ELEMENTS OF
ORGANIC CHEMISTRY

ELEMENTS OF

ALSOPH H. CORWIN, *The Johns Hopkins University*

MAURICE M. BURSEY, *The University of North Carolina*

ORGANIC CHEMISTRY

AS REVEALED BY THE SCIENTIFIC METHOD

ADDISON-WESLEY PUBLISHING COMPANY

READING, MASSACHUSETTS • PALO ALTO • LONDON • DON MILLS, ONTARIO

This book is in the **Addison-Wesley Series in Chemistry**

Consulting Editors

WILLIAM ROBERT MOORE

FREDERICK D. GREENE

The mind is not a vessel to be filled,

but a fire to be kindled.

PLUTARCH

FOREWORD

Since 1885, when Ira Remsen published the first edition of his *Introduction to the Study of the Compounds of Carbon*, the field of organic chemistry has progressed at a rapidly accelerating pace. At that time, however, Remsen took a tremendous forward step in the organization of the subject for teaching purposes. Essentially, he refined the method of Kekulé and presented the subject matter of his course according to the functional groups present, rather than according to the earlier method of treating chemicals as individuals or of considering all substances with the same number of carbons as a group. Remsen's innovation has become standard practice, and organic chemists remain in his debt for initiating the systematic presentation of the subject matter.

The developments of the past century in the field of organic chemistry have matured the basic reasoning of the science so that an organization based on the principles of classification of compounds now appears outmoded. Accordingly, the authors of the present text have abandoned the traditional organization. Instead, they have adopted the point of view that organic chemistry has progressed to the point where it can be regarded as essentially a deductive science with a body of principles which can be taught to the beginner and which will permit him to organize for himself those portions of the tremendous literature of the field that he will use later. The plan of organization of the book has been according to ideas rather than according to classifications of substances.

The authors are strongly of the opinion that the principles of a scientific discipline are deprived of their major pedagogic value if they are presented as dogma. Science has grown and its principles have been elucidated as individual scientists have endeavored to seek the solutions to problems which vexed them. To give the student only the answers which have been found is to rob him of the joys of the chase. To understand how scientists operate, the student must be faced with actual problems; to prepare him to operate as a scientist, he must become a participant in the search for solutions. To do otherwise would be like reading the last page of a detective story first. Consequently, we have endeavored consistently to present the student with research situations beginning with the simplest and progressing to some of the more complex, so that he may understand for himself the intellectual bases of the science and may secure initial practice in the scientific method.

Acknowledgments

The authors wish to thank Professors Paul H. Emmett, Richard J. Kokes, Derek Horton, and Brown Murr and Dr. Milton J. Allen for critical review of portions of the text. They are indebted to Dr. Charles Carlin for material assistance in the preparation of the manuscript and to numerous Junior Instructors and undergraduate students for consultation and suggestions over the years that it was in preparation. Special thanks are due to Messrs. Kevin Sysak, Barry North, and Toby Simon. They also express thanks to Mrs. Elizabeth Ward and Mrs. Marie Gueukmenian for typing the manuscript and to Martin Rosenthal and Laurence Dusold for aid during its revision.

Baltimore, Maryland   A.H.C.
May 1966   M.M.B.

TO THE STUDENT

Reasoning is fun. The ability to reason is the attribute which most clearly distinguishes man from the lower animals. Recreational activities have frequently been built on problem solving. Games of wit and puzzles involving logic have afforded pleasure to millions, and the popularity of detective stories is founded on an implied battle of wits between the author and the reader. The success of these avocations indicates concurrence of a large mass of men in the opinion that reasoning is fun.

The heart of any science is its logical content. Contemporary scholars have sometimes attempted to create an artificial distinction between the sciences and the humanities. In fact, the sciences constitute a major branch of the humanities and illustrate one of the most characteristic of human traits, the ability to engage in subtle reasoning processes.

A much better idea of the essence of a science can usually be obtained by reading current journals in the field than by studying an introductory textbook in the same field. In a journal article, the investigator must present the historical background of his concepts and experiments. He must then describe the new experiments which he has performed. Finally, he must discuss his experiments and draw from them the inferences which they justify. The detailed interweaving of experiment with the resultant logical analysis and synthesis, not the mere accumulation of factual data, constitute the scientific method.

It is the purpose of this book to concern itself with the application to the field of organic chemistry of the central theme of science, the scientific method of reasoning. Because of their advanced and contemporary nature, journals are not well designed for the instruction of the uninitiated, even though they cover the material which it is critically necessary for the beginner to understand. By designing a textbook to accomplish this objective, a critical gap between the inexperience of the beginner and his needs may be bridged.

The general questions at the beginning of each chapter should guide your thinking as you progress through the material. These questions frequently resemble those that might have been framed by the original investigators of the subject. You should attempt to reduce the thought of each chapter to a short answer to the question that precedes it.

The problems at the end of each chapter are not intended to review the chapter because your answer to the prefacing question does that. They are intended to combine new information with the experience of previous study. They attempt to synthesize from these components a situation comparable to that of the first persons to examine these problems. Many of the data in the problems are taken from the experimental sections of original papers in the chemical and biochemical literature. Later chapters will draw equally on the new material contained in the text and that in the problems. The problems are thus an integral part of the course of instruction.

To aid in the mastery of the material, you may find it convenient to attempt various correlations of your own. Thus you may collect and classify synthetic reactions as they appear or you may classify reactions according to functional groups. You will find suggestions along these lines in the Indexes at the end of the text.

While no pretense is made that the subject of organic chemistry does not require hard work for mastery, the procedure of allowing ample sway to the exposition of logical processes will make that work far more enjoyable than the mere drudgery of memorization. In this text you will be able to glimpse some of the enjoyment which comes from a logical conquest and to share vicariously in the satisfaction of solving problems of the sort which scientists engaged in extending the frontiers of knowledge must constantly solve. In this manner we hope that you may come to perceive that science is fascinating and that reasoning is fun.

CONTENTS

BOOK 2

Part 1

ELEMENTS OF CHEMICAL BONDING

Part 2

CHEMICAL TOOLS FOR THE INVESTIGATION OF REACTION MECHANISMS

Part 5

SOME MECHANISMS APPLYING TO BOTH ALIPHATIC AND AROMATIC SYSTEMS

INTRODUCTION

Organic Chemistry

Organic chemistry has been defined as the chemistry of the compounds of carbon. Such a definition, however, gives little idea of the breadth and range of the field. It is more informative to describe the activities of organic chemists. These are highly diverse: some organic chemists who are interested in the organization of matter in living substances devote their time to the isolation of materials from plant or animal sources, to their purification and analysis, and finally to the determination of the arrangement of their component parts in what is called a "structural formula." Other chemists may be interested in the utility of varied substances as pharmaceutical agents, flavors, scents, colors, protective surfaces, or even as structural materials. Such a chemist may devote his time to the artificial production of new materials, never seen in nature, in an effort to improve the desired properties, to eliminate those that are not wanted, and to find cheap means for the production of the natural or artificial substances which he wants to utilize. The studies of the organic chemist may lead him to produce healing substances for use in the treatment of disease or toxic or explosive materials for civil or military use, fuels for the production of heat or power, lubricants for the diminution of wear, coatings for adornment or protection, or new fabrics and building materials. If he is interested in the problem of why these substances function as they do, he will study their chemical transformations in detail to learn more of the relation between chemical structure, on the one hand, and mechanism of action, on the other. He may emphasize either experimental or theoretical studies, depending on his interests and capabilities.

1

The Nature of Chemical Research

Most organic chemists devote their time to some phase of chemical research. If this is directed toward immediate applications, the chemist may seek to improve the properties of known substances or to find new substances for potentially desirable applications. He may attempt to develop a long range application, as was done when the synthetic fibers or the synthetic rubbers were originally studied. If his objectives are longer range, he may ignore foreseeable applications entirely and devote himself to the development of chemical principles or to the uncovering of entirely new principles. Whether his objectives are short range or long range, he will be confronted, in the course of his research, with the problems incident to the exploration of new territory. His path may lead him only a short way from the established guideposts, or it may take him tremendous distances from any ground on which his colleagues have ever stood. Accumulated experience will enable him to choose a path, not necessarily the best one, but because of his position in new territory, nobody will be able to give a dogmatic answer to his problems as they arise. While he may frequently find that his progress is predictable, the trials of research, as well as its outstanding rewards, stem from the fact that the unexpected may occur at any point. This fact creates a continuing challenge to the investigator.

Scope of this Course

The fundamentals of organic chemistry are ideas derived from laboratory experimentation. For the student who will ultimately wish to apply his chemistry to biological, medical, or commercial problems, a sound grasp of these ideas will enable him to approach the applications with assurance. For the student who will ultimately utilize his chemistry in the attempt to discover new ideas, an appreciation of the current ideas will be indispensable as a prerequisite to his further studies. For these reasons, the emphasis of this course will be on the ideas of organic chemistry. These will be suitably illustrated with examples from many fields, but it should be realized that most principles could be illustrated equally well with examples drawn from still different fields. The important consideration in each case is not the field from which an example is drawn but the understanding of the idea that it is intended to illustrate.

Roughly speaking, the ideas fundamental to organic chemistry can be classified according to two broad categories, structure and mechanism. The development of the ideas of structural organic chemistry in the mid-nineteenth century was one of the greatest feats of the human mind up to that time and ranks as a major milestone in man's understanding of the world around him. Through the indirect methods of laboratory experimentation and logical analysis, the organic chemist constructed a method for the study of matter which was so powerful that it may be likened to a "microscope" able to achieve a "magnification" of many millions of times in the examination of chemical molecules. With this tool he could visualize the shapes and detailed geometrical relationships of the molecules that he wished to study. Direct physical methods have not yet achieved such magnification despite the fact that the methods of the organic chemist are now over a century old. An understanding of the reasoning in these processes of the organic chemist is an adventure in the field of human ideas.

Once an understanding of chemical structures was achieved, the chemist naturally turned to a consideration of the processes by which these structures changed from one into another. Mastery of this problem was much more difficult and, indeed, is far from complete at present. One of the major efforts of the contemporary organic chemist is to attempt to throw light on the mechanisms of chemical transformation. The problem is more complicated because it involves not only geometry but time as well. The "microscope" used to study this problem must be one that is capable not only of magnifying millions of times in space but also of slowing down time several millionfold so that we may be able to examine at our leisure a process taking place in approximately a billionth of a second. This "ultraslow-motion microscope" is the instrument of the organic chemical mechanist. Mastery of its use is the key to the control of the processes of organic chemistry in its many practical applications, as well as to the exciting occupation of creating more new organic chemistry.

Historically, understanding of the structural method in organic chemistry had to precede understanding of the mechanisms of chemical transformations. Logically, this order is also the most reasonable one for the student entering on the study of organic chemistry. The materials used in the study of structures are fundamental to those used in the study of reactions. For this reason, this text is divided into two books. The first attempts to answer the question: "How do we know what we know about organic chemical structures?" The second attempts to answer the question: "How do we know what we know about organic chemical reaction mechanisms?" This logical sequence should aid the student in his progression from the simpler fundamental concepts to the more complex ideas which he must ultimately master to move easily in the field of organic chemistry.

The Chemical Literature

The studies referred to in the preceding sections are preserved in the form of an extensive literature which is currently growing at an astounding and accelerating rate. The primary function of the great chemical societies of the world, including the American Chemical Society, which is the largest, is to publish, thus making this literature available to research chemists the world over. One of the objectives of this course of instruction will be to prepare the beginner to read the literature of organic chemistry and to provide him with the materials which he will need for this purpose.

The key to the chemical literature of the world is *Chemical Abstracts*. This is a monumental journal appearing twice a month. It attempts to survey and abstract every chemical publication made anywhere in any language. This process is fantastically expensive and one of the major problems of the American Chemical Society is to provide a sound basis for the financing of the publication of *Chemical Abstracts*. This is especially important now when the literature is growing so rapidly, since the possibility of each chemist's covering all the articles which interest him in the original becomes more and more remote as their volume grows.

Consequently, it is doubly important that this essential service should not be lost just when it is needed most.

An idea of the rate of growth of the chemical literature may be secured by plotting the printed area in the decennial indexes of *Chemical Abstracts* as a function of time as shown in Fig. I–1.

The astounding rate of growth found in the first decade after World War II is being maintained so that it has become necessary to discontinue the publication of decennial indexes because of their bulk. Instead, the next collective index will cover only five years and will be approximately as large as that of the preceding ten years.

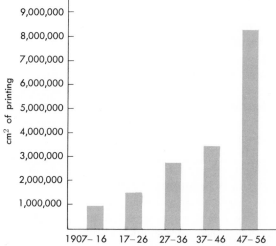

FIG. I–1.   Growth of the decennial indexes to *Chemical Abstracts*.

Because of the fact that the number of journals containing chemical publications throughout the world is so large, the mere task of attempting to read all pertinent tables of contents to find out what is being published has become overpowering. In an attempt to meet this challenge, the American Chemical Society has brought a tremendous computer operation to the aid of the individual chemist. Key words in the titles of chemical publications are listed alphabetically so that the individual may pick the subjects that interest him and find whether or not anything on this subject has been published recently. These lists are issued twice a month in *Chemical Titles*. In addition, authors' names are listed and tables of contents are reproduced. The operation is planned in such a manner that the key word indexes reach subscribers at about the same time as the journals themselves. Thus each investigator has his personal literature search constantly brought up to date. By combining searches of *Chemical Titles* and *Chemical Abstracts*, it is frequently possible to locate necessary literature references and eliminate those which are not important in the study under way. Thus the task of dealing with the tremendous growth in the chemical literature is somewhat lightened by the application of modern methods to the search for information.

BOOK 1

How are organic chemical structures determined?

Part 1

THE STRUCTURAL PROBLEM
OF ORGANIC CHEMISTRY

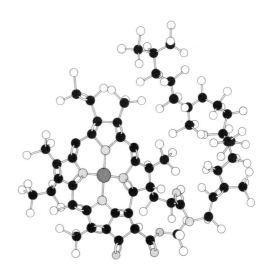

A Look at the Map

Before undertaking the study of the details of organic structural chemistry, we shall take a quick look at a "map" of the territory. For this purpose, we shall review briefly the general approach of the organic chemist to structural problems as a framework into which the details can be fitted later.

*What is the general approach of
the organic chemist to the problems of
chemical structures and mechanisms?*

1

THE CHEMISTRY OF
LIVING MATTER

1-1 Natural Product Chemistry

From time immemorial, man has been interested in the processes of life. His investigations into life processes have taken many paths. In modern science, the study of the gross features of organisms and their microscopic components is the province of biology. The study of the fundamental chemical substances which compose these organized structures, however, is the province of the organic chemist in the specialty of natural product chemistry. The majority of the best leads into the study of organic chemistry have come from the models suggested by these natural product studies. In pursuing his specialty, the natural product chemist starts by purifying a sample of the chemical that interests him and then he examines its structure. Before we undertake a detailed study of the precise methods by which details of structure are established, we may secure a general grasp of the approach used by taking a quick look at an actual example. At this point, the reader should not concern himself with details but should attempt to grasp the general principles used so that this information may serve as a framework on which his later study will build a more complete structure.

As our example, we shall use chlorophyll. This is a complex organic chemical, one of the most important substances to the life processes. We shall attempt to ignore its complexities and cut through to the basic skeleton on which it is constructed.

1–2   Chlorophyll

Chlorophyll is an example of a substance whose investigation extends from the early days of organized organic chemistry to the present, with the most important problem yet to be solved. The structural chemistry of chlorophyll was elucidated by researches in the laboratories of Willstätter in Munich, Stoll in Basle, Conant at Harvard and particularly Hans Fischer in Munich. Two syntheses of chlorophyll have been announced, one by Strell, one of Fischer's students, and the other by Woodward at Harvard. Woodward's synthesis contains many highly original contributions to the chemistry of the field. The ingenuity of this synthesis was a large factor in the award of the 1965 Nobel Prize in Chemistry to Professor Woodward.

The most important outstanding problem in the case of chlorophyll is to answer the question of how it functions in photosynthesis. Numerous aspects of the problem of photosynthesis have been studied in many laboratories all over the world, but the details of the action of chlorophyll in this process have not yet been worked out.

The modern organic chemist, then, has been confronted with two major problems with respect to chlorophyll: (1) its structure and synthesis, (2) the mechanism of its action in the plant. After completion of the first part of this course, the reader should have a basic understanding of the processes by which the first of these problems is solved. After completion of the remainder of the course, he should understand the principles of attack on the second problem. Meanwhile, our look at some of the facts that are known about chlorophyll and related pigments will give a preliminary insight into the general line of approach to the structural problem.

1–3   The Significance of Chlorophyll

Why is it important for the chemist to consider chlorophyll? Ultimately, this substance has been instrumental in providing us with most of our food and all of our organic fuels, such as wood, coal, petroleum, and related substances. As man digs into his reserves of these fuels at an increasing rate, it becomes imperative for him to understand all that he can about the process by which they became available in the first place. This process is called *photosynthesis*. In its course, energy from the sun is absorbed by plants and utilized to break down water, reversing the process of combustion. Oxygen from the water is liberated into the atmosphere and made available for animal respiration. Hydrogen from the water is introduced into a complicated series of reactions which may well be likened to a submicroscopic production line with about twenty "stations" each containing an *enzyme*, a catalyst capable of performing an essential operation on a chemical of biological interest. During photosynthesis, atmospheric carbon dioxide is used by the plant as a source of carbon for building sugars and ultimately other typical plant substances, such as cellulose, the structural material of wood, cotton, and paper. In the reduction process which takes place, energy is fixed; that is, the energy of sunlight is trapped and made available for use by the plant and ultimately by us as fuel.

Animals are parasitic on plants. Carnivorous animals are one step removed from dependence on plants, while herbivorous animals rely directly on the plants for their food. Plants, in their turn, derive their material ultimately from the processes initiated by the action of light on chlorophyll.

Animals, in their turn, supply waste products which can be utilized by plants. The circuit of plants supplying food and oxygen to animals and animals supplying fertilizer and carbon dioxide for plants constitutes a closed biological circuit that is of intense current interest for future exploration of space. The only exceptions which men have been able to devise to this closed circuit are the very few processes which organic chemists have invented in recent years for producing food in factories that do not rely on agricultural raw materials. Even these, as a rule, find it expedient to utilize coal as a raw material, thus again depending on photosynthesis.

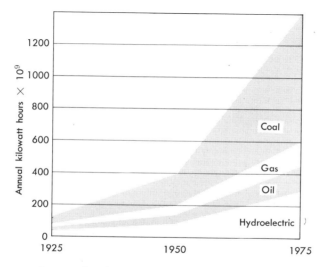

FIG. 1–1.   Sources of energy for electricity, excluding nuclear fission. (Adapted from *Resources for Freedom III*, President's Materials Policy Commission, U. S. Government Printing Office, 1952.)

Our energy sources are also extensively dependent on photosynthesis. In recent years, men have used water power to an increasing extent. Water power is produced from the energy of the sun transmitted without photosynthesis. Currently we are also witnessing the initial phases of the use of atomic energy for commercial power production. Despite these developments, the prime dependence of mankind for energy has been, and will probably be, even well into the twenty-first century, his supply of organic fuels. A projection, which excludes atomic energy, is shown in Fig. 1–1.

Our fossil fuels have come from plant materials built by photosynthesis. The huge tonnages that are involved may be visualized by reference to Fig. 1–2. In this figure, the single circle represents the tonnage of the annual steel production of the entire world, while the sum of the remaining circles represents the annual production of plant material by photosynthesis. Even this huge amount of material

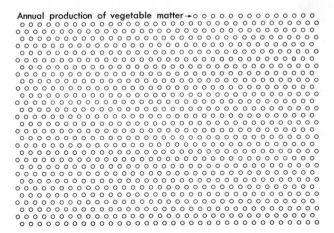

FIG. 1–2. Annual production of vegetable matter.

is due to the fixation of only a very small fraction of the energy falling on the surface of the earth from the sun. Most of the fraction that is fixed is again lost to us by processes of decay so that the total storage of energy by plants is small. In fact, it is estimated that all the energy which can be derived from all the fossil fuels ever available to man is equivalent to that falling on the surface of the earth for only *three* days. The energy of all the remaining two billion or more years has been lost to us. Since we have been able to power so many of our activities with a fraction of three days' energy from the sun, however, we may reasonably hope that knowledge of how to harness the sun more effectively in the future will aid appreciably in solving our increasing power problem. This is one practical significance of the study of the fixation of the energy of the sun by photosynthesis and by other processes.

1–4   Isolation and Purification of Chlorophyll

Before an organic chemist can undertake studies on the structure of a naturally occurring substance, he must devise methods for obtaining it in pure form. In doing this, he starts by destroying the microscopic organization which is one of the chief concerns of the biologist. The plant relies on these relatively gross structures for its functioning, and this explains why the study of these gross structures forms the classical subject matter of biological investigation. The purpose of the chemist in destroying these structures is not to create chaos but to study still more refined organizational features which exist in still smaller entities, the molecules. The information which can be gained by a judicious and exhaustive use of this method is fundamental to ultimate understanding of the microscopic structures which interest the biologist. This is because these larger structures are built from the smaller ones and contribute in the most integral manner to their properties, just as houses built of wood are different from those built of brick.

Alfalfa furnishes a cheap and convenient raw material for the preparation of chlorophyll. Carefully dried leaves are covered with a solvent such as hexane, a purified substance corresponding to light gasoline. It will be seen that the solvent becomes green because of the chlorophyll which it dissolves. However, mixed with the chlorophyll are numerous other substances present in the plant. A preliminary separation of these materials can be obtained by the process known as *chromatography* (Fig. 1–3). To accomplish the separation, the solution of materials which have been extracted from the alfalfa is poured over a column of an adsorbent, such as powdered sugar, contained in a glass tube. The solution will gravitate through the tube, but it will be found that the green color has remained on the sugar. Evaporation of the solvent which goes through the column will show that it contains some colorless materials, giving a preliminary separation of colorless from colored materials. The green fraction may be further purified by a careful washing on the column to "develop the chromatogram." It will be found that the green band consists of a mixture of several yellowish to orange pigments, the carotinoids, and two green pigments, chlorophyll *b* at the top and chlorophyll *a* below it. Chlorophyll *a* is the major green pigment and is distinguished by its bluer shade. Repetition of the process of solution and chromatography, sometimes with the use of different solvent and adsorbent combinations, is capable of yielding a product of high purity, suitable for chemical studies. If enough solvent is passed through the chromatogram or if a change to a better solvent is made, the colored materials can be removed from the column. The process of chromatographic purification is quite general and can be modified to permit the separation of colorless substances. This process is called *elution*.

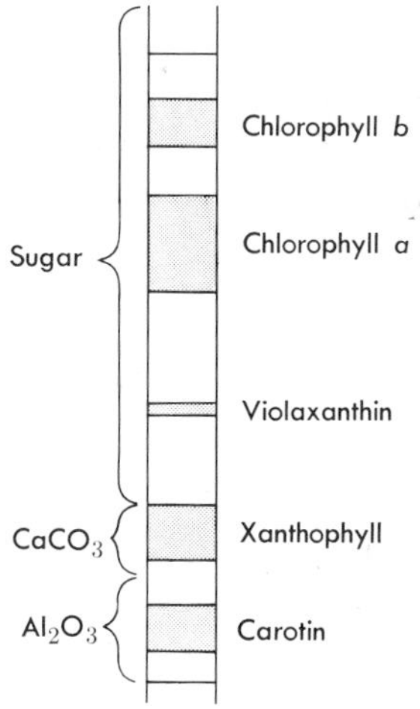

FIG. 1–3. Chromatography of leaf pigments. (From L. Zechmeister, and L. von Cholnoky, *Die Chromatographische Adsorptionsmethode*, Vienna: Springer, 1937.)

1–5   The Structure of Chlorophyll

Figure 1–4 represents a model of the chlorophyll molecule as the organic chemist pictures it today. In this model, each ball represents an atom in approximately its proper position. The large ball in the middle is intended to represent an atom of magnesium. Other balls represent atoms of carbon, nitrogen, oxygen, and hydrogen. In the model there are 55 carbon atoms, 72 hydrogens, 5 oxygens, 4 nitrogens, and 1 magnesium.

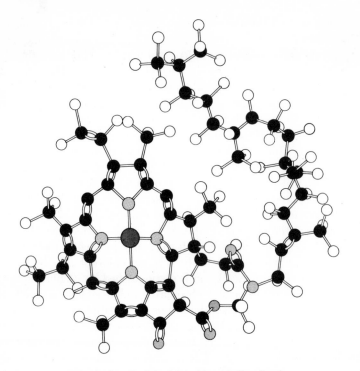

FIG. 1–4.   Model of the chlorophyll molecule.

The model of a simple substance, carbon dioxide, is shown in Fig. 1–5. Clearly this molecule is linear, with one carbon in the center and two oxygens at the ends. Figure 1–6 shows a model of the substance known as "pyrrole." This has four carbon atoms and one nitrogen in a ring with five hydrogens attached on the periphery. Examination of the model of chlorophyll will show that it has four somewhat modified pyrrole rings in it at right angles to each other. They are joined by "bridges" made up of a carbon atom with an attached hydrogen. The whole central structure roughly resembles a doughnut with the hole plugged by the atom of magnesium. Figure 1–7 is a model showing the arrangement of carbons and hydrogens in a molecule of "phytol." Re-examination of the chlorophyll model will show that it has phytol attached to it as a side chain. Because phytol is insoluble in water and soluble in oils, the presence of this side chain contributes a waxy character to the chlorophyll molecule, rendering it insoluble in water and soluble in many oils.

FIG. 1–5.   Model of carbon dioxide.   Fig. 1–6.   Model of pyrrole.

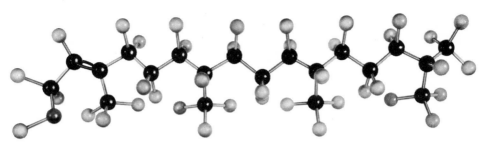

FIG. 1–7. Model of phytol.

The model of chlorophyll will make it clear that it is possible to combine atoms into many types of geometrical arrangement to form molecules. They may form chains, rings, or even three-dimensional space-enclosing figures (Fig. 1–8) of a type not illustrated in the molecule of chlorophyll.

FIG. 1–8. A three-dimensional cage molecule.

As stated above, the processes by which the chemist learns this will be the subject of the first half of the book. In this development, simple structures will be considered first. The examples will then increase in complexity until it becomes possible to see how a really complex structure is determined.

1–6 The Structural Problem: Degradation

Once a chemist has obtained a pure chemical individual for study, the next step is to attempt to elucidate its structure. This is an essential first step before it becomes possible to reason about the relation between structure and activity. Structural deductions are accomplished by a mixture of chemical and geometrical reasoning which differs in detail with each case under study. In the case of chlorophyll, the structural problem was extraordinarily difficult. The substance is sensitive to most chemical reagents, either weak or strong. For example, it will react with the oxygen of the air or with the combination of carbon dioxide and moisture. Weak or strong acids, such as dilute acetic or dilute sulfuric acid, or weak or strong alkalies, such as sodium bicarbonate or sodium hydroxide, will all degrade it. The nature of the process by which reactions such as these are used to establish a chemical structure may be grasped, even without a knowledge of the details, by considering a hypothetical, simplified, "stripped" model from which all the hydro-

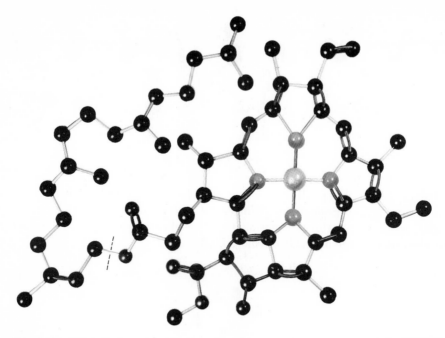

FIG. 1-9. Chlorophyll model, stripped of hydrogens. Cutting at the dashed line produces Fig. 1-10.

FIG. 1-10. Chlorophyllide skeleton. Cutting at the dashed lines produces Fig. 1-11.

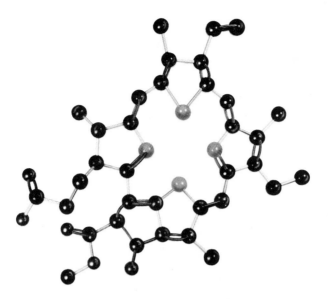

FIG. 1-11. Pheophorbide skeleton.

gens have been eliminated. Such a model is shown in Fig. 1-9. When green leaves are ground, the organization prevailing in the plant is disrupted, and the chlorophyll is exposed to the action of an accompanying enzyme, *chlorophyllase*, which breaks the molecule down into two fragments, phytol and *chlorophyllide*, Fig. 1-10. These substances may be physically separated. This simplifies the problem of structural determination, since the phytol may now be operated on separately, and its structure established by reactions independent of those of the chlorophyllide portion.

When chlorophyll or chlorophyllide is treated with dilute acetic acid of the strength of vinegar, for example, the magnesium is removed from the center. The product of the latter breakdown called *pheophorbide*, and its skeleton is shown in Fig. 1-11. If this substance, in turn, is subjected to the action of heat in the presence of metallic zinc or, preferably, to the action of a powerful reducing agent (hydrogen iodide is used), the whole structure comes apart, leaving fragments which may be examined individually and which may be fitted together tentatively like the parts of a jigsaw puzzle. Some of these fragments are illustrated in Fig. 1-12.

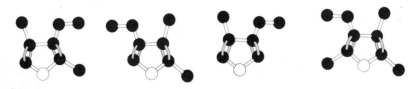

FIG. 1-12. Skeletons of some fragments from the HI reduction of chlorophyll compounds.

1–7   The Structural Problems: Synthesis

The process by which a chemist attempts to reconstruct the original structure of a compound from the fragments resembles that by which an archaeologist attempts to reconstruct an ancient piece of pottery from the available parts. For chlorophyll, the fragments available were pyrrole rings with carbon-containing side chains. The process of reconstruction was accomplished synthetically by trial and error in the laboratory. Numerous hypothetical structures were assumed and then produced synthetically, only to have the chemist discover that they did not resemble the desired material. Finally a synthetic product gave properties closely resembling those of the original. This result showed that the correct general type of structure had been prepared. Refinements were immediately instituted to approach closer and closer to the exact material from which the studies started. Such is the general nature of the interwoven processes of degradation and synthesis on which chemical structures are built. In the particular case of chlorophyll, the final synthesis was rendered especially difficult by the fact that even the sequence of steps in which the building-up process is carried out is important. Chemical reagents strong enough to put together one part of the molecule are frequently strong enough to tear down another part. In fact, it was necessary to invent special methods to accomplish the synthesis of chlorophyll.

1–8   Relation between Chlorophyll and Hemoglobin

One of the amazing facts in the realm of biology is that the most important plant pigment, chlorophyll, and the most important animal pigment, hemoglobin, have colored portions which are closely related chemically. Functionally, these pigments are poles apart. Chlorophyll is an intermediary in the process of photosynthesis; hemoglobin transports oxygen from the lungs, where it enters the body, to the muscles, where it is used. It also assists in carrying the carbon dioxide formed by muscular exertion back to the lungs where it is exhaled. Thus hemoglobin is the prime factor in a relatively efficient system for the transportation of gases essential to life. Two other types of oxygen-carrying pigment are found in nature. One, hemocyanin, is copper-containing. The other, hemovanadin, contains vanadium. Since neither of these substances approaches hemoglobin in efficiency as an oxygen carrier, a barrier standing in the way of further development of the species which rely on these materials is the nature of the blood pigments themselves. Thus it appears that a major step in the evolution of higher animals was the development of the relatively efficient oxygen carrier, hemoglobin. To understand how it functions as it does, the first step is to prepare the material in pure form for chemical investigation.

1–9   Hemin

Hemoglobin is relatively easy to prepare in crystalline form. Starting from centrifuged red blood cells, a saturated solution of the pigment in water is prepared, the acidity is adjusted, and the solution is allowed to stand in a refrigerator. Crystals

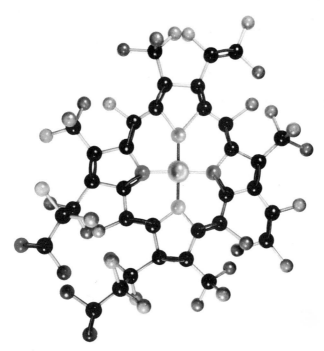

FIG. 1–13. Model of hemin.

of the pigment are slowly deposited. The pigment turns out to be composed of two portions. One is a highly colored, iron-containing substance, heme. The other, comprising 96% of the molecule, is a colorless protein, globin. Heme contains iron in the reduced or ferrous state. Unlike hemoglobin, the iron in this pigment, unprotected by protein, is readily oxidized to the ferric state, producing hemin. For the preparation of hemin, hemoglobin, or even red cells, may be boiled with glacial acetic acid and a little salt. The fine bluish crystals of hemin which form sink and are readily separated by filtration.

Structural investigations on hemin reveal that it has a mosaic type structure, like chlorophyll, made up of four pyrrole rings joined by carbon-hydrogen bridges. A model of hemin is shown in Fig. 1–13. A stripped model of hemin is shown in Fig. 1–14. In this case, the central atom is iron instead of magnesium. The waxy phytol side chain is missing, and the molecule is somewhat soluble in water solutions at pH 7.4, the approximate alkalinity of the blood.

When hemin is treated with acid of the proper strength, the iron atom can be removed from the center. The substance with only the iron of hemin replaced by two hydrogens is called *protoporphyrin*, from the Greek word *protos* meaning "first." When treated with hydrogen and a catalyst, protoporphyrin will absorb hydrogen, giving *mesoporphyrin* (from the Greek *mesos* meaning "middle"). The carbon and nitrogen skeleton of proto- and mesoporphyrins is shown in Fig. 1–15. When mesoporphyrin is subjected to thermal decomposition by heating to about the boiling point of mineral oil, it loses carbon dioxide at the points marked by the

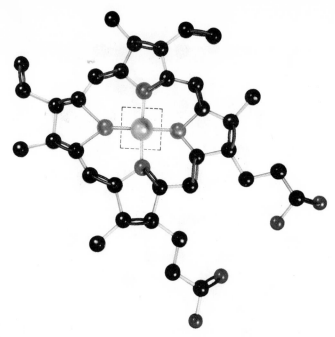

FIG. 1–14.   Skeleton of hemin, stripped of hydrogens. Cutting at the dashed lines produces Fig. 1–15.

FIG. 1–15.   Skeleton of protoporphyrin and mesoporphyrin. Cutting at the dashed lines produces Fig. 1–16.

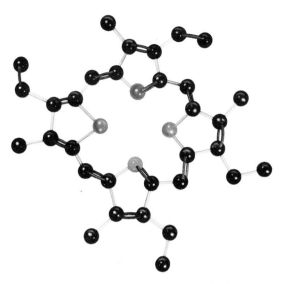

FIG. 1–16. Skeleton of etioporphyrin.

dashed lines in Fig. 1–15 and forms *etioporphyrin* (from the Greek *aitio* meaning "the cause," or in this case, the basic or final degradation product). The carbon and nitrogen skeleton of etioporphyrin is shown in Fig. 1–16. When etioporphyrin is heated with hydrogen iodide, it breaks up, just as pheophorbide does, to form the same characteristic fragments, the substituted pyrrole derivatives shown in Fig. 1–12.

1–10 The Structure of the Porphyrin Skeleton

Because hemin is easier to deal with chemically than chlorophyll, the first step in the elucidation of the structure of chlorophyll was the proof of the structure of hemin. Because of its physical properties, the substance actually chosen for the purpose was mesoporphyrin. Let us still further simplify the schematic representation of these substances by showing mesoporphyrin as in Fig. 1–17. It will be seen that there are two types of pyrrole rings in mesoporphyrin, those represented by the letters M and E, and those represented by the letters M and A. The A groups are the acid groups referred to above.

When the study of hemin began, even the mode of combination between the pyrrole rings was unknown. Methods of degradation were unsuccessful in obtaining information on this point. It was finally decided that synthesis was the only method that could be used for the structural investigation.

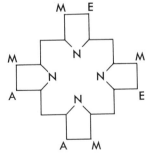

FIG. 1–17.   Schematic representation of mesoporphyrin.

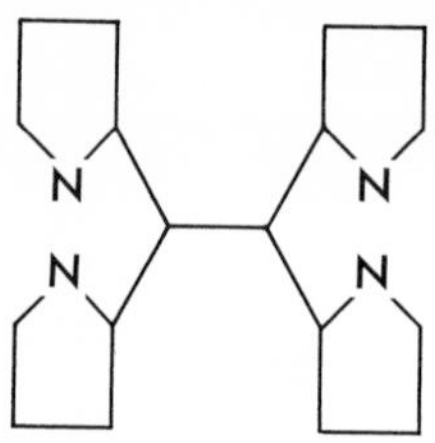

FIG. 1–18. Skeleton of a tetrapyrryl-ethylene.

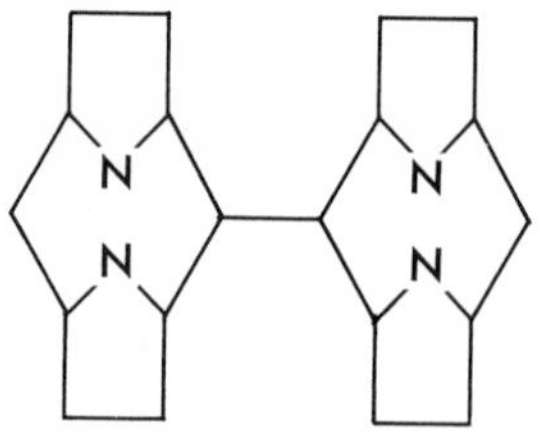

FIG. 1–19. Hypothetical indigoid structure.

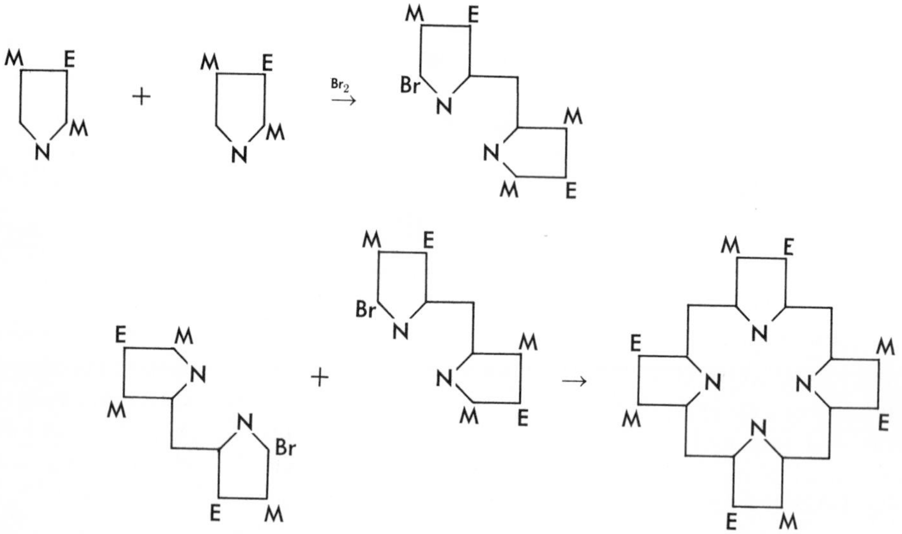

FIG. 1–20. Schematic representation of the synthesis of an etioporphyrin.

Accordingly, several types of combination between pyrrole rings were produced by synthesis. One of these was a so-called "tetrapyrryl-ethylene," Fig. 1–18. Another type of combination which was attempted synthetically without success was that of a so-called "indigoid" structure, Fig. 1–19. It was in an attempt to produce an indigoid structure that Hans Fischer succeeded in making the first synthetic porphyrin, an etioporphyrin. The general scheme of the synthesis can be represented as in Fig. 1–20.

In this synthesis, the M groups on the positions next to the nitrogens in the pentagons serve as the sources of the bridges linking the pyrrole rings.

1–11   The Synthesis of Mesoporphyrin

Once the general skeleton of the porphyrin structure was established by synthesis, it became possible to solve the problem of the geometric arrangement of the groups in mesoporphyrin by the same method. Because mesoporphyrin has two types of pyrrole rings, the number of possible sequences is much greater than for the etioporphyrins. In fact, there are sixteen possible mesoporphyrins. Fischer set out

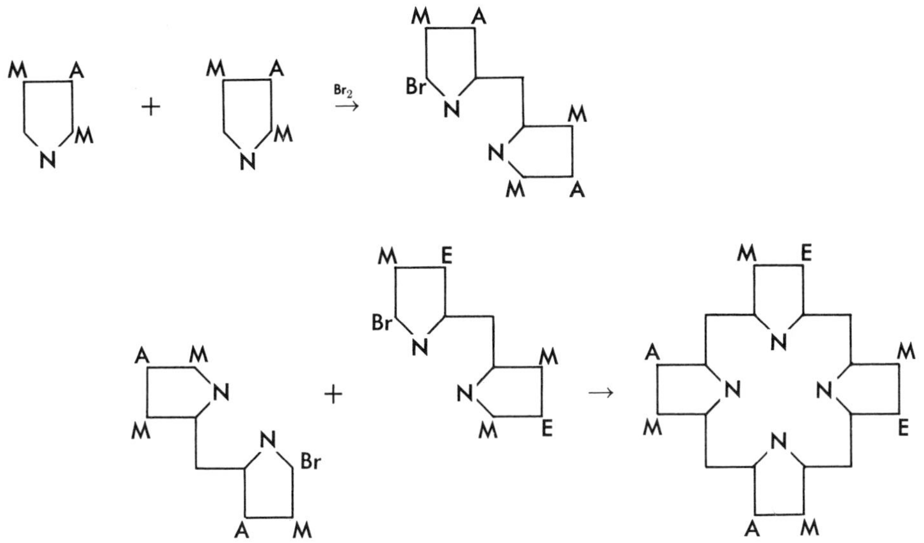

FIG. 1–21.   Representation of the synthesis of an "unnatural" mesoporphyrin.

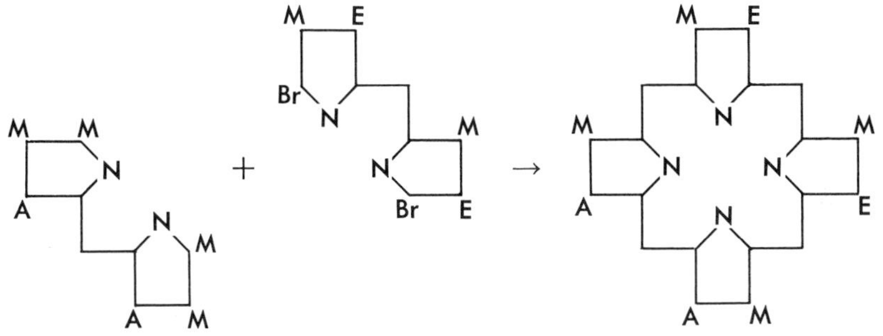

FIG. 1–22.   Synthesis of "natural" mesoporphyrin.

to synthesize as many of the sixteen as was necessary to obtain the one appearing in nature. For example, one synthesis would yield a substance like mesoporphyrin, but with one ring turned around (Fig. 1–21). By a variation on this scheme the desired material, shown in Fig. 1–22, was finally produced. Thus by putting together the building blocks of the large molecule in a predetermined sequence, it was possible to establish the sequence of the groups in the natural product.

Modifications of the synthetic methods used on the structural problem of hemin were applied to the parallel but more complex problem of chlorophyll structure. The surprising conclusion was reached that the sequence of groups in both natural products is the same, despite the fact that one comes from animal sources and the other from vegetables. The solution of the remainder of the problem of the structure of chlorophyll could then be undertaken. This illustrates a principle frequently employed in the structural study of naturally occurring substances. One material may be so complex, so delicate, or so expensive to prepare that its investigation is difficult. By searching throughout the plant and animal kingdoms, the chemist is sometimes able to find another substance chemically related to the first but more amenable to his treatments. In such a case, the solution to the structural problem of the first may be obtained by studying the second and then transferring all pertinent information.

1–12 The Problem of the Mechanism of Action

Chlorophyll divorced from its medium in the chloroplast of the plant is incapable of performing photosynthesis or even of accomplishing the simpler task of fixing light energy by splitting water. In the same manner, hemin divorced from the protein, globin, is incapable of combining with oxygen. In each case, we know where the activity resides, but we do not yet have the key to producing the submicroscopic molecular medium which will permit the activity observed in nature to be reproduced in the laboratory.

If we reduce hemin to heme, that is, if we reduce the iron from ferric to ferrous and then combine it with globin, the artificial material so produced has the power to pick up oxygen and at the same time to resist oxidation back to the ferric state in a water solution. If, instead of globin, we choose any basic substance of known structure for this experiment, we find that the compound made by its union with heme is incapable of transporting oxygen in a water solution and, instead, will be oxidized to the ferric state by it. The clue to the solution of the problem, then, lies in the nature and arrangement of the groupings in globin which are capable of reacting with heme and, in so doing, of protecting it from oxidation and of conferring physiological activity on it. In other words, the clue to the mystery lies in the submicroscopic organization of the atoms into a molecule capable of producing the desired effect. The challenge to the organic chemist is to learn, first, what is the exact nature of the organization which is effective and, second, what is the interrelationship between the molecule under study (hemoglobin) and the substance on which it acts (oxygen) which is responsible for the activity. This final question is the question of the mechanism of action and is fundamental to intelligent understanding of the role of chemical substances and the possible improvement of their properties. How the chemist obtains information about mechanisms will be the subject of the second half of this book.

This discussion has been centered about substances possessing physiological activity in plants and animals since such substances are of universal interest because of the curiosity which each one of us possesses concerning the functioning of life processes. Examples could equally well have been drawn from other fields of chemical activity, however, and the information gained in one field is frequently of surprising pertinence to studies in other fields. In future discussions, examples will be drawn from numerous types of activity. Whatever the field from which they are drawn, they will serve to illustrate general principles that are widely applicable.

PROBLEMS

1–1 The following problem is an exercise in chemical geometry. The only unspecified elements in it are geometrical, and it can be solved on a purely geometrical basis.

Let us suppose that pyrrole may be shown by physical means to have all of its atoms lying in one plane. Let us assume, further, that the molecule possesses a plane of symmetry bisecting it along the axis indicated. The numbers are used to distinguish the various positions and are especially convenient in naming more complicated compounds with the pyrrole ring as their base. The nitrogen distinguishes one vertex of the pentagon from the other four, thus creating a "tag."

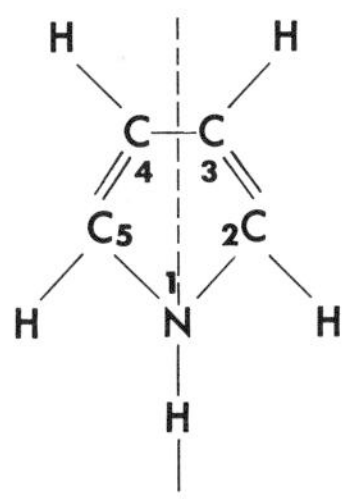

(a) Which positions are equivalent geometrically?

If we could replace any one H on the ring by another atom or group of atoms, there would be five positions on the ring to be substituted. Several of these new compounds made by this substitution would be identical with each other. Let us assume that chemical equivalence corresponds to geometrical equivalence.

(b) How many different pyrroles could be prepared with a single methyl group, CH_3, as a substituent?

We may use the symbol Me for methyl and Et for ethyl, C_2H_5, and write the structure shown at the right for 3-methyl-4-ethylpyrrole.

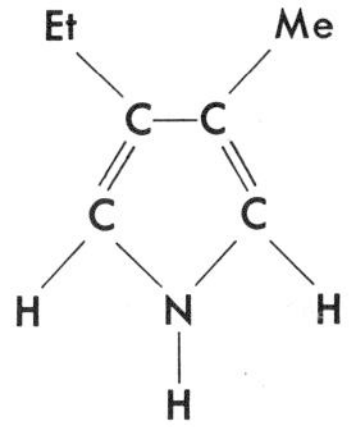

(c) Does this differ geometrically from 4-methyl-3-ethylpyrrole?

Suppose that two of these pyrrole rings are joined, one in the 2-position the other in the 5-position, by a one-carbon bridge to give a "dipyrrylmethane," whose carbon-nitrogen skeleton is given on the right.

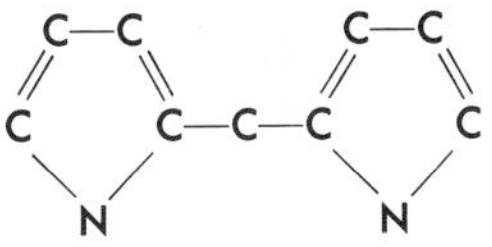

(d) Geometrically, how many dipyrrylmethanes would be possible, using two molecules of 3-methyl-4-ethylpyrrole plus the bridge carbon?

The porphyrin nucleus, of which hemin and chlorophyll are highly substituted examples, can be seen to be made up of four pyrrole rings connected by one-carbon bridges as illustrated in Fig. 1–23. As shown in Section 1–9, hemin can be converted by suitable chemical manipulations into etioporphyrin. Each of the pyrrole rings in etioporphyrin has one methyl group and one ethyl group in positions 3 and 4. On reduction with hydrogen iodide, HI, (Section 1–9), etioporphyrin is broken down into a mixture of the four substituted pyrroles shown in Fig. 1–12. These also have methyls and ethyls and in the 3- and 4-positions. In the 2- and 5-positions these pyrroles have either methyls or hydrogens. Let us represent the methyls and ethyls in the 3- and 4-positions by the abbreviations Me and Et respectively. In the 2- and 5-positions we shall assume that the methyls are residues from the carbon bridges which joined the pyrrole rings together in etioporphyrin and that these bridges were broken in the

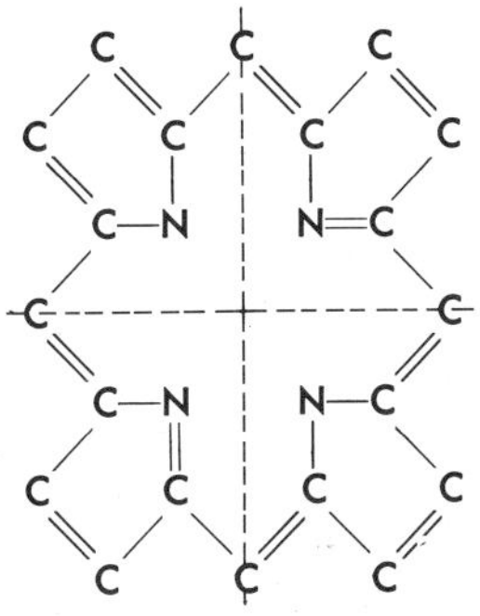

FIGURE 1–23

process of HI reduction which produced the substituted pyrroles. If we look on these bridges as a sort of "ball and socket joint" and represent the 2,5-methyls as the balls and the hydrogens as sockets, we can write the four pyrroles obtained from etioporphyrin as shown below.

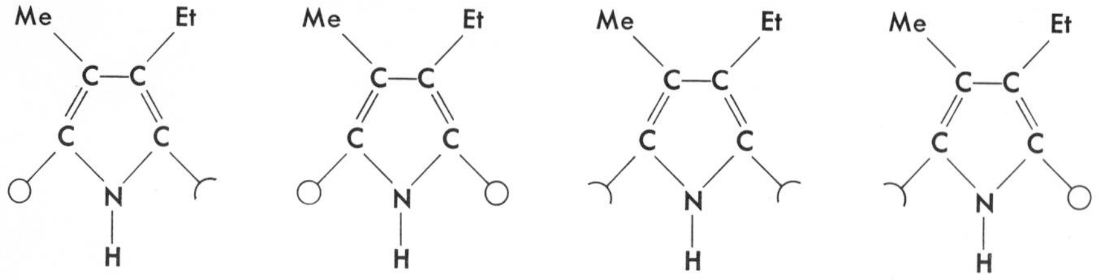

(e) These geometrical figures may be used to reconstruct the larger figure which was broken down to give them. The purpose of describing the 2,5-substituents as balls and sockets is to allow the construction of a set of models. Take a piece of cardboard and, using the four rings above as models, cut out four models of the pyrrole rings. Fit these together so that each ball fits into a socket. Now draw a picture of the resulting structure, which should be a model of etioporphyrin.

(f) If we assume that the HI reaction can split the ball and socket joint on either side of the ball (Fig. 1–24), does the operation that you have just performed determine the sequence of the methyl and ethyl groups in the 3- and 4-positions of the porphyrin?

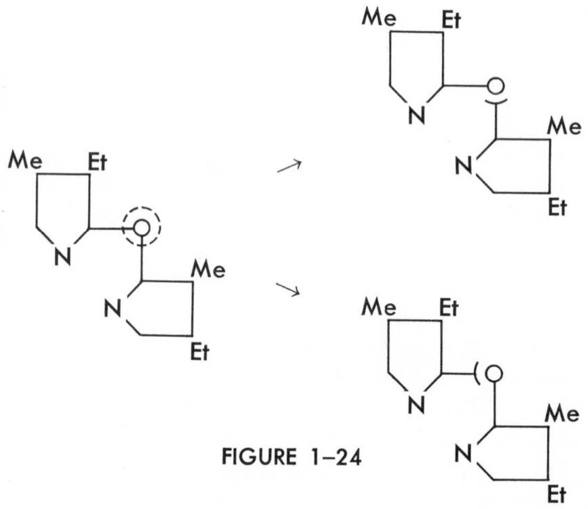

FIGURE 1–24

(g) In how many ways can you arrange the pyrrole rings in etioporphyrin so that each pyrrole ring has one methyl and one ethyl on the 3- and 4-positions? Remember that many of the structures which can be drawn are geometrically equivalent. The answer to this question will tell you how many etioporphyrins are possible. The essence of the remaining structural problem, which must be solved by more refined chemical methods, is to distinguish among these possibilities and to decide which one of the structures fits the natural product.

Part 2

THE BASIC REASONING UNDERLYING ORGANIC STRUCTURES

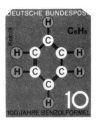

Early chemists found that they could purify volatile substances by distillation. Later it was learned that solids could be purified by crystallization. In the early nineteenth century, organic chemists were equally interested in the problem of the structure of ethanol and in that of morphine. However, the former problem was soon solved, while the latter persisted until recent decades.

In any science, the first few steps toward systematic organization are the most difficult to take. To understand the science, the student must review the initial problems faced by the men who solved them. In organic chemistry, he must understand the basic significance of combustion analysis, the law of definite proportions, the precision conferred by precise symbolism, the contribution to understanding made by Avogadro's hypothesis, the arguments of analogy upon which simple structures were based, and the beginnings of the sophistication of the science with the solution of the problem of the structure of benzene. These subjects will form the material of Part 2.

The stamp on the preceding page is reproduced by courtesy of the ministry for Postal Affairs of the German Federal Republic.

What reasoning underlies the use of
combustion analyses in
the determination of empirical formulas?

2

ORGANIC CHEMICAL FORMULAS

2–1 Greek Cosmology

The ancient Greeks taught that all things were composed of the elements air, water, fire, and earth. Their system was riveted on the minds of men for nearly two thousand years. In some lands, to question it was heresy punishable by the most severe penalties. However, the Renaissance found a new spirit of inquiry abroad which finally led to the overthrow of the Greek cosmology.

2–2 Combustion; Early Experiments

In the middle of the seventeenth century, the English chemist Robert Boyle and his contemporaries reached for, but did not quite grasp, the key which would have opened the door to the mysteries of organic chemistry, the understanding of combustion. During the period of Cromwell's dictatorship and about the time the English seized New Amsterdam from the Dutch and renamed it "New York," Boyle was at work on the study of the process of combustion. In 1659 he invented a method for the collection of gases over water, the forerunner of our pneumatic troughs. Thus for the first time the collection of different gases became possible. Robert Hooke, the physicist, constructed a vacuum pump for Boyle, who proceeded to show that animals would die and flames would be extinguished when the pressure of the air in a container was reduced. Hooke next showed that gunpowder would burn under water and asserted that a substance which would support combustion was present both in air and in saltpeter. Next, Boyle showed that a mouse confined

in a closed glass vessel would slowly suffocate. A few years later, in 1674, John
Mayow showed that air was consumed when a mouse breathed in a closed container and that the combustion of a candle also used up air. He concluded that
a "nitro-aerial spirit" was present, which was required for both combustion and
respiration.

Despite these advances, a more popular theory of combustion was propounded
by a German school, first by J. J. Becher (1635–1682) and later by G. E. Stahl
(1660–1734). These investigators believed that all combustible substances contained a common element of fire which Stahl named "phlogiston." The theory
achieved popularity because it was easy to demonstrate that anyone could see
the fire being given off during combustion. Because of the convincing nature of
this demonstration and the difficulties involved in the quantitative handling of
gases, the phlogiston theory reigned for a century and was passionately and
bitterly supported during its final years, even when laboriously accumulated
evidence and close reasoning had made it untenable.

2–3 The Discovery of Carbon Dioxide

In 1754, coincident with the outbreak of the French and Indian War, Joseph Black,
a young Scotch physician, published an account of his studies on "magnesia alba"
or, as we would call it, magnesium carbonate. Black weighed this material, then
heated it and showed that it lost in weight. He called the gas that was given off
"fixed air" and showed that it could be produced from a variety of "mild alkalies,"
which we would now call carbonates. Medical interest in these substances had been
aroused by the fact that caustic alkalies had frequently been prescribed for the
treatment of urinary stones, but conservative physicians felt that the destructive
action on body tissues should be avoided and milder substances used.

Black took the first critical step toward our modern understanding of the process
of combustion when he demonstrated that the burning of charcoal produced the
same substance as the heating of the "mild alkalies." To prove this, he showed
that the gas produced by these processes would form a milky precipitate with
limewater, while ordinary air failed to do this. The limewater test for carbon
dioxide formed by combustion still remains the standard qualitative test of the
organic chemist for the presence of carbon in an unknown material.

2–4 The Discovery of Oxygen

On Monday, August 1, 1774, approximately eight months after the Boston Tea
Party, Joseph Priestley performed an experiment that became another milestone
in the development of chemistry. In addition to being both a preacher and a
teacher, Priestley was a friend of James Watt, inventor of the steam engine, and
of Benjamin Franklin. His scholarship and research on electricity won him election
as a Fellow of the Royal Academy at the age of 33, in 1766. Two years later he
started experiments in chemistry. In his celebrated experiment, he confined a
sample of so-called "calx of mercury" in a glass vessel over mercury and heated it

with a large burning lens twelve inches in diameter. The red powder gave off an "air" which supported combustion of a candle and a glowing splint of wood much more vigorously than anything observed previously.

After much study of this material and many repetitions of his experiment with suitable variations, Priestley came to the conclusion that this was a substance from which phlogiston had been completely removed and named it "dephlogisticated air." He remarked, ". . . it may be conjectured, that it might be peculiarly salutary to the lungs in morbid cases." He thus foreshadowed the use of oxygen tents in severe cases of pneumonia and heart disease.

Two months after his initial discovery Priestley visited Paris and described his experiments to Antoine Lavoisier. He continued his research and kept in contact with Lavoisier during the next two decades. This was the time of the American Revolution and of the ensuing French Revolution, neither of which were popular with the majority in England. Priestley was a dissenting clergyman, and among other unpopular causes, he espoused the French revolutionaries, although he condemned their excesses. For this position he became the object of mob violence in Birmingham in 1791. His library, laboratory, chapel, and home were destroyed, and he moved to London. Three years later he found it expedient to move to the United States, whose citizens were more in sympathy with his views. His American home located in Northumberland, Pennsylvania, is preserved as a historical shrine.

FIG. 2–1. Antoine Lavoisier and Madame Lavoisier. From the portrait by Jacques L. David, 1788. (Courtesy of The Rockefeller University.)

2–5 Combustion; Lavoisier's Early Studies

Antoine Lavoisier (Fig. 2–1) was a French aristocrat whose influence was felt in diverse fields in addition to chemistry, where his work is best known. As a member of the organization which was entrusted with a monopoly of the collection of taxes, he became interested in economic reform. He was the founder of the system of experimental farms whose distant echoes are still heard in our county agricultural experiment stations. He was a leader in the reform of education in France. He was the originator of the system that is now known as "social security." His research on the production of heat by the human body founded the modern science of physiological chemistry, and similar work on heat production by chemicals laid the basis for modern thermochemistry and thermodynamics. He was the French

Commissioner of Gunpowder and introduced innovations in its manufacture that improved both the quality and the quantity of the product. These studies were one of the sources of Napoleon's early power. One of Lavoisier's friends and collaborators was E. I. du Pont de Nemours. The du Pont family was rendered destitute by the events of the French Revolution and, as a result, emigrated to the United States in 1800. Young Eleuthère Irénée found that gunpowder was in demand in his new home so he used the knowledge gained in his work with Lavoisier in founding the first American powder factory on the Brandywine Creek.

When Lavoisier heard about Priestley's experiments on "dephlogisticated air," he hastened to repeat and extend them. He studied the calcination of mercury and the decomposition of the calx under a variety of conditions. He also studied the same reaction on tin and lead, as well as on phosphorus and sulfur. As a result of this work, he came to the conclusion that ordinary air is a mixture of a *"mofette,"* or asphyxiant, and of another material which he first called "eminently respirable air." This was Priestley's dephlogisticated air. Lavoisier's studies on the combustion of phosphorus and sulfur, however, led him to the further conclusion that the "eminently respirable air" was a constant and necessary constituent of acids, so he decided to rename the substance "oxygen" which means acid-former. Despite the fact that this latter conclusion was later disproved, the name "oxygen" had become so firmly a part of the language that the misnomer could not be corrected, and has persisted.

Supporters of the phlogiston theory had asserted that the process of combustion was limited by the release of phlogiston and that this was the reason that a candle burning in air confined in a glass vessel was extinguished before all the air was consumed. Lavoisier showed quite clearly that when the air was replaced by oxygen no such limitation was present. The limitation on combustion was caused by the presence of the "mofette," and not by the release of phlogiston, for when the same combustion went on even more vigorously in oxygen, no limitation was observed. In Lavoisier's mind and in the minds of certain of his contemporaries, this constituted a death blow to the phlogiston theory. Resistance to the general acceptance of his ideas was present, however, because of the seemingly inexplicable behavior of still another substance, known then as "inflammable air."

2–6   The Discovery of Hydrogen

Robert Boyle had shown in 1659 that the action of diluted "oil of vitriol" (sulfuric acid) on iron nails caused the evolution of an "air" which could be collected in an inverted bottle. It was not until a century later, in 1766, that Henry Cavendish isolated a quantity of this substance and studied its properties. In personality, Cavendish was the prototype of the much-heralded "thinking machine": a careful observer, a skillful experimenter, and a gifted reasoner, with little apparent interest in any activities outside his laboratory. Cavendish recognized the flammability of the "air" produced by the action of acids on certain metals, and the material came to be known as "inflammable air." However, the nature and product of its combustion were unknown.

2–7   The Formation of Water by Combustion

Lavoisier began a study of "inflammable air" in 1774. Probably in 1776 another French investigator, Macquer, set fire to a jet of the substance and observed the condensation of a colorless liquid on a cold surface. This seemed to him to be water, but he did not verify the observation, and its significance was lost. During the next few years a number of investigators examined this combustion and some of them recorded the observation of a "smoke" with the process. Priestley reported that glass vessels in which the combustion, or rather explosion, was performed became "dewy." Cavendish's interest in the material was reawakened and in 1781 he set up a large combustion chamber with two jets leading into it, one of common air, the other of "inflammable air." He states that "as neither inflammable nor common air can burn by themselves, there was no danger of the flame spreading into the magazines from which they were conveyed." He records that he obtained 135 grains or about nine grams of water in the cylinder, "which had no taste or smell, and which left no sensible sediment when evaporated to dryness." Thus Cavendish established unequivocally for the first time that water was formed by the combustion of "inflammable air" in ordinary air. Yet he did not draw the conclusion, obvious to us now, that water was the result of a chemical reaction between the two materials. Rather, he thought that each was a form of water, ordinary air being water with a deficiency of phlogiston, "inflammable air," water with an excess of phlogiston. The release of the phlogiston permitted the condensation of the water.

In passing, it should be noted that at this time Cavendish succeeded in causing an electric spark to burn the nitrogen in air with Priestley's dephlogisticated air to form nitric acid. He observed that in spite of his best efforts, a small bubble of air which could not be burned was left after the combustion. Again, a century was to elapse before this phenomenon was explained by the "discovery" of the rare gases by Rayleigh.

2–8   The Overthrow of Greek Cosmology

Lavoisier was informed of Cavendish's discovery that water could be formed by the combustion of "inflammable air" in ordinary air by a mutual friend, Charles Blagden. His first reaction was one of incredulity, since he believed that oxygen was an acid-former and yet it was obvious that water was not an acid. He soon established the correctness of Cavendish's observations to his own satisfaction and went on to further experiments. Late in 1783, at a meeting of the French Academy Lavoisier challenged a concept which had been held for over two thousand years with his historic memoir entitled, "On the Nature of Water and on Experiments that appear to prove that this Substance is not, properly speaking, an Element, but can be decomposed and recombined." Thus he finally drew the correct conclusion from the experiment of Cavendish, namely, that water is composed of the two substances that we now call "hydrogen" and "oxygen" and that the concept of phlogiston need have no place in the explanation of the process of combustion.

2–9 The Beginning of Modern Chemistry

The understanding of the composition of water was the last barrier to an understanding of the nature of chemical processes, and before long Lavoisier was writing chemical equations, although he used full words in his equations rather than the abbreviated notation which was introduced later. He drew up a table of the chemical elements and discussed at length the problems of chemical nomenclature and "language." He urged that a simplification and sharpening of the language of chemistry would aid in avoiding the acceptance of false presumptions, such as that of phlogiston, and would aid in clear reasoning and analysis. He and his collaborators adopted the definition of a chemical element which had been proposed by Boyle over a century earlier: "A substance that we cannot decompose." In his *Elementary Treatise on Chemistry* published in 1789, he lists the materials then regarded as elements with the admission that later work might show some of them to be capable of decomposition. In the quantitative section of the work, he lists the combining weights of each of the elements. This was the crowning achievement of the new system, enabling the investigator to write an equation for a reaction which would show not only the reagents which went into it and the products formed but also the amounts of each. This was the real beginning of modern chemistry and laid the groundwork for our very adaptable system of chemical formulas and equations.

2–10 Quantitative Combustion

During his last years, Lavoisier initiated the quantitative combustion of organic substances, using a weighed amount of sample and weighing the carbon dioxide and water formed by the combustion. This method is the basis for the modern combustion analysis of organic compounds and permits the determination of their elementary composition. (See Fig. 2–2.)

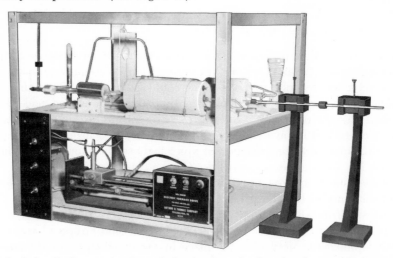

FIG. 2–2. Modern combustion train for the determination of carbon and hydrogen.

The following example shows the type of information the method can give. Using rounded modern values of the atomic weights, we see that a weighed sample of a gas produces 11 mg of carbon dioxide on combustion. If we take the atomic weights of carbon and oxygen as 12 and 16 respectively, the corresponding weight of carbon dioxide is 44, of which $\frac{12}{44}$ or $\frac{3}{11}$ is carbon. Hence the sample contained 3 mg of carbon. The original sample weighed 4 mg so it is $\frac{3}{4}$ or 75% carbon. Combustion also produces 9 mg of water. Taking the atomic weight of hydrogen as 1, we see that water is $\frac{2}{18}$ or $\frac{1}{9}$ hydrogen. This means that the sample contained 1 mg of hydrogen. But its weight was 4 mg so it is $\frac{1}{4}$ or 25% hydrogen.

Lavoisier's political and social activities inevitably involved him in the events of the French revolution. He was one of the leaders in many of the reforms proposed by the revolutionaries including the introduction of the metric system. His studies on the manufacture of gunpowder were critical to the early successes of the revolutionary armies. Yet his membership in the organization of tax collectors and his correspondence with English, Italian, and Spanish scientists may have lent credence in suspicious minds to charges of complicity with foreigners which were brought against him. He was tried in the highly charged atmosphere of the Terror before a warped judge who is reputed to have said, "The Republic has no need of men of science." After a trial that was a mockery of justice, he was condemned and was executed forthwith on the guillotine. Lagrange is said to have remarked the next day, "Only a moment to cut off that head and a hundred years may not give us another like it."

2–11 The Successors of Lavoisier

Lavoisier laid heavy emphasis on the use of quantitative methods, and his work implied quantitative conversions. (Figure 2–3 shows a modern apparatus for quantitative determinations.) His successors set out to exploit these methods and to test their limits. In 1792 Benjamin Richter published his *Outlines of Stoichiometry*, thus coining the term which has persisted to the present for the measurement of the proportions of substances entering into and resulting from chemical reactions. In this work he presents essentially the first table of equivalents. It remained for the French chemist Joseph L. Proust to supply the painstaking work on which the law of constant proportions could be regarded as having been definitely established. In opposition to the views of his colleague Berthollet, Proust undertook careful purifications of his samples for analysis and concluded that the proportions in which the elements entered into chemical combinations were indeed constant. By 1808 the law of constant proportions had been established.

It is interesting to note that in advancing his own case, Berthollet stated that a substance undergoing chemical reaction might divide itself among two others "in proportion to their quantities." This was a statement of the law of mass action which was not established for another sixty years. It was not given due credence at the time, however, because of the demonstration of the presence of impurities in Berthollet's preparations.

FIG. 2–3. Chemical balances have evolved considerably since Lavoisier first stressed their importance in the laboratory. This shows the interior of a modern microchemical balance.

In his studies on both inorganic and organic compounds, J. J. Berzelius, the great Swedish chemist, had established, by 1812, the additional fact that while the proportions of the elements in a given compound were constant in different samples, yet other compounds might contain different ratios of these elements. Examples are the ratios of oxygen to sulfur in the sulfates and sulfites, and of oxygen to nitrogen in the nitrates and nitrites.

2–12 Chemical Symbolism; Communication Theory

Chemists still needed a shorthand system for writing their equations. The alchemists had their symbols which were geometrical in nature. A more modern geometrical system was proposed by John Dalton to support his atomic theory. This was published in 1808. Such geometrical symbols had no intrinsic meaning, however, and could easily lead to ambiguity. A more meaningful system was proposed in 1814 by Berzelius. He used the first letter or two of the name of an element as its symbol. This is the system which was adopted and has been preserved to the present time. Its use is probably the first practical application of the method of symbolic logic, half a century before the term was introduced and the concepts formalized by the English mathematician George Boole and his contemporaries Augustus DeMorgan and Sir William Rowan Hamilton. This method has come to be a powerful tool in the organization of masses of data for purposes of communication and is at the basis of modern communication theory. One of its modern applications is in data storage and retrieval by computers.

2–13 Empirical Formulas

The type of calculation which Berzelius performed can be illustrated by using our previous example. We found this sample to be 75% carbon and 25% hydrogen. We want to find how many atoms of carbon are contained in it and how many atoms of hydrogen. Since the atomic weight of carbon is 12, one unit of the sample would contain 0.75 units of carbon and the atomic fraction would be 0.75/12, or 0.0625. The equivalent weight of hydrogen is 1. One unit of the sample would contain 0.25 units of hydrogen, or 0.25/1 equivalents of hydrogen. The ratio of atoms of carbon to those of hydrogen would be 0.0625/0.25 or $\frac{1}{4}$. Hence the compound would contain carbon and hydrogen in the ratio of one carbon to four hydrogens. Consequently, its formula would be CH_4. A formula determined in this manner is called an "empirical formula."

Berzelius also succeeded in refining analytical methods so that results of greater precision could be obtained. With precision as his objective, however, his procedures were slow, requiring as long as a month for the analytical examination of a single compound. In 1831, Justus von Liebig initiated the use of the carbon and hydrogen train, which was retained for over a century and whose principle is still employed, although on a small scale, in modern microchemical analysis (Fig. 2–4). With the methods of Liebig, chemists were able to examine a wide variety of organic substances and to write formulations based on their analytical compositions. One matter of convenience still remained, however. The determination of nitrogen was clumsy. It required that the volume of the oxygen introduced into a combustion be measured accurately and that the volume of the combustion products be measured again after removal of the carbon dioxide and water. In 1833 Dumas proposed that nitrogen be determined in a separate sample in which the com-

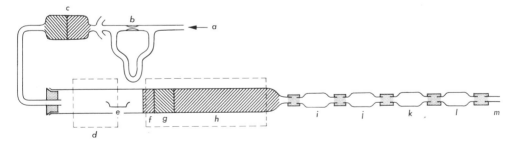

FIG. 2–4. Microchemical carbon and hydrogen train: a, source of oxygen; b, flowmeter; c, guard tube to remove CO_2 and H_2O; d, moving furnace to perform combustion; e, boat to hold sample; f, platinum cracking surface; g, cupric oxide; h, copper chromite combustion catalyst; i, tube to remove halogens (Ag) or sulfur ($PbCrO_4$); j, magnesium perchlorate to remove water; k, hopcalite (CuO-MnO_2) to remove oxides of nitrogen; l, sodium hydroxide-asbestos to remove carbon dioxide; m, capillary tip to prevent back diffusion.

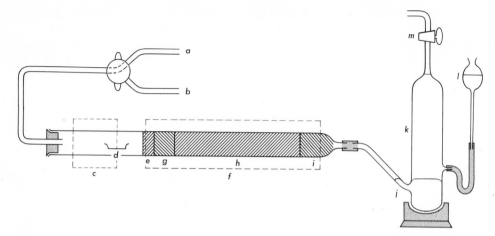

FIG. 2–5. Modern modification of the Dumas apparatus for the determination of nitrogen:
a, source of oxygen; b, source of carbon dioxide; c, moving furnace for combustion; d, boat with
samples; e, platinum cracking surface; f, combustion furnace; g, nickel oxide; h, metallic copper;
i, cupric oxide; j; mercury valve. k, potassium hydroxide solution; l, leveling bulb; m, mercury
displacement system for measurement of nitrogen formed. The sample is burned in the minimum
amount of oxygen and any excess oxygen is absorbed by the copper. The nitrogen bubble is swept
through with carbon dioxide which is removed by the potassium hydroxide. The nitrogen bubble
is then measured by displacement of mercury, which is weighed.

bustion would be performed in admixture with powdered cupric oxide in a current
of carbon dioxide (Fig. 2–5). This was then absorbed in **KOH** solution and the
residual nitrogen formed from the sample was determined volumetrically as
nitrogen gas. With this further refinement, organic chemists were able to explore
alkaloids and other compounds of nitrogen much more freely.

PROBLEMS

2–1   The dry distillation of wood to form charcoal yields wood alcohol, also called "methyl
alcohol," as a fraction of the distillate. The combustion of 5 mg of methyl alcohol yielded
5.625 mg of water and 6.875 mg of carbon dioxide. Calculate the percentage of carbon and
hydrogen in the material.

Qualitative analysis of methyl alcohol shows that no element other than carbon, hydrogen,
and oxygen is present. Calculate the percentage of oxygen in methyl alcohol.

How many equivalents of carbon, hydrogen, and oxygen does methyl alcohol contain?
What is its empirical formula?

2–2   After one eats asparagus, his urine assumes a characteristic repulsive odor. Treatment
of such urine with mercuric chloride yields a precipitate of a "mercaptide." After purification,
the mercury may be removed, and it is found that the odorous substance has been concentrated as a material which boils a few degrees above the melting point of ice and is,
therefore, a gas at room temperature. This substance is called "methyl mercaptan."

The combustion of 5 mg of methyl mercaptan yielded 4.577 mg of carbon dioxide and 3.749 mg of water. Calculate the percentage of carbon and hydrogen in the material.

Qualitative analysis of methyl mercaptan shows that it contains sulfur. Combustion of a 5 mg sample, followed by oxidation of the sulfur dioxide formed with hydrogen peroxide, yielded 10.207 mg of sulfuric acid, which was determined by titration with a standard sample of alkali. Calculate the percentage of sulfur in the compound. What other elements may be present besides carbon, hydrogen, and sulfur?

How many equivalents of carbon, hydrogen, and sulfur does methyl mercaptan contain? What is its empirical formula?

2–3 A 1.458-mg sample of a gas was burned and found to produce 4.937 mg of carbon dioxide and 1.012 mg of water.

(a) Does the gas molecule contain any other element in addition to carbon and hydrogen?

(b) What is the empirical formula for the gas?

(c) Suppose that its molecular weight were determined to be 26. What would the molecular formula of the gas be?

(d) Assume that the molecular weight is 78. What would the molecular formula of the gas be?

2–4 One of the building blocks of penicillin, 6-aminopenicillanic acid, was obtained when certain materials were omitted from the penicillin fermentation liquors. The pure crystalline substance was analyzed, and the data thus obtained indicated an elementary composition of 44.4% carbon, 5.6% hydrogen, 13.0% nitrogen, and 14.8% sulfur. The remainder was assumed to be oxygen.

(a) If one sulfur atom is present in the molecule, what is its molecular formula?

(b) What is the lowest possible molecular weight for 6-aminopenicillanic acid?

Atomic weights of common elements

Bromine	Br	79.909
Carbon	C	12.0115
Chlorine	Cl	35.453
Fluorine	F	18.9984
Hydrogen	H	1.00797
Iodine	I	126.9044
Nitrogen	N	14.0067
Oxygen	O	15.9994
Phosphorus	P	30.9738
Potassium	K	39.102
Sodium	Na	22.9898
Sulfur	S	32.064

How did the discovery of isomerism confront chemists with the problem of structure? Why was the determination of molecular weights necessary to delimit the structural problem? How did Frankland and Kekulé determine molecular weights by progressive substitution? By atomic ratios? How did Avogadro and Cannizzaro determine molecular weights from gas densities?

3

THE THEORY OF ORGANIC CHEMICAL STRUCTURES

3-1 Intercomparison of Samples

As organic chemists explored the wonders of the substances found in plants and animals, new problems arose constantly. To solve these problems, new methods had to be devised. One of the most pressing of the early problems was that of the intercomparison of samples. Suppose that a substance had been obtained from one source and then a sample which appeared to be identical was prepared from another source. How was one to know whether or not they were, in fact, identical? Early solutions to this problem were found which were adequate for the comparison of simple substances, but as the studies of organic chemists have encompassed more and more complex materials, the problem of effective means for intercomparison keeps presenting itself over and over.

The most useful solution to the problem of the proof of identity of two samples was that advanced by Michel Chevreul, who was born in 1786 and lived to the age of 103. Chevreul elected to study the composition of animal fats. He found that the soaps obtained when fats were treated with alkali could be converted into crystalline acids when they were reacted with mineral acids. He purified these fatty acids by recrystallization and decided that he had achieved purity when the melting points became constant. Charles Blagden, the friend of Cavendish who had reported the combustion of hydrogen to Lavoisier, had already made a study

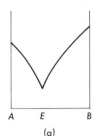 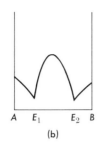 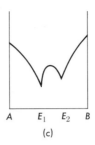 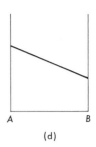

A   E   B   A E_1 E_2 B   A E_1 E_2 B   A   B
     (a)   (b)   (c)   (d)

FIG. 3–1.   Some typical melting point-composition diagrams. In these diagrams the y-coordinate is temperature and the x-coordinate is composition. The latter ranges from 100 mole percent of A at the point marked A to 100 mole percent of B at the point marked B. (a) The usual type of melting point diagram; E is the eutectic. (b) The case in which A and B form a compound which melts higher than either; two eutectics are formed, E_1 and E_2. (c) The case in which A and B form a melting compound lower than either. Again two eutectics are formed. (d) The case in which A and B form a perfect solid solution. In this case the method of mixed melting points fails.

of the effects of impurities on freezing points and had learned that the freezing point of a melt was depressed when a foreign substance was introduced. It was obvious, then, that the removal of the impurity would raise the freezing or melting point. It was but a short step to the powerful method of mixed melting points. Logically, there seemed no reason why two different substances could not have the same melting point and, indeed, cases in which this occurs are now known to be numerous. If one of these substances is different from the other, however, it should act as an impurity in the melt of the other so that the melting point of each would be depressed by the other (see Fig. 3–1). Hence two substances with the same melting point were presumed to be identical when a mixture of the two melted at the same point as the individuals. While rare exceptions to this rule are now known, the method has served well since it was published in 1823.

3–2   Isomerism

Also in 1823, Justus von Liebig published the results of his studies on the salts of fulminic acid. The twenty-year-old Liebig must already have developed careful work habits in the laboratory, since many of the fulminates are notoriously sensitive to shock and will explode if handled carelessly. They are used even now as detonators for explosives. Liebig's analyses of the fulminates were published in the *Annales de Chimie*. A year later Friedrich Wöhler, who was then only twenty-four, published a paper in the same journal on the composition of the cyanates. The editor of the journal was the distinguished French chemist Gay-Lussac. It is apparent that he took his editorial duties seriously, since he called the attention of both young men to the fact that the analyses of the two sets of materials were the same. This discovery brought Liebig and Wöhler together and each soon adopted the habit of submitting papers to the other before publication. In many studies they collaborated and this collaboration lasted throughout their lives.

More discoveries of different substances with identical analyses followed quickly. Berzelius, in stating the law of constant proportions, had also stated its converse, namely, that only a single substance could exist with a given analysis. In 1830 he examined tartaric and racemic acids. These substances have different melting points and therefore could not be identical. Despite this, Berzelius found that the analyses were identical. Faced with his own evidence he was forced to conclude that more than one substance could exist with a single analysis. He coined the word "isomerism," meaning composed of equal parts, to denote this phenomenon.

3–3   The Structural Problem; Kekulé

Recognition of the existence of isomerism immediately brought with it the challenge to explain it. Many of the best chemical brains of the time were devoted to this problem, but its solution was to be delayed for about thirty years. During this time, fact after fact was added to the store, and methods for the manipulation of organic substances were improved. New reactions were discovered and with the gradual accumulation of knowledge, the stage was set for the emergence of one of the most brilliant and fruitful concepts of the nineteenth century, that of structure theory. A central figure in the elucidation of the problem was August Kekulé.

Kekulé was born in 1829. He became fascinated with the study of architecture in his early teens, and at eighteen he went to the University of Giessen to study it. To understand the events that followed, one must know more about the university system in Europe at that time.

Before a young man entered a German university, he would have completed his training at a "gymnasium," where he took an accelerated course leading to a level roughly corresponding to that of a college sophomore here. The student did not work for the baccalaureate, but instead started directly for his doctorate. His first year was spent in attending the lectures of all the outstanding teachers whose work interested him, largely without regard for their fields of specialization, but with some regard to the problem of selecting the professor under whom he wished to pursue his studies. He would then undertake specialization and after several years would complete his doctoral dissertation. In preparing for his doctoral examinations he might also choose to work for a time at universities other than that of his choice to round out his grasp of his field. Finally, he submitted his dissertation and underwent his examinations.

The young student of architecture at Giessen in 1847 heard that one of the most distinguished and interesting lecturers in the university was Liebig. Kekulé was so impressed and enthused by Liebig's lectures and scientific objectives that he abandoned the study of architecture and became a chemist. Yet he could not abandon his feeling for form and structure. The habits of thought that his early interest had aroused persisted. His interest in spatial relationships led him to visualize things in three dimensions, as architects must. He applied these abilities to the problems of chemistry and, in a very real sense, became the first chemical architect.

Kekulé obtained his doctorate in 1852. It is interesting to note that in the academic year 1851–1852, he studied in Paris. In 1853, he went to Switzerland as a postdoctoral student, and in 1854, to London to work with Stenhouse.

3–4 The Oxygen-Sulfur Parallel

Kekulé's first publication came in 1854 and concerned sulfur chemistry. Most people know the odor of hydrogen sulfide, but those of its organic derivatives are not so well known. Their odors are incomparably worse than that of hydrogen sulfide. Being heavier, they are more clinging. They are the standard reference substances for illustrating the extreme limits of the human nose in odor detection. It takes a brave investigator to jeopardize his social standing by undertaking the study of the organic derivatives of hydrogen sulfide. Despite these drawbacks, the prizes to be obtained from the comparison of the properties of sulfur with those of oxygen seemed so important that Kekulé undertook the study.

One of the problems that puzzled chemists during the period from 1830 to 1860 was that of relative atomic and molecular sizes. For example, the relative proportions of hydrogen to oxygen in water were then well known as approximately one to eight. Some reasoned that this meant that an atom of oxygen weighed eight times as much as an atom of hydrogen.

Many contemporary chemists, such as the Frenchman Dumas and his students Laurent and Gerhardt, the German Hermann Kolbe and his English student Edward Frankland, were studying the reactions of organic compounds. As a result, a variety of organic reactions was known. These reactions had been classified, and with them a systematic classification of organic compounds was being evolved. This was the state of knowledge when Kekulé reached London.

Using the knowledge of organic reactions which had been accumulated, it was possible to set up an imposing list of derivatives of water which established by progressive substitution the fact that there were two hydrogens on oxygen in water. Kekulé proceeded to perform the same exercise on sulfur.

Series 1

Kolbe's water series		Kekulé's hydrogen sulfide series	
Water	HOH	Hydrogen sulfide	HSH
Methyl alcohol	CH_3OH	Methyl mercaptan	CH_3SH
Dimethyl ether	CH_3OCH_3	Dimethyl sulfide	CH_3SCH_3

It had been learned that the action of methyl iodide on aqueous alkali would produce methyl alcohol, also called methanol.

$$CH_3I + NaOH \rightarrow CH_3OH + NaI$$

Kekulé found that methyl iodide and sodium hydrogen sulfide would produce methyl mercaptan in a parallel reaction. Williamson had recently found that the action of methyl iodide on a dry methanolic solution of potassium methoxide would produce dimethyl ether. Kekulé, in a parallel reaction, prepared dimethyl sulfide by the action of methyl iodide on the salt of methyl mercaptan.

To confirm the reasoning involved, a second series was constructed. Williamson and Gerhardt had already written acetic acid as a derivative of water and had predicted the discovery of acetic anhydride as a doubly substituted derivative of water. Kekulé extended these formulations to the sulfur series by the use of phosphorus pentasulfide.

Series 2

Williamson and Gerhardt's series		Kekulé's series	
Water	HOH	Hydrogen sulfide	HSH
Acetic acid	C_2H_3O—OH	Thioacetic acid	C_2H_3O—SH
Acetic anhydride	$(C_2H_3O)_2O$	Thioacetic anhydride	$(C_2H_3O)_2S$
Ethyl acetate	C_2H_3O—OC_2H_5	Ethyl thioacetate	C_2H_3O—SC_2H_5

(The prefix "thio" indicates the presence of sulfur.)

It was observed that the action of phosphorus pentachloride on acetic acid produced acetyl chloride.

$$CH_3COOH + PCl_5 \rightarrow CH_3COCl + POCl_3 + HCl$$

This, in turn, would react with water to regenerate acetic acid, thus demonstrating that acetic acid can be derived from water. Kekulé found that phosphorus pentasulfide would react with acetic acid to produce thioacetic acid.

After the prediction of the preparation of acetic anhydride, it was learned that the reaction of acetyl chloride with the sodium salt of acetic acid would, in fact, make acetic anhydride.

$$CH_3COCl + CH_3COONa \rightarrow CH_3COOCOCH_3 + NaCl$$

Kekulé found that if he used the sodium salt of thioacetic acid and reacted it with acetyl chloride, he could produce thioacetic anhydride.

The representative of the mixed type of series 1 and series 2, ethyl acetate, could be prepared by the reaction of alcohol with acetic acid in the presence of a little hydrochloric acid. Kekulé also found that the analogous reaction would proceed in the sulfur series.

3-5   The Molecular Weights of Water and Hydrogen Sulfide

Along with Frankland, Kekulé argued that the possibility of producing two successive substitutions of hydrogen on the water molecule showed that the oxygen atom had two "affinity units" and that, consequently, water should be written as H_2O, not as HO. Since the weight proportions had already been established as one to eight, this meant that the minimum atomic weight of oxygen must be 16, not 8 as some had argued. By the same reasoning, Kekulé argued that the sulfur atom in the organic sulfides which he had prepared had two "affinity units" and that hydrogen sulfide must be written as H_2S. Since the weight proportions in this case had been established as one to sixteen, this meant that the minimum atomic weight for sulfur must be 32.

3-6   The Molecular Weight of Methane

After completing his investigations of the "affinity" of sulfur, Kekulé next turned his attention to the central problem of organic chemistry, the problem of the modes of combination of the carbon atom. This had been the subject of bitter controversies involving Berzelius, Dumas, Laurent, Gerhardt, Frankland and many others prominent in chemistry in the early half of the nineteenth century. Dumas had discovered that hydrogen in some carbon compounds could be replaced by chlorine, a discovery which Berzelius was loath to concede. Dumas drew back from exploiting the implications of this discovery but his pupils Laurent and Gerhardt did not. As a result they earned their master's displeasure and active opposition. Kekulé was prepared to explore these reactions and to proceed with their interpretation. He found that, by one method or another, it was possible to prepare four different chlorine substitution products of methane, namely, methyl chloride, methylene chloride, chloroform, and carbon tetrachloride. He formulated these in the logical manner indicated below.

Chlorine derivatives of methane

Methane	CH_4
Methyl chloride	CH_3Cl
Methylene chloride	CH_2Cl_2
Chloroform	$CHCl_3$
Carbon tetrachloride	CCl_4

Because of the fact that progressive substitution of the hydrogens on the carbon of methane could be achieved one step at a time up to a maximum of four, it followed that methane must be CH_4, not CH_2 as some chemists had insisted. By the same reasoning as that applied to oxygen and sulfur, carbon must have four affinity units. About a decade later, the German chemist Wichelhaus applied the term "wertigkeit" to these affinity units. This was translated into English as "valence." Thus Kekulé's argument was that the valence of carbon was four.

3-7   The Molecular Weights of Proteins; A Modern Application

It is interesting to note that the determination of molecular weights by the method of progressive substitution has recently been revived by Lyman Craig for the vastly more difficult problem of the molecular weights of proteins. Physical methods, when applied to proteins, led to conflicting results. Application of the chemical method demonstrated that the proteins examined had much lower molecular weights than had been thought and opened the door to the application of synthetic methods in this field. This subject will be discussed in Chapter 21.

3-8   The Molecular Weight of Benzene

It was during his stay in London that Kekulé began to worry about the formula for benzene. This was before it was known that the proper formula for benzene was C_6H_6. Some chemists even wrote benzene as CH. Kekulé had been a student of Liebig, who had collaborated with Wöhler in fundamental studies on the reactions of the benzoyl radical. We now know that the formula for the benzoyl radical is C_6H_5CO. This can be thought of as made up of two parts, the CO part, which we can find in other acid radicals such as the acetyl radical, CH_3CO, and the phenyl part, C_6H_5. Kekulé perceived from the analysis and the carbon-to-oxygen ratio that the phenyl part of the benzoyl radical had much more carbon in it than would correspond to the formula CH. By reasoning from the analytical evidence, he was able to arrive at a minimum formula for the benzoyl radical and, from this, ultimately to arrive at a minimum formula for benzene itself. Even though other chemists had not generally accepted the correctness of the formula C_6H_6, Kekulé was sure that it was right and that he would be able to demonstrate this to everyone's satisfaction. So while others were concerning themselves with the problem of the formula for benzene, Kekulé had turned to the problem of the arrangement of the atoms which could constitute its structure.

3-9   The Structure of Benzene

Kekulé, following his architectural bent, liked to attempt to arrange atoms into three-dimensional figures in molecular structures. Yet these structures had to be constrained by the limits of the numbers of "affinity units" which he had learned were present in the building blocks that he had at his disposal. How could he reconcile the fact that carbon had four affinity units, hydrogen had only one, yet in benzene equal numbers of carbons and hydrogens were to be found? Many years later he recounted the following story of a famous dream (for a cartoon of the dream, see Fig. 3-2) which he experienced while in London:

> During my residence in London, I lived for some time on Clapham Road, near the Common. I often spent the evenings in Islington, at the opposite end of that great city, with my friend, Hugo Müller. We talked of many things; chiefly, however, of our beloved chemistry. One beautiful summer evening I was returning on the last omnibus from such a visit. We moved through the then deserted streets of that busy world metropolis. I was riding outside on the top of the omnibus, as was my custom. Soon I fell into a reverie.

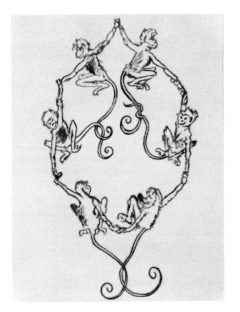
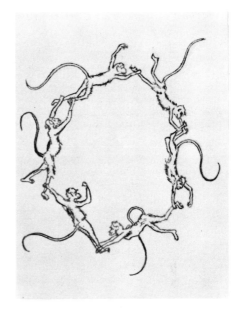

FIG. 3–2. Nineteenth-century cartoonist's conception of Kekulé's dream.

I imagined I saw the atoms dancing around before my eyes. I had dreamed of seeing those diminutive beings in motion before but had never been able to discern clearly the exact nature of their movements. But this time I noted how often two smaller atoms joined themselves together to form a pair; how larger atoms seized hold of two smaller atoms; while still bigger ones attached to themselves three or even four of the smaller ones; and all kept turning in a whirling ring. I saw how the large ones formed a row and dragged the small ones at the ends of the chain.

The cry of the conductor, "Clapham Road," awakened me from my reverie. But I spent a good part of the night in putting on paper at least sketches of those dream shapes. Thus began the theory of molecular structure.*

When he published his textbook of organic chemistry, Kekulé illustrated his concept of the structure of benzene with models which bear a surprising resemblance to modern ball and stick models of molecules. (See the illustration of Kekulé's benzene model in Fig. 3–3.) To preserve the tetravalence of carbon, he proposed that alternate single and double bonds be used between the carbon atoms.

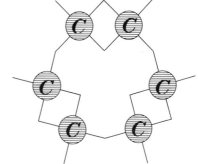

FIG. 3–3. Kekulé's benzene model. (From A. Kekulé, *Lehrbuch der Organischen Chemie*, Stuttgart: F. Enke, 1866.)

* Translated from *Berichte der Deutschen Chemischen Gesellschaft* **23,** 1306 (1890).

3–10   The Congress of Karlsruhe; Cannizzaro

Despite the convincing nature of the arguments which were advanced by Kekulé to support the conclusion that carbon was tetravalent, chemists still clung, sometimes desperately, to earlier theories which led to confusion regarding the nature of the compounds of carbon. For example, in his textbook, Kekulé was able to write a large number of different formulas which had been suggested for acetic acid. In an attempt to clear up this confusion, Kekulé, his friend Weltzien, and Charles Wurtz organized a meeting of chemists from all countries to try to settle disputed points. Thus the First International Chemical Congress, which met in Karlsruhe on September 3, 1860, came about. The Congress did not succeed in its objective of introducing new order into the confusion. Despite this fact, it proved to be the turning point in the history of organic chemistry because of the presence there of a thirty-four-year-old Italian, Stanislao Cannizzaro, who for two years had been Professor of Chemistry at the University of Genoa. In his course in elementary chemistry at the University of Genoa he had been teaching the students modern applications of the hypothesis of Avogadro, which had been formulated fifty years earlier.

Amadeo Avogadro was born in 1776 and died in 1856, just four years before the Congress of Karlsruhe that was to provide the means for the acceptance of his ideas. In 1811 he put forward the hypothesis which bears his name. This was based on an assumption that had been examined even earlier by John Dalton but which he had rejected. The hypothesis was that equal volumes of different gases under the same conditions of pressure and temperature would contain equal numbers of particles. His argument was that atoms of a gas could combine with each other to form molecules. In reactions with other gases, these molecules could then split apart, and the individual atoms could combine with others to form new molecules of a different composition.

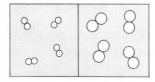   

FIG. 3–4. The diatomic nature of hydrogen and chlorine. Let x = 4 (see text). The product contains eight molecules of hydrogen chloride and consequently eight atoms each of hydrogen and chlorine. Therefore each of the four molecules of hydrogen contains two atoms and each of the four molecules of chlorine contains two atoms.

The acceptance of Avogadro's hypothesis leads to the conclusion that hydrogen and chlorine are diatomic molecules because of their proportions in the formation of hydrogen chloride. One volume of hydrogen combines with one volume of chlorine to form two volumes of hydrogen chloride. If we assume that each volume of hydrogen chloride contains x molecules, then there must be $2x$ atoms of chlorine. But this means that one volume of chlorine, which also contains x molecules contains $2x$ atoms, hence each molecule must contain 2 atoms (see Fig. 3–4).

Continuing the same line of reasoning, we see that each molecule of hydrogen must contain two atoms of hydrogen. But when water is formed from hydrogen and oxygen, it is found that two volumes of hydrogen are consumed, together with one volume of oxygen. The resultant water, in the gaseous state, occupies two volumes. Since each volume of hydrogen contains $2x$ atoms, two volumes will contain $4x$ atoms. After combustion, $2x$ molecules of water will then contain $4x$ atoms of hydrogen. Hence each molecule of water will contain two atoms of hydrogen, and water should have the formula H_2O (see Fig. 3–5).

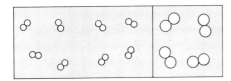 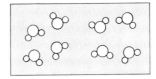

FIG. 3–5. The formula for water. Since eight molecules of water are formed from four molecules of oxygen, each molecule of oxygen must contain two atoms. But eight molecules of hydrogen are required to form eight molecules of water. Each hydrogen molecule contains two atoms. Hence each of the eight molecules of water must contain two atoms each and water is H_2O.

Avogadro concluded that the formula for water was H_2O in 1811, and by similar reasoning the French physicist Ampère reached the same conclusion in 1814. Acceptance of this conclusion was blocked by the influence of Berzelius who had formulated a dualistic hypothesis of chemical union. On the basis of much study of inorganic chemistry, he felt that the fundamental forces which bound atoms together were electrical in nature and that they should be designated as "positive" and "negative." Since two positives should not combine, it followed that two hydrogens should not combine, hence hydrogen molecules could not be diatomic.

If chemists had accepted Avogadro's hypothesis in 1811 instead of 1860, half a century of confusion would have been saved, and organic chemistry would have advanced along different and possibly more fruitful lines. Later research revealed, however, that hydrogen could be replaced by chlorine in combinations with carbon, and this and similar developments cast doubt on the tenability of the concept of Berzelius as applied to organic compounds. Laurent and Gerhardt, in particular, advocated a return to the ideas of Avogadro ten years before Cannizzaro succeeded in bringing this about. Thus at least ten years of wandering might have been spared later in the course of development.

Meanwhile, techniques for the measurement of the densities of gases had been refined. Dumas, who opposed Avogadro's ideas, had initiated a relatively convenient technique for the measurement of gas densities, and work of considerable precision had been carried out by another French chemist, Regnault. The result was that when Cannizzaro set forth his list of atomic and molecular weights, based on Avogadro's hypothesis, he had determinations of satisfactory precision to work with. He applied the method to the interpretation of empirical formulas of organic chemistry and showed, for example, that acetylene should be written as C_2H_2, and benzene as C_6H_6.

Cannizzaro had published his lecture notes in the journal of the University of Pisa and had brought a supply of reprints of this publication to Karlsruhe with him. He perceived that Avogadro's hypothesis provided the missing link in the chain of evidence being constructed by the organic chemists of his time. He argued for the adoption of his views, but was to be disappointed in this objective. The distribution of his reprints eventually turned the trick, since the returning chemists had an opportunity to examine and weigh his arguments at their leisure. As a result, Cannizzaro's use of gas densities to determine molecular weights won acceptance within a few years.

The fact that a method based on an entirely different, but self-consistent principle should lead to the same result as that obtained by Kekulé was the deciding circumstance leading to the adoption of both ideas by contemporary chemists. Cannizzaro gained a most influential supporter in the person of Lothar Meyer, who published a text based on this principle in 1864. The book became popular and rapidly spread Avogadro's ideas and Cannizzaro's application of them to the theory of organic chemistry. So it came about that by the converging of two diverse lines of reasoning, the foundations were laid for the general acceptance of the theories of structural organic chemistry.

PROBLEMS

3–1   A chemist had several bottles on his shelf, each containing some crystalline material melting in the range around 120°C. He obtained some gum benzoin and after treating it with base, eventually produced a tan solid melting at 115–119°C. After several recrystallizations from boiling water, the material was much improved in appearance and was obtained as colorless plates. These were found to melt at 120.5–121°C.

(a) Using the charts of Fig. 3–1, explain what has happened.

The chemist took bottle A from his shelf, found that the contents melted at 120.5–121°C, ground a little of A with the product from gum benzoin and found that the mixture melted at 120.5–121°C.

(b) Are these substances identical?

Bottle B also contained crystalline material melting at 120.5–121°C, but on admixture of compound B and the gum benzoin product the resultant was found to melt at 100–115°C.

(c) What would you conclude about compound B? Make use of the charts of Fig. 3–1. Which ones might be applicable?

Bottle C contained a brownish powder melting at 116–119°C, which on being mixed with the gum benzoin product melted at 116–120°C. Bottle D also contained a brown powder melting at 115–118°C; the mixed melting point with the gum benzoin product in this case was 95–104°C.

(d) Do you think C can be related to the gum benzoin product?

(e) Do you think it would be worthwhile to attempt to recrystallize C from boiling water to raise its melting point?

(f) Would you judge whether A and C might be the same thing in different stages of purity?

(g) Is D the same as the gum benzoin product?

(h) Is it possible that bottles D and B contain the same thing?

(i) Is it necessary that they contain the same thing?

(j) Suppose that it were attempted to recrystallize D from boiling water to raise its melting point. If it did not dissolve, even on prolonged boiling, would this be unexpected?

3–2   C. Wurtz found that treatment of methyl iodide with metallic sodium gave a gas which was later named "ethane." Combustion of 5 mg of ethane gave 14.667 mg of carbon dioxide and 9.000 mg of water.

(a) Calculate the percentage of carbon and hydrogen in this material.

(b) How many equivalents of carbon and hydrogen does it contain?

(c) If one assumed that ethane contains only one carbon atom, what would the formula for ethane be?

(d) Assuming Kekulé's postulate of the tetravalence of carbon, what would the formula for ethane be?

(e) A liter of ethane has a mass of 1.34 g at 760 mm Hg and 0°C. Is this in agreement with Kekulé's postulate?

Methane, CH_4, and ethane are the first two members of a *homologous* series of compounds called the *alkanes*. A homologous series is formed by the addition of one carbon unit at a time. The alkanes have the general formula C_nH_{2n+2}. The names of a few of these compounds are given beside the carbon skeleton of the molecule.

C	methane	C—C—C—C	butane
C—C	ethane	C—C—C—C—C	pentane
C—C—C	propane	C—C—C—C—C—C	hexane

Methyl iodide, CH_3I, is the first member of a series of organic halides called *alkyl iodides.*

(f) Fill in the missing valences on these carbon chains. Do they fit the general formula?

(g) From your knowledge of Greek prefixes, what do you think the formulas and skeletons of heptane and octane would be?

(h) What would be the formula for ethyl iodide?

(i) What would you call $CH_3CH_2CH_2I$?

3–3   Complete the following equations (see Section 3–4).

(a) $CH_3I + NaOH \rightarrow$ formation of *alcohols*
(b) $C_2H_5I + NaOH \rightarrow$

An alcohol may be described as a water molecule in which one hydrogen has been replaced by a hydrocarbon radical. An exception to this definition will be noted later.

(c) $CH_3I + NaSH \rightarrow$ formation of a *mercaptan*

A mercaptan (also called a thiol, or thioalcohol) is the sulfur analog of an alcohol.

(d) $CH_3I + NaOCH_3 \rightarrow$ formation of *ethers*
(e) $C_2H_5I + NaOC_2H_5 \rightarrow$

An ether may be described as a water molecule in which both hydrogens have been replaced by hydrocarbon radicals.

(f) $CH_3I + NaSCH_3 \rightarrow$ formation of a *thioether*

A thioether (or sulfide) is the sulfur analog of an ether.

(g) $CH_3COCl + CH_3COONa \rightarrow$
(h) $CH_3COCl + CH_3COSNa \rightarrow$ formation of *anhydrides*

An anhydride is formally a compound made from two organic acid units with the loss of a molecule of water. The sulfur analogs are called thioanhydrides.

(i) $CH_3COOH + C_2H_5OH \xrightarrow{(H^+)}$ formation of an *ester*

An ester is formally a compound made from an acid and an alcohol with the loss of a water molecule.

(j) $CH_3COOH + C_2H_5SH \rightarrow$ formation of a *thioester*

A thioester is the sulfur analog of an ester.

(k) $(CH_3CO)_2O + H_2O \rightarrow$ *hydrolysis* of an anhydride
(l) $(CH_3CO)_2O + CH_3OH \rightarrow$ *alcoholysis* of an anhydride

Reaction (l) illustrates a second method for the preparation of esters.

The tremendous number of compounds available because of the variety of starting materials and the variety of reactions to be performed on them might be expected to lead to confusion. In the third quarter of the last century, however, it became apparent that order could be brought about by the generalization: *Homologous series of compounds have similar chemical properties.* Hence, a homologous series of alcohols may be expected to be formed by the action of base on a homologous series of alkyl iodides, and a homologous series of ethers may be formed from a set of iodides with sodium methoxide, another series with ethoxide, and so on. This greatly reduces the number of reactions which must be learned, since they can now be generalized to reactions of a given type of atom combination, as we have done in the right-hand column. Such special combinations of atoms which undergo a particular set of reactions are known as *functional groups*. We shall see how the validity of these generalizations may be inferred in the next chapter.

3-4   When acetic acid reacts with phosphorus pentachloride, acetyl chloride, phosphorus oxychloride, and hydrogen chloride are formed. Complete the following equation:

(a) $CH_3COOH + PCl_5 \rightarrow$ formation of an *acid chloride*

An acid chloride is *formally* a compound made from an organic acid molecule and a molecule of hydrochloric acid with the loss of water molecules. Acid halides are therefore formally analogous to organic anhydrides, and they undergo many similar reactions.

(b) How might an ester be prepared starting with an acid chloride?

3-5   In their classic study of organic radicals, Friedrich Wöhler and Justus von Liebig published the results of a study on the oil of bitter almonds made in 1832. When bitter almonds were crushed and then extracted with ether, removal of the ether and subsequent fractional distillation yielded benzaldehyde. Qualitative analysis shows that it contains only C, H, and O. The percentage composition is C, 79.24%; H, 5.66%.

(a) Calculate the atomic proportions of C, H, and O in benzaldehyde.

(b) Assuming that there is only one oxygen per molecule, what is the molecular formula of benzaldehyde?

3-6 Wöhler and Liebig found that if pure dry chlorine was passed through pure benzaldehyde, heat was generated with the evolution of hydrogen chloride. A new lachrymatory liquid containing 25.26% Cl, benzoyl chloride, was formed.

(a) How many hydrogens in benzaldehyde have been replaced to form benzoyl chloride?

(b) What is the molecular formula for benzoyl chloride?

3-7 Treatment of benzoyl chloride with aqueous alkali slowly yields a solution of sodium benzoate, which on acidification gives crystals of benzoic acid. This compound contains 68.84% C and 4.95% H, and no other element except oxygen.

(a) What is the molecular formula for benzoic acid?

(b) Write a partial structure for benzoic acid as a derivative of water.

(c) What is the corresponding partial structure for benzoyl chloride?

(d) Did the treatment of benzaldehyde with chlorine replace hydrogen on the phenyl group or on the aldehyde group of benzaldehyde?

(e) How many hydrogens are contained in the phenyl group?

(f) How many in the aldehyde group?

(g) What is the formula for the aldehyde group? The phenyl group?

3-8 Wöhler and Liebig carried out several other transformations and found that the benzoyl radical could be maintained intact in several new compounds.

(a) What would be the products formed from a mixture of benzaldehyde and bromine?

(b) What product would result by warming benzoyl chloride with potassium iodide?

(c) What product would result from the distillation of benzoyl chloride with finely pulverized lead sulfide?

3-9 (a) If we write R for a generalized monovalent organic radical (for example, an alcohol will be ROH, an acid RCOOH, an alkyl iodide RI) what is the general formula for aldehydes?

(b) What structure can you write to account for the valences assigned by Kekulé to the atoms in this formula?

(c) What is the structure of acetaldehyde, which contains two carbons?

3-10 METHODS FOR DETERMINING MOLECULAR WEIGHTS. The application of Avogadro's hypothesis to the determination of molecular weights by means of gas densities is limited to those cases in which the sample has a significant vapor pressure at an easily attainable temperature. Only a small fraction of the total number of organic compounds now known fulfills this requirement. Other methods have been designed for measuring the molecular weights of the remainder. For substances with molecular weights below 1000, these are usually based on the observation that the boiling points of liquids are raised and their freezing points are depressed by the presence of nonvolatile substances as solutes. The increment or decrement in temperature caused by the solute is proportional to the number of its molecules in the solution. Special methods applicable to large molecules have been devised and one of these will be considered when we discuss the chemistry of proteins.

By far the most accurate method for the determination of molecular weights of substances in the lower range is the method of mass spectrometry. This method has the additional advantage that under certain circumstances, much more information than just the molecular weight may be obtained from it.

Molecular weights and mass spectrometry. In 1898 Wien was able to demonstrate that positive rays could be deflected by electric and magnetic fields. Beams of positively or negatively charged particles, for example, electrons, may be bent by the force field of a magnet (Fig. 3–6).

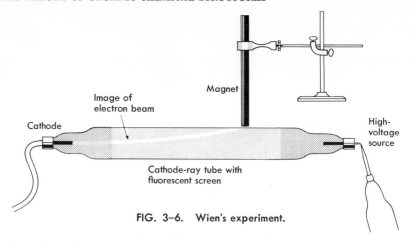

Magnet

Image of
electron beam

Cathode

High-
voltage
source

Cathode-ray tube with
fluorescent screen

FIG. 3–6.   Wien's experiment.

The deflection is dependent on the mass of the charged species as well as the charge. In 1912 Thomson showed the existence of two isotopes of neon, Ne^{20} and Ne^{22}, because ions produced from neon were deflected to different degrees in a uniform magnetic field and gave two different signals in the detector (Fig. 3–7).

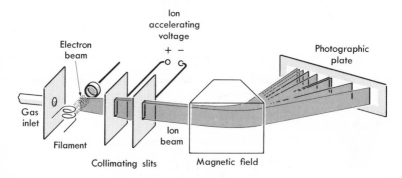

Ion
accelerating
voltage

Electron
beam

+ −

Photographic
plate

Gas
inlet

Ion
beam

Filament

Collimating slits

Magnetic field

FIG. 3–7.   Separation of charged isotopes by a magnetic field. (From B. H. Mahan, *University Chemistry*, Reading, Mass.: Addison-Wesley, 1965.)

It follows that if ions can be produced from a molecule and then passed through a uniform magnetic field so that they are sorted into groups with the same mass, the mass of each kind of ion may be determined on a previously calibrated detector. In fact, even the molecular formula may be determined if the instrument is made accurate enough, because each isotope of each element differs from an integer by a different amount. The deviation from an integer of the molecular ion is the sum of the deviations of all the atoms in it, so that a ready solution of the formula is possible. For example, if two molecules form ions with mass 62, we could distinguish them by a more careful study which might show one to have mass 62.0368 and the other 62.0190. In this case, comparison with tables of isotope masses would indicate molecular formulas of $C_2H_6O_2$ and C_2H_6S, respectively, based on the values of the common isotopes for the elements. Possible structures could be $HOCH_2CH_2OH$ and CH_3SCH_3 or CH_3CH_2SH.

All that is required therefore is that ions be formed from a sample with a slight vapor pressure. Both positive and negative ions may be produced by bombarding an organic

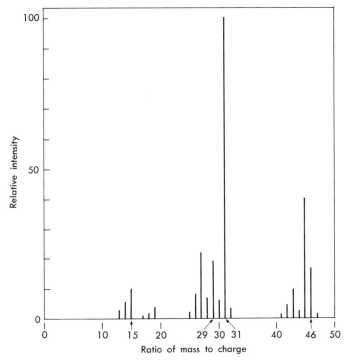

FIG. 3–8. Mass spectrum of ethanol. (After K. Biemann, *Mass Spectrometry: Organic Chemical Applications*, New York: McGraw-Hill, 1962.)

vapor with electrons. Possible modes of formation are:

$$e^- + R = R^+ + 2e^-, \quad e^- + R = R^-$$

Curiously, the positive ions predominate, and most studies have been performed on them.

A molecule ionized in this fashion has a great deal of excess energy, simply from the way in which it was formed. It is no wonder then that the molecular ions have a tendency to "fall apart" into smaller fragments. The mass spectrum of ethyl alcohol (Fig. 3–8), whose structure we shall momentarily assume, has been determined.

This profusion of ions, far from complicating the picture, gives valuable information about the structure. A picture frequently drawn correlates some of the important peaks in the spectrum to fragments of the molecule formed by cleavage of a bond it contains.

$$(CH_3\!\!-\!\!\overset{46}{CH_2}\!\!-\!\!OH)^+ \rightarrow CH_3 \!\!\mid\!\! \overset{31}{CH_2OH^+}$$

$$\rightarrow CH_3\!\!-\!\!CH_2 \!\!\mid\!\! \overset{17}{OH^+}$$

$$\rightarrow CH_3\!\!-\!\!\overset{45}{CH}\!\!-\!\!OH^+ \atop {-\!-\!\!\mid\!\!-\!- \atop H^1}$$

$$\rightarrow {}^{+}\overset{15}{CH_3}\!\!\mid\!\!CH_2OH$$

$$\rightarrow {}^{+}CH_3\!\!-\!\!\overset{29}{CH_2}\!\!\mid\!\!OH$$

One field of research currently being pursued is the demonstration that this type of fragmentation is not random, but can be explained and predicted. For the present, we shall not consider these as typical reactions of organic molecules because of the extreme conditions under which they take place. Their utility is nevertheless evident.

The most intense peaks in the mass spectrum of benzaldehyde occur at M/e = 106, 105, and 77. What molecular fragments are involved? Is the structure of the ion with mass 105 uniquely determined?

An isotopically substituted benzaldehyde may be synthesized with a deuterium instead of a hydrogen atom in the aldehyde group. When this compound is examined mass spectroscopically, the most intense peaks occur at 107, 105, and 77. What now must be the structure of the ion of mass 105?

3-11 Two volatile liquids are found in the laboratory in unlabeled bottles. Neither of them can be made to react with any of the reagents we have mentioned in this chapter. A mass spectrum of each of them is recorded: Compound A has major ions of mass 29, 45, and 59, and a parent peak at 74. Compound B has major ions of mass 15, 29, 43, and 59, and a parent peak at 74. From this information the main features of the structure can be determined.

(a) Can a compound of molecular weight 74 be an alkane? How many oxygens could it contain?

(b) What kinds of compounds that we have discussed contain this many oxygens? What class is excluded by the lack of reactivity?

(c) Write possible structures for A and B. On the basis of the fragments likely to occur from each of your structures, assign likely structures to A and B.

How is the reaction with sodium used as a diagnostic test for OH groups?
How does its application lead to the structure of methanol?
What additional evidence is used to establish the structure of ethanol?
What further principles are used in establishing the structure of acetic acid?

4

THE STRUCTURES OF ALCOHOLS AND CARBOXYLIC ACIDS

4–1 Introduction

In 1807 Sir Humphrey Davy succeeded in isolating metallic sodium by the electrolysis of sodium hydroxide. The availability of this chemical element provided organic chemists with a powerful tool for synthesis and for structural diagnosis. Chemists soon learned that methane, for example, is completely inert to the action of sodium. This was also found to be true of other paraffinic hydrocarbons so that these substances could be used to protect metallic sodium from the action of atmospheric oxygen, water, and carbon dioxide.

Water, on the other hand, was found to react violently with sodium with the formation of hydrogen gas and sodium hydroxide. The violence of the reaction is so great that a flame is formed from a small amount of sodium, while a larger amount will explode. Molten sodium hydroxide will undergo further reaction with metallic sodium to replace a second hydrogen with the formation of sodium oxide.

4–2 The Structure of Methanol

Methanol or methyl alcohol, sometimes also called "wood alcohol" because it was historically prepared from wood in the process of forming charcoal, is a liquid which boils at 64.7°. When sodium metal is dropped into methanol, a violent reaction takes place, and hydrogen is liberated. As a rule, no flame is formed in this case, indicating a less violent reaction than that with water. The solid product from this reaction, which can be isolated by distilling off the excess methanol, is a white solid which analyzes for the empirical formula CH_3ONa. It will be seen that if we desire to preserve the concept of the tetravalence of carbon, the divalence of oxygen, and the monovalence of hydrogen (and of sodium as well), then there is only one formula that can be written for sodium methoxide.

$$
\begin{array}{c}
\text{H} \\
| \\
\text{H—C—O—Na} \\
| \\
\text{H}
\end{array}
$$

This is, in fact, the formula that organic chemists used for this substance for many years. Electrical studies on sodium methoxide show, however, that this formula does not correctly represent the electrical properties of the substance. A solution of sodium methoxide in methanol can carry an electric current, and it was discovered that the sodium ion migrates toward the negative electrode, showing that it carries a positive charge, while the methoxide ion migrates as a unit to the positive pole, showing that it carries a negative charge. Electrical studies such as this were being made with increasing frequency during the middle of the nineteenth century, but it was not until the end of the century, with the work of Arrhenius, that the modern interpretation of these phenomena as caused by the presence of ions in solution was advanced. We shall not discuss these electrical phenomena in greater detail at the present time, but it will be advantageous to correct the formula for sodium methoxide that was first drawn over a century ago by indicating its ionic nature. Thus we now write:

$$
\begin{array}{c}
\text{H} \\
| \\
\text{H—C—O}^- \; \text{Na}^+ \\
| \\
\text{H}
\end{array}
$$

as the formula for sodium methoxide.

An attempt to react sodium methoxide with more metallic sodium turns out to be futile: no further reaction will take place. Thus we may conclude that whereas water has two hydrogen atoms that are displaceable by sodium, methanol has only one such hydrogen atom. The characteristic of the hydrogens of water is that they are bound to oxygen. Hence the organic chemist concludes, tentatively, that it may be a property of a hydrogen bound directly to an oxygen that it is displaceable by sodium on treatment with sodium metal. If this is true, then methanol has one such hydrogen and only one. In contrast, the lack of reactivity of methane toward metallic sodium indicates that it is a property of a hydrogen atom bound to carbon that it is inert to metallic sodium. The lack of further reactivity of sodium methoxide toward metallic sodium confirms the initial conclusion that sodium methoxide has three hydrogens bound to carbon.

From the foregoing observations, i.e., the reactivity of methanol toward sodium, the reactivity of water toward sodium, the inertness of sodium methoxide toward sodium, and the inertness of methane toward sodium, we have the materials for the logical deduction of a structural formula for methanol.

$$
\begin{array}{c}
\text{H} \\
| \\
\text{H}-\text{C}-\text{O}-\text{H} \\
| \\
\text{H}
\end{array}
$$

This is an example of reasoning by analogy. In many walks of life, reasoning by analogy is dangerous to reliable conclusions. In organic chemistry, the method is widely used but is also capable of giving erroneous conclusions on occasion. In general, errors arise from the fact that two analogous cases are never identical. We must be sure that the item which is changed in going from one case to another is not an item which is critical to the tenability of the conclusion. To do this, one feature at a time is chosen for variation, to see whether or not the proposed generalization still holds true after the change is made. If the generalization holds true through a sufficient number of changes, then it may be concluded that the features being changed do not make a decisive difference, and the probability of the reliability of the generalization is thus increased. We shall test our generalization with respect to the nature of the reactivity of O—H bonds toward sodium by examining more alcohols.

4–3　The Structure of Ethanol

From time immemorial, men have known that fruit juices, on standing, underwent a process of fermentation yielding an intoxicating beverage. The discovery of the process of distillation (Fig. 4–1) is usually attributed to the Arabs of the tenth century and the term "alcohol," applied to the essential intoxicating substance in fermented beverages, is derived from the Arabic, although its progenitor was used by them to designate an extremely finely powdered cosmetic, antimony sulfide. Chemically, the spirit of wine is termed *ethanol* or *ethyl alcohol*. Ethanol obtained by distillation is only 95% pure, since this mixture with water has a lower boiling point than pure ethanol. Such a low-boiling mixture is called an *azeotrope*. In the laboratory, anhydrous ethanol can be obtained by treating 95% alcohol with quicklime, CaO, or with magnesium ethoxide, $Mg(OC_2H_5)_2$. Industrially, anhydrous ethanol is obtained by taking advantage of the formation of a ternary azeotrope, water, alcohol, and benzene, which boils at a still lower temperature than 95% alcohol. (See Fig. 4–2 for a diagram of a laboratory fractionating column.) The resultant mixture of ethanol and benzene, which cannot be separated by distillation at atmospheric pressure, can be separated in a still under pressure. Its formula is found by analysis to be C_2H_6O, and on reaction with metallic sodium it is found that only one hydrogen is displaceable. The white residue which remains after the distillation of the excess ethanol is sodium ethoxide, C_2H_5ONa. Like

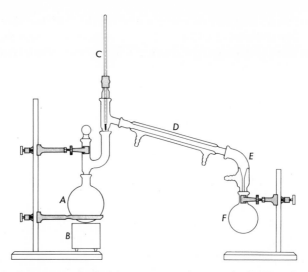

FIG. 4–1. Simple laboratory distillation apparatus showing A, distilling flask; B, heater; C, thermometer; D, condenser; E, adapter; F, receiver.

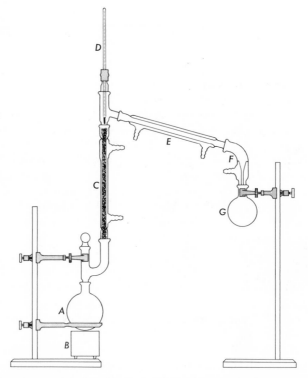

FIG. 4–2. Laboratory fractionating column showing A, distilling pot; B, heater; C, fractionating column with packing; D, vapor thermometer; E, condenser; F, adapter; G, receiver.

sodium methoxide, it conducts a current and resists further action by metallic sodium. Hence, by analogy, the five hydrogens are assigned to bonding with carbon and the displaceable hydrogen to bonding with oxygen. We may thus write a structural formula for ethanol as follows.

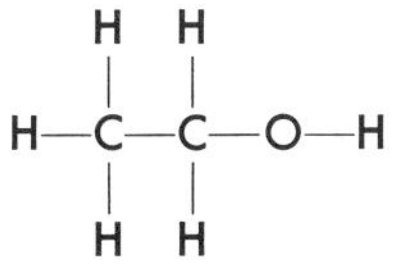

$$\begin{array}{ccc} H & H & \\ | & | & \\ H-C-C-O-H \\ | & | & \\ H & H & \end{array}$$

Consideration of the empirical formula C_2H_6O will show that the structure assigned to ethanol is not the only one that can be written which will preserve the monovalence of hydrogen, the divalence of oxygen, and the tetravalence of carbon. In fact, treatment of methyl iodide with sodium methoxide yields a gas which condenses at $-24°$ and which analyzes for C_2H_6O. The method of preparation suggests that the gas should have the structure of dimethyl ether.

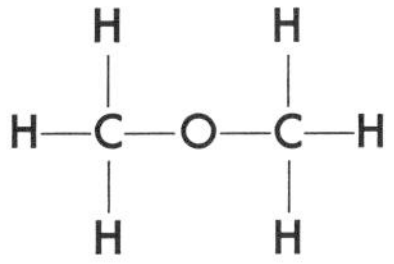

$$\begin{array}{ccc} H & & H \\ | & & | \\ H-C-O-C-H \\ | & & | \\ H & & H \end{array}$$

Since this substance contains no hydrogens bound to carbon, it would not be expected to react with metallic sodium. Experiment verifies this assumption, which is based on reasoning by analogy. A variety of experiments shows that the ether linkage, $C-O-C$, is quite stable to chemical reagents. It can be broken by treatment with strong mineral acids, however, and the acid chosen for structural investigations is hydriodic acid.

Treatment of methanol with hot hydriodic acid yields methyl iodide.

$$CH_3OH + HI \rightarrow CH_3I + H_2O$$

The reaction of dimethyl ether with hydrogen iodide requires a temperature as high as that necessary to form methyl iodide from methanol so that the reaction yields only methyl iodide as an organic product.

$$CH_3OCH_3 + HI \rightarrow CH_3OH + CH_3I$$
$$CH_3OH + HI \rightarrow CH_3I + H_2O$$

We thus find that a characteristic reaction of an ether is that of cleavage with HI. It would be instructive to attempt this reaction on ethanol. When tried, the experiment yields ethyl iodide:

$$C_2H_5OH + HI \rightarrow C_2H_5I + H_2O$$

Thus ethanol reacts with HI in a manner analogous to methanol, with the formation of an iodide containing the same number of carbon atoms as the original alcohol, whereas dimethyl ether, a two-carbon compound, on treatment with HI, yields methyl iodide, a one-carbon compound.

We see a process of reasoning by interlocking analogies at work here. A reaction of water is found to have an analogy in the behavior of methanol. A property of methane is found to have an analogy in the behavior of sodium methoxide. On these bases, analogies are found in the behavior of ethanol which lead to the writing of a structural formula. An alternative possibility is conceived in dimethyl ether. A straightforward synthetic reaction permits the preparation of this substance for investigation, and analogies with the behavior of methane confirm its structure. It is found that HI characterizes a $C—O$ bond by cleavage with the formation of an alkyl iodide. This reaction proceeds with methanol and with dimethyl ether, and the behavior of ethanol is analogous. Where reliance on a single analogy might be hazardous, the erection of a logical structure built on many interlocking analogies gives an increasing degree of probability to the reliability of the conclusions drawn from it. It is by this process of building from simple cases to cases of increasing complexity that the most complicated organic chemical structures are elucidated. The first book of this text will present selected cases of increasing complexity to illustrate the processes.

The case of dimethyl ether is a simple example of another type of reasoning which is relied on systematically by structural organic chemists. This material was prepared by synthesis, using a process that established its structure. It was then degraded by a chemical reaction that was also sufficient to establish its structure. This double attack on structure, by degradation and by synthesis, is a standard method used by organic chemists to check the reliability of their structural conclusions. As a rule, the two methods utilize procedures which are so different that agreement between them vastly increases the probability that a conclusion drawn from both is reliable.

4–4 The Structure of Acetic Acid

When Kekulé published his textbook of organic chemistry a century ago, he noted that eighteen structural formulas had been proposed for acetic acid. It is difficult for modern chemists to conceive of such variety of formulations for a simple chemical. The explanation, of course, lies in the fact that many of the formulas proposed did not conform to Kekulé's postulates concerning valence. Let us examine a few of the possibilities in the light of the reactions of acetic acid, whose empirical formula is $C_2H_4O_2$.

For acetic acid, the diagnostic reaction with metallic sodium is a dangerous one and proceeds with such violence that it is usually discarded for practical studies. However, since the objective of the reaction is to prepare a sodium salt, the purpose may be accomplished in this case by a much more easily controlled reaction, that with sodium hydroxide. It is found, on experiment, that one hydrogen of acetic acid is displaceable with sodium hydroxide.

$$C_2H_4O_2 + Na^+ OH^- \rightarrow C_2H_3O_2^- Na^+ + H_2O$$

By analogy, the presence of a displaceable hydrogen indicates the presence of an OH bond, although it must be recognized that in this case, the analogy is not a perfect one: the displacement in the case of acetic acid takes place appreciably more readily than in the case of methanol or ethanol, even much easier than in the case of water. A confirmation is necessary.

Confirmation of the presence of an OH group can be obtained by the use of PCl_5 (see Section 3–4).

$$C_2H_4O_2 + PCl_5 \rightarrow C_2H_3OCl + POCl_3 + HCl$$

Acetyl chloride, the organic product of the reaction with acetic acid, is a corrosive liquid which boils at 51° and, as we have seen, is capable of entering into a variety of reactions useful in synthesis.

Having set off one hydrogen as different from the other three, we may hazard the hypothesis that the other three hydrogens are attached to a carbon atom in the form of a methyl group. Confirmation for this concept is obtained from a relatively drastic degradation of sodium acetate.

$$C_2H_3O_2^- Na^+ + NaOH \quad \text{(with } Ca(OH)_2 \text{ as soda lime)} \xrightarrow{400°} CH_4 + Na_2CO_3$$

The formation of methane by decomposition of acetic acid indicates that acetic acid is itself a derivative of methane and gives reason for writing the remaining three hydrogens as attached to a carbon atom in a methyl group. This gives us a partial formula for acetic acid with the following structural features established.

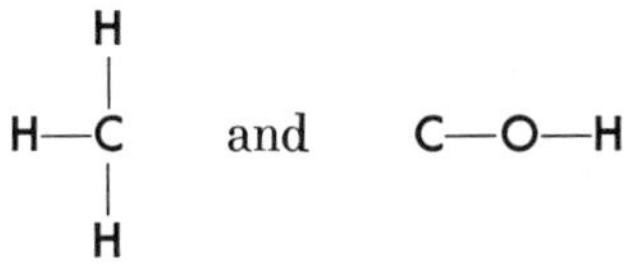

$$
\begin{array}{ccc}
& \text{H} & \\
& | & \\
\text{H—C} & \text{and} & \text{C—O—H} \\
& | & \\
& \text{H} &
\end{array}
$$

We have yet to find the nature of the second oxygen atom and the nature of the linkage of the two carbons. Two possibilities exist: the carbons might be linked directly, or they might be linked through the second oxygen. The latter possibility would require a divalent carbon, as shown below.

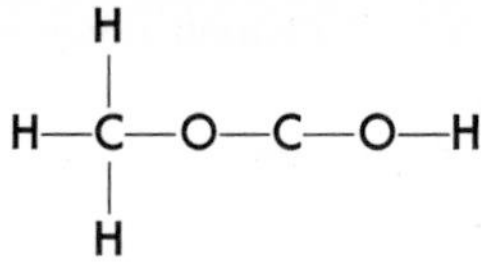

$$\begin{matrix} & & H & & & & \\ & & | & & & & \\ H & - & C & - O - C - O - H \\ & & | & & & & \\ & & H & & & & \end{matrix}$$

In Kekulé's time, such a possibility could not be dismissed out-of-hand but required experimental examination.

Hydriodic acid is our diagnostic reagent for a C—O—C linkage so we may examine its action on acetic acid. Experiment shows that acetic acid is quite stable to hydriodic acid. In fact, it is frequently used as a solvent for hydriodic acid to increase the solubility of organic compounds in the acid for purposes of chemical degradation. This stability indicates that the formulation with a C—O—C linkage is probably not correct, leaving the direct carbon-to-carbon linkage as the preferable alternative.

The remaining problem of the assignment of the second oxygen requires a different type of approach. It is possible to write a structure for a hypothetical compound which has two hydroxyl groups attached to a single carbon atom.

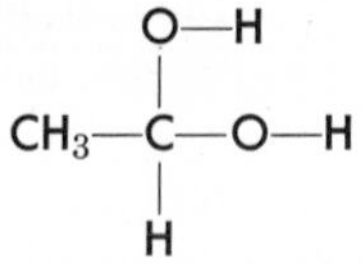

$$\begin{matrix} & & O-H & \\ & & | & \\ CH_3 & - & C & -O-H \\ & & | & \\ & & H & \end{matrix}$$

The empirical formula for this compound is $C_2H_6O_2$, which has two hydrogens more than acetic acid has. The fact that two hydrogens would have to be removed to form acetic acid suggests that the answer to the problem may be found in multiple bonding, of the sort proposed by Kekulé to preserve the tetravalence of carbon in his formula for benzene. A possible solution is to write a double bond between the carbon and the second oxygen, as shown below.

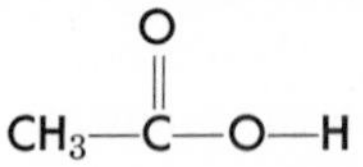

$$\begin{matrix} & & O & \\ & & \| & \\ CH_3 & - & C & -O-H \end{matrix}$$

This formula preserves the assigned valences of carbon, oxygen, and hydrogen and accounts for all the reactions which have been presented. We have not yet presented a confirmatory reaction for the C=O group. Later we shall find a number of these reactions and shall then apply them to acetic acid and its derivatives. Meanwhile, we may seek synthetic confirmation of the structural features that we have arrived at by the methods of chemical degradation.

We have already established the presence of a C—C linkage in ethanol. Early chemists were aware of the fact that ethanol could be oxidized to yield acetic acid. The balanced equation is

$$3CH_3CH_2OH + 2H_2Cr_2O_7 + 6H_2SO_4 \rightarrow 3CH_3COOH + 2Cr_2(SO_4)_3 + 11H_2O$$

As a matter of convenience, this is frequently written as follows.

$$CH_3CH_2OH \xrightarrow[H_2SO_4]{CrO_3} CH_3COOH$$

This reaction confirms the presence of the C—C linkage in acetic acid.

The presence of the CH_3 group can be confirmed by the synthesis of acetic acid from methyl iodide.

$$CH_3I + NaCN \rightarrow CH_3CN + NaI$$
$$CH_3CN + 2H_2O + HCl \rightarrow CH_3COOH + NH_4Cl$$

Thus we see that both chemical degradation and synthesis lead to the same conclusion with respect to the structure of acetic acid. The conclusion drawn may require modification or refinement later as new facts are uncovered, but the structural features discussed seem to have acquired a relatively high degree of probability because of the number of test methods used to establish them. Reasoning of the type advanced for methanol, dimethyl ether, ethanol, and acetic acid is frequently referred to by organic chemists as a "structural proof." It should be recognized, however, that such a "proof," while establishing a high degree of probability for certain structural features, is silent with respect to many precise details (for example, exact bond lengths) and lacks any ultimate, absolute character that would endow it with philosophical certainty. It does, however, afford us a useful basis for the correlation of the possible chemical reactions of materials so that the structural formulas of organic chemists are more than the representation of a model of how a molecule might be expected to look, given sufficient magnification. They are a condensation of knowledge of how compounds react. As the student acquires more and more familiarity with his subject, these formulas will acquire correspondingly increased utility in the correlation of possible experimental behavior of the substances involved.

4–5 Methods of Preparation

It is well at this time to call attention to differences between various possible reactions for preparing organic chemicals. In the preceding presentation, emphasis was on diagnostic methods useful for structural determinations. When structural diagnosis is the objective, the chemist can afford to use expensive chemicals, because the preparation and identification of a small amount of a substance will suffice for the purposes of a structural investigation. Even in laboratory synthesis where a greater quantity of a material may be desired, relatively expensive chemicals may be employed to save time in synthesis or to save the construction of costly special equipment which might be required to prepare the same substance from less expensive chemicals. With industrial preparations of organic chemicals, on the other hand, the cost of the raw materials entering into a synthetic process becomes a matter of prime concern. If the projected volume of production is great enough, it may pay to build plants requiring tremendous capital outlays to secure a sufficiently low cost per unit of the product. These considerations, and others respecting relative availability of alternative raw materials in a given location or for a given plant, will determine the method used to produce a given chemical.

For example, iodine is quite expensive, and it would be economically prohibitive to make acetic acid from methyl iodide and sodium cyanide. On the other hand, in certain locations where ethanol is cheap, acetic acid is produced commercially by the oxidation of ethanol. This may be done by bacterial fermentation by the so-called "quick vinegar" process. Most of the acetic acid used for food purposes is produced by this process. At one time the best source of commercial acetic acid was as a by-product from the manufacture of charcoal. At the present time, it would not pay to build a plant to make acetic acid by this process for the acetic acid alone. When there is a market for charcoal, however, it pays to recover the acetic acid formed as a by-product, and a few percent of the total production of acetic acid is made in this way.

The advent of commercial methods for performing reactions under high pressure and at elevated temperatures and increasing knowledge about the action of catalysts has made feasible large-scale catalytic processes starting with the cheapest raw materials. Such processes require enormous capital outlays, but are capable of yielding high production capacity and, therefore, low unit costs. As an example, coke may be treated with water at red heat to give carbon monoxide and hydrogen.

$$C + H_2O \rightarrow CO + H_2$$

The mixture so obtained is fortified by the addition of more hydrogen and is then passed over a catalyst containing mixed oxides of zinc, chromium, manganese, or aluminum at a pressure of 3000 to 5000 psi and a temperature of 300°C. Under these conditions, methanol of high purity is obtained along with some unreacted starting gases which can be recycled. The equation is

$$CO + 2H_2 \rightarrow CH_3OH$$

A company equipped to produce methanol by this process can extend the method to produce acetic acid according to the following equation.

$$CH_3OH + CO \rightarrow CH_3COOH$$

The reaction is run in the presence of a large excess of carbon monoxide. The catalyst is a special activated carbon "promoted" by the use of a few percent of TiO_2, Al_2O_3, or SiO_2. The reaction is carried out at pressures exceeding 10,000 psi and at temperatures ranging from below 300° to about 350°C. As the temperature is increased, the speed of the reaction is increased, but more and more methyl acetate is formed at the higher operating temperatures.

The production of methanol and acetic acid by high-pressure synthesis would probably be the method chosen by a large organization with sufficient capital for the required investment and with sufficient assurance of a market, while these methods would be out of the question for a university laboratory that wanted, for some reason, to synthesize samples of either methanol or acetic acid.

PROBLEMS

4-1 Using the information developed in this chapter and earlier ones, devise a synthesis of phenylacetic acid, $C_6H_5CH_2COOH$, from benzyl bromide, $C_6H_5CH_2Br$.

4-2 How might the ethyl ester of propionic acid, CH_3CH_2COOH, be prepared using ethyl iodide as the sole organic starting material for the synthesis, and assuming the availability of all necessary reagents?

You should be able to think of several schemes, of which one requires the use of Eq. (i) Problem 3-3. A catalyst is usually required in the laboratory for this esterification procedure; the organic acid and dry alcohol are mixed with either a few drops of concentrated sulfuric acid or with gaseous hydrogen chloride. We shall see why the catalyst is used in Book 2.

4-3 We have seen that alcohols may be oxidized to acids using CrO_3 and H_2SO_4. The reverse reactions, that is, the direct reduction of acids to alcohols, was not achieved until the late 1940's when a reagent was found for this purpose, $LiAlH_4$. This is one of the most powerful reducing agents known, and we shall see it used in several places in the following pages; it forms a salt of the alcohol desired, which then may be obtained by hydrolysis of the salt.

Suppose that for some reason it became necessary to synthesize ethyl acetate labeled with carbon-14 in each position, that is, as shown below:

$$\overset{*}{C}H_3CH_2OCOCH_3 \qquad CH_3\overset{*}{C}H_2OCOCH_3$$

$$CH_3CH_2O\overset{*}{C}OCH_3 \qquad CH_3CH_2OCO\overset{*}{C}H_3$$

It is possible to buy $C^{14}H_3I$ and $NaC^{14}N$. Using these compounds, show how you could produce each of the specifically labeled ethyl acetate samples required.

4-4 An earlier (and still useful) method for reducing an acid requires the preparation of an ester, which is then dissolved in alcohol. Small pieces of sodium metal are added to the reaction mixture, and the product which would be obtained if the reaction mixture were evaporated to dryness afterward would consist of as many as three sodium salts of alcohols— or alkoxides: one would be the sodium salt of the alcohol used as solvent (of course, only if there were excess sodium); another would be the alkoxide formed from the alcohol used to esterify the original acid; and the third would be the salt of the desired alcohol. These may, in general, be separated after hydrolysis by careful fractional distillation, or by simply evaporating to dryness, if the alcohol has such a high molecular weight that it is a solid at ambient temperatures. The oil expressed from nutmeg yields an ester which on purification and subsequent hydrolysis yields an acid, myristic acid. Myristic acid was found to contain 73.63% C and 12.36% H, and gave negative tests for halogen, sulfur, nitrogen, and phosphorus. The molecular weight was found to be about 227. The acid was boiled overnight with methanol containing dry hydrogen chloride. Evaporation of the reaction mixture gave an oil which after purification froze somewhat below room temperature (18.5°C). Reduction of the oil with sodium and alcohol gave a solid with melting point 39–39.5°C, after recrystallization from aqueous alcohol.

(a) What is the formula for the solid melting at 39–39.5°C?

(b) Suppose that no carbon in this compound has more than two other carbons attached to it. What would the structure of this substance be?

(c) On this same assumption, what is the structure of myristic acid?

It is interesting that of the higher acids, those with even numbers of carbons are found frequently, but those with odd numbers of carbons are rarely found. This indicates something about their mode of formation. The naturally occurring alcohols and some other compounds also seem to follow this rule. For the alcohol corresponding to myristic acid, the natural source is so exotic (head oil of porpoises) that laboratory synthesis from readily available products is the method of choice for production.

How do we know the geometrical structure of benzene and of the compounds based on it?

5

THE CONSTITUTION OF BENZENE

5–1 Introduction

We saw in Chapter 3 that the intuition of Kekulé was sufficiently penetrating to devise a structural formula for benzene which preserved the tetravalence of carbon. It remained for this formula to withstand many critical tests in the laboratory before it could be regarded as logically established. All the evidence which was obtained in the laboratory and all the arguments which were put forward by chemists, whether in support of the structure or in attempts to disprove it, were necessarily indirect. The atoms which constitute the building blocks of organic molecules were far too small to be seen directly.

Even at the present time it has proved impossible to secure direct geometrical evidence for the type of structure which we write for organic compounds. The crystal structure investigations of the x-ray specialist involve indirect physical methods, just as those of the organic chemist involve indirect chemical methods. It is now possible to predict that by means of an electron microscope or a proton microscope, we may obtain photographs of the arrangements of atoms in organic compounds, showing the relative positions of carbons, oxygens, and nitrogens. It is also possible to predict with confidence what will be found. Lacking direct methods for accomplishing their purpose, men have nevertheless succeeded in creating the indirect equivalent of a microscope with a magnification factor of ten million. It is to the details of the construction and use of this powerful creation of the human mind that we shall now turn our attention. As an example, we shall study the logical arguments concerning the structure of benzene. Our first assumption is that there is a causal relationship between the structure of benzene and its chemical properties. To learn about the geometry of benzene, we shall study its chemistry. Then by the juxtaposition of geometrical arguments and chemical arguments, we shall test for consistency.

5–2 An Objection to Kekulé's Benzene Formula

Kekulé proposed to represent benzene with a formula in which the carbon atoms form a regular hexagon with a hydrogen attached at each vertex. To satisfy the assumption of tetravalence for each carbon, he drew alternate single and double bonds between carbons in the ring, arriving at the formula shown in Fig. 5–1.

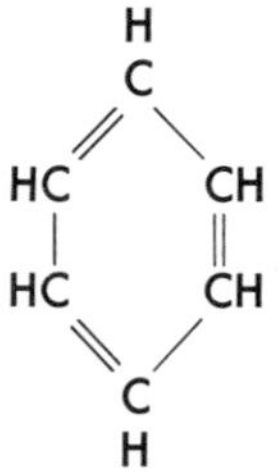

FIGURE 5–1

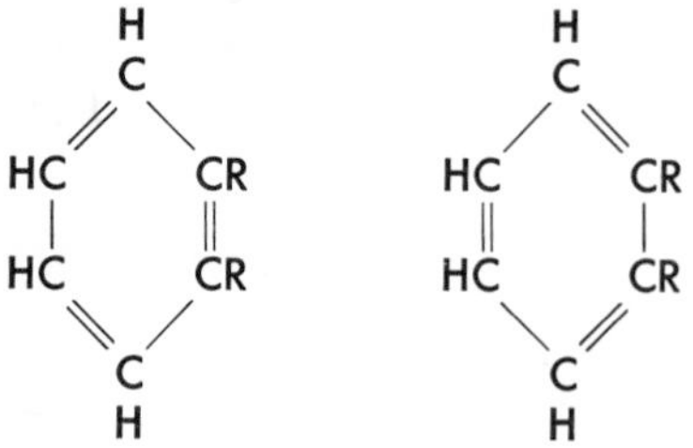

FIGURE 5–2

(a)   (b)

Shortly after Kekulé's proposal was advanced, it suffered its first defeat. It was pointed out that there were two such formulas which would be interchanged by flipping the double bonds to single bond positions and *vice versa*. For benzene itself, such a change would make no difference, but if two substituents other than hydrogen were introduced in adjacent positions, then there would be a difference (Fig. 5–2).

The compound represented by formula (a) has the two carbons with R groups separated by a double bond, while (b) has them separated by a single bond. The compounds should be different and capable of isolation. Thus a prediction was made which has not been capable of verification up to the present. Chemists set to work on the problem and were soon discouraged in their efforts to separate such compounds. Some saw this as proof that Kekulé's structure was incorrect. Kekulé himself replied that the difficulty probably lay in the assumption that the two substances were sufficiently different to be capable of isolation. He said that it was equally reasonable to suppose that they would be in a process of constant interconversion and would, therefore, prove incapable of isolation. Thus he modified his theory in the face of adverse experimental results and assumed that the alternate single and double bonds were in a state of dynamic equilibrium.

Kekulé's concept of dynamic equilibrium between isomers implied that the two are equally stable and interchange readily. Time has brought about a revision of this concept, leading to the idea that the interchange is one that takes place with the speed of light and thus introduces a qualitative difference from the picture in which the individual bonds can be regarded as having a finite survival time. In the modern concept, real benzene is appreciably more stable than Kekulé's fixed-bond isomers. The stabilization is due to "resonance" or "mesomerism" or "bond delocalization," terms whose origins and more precise meanings we shall leave for fuller discussion in the second book. For the moment, it will be sufficient to know that "Kekulé isomers" have remained incapable of separation.

5–3   Hexagonal Shape of Benzene; Körner's Principle

The problem of the hexagonal shape of benzene proved to be more amenable to experimental verification. The investigation of this problem was undertaken by one of Kekulé's students, Wilhelm Körner (1839–1925). Examination of the hexagonal structure showed that all six positions were equivalent, so only one monosubstitution product of benzene should be formed. Experiment bore this out. Further examination showed that three disubstitution products were possible, numbered 1-2, 1-3, and 1-4 and named *ortho*, *meta*, and *para* (Fig. 5–3).

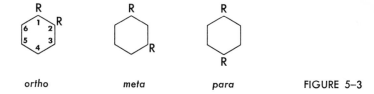

ortho   meta   para   FIGURE 5–3

Körner reasoned that these could be distinguished by the number of trisubstituted compounds that could be formed from them, in the manner illustrated in Fig. 5–4.

In the example given, *ortho* dibromobenzene can be identified as the substance capable of giving two dibromonitrobenzenes, *meta*, as that capable of giving three, while *para* is the substance that gives only one dibromonitro derivative. While systematic advancement of the nitro group around the positions in the ring will seem to give more substances, re-examination will show that these other formulas stand, in reality, for the same materials with the formulas turned in different directions.

Körner went to the laboratory, prepared the indicated dibromobenzenes, found only the expected three, and identified them through their reactions with nitric acid in sulfuric acid, the so-called "nitrating mixture." He succeeded in isolating six and only six dibromonitrobenzenes and found that one of the dibromobenzenes gave one nitro derivative, one gave two, and one gave three, in agreement with the prediction of the hexagonal formula.

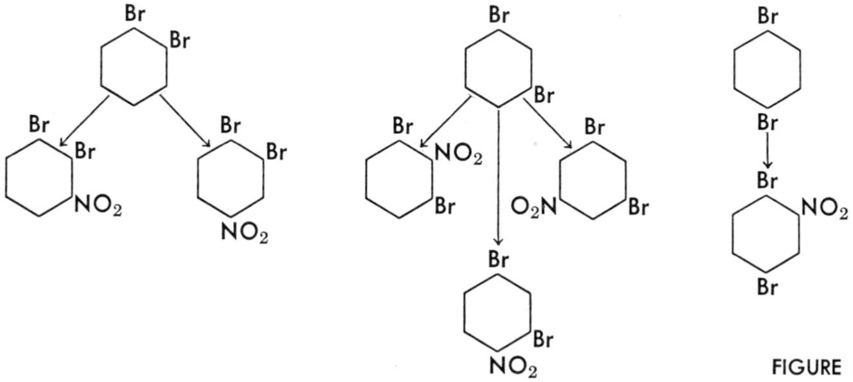

FIGURE 5–4

5-4   Alternatives to the Hexagon for Benzene

Körner's method has been utilized as the basis for the absolute determination of the sequence of groups in many derivatives of benzene. Actually, it is much more. Since the number of substances found in the laboratory is the same as the number predicted by the assumption of a regular hexagon, it constitutes a verification of the hexagonal shape. To illustrate that this result is not a necessary one for all possible arrangements of six carbons and six hydrogens, let us consider the case of fulvene, an isomer of benzene. Fulvene is represented by the formula shown in Fig. 5-5.

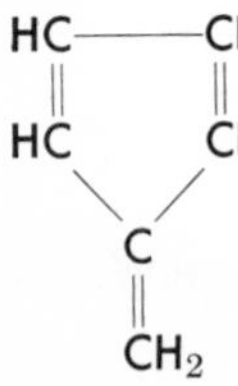

HC———CH
‖   ‖
HC   CH
  \ /
   C
   ‖
  CH$_2$

HC———CR
‖   ‖
HC   CH
  \ /
   C
   ‖
  CH$_2$
   (a)

HC———CH
‖   ‖
HC   CR
  \ /
   C
   ‖
  CH$_2$
   (b)

HC———CH
‖   ‖
HC   CH
  \ /
   C
   ‖
  CHR
   (c)

FIG. 5-5. Fulvene. 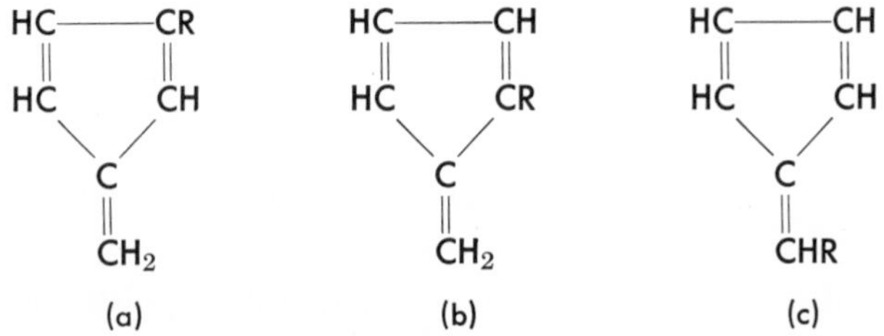   FIG. 5-6. Monosubstituted fulvenes.

In this case, departure from the behavior of a hexagon is observed immediately at the state of monosubstitution, since three monosubstituted fulvenes (Fig. 5-6) are possible.

Körner established the fact that the di- and tri-substituted benzenes formed isomers in numbers consistent with the hexagonal formula. Immediately the question arose as to whether or not it was possible to find another type of geometrical figure which would also be consistent with Körner's experimental results. Two further figures which have six vertices are the octahedron and the triangular prism. We shall examine these next.

Figure 5-7 shows an octahedron. The first objection which can be raised to the use of an octahedron to represent benzene is that it is not possible to bond each carbon to each of its neighbors and still join it to a hydrogen atom. Since each carbon has four neighbors, the necessary junctions would raise the minimum acceptable valence of carbon to five, in contradiction to our assumption of its tetravalence. If we ignore this objection, however, we immediately reach another. While it is true that a regular octahedron has six equivalent vertices, the number of disubstitution products to be formed would be two, not three. These are 1-3 and 1-6; 2-3 is equivalent to 1-2 and 2-4 is equivalent to 1-6.

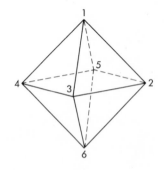

FIG. 5-7. An octahedron.

Table 5–1 presents the contrast with varying degrees of substitution between the isomers which can be experimentally prepared from benzene and those predicted on the basis of an assumed octahedral structure.

Table 5–1

	Mono	Di	Tri	Tetra	Penta	Hexa	Total
Benzene, experimental	1	3	3	3	1	1	12
Octahedron	1	2	2	2	1	1	9

5–5 Ladenburg's Triangular Prism

The triangular prism, on the other hand, has most of the symmetry elements of the hexagon. It was proposed by Ladenburg as a geometrical alternative to the hexagon. Let us examine its predicted substitution products and compare them with those found for the substitution of benzene.

Since all six positions on the triangular prism are identical, only one monosubstitution product will be possible. The di- and tri-substituted products are listed in Table 5–2, with those for the hexagon included for comparison.

Table 5–2

	Mono	Di	Tri	Tetra	Penta	Hexa	Total
Hexagon	1	3	3	3	1	1	12
	1	1-2	1-2-3				
		1-3	1-2-4				
		1-4	1-3-5				
Triangular prism	1	3	3	3	1	1	12
	A	A-B	A-B-C				
		A-C	A-B-F				
		A-D	A-B-E				

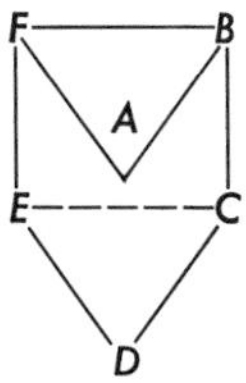

Examination of the table will show that the number of derivatives in each class is identical for the two geometric figures and both agree with those found experimentally. From these facts, it follows further that Körner's principle will be followed for both figures. The results of its application to these figures are given in Table 5–3.

Table 5–3

APPLICATIONS OF KÖRNER'S PRINCIPLE

	Hexagon		Triangular prism	
1-2	1-2-3, 1-2-4		A-B	A-B-C, A-B-F, A-B-E
1-3	1-2-3, 1-3-4, 1-3-5		A-C	A-B-C, A-B-E
1-4	1-2-4		A-D	A-B-C

Therefore $A = 1, D = 4, C = 2, B = 3$ Ortho = 1-2 = A-C   Meta = 1-3 = A-B

    Para = 1-4 = A-D

5–6   Distinction Between the Hexagon and the Triangular Prism

It can be seen that a more subtle approach would be necessary to distinguish between the hexagon and the triangular prism. The abandonment of the prismatic formula for benzene resulted from an increasing knowledge of the nature and extent of bond strains, a subject that we shall postpone for a short time. Some years after acceptance of the hexagon, a more rigorous chemical-geometrical approach became possible.

Study will show that the true difference between the hexagon and the triangular prism is in the "extra" bonds joining the carbons. In the hexagon, the three extra bonds are "double" linkages, while in the prism, all linkages are single. By the cancellation of these extra bonds in the triangular prism, it is possible to transform it stepwise into a hexagonal shape. The same end can be achieved with the hexagon by the "saturation" of the "double" bonds.

After Kekulé's structure had been accepted, chemists learned how to add hydrogen to multiple bonds and achieve saturation. The first method that was used was the relatively drastic one of boiling the compound with sodium and alcohol. Later it was found that the reaction could be performed with the aid of gaseous hydrogen in the presence of a metallic catalyst such as nickel or platinum. The results of this reaction, suitably applied, can achieve the logical differentiation between the two geometric figures under examination as possible formulas for benzene.

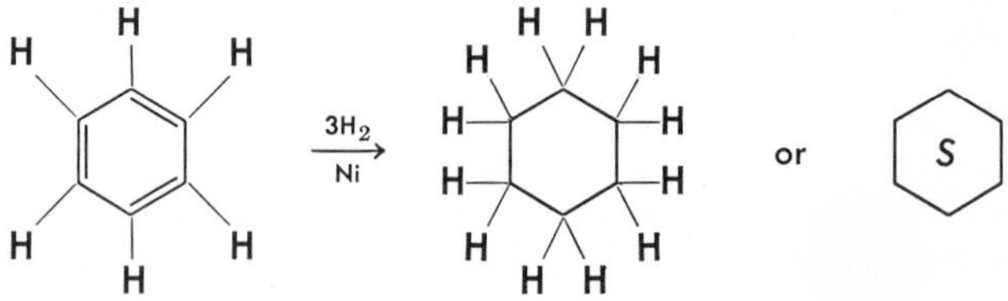

FIGURE 5–8

The multiple bonds of benzene can be saturated geometrically in only one manner. This is represented in Fig. 5–8.

In Fig. 5–8, the central S is understood to mean that the molecule is "saturated" with hydrogen. Each vertex now has a CH$_2$ group instead of a CH group as in benzene. The formula for the substance formed is C$_6$H$_{12}$, and its name is cyclohexane. It can be prepared in good yield by this method. Since there is only one monobromo derivative of cyclohexane, all of the hydrogens are equivalent.

In the triangular prism, all of the "extra" bonds are single bonds, so the assumption of this formula for benzene would make it necessary to break these bonds by hydrogenation to prepare cyclohexane. Geometrically, there are three different ways in which this can be done and only three. While the sequence of the operations may be varied, all three possible results can be obtained if one bond on the side of a square is broken first in the first sequence, the second such bond in the second sequence, and the third bond in the third. This geometrical process is illustrated in Fig. 5–9.

The dimethyl derivatives of benzene are known as xylenes. Three xylenes are known, *ortho*, *meta*, and *para*. Let us suppose that the triangular prism formula is substituted with methyl groups at the A-B positions. Hydrogenation should produce all three sequences with approximately the same ease. However, the A-B substituted material corresponding to formula I would be identical with that corresponding to formula II, while that of formula III would be different. Hence two different dimethylcyclohexanes would be formed, I and III. Xylene A-C would also give two dimethylcyclohexanes, I and III. Xylene A-D would give two, I and II. The characteristic behavior of such a formula then would be that each disubstituted derivative would give two different substances on hydrogenation and that while there would be only three such substances with the three possible geometrical relationships, each one of them could be formed from two different xylenes. (In this argument we are disregarding possible differences between the back and front of the ring in cyclohexane and only considering the differences around the periphery.)

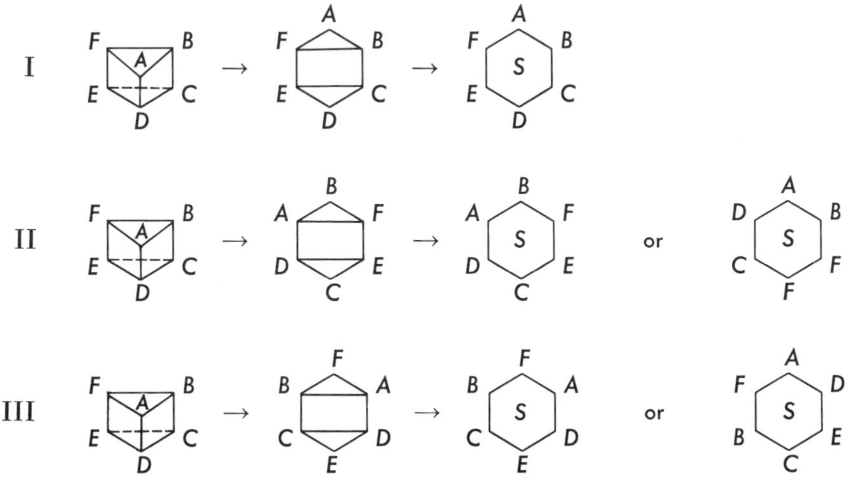

FIGURE 5–9

Referring back to Fig. 5–9, we see that the 1-2 xylene will give only one positional isomer of dimethylcyclohexane, the 1-2 derivative; 1-3 and 1-4 will likewise give but one positional isomer each. None of these substances will be capable of formation from two different xylenes.

A critical distinction between the hexagonal formula and the triangular prism formula can be made, therefore, by examining the experimental results of the hydrogenation of the xylenes. Can each of the dimethylcyclohexanes be formed from two xylenes or only from one? If from two, we must decide in favor of the prism. If from one only, we must decide in favor of the hexagon.

When the experiment is performed, it is found that each of the dimethylcyclohexanes can be formed from one xylene only, confirming the hexagonal structure for benzene. Thus by a combination of chemical and geometrical reasoning, it is possible to achieve a definite logical distinction between the two possible formulas. Because of bond strains, the isomer of benzene with Ladenburg's triangular prism formula, prismane, has not yet been prepared. Recently, however, a substituted prismane has been reported.

5–7 The Scientific Method

The process of establishing the structure of benzene is an excellent example of the scientific method. In this, the first step is the general one of classification of observations, in this case compounds and their reactions. The next step is induction, or reasoning from many particular cases to a generalization. Here the generalization was the hypothesis that benzene and its derivatives can be represented by hexagonal formulas. The next step is deduction and verification. In this case the first deduction, or "prediction" as we usually say, was that there should be two ortho-disubstituted benzene derivatives. This proved to be untrue so the theory was suitably modified to take account of this fact. The modified theory was then resubmitted to a process of deduction and verification. Predictions were made as to the number of trisubstituted isomers which should be formed from each disubstituted isomer. These were borne out. Finally, an alternative hypothesis, the triangular prism, was found which would explain the experimental facts, as far as they were known. Deductions were made from each alternative hypothesis, and it was found that one would fit additional experimental facts, the other would not. Such an experiment which distinguishes between two alternative hypotheses is called a "critical" or "crucial" experiment. Thus by repeated deduction and verification, the hypothesis was established.

The more deductions or "predictions" that can be made from a hypothesis, the more valuable it is. The scientist thus tries to refine his hypotheses to the point of maximum predictive utility by repeated deduction and verification, making whatever modifications are necessary to fit his hypothesis to the mold required by the experimental facts.

PROBLEMS

5–1 Benzene boils at 80.1°C, toluene (methylbenzene) at 110.8°C, and the three xylenes (dimethylbenzenes) at 138.4°C, 139.3°C, and 144.1°C. All are present in coal tar and fractions containing them can be separated by distillation. For more complete purification, special methods are usually used.

(a) The xylene boiling at 138.4° can be nitrated with a mixture of sulfuric and nitric acids to yield a single mononitroxylene. That boiling at 139.3° yields three mono-nitro compounds. The isomer boiling at 144.1° gives two mono-nitro derivatives. What are the structures of the three xylenes?

(b) Oxidation of the xylene boiling at 144.1° by means of dichromate in sulfuric acid gives phthalic acid, $C_8H_6O_4$. What is the structure of phthalic acid?

(c) Oxidation of the xylene boiling at 139.3° gives isophthalic acid. What is the structure of isophthalic acid?

(d) Oxidation of the xylene boiling at 138.4° gives terephthalic acid. What is its structure?

(e) Oxidation of any mono-alkylbenzene produces benzoic acid, regardless of the length or structure of the alkyl group. Keeping this in mind, what other substituted benzene of the formula C_8H_{10} can be distinguished experimentally from the xylenes?

5–2 We have noted earlier (Problem 3–4) that anhydrides may be formed from two units of an organic acid with the elimination of a water molecule. The geometry of phthalic acid permits the formation of steam and *phthalic anhydride*, $C_8H_4O_3$, when phthalic acid is heated above its melting point.

(a) Write the structure of phthalic anhydride.

Isophthalic acid and terephthalic acid do not form cyclic anhydrides of similar molecular formula. Instead, they form polymeric chains; that is, carboxylic acid groups from two different molecules are joined with the loss of water, and the link may be repeated many times. We may designate the different behavior of phthalic acid as a proximity effect.

(b) Using the above information, design a separate proof that benzene is hexagonal and not prismatic.

5–3 The orientation of groups entering the benzene ring is controlled primarily by those already present. Although, in general, all possible isomers will be formed in a given substitution reaction, very often one isomer or another will predominate. For example, when toluene is nitrated, 4% of the *meta* isomer is formed, 59% of the *ortho*, and 37% of the *para*. On the other hand, when benzoic acid is nitrated, 80% of the *meta* isomer, 19% of the *ortho*, and 1% of the *para* are formed. Again, the bromination of nitrobenzene using ferric bromide as the catalyst leads to a preponderance of the *meta*-disubstituted compound, but the nitration of bromobenzene leads to a 42:58 mixture of the *ortho*- and *para*-disubstituted compounds. Positional isomers may be separated by a variety of physical techniques; fractional distillation and fractional crystallization are among the most useful.

Since the benzene ring is resistant to most common reducing agents, it is frequently possible to reduce a substituent selectively. One of the most common reductions is that of nitrobenzene, carried out with tin or iron and hydrochloric acid, giving aniline, $C_6H_5NH_2$. Aniline is very easily oxidized to a variety of products; for this reason no oxidation step could follow the formation of the RNH_2 in a synthesis. We shall see later that there are ways to protect this group against oxidation, however.

Hydroxybenzene, C_6H_5OH, commonly called phenol, may be prepared by heating bromobenzene with strong sodium hydroxide to about 200°. Although it fits the formula ROH for alcohols, only some of its reactions are analogous to those of alcohols. It differs, for example, in that it is more acidic than alcohols, but not as strong as a carboxylic acid.

(a) Give a synthetic scheme for producing m-aminobenzoic acid in high yield.

(b) Devise a scheme for the production of p-aminobenzoic acid. Is a different sequence of steps advisable to produce the greatest possible yield of desired material?

(c) How could you produce o-bromoaniline? m-bromoaniline?

(d) How might p-nitroanisole be prepared? (Anisole is methyl phenyl ether.)

5–4 Six dinitroanilines are known. These are listed by melting points in the first column of Table 5–4. Each of these can be converted into a dinitrobenzene by diazotization and removal of the resulting diazonium group. The dinitrobenzene obtained from each of the dinitroanilines is listed opposite it in the second column. Oxidation of the dinitroanilines with trifluoroperacetic acid yields corresponding trinitrobenzenes. These are listed on the same line in the third column. Write the correct structures for all twelve compounds designated below by their melting points and show how you arrived at your conclusions.

Table 5–4

Dinitroanilines	Dinitrobenzenes	Trinitrobenzenes
127°	118°	128°
188°	88°	58°
137°	174°	58°
142°	88°	128°
154°	118°	58°
159°	88°	123°

5–5 In planning an experiment to utilize Körner's principle to differentiate between *ortho*, *meta*, and *para* derivatives of benzene, four possibilities were considered: (a) the three derivatives could have both groups identical and could be substituted with a reagent to introduce a third identical group; (b) the original two groups could be identical, but a reagent to introduce a different group could be used; (c) the original two groups could be different, and the substituting agent could introduce a group identical with one of them; (d) the original groups could be different, and the substituting agent could introduce a third different group. Which of these possible experiments could differentiate all three isomers? What is the most structural information that could be obtained from each of the remaining methods?

Part 3

ELEMENTS OF CHEMICAL GEOMETRY

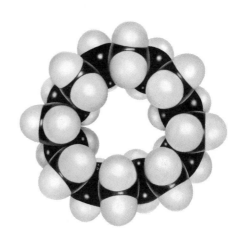

Even before Kekulé's work on organic structures, Pasteur had pointed out that molecules must be three-dimensional. In spite of this, the world of the structural organic chemists remained flat for about two decades. In 1874 it began to take on its third dimension. The introduction of the third dimension started men thinking about other aspects of chemical geometry than the structural ones. Among these were the bending of bonds to cause strains in molecules, the internal and external sizes of molecules, the nature of the vibrations which are induced by collisions and by heating, and the nature of the differences between the rotations about single and double bonds. These subjects will be considered in Part 3.

What observations and experiments led to the
distinction between a two-dimensional model of carbon and
a three-dimensional model?
What are the chemical consequences
of the three-dimensional model?

6

THE ARRANGEMENT OF
ATOMS IN SPACE

6–1 Background

The problem of the valences of oxygen, sulfur, and carbon was solved by the comparison of experimental results with those expected by the use of a simple quasi-geometrical model. The geometrical method was then applied to a more complex problem, that of the structure of benzene. After suitable refinements, it was again successful. The next important extension of the method of geometrical reasoning to the solution of a chemical problem was used in obtaining an insight into the arrangement of atoms in space. The groundwork for this advance was laid by Pasteur before valence theory was developed. When an adequate basis for understanding had been reached, the solution to the problem was contributed by J. H. van't Hoff, although essentially the same reasoning was employed on a somewhat less extensive scale by J. A. le Bel in an independent publication which appeared two months after that of van't Hoff, but which reached the active European scientific community first because van't Hoff's paper was published in Dutch. The phenomena with which these investigators worked were based on the polarization of light.

Two centuries earlier, it had been discovered that transparent crystals of calcium carbonate, "Iceland spar," possess the peculiar property of splitting an incident ray of light into two rays, called the *ordinary ray* and the *extraordinary ray*. This phenomenon can be easily observed. When looking at a dot through the crystal, one sees two dots. This phenomenon is known as *birefringence*.

It was learned that these two rays are vibrating in mutually perpendicular planes. Such rays are said to be "plane polarized." No application of these discoveries was made to chemistry for a century and a quarter. Then it was discovered that a quartz crystal or a solution of sugar would rotate the plane of polarized light. (See Fig. 6–1.) Such a preparation is said to be *optically active*. The same effect could be achieved with turpentine in the gaseous state, showing that the property is not necessarily associated with fixation of molecules into organized patterns, but occurs even when their arrangement is as nearly random as it is possible to make it.

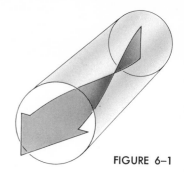

FIGURE 6–1

6–2 Instrumentation

Finally, in 1828, a Scottish physicist, William Nicol, perfected an optical device, the Nicol prism, for separating the two rays of Iceland spar in a convenient manner and thus made the investigation of polarized light in the laboratory a relatively simple matter. The Nicol prism consists of two pieces of Iceland spar carefully cut to predetermined angles and then cemented together so that the ordinary ray reaches the cemented layer at the angle of total reflection, thus eliminating it and leaving only the extraordinary ray (Fig. 6–2).

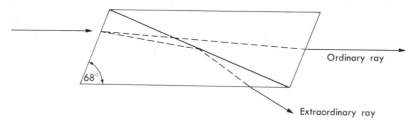

FIG. 6–2. Principle of construction of the Nicol prism.

A device called a "polarimeter" or "polariscope" is used to measure the optical activity of fluids. The simplest type of polariscope is constructed by mounting a monochromatic light source, which supplies polarized light to a sample, in back of a fixed Nicol prism, called a *polarizer*. Next is placed the tube containing the sample. Finally, a second Nicol prism, mounted on a graduated circle that can be rotated about the axis of the instrument, follows (Fig. 6–3).

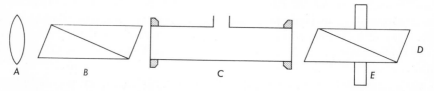

FIG. 6–3. Rudiments of a polariscope: *A*, monochromatic light source; *B*, polarizer; *C*, sample tube; *D*, analyzer; *E*, graduated circle.

When the instrument does not contain a sample, setting the analyzer at precisely 90° from the angle of the polarizer blacks out the light beam. When an optically active sample is then placed in the instrument, rotation of the beam causes light to appear in the analyzer. A compensating rotation of the analyzer will then return the reading to its original state with the light blacked out. The angle of rotation of the analyzer required to bring about compensation permits the extent of the optical activity of the compound under examination to be calculated.

Modern polariscopes can be fitted with various additional optical devices to permit more light to be passed through the sample and to increase the sensitivity of detection of the balance point of the instrument. A recent innovation is the use of a Faraday cell, an electrical device to bring about optical compensation, so that all readings may be performed electrically. This permits approximately a hundredfold increase in sensitivity.

6–3   Investigations of Optically Active Materials

Once the polariscope was available, studies on optically active substances became much more convenient to make. As a result, chemists industriously set about the examination of naturally occurring organic materials to learn the conditions of optical activity. Biot, who had observed the optical activity of gaseous turpentine in 1819, turned his attention increasingly to the study of solutions. He made an especially significant series of studies on tartaric acid. One of the by-products of wine making is cream of tartar, potassium acid tartrate. Acidification of this produces tartaric acid. Biot discovered that this acid rotates the plane of polarized light to the right. It is therefore called *dextro-rotatory*. Tartaric acid had long been known, having been isolated by Scheele. Later another acid was isolated from grapes and marketed under the mistaken impression that it was oxalic acid, the sour principle of rhubarb. Gay-Lussac discovered that this material was not oxalic acid and named it "racemic acid." As was pointed out earlier in this text (Section 3–2) Berzelius, in 1820, convinced himself that racemic acid and tartaric acid both had the same composition and coined the term "isomerism" to designate the phenomenon. It was found, however, that racemic acid is incapable of rotating the plane of polarized light. This, as well as a marked difference in melting point, served to distinguish the two substances.

6–4   Resolution

In 1848, Louis Pasteur started the study of crystals of optically inactive sodium ammonium racemate. His careful examination of these crystals showed that they could be separated into two groups which were mirror images of each other but not superimposable. Such crystals are known as *hemihedral*. On dissolving one set in water, it was found that the solution was identical to that of sodium ammonium tartrate, even to its optical activity. The other set was found to rotate the plane of polarized light an exactly equal amount in the opposite direction. When mixed in equal proportions, the crystals gave a solution which was optically inactive and identical with that of sodium ammonium racemate. This demonstrated that racemic acid is a mixture of two optical isomers with equal and opposite optical activities. These *dextro* and *levo* substances whose crystals are mirror images are sometimes called *optical antipodes*. A more precise name for them is *enantiomorphs*, from the Greek for opposite. Their separation is termed *resolution*.

The hand separation of crystals into sets of mirror images is laborious and time-consuming. In addition, it is strictly limited as a means of resolution, since only a very few materials will separate as does sodium ammonium racemate. Pasteur immediately began the search for other more convenient methods of resolution of optical isomers. His next success in this field provided one of the key discoveries in the field of biological chemistry. He found that he could culture a mold, *Penicillium glaucum*, on ammonium racemate and that the mold would use the *dextro* form as food and leave the *levo* form in the culture medium. This demonstrated the important principle that living organisms possess an optical bias. It was soon found that the general method could be applied to a large number of resolutions. It had the obvious disadvantage that half the starting material was destroyed. Nevertheless it provided a source of optically active materials for study.

Continuing his studies, Pasteur found that racemic acid could be resolved by reaction with an optically active base. Combination of two enantiomorphs with the same chemical substance produces two different materials which are not mirror images. Such pairs are known as *diastereoisomers*. The principle involved can be illustrated symbolically. Let A^+ and A^- represent the enantiomorphs. Let B^- represent the optically active material which is to combine with them. The reaction is as follows.

$$\text{(enantiomorphs)} \quad \begin{array}{c} A^+ \quad A^- \\ + \\ 2B^- \end{array} \rightarrow \begin{array}{c} A^+ \\ | \\ B^- \end{array} + \begin{array}{c} A^- \\ | \\ B^- \end{array} \quad \text{(diastereoisomers)}$$

The substance

$$\begin{array}{c} A^+ \\ | \\ B^- \end{array}$$

may be likened to a black right glove joined to a white left glove, while the substance

$$\begin{array}{c} A^- \\ | \\ B^- \end{array}$$

may be likened to a black left glove joined to a white left glove (Fig. 6–4). Compounds such as these will not fit into the same crystals and will, therefore, be separable by crystallization. In practice, the optically active naturally occurring base L-brucine is usually used for these resolutions. The modern variant of this method was introduced by Pope. This depends on the fact that the two enantio-

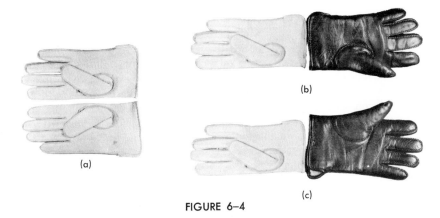

(b)

(a)

(c)

FIGURE 6–4

morphous acids react with the same base with different energies. Thus not only is the geometry of the resulting compounds different, but their energies of formation and stabilities are also different. Accordingly, if two moles of a racemic mixture of acids are treated with one mole of an optically active base, one diastereoisomer forms to the almost total exclusion of the other. The resultant mixture of an acid and a salt,

$$A^+ + A^- + B^- \rightarrow A^-B^- + A^+,$$

is much easier to separate than a mixture of two different salts, such as that resulting from the application of the original Pasteur method.

Pasteur's biochemical method has also been improved recently by Greenstein. In this method a mixture of enantiomorphous bases is reacted with acetic anhydride to give acetylated derivatives. These are then treated with a specific enzyme or biocatalyst capable of removing the acetyl group by hydrolysis. We shall refer to enzymes in Chapter 21 and succeeding chapters. For the present it is sufficient to know that they are complex chemical substances which are optically active. Because of the optical bias of the enzyme, hydrolysis will take place very much more rapidly on one of the enantiomorphs, giving an approach to absolute specificity. This will result in a mixture of a free base of one rotation with an acetylated compound of the opposite rotation. Again the separation of two such dissimilar compounds is relatively simple. This method has the great advantage that subsequent hydrolysis of the acetylated compound yields the second enantiomorphous base so that there is no loss of substance in the process. Application of Greenstein's method has made a variety of optically active compounds available in quantity.

6–5 Optical Activity and Dissymmetry

In 1820 Herschel discovered that the two crystalline forms of quartz, discovered some years previously, possess the property of rotating the plane of polarized light in opposite directions. Pasteur discussed the structural implications of this and later discoveries in 1860 in the following terms:

> When we study material things of whatever nature, as regards their forms and the
> repetition of their identical parts, we soon recognize that they fall into two large classes
> of which the following are the characters. Those of the one class, placed before a mirror,
> give images which are superposable on the originals; the images of the others are not
> superposable on their originals, although they faithfully reproduce all the details. A
> straight stair, a branch with leaves in a double row, a cube, the human body—these
> are of the former class. A winding stair, a branch with the leaves arranged spirally, a
> screw, a hand, an irregular tetrahedron—these are so many forms of the other set. The
> latter have no plane of symmetry.*

The two forms of quartz lose their optical rotatory power when they are either
dissolved or fused. It was concluded, then, that the dissymmetry of quartz depends
on the structure of the crystal and not on the molecules of silica.

> Imagine a spiral stair whose steps are cubes, or any other objects with superposable
> images. Destroy the stair and the dissymmetry will have vanished. The dissymmetry
> of the stair was simply the result of the mode of arrangement of the component steps.†

With organic substances which retain their optical activity in solution, an
explanation based on the arrangement of the molecules alone cannot be valid.
Pasteur, therefore, attributed their optical activity to *molecular dissymetry*. This
phrase is inscribed as a key word in his mausoleum in the Pasteur Institute in
Paris. The discovery of the hemihedral forms of the tartrates substantiated this
concept, since each of the forms crystallized true from its solution.

Molecular dissymmetry is impossible in figures which are confined to two
dimensions. For this reason Pasteur postulated that molecules must be three-
dimensional figures with atoms linked in a definite arrangement. This postulate
stamps Pasteur as the originator of the concept of chemistry in space, or *stereochemistry*, as it is now called. Pasteur's work in the field was terminated in 1853,
however, and at that time the structural work of Kekulé and others was still
in the future, and the method for determining the relative positions of atoms in
molecules was not available. Pasteur thus put his ideas about the structure of
tartaric acid in the form of a question which was remarkably prescient:

> Are the atoms of the dextro-acid grouped on the spirals of a dextrogyrate helix, or placed
> at the summits of an irregular tetrahedron, or disposed according to some particular
> dissymmetric grouping or other? We cannot answer these questions. But it cannot be
> doubted that the atoms are grouped in some dissymmetric order having a non-super-
> posable image. It is not less certain that the atoms of the laevo-acid have precisely the
> opposite dissymmetric grouping.‡

---

* Lowry, T. M., *Optical Rotatory Power*, Dover Publications, New York, 1964, p. 27;
originally published by Longmans, Green and Co., London, 1935.
  † *Ibid.* p. 27.
  ‡ *Ibid.* p. 37.

Commenting on this three quarters of a century later, Lowry states:

In this passage Pasteur puts forward the irregular tetrahedron, which even at the present day provides the simplest and commonest illustration of molecular dissymmetry, as a basis of optical rotatory power; and he also foreshadows the helical or spiral structure, which was detected in the structure of crystalline tartaric acid sixty years later by Astbury with the help of x-ray analysis. It is therefore not surprising that, when the quadrivalency of carbon was clearly established, the tetrahedral model was adopted almost immediately as a correct representation of the carbon atom in space of three dimensions, and was used as a basis for explaining isomerism (or the absence of isomerism) amongst carbon compounds.*

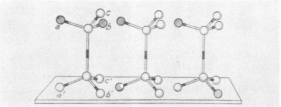

FIG. 6–5.   Paterno's models of dichloroethane (1869). [From *Giorn. Sci. Palermo* **5**, 117 (1869).]

Tetrahedral models of carbon were used in 1869 by Paterno to explain the existence of three supposed isomers of dichloroethane, $C_2H_4Cl_2$. It was further postulated that rotation about the single carbon-carbon bond was restricted. His models are shown in Fig. 6–5.

Paterno's claim to priority in the use of tetrahedral models to explain demonstrable facts of organic chemistry was lost when it was found that the supposed isomers of ethylene chloride, CH_2Cl—CH_2Cl, did not exist as separable substances. This also demonstrated that rotation about a carbon-carbon single bond was possible.

6–6   A Model Correlating Optical Activity with Chemical Structure

In 1874, van't Hoff, then twenty-two, was engaged in the study of optically active substances in an attempt to correlate optical activity with chemical structure. His first attempt at an explanation led to some contradictions, but on further investigation he came to the conclusion that each of the apparent contradictions could be explained. He then proceeded to set forth his correlations between experimental observations and his proposed theory.

Van't Hoff first examined the assumption that the atoms around methane might all lie in a plane. The number of isomers to be expected on this assumption was greater than the number found in the laboratory. On the other hand, if one assumed a tetrahedron with the carbon at its center and the valences directed toward the vertices, the right number of isomers was predicted with a single exception, that of the figure in which all four substituents were different. In this

---

* *Ibid.* p. 37.

Table 6–1

ISOMERS OF SUBSTITUTED METHANES

	Plane model	Tetrahedral model	Experimental
CH_2R'	1	1	1
CH_2R_2'	2	1	1
$CH_2R'R''$	2	1	1
$CHR_2'R''$	2	1	1
$CHR'R''R'''$	3	2	?
$CR'R''R'''R''''$	3	2	?

case some anomalies appeared. The relationships are shown in Table 6–1 and in Fig. 6–6. It is easy to see that the tetrahedral model fits the experimentally determined number of isomers better than the plane model. The problem of the last two categories remained to be considered, however.

Carbons such as the last two in the table, that is, those combined with four different univalent groups, were called "asymmetric"* by van't Hoff. Drawing on his reading and research he made the generalization that all of the compounds of carbon which in solution rotate the plane of polarized light possess an asymmetric carbon atom.†

Despite the fact that the determination of the structures of naturally occurring substances was still in its infancy, van't Hoff was able to present a list of over thirty optically active substances about which enough was known to assure that they contained asymmetric carbon atoms. The sole exception to the rule that had been reported was a sample of "active propyl alcohol" which was later reported to be impure and still later was shown to contain active amyl alcohol.

Van't Hoff next pointed out that numerous cases were known in which a chemical reaction was performed on a compound containing an asymmetric carbon so as to destroy the asymmetry, a reaction called *racemization*. In each of these cases the optical activity disappeared at the same time as the last asymmetric carbon. He also noted that not all compounds which could be formulated with asymmetric carbons were optically active. The most important reason for this was that such compounds might be mixtures of enantiomorphs which had not yet been resolved. Van't Hoff proceeded with a series of predictions about which substances should be optically active and which should not be. Some of these turned out to present

---

* An *asymmetric* object, such as a single carbon atom or a molecule, has no symmetry whatever. The word *dissymmetric* has been used in two different senses. In one sense it is interchangeable with *asymmetric*. In the other sense, however, it means that the object has neither plane nor center of symmetry. Reflecting a dissymmetric object in a plane yields its enantiomorph or mirror image. In this sense, a *dissymmetric* object means one of a pair. This is implied by the second sense of the prefix *dis-*, meaning *double* or *twofold*. Because of the ambiguity, it is probably best to drop the word *dissymmetric* and to use the term *enantiomorph* or *enantiomer*.

† Van't Hoff, J. H., *Die Lagerung der Atome in Raume*, Vieweg und Sohn, Braunschweig, 1894, p. 7.

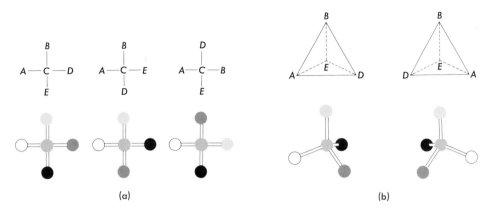

FIG. 6–6.   (a) Plane model and (b) tetrahedral model of methane.

difficulties in resolution that were not overcome for a long period of time, but now all of his predictions have been confirmed experimentally.

The major anomaly brought out in this investigation was the presence of only a single isomer in some of the cases in which two were expected on the tetrahedral theory. This anomaly disappeared when with improved techniques, all the substances containing asymmetric carbons were finally resolved into their enantiomorphs. Thus complete agreement was found between the conclusions drawn for the tetrahedral model and those found experimentally.

The concept of the tetrahedral carbon atom greatly strengthened the ability of organic chemists to visualize the spatial arrangement of atoms in molecules and completed the necessary conceptual basis for the elucidation of the structures of a tremendous number of naturally occurring substances. These ideas also laid the foundation for a rational approach to the problems of synthesis.

Van't Hoff's original concept was soon extended to include asymmetric atoms other than the carbon atom and finally to include molecules which contained no asymmetric atom but which were, nevertheless, so constructed as to be asymmetric.

6–7   Two-Dimensional Representation

The problem of the representation of tetrahedra in two dimensions is one which can cause confusion. One convenient method of representation is due to Emil Fischer and such formulas are known as "Fischer projections." The principle behind the Fischer projections is illustrated in Fig. 6–7.

Models (a) and (b) are representations of asymmetric tetrahedra. The basis of their asymmetry lies in the differences between the four attached substituents, a, b, c, and d. They are mirror images and not superimposable. If we rock (a) and (b) back on the vertices d, the intersection cd will lie on the bottom and ab will be visible from the top. This condition is shown in models (c) and (d). Instead of drawing in the sides ad, db, bc, and ca, the Fischer convention is to draw in only the sides ab and cd. This gives the Fischer projections, (e) and (f). Although it is a

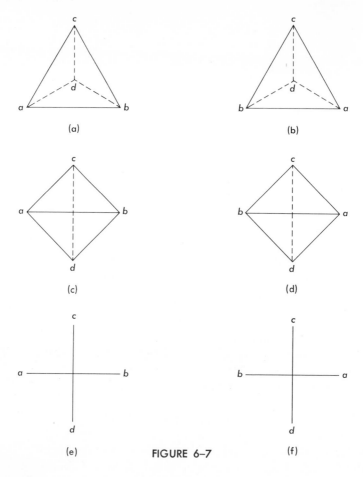

FIGURE 6–7

two-dimensional model, it is understood to represent a three-dimensional object. If we assume that the carbon atom lies in the plane of the paper, the intersection *ab* is understood to be above the paper and the intersection *cd* below.

6–8   Number of Isomers

Using Fischer projections, it is possible to show that the number of isomers predicted doubles with the addition of each new center of asymmetry.

Isomers of a substance with two asymmetric carbons

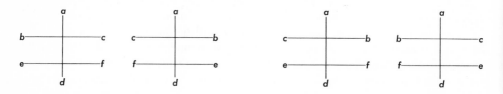

Accordingly, the number of isomers to be expected with n asymmetric centers is 2^n. If some of the substituting groups are identical, it is possible to have a molecule which is internally compensated. This is called the *meso* form. Each such case reduces the number of isomers to be expected by one.

Isomers with internal compensation

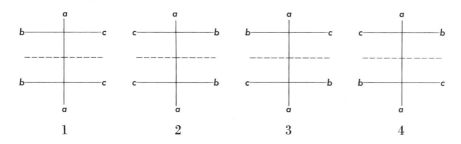

Examination will show that models 1 and 2 have a plane of symmetry passing through the center of the axis aa. This is indicated in projection by the dashed line. Hence, although these are shown as mirror images, they are also superimposable and are not enantiomorphs. Models 3 and 4, on the other hand, have no such plane of symmetry because they are differently arranged. Consequently, they are enantiomorphs. This model, then, exists in three forms instead of four.

To the chemist engaged in organic synthesis, the theory of the tetrahedral carbon has immediate implications with respect to the number of products which he must expect to form in his work. If he works with unresolved starting materials, each time he joins two to make a molecule with multiple centers of asymmetry, he will create new sets of diastereoisomers. Since these will have different physical properties and different melting points, the problems of separation and identification will be multiplied. Accordingly, when asymmetric centers are involved, it is desired to work with optically active starting materials so that the number of products formed will be minimal.

All of these consequences of the theory of the tetrahedral carbon were formulated by van't Hoff. The predictions of the number of isomers to be found with multiple asymmetric centers were verified before the turn of the century by the work of Emil Fischer on sugars, which will be presented in some detail in later chapters. Despite this firm empirical basis, the theory was not quite completely satisfying as a scientific concept because nobody really understood why random aggregates of asymmetric molecules should rotate the plane of polarized light. The answer to this question was not attained for another half-century. To understand it, it is necessary to learn more about polarized light. This will be the subject of the next chapter.

PROBLEMS

6–1   Examine a molecular model of propane and of butane.   Why are two isomers of propane, I and II, not possible?

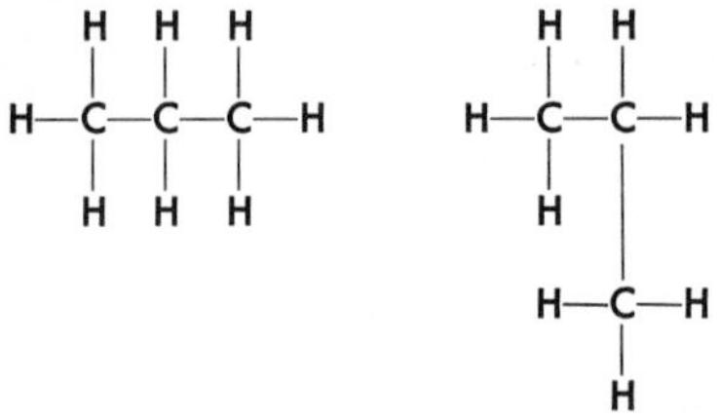

$$
\begin{array}{cccc}
 & H & H & H \\
 & | & | & | \\
H- & C- & C- & C-H \\
 & | & | & | \\
 & H & H & H
\end{array}
\qquad
\begin{array}{ccc}
 & H & H \\
 & | & | \\
H- & C- & C-H \\
 & | & \\
 & H & \\
 & | & \\
H- & C- & H \\
 & | & \\
 & H &
\end{array}
$$

I   II

In two-dimensional representation of alkanes, therefore, what determines the number of isomers:

(a) the *number* of carbons and hydrogens to which each individual carbon is bonded, or

(b) in addition, the *angle* at which the bond is drawn on paper?

6–2   (a) Which of the structures below are equivalent?

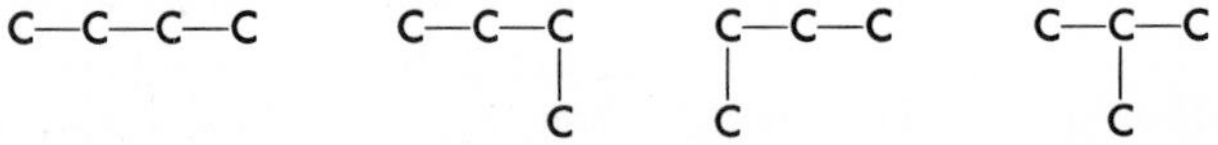

$$
\text{C-C-C-C} \qquad
\begin{array}{c}\text{C-C-C}\\ |\\ \text{C}\end{array} \qquad
\begin{array}{c}\text{C-C-C}\\ |\\ \text{C}\end{array} \qquad
\begin{array}{c}\text{C-C-C}\\ |\\ \text{C}\end{array}
$$

(b) How many isomers of butane, C_4H_{10}, are possible?

(c) What is the structure of the smallest alkane which could have dextro and levo forms?

6–3   IUPAC RULES.   Designation of isomers corresponding to a given formula becomes a tedious process as the number of isomers increases.   Let us concern ourselves only with the simpler cases here.

We have already named the lower alkanes containing straight chains.   When branching of the carbon skeleton occurs, the International Union of Pure and Applied Chemistry suggests that the longest carbon chain be chosen and numbered so that substituents have the lowest number.   For example:

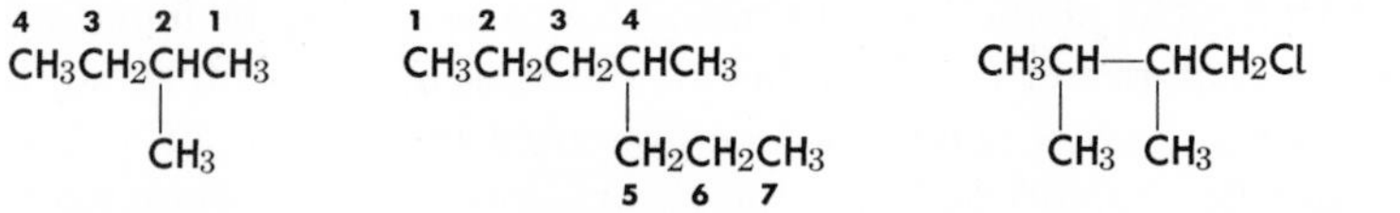

$$
\begin{array}{l}
\overset{4}{}\ \overset{3}{}\ \overset{2}{}\ \overset{1}{}\\
CH_3CH_2CHCH_3\\
\qquad\quad |\\
\qquad\quad CH_3
\end{array}
\qquad
\begin{array}{l}
\overset{1}{}\ \overset{2}{}\ \overset{3}{}\ \overset{4}{}\\
CH_3CH_2CH_2CHCH_3\\
\qquad\qquad\quad |\\
\qquad\qquad\quad CH_2CH_2CH_3\\
\qquad\qquad\qquad \overset{5}{\ }\ \overset{6}{\ }\ \overset{7}{\ }
\end{array}
\qquad
\begin{array}{l}
CH_3CH{-}CHCH_2Cl\\
\quad\ \ |\quad\ |\\
\quad\ \ CH_3\ \ CH_3
\end{array}
$$

2-methylbutane   4-methylheptane   1-chloro-2,3-dimethylbutane
(not 3-methylbutane)   (not 2-propylpentane)

Name the following compounds.

$$
\text{(a)}\quad CH_3CH_2CH\overset{\displaystyle CH_3}{\underset{\displaystyle CH_3}{<}}
\qquad\qquad
\text{(b)}\quad \overset{\displaystyle CH_3}{\underset{\displaystyle CH_3}{>}}CHCH_2CH_2CH_2Cl
$$

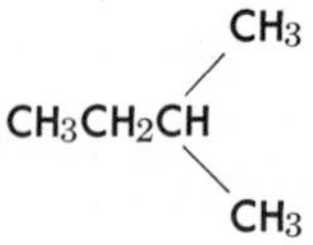

(if CH_3I is iodomethane)

(c) 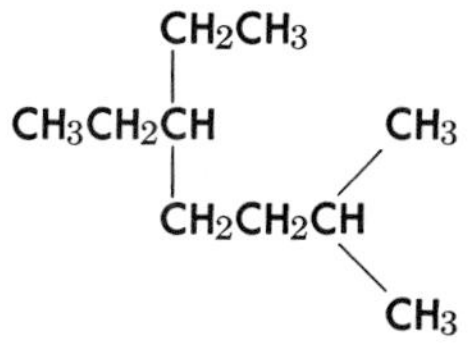   CH₃CH₂ĊH — with CH₂CH₃ above, and CH₂CH₂ĊH below attached to CH₃ and CH₃

(d) 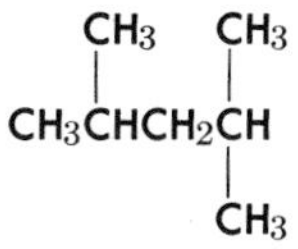   CH₃CHCH₂CH with CH₃ CH₃ above and CH₃ below

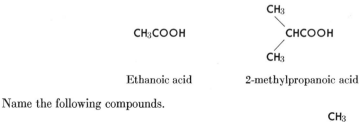

Alcohols are named according to a similar pattern:

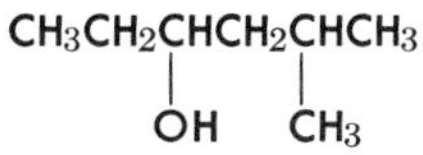

CH₃CH₂CHCH₂CHCH₃
| |
OH   CH₃

2-methylhexan-4-ol

Name the following compounds.

(e) 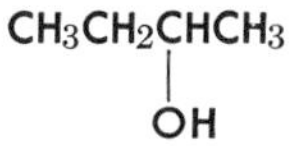   CH₃CH₂CHCH₃
|
OH

(f) 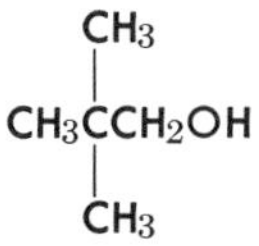   CH₃CCH₂OH with CH₃ above and CH₃ below

(g)   ClCH₂CH₂OH

(h) 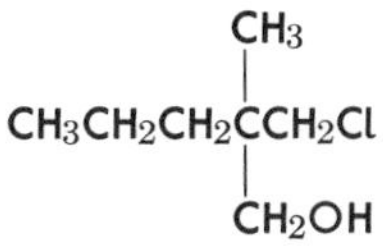   CH₃CH₂CH₂CCH₂Cl with CH₃ above and CH₂OH below

(If —CH₃ is a methyl group, what is the name for —CH₂Cl, as part (b) suggests?)

Acids are also named as derivatives of hydrocarbons in the IUPAC system:

CH₃COOH

CH₃
\
CHCOOH
/
CH₃

Ethanoic acid   2-methylpropanoic acid

Name the following compounds.

(i) 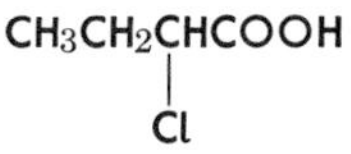   CH₃CH₂CHCOOH
|
Cl

(j) 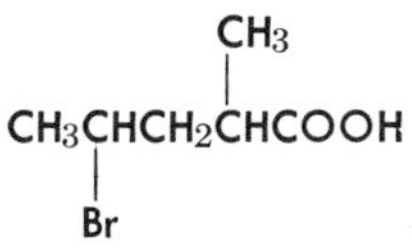   CH₃CHCH₂CHCOOH with CH₃ above and Br below

(k)   HOCH₂CH₂CH₂COOH

(l) 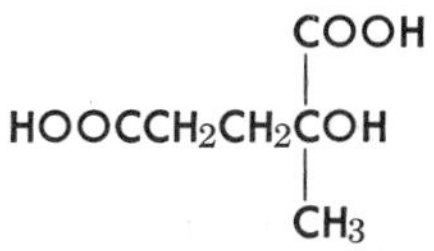   HOOCCH₂CH₂COH with COOH above and CH₃ below

(if HOCH₂CH₂OH is ethane-1,2-diol and
HOOCCH₂CH₂COOH is butane-1,4-dioic acid)

6–4 TRIVIAL NAMES. The systematic names are not often used for the lower members of these series. Often trivial names which may reflect the source from which the material was obtained are used.

Hydrocarbons with a methyl branch one carbon from the end are given the prefix *iso-*.

$$CH_3CHCH_2CH_3 \qquad CH_3CHCH_2CH_2CH_3$$
$$\qquad | \qquad\qquad\qquad\qquad |$$
$$\qquad CH_3 \qquad\qquad\qquad\qquad CH_3$$

*iso*pentane   *iso*hexane

According to this scheme straight-chain hydrocarbons have the prefix *n-* (for normal).

$$CH_3CH_2CH_2CH_2CH_3$$

n-pentane

We shall mention one parent hydrocarbon whose trivial name follows no rule

$$CH_3$$
$$|$$
$$CH_3CCH_3$$
$$|$$
$$CH_3$$

*neo*pentane

and the sole exception to the *iso-* rule, *iso*octane, which is really 2,2,4-trimethylpentane.

(a) Draw the structure for *iso*octane.

(b) Name as many of the hydrocarbons in Problem 6–3 as possible by trivial names.

Alcohols are named as derivatives of the alkanes. An alcohol whose oxygen is attached to a carbon bearing one other carbon is termed a *primary* alcohol; if the carbon is attached to two carbons, it is a *secondary* alcohol, if to three carbons, *tertiary*. The trivial names of the C_4-alcohols will illustrate the system.

$$CH_3CH_2CH_2CH_2OH \qquad CH_3CH_2CHCH_3 \qquad CH_3COH \qquad CH_2CH_2OH$$

n-butyl alcohol   Secondary butyl alcohol   Tertiary butyl alcohol   *iso*butyl alcohol
(or *s*-butyl alcohol)   (or *t*-butyl alcohol)   (or *i*-butyl alcohol)

(c) Is isobutyl alcohol primary, secondary, or tertiary?

(d) The C_5-alcohols are called amyl alcohols. Give structures for *n*-amyl alcohol, secondary amyl alcohol, and tertiary amyl alcohol.

(e) Name as many alcohols in Problem 6–3 as possible by trivial names.

The lower carboxylic acids bear the following names.

$$CH_3COOH \qquad CH_3CH_2COOH \qquad CH_3CH_2CH_2COOH \qquad CH_3CH_2CH_2CH_2COOH$$

Acetic acid   Propionic acid   Butyric acid   Valeric acid

An alcohol or acid may be called *iso-* only if the methyl branch is at the "far" end of the molecule.

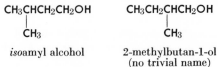

*iso*amyl alcohol   2-methylbutan-1-ol
(no trivial name)

Greek letters may be used to indicate substituent positions. The letter α indicates that a substituent is on a carbon next to a functional group, β, that it is one carbon removed.

$$ClCH_2CH_2COOH$$

β-chloropropionic acid

(f) Draw structures for isobutyric acid and isovaleric acid. What are their IUPAC names?

(g) Name as many acids in Problem 6–3 as possible by trivial names.
Name the following compounds.

(h) CH_3CCl_2COOH

(i) 
$$\begin{array}{c} CH_3 \\ \diagdown \\ CHCH_2CHCOOH \\ \diagup \\ CH_3 \end{array}$$

(j) $CH_3CH_2CH_2COCl$

(What is CH_3COCl? See Section 3–4.)

(k) 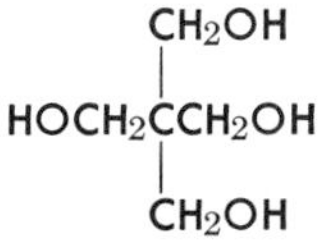
$$\begin{array}{c} CH_2OH \\ | \\ HOCH_2CCH_2OH \\ | \\ CH_2OH \end{array}$$

Pentaerythritol

(What should the —CH_2OH group be called? See Problem 6–3h.)

6–5   Which of the following compounds contain an asymmetric carbon? Which may be resolved into enantiomers? Write Fischer projection formulas for all the possible isomers of each compound, indicating planes of symmetry in applicable cases.

(a) 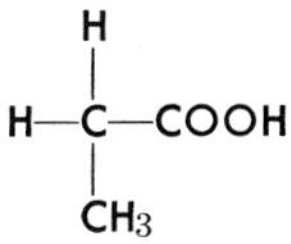
$$\begin{array}{c} H \\ | \\ H-C-COOH \\ | \\ CH_3 \end{array}$$

(b)
$$\begin{array}{c} H \\ | \\ HO-C-COOH \\ | \\ CH_3 \end{array}$$

(c)
$$\begin{array}{c} H\ \ H \\ |\ \ \ | \\ HOOC-C-C-COOH \\ |\ \ \ | \\ OH\ H \end{array}$$

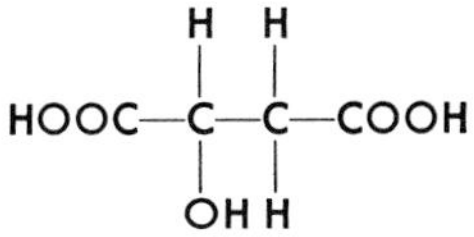

(d) 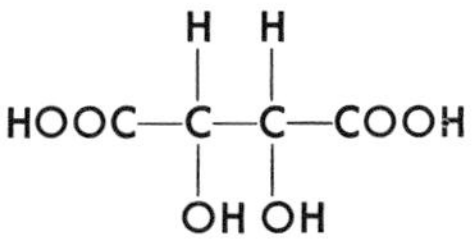
$$\begin{array}{c} H\ \ H \\ |\ \ \ | \\ HOOC-C-C-COOH \\ |\ \ \ | \\ OH\ OH \end{array}$$

(e) 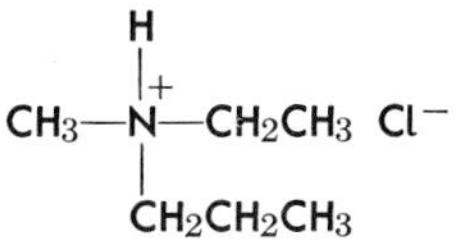
$$\begin{array}{c} H \\ |+ \\ CH_3-N-CH_2CH_3\ \ Cl^- \\ | \\ CH_2CH_2CH_3 \end{array}$$

(f) 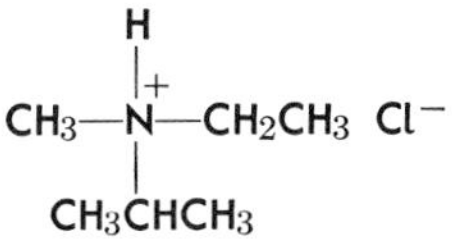
$$\begin{array}{c} H \\ |+ \\ CH_3-N-CH_2CH_3\ \ Cl^- \\ | \\ CH_3CHCH_3 \end{array}$$

Compounds (e) and (f) are analogous to

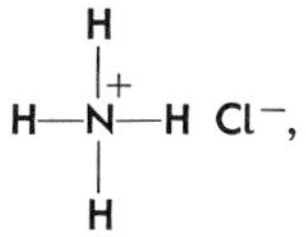

$$\begin{array}{c} H \\ |+ \\ H-N-H\ \ Cl^-, \\ | \\ H \end{array}$$

as we shall see later.

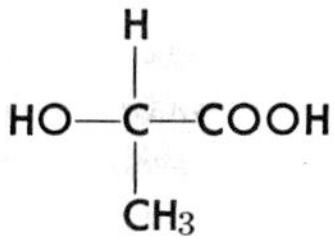

(g) 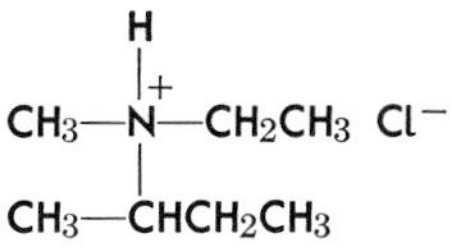
$$\begin{array}{c} H \\ |+ \\ CH_3-N-CH_2CH_3\ \ Cl^- \\ | \\ CH_3-CHCH_2CH_3 \end{array}$$

(h)
$$\begin{array}{c} H \\ | \\ CH_3-C-CH_2CH_3 \\ | \\ CH_3-CH-CH_2-CH_3 \end{array}$$

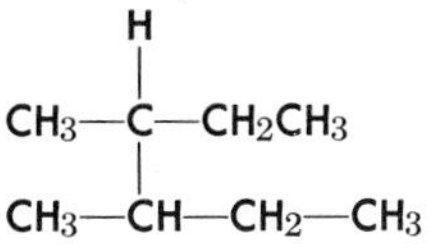

6-6 Suppose that we have three carbon atoms in a ring, defining a plane as shown in Fig. 6–8. In addition, suppose that there are hydrogens attached to each carbon above and below this plane, making a symmetrical molecule, cyclopropane, as shown in Fig. 6–9.

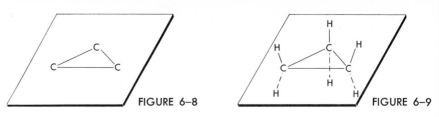

FIGURE 6–8   FIGURE 6–9

How many isomers of the following compounds would be possible? How many of them are enantiomers of one another?

(a) CH₂⎯CHCl   (b) CHCl⎯CHCl   (c) CHCl⎯CHBr

$\quad$ CHCl   CHCl   CHCl

6-7 The formula below was found to be that of cholesterol. How many asymmetric carbons would it contain?

$$CH_3CH(CH_2)_3CH(CH_3)_2$$

6-8 The reagent for nickel, dimethylglyoxime, chelates the metal, giving a product of the type shown below.

VII   VIII

Any isomers like VII and VIII, differing only in the position of an H atom, would not be capable of separation if they actually existed as separate isomers; experimentally, then, we may think of them as indistinguishable.

Two products with different melting points result from the use of benzylmethyl glyoxime (IX) as the chelating agent.

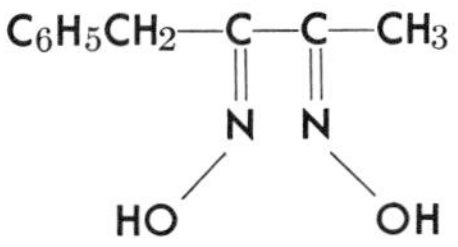

$$C_6H_5CH_2-C-C-CH_3$$

$$\underset{HO}{\underset{N}{\|}}\quad\underset{OH}{\underset{N}{\|}}$$

IX

What, therefore, must be the arrangement of N-atoms around nickel in the complex with benzylmethylglyoxime? What is the arrangement in nickel dimethylglyoxime by analogy?

What is responsible for the rotation of the plane
of polarized light? How can the randomly oriented molecules
in a gas or liquid rotate the plane of polarized light? How are the absolute
spatial positions of groups on a molecule determined?

7

THE BASIS OF THE OPTICAL
ROTATORY POWER OF
ORGANIC MOLECULES

7-1 Types of Polarized Light

It is possible to produce three kinds of polarized light: plane polarized, elliptically polarized, and circularly polarized. Of these, plane polarized and circularly polarized light are the two types that will interest the organic chemist. If we imagine a rope supported at one end and held by a man at the other so that it is parallel to the ground, the man may start a series of vibrations up and down that will be transmitted along the rope as waves. If he is careful to make his hand travel accurately up and down in a straight line, the extension of that line in space which is traced by the waves in the rope will be a plane. Such waves are said to be "plane polarized." It is one of the anomalies of physical optics, however, that the plane which has been assigned as the "plane of polarization" of a light beam is actually the plane perpendicular to the one in which the advancing wavefront oscillates. This anomalous assignment of planes need not interfere with our subsequent analyses, however.

If the man with the rope uses his hand to generate a circle, the rope will respond with a series of waves which will trace out a helix. Such a wave motion is termed "circularly polarized," rather than "helically polarized" as might be expected.

7-2 Analysis of Plane-Polarized Light

Let us consider a ray of light that is plane polarized at an angle of 45° to the horizontal, as in Fig. 7–1(a). For the purpose of physical analysis, such a ray may be considered to result from the action of two rays at right angles, as in Fig. 7–1(b).

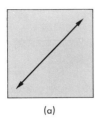 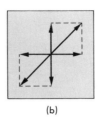

(a)   (b)

FIGURE 7–1

Quartz crystal, like Iceland spar, is capable of splitting light that enters it at certain angles into two rays perpendicular to each other. These travel at different speeds in the quartz. The extraordinary ray travels faster than the ordinary ray. If a piece of crystalline quartz is cut into a flat plate at an angle such that it can split light into two such rays, and plane-polarized light is allowed to fall on it, the light will be split into two rays at right angles to each other, each plane polarized but at 90° to the other. The extraordinary ray, traveling faster than the ordinary ray, will get out of phase with it. Suppose that the quartz plate is made of such a thickness that the ordinary ray falls behind just one-quarter of a vibration before it emerges. Such a plate is called a "quarter-wave plate." Polarized light emerging from a quarter-wave plate will perform a helical motion and is said to be circularly polarized. The reason for the helical motion can be seen by following the analysis in Fig. 7–2.

 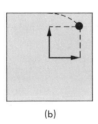  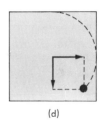

(a)   (b)   (c)   (d)

FIGURE 7–2

Reference to Fig. 7–2(a) shows that the vertical vector has just reached its top point at the time when the horizontal vector has reached the center of the square. Thus the horizontal vector is one-quarter of a wave out of phase with the vertical one. The result of the addition of the two vectors is represented by the dot. In 7–2(b), where each vector has progressed one-eighth of a vibration, the resultant has moved along the circumference of a circle down to the point indicated by the new dot. At one-quarter of a vibration from the start, the resultant is as shown in 7–2(c); after three-eighths, it is as in 7–2(d). A continuous line joining the dots in the figures traces out the circle shown being inscribed in the square. Therefore, the projection of the light path in a plane is a circle, and the light is progressing with a helical motion.

Let us next imagine a wave generator capable of forming two helical waves simultaneously. One of these progresses in a right-handed helix, the other in a left-

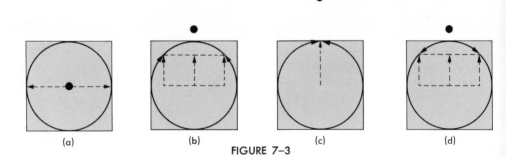

FIGURE 7–3

handed helix. The waves are of equal amplitude and are progressing at the same velocity. The resulting motion is shown in Fig. 7–3.

In Fig. 7–3(a), both helices are moving upward. Their resultant lies halfway between, and is shown by the dot. In 7–3(b), they have progressed halfway from the center to the top. Each one projects to a vector as shown. Addition of these vectors gives the result shown by the dot. In 7–3(c), each has reached the top of its path. The resultant is thus twice this distance from the center. In 7–3(d), the two are receding and the resultant has moved down. The path that the resultant is tracing is a straight line. Extension of the line through space along the path of the light generates a plane. Hence the resulting light is plane polarized. Therefore, plane-polarized light may be treated analytically as if it were made up of the sum of two beams of circularly polarized light moving in opposite directions. This proposition was first advanced by the physicist, Fresnel, who then proceeded to explain the rotation of the plane of polarization.

7–3   Rotation of the Plane of Polarization

Let us imagine that a beam of plane-polarized light passes through a medium, either solid, liquid, or gaseous, which is so constituted that its refractive index for a beam of right circularly polarized light is different from that for left circularly polarized light. Plane-polarized light emerging from such a medium will have had one of its components slowed more than the other so that the resulting motion will be as sketched in Fig. 7–4.

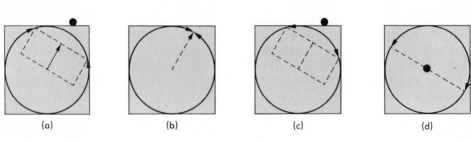

FIGURE 7–4

It will be seen that the motion of the resultant of the emerging beams in Fig. 7–4 is again a straight line but that because of the phase change, the line has been rotated from that in Fig. 7–3. Thus a medium that slows up a beam of circularly polarized light moving in one direction more than that moving in the other will rotate the plane of the resultant plane-polarized light. A medium which has this property is said to be *anisotropic*.

Once Fresnel had advanced this explanation, verification was undertaken by actual measurements of the refractive indices of right and left circularly polarized light passing through a medium that rotated the plane of polarized light, and it was found that, in fact, the two were different. Thus the hypothesis was verified.

7–4   Conditions Necessary for the Rotation of the Plane of Polarization

It is not too difficult to imagine that molecules in a solid might be lined up so as to affect right and left helices differently. Indeed, if the molecules were lined up in a helix, such an effect would be accomplished. It is not so easy to picture why it is that a liquid or a gas could have such a property. Superficially, it would seem that by random orientation of molecules, any effect remaining from the passage of light through one molecule would be canceled by passage through another oppositely oriented. Closer analysis will reveal that this is not true, however.

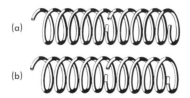

(a)

(b)

FIGURE 7–5

The reader should secure two helical springs wound in the same direction or, alternatively, cut one spring into two. He can then quickly verify the fact that turning one spring end for end does not change the "handedness" of the helix. If both springs are wound clockwise, a particle rolling around one of them so that it would perform a helical motion in space would, on passing from the first to the second, continue to roll in the same direction, whichever end of the second was presented to the outlet from the first. Thus any motion traced during the passage through the first would not be undone by passage through the second, but would rather be reinforced. This is illustrated in Fig. 7–5, in which the right helix is reversed from (a) to (b).

7–5   Models for Molecular Asymmetry

It can be seen that, as Pasteur stated, the condition necessary for a molecular aggregate to rotate the plane of polarized light is that the individual molecules have helical asymmetry with respect to their action on light. To complete the explanation of the phenomenon of optical activity, it is necessary to learn how a molecule can have helical asymmetry in its action on light.

Speculations concerning the interaction between light and matter to produce optical activity were made during the nineteenth century, but the beginning of the modern attack on the problem came in 1915 with the publication of a paper by Born showing that an asymmetric system consisting of harmonic resonators coupled by electrical or magnetic forces is sufficient to produce the phenomenon. Although the problem is a quantum-mechanical one, this classical system is capable of replacing the quantum-mechanical model.

One of the earliest mechanical models which served to demonstrate the principle was described by H. G. Tanner in 1929. This model had the essential properties of an asymmetric carbon atom. In it, the four vertices of a tetrahedron were attached to four springs. Each of the springs was set to a different tension, giving the tetrahedron a type of asymmetry. A long cable was attached to the center of the tetrahedron and arranged so that it could be vibrated mechanically. It was then observed that vibration of this cable in a straight line would propagate a wave of "plane-polarized" vibration down as far as the center of the tetrahedron. When the emergent vibration passed beyond this point, its plane of vibration was rotated. Similarly, the machine showed different resistance to the passage of right and left circularly polarized vibrations. Thus the model served to illustrate the action of an asymmetric carbon atom. This device is, in fact, an analog computer with which it is possible to study details of the interaction of the vibrating cable with the asymmetric carbon model much more simply than is possible with a mathematical model.

Following Born's publication, a series of mathematical models for the optically active carbon atom was published by various investigators. The essence of all these models is the idea that the substitution of four different groups on a central carbon atom would create a sort of helical asymmetry with respect to its interaction with light so that an emergent beam would have its plane of polarization rotated. With these models it was possible to establish a relationship between refractivities of groups and their effects on polarized light and to find a basis for the assignment of the absolute configurations of molecules in space as a function of the direction in which they would rotate polarized light.

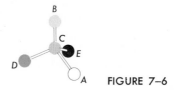

FIGURE 7-6

A rough analogy to the mathematical models may be obtained by considering Fig. 7-6. Imagine a wave advancing in a helical path in a clockwise direction. It comes into contact with the molecule whose central carbon, C, has four different groups attached, A, B, D, and E; A projects in front of C, B is vertically above C, and E and D are behind C. The beam first hits at A, then advances clockwise at such velocity that its next contact is at B. Continuing, it reaches E

and then leaves the molecule. Since D is at the same distance behind C as is E, the wave never comes into contact with D. Hence its path through the molecule may be described as ABE.

Now imagine a second wave, exactly like the first except that its motion is counterclockwise. It comes into contact first at A, passes counterclockwise to B, and then reaches D before leaving the molecule. It never touches E. Hence its path may be described as ABD.

It is characteristic of the passage of light through matter that the denser the medium, the slower the passage of light through it. If groups D and E have different densities so that one slows light more than the other, the rate of passage of the helix tracing the path ABE through the molecule will be different from that tracing the path ABD. But this is the condition that is necessary to secure rotation of the plane of polarized light. Thus we see that an asymmetric molecule presents helical asymmetry to a helical beam of light and, as a result, random distribution of an aggregate of such molecules will not cancel the effect on light of passage through a single one.

The reader should understand that the mechanical analogy presented does not precisely describe the mode of interaction of the wavefront of light with a molecule. Despite this, the essential geometrical features of the interaction are as presented so that the analogy permits an understanding of the geometrical relationships responsible for the rotation of the plane of polarization of light.

7–6   Absolute Configuration

We saw in Chapter 6 how it is possible to represent tetrahedral carbons by two-dimensional models. However, two models, mirror images, representing each asymmetric carbon are possible. Only one of these can properly represent the *dextro* configuration, and the other must represent the *levo*. The question of which is which then arises. When this problem became acute during his studies on the optical activity of sugars, Emil Fischer resolved it by an arbitrary choice which obviously had a 50-50 chance of being correct. As we shall see in Chapter 22, the fifth carbon of glucose was chosen as the standard, and means were then devised for comparing others with it. Only in comparatively recent times has it become possible to test the correctness of Fischer's arbitrary assignment of configuration.

Assignments of absolute configuration on the basis of mathematical models were made by W. Kuhn in 1929 and by Boys in 1934. The first direct experimental test of Fischer's assignment was made in 1951 by Bijvoet and his collaborators by means of x-ray diffraction. We shall refer to this method in more detail in the next chapter. The method was used to determine the structure of tartaric acid,

$$HOOC\text{—}CHOH\text{—}CHOH\text{—}COOH$$

by examination of its rubidium salt. It was found that Fischer's assignment had been correct.

For chemical convenience, the modern standard for configuration is D-glyceralde-hyde. This has the absolute configuration shown below.

$$
\begin{array}{c}
\text{CHO} \\
|\\
\text{H—C—OH} \\
|\\
\text{CH}_2\text{OH}
\end{array}
$$

D-(+)-glyceraldehyde

In this formula the group —CHO is the aldehyde group. Since chemical means have been found for comparing Fischer's standard carbon on glucose with D-glyceraldehyde, all the earlier comparisons which were made can be immediately related to D-glyceraldehyde. In the notation adopted, the small capitals D and L refer to absolute configuration, while the signs (+) and (−) refer to the *dextro* or *levo* rotation of the substance in a polariscope. The two are not always the same, and even such changes as esterification or salt formation may alter the sign of rotation without affecting the absolute configuration.

7–7 Rotatory Dispersion

In 1817 Biot discovered that the value obtained for the optical rotation of sub-stances under examination was dependent on the wavelength of the light used to measure the rotation. For most chemists, this simply meant that rotations must be uniformly specified at a particular wavelength, and the wavelength of the yellow sodium D-line (589.2 mμ) has been widely adopted as the standard.

With most organic substances it was observed that the extent of optical rotation would increase as the wavelength became shorter. When such curves were pursued into the region of the spectrum at which absorption takes place, it was observed that the optical rotatory power would increase very rapidly to a maximum, then diminish sharply through zero and reverse its sign. This phenomenon is called *anomalous dispersion*. An anomalous dispersion curve is shown in Fig. 7–7.

The anomalous dispersion curve of the *levo* isomer of the substance shown in Fig. 7–7 would be the mirror image of the curve shown. In the cases where more

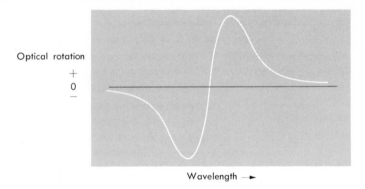

Optical rotation

Wavelength →

FIGURE 7–7

than one center is present, composite curves will be obtained which represent additions or subtractions of two or more anomalous dispersions such as the curve of Fig. 7–7. If two or more such centers are present but their absorptions are spaced a considerable distance apart, the rotation at a wavelength relatively far from that of the anomalous dispersion will usually be controlled by the center nearest the wavelength used for measuring.

During the past decade, spectropolarimeters have become available which have made the measurement of optical rotatory dispersion (ORD) a much simpler process than it was during the past century. The result is that numerous correlations have been derived between the shapes and positions of the optical rotatory dispersion curves and the structures of the compounds in question. If a suitable absorbing group is present in the molecule, its position with respect to the center of asymmetry will determine the shape and position of the anomalous dispersion curve. Hence, with the use of reference standards whose absolute configurations are known, the assignment of absolute configurations to new compounds becomes possible through the measurement of the optical rotatory dispersion of the known and unknown substances. This is a much simpler task than the individual chemical or x-ray examination of each substance. As a result, the number of substances whose absolute configurations are known is increasing rapidly.

PROBLEMS

7–1 Which of these Fischer representations corresponds to D-(+)-glyceraldehyde and which to L-(−)-glyceraldehyde?

(a) 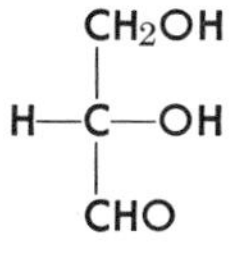
$$
\begin{array}{c}
CH_2OH \\
| \\
H-C-OH \\
| \\
CHO
\end{array}
$$

(b) 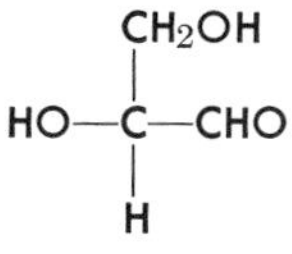
$$
\begin{array}{c}
CH_2OH \\
| \\
HO-C-CHO \\
| \\
H
\end{array}
$$

(c)
$$
\begin{array}{c}
CHO \\
| \\
H-C-CH_2OH \\
| \\
OH
\end{array}
$$

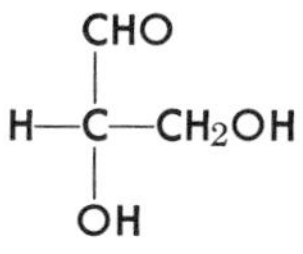

(d) 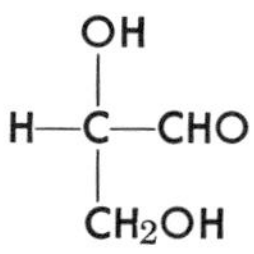
$$
\begin{array}{c}
OH \\
| \\
H-C-CHO \\
| \\
CH_2OH
\end{array}
$$

Therefore in manipulating these projection formulas, does one invert or retain configuration by
  (i)   interchanging the top and bottom groups,
  (ii) interchanging the left- and right-hand groups,
  (iii) turning the whole figure 180° in the plane of the paper, or
  (iv) turning the whole figure 180° out of the plane of the paper (turning the paper over)?

7–2 (a) Can there be a compound D-(−)-glyceraldehyde?
  (b) Can there be any D-(−)-compound at all?

7-3 Cinnamic acid (I) may be dimerized to compounds like II and III under the influence of light. Assuming a planar ring with substituents above and below it, determine how many dimers are possible, which of these contain asymmetric carbons, which contain planes of symmetry, and which contain other kinds of symmetry.

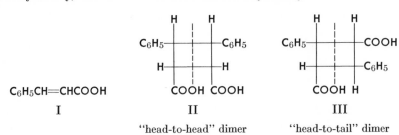

$C_6H_5CH{=}CHCOOH$

I

II

"head-to-head" dimer

III

"head-to-tail" dimer

Show now that the lack of a plane of symmetry does not insure that a molecule is internally compensated. Is the superimposability of mirror images a more general test?

7-4 Trithioformaldehyde (IV) can be oxidized to a number of disulfoxides (V, VI, VII) where the oxygen in each case is either above or below the ring. Because of experimental difficulties it is not possible to resolve the D- and L-forms at room temperature; therefore an unknown sample having no activity could be either a DL-mixture or a meso compound, but the way to eliminate one of these possibilities is not immediately obvious.

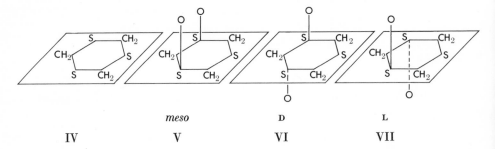

IV

meso

V

D

VI

L

VII

The problem may be solved if hydrogen peroxide is used to oxidize the remaining sulfur to a third sulfoxide group, where again the oxygen may be above or below the ring. Demonstrate how this is so; the method is vaguely reminiscent of Körner's method for substituted benzenes.

7-5 Phytol isolated from chlorophyll has an extremely low rotation at the sodium D-line; in fact, some workers had thought it racemic in earlier times. Carefully prepared degradation

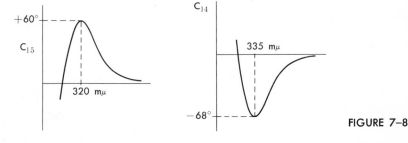

FIGURE 7–8

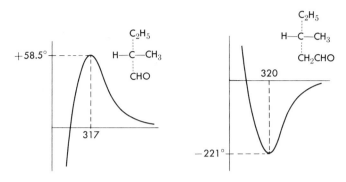

FIGURE 7–9

products show ORD-curves with anomalous dispersion, however. In fact, the absolute configuration of the asymmetric carbon nearest the alcohol function was determined by comparison with curves of standards.

(a) Phytol (Fig. 1–7) has the following formula.

$$(CH_3)_2CHCH_2CH_2CH_2CHCH_2CH_2CH_2CHCH_2CH_2CH_2C\!\!=\!\!CHCH_2OH$$
$$\overset{|}{CH_3}\qquad\overset{|}{CH_3}\qquad\overset{|}{CH_3}$$

How many asymmetric carbons does it have?

(b) Stepwise degradation of phytol, by methods which will be presented later, yielded a C_{15} aldehyde,

$$(CH_3)_2CHCH_2CH_2CH_2CHCH_2CH_2CH_2CHCH_2CHO$$
$$\overset{|}{CH_3}\qquad\overset{|}{CH_3}$$

and a C_{14} aldehyde,

$$(CH_3)_2CHCH_2CH_2CH_2CHCH_2CH_2CH_2CHCHO$$
$$\overset{|}{CH_3}\qquad\overset{|}{CH_3}$$

These had the dispersion curves shown in Fig. 7–8 which may be compared with the ORD curves of the compounds whose absolute configurations are shown in Fig. 7–9.

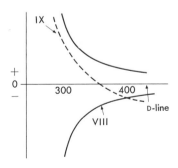

FIGURE 7–10

Given the information that replacement of C_2H_5 by another alkyl group does not alter the curves appreciably, what is the absolute configuration of the carbon in question in phytol? The other asymmetric center was found to have the same configuration by a synthetic route, which also corroborated the present proof for this center at the same time.

7-6 Chemical degradation of a number of crystalline products found in tannins gave a series of disubstituted isopropanols.

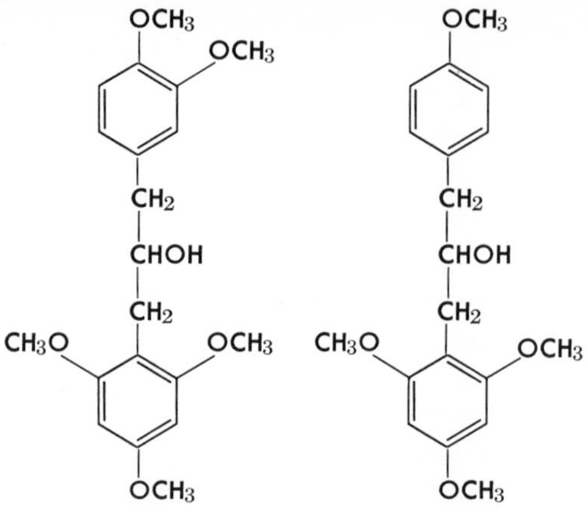

VIII   IX

At the usual wavelength these both had slight negative rotations, and it was assumed that they were both of the same family. However, when the optical rotatory dispersion curve of each compound was compared with that of the enantiomer of VIII, the graph shown in Fig. 7–10 was obtained.

(a) Would you conclude on this basis that VIII and IX are of the same or different families?

(b) Would you place complete confidence in measurements at the sodium D-line as a criterion of absolute configuration?

*What kinds of geometrical models explain the
existence of isomers other than optical isomers?
What other geometrical factors can be built into a model
to explain chemical observations?
What observations do these explain?*

8

STEREOISOMERISM AND ITS
REPRESENTATION BY MODELS

8–1 Geometrical Isomerism

The study of the arrangement of atoms in space is called *stereochemistry*, and the chemical isomers which differ only by their spatial arrangement are called *stereoisomers*. Van't Hoff assumed that C—C single bonds were free to rotate and that as a consequence, a substance like 1,2-dichloroethane, $ClCH_2CH_2Cl$, would exist in only one form. Following Kekulé's ideas, however, chemists found a whole group of hydrocarbons in which the number of hydrogens present was short of that required for the "saturated," paraffin hydrocarbons. The simplest example is ethylene, C_2H_4, which was assigned the formula

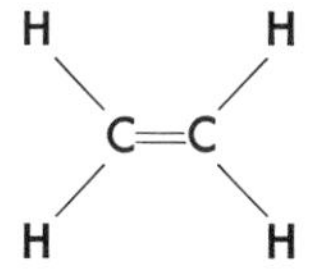

In addition to the hydrocarbons, many derivatives of these "unsaturated" compounds had also been found. Van't Hoff reasoned that joining two carbons by a double bond would restrict rotation so that for properly substituted doubly bonded substances, isomers could be formed that would be true stereoisomers but would not possess optical activity because they would possess symmetry. Such isomers he called "geometrical isomers."

As an example of geometrical isomerism van't Hoff cited the case of maleic and fumaric acids, substances whose relationship had been puzzling up to that time. Both of these substances are dicarboxylic acids with the formula $C_4H_4O_4$. They had been assigned the formula $HOOC$—CH=CH—$COOH$, but the puzzling fact was that although the properties of each agreed with this formula, the two substances were demonstrably different. Maleic acid was a solid melting at

130–131°C, while fumaric acid was a solid with a much higher melting point, about 290°C. When maleic acid was heated to its melting point and maintained at that temperature for a time, it was found that water would distill off with the formation of an anhydride, maleic anhydride. This is a substance which melts at 53°C and fits the analysis for $C_4H_2O_3$. Fumaric acid, on the other hand, proved to be stable at temperatures much above 130–140°C, but when held at its melting point, in the neighborhood of 300°C, it would also slowly lose water to form an anhydride which was at first called fumaric anhydride. The experiment was difficult to perform because of the volatility of fumaric acid which was so great that the material tended to sublime before melting. The experiment could best be performed in a closed container, but this also proved to be difficult to carry out because of the tendency of the container to explode from the pressure built up inside it by the decomposition. Ultimately it was learned, however, that the anhydride formed on heating fumaric acid is identical to that formed from maleic acid.

From the experimental facts concerning maleic and fumaric acids, van't Hoff formulated a structural hypothesis which would account for the observations. He said that maleic acid should be assigned the formula

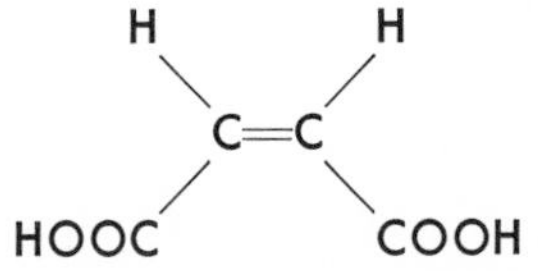

which he called ethylene *cis*-dicarboxylic acid, while fumaric acid should be assigned the formula

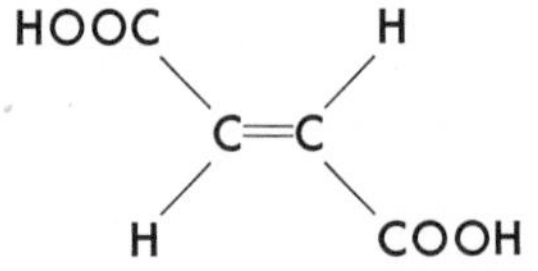

which he called ethylene *trans*-dicarboxylic acid. He reasoned that the two carboxyl groups in maleic acid would be close enough to lose water readily, forming a five-membered ring.

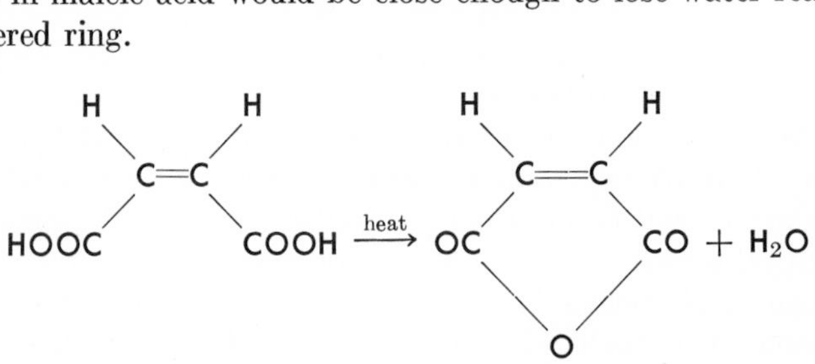

Maleic acid   Maleic anhydride

It was already known from the work of Kekulé and others that both five- and six-membered rings formed easily. For fumaric acid, van't Hoff reasoned that the carboxyl groups were so far away as to prevent the formation of a true anhydride of fumaric acid. However, he believed that the restriction to rotation about the double bond could be gradually overcome by high temperature achieved by prolonged heating, bringing about the decomposition of fumaric acid to form maleic acid. Since the temperature required for this change was far above that required to form maleic anhydride from the acid, the only recognizable organic product from the reaction would be maleic anhydride, the product actually observed. Thus he believed that the new hypothesis of bonds directed in space was capable not only of accounting for the existence of two ethylene dicarboxylic acids, but also of providing a basis for distinguishing between them.

Van't Hoff's hypothesis concerning the possibility of forming *cis* and *trans* isomers about a double bond has proved fruitful. In every case in which such isomers are predicted, experimental verification of their existence has been attainable.

Pursuing the matter still further, van't Hoff reasoned that joining two carbon atoms at three points to form a triple bond would leave the two remaining groups at an angle of 180° to each other so that there should be but a single substance with the structure of acetylene dicarboxylic acid.

$$H—C\equiv C—H \qquad\qquad HOOC—C\equiv C—COOH$$

Acetylene   Acetylene dicarboxylic acid

Experiment also verified this prediction.

8–2 Early Molecular Models

Numerous drawings exist of early molecular models designed to illustrate different chemists' concepts of the rearrangement of atoms in space. Apparently Kekulé was the inventor of "ball and stick" models designed to show the type of chemical structure which he postulated. Although the sticks were rigid and held at 90° angles in the balls, joining two pairs of sticks would form double bonds, and benzene rings could be made with these models.

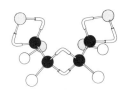

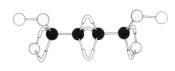

◀ FIG. 8–1. Early model of maleic acid.

FIG. 8–2. Early model of acetylene dicarboxylic acid.

The angles from the center to the vertices of a tetrahedron are 109° 28′. Van't Hoff's postulation of tetrahedral carbons led to a revamping of models to conform to the new theory. Such "ball and stick" models with "valence angles" of about $109\frac{1}{2}°$ permitted a vast extension of organic structural theory and went far to explain many reactions. Maleic acid, for example, could be represented as in Fig. 8–1 and acetylene dicarboxylic acid, as in Fig. 8–2. One of the first triumphs of the new models was the enunciation of the Baeyer "strain theory."

Table 8-1

HEATS OF COMBUSTION OF THE LOWER CYCLOPARAFFINS

	kcal/mole	kcal/CH_2 unit
Cyclopropane	499.5	166.5
Cyclobutane	654.2	163.8
Cyclopentane	798.5	158.7
Cyclohexane	943.2	157.2
Aliphatic CH_2 unit	–	157.5

8-3 Baeyer's Strain Theory

In the great flowering of organic chemistry that took place after the promulgation of Kekulé's hypothesis and Cannizzaro's molecular weight method, a large number of new synthetic compounds was prepared. For nearly twenty years, however, chemists found only five- and six-membered rings among the ring compounds they examined. In 1879, however, Markovnikov synthesized a four-membered ring. This proved to be less stable than the known five- and six-membered rings. In 1882 Freund prepared a three-membered ring. This proved to be still less stable. These substances aroused the interest of Adolph von Baeyer, often referred to as the "king of organic experimentalists." Baeyer pointed out that the normal tetrahedral angle of $109\frac{1}{2}°$ is very close to the internal angle of a pentagon, 108°. He reasoned that a cyclopentane ring should, therefore, be a very stable ring because of the excellent fit of the bond angles. A four-membered cyclobutane ring, on the other hand, would have its bonds bent from their normal $109\frac{1}{2}°$ separation to 90°, creating a strain which would diminish the stability of the system. A three-membered cyclopropane ring would have its bonds bent still more to 60°, creating still greater strain and thus greater instability. This picture, although refined by modern studies, still remains the essence of the explanation offered for the behavior of compounds with rings containing less than five members.

One method by which chemists can estimate the stability of substances is to burn them and find the quantity of energy released. The greater the energy release, the greater the initial energy content and, therefore, the less stable the compound. A simple mechanical analogy for this concept is that of the stone on the hill. When the stone is at the top of the hill, it has a high energy content and is in an unstable condition. When it releases its energy by rolling to the bottom of the hill, it assumes a more stable condition.

For the cycloparaffins, heats of combustion verify the concept of the instability of the lower members of the series, as shown in Table 8-1. It will be noted that the heats of combustion diminish with increase in size of the ring up to cyclohexane, showing an increase in stability with increasing ring size.

8-4 Large Rings

Unfortunately, Baeyer also extended his argument in the direction of large rings. Arbitrarily, he assumed that there is a force that tends to make rings planar. Assuming that their shape is planar, then rings larger than five would have a strain in the opposite direction from the small rings, that is, an outward strain instead of an inward strain. This assumption was questioned almost immediately by Werner who could picture no force tending to keep rings planar. Experimentally, however, rings larger than six membered remained elusive for many years. Gradually, however, such rings were produced, and in the period from 1920 on, the Swiss investigator, Ruzicka, succeeded in finding the conditions necessary for the preparation of very large rings. Essentially, his experiments showed that the reason for the difficulty in preparing rings larger than six was the improbability of the two ends of a long chain colliding in the position required for them to undergo reaction. A chain of tetrahedra tends to form zig-zags or spirals which on being struck, seldom assume the exact position required to bring the ends together. Once the very large rings are formed, however, study showed them to be quite stable, thus disproving Baeyer's hypothesis of a planar-constraining force.

As chemists studied the formation and properties of large rings with greater care, however, a curious fact emerged. One method for preparing a cyclic hydrocarbon is to modify the Wurtz synthesis.

$$2CH_3I + 2Na \rightarrow CH_3CH_3 + 2NaI$$

Wurtz reaction

$$BrCH_2CH_2CH_2CH_2CH_2CH_2Br + Mg \rightarrow CH_2 \begin{array}{c} CH_2CH_2 \\ \diagup \quad \diagdown \\ \\ \diagdown \quad \diagup \\ CH_2CH_2 \end{array} CH_2 + MgBr_2$$

Hexamethylene dibromide   Cyclohexane

On attempting to apply this reaction to decamethylene dibromide, Carothers and Hill found that the most easily isolated products were polymers instead of a ring. Other reactions designed to give rings larger than seven-membered were frequently found to give rings of twice the expected size even more readily. Syntheses designed to give eight-membered rings gave fair amounts of sixteen-membered rings, and those designed to give nine-membered rings gave fair amounts of eighteen-membered rings. These findings not only refuted Baeyer's hypothesis with respect to the instability of large rings, they actually inverted it.

As shown in Table 8–2 measurement of heats of combustion confirmed the trend toward instability with increasing ring size indicated by the work of Hill and Carothers.

Table 8–2

HEATS OF COMBUSTION PER CH_2 UNIT OF HIGHER CYCLOPARAFFINS

Compound	kcal
Aliphatic CH_2	157.5
Cyclohexane	157.2
Cycloheptane	158.2
Cyclooctane	158.5
Cyclononane	158.7

Knowing that cyclooctane is harder to prepare and less stable than cyclohexane, we must still explain why it is that cyclohexadecane should be more stable and easier to prepare than cyclooctane. Part, at least, of the answer had laid dormant in physical chemical measurements for fifty years. The remainder had been building up for a couple of decades by the time the development of organic chemistry required its application. The answer lay in a more precise study of the distances between atoms and of the space they occupy.

8–5 Interatomic Distances; Bond Radii

As early as 1890, Victor Meyer was arguing that the size of atoms in molecules was important to their chemical behavior. However, Meyer had no way to measure their size except by their weight. It remained for investigators of x-ray diffraction, especially von Laue and the Braggs, to find how to estimate the distances separating atoms in molecules. X-rays are electromagnetic radiations with wavelengths which have been found to correspond approximately to interatomic distances. As such they can be used as probes to study the spacings of atoms. Crystals are made of extended lattices of molecules or (with ionic crystals) of ions or (with metals) of atoms. The regular arrangement of the atoms within a crystal creates a series of reinforcements in the x-ray diffraction patterns. A photograph of an x-ray diffraction pattern is shown in Fig. 8–3.

The analysis of these reinforcements roughly resembles the analysis which an observer passing a carefully planted cornfield could use to reconstruct the pattern of planting. As he sights down the field he will observe rows whose spacings will

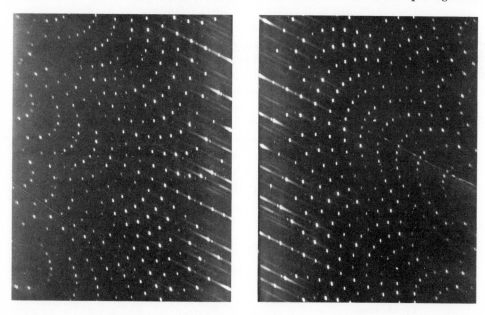

FIG. 8–3. Courtesy of Donnay and Donnay, Crystallographic Laboratories, The Johns Hopkins University.

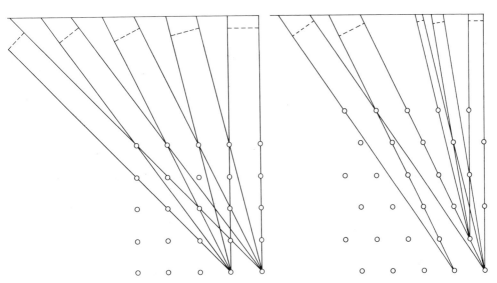

FIG. 8–4.   Reinforcement angles in a two-dimen-   FIG. 8–5.   Reinforcement angles in a two-
sional square lattice.   dimensional face-centered hexagonal lattice.

vary with his angle of vision (Figs. 8–4 and 8–5). The appearance of rows is due to
"reinforcement" caused by the stalks which line up in contrast to the lack of reinforcement in the spaces. By suitable measurements of the angles at which rows
appear, it would be possible to reconstruct the pattern by which the cornfield was
planted. Thus the observer moving past a field planted with a different lattice
arrangement would observe a different sequence of rows and spaces.

Table 8–3

BOND RADII IN ANGSTROM UNITS (10^{-10} m)

C, 0.77	N, 0.70	O, 0.66	F, 0.64
			Cl, 0.99
			Br, 1.11
			I, 1.28

   A somewhat similar type of reinforcement occurs when x-ray beams encounter
atoms in a crystal lattice, so that it is possible for a skilled observer, with the aid
of a computer, to reconstruct the pattern that must have been responsible for the
observed x-ray diffraction. In this manner it is possible to estimate interatomic
distances with a precision somewhat greater than 1%. While it has been found
that a C—C single bond, for example, will not have precisely the same length in all
different compounds, an average value can be used for the construction of a model
which will permit a great increase in precision over the nineteenth century scheme
of representing all atoms with essentially the same radii or, alternatively, of
representing them according to their weights. A representative table of such
average values for a few elements is given in Table 8–3.

8–6   Interference Distances; van der Waals Radii

Soon after reliable x-ray estimations of bond distances became available, models constructed to these relative sizes were prepared. While intellectually more satisfying than their less precise forerunners, these models fell short of explaining many phenomena which had been observed experimentally. For example, they offered no solution to the problem of the diminished stability of eight-membered rings as compared to sixteen-membered rings. Nor did they offer a solution to an even simpler phenomenon. Using these models made up as spheres to construct a model of a hypothetical highly compressed gas or of a liquid, it was found that the actual liquids and highly compressed gases occupied appreciably larger volumes than the models predicted. It was argued, on the one hand, that the x-ray results were not reliable or, on the other hand, that the compressibility data were not reliable.

The volume which should be occupied by the molecules of a highly compressed gas was first calculated in 1874 by Budde according to the equation

$$P(V - b) = RT$$

While this gave a closer approximation to the behavior of an actual gas than did the perfect gas law,

$$PV = RT$$

yet measurements soon showed that it was not good enough and that in addition to the repulsive force exerted by the molecules on each other when highly compressed, there was another force, a force of attraction that acted in the opposite direction. This was formulated by van der Waals in 1879 as follows:

$$(P + a/V^2)(V - b) = RT$$

The van der Waals equation remains one of the best of the so-called "equations of state" for gases, and the corrected values for the quantity b give an approximation to the volumes occupied by the molecules of various substances. Knowing the atomic composition of these molecules, it is possible to calculate so-called "van der Waals radii" of atoms, that is, their exterior diameters. It is interesting to note that the nineteenth century organic chemists who were arguing about the size of atoms had measurements of these sizes available to them even before their controversies arose. This is still another example of the lag caused by difficulties in communication between practitioners of different branches of science. A few van der Waals radii are presented in Table 8–4.

It will be noted that these radii are substantially larger than the interatomic radii given in Table 8–3. Evidence accumulating

Table 8–4.   VAN DER WAALS RADII IN ANGSTROM UNITS

N, 1.5	O, 1.4	F, 1.35
		Cl, 1.80
		Br, 1.95
		I, 2.15

from still other sources, such as studies on the viscosities of liquids, finally led to the conclusion that a properly constructed atomic model would require the use of *both sets* of radii, a small internal radius to represent the closest approach of atoms in bonding, and a larger external radius to represent the closest approach of atoms that are not bonded. The method chosen to represent these two radii is to cut a sphere to the external or interference radius and then truncate it so that the distance from the center to the bonding point would represent the interatomic radius, as shown in Fig. 8–6.

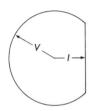

FIG. 8–6. Atomic model, V = van der Waals radius, I = interatomic radius.

FIG. 8–7. Courtaulds model of benzene.

Models of the type shown in Fig. 8–6 are known as Stuart-Briegleb models. The interference radii employed in these are smaller than van der Waals radii. To justify this, it is argued that the organic chemist is seldom interested in models with full van der Waals radii, since he is usually interested in reaction chemistry. Van der Waals radii show the closest approach of atoms under normal compressions, but under the much higher stresses of reaction conditions, closer approaches than the van der Waals radii occur on collision. It is probable that the smaller distances used in the Stuart-Briegleb models give a closer approximation to the reaction conditions that frequently interest the organic chemist than would full van der Waals radii.

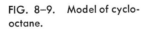

FIG. 8–8. Godfrey model of benzene.

FIG. 8–9. Model of cyclooctane.

In spite of this argument, models with full van der Waals radii have appeared on the market. One type, shown in Fig. 8–7, is a Courtaulds model of benzene. A second type, shown in Fig. 8–8, is a Godfrey model of benzene.

Using Stuart-Briegleb models, the remaining mystery concerning large rings begins to dissolve. It will be seen from Fig. 8–9 that the relatively small transannular distance in cyclooctane is too small to accommodate the relatively large van der Waals radii of the hydrogens with any freedom for motion. Instead, the hydrogens tend to occupy the internal space of the ring completely, freezing the model so as to prevent rotation about the single bonds joining the carbons. Cyclohexadecane, on the other hand, has a relatively large transannular distance, as shown in Fig. 8–10. In this model, the distance is great enough to accommodate the hydrogens and still permit some rotation about the carbon-carbon single bonds. When full van der Waals radii are used, the effect is even more striking. The crowding effect visible in the model of cyclooctane persists in models of nine-, ten-, and eleven-membered rings. By the time that the fourteen-membered ring has been reached, the ring opens up enough to accommodate the interference radii of the hydrogens.

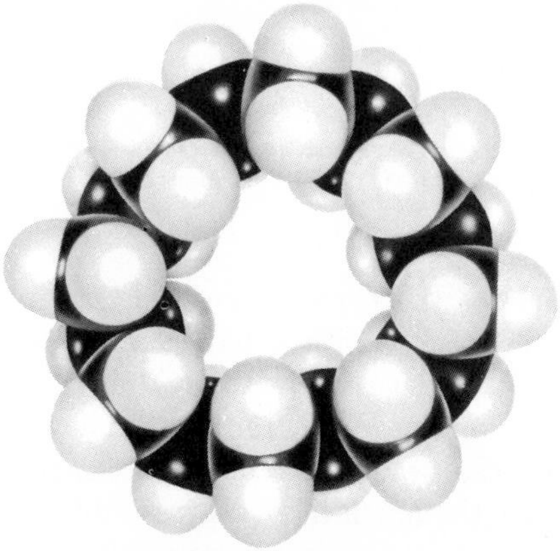

FIG. 8–10. Model of cyclohexadecane.

It is an extraordinary twist of fate that physical measurements were first made in 1874 by Budde that would have helped to solve a problem propounded by Baeyer in 1885. The solution to this problem had to wait for bits of evidence from several fields of chemistry to be assembled in the 1930's. This time lag between observation and interpretation is being reduced by modern communication but it may not be wise to be overconfident on this score. It is highly probable that observations have already been made that are capable of solving some of our most perplexing problems, if we only knew enough to look in the right places for the key clues.

PROBLEMS

8-1 Compounds with C—C double bonds are called *alkenes* or *olefins*. They are named by changing the -ane of the corresponding alkane to -ene. Prefixed numbers should be the lowest possible. (See 1-butene on the left below.) The number may be suffixed to avoid confusion. (See right below.)

$$H_2C=CHCH_2CH_3$$

$$\begin{array}{ccc} CH_3 & & CH_3 \\ \diagdown & & \diagup \\ & C=C & \\ \diagup & & \diagdown \\ CH_3 & & H \end{array}$$

1-butene   2-methylbutene-2

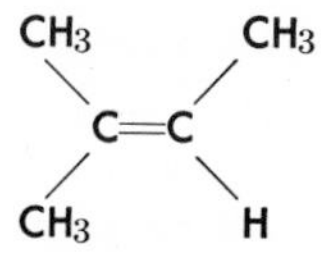

Compounds with 2 double bonds are called *dienes*.

$$CH_2=CH-CH=CH_2 \qquad\qquad CH_3C=CCl-CH=CH_2$$
$$\qquad\qquad\qquad\qquad\qquad\qquad\qquad\qquad\; |$$
$$\qquad\qquad\qquad\qquad\qquad\qquad\qquad\quad CH_3$$

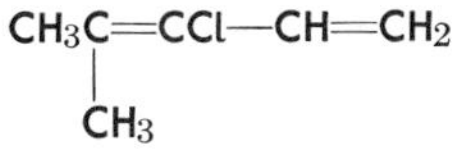

1,3-butadiene   2-methyl-3-chloropenta-2,4-diene

Compounds with triple bonds are called *alkynes*. The nomenclature rules are similar to those for alkenes.

$$HC\equiv CCH_2CH_2CH_3 \qquad HC\equiv C-C\equiv C-CH_3 \qquad H_2C=CH-CH_2C\equiv C-CH_2CH_3$$

1-pentyne   1,3-pentadiyne   hept-1-ene-4-yne

Name the following compounds.

(a) 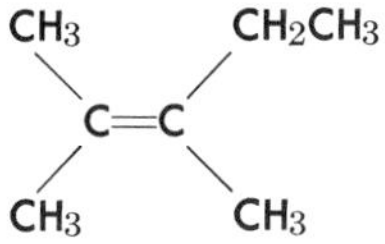
$$\begin{array}{ccc} CH_3 & & CH_2CH_3 \\ \diagdown & & \diagup \\ & C=C & \\ \diagup & & \diagdown \\ CH_3 & & CH_3 \end{array}$$

(b) $CH_3CH=CHCH_2OH$

(c) 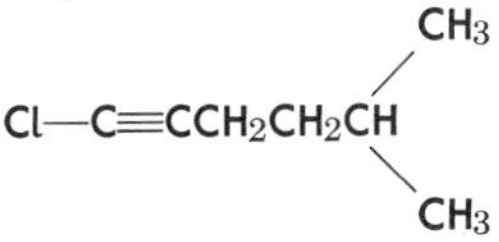 $Cl-C\equiv CCH_2CH_2CH$
$$\qquad\qquad\qquad\qquad\qquad \diagup\;\;\diagdown$$
$$\qquad\qquad\qquad CH_3 \qquad CH_3$$

(d) $HOCH_2CH_2CH=CH-CH=CHCH_2CH_3$

Give the structures of the following compounds.

(e) 4-pentenoic acid

(f) 1,3,5-hexatriene

(g) isobutylene

(h) allyl alcohol (prop-2-en-1-ol)

8–2 (a) How many isomers of 2-butene are possible?

(b) How many isomers of 2-methyl-2-butene are possible?

8–3 Only one cyclopentene (I) is known to exist. Would you expect it to have a *cis*-substituted double bond or a *trans*-substituted one? Why?

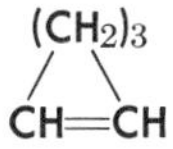

$$\begin{array}{c} (CH_2)_3 \\ \diagup \quad \diagdown \\ CH=CH \end{array}$$

I

8–4 Using van't Hoff's tetrahedral-carbon postulate, construct a model of 4-bromohexa-2,3-diene. Should this compound exhibit optical activity? Does it have any geometrical isomers?

8–5 Consecutive double bonds are known as *allenic* double bonds. The parent compound

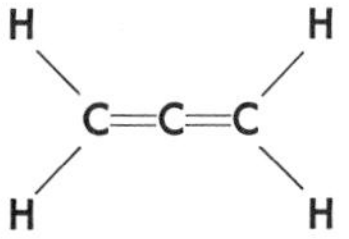

$$\begin{array}{ccc} H & & H \\ \diagdown & & \diagup \\ & C=C=C & \\ \diagup & & \diagdown \\ H & & H \end{array}$$

is known as *allene*. Should penta-2,3-diene be resolvable into optical isomers or geometrical isomers?

8-6   Alkanes may be prepared by the catalytic hydrogenation of unsaturated hydrocarbons. A catalyst, for example, finely divided platinum, palladium, or nickel, is used.

$$CH_3CH{=}CHCH_2CH_3 \xrightarrow[25°]{H_2/Pd} CH_3CH_2CH_2CH_2CH_3$$

Complete the following equations.

(a)   maleic anhydride $\xrightarrow[25°]{H_2/Pd}$ A

(b)   A $\xrightarrow[H_2O]{NaOH}$ B

(c)   B $\xrightarrow[H_2O]{HCl}$ C

(d)   C $\xrightarrow[C_2H_5OH]{HCl}$ D

(e)   D $\xrightarrow[C_2H_5OH]{Na}$ E

(f)   E $\xrightarrow[HBr]{concentrated}$ F

(g)   F $\xrightarrow{Mg}$ G

(h) What reagent might have been used to effect a one-step transformation of C to E? [A could also have been carried to E in this fashion.]

8-7   Alkenes may be prepared by the dehydration of alcohols. If an alcohol is stable at the temperatures required, it may be passed through a column of specially prepared ("activated") alumina at 350–450°. Under these conditions the molecule loses water and forms an olefin.

$$CH_3CH_2CH_2CH_2OH \xrightarrow[450°]{Al_2O_3} CH_3CH_2CH{=}CH_2$$

(a) What compound might be prepared from compound E of Problem 8–6 by this route?

(b) How could you prepare 1,2-diphenylethane from 1,2-diphenylethanol?

8-8   Unsaturated compounds form 1,2-dihalohydrocarbons when one mole of chlorine or bromine is added to the unsaturated link. This reaction is called an *olefin* reaction (oil former).

$$CH_2{=}CH_2 + Cl_2 \rightarrow ClCH_2CH_2Cl$$

How could 1,1,2,2-tetrachloroethane be prepared?

What kind of information can we obtain from models
which demonstrate internal movements of molecules?
How do the forces that cause restriction
of rotation about a single bond bring about energy
differences between ring conformers?

9

DYNAMIC MODELS, INFRARED SPECTRA, AND CONFORMATION

9–1 Molecular Collisions

The development of the kinetic theory of gases led to the realization that molecules at ordinary temperatures are undergoing a series of forceful collisions. In 1860 Maxwell published a work on the application of statistical procedures to the solution of the problem of the distribution of energies between the molecules of a gas. This work was extended by Boltzmann in a series of studies from 1868 to 1875. A typical energy-distribution curve is shown in Fig. 9–1.

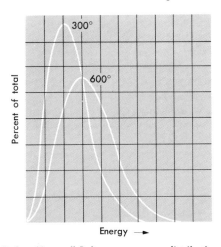

FIG. 9–1. Maxwell-Boltzmann energy-distribution curve.

9-2 Elastic Bonds

Continuing studies on the nature of bonds in molecules led to the realization that to represent bonds as being rigid, as in the models of most organic chemists, is misleading. The prime source of information on this point is the study of the infrared absorption spectra of molecules. Studies on infrared spectra have shown that the substitution of strong springs for rigid bonds gives a closer approach to the observed behavior of molecules.

9-3 Infrared Spectroscopy

Electromagnetic radiations in the infrared region of the spectrum encompass the region which we would ordinarily classify as "heat waves." When a suitable heat-wave generator, such as a moderately glowing electric filament, is used as a source of energy, this energy can then be passed through a prism and spread out into an invisible infrared spectrum. By using sensitive thermocouples as detectors, it is possible to record the energy emitted at each wavelength (Fig. 9-2). If a cell

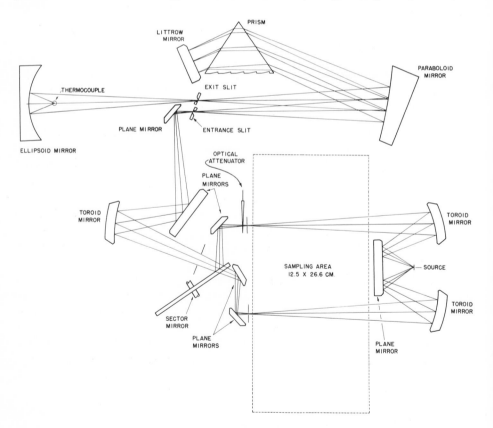

FIG. 9-2. Infrared spectrophotometer, schematic. (Courtesy of the Perkin-Elmer Corporation.)

containing an organic chemical is then placed in the beam, it is found that the chemical will absorb infrared energy at certain wavelengths and not at others. By referring again to the thermocouple, the exact amount of absorption at each wavelength can be determined. Automatic instruments for making such plots are called "recording infrared spectrophotometers" and are widely used in laboratories of organic chemistry at the present time.

Some of the first infrared spectra were obtained by R. W. Wood, working in the Hopkins Physics Labortories. One of his students, Coblentz, working at the National Bureau of Standards, recorded the infrared absorption spectra of numerous organic chemicals in 1906, but at that time organic chemists were not psychologically equipped to take advantage of the information made available to them by these physical studies. Technical and theoretical advances in the study of infrared spectra were made by Wood and A. H. Pfund, and other laboratories accelerated these studies. These physical studies showed that infrared absorptions were, in general, due to the utilization of the heat energy by molecules to stimulate rhythmic stretching vibrations, for shorter infrared waves, and rhythmic bending vibrations, for longer infrared waves. The attribution of precise bond behavior to observed absorptions, so-called "frequency assignments," remained a difficult problem.

9–4   Frequency Assignments

In 1930 D. H. Andrews published a description of a method of frequency assignment by the use of models. The problem to which he addressed himself can be simply stated. From a knowledge of the action of springs in general, it is easy to conclude that it takes more energy to stretch a spring than to bend it. Applying this generalization to bonds in molecules, one would conclude that higher-energy heat absorption might correspond to bond-stretching frequencies, and lower-energy absorptions might correspond to bond-bending frequencies. Studying a model of an organic molecule, however, experimenters soon realized that there would be several bond-stretching frequencies in most molecules, corresponding to different types of internal molecular motion, as well as several bond-bending frequencies. It was not always easy to discover which of the individual molecular motions that could be postulated would correspond to the absorption that was actually observed.

Andrews' approach to the problem of frequency assignment was to construct a dynamic model of an organic chemical molecule, using balls of steel for the atoms and joining them by stiff steel springs. As an example, we may take a dynamic model of benzene (Fig. 9–3). This was mounted on a frame and suspended by rubber bands whose strength was small compared to that of the steel springs representing bonds. The model was then set into oscillation by a motor whose speed could be varied and measured. Each stroke of the oscillator was set to flash a neon light which thus constituted a stroboscope for the observation of the nature of the motion of the model.

It was found that the dynamic benzene model underwent certain recognizable stretching and bending motions at certain frequencies and, by trial and error, it

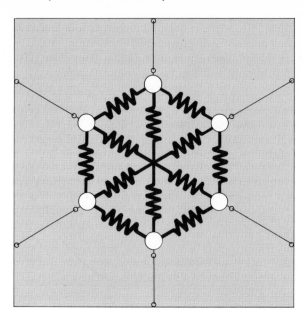

FIG. 9–3.   Vibrating model of benzene.

was possible to construct a model in which these frequencies bore the same numerical relationships to each other as did the infrared frequencies observed for benzene. By this method it was possible to identify infrared frequencies with types of molecular motion that could be analyzed visually on the model, with the result that the infrared frequencies were thus assigned to characteristic molecular motions. This method of analysis permitted the assignment of force constants to the bonds holding the benzene molecule together, and once the relative stretching and bending force constants were known, it was possible to complete the solution to the problem of the assignment of the remaining frequencies by a mathematical analysis.

The Andrews method was applicable to the carbon skeletons of organic molecules but for technical reasons proved to be too difficult to use in the assignment of frequencies to C—H bonds. The problem of the assignment of C—H frequencies was solved nearly simultaneously by a happy scientific coincidence.

9–5   Isotopic Substitution

H. C. Urey devoted himself to a detailed study of the spectrum of hydrogen. In the course of this work he found absorption frequencies that defied explanation on the basis of the assumption that all the molecules he was dealing with had the formula H—H. Urey postulated that there might be a heavier isotope of hydrogen present with double the atomic weight of ordinary hydrogen. This postulate seemed to bring his spectra into agreement, so he set out to isolate "heavy hydrogen." The quest was finally successful, and heavy hydrogen or "deuterium" was isolated and shortly became commercially available as a tool for general use in chemical research.

R. C. Lord, who had worked with Andrews on the benzene problem, perceived that deuterium provided a powerful tool for the investigation of infrared spectra. Lord collaborated with Langseth at Copenhagen on the preparation of benzenes with deuterium atoms substituted at known spots in the molecule for hydrogen atoms. Armed with these "tracer" molecules, infrared spectra were studied with and without deuterium. Substitution at one point would cause the disappearance of certain absorptions and the appearance of new ones. Since the precise changes in mass involved were known, these substitutions permitted the calculation of the C—H and C—D force constants and, ultimately, of the infrared frequencies of all characteristic types of motion present in the benzene ring. The method was soon applied to many other organic compounds, and the detailed interpretation of infrared spectra thus became possible.

Still another student of Wood and Pfund, R. B. Barnes, played an important part in spreading the use of infrared spectra among organic chemists. He measured spectra, used them for analytical purposes, sought to improve instrument design, and sought the attention of organic chemists individually and in meetings to acquaint them with the utility of the method. As a result of both the scientific and the technological advances in the field, the recording and interpretation of infrared spectra has become one of the most useful tools in the qualitative investigation of organic chemical structures. Generally speaking, however, the method rests on structural analogies established by means of known compounds so that, with few exceptions, the method must be looked on as a source of structural information derived from analogies established by other means. The other means used by the organic chemist are based on the geometrical type of reasoning with which we have become familiar. Further examples of the primary structural determinations of the organic chemist will be given in succeeding chapters to familiarize the reader with the reasoning on which infrared and still other physical methods of structural determination are based.

9–6 Models as Analog Computers

It will be appreciated that the Andrews benzene model is, in reality, an analog computer permitting certain numerical relationships to be determined by analogy when they were not available to direct calculation. This type of application of models has been made in still other connections. The visualization of the interference between hydrogens in an eight-membered ring requires the use of models for the measurement of two distances, the transannular carbon skeleton distance and the interference reach of the attached hydrogens. While this problem is theoretically capable of solution by the methods of solid geometry, it would be a complex undertaking, while the problem is solved quickly and easily with models. Models are currently available in which bond distances and angles have been constructed with relatively high precision to permit such measurements to be made routinely when they are desired for the interpretation of chemical reactions.

In the same manner that the Stuart-Briegleb models make it possible to estimate interference parameters of molecules, the Andrews models open the possibility of measuring parameters related to internal strains of molecules. An interesting case in current natural product chemistry occurs in the chlorophyll molecule. A five-membered isocyclic ring, that is, one with five carbon atoms, is grafted on one of the five-membered pyrrole rings. The external angle of a pentagon is 252° so that the bond angle of a substituent on pyrrole would tend to assume an angle of 126°. Joining a five-membered ring to a pyrrole ring, however, constrains the external pyrrole bond to a value of 108°, the angle of the interior of a pentagon. It is obvious that this will create strains which will distort the chlorophyll molecule from the symmetrical shape which it would have in the absence of this source of strain.

Basing the reasoning on the Andrews benzene model, an analog computer for chlorophyll strains was constructed (Fig. 9–4). This model shows the type of distortion to be expected in the chlorophyll molecule by the closure of an isocyclic ring as well as making available a means of studying the effects of still other types of strain on the molecule.

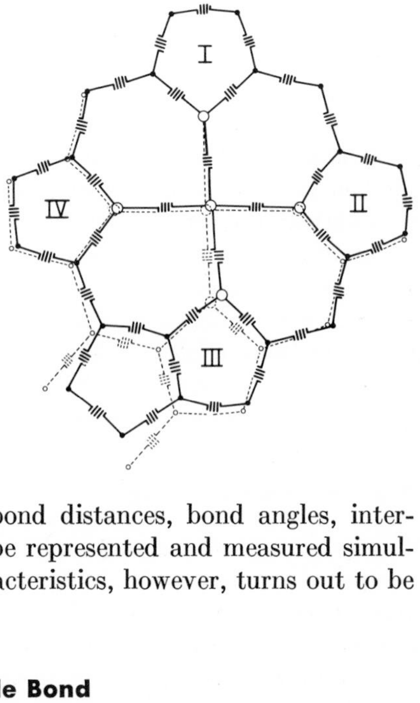

FIG. 9–4. Analog computer for chlorophyll strains. [From A. H. Corwin, J. A. Walter, and R. Singh, J. Org. Chem. 27, 4284 (1962).]

Ideally, molecular models should permit bond distances, bond angles, interference distances, and internal strains all to be represented and measured simultaneously. A model combining all these characteristics, however, turns out to be mechanically quite difficult to devise.

9–7   Restriction of Rotation about a Single Bond

In addition to the complications listed above that should be represented by a satisfactory molecular model, still another phenomenon occurs which is of interest to the organic chemist and which, ideally, should be capable of visualization with models. This is restriction of rotation about a single bond.

As one approaches the absolute zero, −273.16°C, more and more of the motion of molecules is frozen out. By warming helium 4.26° above this temperature, enough translational energy is imparted to it to overcome the intermolecular forces, converting it into a gas. At this temperature, all substances except helium are still frozen solid. Allowing the temperature to rise to 14.02°K, we reach the melting point of hydrogen and then, at 20.36°K, enough energy has been added to hydrogen to cause it to boil. At this temperature, the amount of energy available is still very tiny, and all substances except hydrogen and helium are still solid. The next melting point to be reached is that of neon at 24.49°K, then fluorine at 50°K, then oxygen at 55°K, then nitrogen at 63°K before we finally reach the melting point of the first carbon-containing compound, carbon monoxide, which melts at 66°K. Methane melts at 89°K and boils at 111.7°K or −161.5°C.

Once they have reached the gaseous state, we might expect that further acquisitions of energy could only increase the translational motion of molecules, causing them to collide with each other with increasing violence. To test this concept, careful measurements were made of the heat capacities of gases, that is, the amount of heat required to warm them in the low temperature range. It is also possible to calculate the heat capacities of gases. With gases whose molecules are simple, these calculations agree with experiment to a high degree of precision. With hydrocarbons, however, the agreement obtained by the assumption that the energy was going exclusively into translation turned out to be very poor. Experiment and theory were brought into agreement in 1937 when Kemp and Pitzer showed that the assumption of the existence of an energy barrier of 3150 cal/mole to free rotation of the two methyl groups in ethane would permit the best fit with the experimental data. This assumption was then carried on to more complex hydrocarbons and was found to bring the theoretical calculations into agreement with the experimental observations in these cases as well. From these measurements and calculations chemists began to assume the existence of such a barrier and to correct their models and their reasoning accordingly. In this case, the time lag between discovery and utilization was not as great as in earlier cases that we have studied, but the full impact of the discovery of a barrier to free rotation was not felt by organic chemists for about twenty years.

In gaseous collisions, an energy of 3150 cal/mole is not very large. At room temperature, statistical calculations from the Boltzmann distribution relationship show that 0.5% of the molecules of a gas have collisional energy of 3150 cal/mole or greater. Since, according to the Maxwell-Boltzmann distribution curve, the number of collisions taking place in a gas at room temperature is of the order of 10^{11} moles/liter-sec, this means that at room temperature there would be sufficient collisions with energy greater than 3150 cal to cause the rotation of approximately 5×10^8 moles of ethane through the energy barrier per second in each liter. It can be seen from this that it would be futile to expect to isolate molecules which differed from each other only by the phase of their rotation about a single bond. Despite this limitation, however, the restriction of rotation is great enough to exert a measurable effect on the reactions of many compounds. The study of the effects of such restrictions is called *conformational analysis* and the stable phases of molecules during these rotations are called their *conformations*. Substances which differ only in their conformations are called *conformers*.

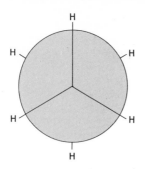

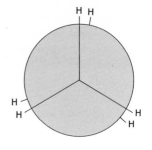

FIG. 9–5.   Projection of stable conformation
of ethane.

FIG. 9–6.   Projection of unstable conformation
of ethane.

9–8   Conformational Analysis

Let us imagine that we are sighting down a model of a molecule of ethane along
the line joining the two carbons. The stable conformation would then be represented
as in Fig. 9–5. Such a projection is known as a *Newman projection* and the stable
form shown is called the *staggered conformation*. Rotation of one methyl group
through 60° produces the *eclipsed conformation* shown in Fig. 9–6. If we draw a
plot of the relation between the energy of a molecule and its conformation, we
should expect to obtain the graph shown in Fig. 9–7.

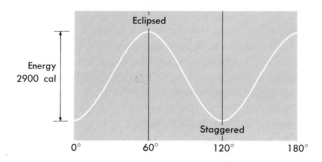

FIG. 9–7.   Relation between conformation and energy of ethane.

It can thus be seen that it is not quite accurate to speak of "free rotation" about
a single bond. Rotation about a single bond, while rapid, is restricted by a small
force of repulsion between the hydrogens attached to carbons. The interference
distances of most molecular models are too small to show this repulsion between
hydrogens, indicating still another source of information available to us which has
not been incorporated into the working models of the organic chemist.

Conformational studies become of special importance in the chemistry of
saturated ring compounds. A model of cyclopentane (Fig. 9–8) will show that it
is impossible to rotate the bonds into such a position as to produce all staggered
conformations. Referring back to the table of heats of combustion of cyclic hydrocarbons, Table 8–1, we see that the heat content of cyclopentane is 1.2 kcal/CH_2

FIG. 9–8.   Models of cyclopentane.

higher than that of an average aliphatic CH_2. This energy differential is ascribed to conformational repulsion.   In cyclohexane, on the other hand, it is possible to construct a model with all methylene groups staggered (Fig. 9–9).   This accounts for the greater stability of cyclohexane already noted.

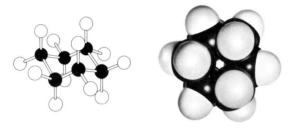

FIG. 9–9.   Models of cyclohexane.

To convert one conformer of a chain compound, like ethane, into another conformer will require a process of rotation about only one bond.   With a ring compound, on the other hand, the conversion of one conformer into another will, for geometrical reasons, require simultaneous rotation about at least two bonds.   Trial with ball and stick models is the best means for ascertaining this fact.   The result is that the barrier to conversions of ring conformers into each other is greater than that of chain conformers.   Indeed, it is in the study of ring conformations that this branch of stereochemistry assumes its greatest importance.

If all the methylene groups in cyclohexane are placed in staggered conformations, the resulting zig-zag figure joining the centers of carbon atoms is the one shown in Fig. 9–10.   This figure is called the *chair conformation.*

If two methylene groups are rotated, a new conformation is created, the *boat conformation* (Fig. 9–11).   When constructed with Stuart models (Fig. 9–12), the

FIG. 9–10.   Stable or chair conformation of cyclohexane.

FIG. 9–11.   Unstable or boat conformation of cyclohexane.

FIG. 9–12. Model of cyclohexane with hydrogens re-
moved; chair form.

FIG. 9–13. Cyclohexane
model with hydrogens on
equatorial plane only; chair
form.

FIG. 9–14. Cyclohexane
model with axial hydrogens
only; chair form.

carbon skeleton of cyclohexane appears to be nearly planar because of the fact that the zig-zag shape of the molecule can be traced above and below the plane equally. The plane connecting the centers of successive bonds in this model is called the *equatorial plane*. When hydrogens are attached, half of them lie in the equatorial plane (Fig. 9–13). Consequently, they are called *equatorial hydrogens*.

A straight line passing through the center of the equatorial plane and perpendicular to it constitutes the "axis" of the molecule. Half of the hydrogens of the chair form will be found joined to the molecule parallel to this axis, three of them pointing up, the other three down (Fig. 9–14). These are designated *axial hydrogens*.

To permit easy visualization of the bond positions in cyclic compounds, skeleton models have been constructed which emphasize the bonds at the expense of the interferences of the atoms attached. These are usually made so that rotation about a bond is relatively easy without detachment of the atoms, permitting easy transformations between conformations. Several types of such models are shown in Fig. 9–15.

Our survey of molecular models shows that special models exist to illustrate one or more of the special attributes of organic molecules. Each of these may be considered as a "cartoon," caricaturing the molecule by its emphasis on one point to the neglect of another. Despite this, these models serve well as aids in our thinking about chemical geometry. In addition, still other types of models have been constructed to aid in our thinking about the force surrounding molecules. These will be discussed in Book 2.

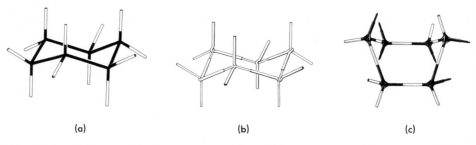

(a)   (b)   (c)

FIG. 9–15. Skeleton models of cyclohexane; (a) and (b) chair form and (c) boat form. (a) is a framework molecular model, (b) is a Dreiding model, and (c) is a Fieser model.

PROBLEMS

9–1   The vibrational spectra of organic molecules are powerful research tools in the modern laboratory. Absorptions of energy of wavelengths between 2 and 15 microns (the visible spectrum extends from 0.4 to 0.7 microns) can be determined semiquantitatively within a few minutes.

The great value of infared spectra results from the fact that the regions of energy absorption of a given functional group (for example, an alcohol group or a carboxylic acid group) do not greatly vary from compound to compound. Comparison of spectra of a number of compounds containing the same type of functional group will often allow the assignment of certain bands present in all of these spectra to the vibrations connected with the group. Those regions of absorption used most by organic chemists in assigning or confirming new structures are those in the region from 2.5 to 3.7 microns, and from 5.4 to 6.6 microns. The former region contains the absorption spectra of hydrogen-to-carbon, hydrogen-to-nitrogen, and hydrogen-to-oxygen stretching vibrations, and the latter contains the absorptions connected with double-bond stretching. This does not imply, of course, that absorptions in other regions of the spectrum are of less value in assigning structures to molecules.

If we examine representative spectra of some simple molecules, we may select a few useful absorptions for reference. Usually only the strongest absorptions will be helpful in assigning structure.

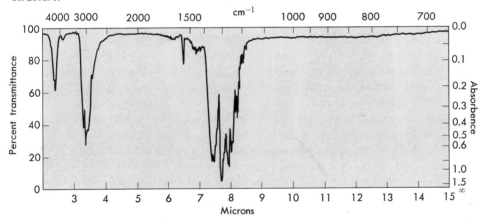

FIG. 9–16.   CH₄, methane. [From R. H. Pierson, A. N. Fletcher and E. St. Clair Gautz, *Anal. Chem.* **28**, 1218 (1956). Reproduced by permission.]

Methane, Fig. 9–16, has two principal absorptions, one from 3.2 to 3.4 microns, which is assigned to the stretching of the H—C bond, and a broad absorption from 7.2 to 8.2 microns, which represents the bending modes of the H—C bond. The spectra are complicated by fine structure, which is ascribed to superposition of different rotational absorptions onto the proper vibrational absorption.

In methyl alcohol, Fig. 9–17, we see the C—H stretching and C—H bending in approximately the same positions as in methane. In addition, there is a sharp peak at 2.75 microns, which is assigned to O—H stretching, and a strong one from 9.5 to 10.0 microns, connected with the C—O single bond stretch.

In ethyl chloride, Fig. 9–18, the C—H stretching and C—H bending vibrations occur at approximately the same positions as in methane; the C—H bending vibrations are spread

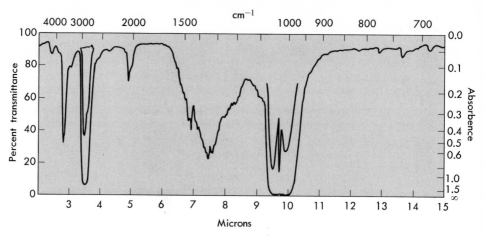

FIG. 9–17.   CH$_3$OH, methyl alcohol. [From Pierson, et al., *Anal. Chem.* **28,** 1218 (1956). Reproduced by permission.]

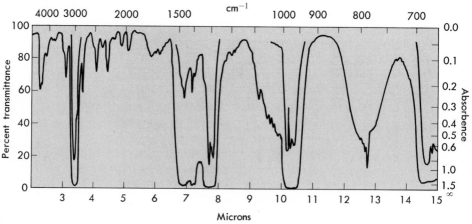

FIG. 9–18.   C$_2$H$_5$Cl, ethyl chloride. [From Pierson, et al., *Anal. Chem.* **28,** 1218 (1956). Reproduced by permission.]

over a wider range, however. The strong absorption from 10 to 10.5 microns is associated with C—C stretching and the absorption from 14.5 to the end is a C—Cl stretching vibration. The weaker absorption centered at 12.7 microns is another type of CH$_2$-group vibration.

From about 7 microns and outward, assignment of functional group absorptions is very difficult. Toward the end of the region, absorptions occur which involve more than one bond in the molecule, and consequently the position of absorption of a group is influenced very strongly by the character of the other bonds near it. This region is called the fingerprint region; it is often difficult to assign absorptions because the pattern will be characteristic of only one molecule.

Figures 9–19 and 9–20 show the infrared spectra of two compounds having the analysis C, 52.1; H, 13.1. Combustion analysis of the samples indicates the absence of halogens, nitrogen, and sulfur. Some idea of the molecular weight can be gained by the fact that the spectra were recorded in the gas (or vapor) phase near room temperature. Assign structures

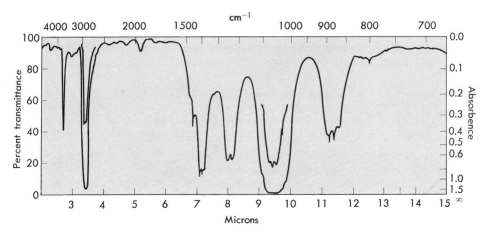

FIG. 9–19.   From Pierson, *et al., Anal. Chem.* **28**, 1218 (1956).   (Reproduced by permission.)

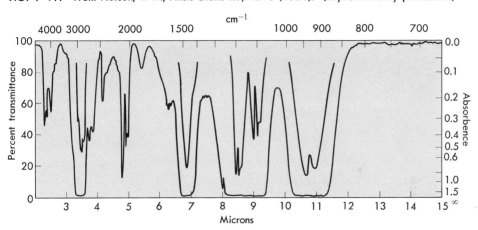

FIG. 9–20.   From Pierson, *et al., Anal. Chem.* **28**, 1218 (1956).   (Reproduced by permission.)

to the two species; it is unnecessary for you (and difficult even for experts) to make complete assignments of all the infrared absorptions.

9–2   (a) Draw a Newman projection of 1,2-dichloroethane.

(b) How many geometrically different conformations might be expected with the hydrogens and chlorines staggered?

(c) With the hydrogens and chlorines eclipsed?

(d) Which pair of substituents will offer the greater barrier to internal rotation, hydrogen-hydrogen or hydrogen-chlorine?

(e) Which pair of substituents will offer the greater barrier, hydrogen-chlorine or chlorine-chlorine?

(f) Draw a rough diagram of energy vs. angle of rotation for 1,2-dichloroethane (similar to Fig. 9–7). Specify that the angle of rotation is that between the two chlorine atoms on the Newman projection.

9-3   (a) Less energy is absorbed by a molecule at low temperatures because the rotation about the bond is forbidden by the barrier. At higher temperatures more energy is absorbed because some of it is "diverted" into rotation around bonds. Consider the heat capacity of 1,2-dibromoethane. At room temperature, would you expect it to be higher than, the same as, or lower than the heat capacity at 20°K?

(b) Compare these predictions with a similar set for 1,2-dibromoethylene.

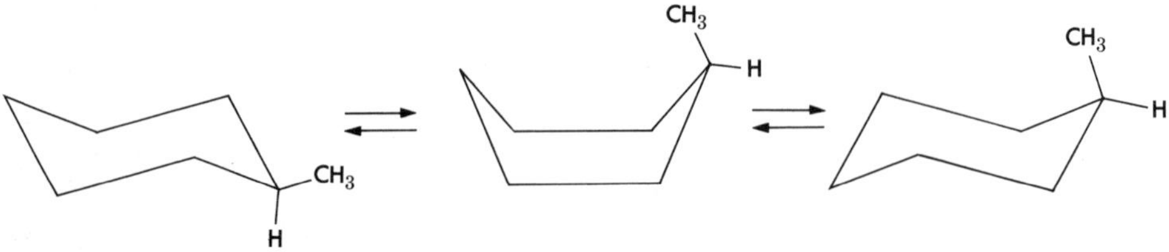

FIGURE 9–21

9-4   The boat and chair forms of cyclohexane are readily interconvertible, but the chair form is more stable. If the ring is substituted, two chair forms are possible, one with the substituent in an axial position and one with the substituent in an equatorial position, as in Fig. 9–21. The axial form is less stable because of inter- actions of a type similar to those which were found in ethane (see Figs. 9–7 and 9–22). Which would have the largest equilibrium constant,

$$K_{eq} = \frac{\text{equatorially substituted form}}{\text{axially substituted form}}$$

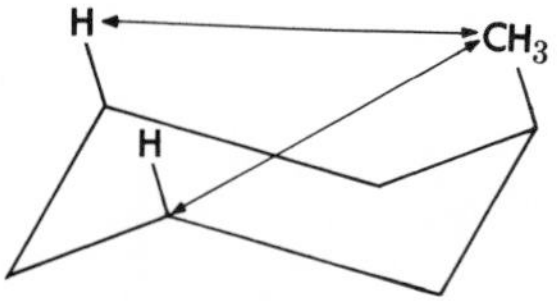

FIGURE 9–22

cyclohexyl fluoride, cyclohexyl chloride, or cyclohexyl bromide?

9-5   Do you think it would be possible to prepare optically active 1,2-, 1,3-, and 1,4- dimethylcyclohexanes?

Part 4

SOME BASIC METHODS FOR STRUCTURAL DETERMINATION

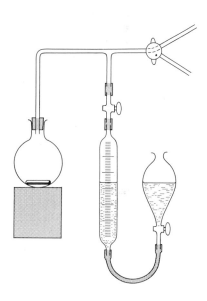

Just as the introduction of sodium as a diagnostic reagent for hydroxyl groups led to the determination of the structure of methanol, so the introduction of a variety of other diagnostic reagents has led to the possibility of determining more complex structures. As the molecules under study became larger, the organic chemist resorted to fragmentation and study of the identities of the fragments in his efforts to reconstruct mentally the architecture of the original material. A series of such diagnostic agents and methods will form the subject matter of Part 4.

What reactions can be used to establish the structures of olefins?

10

THE STRUCTURES OF ALKENES; CARBOXYLIC ACIDS AND THE SYNTHESIS OF DERIVATIVES FOR THEIR IDENTIFICATION

10–1 Alkenes as Structural Reference Compounds

We have now reviewed the primary assignments of the structures of organic molecules and shown how they rest on geometrical principles. We shall next amplify this approach by considering the problems involved in establishing the structures of compounds containing a double bond, such as the alkenes or olefins. The choice of alkenes for this purpose rather than alkanes rests on practical grounds. While alkenes can be converted to alkanes by hydrogenation, the resultant alkanes frequently turn out to be poorly suited to identification. In particular, because of their lack of reactivity, it is usually impossible to convert them into related derivative compounds to make identifications more secure. In brief, alkanes are poor standard reference compounds.

Alkenes, on the other hand, form excellent reference compounds. In the first place, as we shall see, their chemical reactivity permits them to be degraded into readily identifiable substances so that their structures may be established. In the next place, the ease with which they add chlorine and bromine often makes it possible to identify them directly as their halogen derivatives.

$$CH_2{=}CH_2 + Br_2 \rightarrow BrCH_2CH_2Br$$

In addition to its use in identification, this reaction can be used for purification of olefins. In the example given, ethylene is a gas whose condensation temperature is $-104°C$; 1,2-dibromoethane (ethylene bromide) is a liquid whose boiling point is $132°C$. If a gaseous or liquid olefin were accompanied by impurities with nearly the same boiling point, conversion into the dihalide would greatly facilitate purification. The olefin could then be regenerated by dehalogenation.

$$BrCH_2CH_2Br + Zn \rightarrow CH_2{=}CH_2 + ZnBr_2$$

Because of the ease with which olefins can be identified, means are frequently sought for converting other types of compounds of unknown structure into olefins to secure a structural assignment. Our study of means for structural assignment will, accordingly, begin with the problem of the determination of the structure of an unknown olefin.

10–2 Starting a Simple Structural Determination

Let us suppose that we have an unknown gas which analyzes for C_4H_8. If it were a saturated hydrocarbon, its analysis would be C_4H_{10}, or C_nH_{2n+2}. The fact that it is two hydrogen atoms short of this formula would be interpreted to mean that the material contained either a double bond or a ring. This type of deduction from the molecular formula for the unknown is always the first step in a structural determination, since it paves the way for a systematic attack on the structural problem by posing alternatives that can be tested experimentally.

10–3 Discriminating Between Rings and Double Bonds

In the case we are considering, the alternatives of ring or double bond can be tested experimentally by several procedures. One of the earliest, still useful when applied properly, is the test with neutral permanganate devised by Baeyer. Chemists had already discovered that in acidic solutions permanganate was a relatively powerful but somewhat selective reagent, oxidizing numerous types of organic compounds, but failing to oxidize some. In strongly alkaline solutions permanganate is also a powerful oxidizing agent, converting most organic compounds to either carbonate or carbon monoxide, but leaving a few acids and especially stable compounds untouched.

Baeyer found that in neutral solutions olefins could be cleanly hydroxylated with permanganate and that if precautions were taken to keep the solutions neutral, the reaction would stop there.

$$3CH_2{=}CH_2 + 2MnO_4^- + 4H_2O \rightarrow 3HOCH_2CH_2OH + 2MnO_2 + 2OH^-$$

Ethylene glycol

Later investigations have shown that, as a preparative method for glycols, permanganate is somewhat inferior to a combination of hydrogen peroxide and osmium tetroxide.

$$CH_2{=}CH_2 + HOOH \xrightarrow{OsO_4} HOCH_2CH_2OH$$

It is also possible to make osmate esters directly by reaction of an olefin with an equivalent amount of osmium tetroxide. These esters can then be reduced to glycols. Osmium tetroxide, on the other hand, is expensive, volatile, and toxic. Its special hazard is the possibility of depositing an osmium mirror over the eyeball. Hence permanganate, because of its cheapness, safety, and availability, is the reagent chosen for use in detecting double bonds, especially in undergraduate laboratories.

As a diagnostic reagent, permanganate must be used with discretion. The equation shows that the addition of permanganate to a double bond generates hydroxyl ions. As a result, the solution becomes more alkaline as the oxidation proceeds. This, in turn, increases the power of the permanganate to the point where it will, ultimately, lose its discrimination and attack many types of groupings. To prevent this, the permanganate is used in the presence of a buffering agent. It is important to observe this precaution, since a solution may contain just enough olefinic impurity to start the permanganate reaction and thus generate enough base to attack a major nonolefinic component.

The value of Baeyer's reagent in diagnosis is that it will not attack a cyclopropane ring or a cyclobutane ring and thus will discriminate between small rings and double bonds.

Another means of discriminating between small rings and double bonds is by their different reactions to catalytic hydrogenation. These differences were first noted by Willstätter.

$$CH_2{=}CH_2 + H_2 \xrightarrow[20°]{Pt} CH_3CH_3$$

$$\begin{array}{c} CH_2 \\ \diagup \ \diagdown \\ CH_2{-}CH_2 \end{array} + H_2 \xrightarrow[80°]{Pt} CH_3CH_2CH_3$$

$$\begin{array}{c} CH_2{-}CH_2 \\ |\qquad| \\ CH_2{-}CH_2 \end{array} + H_2 \xrightarrow[120°]{Pt} CH_3CH_2CH_2CH_3$$

Cyclopentane and cyclohexane are stable to catalytic hydrogenation at still higher temperatures, but eventually a temperature is reached at which the power of the catalyst is sufficient to cause cleavage even of saturated hydrocarbons. Naturally, at these temperatures the cycloparaffins will also be attacked.

While ethylene is attacked readily by hydrogen at room temperature, some double bonds deeply buried in ring systems are harder to hydrogenate. In these cases, hydrogenation can usually be accomplished slowly at room temperature by adding more catalyst, but as a practical matter the chemist will usually increase the temperature to diminish the waiting time. Even in such cases, however, selectivity between olefinic bonds and small rings can usually be achieved.

10–4   Continuing the Structural Determination

To return to the discussion of our compound, C_4H_8, we have seen that we must differentiate between the possibility that it is an olefin or that it is methylcyclopropane or cyclobutane. Treatment with neutral permanganate established that it had a double bond, and this was confirmed by catalytic hydrogenation.

$$C_4H_8 \xrightarrow{\text{KMnO}_4} C_4H_{10}O_2{}^*$$

$$C_4H_8 + H_2 \xrightarrow[200°]{\text{Pt}} C_4H_{10}$$

The diagnostic process has eliminated cyclic compounds from consideration and reduced the possibilities to four. Of these, three have straight chains and one has a branched chain.

Straight chain

$CH_3CH_2CH{=}CH_2$ $CH_3CH{=}CHCH_3$

1-butene   2-butene (*cis* or *trans*)

Branched chain

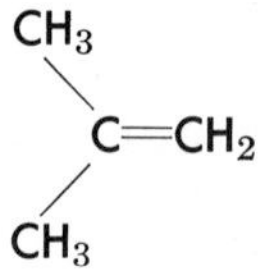

$$\begin{array}{c} CH_3 \\ \diagdown \\ \quad\;\; C{=}CH_2 \\ \diagup \\ CH_3 \end{array}$$

2-methylpropene (Isobutylene)

The assignment of *cis* and *trans* configurations is sometimes much more difficult than the assignment of the position of a double bond in a chain. For this reason we shall limit our first structural investigations to those means used for the assignment of the positions of double bonds.

10–5   Degradation by Oxidation

A reagent which is widely used in structural studies on olefins is Beckmann's reagent, familiarly known as "cleaning solution." This consists of a solution of dichromate in partially aqueous sulfuric acid, giving CrO_3 and H_2SO_4. This

---

* To calculate the amount of a reagent required in a reaction, it is frequently essential to balance the equation, as is done for a permanganate oxidation in Section 10–3. When attention is focused on the organic reagents and products, however, other reagents may be written above or below the arrow to indicate their nature, but not their equivalence.

reagent attacks double bonds, converting the RCH= group into RCOOH. In some laboratories an acidic solution of permanganate is preferred because weaker sulfuric acid can be used, thus giving a reagent less susceptible to possible errors due to initial attack of the acid on the hydrocarbon.

If we consider only the straight-chain possibilities for the present, oxidation with either CrO_3 or $KMnO_4$ in acid will yield only acetic acid, in the case of 2-butene.

$$CH_3CH=CHCH_3 \xrightarrow[H_2SO_4]{CrO_3} 2CH_3COOH + H_2O$$

For 1-butene, we might expect the oxidation to yield propionic and formic acids. Formic acid, however, is not stable to oxidizing agents in acidic solutions and is further oxidized. If stronger acid is used, acid decomposition predominates and some carbon monoxide is formed. If weaker acid and stronger oxidizing agent is used, more carbon dioxide is formed. We shall formulate the reaction as if the conditions chosen were ideal for oxidation.

$$CH_3CH_2CH=CH_2 \xrightarrow[H_2SO_4]{KMnO_4} CH_3CH_2COOH + [HCOOH]$$

$$HCOOH \xrightarrow[H_2SO_4]{KMnO_4} CO_2 + H_2O$$

(The reader should note that a mixture of $KMnO_4$ with concentrated sulfuric acid will sometimes explode. Oxidations are performed with dilute acid.)

Let us alter our original premise slightly and consider the possibility that in one bottle we had a sample of 1-butene, and in a second we had a sample of 2-butene. Both of these are gases at room temperature, condensing to liquids slightly below and slightly above the freezing point of water, respectively. Under pressure, both can be kept in the liquid state at room temperature. Let us suppose that we devise a suitable "scrubber" so that the gases can be exposed to the action of the oxidizing agent by repeated contact of bubbles with the reagent so that none of the gas will escape without reaction. Under these conditions, we might expect one scrubber, after reaction, to contain acetic acid; the other would contain half as many equivalents of propionic acid.

$$CH_3CH_2CH=CH_2 \xrightarrow{oxidation} CH_3CH_2COOH + CO_2$$

$$CH_3CH=CHCH_2 \xrightarrow{oxidation} 2CH_3COOH$$

Our problem is to isolate, recognize, and identify the products.

10–6 Identification of Acids

Higher aliphatic acids are insoluble in aqueous acid solutions, but both acetic and propionic acids are soluble. To isolate them for identification, extraction with an immiscible solvent is the method usually employed. For this purpose, ether is a suitable choice. The acidic solution should be either diluted or partially neutralized first, since ether is quite soluble in strong acids, but becomes less and less soluble as the acid is diluted or the salt concentration is increased. Because of the low boiling point of ether, the solution should also be cold when the extraction is undertaken.

By repeatedly extracting the acidic solution with ether, the organic acids may be removed. The further treatment will then depend on the exact type of identification desired. Suppose, for example, that we desired to identify the acids directly by their boiling points. In this case, the ether solution would be washed first with a little distilled water to remove traces of mineral acid and then dried with sodium sulfate or other suitable drying agent. Because of its low boiling point, the ether could then be distilled off, and the residue in the distilling flask would be acetic acid, in one case and propionic acid, in the other. Boiling points of organic liquids can be determined even in very small quantities with suitable arrangements. With larger amounts, the problem becomes simpler. If the amount is sufficient, an ordinary distilling flask with a fractionating side-arm, as shown in Fig. 10-1, may be used. It would then be found that one sample boiled at 118 C. This would be identified as acetic acid. The other sample would boil at 140°C. This would be identified as propionic acid. A flow diagram illustrating the sequence of operations for the isolation of acetic acid is shown in Fig. 10-2.

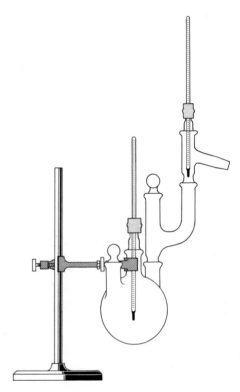

FIG. 10-1. Distilling flask with fractionating side-arm.

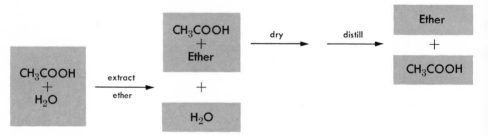

FIG. 10-2. Isolation of acetic acid.

10–7   Substituted Phenacyl Esters

While it is possible to identify less than a milligram of liquid by its boiling point, it is more convenient to manipulate solids than liquids. For this reason organic chemists prefer to convert liquids into solid derivatives, whenever possible. For the acids, it has been found possible to prepare solid esters of acids by a modification of the esterification process given in Problem 4–2. The most commonly employed derivatives for this purpose are *para*-substituted phenacyl esters, made as follows:

$$RCOO^- Na^+ + XC_6H_4\overset{\overset{\displaystyle O}{\|}}{C}CH_2Br \rightarrow RCOOCH_2\overset{\overset{\displaystyle O}{\|}}{C}C_6H_4X + Na^+ Br^-$$

Substituted   Substituted
phenacyl bromide   phenacyl ester

The X groups used in identification have been H, C_6H_5, Cl and Br. Of these, the bromophenacyl derivatives are possibly the most satisfactory. They have the advantage that a quantitative determination of the bromine content also gives the equivalent weight of the ester. Melting points of a number of *p*-bromophenacyl esters of acids which are ordinarily liquids are listed in Table 10–1.

The trivial names of certain of these acids are interesting. The word "butyric" is derived from the same root as "butter" and butyric acid is the main odorous constituent of rancid butter. In sweet butter, the acid is esterified with glycerin. On standing, enzymatic action causes hydrolysis of the esters with liberation of the acids and resulting rancidity. As the chain length of the acid increases, the disagreeable quality of the odor increases until the diminution in volatility reverses the trend. These acids are found in perspiration and are partly responsible for its offensive residual odors. The three acids, caproic, caprylic, and capric are obviously derived from the same root, the Latin word for "goat." These acids are found in the skin secretions of the goat and are responsible for the odor of goats.

Table 10–1

Acid	Formula	b.p., °C	Ester m.p., °C
Formic	HCOOH	101	135
Acetic	CH_3COOH	118	85
Propionic	C_2H_5COOH	140	63
Isobutyric	$(CH_3)_2CHCOOH$	155	77
n-butyric	C_3H_7COOH	163	63
Isovaleric	$(CH_3)_2CHCH_2COOH$	176	68
n-valeric	C_4H_9COOH	186	75
n-caproic	$C_5H_{11}COOH$	205	72
Oenanthic	$C_6H_{13}COOH$	224	72
n-caprylic	$C_7H_{15}COOH$	236	67
Capric	$C_9H_{19}COOH$	270	67
Undecanoic	$C_{10}H_{21}COOH$	275 (dec)	68

Table 10–2

Acid	Formula	m.p., °C	Ester m.p., °C
Capric	$C_9H_{19}COOH$	30	67
Lauric	$C_{11}H_{23}COOH$	44	76
Myristic	$C_{13}H_{27}COOH$	54	81
Margaric	$C_{16}H_{33}COOH$	60	83
Palmitic	$C_{15}H_{31}COOH$	62	86
Stearic	$C_{17}H_{35}COOH$	69	90
Phenylacetic	$C_6H_5CH_2COOH$	76	89
o-toluic	$CH_3C_6H_4COOH$	102	57
m-toluic	$CH_3C_6H_4COOH$	110	108
Benzoic	C_6H_5COOH	121	119
o-chlorobenzoic	ClC_6H_4COOH	140	106
m-nitrobenzoic	$NO_2C_6H_4COOH$	140	132
o-nitrobenzoic	$NO_2C_6H_4COOH$	146	107
m-chlorobenzoic	ClC_6H_4COOH	158	116
p-toluic	$CH_3C_6H_4COOH$	177	153
p-nitrobenzoic	$NO_2C_6H_4COOH$	241	137

Some of the aliphatic acids and many of the other types of acid known to organic chemists are ordinarily isolated as solids. Those with low melting points may be isolated either as the solid or as the liquid. Even in the case of solid acids, however, the possibility of forming a solid derivative with a characteristic melting point provides an excellent check of identity, since samples which are not rigorously pure may melt a few degrees lower than the pure substances. Melting points of the p-bromophenacyl esters of some solid monobasic acids are given in Table 10–2.

The preponderance in nature of acids with even numbers of carbons (Problem 4–4) reflects the results of the biosynthetic mechanisms operating in plants and animals, which produce these materials almost exclusively. These acids, in the form of their glyceride esters, are normal constituents of plant and animal fats. Hard fats contain more of the saturated fatty acid glycerides and softer fats and oils contain more of the unsaturated, olefinic acid glycerides. Both saturated and unsaturated esters contain acids with even numbers of carbon atoms, however.

10–8   Solid Esters of Dibasic Acids

As we have seen, it is possible to prepare dibasic organic acids as well as monobasic acids. Table 10–3 lists some dibasic acids and the melting points of their p-bromophenacyl esters.

10–9   Distinction Between the Butenes

To return to the problem of the butenes: If we desired to identify the products of an oxidation as solid phenacyl esters rather than as the pure liquid acids, then we would separate the ethereal extract of the acid and treat it with an alkaline

Table 10–3

Acid	Formula	m.p., °C	Di-ester m.p., °C
Glutaric	$HOOC(CH_2)_3COOH$	97	137
Pimelic	$HOOC(CH_2)_5COOH$	105	137
Azelaic	$HOOC(CH_2)_7COOH$	106	131
Maleic	$HOOCCH{=}CHCOOH$	130	168
Sebacic	$HOOC(CH_2)_8COOH$	133	147
Suberic	$HOOC(CH_2)_6COOH$	140	144
Adipic	$HOOC(CH_2)_4COOH$	152	154
Phthalic	$C_6H_4(COOH)_2$	184 (dec)	153
Succinic	$HOOC(CH_2)_2COOH$	188	211
Isophthalic	$C_6H_4(COOH)_2$	300	179
Terephthalic	$C_6H_4(COOH)_2$	300 (subl)	225

aqueous solution. If, for some reason, we wanted to separate carboxylic acids from other less acidic materials, the aqueous solution we used would be sodium bicarbonate. This has the disadvantage of forming bubbles, however, so that if a fractionation were not needed at this point, a dilute solution of sodium hydroxide would cause less disturbance to the highly volatile ether layer. At any rate, the acid materials would be extracted into the aqueous layer by the base and the resultant solution would contain the sodium salt of the acid. Ethanol would be added to dissolve the reactants, the excess base would be neutralized until the solution was just faintly acid to litmus and the *p*-bromophenacyl bromide reagent added. The solution would then be allowed to reflux to complete the ester formation. On cooling, the ester would solidify. The equations for these reactions are:

$$CH_3COOH + HO^- \rightarrow CH_3COO^- + H_2O$$

$$CH_3COO^- + BrC_6H_4\overset{O}{\overset{\|}{C}}CH_2Br \rightarrow CH_3COOCH_2\overset{O}{\overset{\|}{C}}C_6H_4Br + Br^-$$
$$\text{(m.p. }85°C\text{)}$$

$$C_2H_5COOH + OH^- \rightarrow C_2H_5COO^- + H_2O$$

$$C_2H_5COO^- + BrC_6H_4\overset{O}{\overset{\|}{C}}CH_2Br \rightarrow C_2H_5COOCH_2\overset{O}{\overset{\|}{C}}C_6H_4Br + Br^-$$
$$\text{(m.p. }63°C\text{)}$$

A flow diagram illustrating the steps in the separation of an acid as a bromophenacyl ester is given in Fig. 10–3.

The bromophenacyl ester formed in the preceding reaction could be purified by recrystallization and, after drying, its melting point could be determined. In our case, one sample, that forming the acid boiling at 118°, would form a bromophenacyl

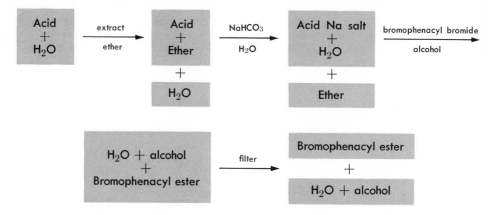

FIG. 10–3.   Identification of an acid as its bromophenacyl derivative.

ester melting at 85°, while the one forming an acid boiling at 140° would form a bromophenacyl ester melting at 63°. This would complete the identification of the two olefins.

10–10   Structure of a More Complex Unknown; Hydrogenation

Now let us suppose that we had a liquid which analyzed for C_6H_{10}. First we must ask how many hydrogens it has short of the saturated C_6 compound. Then this must be interpreted. A room-temperature hydrogenation is undertaken with a platinum catalyst and the resulting product is found to have the formula, C_6H_{12}. This much information permits the elimination of many alternative formulas but still stops short of a final answer concerning the structure. Before going on, however, another piece of information useful in structural determinations will be in order.

In the case given, the critical information was the number of hydrogens that would be absorbed by the compound on hydrogenation. The answer could be obtained in either or both of two ways. As indicated, the substance could be hydrogenated and the product analyzed to find the gain in hydrogen. Alternatively, it is possible to measure the uptake of hydrogen directly, an intrinsically more accurate procedure.

There are two types of apparatus for the measurement of the uptake of hydrogen during hydrogenation. One measures the change in volume at constant pressure, the other measures the change in pressure at constant volume. A constant-pressure type hydrogenation apparatus is shown in Fig. 10–4.

With apparatus of this type, it is possible to follow both the rate and the extent of hydrogenation. If two reducible groups are present, it is sometimes possible to secure selectivity between them by noting a change in the rate of hydrogenation after one has reacted. In any case, it is possible to find how many groups react

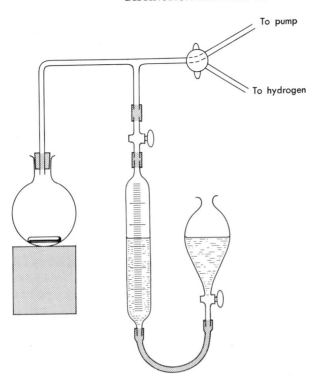

To pump

To hydrogen

FIG. 10–4. Apparatus for hydrogenation at constant pressure.

with hydrogen, thus answering immediately the important question for structural analysis.

In the case of our unknown, it was found that the equation shown below described the course of the experiemnt.

$$C_6H_{10} + 1H_2 \xrightarrow{Pt} C_6H_{12}$$

What conclusion can be drawn from this experiment with respect to the structures of C_6H_{10} and of C_6H_{12}?

Following the course suggested by the outcome of the hydrogenation experiment, the compound C_6H_{10} was treated with an oxidizing agent. After extraction and purification, an acid melting at 152°C was obtained. This, on preparation of the bromophenacyl ester, gave a derivative melting at 154°C. What conclusion can be drawn about the structure of the compound C_6H_{10}?

10–11 Distinction Between Chains and Rings

The preceding example shows that different results are obtained when an open chain compound and a cyclic compound are oxidized. As seen earlier, oxidation breaks a double bond. For an open chain compound, this cleavage will reduce the molecule to fragments containing fewer carbons than the original compound. On the other hand, for a cyclic olefin, cleavage of the ring will produce an open chain with the same number of carbons.

$$RCH{=}CHR' \rightarrow \text{Two fragments} \qquad \begin{matrix} CH \\ -\!-\|-\!- \\ CH \end{matrix} \rightarrow \text{One product}$$

10–12   Distinction Between Olefins and Benzenoid Hydrocarbons

While it is possible to hydrogenate benzene very slowly at room temperature, elevated temperatures are much preferred for this purpose. In fact, the benzene ring is so resistant to hydrogenation that it is not difficult to achieve a selective hydrogenation of an ethylenic double bond on a molecule containing a benzene ring.

A solid melting at 45°C was isolated from a reaction mixture. On analysis this proved to have the formula $C_{16}H_{16}$. Hydrogenation consumed one mole of hydrogen per mole of compound to produce the hydrocarbon $C_{16}H_{18}$, melting at 52° C and boiling at 317°C. Treatment of the solid melting at 45°C with chromic-sulfuric acid mixture and extraction gave a solid melting at 76°C. This had an equivalent weight of 136, as determined by titration with a standard base, and yielded a bromophenacyl derivative with a melting point of 89°C. From this information it should be possible to reconstruct the structural formula of the solid melting at 45°C and the one melting at 52°C.

What information does the preceding experiment give you about the stability of the benzene ring to oxidation?

10–13   Stability of Aromatic Compounds

Numerous experimental observations of the stability of benzenoid hydrocarbons and other aromatic-type compounds to both reducing and oxidizing agents have forced modern chemists to revise still further the concepts of Kekulé with respect to the significance of the nonisolation of the "double bond isomers" of o-xylene, for example. In Kekulé's time it was argued that such isomers could not be isolated because they are interconverted too rapidly for isolation. Now it is argued that the stability of these compounds toward chemical reagents shows that the actual compounds are more stable than the hypothetical "unsaturated" compounds which the formulas seem to represent. As a result, it is argued that the "unsaturated" benzenoid isomers do not exist and that the species that actually exists is more stable than these and should be thought of as a "hybrid" of the two, neither one nor the other but both, combined to give a more stable species. It is argued, further, that such hybridization takes place whenever it is possible to write two equivalent structures which can be interconverted by moving only bonds and not atomic nuclei. Detailed explanations of this concept will be postponed for Book 2.

PROBLEMS

10-1   (a) A compound has the formula C_7H_{14}. To which saturated hydrocarbon does it correspond?

(b) How many hydrogens does it lack?

(c) What is the total number of rings and/or double bonds that must be incorporated into its structure to account for the missing hydrogens?

(d) Hydrogenation at room temperature yields C_7H_{16}. How many rings does the compound have? How many double bonds?

(e) If the hydrogenation were carried out at 100°C, would the result differ?

(f) The olefin is oxidized with chromic acid-sulfuric acid. Two acids are obtained which may be separated by fractional distillation. The low-boiling fraction, after purification, boils at 118°C and forms a p-bromophenacyl ester melting at 85°C. The high-boiling fraction is characterized by the same reagent and the ester is found to melt at 68°C. What are the two acids?

(g) What is the structure of the olefin (or olefins) which forms a mixture of these two acids on strong oxidation?

(h) How might 3-methylbutene-1 be prepared from one of the acids? (See Problems 4-4 and 8-7.)

10-2   An isomer of the C_7H_{14} mentioned above was oxidized in the same way. Only one acid was isolated from the reaction mixture. It formed a *para*-bromophenacyl ester with a melting point of 72°C.

(a) What was the olefin?

(b) Devise a synthesis for the olefin from a reasonable starting material.

10-3   (a) A compound has the formula C_6H_{10} and on hydrogenation yields C_6H_{14}. Does it contain a ring?

(b) Oxidation of this compound gives a mixture of acids which are separated by careful fractional distillation. On neutralization, one was found to have an equivalent weight of 60, the other 88. (This is the determination of the *neutralization equivalent.*) What structures are possible for the acids? How could you differentiate between possibilities in the laboratory?

(c) Preparation of the p-bromophenacyl esters of both acids gives two compounds with melting points of 85°C and 63°C. Does this additional data identify the acids?

(d) What structure can you write for the original compound to accommodate all the data given? Thus a different kind of unsaturation is sometimes a possibility in these degradative studies. The similarity in reactivity to double bonds carries over to many other kinds of reactions; you should note analogies when they appear.

10-4   (a) A molecule has the formula $C_{18}H_{18}$. How many hydrogens is it lacking?

(b) What clue does the large number of missing hydrogens furnish about the structure?

(c) The usual oxidation procedure is carried out, and, after careful separation, two acids are obtained in crystalline form. One melts at 121°C and the other at 188°C. The first has a neutralization equivalent of 122, and the second has one of 59. What structure for the original molecule will accommodate these facts?

(d) When the molecule is oxidized, would you expect the two acids to be formed in equimolar amounts?

(e) Suppose that the molecule had been hydrogenated at room temperature and then oxidized under more severe conditions than those commonly used for this type of reaction. What product could you predict would form?

10-5 (a) A compound has the formula $C_{14}H_{16}O$. How many hydrogens is it lacking? [*Hint:* Compare the empirical formulas for methane and methanol. Does the presence of singly bonded oxygen in a molecule alter the number of hydrogens present in the parent hydrocarbon?]

(b) Oxidation with chromic-sulfuric acid yields only two isolable fragments. Both are acids fairly soluble in hot water. One has a melting point of 184°C and the other has a melting point of 97°C. The latter has a neutralization equivalent of 66 and forms a *p*-bromophenacyl derivative with a melting point of 137°C. What is the latter acid?

(c) When *p*-cresol (*p*-methylphenol) is treated with sodium hydroxide, the sodium salt is formed. Treatment of this salt with methyl iodide, followed by oxidation of the reaction product with strong hot chromic-sulfuric acid yields a material with a melting point at 184°C. Admixture of this material and that of similar melting points obtained from the olefin gives no melting point depression. What is the structure of the acid from the olefin?

(d) Do these two fragments account for all the carbons present in the olefin?

(e) What is the structure of the olefin?

BRANCHED-CHAIN OLEFINS
AND THEIR SYNTHESIS.
ACETYLENES AND CARBONYL
COMPOUNDS

11-1 General

Most hydrocarbons encountered in the study of organic chemistry are branched-chain olefins. The group includes a host of natural products, both open chain and cyclic, such as essential oils and flavoring materials as well as structural and functional substances occurring in plant and animal organisms. In addition, many other such substances have hydroxyl or other groups that can easily be removed to form unsaturated hydrocarbons so that the study of the unsaturated hydrocarbons themselves is basic to structural work.

11-2 Cleavage to a Ketone

Let us examine a simple branched-chain, unsaturated hydrocarbon, 2,3-dimethyl-2-butene.

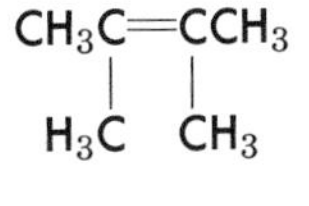

$$CH_3C\!\!=\!\!CCH_3$$
$$H_3C \quad CH_3$$

Oxidation of this substance by chromic-sulfuric acid mixture will yield a single cleavage product, acetone, CH_3COCH_3. Acetone is the simplest representative of the class of compounds called *ketones*. Ketones and another class of compounds called *aldehydes* are both types of *carbonyl compounds*, that is, compounds containing the $C\!\!=\!\!O$ group. The distinction between them is that the carbonyl carbon is attached to two carbons in a ketone, but in an aldehyde at least one of the attached atoms must be hydrogen. As a result, much of the chemistry of these two classes is similar, but there are important differences. Aldehydes, for example,

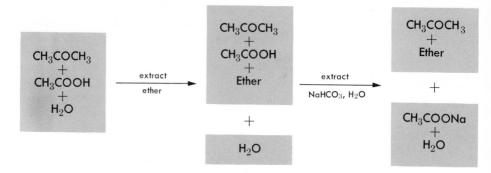

FIG. 11–1.   Separation of acetone and acetic acid.

are readily converted to the corresponding carboxylic acids by oxidation. Ketones are much more resistant to oxidation. Acetone is much more stable to oxidizing agents than is an olefin, with the result that it is easily possible to stop an oxidation reaction at the ketone stage. It is true that the reaction can be carried further, however, so that by using a stronger reagent and, in particular, by using elevated temperatures, it is possible to cleave an aliphatic ketone. For ordinary structural determinations, however, the reaction is carried out under milder conditions that do not seriously attack ketones.

Acetone is a volatile liquid boiling at 57°C. Here again the chemist confronts the problem of finding a suitable means of identification. If we were to isolate the product of the oxidation of 2-methyl-2-butene, $(CH_3)_2C{=}CHCH_3$, in the manner described for an acid, acetone would be extracted into the ether layer along with acetic acid. A careful wash with an alkaline solution would remove the acid, leaving the nonacidic ketone behind in the ether layer. A flow diagram showing the separation of acetone and acetic acid is given in Fig. 11–1.

Since ether boils at 35°C and acetone at 57°C, separation of the two would not be impossible. Under the usual working conditions, however, there would be a large excess of the ether and a small amount of acetone so that there would be a tendency to lose the acetone unless special precautions were taken to fractionate it out of the ether. Obviously a better procedure would be desirable.

11–3   Identification of Carbonyl Compounds

Carbonyl compounds, such as acetone, are usually identified by means of their reactions with nitrogenous bases. One of the earliest reagents for this purpose was hydroxylamine.

$$\begin{array}{c} CH_3 \\ \diagdown \\ CO \ + \ H_2NOH \ \rightarrow \\ \diagup \\ CH_3 \end{array} \qquad \begin{array}{c} CH_3 \\ \diagdown \\ C{=}NOH \ + \ H_2O \\ \diagup \\ CH_3 \end{array}$$

The product formed is called an *oxime*. In this particular case, it is acetone oxime. Unlike acetone, it is a solid, melting at 59°C. With a very few exceptions, oximes can be prepared for identification of ketones.

Some of the oximes have melting points so low that it is difficult to crystallize them. For this reason, other nitrogenous bases have been substituted, some of them derivatives of hydrazine, H_2NNH_2. One such base that has enjoyed wide popularity for purposes of identification is phenylhydrazine.

$$\begin{matrix} CH_3 \\ \diagdown \\ CO \\ \diagup \\ CH_3 \end{matrix} + H_2NNHC_6H_5 \rightarrow \begin{matrix} CH_3 \\ \diagdown \\ C{=}NNHC_6H_5 \\ \diagup \\ CH_3 \end{matrix} + H_2O$$

The product is called *acetone phenylhydrazone*.

In the particular case of acetone, there is no advantage in using phenylhydrazine instead of hydroxylamine, since the phenylhydrazone has an even lower melting point than the oxime, 42°C instead of 59°C. In most cases, however, phenylhydrazones melt at higher temperatures than oximes.

While a number of phenylhydrazones have proved to be satisfactory for purposes of identification, a series of derivatives with still higher melting points was desired. This was found in the semicarbazones, formed by reaction with semicarbazide.* Its reaction with ketones is similar to those given above.

$$\begin{matrix} CH_3 \\ \diagdown \\ CO \\ \diagup \\ CH_3 \end{matrix} + H_2NNHCONH_2 \rightarrow \begin{matrix} CH_3 \\ \diagdown \\ C{=}NNHCONH_2 \\ \diagup \\ CH_3 \end{matrix} + H_2O$$

In general, semicarbazones have suitably high melting points for purposes of identification, and they have been used for this purpose for years. Acetone semicarbazone, for example, melts at 187°C.

In some cases difficulties have been encountered in inducing semicarbazones to crystallize, even though the products were solids. Organic chemists sought still other reagents and finally chose 2,4-dinitrophenylhydrazine. The 2,4-dinitrophenylhydrazones usually crystallize with ease and form readily in strongly acidic

---

* Regarding the nomenclature, amides, in general, are derivatives of acids in which the acidic OH has been replaced by an NH_2 group or by a substituted NH_2 group such as NHR or NR_2, where R is usually a hydrocarbon radical. Urea, H_2NCONH_2, is the amide of carbonic acid and is sometimes called "carbamide." The corresponding amide in which hydrazine is substituted for ammonia is called "carbazide," $H_2NNHCONHNH_2$. Semicarbazide, $H_2NNHCONH_2$, is so-called because it is halfway between carbamide and carbazide.

solutions. This reaction is similar to the preceding one:

$$CH_3\!\!-\!\!CO + H_2NNH\!\!-\!\!\langle\ \rangle\!\!-\!\!NO_2 \ (NO_2) \rightarrow \ CH_3\!\!-\!\!C\!\!=\!\!NNH\!\!-\!\!\langle\ \rangle\!\!-\!\!NO_2 \ (NO_2) + H_2O$$

Acetone dinitrophenylhydrazone melts at 126°C. The dinitrophenylhydrazones are usually either yellow or orange in color. The color of the derivatives can be useful on occasion, since it permits the formation of a derivative to be observed by a color change. It is also possible to measure the change in color quantitatively with a colorimeter and thus assay the carbonyl compound.

To return to the problem of separation of the products of oxidative cleavage, an ethereal solution of acetone can be treated with an alcoholic solution of 2,4-dinitrophenylhydrazine and the ether removed by evaporation. On addition of hydrochloric acid and boiling, the dinitrophenylhydrazone will form and will crystallize readily on cooling. This is probably the most convenient method for identifying ketones in the products of the oxidation of an olefin.

11-4   Preparation of Olefins from Alcohols; Migration of a Double Bond

We have already seen that alcohols can be dehydrated to yield olefins. One reagent for accomplishing this is sulfuric acid. The reaction is reversible, however, so that alcohols can be made by the hydration of olefins. In fact, large quantities of ethanol and isopropanol are prepared by this process. Stronger acid and higher temperatures favor the dehydration reaction, and somewhat weaker acid with lower temperatures tend to favor the hydration. Experience has shown, however, that the hydration which takes place is not always an exact reversal of the dehydration. For example, a primary alcohol, that is, one with no more than one carbon attached to the alcoholic group, would dehydrate to an olefin, but on hydration might form a secondary alcohol, that is, one with two carbons attached to the alcoholic group.

$$CH_3CH_2CH_2CH_2OH \xrightarrow{\ H_2SO_4\ } CH_3CH_2CH\!\!=\!\!CH_2 + H_2O$$

$$CH_3CH_2CH\!\!=\!\!CH_2 + H_2O \xrightarrow{\ H_2SO_4\ } CH_3CH_2CHOHCH_3$$

The rule with respect to the directive influence in hydration of olefins is called the *Markovnikov rule*, after its discoverer. It applies only to hydrocarbons and states that on addition of HX to a double bond, the X group, OH, Cl, Br, or I, will preferentially go to a tertiary carbon rather than a secondary carbon and to a secondary carbon rather than a primary carbon. An exposition of the factors governing this orientation rule and its exceptions will be presented in Book 2.

Following the hydration of 1-butene to 2-butanol, further dehydration will yield 2-butene.

$$CH_3CH_2CHOHCH_3 \xrightarrow{H_2SO_4} CH_3CH{=}CHCH_3 + H_2O$$

The rule concerning the direction of dehydration of alcohols in acid is called the *Saytzev rule*, after its discoverer. The rule is that in acid dehydration the removal of a hydrogen from a tertiary carbon will take precedence over the removal from a secondary carbon and the removal of a hydrogen from a secondary carbon will take precedence over the removal from a primary carbon. The factors governing dehydration reactions will also be presented in Book 2.

It will be seen that the sequential operation of the Markovnikov rule and the Saytzev rule on an olefin can accomplish the migration of a double bond. In the case cited, 1-butene was converted into 2-butene by sulfuric acid. While it is true, as stated, that the ideal conditions for the hydration reaction differ from those for dehydration, both may proceed to some extent in a single reaction mixture. For this reason, reagents containing sulfuric acid or other mineral acids are not always completely reliable in the determination of the structures of olefins. In most cases it has proved possible to establish structures with these reagents, but there have been just enough anomalous results obtained to make organic chemists search for a reagent which would cleave a double bond without the use of mineral acids.

11–5 Cleavage by Ozonolysis

A reagent capable of cleaving double bonds without the addition of mineral acids was discovered by Harries and investigated extensively by Staudinger. This is ozone, O_3. Ozone is an extremely powerful oxidizing agent and is capable of attacking most organic substances. In some cases the resulting products are explosive so that they are seldom concentrated or purified before work-up. It is because of the great reactivity of ozone that care must be exercised in the choice of a solvent for its employment. In general, carbon tetrachloride is used wherever possible. This substance is relatively inert to the action of ozone and is thus a suitable reaction solvent.

The virtue of ozone in structural determinations is that it attacks olefinic compounds much more rapidly than it does most other types of compounds. The reaction is usually so fast that, with proper gas-liquid mixing during its course, it is possible to exhaust the olefin quantitatively before appreciable attack occurs at another grouping. If an ozonizer is set up so that its output is constant, that is, if the flow rate and temperature are maintained constant, then the percentage of ozone present can be analyzed and the reaction performed quantitatively. Immediately on exhaustion of the olefin, free ozone will appear at the outlet of the gas system and it can be detected with moist starch-iodide paper, since its reaction with iodide ion to give iodine is also instantaneous. No acidic or basic catalyst is required for the reaction of ozone with an olefin. The practical result

Table 11–1

KETONES, LIQUID

Compound	Formula	b.p., °C	m.p. Semicarb, °C	m.p. 2,4-DNP, °C
Acetone	CH_3COCH_3	56	187	126
Methyl ethyl ketone	$CH_3COC_2H_5$	80	135	111
Diacetyl	$CH_3COCOCH_3$	88	278	315
Isopropyl methyl ketone	$(CH_3)_2CHCOCH_3$	94	113	117
Methyl n-propyl ketone	$CH_3COC_3H_7$	102	110	144
Diethyl ketone	$C_2H_5COC_2H_5$	102	139	156
Pinacolone	$CH_3COC(CH_3)_3$	106	157	125
Isobutyl methyl ketone	$(CH_3)_2CHCH_2COCH_3$	119	135	95
Methyl neopentyl ketone	$CH_3COCH_2C(CH_3)_3$	124	176	101
Di-isopropyl ketone	$(CH_3)_2CHCOCH(CH_3)_2$	125	160	–
Methyl n-butyl ketone	$CH_3COC_4H_9$	129	122	106
Cyclopentanone	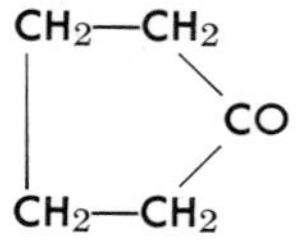 $\begin{array}{c}CH_2-CH_2\\ \diagdown\quad CO\\ CH_2-CH_2\end{array}$	131	205	147
Acetylacetone	$CH_3COCH_2COCH_3$	139	–	209
Di-n-propyl ketone	$C_3H_7COC_3H_7$	145	133	75
Methyl n-amyl ketone	$CH_3COC_5H_{11}$	151	127	89
Cyclohexanone	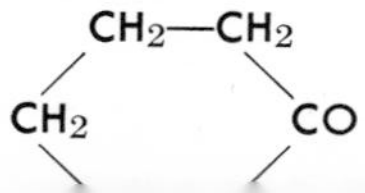 $\begin{array}{c}CH_2-CH_2\\ CH_2\qquad CO\\ CH_2-CH_2\end{array}$	155	166	162

Compound	Formula	m.p., °C	m.p. Semicarb, °C	m.p. 2,4-DNP, °C
2-methyl cyclohexanone	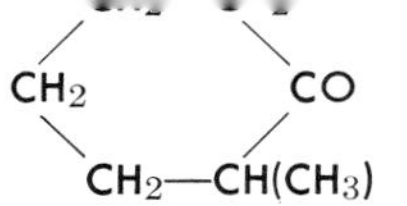 (ring) CO / CH$_2$—CH(CH$_3$) / CH$_2$ CH$_2$—CH$_2$	163	195	137
Di-isobutyl ketone	(CH$_3$)$_2$CHCH$_2$COCH$_2$CH(CH$_3$)$_2$	166	121	—
3-methyl cyclohexanone	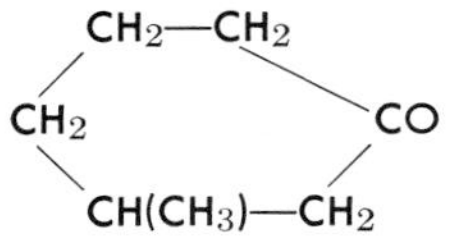 (ring) CO / CH$_2$ CH(CH$_3$)—CH$_2$ / CH$_2$—CH$_2$	169	180	—
4-methyl cyclohexanone	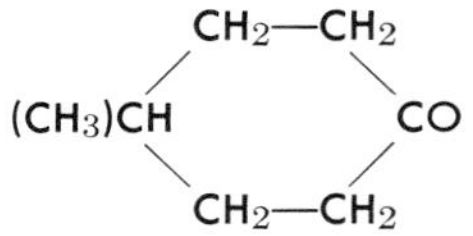 (ring) CO / CH$_2$—CH$_2$ / (CH$_3$)CH CH$_2$—CH$_2$	169	199	—
Methyl n-hexyl ketone	CH$_3$COC$_6$H$_{13}$	172	122	58
Cycloheptanone	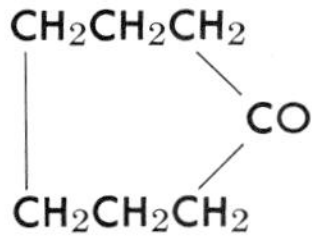 (ring) CO / CH$_2$CH$_2$CH$_2$ CH$_2$CH$_2$CH$_2$	181	163	148
Di-n-butyl ketone	C$_4$H$_9$COC$_4$H$_9$	187	90	—
Acetophenone	CH$_3$COC$_6$H$_5$	200	198	250
Benzyl methyl ketone	C$_6$H$_5$CH$_2$COCH$_3$	216	198	—
Propiophenone	C$_2$H$_5$COC$_6$H$_5$	218	174	—
Phenyl n-propyl ketone	C$_6$H$_5$COC$_3$H$_7$	220	184	—
Methyl p-tolyl ketone	CH$_3$COC$_6$H$_4$CH$_3$	222	205	—

KETONES, SOLID

Compound	Formula	m.p., °C	m.p. Semicarb, °C	m.p. 2,4-DNP, °C
Benzophenone	C$_6$H$_5$COC$_6$H$_5$	48	202	239

of this is to cause a reaction without a "molecular rearrangement," the term applied to a case such as that of the transformation of 1-butene into 2-butene cited in the preceding section. All organic structural "determinations" are carried on with the tacit hope that no molecular rearrangements have taken place during their course, and structures are said to be established, "barring molecular rearrangements." By making a special study of molecular rearrangements, however, organic chemists have learned about the conditions under which they are likely to occur and those under which they are rare or absent. This study has greatly added to the reliability of organic structural determinations.

The reaction of ozone with an olefin gives an ozonide. There has been some controversy about the structures of ozonides, particularly because they are explosive, making precise work with them difficult. The structure usually assigned is shown below.

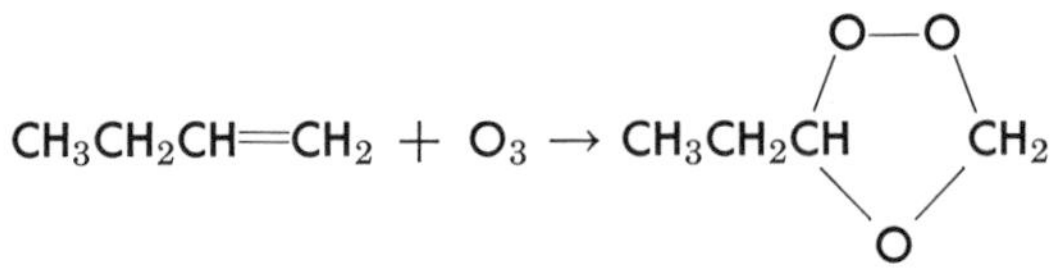

$$CH_3CH_2CH{=}CH_2 + O_3 \rightarrow CH_3CH_2\overset{O-O}{\underset{O}{CH \quad CH_2}}$$

Hydrolysis of an ozonide will not give a single set of products. The state of oxidation of an ozonide is midway between that of an aldehyde and an acid.

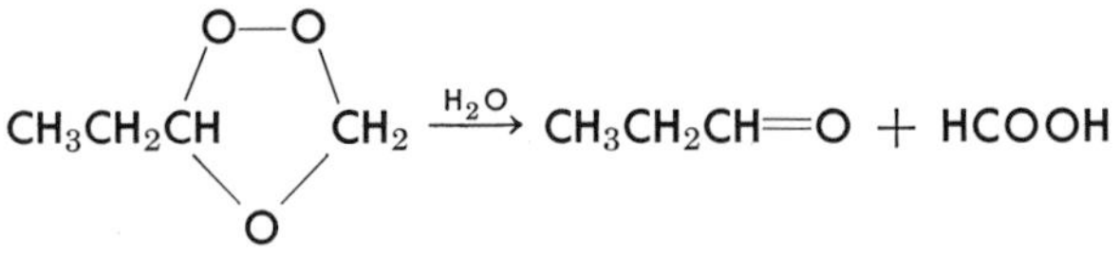

$$CH_3CH_2\overset{O-O}{\underset{O}{CH \quad CH_2}} \xrightarrow{H_2O} CH_3CH_2CH{=}O + HCOOH$$

To prevent the formation of a mixture, ozonides are worked up by a process called *reductive cleavage*. This hydrogenates the O—O linkage and forms two molecules of carbonyl compound instead of one of acid plus one of carbonyl. One reagent which has been used for this purpose is zinc and acetic acid but the reagent chosen is usually hydrogen with a platinum catalyst.

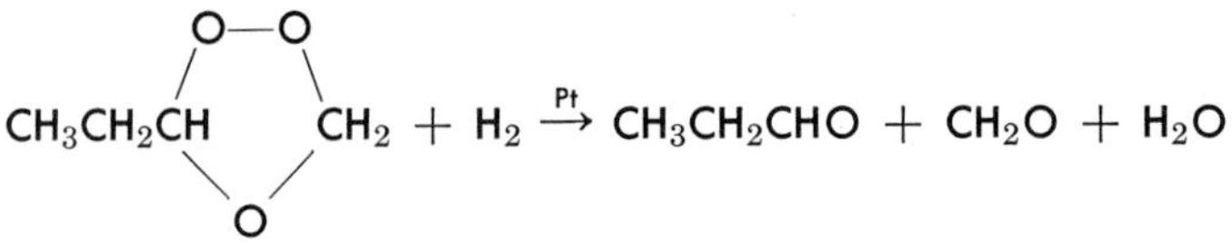

$$CH_3CH_2\overset{O-O}{\underset{O}{CH \quad CH_2}} + H_2 \xrightarrow{Pt} CH_3CH_2CHO + CH_2O + H_2O$$

Again, it will be seen that our structural problem has been reduced to the isolation and identification of the derivatives of carbonyl compounds, in this case of aldehydes. In addition to avoiding the possibility of a rearrangement, this structural reaction has the further advantage that the one-carbon fragment, formaldehyde, can be isolated, whereas for the acid oxidations it went off as a gas, either carbon monoxide or carbon dioxide. Historically, many structural determinations were made with the acidic reagents before the discovery of ozonolysis and even today there may be occasions when these reagents are desirable. When a question of rearrangement arises, however, ozonolysis is the method of choice in structural determinations.

11–6 Ketone Derivatives

For purposes of identification, Table 11–1 gives the physical properties of a group of ketones and their derivatives.

11–7 Aldehyde Derivatives

Table 11–2 gives the properties of selected aldehydes and their derivatives for purposes of identification.

Table 11–2. (a) ALDEHYDES, LIQUID

Compound	Formula	b.p., °C	m.p. Semicarb, °C	m.p. 2,4-DNP, °C
Formaldehyde	CH_2O	−21	169	166
Acetaldehyde	CH_3CHO	21	162	168
Propionaldehyde	C_2H_5CHO	50	89, 154	154
Glyoxal	$OHCCHO$	50	270	328
Isobutyraldehyde	$(CH_3)_2CHCHO$	64	125	182
n-butyraldehyde	C_3H_7CHO	74	106	122
Trimethylacetaldehyde	$(CH_3)_3CCHO$	74	191	210
Isovaleraldehyde	$(CH_3)_2CHCH_2CHO$	92	107	123
n-valeraldehyde	C_4H_9CHO	103	–	98
n-capronaldehyde	$C_5H_{11}CHO$	128	115	104
n-heptaldehyde	$C_6H_{13}CHO$	156	106	108
Benzaldehyde	C_6H_5CHO	179	222	237
Phenylacetaldehyde	$C_6H_5CH_2CHO$	194	156	121
m-tolualdehyde	$m\text{-}CH_3C_6H_4CHO$	199	204	–
o-tolualdehyde	$o\text{-}CH_3C_6H_4CHO$	200	218	–
p-tolualdehyde	$p\text{-}CH_3C_6H_4CHO$	204	234	234
o-chlorobenzaldehyde	$o\text{-}ClC_6H_4CHO$	208	225	207
m-chlorobenzaldehyde	$m\text{-}ClC_6H_4CHO$	208	228	–
Hydrocinnamaldehyde	$C_6H_5CH_2CH_2CHO$	224	127	–
Anisaldehyde	$p\text{-}CH_3OC_6H_4CHO$	247	203	254 (dec)

(b) ALDEHYDES, SOLID

Compound	Formula	m.p., °C	m.p. Semicarb, °C	m.p. 2,4-DNP, °C
o-Nitrobenzaldehyde	$o\text{-}NO_2C_6H_4CHO$	44	256	250 (dec)
p-Chlorobenzaldehyde	$p\text{-}ClC_6H_4CHO$	47	230	–
m-Nitrobenzaldehyde	$m\text{-}NO_2C_6H_4CHO$	58	246	293 (dec)
p-Nitrobenzaldehyde	$p\text{-}NO_2C_6H_4CHO$	106	221	320

As we have seen, it is characteristic of aldehydes that acidic dichromate or permanganate will oxidize them further to the corresponding acids.

$$C_2H_5CHO \xrightarrow[H_2SO_4]{CrO_3} C_2H_5COOH$$

For this reason, aldehydes are not isolated when structural determinations are performed with acidic oxidizing agents.

11–8   Structures of the Di-isobutylenes

We are now in a position to examine the structures of more complicated olefins. As an example, let us consider the so-called "di-isobutylenes."

Both 1-butene and 2-butene occur in the cracking gases from gasoline production along with isobutylene, $(CH_3)_2C{=}CH_2$. As indicated above, addition of water by means of sulfuric acid takes place more readily with the branched-chain olefin than with the straight. Advantage is taken of this fact to effect a separation and purification. The gases are first treated with a dilute sulfuric acid solution which removes the isobutylene. The hydration of isobutylene, according to the Markovnikov rule, yields tertiary butyl alcohol, $(CH_3)_3COH$. On dehydration with stronger sulfuric acid, tertiary butyl alcohol yields isobutylene, free from 1- and 2-butenes. When either tertiary butyl alcohol or isobutylene is allowed to stand with the sulfuric acid, however, a further reaction takes place and a mixture of di-isobutylenes is formed. Analysis shows that these have the formula C_8H_{16}. Thus the contact with sulfuric acid has caused the isobutylene to "dimerize."

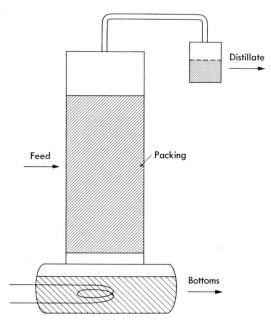

FIG. 11–2.   Commercial distilling column.

Fractionation of the di-isobutylenes shows that there are two hydrocarbons present, one boiling at 101.2°C, the other at 104.5°C. These can be separated in the excellent commercial stills that are industrially available for the purpose. (See Fig. 11–2.)

Oxidation of the mixed di-isobutylenes with dichromate and sulfuric acid yields several products of which the major one has the composition $C_7H_{14}O$. Since an aldehyde would be oxidized under the conditions of formation, this substance must be a ketone. Its boiling point is 124°C. It forms a semicarbazone melting at 176°C and a dinitrophenylhydrazone melting at 101°C. What is the ketone? (See Table 11–1.)

Ozonolysis of the liquid boiling at 101.2°C and subsequent formation of the semicarbazones yields a mixture of substances from which two crystalline products can be separated. One melts at 176°C and is identical with that prepared from the ketone made with dichromate-sulfuric acid. The other melts at 169°C. What is the structure of the liquid boiling at 101.2°?

Ozonolysis of the liquid boiling at 104.5°C and subsequent formation of the semicarbazones yields a mixture of substances from which two different crystalline products can be separated. One melts at 191°C and has the composition $C_6H_{13}ON_3$. The second melts at 187°C and has the composition $C_4H_9ON_3$. What is the structure of the liquid boiling at 104.5°?

Hydrogenation of the mixed di-isobutylenes yields a saturated hydrocarbon, C_8H_{18}. This material is prepared on a large scale commercially under the name "iso-octane," a misnomer, and is used as the standard for the determination of the anti-knock values for automotive fuels. What is the structure of "iso-octane" (Fig. 11–3)?

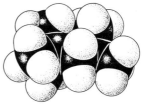

FIGURE 11–3

11-9   Example of Another Degradation

Suppose that a synthetic procedure produced a hydrocarbon analyzing for C_6H_{10}. What information does this analysis convey? Hydrogenation gives an uptake of two molecules of hydrogen with the formation of C_6H_{14}. What information does this convey? Oxidation with chromic-sulfuric acids yields a mixture of acids, one boiling at 118°C, the other at 163°C. The acid boiling at 118° gives a bromo-phenacyl ester melting at 85°, while the acid boiling at 163° gives a bromophenacyl ester melting at 63°. What is the structure of C_6H_{10}?

11-10   The Use of Synthesis in Structural Confirmations

The steps in establishing the structure of an unsaturated hydrocarbon involve not only its degradation but also its synthesis. The unknown sample must be prepared in the highest possible state of purity, and its physical constants established. Spectral data are then recorded for purposes of identification and comparison. After degradation has established the probable structure, the material is prepared by synthesis. The physical and chemical properties of the unknown and the synthetic material are then carefully compared and, in particular, the various spectra of the synthetic material are compared in detail with that of the unknown. Only after exhaustive comparisons of this sort can the structure be considered as established.

We have already encountered some methods for the synthesis of olefins. Others will be presented in the future in connection with types of compounds not yet met in this survey. One method of quite general application is by the alcoholic alkaline dehydrohalogenation of alkyl halides.

$$C_2H_5Br + KOH \xrightarrow{C_2H_5OH} C_2H_4 + KBr$$

In this reaction, as in the dehydration of alcohols, the Saytzev rule applies in most cases. Thus

$$(CH_3)_2CHCHBrCH_3 + KOH \xrightarrow{C_2H_5OH} (CH_3)_2C{=}CHCH_3 + KBr$$

This reaction can be extended to dihalides. Thus an aldehyde, on treatment with phosphorus pentachloride, yields a dichloride:

$$CH_3CH_2CHO + 2PCl_5 \rightarrow CH_3CH_2CHCl_2 + 2POCl_3 + 2HCl$$

On treatment with alcoholic KOH this will yield methyl acetylene.

$$CH_3CH_2CHCl_2 + KOH \xrightarrow{C_2H_5OH} CH_3C{\equiv}CH + 2KCl$$

Acetylene itself is prepared by a unique synthesis from lime and coke.

$$3C + CaO \xrightarrow{2000°} CO + CaC_2$$

The calcium carbide obtained in this manner is treated with water to yield acetylene.

$$CaC_2 + H_2O \rightarrow Ca(OH)_2 + HC{\equiv}CH$$

This method for the production of acetylene was extensively exploited by the Germans under Hitler when their autarkic policies led to the severance of trade relations with countries usually supplying them with other raw materials. Through the studies of Reppe and his research teams, numerous applications of acetylene to the synthesis of complex organic compounds were exploited industrially. Most of these reactions require equipment and precautions not usually available in a university laboratory so that simpler syntheses with acetylene are of interest here.

Acetylene is distinguished from olefinic hydrocarbons by its acidity and its reactivity with metallic ions. Thus cuprous ammonia complex or argentous ammonia complex will react with acetylene to give a precipitate of the corresponding cuprous or argentous acetylide. These reactions can be carried out easily for purposes of identification. Care must be taken with the products, however, since both of these heavy metal acetylides are explosive when dry. On the other hand, treatment of acetylene in liquid ammonia with metallic sodium or potassium or with the amides yields the corresponding alkali metal acetylides. These substances are not explosive when dry and can be used in organic synthesis.

$$HC{\equiv}CH + Na \rightarrow NaC{\equiv}CH + \tfrac{1}{2}H_2$$

$$NaC{\equiv}CH + Na \rightarrow NaC{\equiv}CNa + \tfrac{1}{2}H_2$$

$$CH_3I + NaC{\equiv}CH \rightarrow CH_3C{\equiv}CH + NaI$$

$$2CH_3I + NaC{\equiv}CNa \rightarrow CH_3C{\equiv}CCH_3 + 2NaI$$

An important commercial application of acetylene is in the preparation of acetaldehyde.

$$HC{\equiv}CH + H_2O \xrightarrow[\text{H}_2\text{SO}_4]{\text{HgSO}_4} [CH_3CH(OH)_2] \rightarrow CH_3CHO + H_2O$$

Most substances with two hydroxyl groups on the same carbon are found to lose water spontaneously. Because of its low boiling point, the acetaldehyde distills out as it is formed. It will be seen that this double hydration reaction follows Markovnikov's rule at each step. Likewise, the addition of HBr to acetylene follows Markovnikov's rule.

$$HC{\equiv}CH + 2HBr \rightarrow H_3CCH(Br)_2$$

For purposes of identification, substituted acetylenes having one hydrogen linked to the acetylenic group will react with cuprous or argentous ammonia solutions to give precipitates of the metal acetylides. Dialkylacetylenes, on the other hand, will not undergo this reaction.

PROBLEMS

11–1 The common names for most of the aldehydes and ketones which have common names are given in Tables 11–1 and 11–2. You should be able to formulate a set of rules for many of the trivial names listed.

The IUPAC names for aldehydes are made by dropping the -e from the hydrocarbon name and adding -al. Ketones add -one after dropping -e. The examples given below will illustrate the procedure.

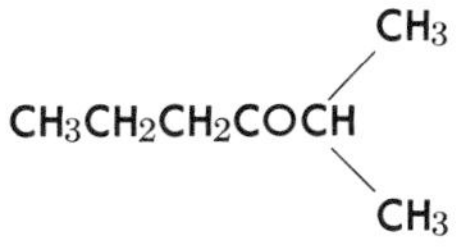

$$CH_3CH_2CH_2CO\overset{\displaystyle CH_3}{\underset{\displaystyle CH_3}{CH}}$$ $$CH_3CH{=}CHCH_2CH_2CHO$$ $$HOCH_2CH_2CH_2COCH_2COCH_3$$

2-methylhexanone-3   Hex-4-enal   1-hydroxyheptane-4,6-dione

Name the following compounds given in Tables 11–1 and 11–2 by the IUPAC rules.

(a) Diacetyl   (b) Pinacolone   (c) Acetylacetone   (d) Hydrocinnamaldehyde

Which of the following compounds are incorrectly named?

$$\text{CH}_3$$
$$/$$
(e) $\text{CH}_3\text{COCH}_2\text{CH}_2\text{CCl}$ (f) $\text{CH}_2=\text{CHCOCH}_2\text{CH}_2\text{CH}_2\text{OH}$
$$\backslash$$
$$\text{CH}_3$$

5-chloro-5-methylhexanone-2   6-hydroxyhept-1-en-3-one

(g) $\text{C}_6\text{H}_5\text{CH}=\text{CH}-\text{CH}=\text{CH}-\text{CH}=\text{CH}-\text{CHO}$

7-phenylhept-2,4,6-trienal

11–2 Isoprene can be obtained by the pyrolysis of rubber and of many other naturally occurring compounds. Its formula is C_5H_8. A careful hydrogenation was performed on it with the following results.

$$100\text{C}_5\text{H}_8 \rightarrow 30\text{C}_5\text{H}_{12} \ (A) + 15\text{C}_5\text{H}_{10} \ (B) + 13\text{C}_5\text{H}_{10} \ (C) + 12\text{C}_5\text{H}_{10} \ (D)$$
$$+ \ 30\text{C}_5\text{H}_8 \ \text{(unchanged)}$$

(a) What information about the structure of isoprene does the formation of A give?

(b) Ozonolysis of B followed by treatment with 2,4-dinitrophenylhydrazine gave two compounds with melting points of 168°C and 126°C. What is B?

(c) Ozonolysis of C followed by formation of 2,4-dinitrophenylhydrazone derivatives gave two compounds, melting points 166°C and 111°C. What is C?

(d) Ozonolysis of D followed by formation of 2,4-dinitrophenylhydrazone derivatives gave two compounds, melting points 166°C and 182°C. What is D?

(e) From these data, can you suggest a reasonable structural formula for isoprene?

(f) What would be the reaction of isoprene with hydrogen to yield B?

(g) What is the structure of A?

11–3 A solid organic compound, melting point 45 to 46°C, was obtained by extraction of the roots of *Angelica archangelica*. Analysis pointed to the formula $\text{C}_5\text{H}_8\text{O}_2$. Mild hydrogenation yielded $\text{C}_5\text{H}_{10}\text{O}_2$, and the resulting compound was soluble in dilute aqueous alkali.

When the original natural product was ozonized and the reaction worked up under reducing conditions, two materials were formed. One of the semicarbazones prepared after separation of the mixture melted at 162°C; the other, whose analysis fit the formula $\text{C}_4\text{H}_7\text{O}_3\text{N}_3$, did not melt sharply but decomposed at about 200°C.

A compound identical to the latter was prepared by the following route. Acetyl chloride in ether solution was treated with anhydrous hydrogen cyanide and pyridine (cf., the reaction of methyl iodide with cyanide, Section 4–4) and the resulting compound was hydrolyzed in aqueous acid. After very careful isolation, the product was characterized by reaction with semicarbazide and gave the same $\text{C}_4\text{H}_7\text{O}_3\text{N}_3$ mentioned above. How useful would a mixed melting point determination be in this case?

How much of the structure of the natural product can you determine from this information? Is it surprising to learn that another compound, melting point 64°C, isolated after hydrolysis of the glycerides of *Croton tiglium*, gave exactly the same products as described above?

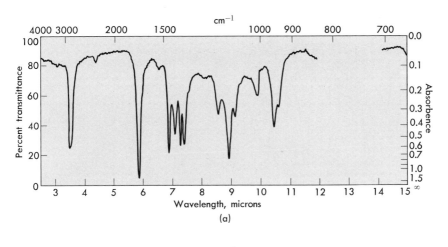

(a)

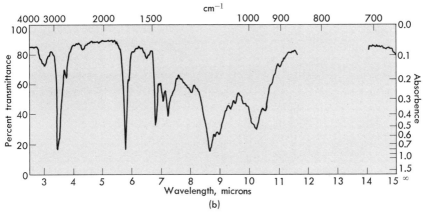

(b)

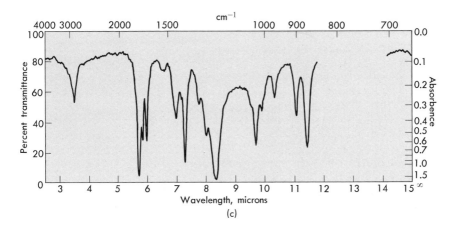

(c)

FIG. 11–4. (a) Diethyl ketone, (b) n-butyraldehyde, (c) isopropenyl acetate.

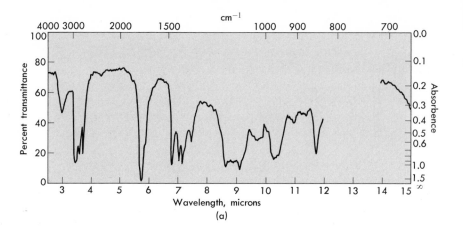

(a)

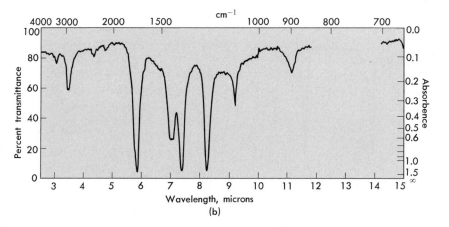

(b)

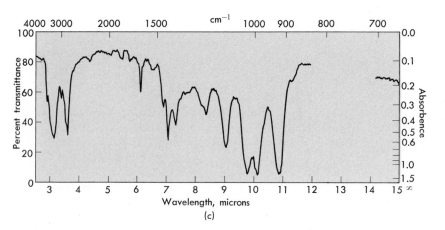

(c)

FIGURE 11–5

11-4 A compound $C_{18}H_{32}O_2$, melting point 50°C, isolated by hydrolysis of the glycerides from the seed fat of a Guatemalan tree, *Picramnia tariri*, was found to yield lauric and adipic acids on oxidation.

(a) Considering the method of isolation, what would be a likely functional group in this compound?

(b) What must the structure be from the oxidation data?

(c) Devise a synthetic method to prove or disprove your answer to part (b). Bear in mind that carboxylic acids are stronger acids than any hydrocarbon you could properly employ.

11-5 The absorption of carbonyl groups in the infrared is one of the most frequently used data in the research laboratory. Not only are carbonyl absorptions sharp and intense, but they occur in a region of the spectrum where very little else absorbs. The precise frequency of the carbonyl group is dependent on its nature: thus aliphatic aldehydes absorb at 5.7 to 5.8 and ketones at 5.8 to 5.85 microns; acids at 5.8 to 5.85 microns; esters at 5.7 to 5.75 microns. (These figures pertain to saturated aliphatic compounds only.) The latter two may be differentiated from the former by other vibrations, for example, the very characteristic O—H absorption of carboxylic acids, and the single bond C—O of acids and esters.

The spectra presented in Figs. 11–4 and 11–5 were recorded using about 2% solutions of the compound in carbon tetrachloride. This is a particularly useful solvent, since CCl_4 itself absorbs strongly only from about 12 to 14 microns, leaving the rest of the spectrum "open" for observation of solute absorptions. In these spectra the region of interference has been left blank.

In the spectrum of diethyl ketone, Fig. 11–4(a), there is a strong carbonyl absorption at 5.8 microns. We could decide that this is an aliphatic ketone from the following data:

It cannot be an acid (no O—H stretch at 2.7 to 2.8).

It cannot be an ester (no strong absorption for C—O from 9.5 to 10.0).

It cannot be an aldehyde (see below).

The region is not characteristic of other types of carbonyl groups.

The spectrum of butyraldehyde likewise shows a characteristic carbonyl absorption at 5.8 microns. The C—H stretching region shows, in addition to the usual strong peak at 3.5, another sharp peak at 3.8, which is characteristic for the H—C of the aldehyde group. No other group absorbs in this region so sharply.

There is a small, broad O—H peak in this spectrum and a side peak on the main carbonyl peak. Aldehydes are known to be unstable to air; they are oxidized slowly to carboxylic acids. It is likely that this sample contained a small amount of the corresponding oxidation product. What would that be?

The spectrum of isopropenyl acetate shows an ester carbonyl absorption at 5.7. In addition, there is a sharp C=C absorption at 6.0 microns, at a slightly longer wavelength than the aliphatic carbonyl region. This is not intense, but nevertheless is fairly characteristic of a carbon-carbon double bond. Many double bonds absorb either weakly or not at all; we shall see later why this is so.

Figure 11–5 shows three spectra of liquids recorded as 2% solutions in CCl_4. Each of these compounds has the empirical formula C_3H_6O. By using the characteristic absorption patterns from the preceding three spectra, you should be able to write reasonable structures for the three compounds. One further bit of information: the structure CH_3—CH=CHOH is not stable under these conditions.

*What classes of reactions do alkylmagnesium
halides undergo? How may these reactions be adapted to
structural determination? What
syntheses may be performed with their aid?*

12

THE GRIGNARD REAGENT;
ITS USE IN SYNTHESES AND
STRUCTURAL DETERMINATIONS

12-1 Organozinc Compounds

In the 1840's Wurtz, Bunsen, Frankland and others attempted to prepare free
radicals by numerous methods. In 1849 Frankland attempted to prepare free ethyl
radicals by reacting ethyl iodide with a zinc-copper couple. He found that he could
isolate ethyl zinc iodide from the reaction $C_2H_5I + Zn(Cu) \rightarrow C_2H_5ZnI$. On
heating, this compound would disproportionate to form diethyl zinc and zinc
iodide.

$$2C_2H_5ZnI \rightarrow (C_2H_5)_2Zn + ZnI_2$$

Diethyl zinc is a colorless liquid boiling at 118°C. By a similar process it was
found possible to prepare dimethyl zinc, a colorless liquid boiling at 46°C. These
substances are extremely reactive and for many years they were used by organic
chemists for synthetic purposes. Both substances are toxic and spontaneously
inflammable in the air, so that working with them is a hazardous task. A standard
laboratory test to determine the fitness of a candidate to undertake doctoral
research was to complete a preparation successfully with one of these two substances. The materials are self-testing: the candidate does not have to be told by
the instructor when he fails the test.

12-2 Grignard Reagents

Fifty years after Frankland's discovery, Barbier found that alkyl zincs could be
replaced in synthetic reactions by using a mixture of an alkyl halide in ether with
magnesium metal and the substance with which it was desired to effect a reaction.

The next year, 1900, his pupil Victor Grignard improved and simplified the method by allowing the reaction between the alkyl halide and the magnesium to proceed to completion in the ether before the addition of the second organic reagent. This *Grignard reaction* strictly paralleled the zinc reaction discovered by Frankland a half-century earlier.

$$CH_3I + Mg \xrightarrow{\text{ether}} CH_3MgI$$

The Grignard reaction has proved to be one of the most useful synthetic tools available to the organic chemist and has remained a subject of intense research efforts during the entire twentieth century to date. It will well repay study.

Grignard reagents react with water and with atmospheric carbon dioxide, as well as with oxygen, more slowly. For these reasons, moisture and air must be excluded to obtain the best yields. The reaction is performed in sharply dried ether, and it is advantageous to perform a preliminary drying operation on all the glassware intended for use in the reaction. In ordinary practice, air is partially excluded by keeping the ether at the boil during the reaction, but in critical cases a stream of dry nitrogen is passed over the reaction mixture. A drying tube is always used beyond the condenser to exclude moisture and carbon dioxide. The alkyl halide is also sharply dried. If these precautions are observed, the reaction with dried magnesium turnings usually starts without difficulty. In some cases, however, a catalyst is desirable and a small crystal of iodine may be used for this purpose. In general, iodides start more readily than bromides which, in turn, react more readily than chlorides, although the yields may be in the reverse order. Methyl and ethyl iodides are commonly employed because of the greater volatility of the bromides and chlorides. In the aromatic series, bromobenzene is usually used.

12–3   Syntheses with Grignard Reagents

The synthetic reactions of Grignard reagents are numerous. Only a few examples will be given here.

One of the most useful reactions of Grignard reagents is with carbonyl compounds. With formaldehyde, it is possible to prepare primary alcohols with one more carbon than the alkyl halide.

$$CH_3MgI + CH_2O \rightarrow CH_3CH_2OMgI$$

$$CH_3CH_2OMgI + HCl \rightarrow CH_3CH_2OH + MgICl$$

Because of the violence of the reaction with HCl, the second hydrolysis is frequently performed with aqueous ammonium chloride. This is sufficiently acidic to carry the reaction to completion in most cases.

It will be noted that the characteristic of the Grignard reagent is to form a new carbon-carbon bond by the attack of the carbon of the reagent on the carbon

of the carbonyl group. The same reaction proceeds with higher aldehydes with
the formation of secondary alcohols.

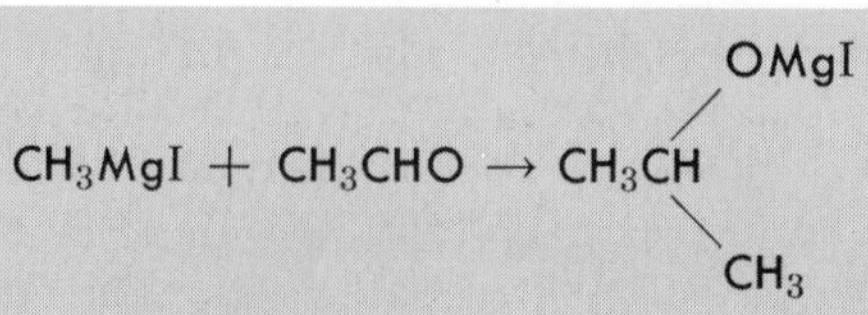

$$CH_3MgI + CH_3CHO \rightarrow CH_3CH \begin{smallmatrix} OMgI \\ \\ CH_3 \end{smallmatrix}$$

$$(CH_3)_2CHOMgI + H_2O \xrightarrow{NH_4Cl} (CH_3)_2CHOH + Mg(OH)I$$

With esters, the reaction proceeds further. Since esters have a carbonyl group,
we should expect the first reaction to be an attack at the carbonyl group similar
to that occurring with aldehydes and ketones. Indeed, when the reaction is run
at dry ice temperatures, this is the reaction that takes place.

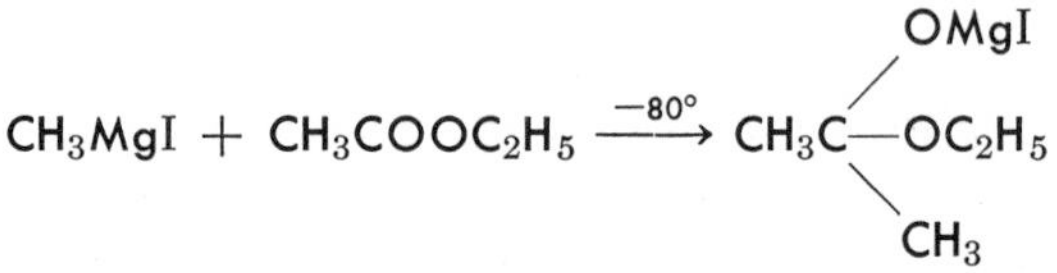

$$CH_3MgI + CH_3COOC_2H_5 \xrightarrow{-80°} CH_3C \begin{smallmatrix} OMgI \\ \\ CH_3 \end{smallmatrix} OC_2H_5$$

At ordinary reaction temperatures, however, a second reaction occurs. The Grignard
reagent is such a powerful base that it is capable of cleaving highly reactive C—O—C
bonds of the type formed in this intermediate.

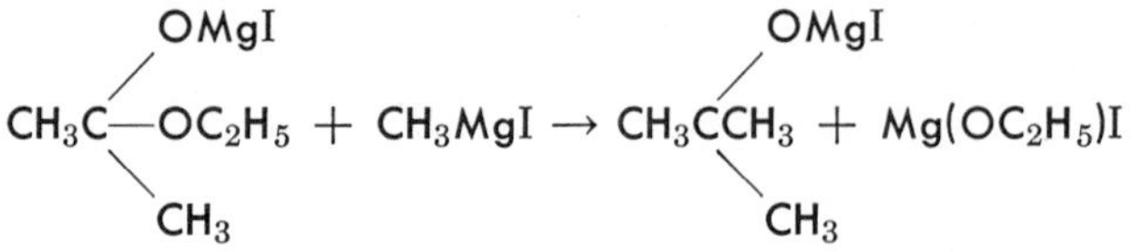

$$CH_3C \begin{smallmatrix} OMgI \\ \\ CH_3 \end{smallmatrix} OC_2H_5 + CH_3MgI \rightarrow CH_3C \begin{smallmatrix} OMgI \\ \\ CH_3 \end{smallmatrix} CH_3 + Mg(OC_2H_5)I$$

$$(CH_3)_3COMgI + H_2O \rightarrow (CH_3)_3COH + Mg(OH)I$$

A variety of tertiary alcohols can be formed by this reaction. Thus the Grignard
reaction makes it possible to prepare primary, secondary, and tertiary alcohols in
great numbers. It should be noted in passing that this reaction provides confirmatory evidence of the presence of a carbonyl group in ethyl acetate and thus
in acetic acid.

The reaction of Grignard reagents with carbon dioxide can be utilized to prepare
carboxylic acids.

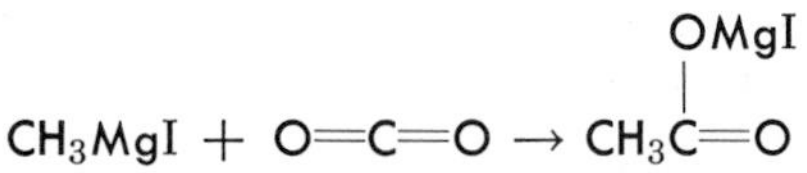

$$CH_3MgI + O{=}C{=}O \rightarrow CH_3C \begin{smallmatrix} OMgI \\ | \\ {=}O \end{smallmatrix}$$

$$CH_3COOMgI + HCl \rightarrow CH_3COOH + MgClI$$

12–4 "Active Hydrogen" Determinations

For the purposes of structural investigations, one of the most useful reactions of Grignard reagents is the reaction with so-called "active hydrogens," that is, hydrogens reactive to the Grignard reagent. Such hydrogens are the acidic hydrogens of water, alcohols, ammonia and amines, mineral acids, carboxylic acids.

$$CH_3MgI + H_2O \rightarrow CH_4 + Mg(OH)I$$

$$CH_3MgI + CH_3OH \rightarrow CH_4 + Mg(OCH_3)I$$

$$CH_3MgI + CH_3NH_2 \rightarrow CH_4 + Mg(NHCH_3)I$$

$$CH_3MgI + HCl \rightarrow CH_4 + MgClI$$

$$CH_3MgI + CH_3COOH \rightarrow CH_4 + Mg(OCOCH_3)I$$

Accordingly, the Grignard reaction provides a means for going from an alkyl halide to the corresponding alkane.

This reaction of Grignard reagents with active hydrogens makes it possible to estimate quantitatively the number of such reactive groups in an unknown compound. The procedure was first used by Chugaev and was developed and refined by his student Zerevitinov. For this reason it is referred to as the *Zerevitinov active hydrogen determination*. A simplified form of the apparatus used is sketched in Fig. 12–1. For the purpose of the determination, a high-boiling ether is substituted for ethyl ether to permit the removal of the methane formed without serious contamination by the volatility of the ether. Isoamyl ether is frequently used for this purpose.

In this apparatus, the Grignard reagent is introduced into one leg and the unknown into the second leg. After equilibration with the stopcock open, the stopcock is closed and the contents of the two legs are mixed. Methane is evolved and the amount is read in the gas burette. After reduction to standard conditions, the weight of methane evolved from a given weight of the sample may be calculated and from this the total amount of "active hydrogen" in the sample estimated.

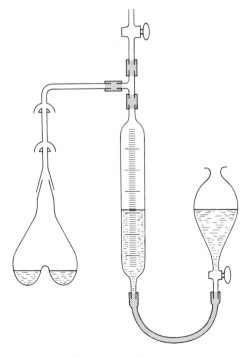

FIG. 12–1. Zerevitinov apparatus.

A refinement of the Zerevitinov apparatus was introduced by Kohler and his students in the so-called "Grignard machine." This apparatus permits both the amount of active hydrogen evolved and the amount of Grignard reagent consumed to be estimated. Preliminary standardization of the reagent with water permits the strength of the reagent to be determined. When the amount of reagent added is known, the amount of methane evolved by reaction with the unknown is measured and subtracted from the total available. After the reaction is complete, the residual reagent is then determined by liberating methane with water. Any reagent used by the unknown for reactions other than the liberation of methane may then be calculated. An example may clarify the procedure.

Let us suppose that we were to treat hydroxyacetone with methyl magnesium iodide in a Grignard machine. We might add three equivalents of reagent initially. Then we would have the following situation:

$$3CH_3MgI + CH_3COCH_2OH \rightarrow CH_4 + CH_3C(OMgI)CH_2OMgI + 1CH_3MgI \quad (1)$$
$$|$$
$$CH_3$$

After this reaction was carried to completion and the methane measured, water would be added. This would react with the residual Grignard reagent to form additional methane.

$$1CH_3MgI + H_2O \rightarrow CH_4 + Mg(OH)I \quad (2)$$

From reaction (1) we find that the number of active hydrogens in the unknown (hydroxyacetone) is one. From reaction (2) we find that there is one mole of residual reagent after the reaction. But since three moles were taken originally and only two have been accounted for as methane, one was used in a reaction with another group, in this case a ketone group. It is obvious that either an aldehyde or a ketone would use one mole of reagent while an ester would use two.

12–5   The Barbier-Wieland Degradation

The use of the Zerevitinov determination and the Grignard machine gives two powerful tools for the investigation of functional groups present in unknown substances. The Zerevitinov determination, in particular, has been widely used in structural determinations. Findings made in this manner can now be confirmed by infrared determinations, which add still more to the information available on an unknown. One further use of the Grignard reagent in structural determinations has also proved of great value. This is the use of phenylmagnesium bromide in the systematic degradation of acids, aldehydes, or ketones to determine their structures.

As complex natural products were degraded, acids or ketones would frequently be encountered whose structures had not been determined. Hence the observation of the physical properties of their derivatives would not provide sufficient evidence for their structural determinations. A method was required which would permit these to be taken apart a step at a time until a known substance was finally obtained. Such a method was devised from the materials that we have already encountered in our survey.

We have seen that tertiary alcohols are dehydrated to olefins in the presence of sulfuric acid and that subsequent treatment with chromic acid then cleaves the double bond. If the tertiary alcohol were one made with an aliphatic Grignard reagent, there would be alternative positions at which the dehydration could occur. Let us suppose that we had treated ethyl butyrate with ethyl magnesium iodide.

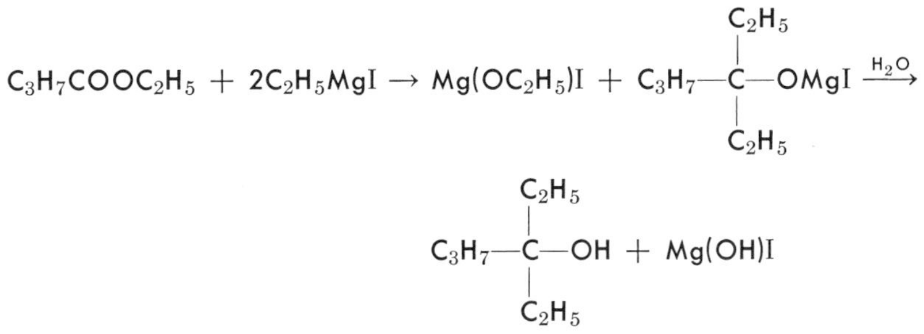

$$C_3H_7COOC_2H_5 + 2C_2H_5MgI \rightarrow Mg(OC_2H_5)I + C_3H_7-\underset{\underset{C_2H_5}{|}}{\overset{\overset{C_2H_5}{|}}{C}}-OMgI \xrightarrow{H_2O}$$

$$C_3H_7-\underset{\underset{C_2H_5}{|}}{\overset{\overset{C_2H_5}{|}}{C}}-OH + Mg(OH)I$$

The 3-ethylhexanol-3 formed by the condensation could then dehydrate to form either 3-ethylhexene-3 or 3-ethylhexene-2.

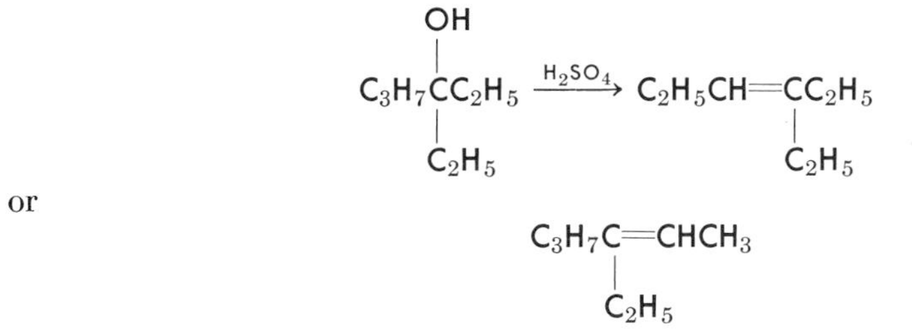

$$C_3H_7\underset{\underset{C_2H_5}{|}}{\overset{\overset{OH}{|}}{C}}C_2H_5 \xrightarrow{H_2SO_4} C_2H_5CH=\underset{\underset{C_2H_5}{|}}{C}C_2H_5$$

or

$$C_3H_7\underset{\underset{C_2H_5}{|}}{C}=CHCH_3$$

This type of alternative can be blocked and the direction of dehydration forced by the use of a Grignard reagent that has no hydrogen attached to the magnesium-bearing carbon. Such a group is the phenyl group. Thus in the reaction

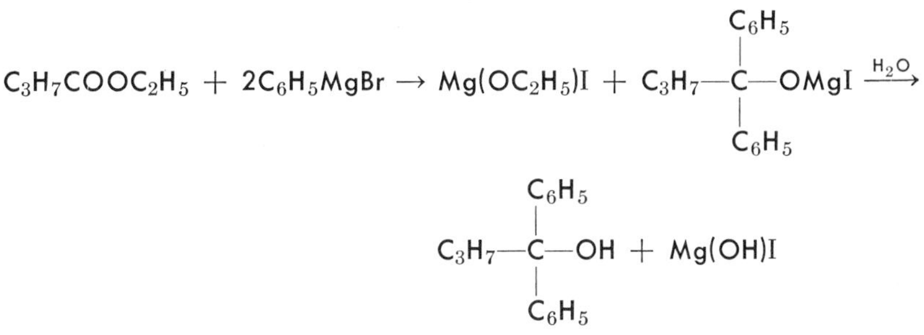

$$C_3H_7COOC_2H_5 + 2C_6H_5MgBr \rightarrow Mg(OC_2H_5)I + C_3H_7-\underset{\underset{C_6H_5}{|}}{\overset{\overset{C_6H_5}{|}}{C}}-OMgI \xrightarrow{H_2O}$$

$$C_3H_7-\underset{\underset{C_6H_5}{|}}{\overset{\overset{C_6H_5}{|}}{C}}-OH + Mg(OH)I$$

a tertiary alcohol is formed that can only dehydrate in one direction, shown below:

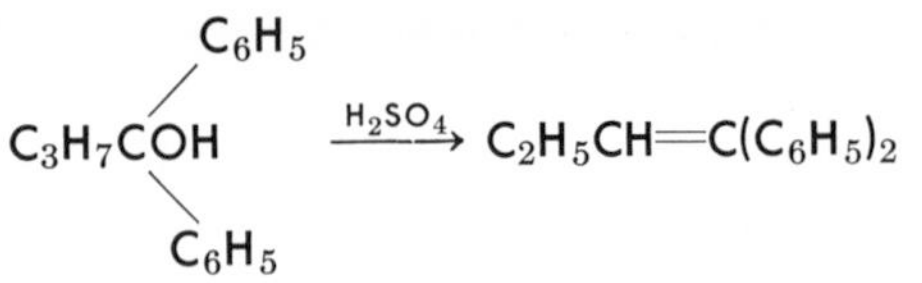

$$C_3H_7\underset{\overset{|}{C_6H_5}}{\overset{\overset{C_6H_5}{|}}{C}}OH \xrightarrow{H_2SO_4} C_2H_5CH\!=\!C(C_6H_5)_2$$

This product, on oxidation with chromic acid, can yield only propionic acid and benzophenone.

$$C_2H_5CH\!=\!C(C_6H_5)_2 \xrightarrow[H_2SO_4]{CrO_3} C_2H_5COOH + (C_6H_5)_2CO$$

Because of its excellent tendency to crystallize, benzophenone is easily separated from the oxidation mixture, even in cases in which the other product is a ketone. This series of reactions has thus produced an acid with one carbon fewer than the acid whose ester was originally used. By esterification and repetition of the degradation, another carbon can be removed and a systematic, step-by-step degradation performed. This process is known as the *Barbier-Wieland degradation*.

A point of branching in the chain will lead to the formation of a ketone instead of an acid.

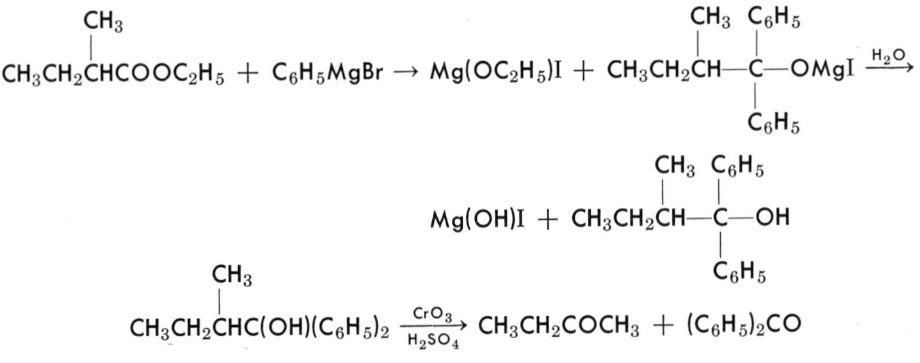

$$CH_3CH_2\underset{\overset{|}{CH_3}}{CH}COOC_2H_5 + C_6H_5MgBr \rightarrow Mg(OC_2H_5)I + CH_3CH_2\underset{\overset{|}{C_6H_5}}{\overset{\overset{CH_3}{|}}{CH}}\!-\!\underset{}{\overset{\overset{C_6H_5}{|}}{C}}\!-\!OMgI \xrightarrow{H_2O}$$

$$Mg(OH)I + CH_3CH_2\underset{\overset{|}{C_6H_5}}{\overset{\overset{CH_3}{|}}{CH}}\!-\!\overset{\overset{C_6H_5}{|}}{C}\!-\!OH$$

$$CH_3CH_2\underset{\overset{|}{CH_3}}{CH}C(OH)(C_6H_5)_2 \xrightarrow[H_2SO_4]{CrO_3} CH_3CH_2COCH_3 + (C_6H_5)_2CO$$

Another repetition of the reaction would then continue the degradation.

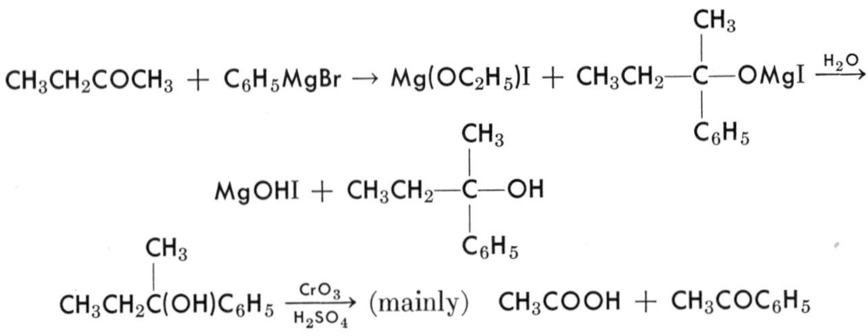

$$CH_3CH_2COCH_3 + C_6H_5MgBr \rightarrow Mg(OC_2H_5)I + CH_3CH_2\!-\!\underset{\overset{|}{C_6H_5}}{\overset{\overset{CH_3}{|}}{C}}\!-\!OMgI \xrightarrow{H_2O}$$

$$MgOHI + CH_3CH_2\!-\!\underset{\overset{|}{C_6H_5}}{\overset{\overset{CH_3}{|}}{C}}\!-\!OH$$

$$CH_3CH_2\underset{\overset{|}{CH_3}}{C}(OH)C_6H_5 \xrightarrow[H_2SO_4]{CrO_3} \text{(mainly)}\quad CH_3COOH + CH_3COC_6H_5$$

In the latter reaction, the dehydration preceding oxidation could have proceeded in either direction, formally, but reference to the Saytzev rule would indicate that the major products would be those shown.

The Barbier-Wieland degradation has been extensively used in establishing the structures of complex natural products, especially in the field of substances related to the sex hormones, vitamin D, cholesterol and other steroids.

12–6   Syntheses of Alcohols and Olefins

The foregoing reactions of Grignard reagents supply us with tools for the preparation and structural determinations of nearly all the materials that we have dealt with up to this point. For example, in Problem 8–6, 2-pentene was used for hydrogenation. This could be prepared as follows:

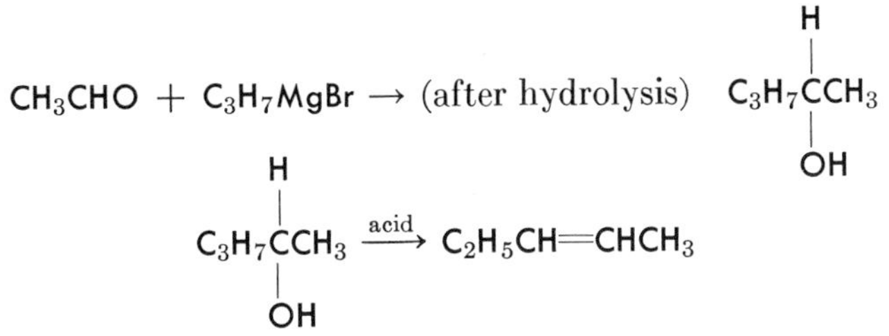

$$CH_3CHO + C_3H_7MgBr \rightarrow \text{ (after hydrolysis) } \underset{\underset{OH}{|}}{\overset{\overset{H}{|}}{C_3H_7CCH_3}}$$

$$\underset{\underset{OH}{|}}{\overset{\overset{H}{|}}{C_3H_7CCH_3}} \xrightarrow{acid} C_2H_5CH{=}CHCH_3$$

or

$$C_2H_5CHO + C_2H_5MgI \rightarrow \text{ (after hydrolysis) } C_2H_5CH(OH)C_2H_5$$

$$C_2H_5CH(OH)C_2H_5 \xrightarrow{acid} C_2H_5CH{=}CHCH_3$$

Which of the dehydration reactions would you expect to proceed with the higher yield?

In Problem 8–1(a), the compound shown at the right was given.

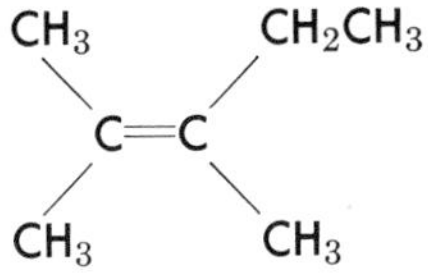

$$\underset{CH_3}{\overset{CH_3}{{\Large\diagdown}}} C{=}C \underset{CH_3}{\overset{CH_2CH_3}{{\Large\diagup}}}$$

This compound could be prepared by either of the following reactions:

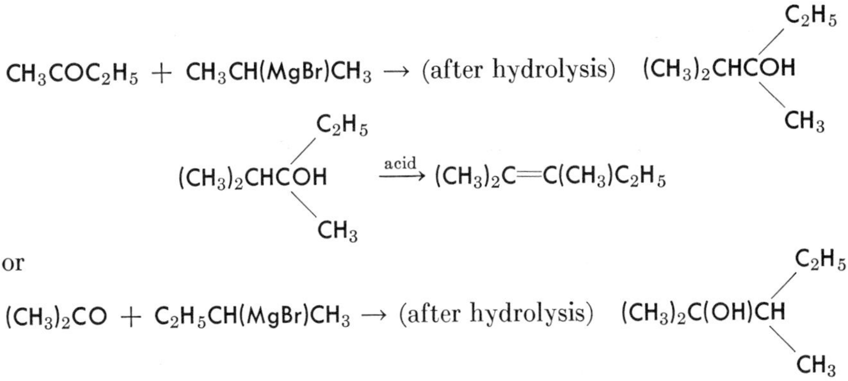

$$CH_3COC_2H_5 + CH_3CH(MgBr)CH_3 \rightarrow \text{ (after hydrolysis) } (CH_3)_2CHC\underset{CH_3}{\overset{C_2H_5}{{\Large\diagup}}}OH$$

$$(CH_3)_2CHC\underset{CH_3}{\overset{C_2H_5}{{\Large\diagup}}}OH \xrightarrow{acid} (CH_3)_2C{=}C(CH_3)C_2H_5$$

or

$$(CH_3)_2CO + C_2H_5CH(MgBr)CH_3 \rightarrow \text{ (after hydrolysis) } (CH_3)_2C(OH)\underset{CH_3}{\overset{C_2H_5}{{\Large\diagup}}}CH$$

12–7 Planning an Organic Synthesis

If a chemist has completed a structural determination by methods involving degradation, the next step in confirming the structural assignment will be the synthesis of the compound. In addition to this, many other reasons exist for undertaking syntheses. One of the most frequently recurring of these reasons is that a material with a certain structure has, or is thought to have, properties that are desirable. It may be that a substance obtained from a natural source is so rare as to be prohibitively expensive. In this case, a synthetic preparation may make it available cheaply and in quantity. Whatever the reason, the organic chemist must be prepared to undertake syntheses, either simple or complex, as a regular part of his work.

As a rule, the best approach to a synthetic problem is backward, from the product back toward available starting materials. The reader should write the formula for the final product and recall as many ways as possible to arrive at it with a single reaction. Such a final reaction might not involve a change in the number of carbon atoms. Thus it might be a hydrogenation, dehydrogenation, halogenation, dehalogenation, hydrohalogenation, hydration, dehydration, or other similar reaction. On the other hand, means may exist for preparing the compound from carbon compounds with fewer carbons or even by cleavage of a substance with more carbons. After a number of possible alternatives have been found, each of these compounds is submitted, in turn, to the same process which will thus ultimately lead back to simple or readily available starting materials.

If a synthesis involves many steps, the deciding factor in the choice of a synthetic route may well be the yield to be obtained in the successive steps. Even with high yields, the overall yield falls rapidly as the number of steps increases. Thus a four-step synthesis in which each step gave 50% yield would give an overall yield of $(\frac{1}{2})^4$ or 6.25%. A three-step synthesis in which each yield is 80% would give a 51% yield overall and thus a twelve-step synthesis with each yield 80% would give 6.87% overall. Some complicated syntheses require many more steps than twelve, so high yields are essential to a successful outcome.

In planning a multistep synthesis, the research chemist is often faced with a dilemma. The steps in his synthesis whose results are most problematical will usually occur toward the end of the synthesis. Initial condensations will usually be performed on relatively simple substances whose chemistry is better understood. As a result, he will be forced to do his most difficult experimentation on materials which are themselves the results of multistep syntheses and therefore only available in small quantity. One method for resolving this dilemma may be to design parallel reactions for the unknown steps on materials as closely related to the unknown substances as possible.

In the work which follows, stress will be laid on developing facility with the design of alternative syntheses so that the reader will be in a position to choose the most feasible route to the end product.

PROBLEMS

12-1 Using appropriate Grignard reagents, show how the following compounds could be prepared:

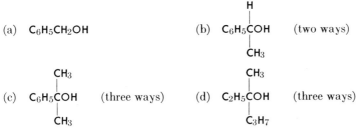

(a) $C_6H_5CH_2OH$

(b) $C_6H_5\overset{\displaystyle H}{\underset{\displaystyle CH_3}{C}}OH$ (two ways)

(c) $C_6H_5\overset{\displaystyle CH_3}{\underset{\displaystyle CH_3}{C}}OH$ (three ways)

(d) $C_2H_5\overset{\displaystyle CH_3}{\underset{\displaystyle C_3H_7}{C}}OH$ (three ways)

12-2 Occasionally it is necessary to prepare simple molecules with labels in various positions to test theories of structure and reactivity. How might the following deuterated ethanol molecules be synthesized? You may assume the availability of any necessary starting material.

(a) CH_3CD_2OH (b) CD_3CH_2OH (c) CH_3CH_2OD

(d) How might you prepare the following?

(e) If H_2SO_4 were used in this step, would you be surprised to find a small amount of

admixed, even though the alcohol used at the beginning was isotopically pure?

12-3 Magnesium metal was added to a solution of C_3H_7Br (A) in refluxing ether. When nothing happened, a crystal of iodine was added to the reaction mixture. After scratching the surface of the magnesium, an exothermic reaction occurred, yielding C_3H_7MgBr. To this an ether solution of $C_9H_{10}O_2$ (B) was added, and the reaction product was hydrolyzed with concentrated aqueous ammonium chloride. Careful purification yielded $C_{13}H_{20}O$ (C), which was dehydrated with extreme ease to $C_{13}H_{18}$ (D). When this olefin was oxidized with chromic-sulfuric acid, two products were isolated, one a pleasant-smelling liquid, the other a liquid of unpleasant odor. The two were separated by treating an ether solution of the mixture with an aqueous sodium bicarbonate solution. After this treatment, the ether phase no longer had an unpleasant odor. Evaporation of the ether yielded a high-boiling oil which formed a semicarbazone melting at 184°C and fit the analysis $C_{11}H_{15}ON_3$ (E). The sodium bicarbonate layer was reduced to a small volume and treated with a solution of p-bromophenacyl bromide in ethanol. The product which resulted had an analysis corresponding to $C_{11}H_{11}BrO$ (F) and melted at 63°C.

(a) What is the structure of F? What is the compound from which it was formed?

(b) What is the structure of E? What is the structure of the compound from which it was formed?

(c) What is the structure of D? What alcohols might have been dehydrated to give D?

(d) Note that C gave rise to only one dehydration product, D. What must C therefore be?

(e) In going from $A + B$ to C, an oxygen atom was lost. What group of compounds must lose an oxygen (and other atoms too, of course) in this reaction?

(f) Compound B gained four carbons in the reaction. It must therefore have added more than one mole (accounting for only three carbons) of A. Does the class of compounds named in your answer to (e) add more than one mole of Grignard reagent? Does this class also lose any carbon-containing fragments in this reaction?

(g) What fragment must have been lost from B in the Grignard step? What is the structure of B?

(h) What is the structure of A?

12–4　For the present we shall examine two types of reductions of ketones and aldehydes to relate them to alcohols and hydrocarbons. First, these compounds may be reduced to alcohols by lithium aluminum hydride or by catalytic hydrogenation over platinum or palladium.

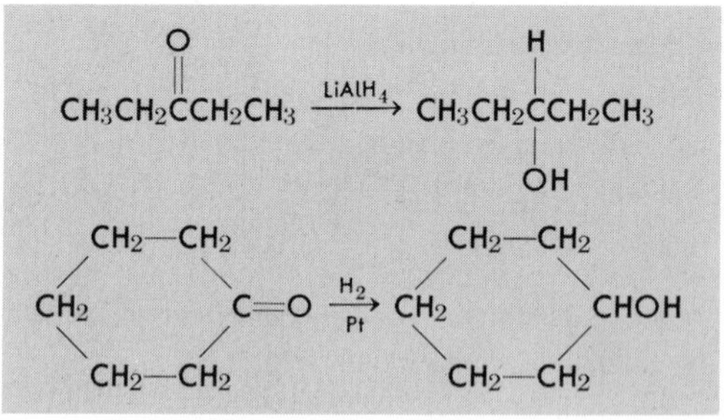

Second, the carbonyl group may be reduced directly to a methylene, CH_2, group by heating to 200° with hydrazine in the presence of strong base (Wolff-Kishner reduction) or by boiling the ketone with hydrochloric acid and zinc amalgam (Clemmensen reduction).

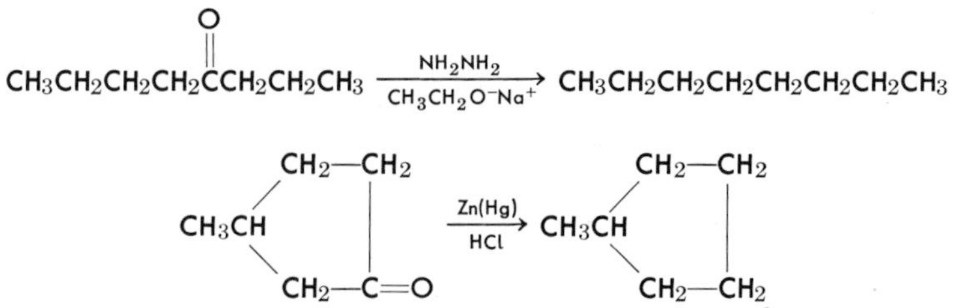

The compound $C_5H_{10}O_2$ (A) was found to liberate one mole of CH_4 when three moles of CH_3MgI were added. Addition of water liberated one more mole of CH_4. The Grignard product was hydrolyzed with concentrated ammonium chloride and the new compound, $C_6H_{14}O_2$ (B), was passed over hot alumina, giving C_6H_{10} (C). Ozonolysis followed by reductive workup yielded a mixture of three new volatile compounds. They were separated by reaction of the mixture with 2,4-dinitrophenylhydrazine and chromatography of the products. One of these was found to melt at 126°C (the 2,4-DNP of D) and another at 166°C (the 2,4-DNP of E), but the third (the 2,4-DNP of F) did not melt below 300°C.

(a) What is D?

(b) What is E?

Compound A was treated with hydrogen over platinum, absorbing one mole and forming G. When G was dehydrated over hot alumina, C_5H_8 (H) was formed. Ozonolysis followed by treatment of the ozonide with hydrogen and platinum yielded a mixture of three volatile compounds again. The 2,4-dinitrophenylhydrazones of these were prepared and separated as before. One had a melting point of 166°C and on admixture with an equal amount of the 2,4-DNP of E still melted at 166°. Another did not melt below 300°C, but its infrared spectrum was identical to that of 2,4-DNP of F. The third (the 2,4-DNP of I) melted at 168°C.

(c) What is I?

The 2,4-DNP of F was hydrolyzed back to the original carbonyl compound in aqueous acid. On standing, the solution slowly oxidized, and the new product (J) was extracted into ether. This proved to be a poor procedure because the compound was not very soluble in ether; J was found to be acidic and on neutralization gave a sodium salt which had the empirical formula CO_2Na.

(d) What is the molecular formula for the sodium salt of J?

(e) What is J?

(f) What is F, if it is not acidic?

(g) Knowing the formulas for D, E, and F, reconstruct the formula for C.

(h) With the mode of formation of B from A in mind, reconstruct the most probable formulas for B.

(i) Chromic-sulfuric acid oxidation of A produces an oil soluble in sodium bicarbonate but not in neutral water. What is the most probable formula for A?

(j) Using this formula for A, what is the structure of G?

(k) What is H?

(l) Is your formula for H consistent with your structure for I?

12-5   Determine the structures of the compounds in the following scheme:

(a) $C_{14}H_{12}O_2 \xrightarrow[H^+]{CH_3OH} C_{15}H_{14}O_2$
   (m.p. 148°)   (m.p. 60°)

(b) $C_{15}H_{14}O_2 \xrightarrow[\text{(2) } NH_4Cl \text{ in } H_2O]{\text{(1) } C_6H_5MgBr} C_{26}H_{22}O \longrightarrow C_{26}H_{20}$
   (m.p. 60°)   (not isolated)   (m.p. 223–224°)

(c) $C_{26}H_{20} \xrightarrow{CrO_3/H_2SO_4} 2C_{13}H_{10}O$
   (m.p. 223–224°)   (m.p. 48°)

12-6   Compound A, $C_7H_{14}O_2$, on treatment with NH_2NH_2 and sodium ethoxide produced B, $C_7H_{16}O$. This could be converted to a suitable derivative, melting point, 47°C, with 3,5-dinitrobenzoyl chloride. The analysis of this derivative gave the formula $C_{14}H_{18}O_6N_2$.

(a) To what class of compounds does A belong? Base your answer on the analysis and analogy with known reactions.

Alternatively B could be oxidized to C, $C_7H_{14}O_2$, which reacted with bromophenacyl bromide to give an ester, melting point, 72°C.

(b) Give an acceptable structure for B and several for A, assuming that C can be found in the tables of Chapter 10.

On standing in the air, A is converted to D, $C_7H_{14}O_3$, which can be titrated with NaOH. Chromic-sulfuric oxidation of A gives E, $C_7H_{12}O_4$, melting point, 105°C, which forms a bromophenacyl derivative with melting point of 137°C.

(c) What are the structures for E and D?

(d) What is the structure of A?

(e) Which is evidently oxidized more easily, an aldehyde or an alcohol? Would it be feasible to prepare an aldehyde by strong oxidation of an alcohol if the aldehyde could not be removed somehow as rapidly as it was formed, perhaps by boiling?

(f) From your results, here, are alcohols affected under Wolff-Kishner reaction conditions? The same is true of the Clemmensen reaction.

(g) Compare the probable action of a molecule of hydrazine with that of a derivative-forming reagent on a carbonyl compound. What intermediate could exist in the Wolff-Kishner reaction?

(h) On treatment with acid, D could form a polymeric ester or a cyclic ester. Which would be more likely to form from steric considerations?

12–7   Independently of each other, Barbier and Wieland developed the method of degradation which bears their names to study the structure of the bile acids and related compounds. A reference compound for the bile acids, cholanic acid, $C_{24}H_{40}O_2$, was known to be related to cholesterol by sequences of steps leading to the same product from the two compounds. It was known that both had the same C_{19} nucleus and that the side chain was attached to the same carbon on this nucleus in both cholanic acid and cholesterol.

Methyl cholanate reacted with methylmagnesium bromide to give a compound $C_{26}H_{44}O$, which yielded a new acid, norcholanic acid, on CrO_3 oxidation. Methyl norcholanate gave another new acid, bisnorcholanic acid, on repetition of this reaction sequence. When methyl bisnorcholanate was treated with phenylmagnesium bromide and the resulting product ozonized, a ketone was obtained.

(a) Writing the C_{19} portion of the molecule as a single radical R, show how this sequence of steps proves the structure of the side chain of cholanic acid.

(b) Assuming the structure of the four-ring nucleus given earlier for cholesterol (Problem 6–8), does cholanic acid contain either a double bond or alcohol function as cholesterol does?

(c) Write the structure of cholanic acid. What features cannot be indicated in your structure on the basis of the information given?

What new principle appears in the determination of the structures of ring compounds? How does the presence of a second carboxylic acid group affect the reactivity of carboxylic acids? How may changes in structure and changes in reactivity be correlated in this series?

13

STRUCTURES OF RING COMPOUNDS; DIBASIC ACIDS; SYNTHESES OF ACIDS AND CYCLIC KETONES

13–1 Formation and Degradation of a Cyclo-Olefin

The hydrogenation of molten phenol yields cyclohexanol.

$$C_6H_5OH + 3H_2 \xrightarrow[175°]{Ni} C_6H_{11}OH$$

Cyclohexanol, on acid dehydration, yields cyclohexene.

$$C_6H_{11}OH \xrightarrow{acid} C_6H_{10}$$

Cyclohexene, on oxidation with chromic-sulfuric acids, yields adipic acid.

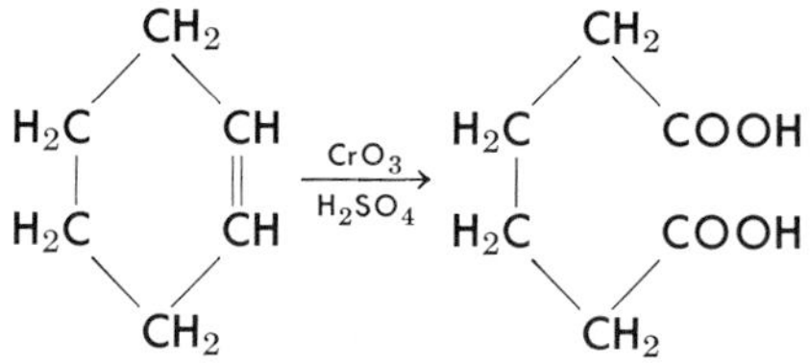

We have seen earlier that the cleavage of a double bond in the center of a chain causes the formation of two fragments, each with fewer carbons than the original chain. Cleavage of a double bond in a ring, however, leaves the fragments still joined, causing the formation of a cleavage product which, as a rule, will have the same number of carbons as the original compound. Thus the presence or absence of fragmentation in an oxidative degradation shows whether a double bond is in a chain or in a ring.

13-2 Nylon 66

We may digress from the structural story at this point to call attention to the industrial use of adipic acid. This is the intermediate in the production of the original nylon, nylon "66." Industrially, adipic acid can be made from cyclohexanol, cyclohexanone, or from cyclohexane directly. As mentioned above, cyclohexanol can be produced from phenol. Cyclohexane, however, can be produced from benzene, which is cheaper than phenol. Air oxidation of liquid cyclohexane in the presence of a catalyst, such as cobalt acetate, gives a high yield of a mixture of cyclohexanol and cyclohexanone. Industrially it has been found unnecessary to use the expensive chromic-sulfuric acid mixture for the oxidation to adipic acid. Instead, the liquid mixture of cyclohexane, cyclohexanone and, sometimes, cyclohexanol is diluted with acetic acid, a little hydrochloric acid and cobalt catalyst. The mixture is heated to 95°C and is then oxidized with air at a pressure of 150 pounds per square inch. After suitable purification, the adipic acid is crystallized out.

Treatment of acetic acid with ammonia yields ammonium acetate. When this is heated it will ultimately decompose with the loss of water to yield acetamide.

$$CH_3COO^- NH_4^+ \xrightarrow{\text{heat}} CH_3CONH_2 + H_2O$$

In the same manner, ammonium adipate can be heated to give the diamide of adipic acid.

$$NH_4^+ {}^-OOC(CH_2)_4COO^- NH_4^+ \rightarrow H_2NCO(CH_2)_4CONH_2 + 2H_2O$$

On heating to a still higher temperature in the presence of a suitable catalyst, further dehydration can be forced with the formation of adiponitrile.

$$H_2NCO(CH_2)_4CONH_2 \xrightarrow[\text{boron phosphate}]{350°} N{\equiv}C(CH_2)_4C{\equiv}N + 2H_2O$$

Finally, hydrogenation of the nitrile yields hexamethylenediamine.

$$N{\equiv}C(CH_2)_4C{\equiv}N + 4H_2 \xrightarrow{\text{Ni (NH_3)}} H_2N(CH_2)_6NH_2$$

Ammonia is added to this reaction to prevent unwanted by-reactions from occurring.

When adipic acid and hexamethylenediamine are mixed, a long-chain salt is formed.

$$nHOOC(CH_2)_4COOH + nH_2N(CH_2)_6NH_2 \rightarrow$$

$${}^-OOC(CH_2)_4COO^-[H_3N^+ (CH_2)_6NH_3^+ \ {}^-OOC(CH_2)_4COO^-]_{(n-1)}H_3N^+ (CH_2)_6NH_3^+$$

This substance is known as "nylon salt." On heating, it loses water to form the amide, as did the ammonium salts dealt with previously.

$$^-OOC(CH_2)_4COO^-[H_3N^+(CH_2)_6NH_3^+ \ ^-OOC(CH_2)_4COO^-]_{(n-1)}H_3N^+(CH_2)_6NH_3^+ \rightarrow$$

$$^-OOC(CH_2)_4CO-[NH(CH_2)_6NHCO(CH_2)_4CO]_{(n-1)}-NH(CH_2)_6NH_3^+ + (2n-1)H_2O$$

This amide is known as nylon 66, indicating that the repeating units in it have 6 carbons in both the acid and base constituents forming the chain. This type of long chain compound is known as a *condensation polymer* to distinguish it from a true polymer which would have the same empirical formula as the monomer. In this case, polymer has been formed from monomer with the loss of water and thus a condensation has taken place. Other nylons can be prepared by using acids or bases of different chain lengths, and the properties of the product vary accordingly. While the process sketched above was the first used for the formation of nylon, the availability of other raw materials at more economical prices frequently makes alternative methods for preparing the intermediates cheaper. The relationship of chemistry to economics is an interesting study, but we shall focus our attention on other facets of the story of organic chemistry.

As produced commercially, the molecular weight of nylon 66 is about 10,000 and the melting point is about 260°C, a temperature easily exceeded by a hot iron. It is insoluble in most common solvents, but can be dissolved in formic acid, phenol, dimethyl formamide, $(CH_3)_2N-CHO$, and monomethyl formamide. For use it is either extruded, for larger objects, or spun for filaments. The advent of nylon has had a tremendous impact on the silk industry, which was essentially an agricultural pursuit in the Orient. The cultivation of mulberry trees for the feeding of silkworms has given way on an increasing scale to the factory production of nylon leaving acres available for the raising of food, at lower cash return. This is another economic effect of applied chemistry which is a repetition of earlier experiences with synthetic production methods, especially of indigo and alizarin, two dyes which used to be produced agriculturally on a large scale, but which are now prepared exclusively by synthesis.

13-3 The Dicarboxylic Acids

To return to the structural problem, rings of varying sizes can be degraded with the formation of dicarboxylic acids. The properties of these compounds vary characteristically with the molecular size. A survey of their behavior on heating will be especially valuable with respect to use in possible structural investigations.

13-4 Oxalic Acid

The smallest dicarboxylic acid is oxalic acid, $HOOCCOOH$. The juxtaposition of two carboxyl groups acts to strengthen each so that oxalic acid is a very strong acid, 3000 times as strong as acetic acid. The reason for this great effect on acidity will be discussed in Book 2. Potassium acid oxalate is the acidic constituent of sorrel (genus *oxalis* from the Greek word for "sharp," from the same root as *oxygen*, acid-former), commonly known as "sour grass." It is also the acidic constituent of rhubarb and occurs in a variety of other plants. It forms an insoluble calcium salt which may cause kidney stones.

With care, anhydrous oxalic acid can be sublimed. Under ordinary conditions, however, heat decomposes the acid.

$$HOOCCOOH \xrightarrow{heat} CO_2 + HCOOH \rightarrow CO + H_2O$$

At the temperature of the decomposition of oxalic acid, formic acid also tends to be unstable so that at least part of this product is further decomposed as indicated. These reactions of the acid reverse synthetic reactions which are used to produce both formic acid and oxalic acid industrially.

$$CO + Na^+ OH^- \xrightarrow[\text{100 to 150 psi}]{200°} HCOO^- Na^+ \quad (90 \text{ to } 95\% \text{ yield})$$

$$2HCOO^- Na^+ \xrightarrow{375°} H_2 + Na^+ {}^-OOCCOO^- Na^+$$

Formic acid is prepared from sodium formate by cold neutralization in preformed formic acid with concentrated sulfuric acid. The sodium sulfate is then filtered off. Oxalic acid is prepared by first precipitating insoluble calcium oxalate and then treating this carefully with sulfuric acid to form insoluble calcium sulfate and oxalic acid. Both formic and oxalic acids are sensitive to the action of sulfuric acid so that care must be taken to keep the temperature low and to keep from adding more sulfuric acid than corresponds to the salt taken.

When dilute sulfuric acid and permanganate are used to oxidize olefins, any oxalic acid formed would probably be converted to carbon monoxide. With sulfuric acid, decomposition to carbon dioxide and carbon monoxide takes place, but chromic acid can convert more or less of the carbon monoxide to carbon dioxide, depending on the exact concentrations and temperatures. For these reasons, oxalic acid is seldom isolated as a cleavage product of olefins, although it has been reported by workers who controlled temperatures and concentrations carefully.

13–5 Malonic Acid

The next higher dicarboxylic acid is malonic acid. This is prepared from the sodium salt of chloroacetic acid.

$$^-OOCCH_2Cl + CN^- \rightarrow {}^-OOCCH_2CN + Cl^-$$

$$^-OOCCH_2CN + 2C_2H_5OH + 2HCl \rightarrow C_2H_5OOCCH_2COOC_2H_5 + 2Cl^- + NH_4^+$$

The ester is then hydrolyzed to the free acid, preferably by allowing it to stand in the cold with strong hydrochloric acid.

$$C_2H_5OOCCH_2COOC_2H_5 + 2H_2O \xrightarrow{HCl} HOOCCH_2COOH + 2C_2H_5OH$$

The reason that it is advantageous to prepare the ester as an intermediate in the synthesis of the acid is that malonic acid is unstable to heating under acidic conditions, especially in water.

$$HOOCCH_2COOH \xrightarrow[H_2O]{heat} CO_2 + CH_3COOH$$

The insertion of a CH_2 group between the two carboxyl groups separates these groups and diminishes their action on each other. The result is that malonic acid is only 0.025 times as strong as oxalic acid, although it is still 75 times as strong as acetic acid.

The ready decarboxylation of malonic acid by heating is characteristic also of the substituted malonic acids, most of which decompose with even greater ease. This is true whether the substitution has taken place at one or both hydrogens.

$$HOOCC(CH_3)_2COOH \xrightarrow{heat} CO_2 + (CH_3)_2CHCOOH$$

This property limits the isolation of malonic acids from olefin decompositions, since under the conditions of the acid degradation, decarboxylation to the corresponding acetic acid would take place. Hence in a degradation reaction, the formation of acetic acid must always be interpreted with caution, since it may have arisen from malonic acid by decarboxylation.

13–6 Succinic Acid

Neither oxalic nor malonic acid is converted to an anhydride by heating. It has already developed, however, that maleic acid is readily converted to its anhydride, a five-membered ring, on heating. Since succinic acid forms a five-membered anhydride ring, this reaction also takes place readily.

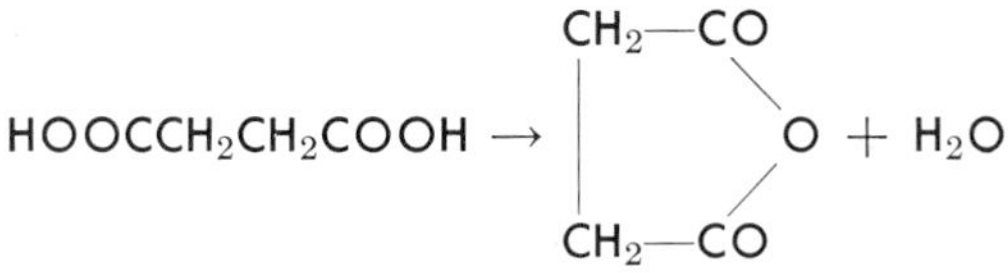

$$HOOCCH_2CH_2COOH \rightarrow \begin{matrix} CH_2-CO \\ | \quad\quad\ \diagdown \\ \quad\quad\quad O \\ | \quad\quad\ \diagup \\ CH_2-CO \end{matrix} + H_2O$$

It must be obvious that stereochemical considerations enter into these contrasts. Succinic anhydride is a five-membered ring and, therefore, relatively stable. The hypothetical malonic anhydride would be a four-membered ring and therefore strained. The hypothetical oxalic anhydride would be a three-membered ring and therefore still more highly strained. Recent studies in organic chemistry have laid great stress on the preparation of unstable ring compounds, but these two simple anhydrides still challenge the preparative skill of organic chemists.

The separation of the two carboxyl groups by still another methylene in succinic acid reduces the acid strength by a factor of approximately 11, leaving succinic acid roughly 7 times as strong as acetic acid.

Succinic acid was first prepared over four hundred years ago by the distillation of amber, from which it derives its name (the Latin name for amber is *succinum*). Maleic anhydride is prepared from benzene by catalytic oxidation.

$$\underset{\substack{\text{HC}\diagdown\quad\diagup\text{CH}\\ \| \qquad \|\\ \text{HC}\diagup\quad\diagdown\text{CH}}}{\overset{\substack{\text{CH}\\ \diagup\quad\diagdown}}{\underset{\text{CH}}{}}} + 2O_2 \xrightarrow[450°]{V_2O_5} \underset{\substack{\text{HC}\diagdown\\ \|\\ \text{HC}\diagup}}{\overset{\substack{\text{CO}\\ \diagup\quad\diagdown}}{}} O + 2CO + 2H_2O$$

Hydrogenation of either maleic anhydride or maleic acid will then yield the corresponding succinic acid derivative.

$$HOOCCH{=}CHCOOH + H_2 \xrightarrow{Ni} HOOCCH_2CH_2COOH$$

$$\underset{\substack{\text{CH}-\text{CO}\\ \|\qquad\qquad\diagdown\\ \|\qquad\qquad O\\ \text{CH}-\text{CO}\cdot}}{} + H_2 \xrightarrow{Ni} \underset{\substack{\text{CH}_2-\text{CO}\\ |\qquad\qquad\diagdown\\ |\qquad\qquad O\\ \text{CH}_2-\text{CO}}}{}$$

13–7 Glutaric Acid

Glutaric acid, $HOOC(CH_2)_3COOH$, behaves as succinic acid does on heating.

$$\underset{\substack{\text{CH}_2\text{COOH}\\ \diagup\\ \text{CH}_2\\ \diagdown\\ \text{CH}_2\text{COOH}}}{} \xrightarrow{\text{heat}} \underset{\substack{\text{CH}_2-\text{CO}\\ \diagup\qquad\qquad\diagdown\\ \text{CH}_2\qquad\qquad O\\ \diagdown\qquad\qquad\diagup\\ \text{CH}_2-\text{CO}}}{} O + H_2O$$

The anhydride formed in this case is a six-membered ring, which belongs to the class that is stereochemically favored, both for stability and for ease of formation. These assumptions are borne out by the ease of formation of glutaric anhydride and by its stability.

One of the best methods for the preparation of glutaric acid is by the nitric acid oxidation of cyclopentanone. This reaction (see the top of p. 187) illustrates the fact, alluded to earlier (Section 11–2), that under drastic oxidizing conditions ketones can be cleaved.

$$\begin{matrix} CH_2-CH_2 \\ | \qquad\quad \diagdown \\ \qquad\qquad CO \xrightarrow{HNO_3} HOOCCH_2CH_2CH_2COOH \\ | \qquad\quad \diagup \\ CH_2-CH_2 \end{matrix}$$

Glutaric acid is only about 2.5 times as strong as acetic acid. Since it has two carboxyl groups, one would expect it to be a minimum of twice as strong, based on statistical considerations alone. For this reason, it can be concluded that the three methylene groups act to shield the carboxyl groups nearly completely from each other.

13–8   Adipic Acid

We have already learned how adipic acid can be produced. Its reactions on heating provide an interesting contrast to those of succinic and glutaric acids. Heating of adipic acid produces a polymeric anhydride. This is in line with expectations concerning the difficulty of bringing two groups separated by this distance together to form a seven-membered ring. On the addition of a small amount of $CaCO_3$ to the heated acid, a new reaction ensues. This reaction has its counterpart in a reaction long used for the preparation of acetone from acetic acid.

$$2CH_3COOH + Ca^{++}(OH)_2^{=} \rightarrow (CH_3COO)_2^{=} Ca^{++} \rightarrow CH_3COCH_3 + Ca^{++}CO_3^{=}$$

$$\begin{matrix} CH_2-CH_2-COOH \\ | \qquad\qquad\qquad + Ca^{++}CO_3^{=} \rightarrow \\ CH_2-CH_2-COOH \end{matrix} \quad \begin{matrix} CH_2-CH_2-COO^- \\ | \qquad\qquad\qquad Ca^{++} + CO_2 \xrightarrow{heat} \\ CH_2-CH_2-COO^- \end{matrix}$$

$$\begin{matrix} CH_2-CH_2 \\ | \qquad\quad \diagdown \\ \qquad\qquad CO + Ca^{++}CO_3^{=} \\ | \qquad\quad \diagup \\ CH_2-CH_2 \end{matrix}$$

The formation of cyclopentanone by the catalytic action of calcium carbonate is typical of a general reaction of dibasic acids with six or more carbons in a chain. Hill and Carothers showed that when dibasic acids with eight to twelve carbons are heated without a catalyst, relatively good yields of the dimeric anhydrides are formed, illustrating trans-annular interference. (See Fig. 13–1.)

$$\begin{matrix} && CH_2 & CH_2 & CH_2 \\ & CH_2 & CH_2 & CH_2 & COOH && O & CH_2 & CH_2 & CH_2 \\ \diagup & \diagdown & \diagup & \diagdown & \diagup & && \| \diagup & \diagdown & \diagup & \diagdown & \diagup & \diagdown \\ 2HOOC && CH_2 & CH_2 & CH_2 & \rightarrow & C & CH_2 & CH_2 & CH_2 & C=O \\ &&&&&& \diagup &&&& | \\ && && && O &&&& O \\ && && && | &&&& \\ && && && O=C & CH_2 & CH_2 & CH_2 & C=O \\ && && && \diagdown & \diagup & \diagdown & \diagup & \diagdown & \diagup \\ && && && CH_2 & CH_2 & CH_2 \end{matrix}$$

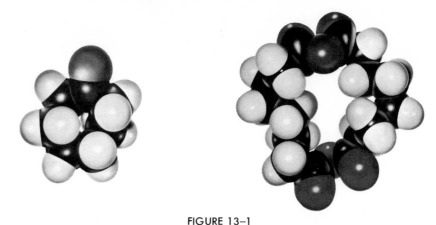

FIGURE 13-1

In the presence of the catalyst, however, it is possible to prepare the cyclic ketones with one less carbon than the parent acid. As the ring size increases, calcium carbonate becomes less and less efficient as a catalyst. Experimentation by Ruzicka showed that ThO_2 is a more satisfactory catalyst for the formation of these larger rings, possibly because of the larger size of the thorium atom.

13-9   Blanc's Rule

The varying reactions of dibasic acids to heat, especially in the presence of catalysts such as CaO and ThO_2, have resulted in the formulation of a generalization known as Blanc's rule. This rule has proved useful in structural investigations of more complex unsaturated rings. The rule is that heating of a substituted succinic or glutaric acid will yield an anhydride, while heating of a substituted adipic acid with CaO or ThO_2 will yield a ketone with one less carbon atom. Thus two isomeric dibasic acids with the formula $C_6H_{10}O_4$ might be distinguished by their varying reactions to $CaCO_3$. The one which gave a cyclic ketone would have to be adipic acid. Another which gave only an anhydride, however, might have any of the structures shown below.

$$HOOCCH(CH_3)CH_2CH_2COOH \qquad HOOCCH_2CH(CH_3)CH_2COOH$$

(a)   (b)

$$HOOCC(CH_3)_2CH_2COOH \qquad HOOCCH(CH_3)CH(CH_3)COOH$$

(c)   (d)

or

$$HOOCCH(C_2H_5)CH_2COOH$$

(e)

As shown earlier, adipic acid would be formed from the oxidation of cyclohexene.

The other compounds would be formed from the oxidations of the following cyclic olefins.

(a)   from $CH_3CH{-}CH$ (b)   from $CH{-}CH_2$ (c)   from $(CH_3)_2C{-}CH$

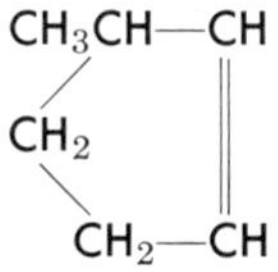

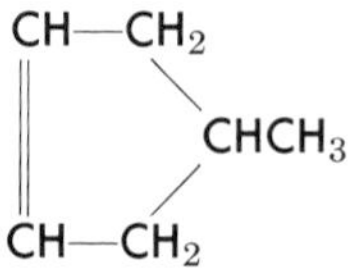

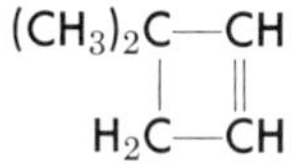

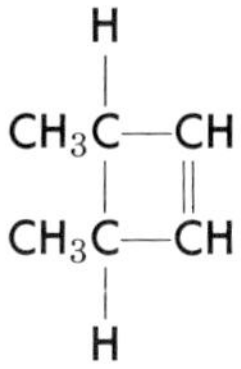

(a')   (b')   (c')

(d)   from $CH_3\overset{H}{C}{-}CH$ (e)   from $C_2H_5\overset{H}{C}{-}CH$

(d')   (e')

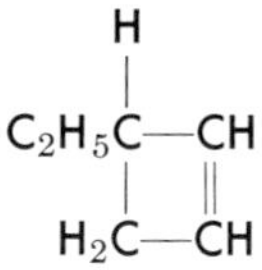

Discrimination between the acids (a), (b), (c), (d), and (e) would have to be obtained by methods other than those which we have used so far. How might you discriminate between the group (a'), (b') and the group (c'), (d'), and (e')?

13–10   Determination of Structure by Synthesis; the Malonic Ester Synthesis

It is apparent that one means to distinguish between alternative structures is to synthesize at least some of the alternatives. Degradation reactions can frequently eliminate certain possibilities. This method should be used to reduce the possibilities to the smallest number. Synthesis can then be applied to complete the problem.

One very useful synthetic method for the preparation of a variety of substituted acetic acids relies on a distinctive reaction of malonic ester. The presence of two carboxylic ester groups on the same carbon "activates" the carbon, markedly increasing the acidity of the attached hydrogens. With strong bases such as sodium ethoxide in anhydrous ethanol or sodamide, which is many orders of magnitude stronger, suspended in ether, a salt of malonic ester may be obtained.

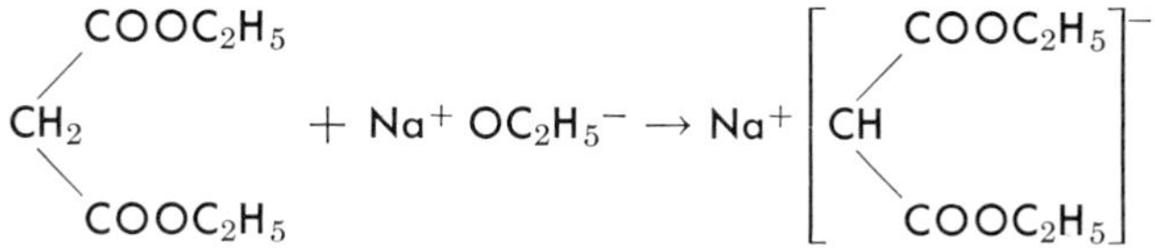

$$CH_2{\overset{\textstyle COOC_2H_5}{\underset{\textstyle COOC_2H_5}{\Big<}}} \ + \ Na^+ OC_2H_5^- \rightarrow Na^+ \left[CH{\overset{\textstyle COOC_2H_5}{\underset{\textstyle COOC_2H_5}{\Big<}}} \right]^-$$

This salt will then react with an alkyl iodide very much as sodium cyanide would to give an alkylated derivative. (See the reactions at the top of page 190.)

$$CH_3I + CN^- \rightarrow CH_3CN + I^-$$

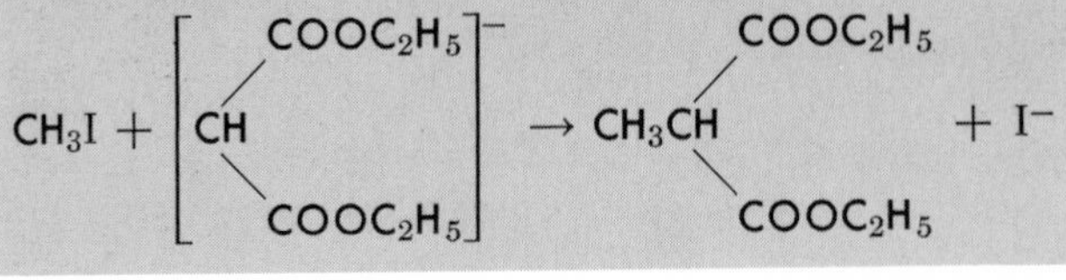

$$CH_3I + \begin{bmatrix} CH \begin{matrix} COOC_2H_5 \\ \\ COOC_2H_5 \end{matrix} \end{bmatrix}^- \rightarrow CH_3CH \begin{matrix} COOC_2H_5 \\ \\ COOC_2H_5 \end{matrix} + I^-$$

Heating this substituted malonic ester with aqueous mineral acid will then hydrolyze the ester and finally decarboxylate the substituted malonic acid.

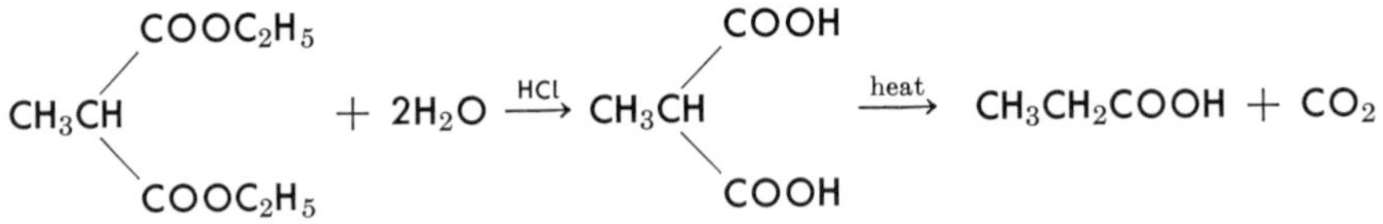

$$CH_3CH \begin{matrix} COOC_2H_5 \\ \\ COOC_2H_5 \end{matrix} + 2H_2O \xrightarrow{HCl} CH_3CH \begin{matrix} COOH \\ \\ COOH \end{matrix} \xrightarrow{heat} CH_3CH_2COOH + CO_2$$

It will be seen that the intermediate singly methylated malonic ester still has one replaceable hydrogen. If it is treated with another mole of ethoxide and a second mole of methyl iodide, further alkylation will take place.

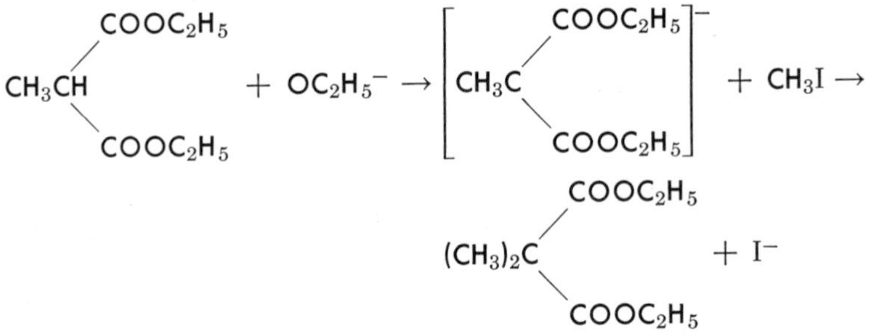

$$CH_3CH \begin{matrix} COOC_2H_5 \\ \\ COOC_2H_5 \end{matrix} + OC_2H_5^- \rightarrow \begin{bmatrix} CH_3C \begin{matrix} COOC_2H_5 \\ \\ COOC_2H_5 \end{matrix} \end{bmatrix}^- + CH_3I \rightarrow$$

$$(CH_3)_2C \begin{matrix} COOC_2H_5 \\ \\ COOC_2H_5 \end{matrix} + I^-$$

On hydrolysis, this new product will yield a doubly substituted acetic acid.

$$(CH_3)_2C \begin{matrix} COOC_2H_5 \\ \\ COOC_2H_5 \end{matrix} + 2H_2O \xrightarrow{HCl} (CH_3)_2C \begin{matrix} COOH \\ \\ COOH \end{matrix} \xrightarrow{heat} (CH_3)_2CHCOOH + CO_2$$

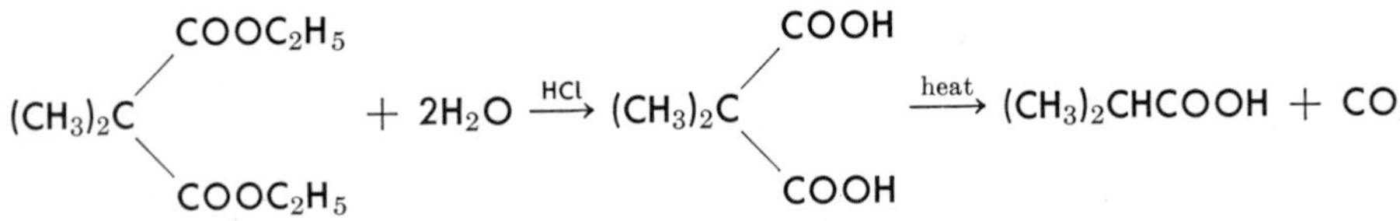

Thus we see that it is possible to prepare either singly or doubly substituted acetic acids by this method. Why is it not possible to prepare a tri-substituted acetic acid this way?

This method of synthesis is quite general and is referred to as the *malonic ester synthesis*. By performing the alkylations stepwise it is possible to prepare unsymmetrically substituted malonic esters and, from these, acetic acids with two different substituents.

13–11   Synthesis of Dibasic Acids

An interesting variant of the malonic ester synthesis permits the preparation of certain dibasic acids. Thus succinic acid may be prepared from sodiomalonic ester by the following reactions:

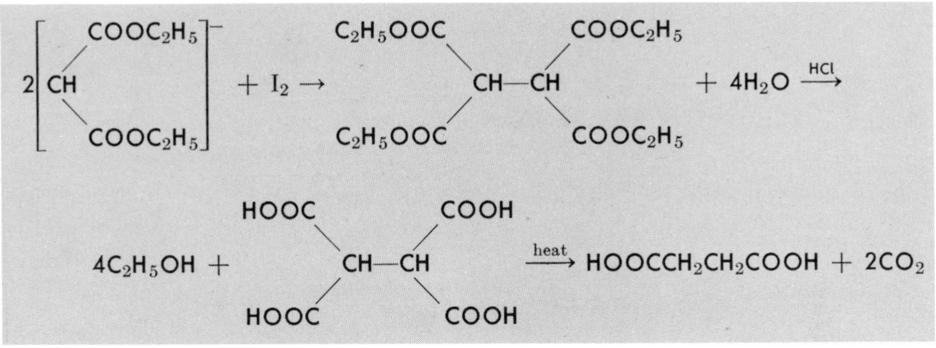

$$2 \left[\begin{array}{c} COOC_2H_5 \\ CH \\ COOC_2H_5 \end{array} \right]^- + I_2 \rightarrow \begin{array}{c} C_2H_5OOC \qquad COOC_2H_5 \\ CH—CH \\ C_2H_5OOC \qquad COOC_2H_5 \end{array} + 4H_2O \xrightarrow{HCl}$$

$$4C_2H_5OH + \begin{array}{c} HOOC \qquad COOH \\ CH—CH \\ HOOC \qquad COOH \end{array} \xrightarrow{heat} HOOCCH_2CH_2COOH + 2CO_2$$

How could you prepare $HOOCCH(CH_3)CH(CH_3)COOH$ (compound d)?

The reaction of iodine with sodiomalonic ester is assumed to form iodomalonic ester as an intermediate. This will react readily with sodiomalonic ester to give the observed product.

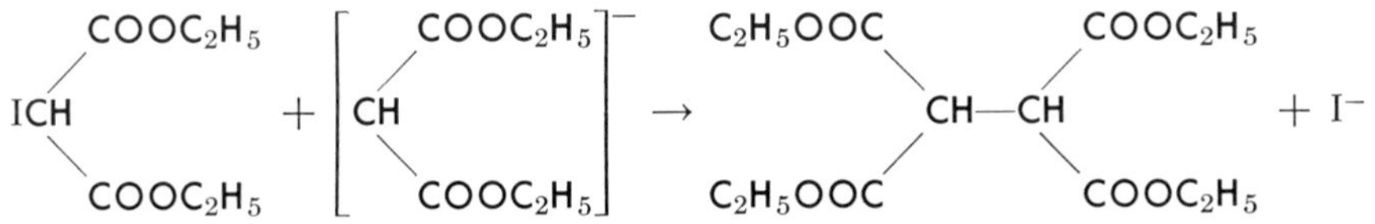

$$\begin{array}{c} COOC_2H_5 \\ ICH \\ COOC_2H_5 \end{array} + \left[\begin{array}{c} COOC_2H_5 \\ CH \\ COOC_2H_5 \end{array} \right]^- \rightarrow \begin{array}{c} C_2H_5OOC \qquad COOC_2H_5 \\ CH—CH \\ C_2H_5OOC \qquad COOC_2H_5 \end{array} + I^-$$

Iodomalonic ester is difficult to work with. Hence, when an unsymmetrical synthesis is desired, bromomalonic ester is usually chosen.

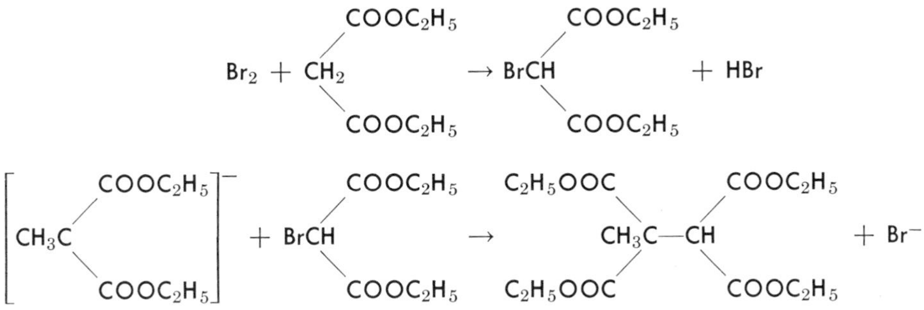

$$Br_2 + \begin{array}{c} COOC_2H_5 \\ CH_2 \\ COOC_2H_5 \end{array} \rightarrow \begin{array}{c} COOC_2H_5 \\ BrCH \\ COOC_2H_5 \end{array} + HBr$$

$$\left[\begin{array}{c} COOC_2H_5 \\ CH_3C \\ COOC_2H_5 \end{array} \right]^- + \begin{array}{c} COOC_2H_5 \\ BrCH \\ COOC_2H_5 \end{array} \rightarrow \begin{array}{c} C_2H_5OOC \qquad COOC_2H_5 \\ CH_3C—CH \\ C_2H_5OOC \qquad COOC_2H_5 \end{array} + Br^-$$

How could you make $HOOCCH(C_2H_5)CH_2COOH$ (compound e)?

Sodiomalonic ester will react with methylene iodide to yield a product which is an intermediate in the synthesis of glutaric acid. (See page 192.)

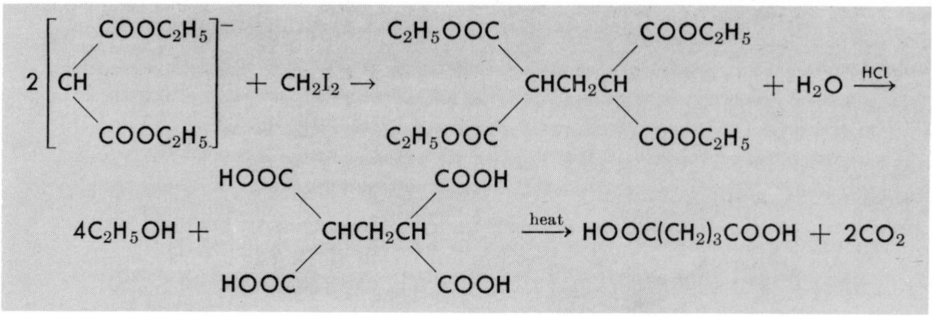

$$2 \begin{bmatrix} CH \overset{\textstyle COOC_2H_5}{\underset{\textstyle COOC_2H_5}{}} \end{bmatrix}^- + CH_2I_2 \rightarrow \quad \overset{C_2H_5OOC}{\underset{C_2H_5OOC}{}} CHCH_2CH \overset{COOC_2H_5}{\underset{COOC_2H_5}{}} \quad + H_2O \overset{HCl}{\longrightarrow}$$

$$4C_2H_5OH + \quad \overset{HOOC}{\underset{HOOC}{}} CHCH_2CH \overset{COOH}{\underset{COOH}{}} \overset{heat}{\longrightarrow} HOOC(CH_2)_3COOH + 2CO_2$$

What would you require to synthesize $HOOCCH_2CH(CH_3)CH_2COOH$ (compound b)?
Can you think of a method by which a bromide suitable for this synthesis might be prepared?

Bromination of ethyl *iso*butyrate gives the α-bromo ester.

$$(CH_3)_2CHCOOC_2H_5 + Br_2 \rightarrow (CH_3)_2CBrCOOC_2H_5$$

How could you prepare compound (c)?

13-12 The Michael Condensation

It is characteristic of β-halogenated carboxylic acids and esters that loss of hydrogen halide takes place readily in basic solutions.

$$ICH_2CH_2COOC_2H_5 + OC_2H_5^- \rightarrow H_2C{=}CHCOOC_2H_5 + I^- + C_2H_5OH$$

For this reason, alkylations are not performed with these esters. Michael discovered, however, that in those cases in which olefin formation takes place so readily, the unsaturated ester may itself be used as if the halogen were there. Alkylation of an organic anion by an "activated" double bond is called a *Michael condensation*.

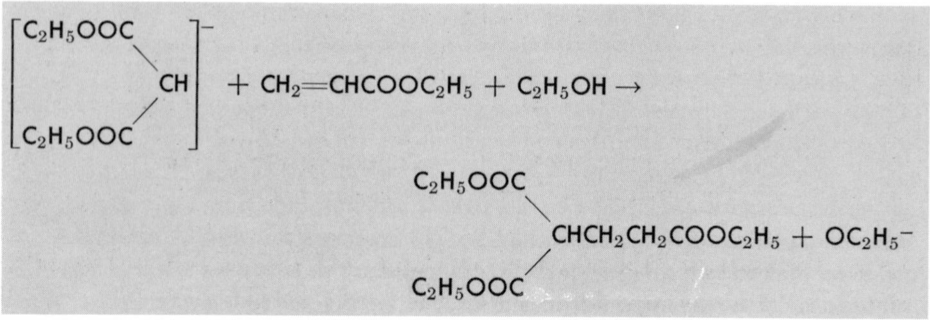

$$\begin{bmatrix} \overset{C_2H_5OOC}{\underset{C_2H_5OOC}{}} CH \end{bmatrix}^- + CH_2{=}CHCOOC_2H_5 + C_2H_5OH \rightarrow$$

$$\overset{C_2H_5OOC}{\underset{C_2H_5OOC}{}} CHCH_2CH_2COOC_2H_5 + OC_2H_5^-$$

Since the ethoxide ion is regenerated, it is only necessary to add catalytic quantities for the reaction to proceed.

Hydrolysis and decarboxylation of this compound will give glutaric acid.

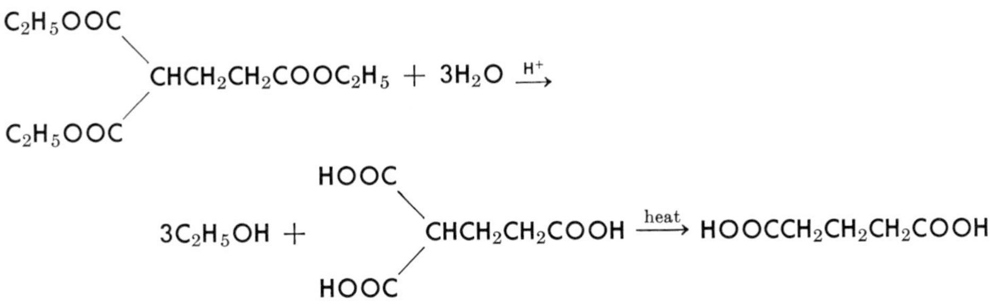

$$C_2H_5OOC \diagdown$$
$$CHCH_2CH_2COOC_2H_5 + 3H_2O \xrightarrow{H^+}$$
$$C_2H_5OOC \diagup$$

$$HOOC \diagdown$$
$$3C_2H_5OH + \qquad CHCH_2CH_2COOH \xrightarrow{heat} HOOCCH_2CH_2CH_2COOH$$
$$HOOC \diagup$$

With these facts in mind, how could you prepare compound (a)?

The nature of the process by which carboxylic ester groups produce the "activation" necessary to bring about the Michael condensation will be discussed in Book 2.

PROBLEMS

13-1 Using the malonic ester synthesis, write reactions for the preparation of the following compounds:

$$\begin{array}{c} CH_3 \\ \diagdown \\ (a) \qquad CH—COOH \\ \diagup \\ CH_3 \end{array} \qquad \begin{array}{c} CH_2—CH_2 \quad COOH \\ \diagup \qquad\qquad \diagdown \quad | \\ (b) \quad CH_2 \qquad\qquad CHCCH_3 \\ \diagdown \qquad\qquad \diagup \\ CH_2—CH_2 \end{array}$$

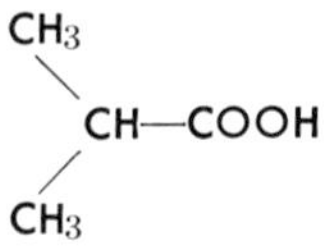

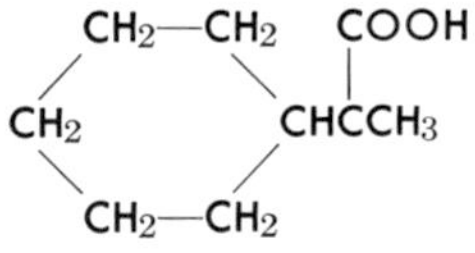

13-2 Using the Michael reaction, work out the following synthesis:

$$C_6H_5CH{=}CHCOOH \rightarrow \beta\text{-phenylglutaric anhydride}$$

Cinnamic acid

13-3 One of the products obtained from the extraction of beet roots is aconitic acid. Michael found that he was able to synthesize this material using a variation of the reaction which he developed. He mixed diethyl malonate, diethyl acetylenedicarboxylate, and sodium ethoxide and carefully hydrolyzed the resulting ester to give the desired acid, $C_6H_6O_6$. The addition of one mole of malonic ester to an activated triple bond is analogous to its addition to an activated double bond. What structure can you write for aconitic acid? What feature is still uncertain about the structure? Should the usual type of olefin degradation solve this point?

13-4 A hydrocarbon boiling at 126°C has the formula C_8H_{14}. On hydrogenation it yields C_8H_{16}.

(a) How many rings and multiple bonds does the molecule contain? Oxidation with chromic-sulfuric acid yielded $C_8H_{14}O_4$. What kind of compound is this? What information does it give about the location of the unsaturation?

(b) When this acid was heated with $CaCO_3$, $C_7H_{12}O$ was formed. What information does this give concerning the type of acid involved?

(c) Anhydrides show a double carbonyl absorption in the infrared, between 5.35 and 5.7 microns. Five-membered ring ketones absorb near 5.7 to 5.75 microns and six- and seven-membered ones near 5.8 to 5.85. The material in question had a single absorption at 5.75 microns. Write several possible structures for $C_7H_{12}O$ with this information. What size ring must the original C_8H_{14} contain?

(d) The corresponding aromatic compound may be obtained by reversing the hydrogenation methods used to make cyclohexane, that is, by heating the nonaromatic compound with platinum or with some other aromatizing agent. In the case of cyclohexane, benzene would be produced. Methylcyclohexane would yield toluene.

$$C_6H_6 + H_2 \overset{Pt}{\rightleftarrows} C_6H_{12}$$

While platinum is suitable as a catalyst for the reaction in either direction, dehydrogenations are usually performed with less active catalysts, such as specially prepared copper. For producing aromatic compounds from hydroaromatic compounds, the usual reagent is selenium.

$$C_{10}H_{18} + 5Se \rightarrow C_{10}H_8 + 5H_2Se$$

Decahydro-   Naphthalene
naphthalene

When this dehydrogenation is carried out on our C_8H_{14}, a moderate yield of a liquid boiling at 139°C is obtained. This may be oxidized with hot chromic-sulfuric acid to yield a crystalline acid with melting point 300°C forming a p-bromophenacyl ester melting at 179°C.

What must be the structure of the olefin C_8H_{14} if no rearrangements take place during the aromatization step?

*What general similarities and
dissimilarities exist between the reactions of
keto acids and dibasic acids?
How can these reactions be used in the synthesis of
reference materials for the study of structure?*

14

KETO ACIDS AND DIKETONES;
THE CLAISEN ESTER CONDENSATION
AND THE ACETOACETIC
ESTER SYNTHESIS

14-1 Multifunctionality

Many of the interesting and unique properties of organic compounds result from the interactions of groups in bifunctional and multifunctional compounds. In the preceding chapter, we saw that one acid group can profoundly influence the properties of another. For oxalic acid, both the acid strength and the reactivity were altered by the presence of another carboxyl group. The same was true in different measure with malonic acid. As the distance between the two groupings increased, the interaction diminished, as would be expected. These changes caused by the interaction of two groups are characteristic of bifunctionality in general. The nature of the specific alterations brought about by different groups will obviously differ. Nevertheless, the introduction of a new chemical group into a molecule at a position close to that of another group will affect the chemistry of the group already present. The chemistry of the entering group will also be affected by the original group. This property of mutual interaction is responsible for the tremendous variety of the properties of organic compounds and for the subtle control over these properties which the organic chemist can exercise. These interactions will repay careful study.

We have surveyed a few of the outstanding characteristics of monofunctional ketones, of monobasic carboxylic acids, and of dibasic acids. We shall now turn our attention to some properties of other classes of bifunctional compounds, starting with the keto acids. It is easy to see that oxidations of ring compounds might yield either dibasic acids, keto acids, or diketones.

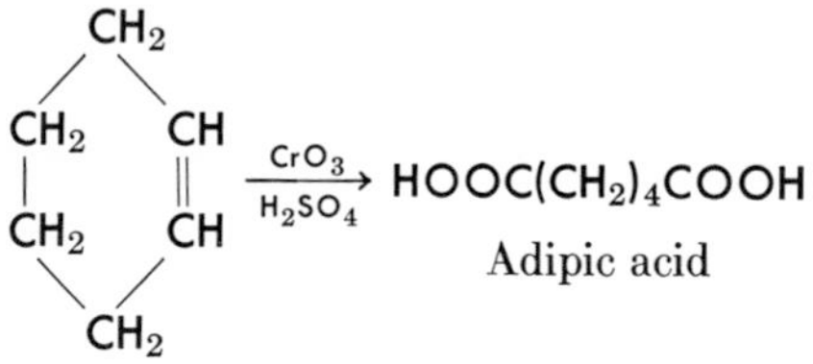

HOOC(CH₂)₄COOH

Adipic acid

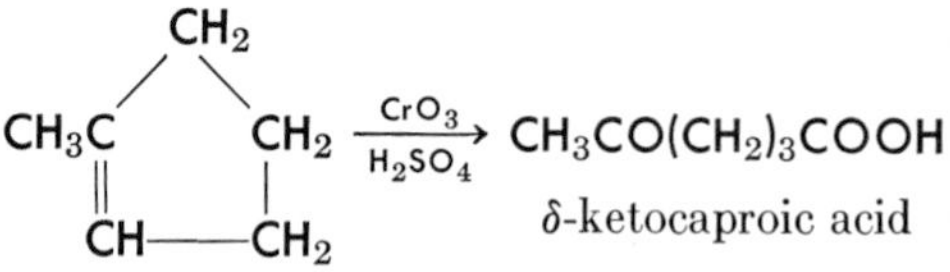

$$\text{HOOC(CH}_2)_4\text{COOH}$$

δ-ketocaproic acid

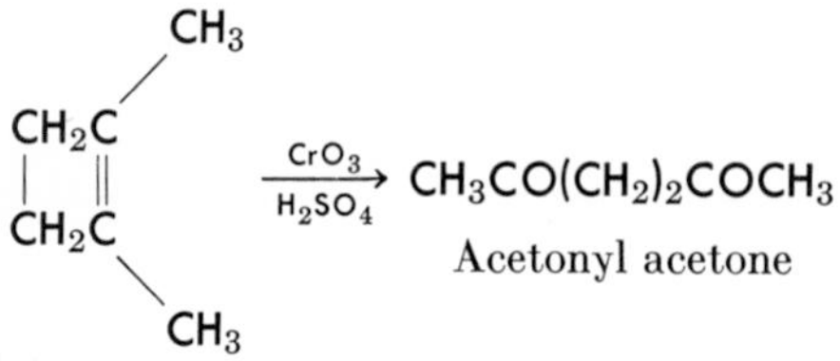

$$CH_3CO(CH_2)_3COOH$$

Acetonyl acetone

$$CH_3CO(CH_2)_2COCH_3$$

Identification of these substances will depend on a knowledge of their properties and, ultimately, on possessing methods for their synthesis. The synthetic methods used for these preparations are based on observations made by chemists a century ago.

14–2 Ethyl Acetoacetate

At the time when Kekulé was proposing his formula for acetic acid, other investigators were at work studying acetic acid and its derivatives to learn their properties. One of these men was Geuther, who believed that acetic acid had two hydrogens replaceable by sodium. To prove this, in 1863 he prepared ethyl acetate, in which the easily replaceable hydrogen had been replaced by the ethyl group, and then proceeded to treat the ethyl acetate with metallic sodium. He observed that, in fact, hydrogen was evolved in the amount of one atom of hydrogen for each molecule of ethyl acetate used. Unlike other reactions of the type, however, Geuther's reaction did not produce a single product. He isolated sodium ethoxide as one product. The other was a crystalline compound with the formula $C_6H_9O_3Na$. The reaction can be formulated:

$$2CH_3COOC_2H_5 + 2Na \rightarrow C_2H_5ONa + C_6H_9O_3Na + H_2$$

The compound $C_6H_9O_3Na$ is the salt of a very weak acid which can be liberated by treatment with dilute mineral acid.

$$C_6H_9O_3Na + HCl \rightarrow C_6H_{10}O_3 + NaCl$$

The compound $C_6H_{10}O_3$ is soluble in organic solvents and insoluble in water. It is neutral to litmus, but its weak acidic properties can be demonstrated with strong bases. A particularly suitable base is sodium ethoxide. This regenerates the original sodium salt.

$$C_6H_{10}O_3 + C_2H_5O^- \rightarrow C_6H_9O_3^- + C_2H_5OH$$

Further investigation of the weak acid, $C_6H_{10}O_3$, showed that it is the ethyl ester of a stronger acid, since hydrolysis gives ethanol and an acid.

$$C_6H_{10}O_3 + H_2O \xrightarrow{H^+} C_4H_6O_3 + C_2H_5OH$$

The acid, $C_4H_6O_3$, turns out to be more than ten times as strong as acetic acid and is readily titratable with dilute alkalis. It was thus quickly recognized as a carboxylic acid. This conclusion was confirmed when it was found that the acid would undergo ready decarboxylation to yield acetone.

$$C_4H_6O_3 \xrightarrow{heat} CH_3\overset{\overset{\displaystyle O}{\|}}{C}CH_3 + CO_2$$

Since the compound was originally formed from ethyl acetate by a condensation process, it was natural to expect to find an acetyl group in it. This was confirmed by the formation of acetone, which is acetyl methane. Chemists also reasoned that the loss of carbon dioxide was reminiscent of the removal of carbon dioxide from acetic acid (Section 4–4) even though the new reaction took place much more readily than the older one. This latter fact allowed them to write:

$$R-COOH \rightarrow RH + CO_2 \quad \text{or} \quad (C_3H_5O)COOH \rightarrow CH_3\overset{\overset{\displaystyle O}{\|}}{C}CH_3 + CO_2$$

Both the mode of formation and the production of acetone lead to the formulation of the group (C_3H_5O) as

$$CH_3\overset{\overset{\displaystyle O}{\|}}{C}CH_2-$$

Thus the reconstructed formula for $C_4H_6O_3$ would be

$$CH_3\overset{\overset{\displaystyle O}{\|}}{C}CH_2COOH$$

and its decomposition to acetone would be represented by the equation:

$$CH_3\overset{\overset{\displaystyle O}{\|}}{C}CH_2COOH \xrightarrow{heat} CH_3\overset{\overset{\displaystyle O}{\|}}{C}CH_3 + CO_2$$

It is now possible to retrace still another step in the degradation and write the formula for the ethyl ester, since we have recognized its decomposition by hydrolysis. The ester would be

$$\overset{\displaystyle O}{\underset{\displaystyle \|}{}}$$
$$CH_3CCH_2COOC_2H_5$$

and its hydrolysis would be represented by the equation:

$$CH_3COCH_2COOC_2H_5 + H_2O \xrightarrow{H^+} CH_3COCH_2COOH + C_2H_5OH$$

The reader will recognize that this ester, called ethyl acetoacetate, possesses a methylene group between two carbonyl groups, similar to malonic ester. Hence it will not now be surprising that the ester reacts with sodium ethoxide to form a sodium salt.

$$CH_3COCH_2COOC_2H_5 + C_2H_5O^- Na^+ \rightarrow (CH_3COCHCOOC_2H_5)^- Na^+ + C_2H_5OH$$

14–3 The Acetoacetic Ester Controversy

Geuther's observations precipitated a structural controversy which lasted for decades and whose overtones extend into modern chemistry. He used metallic sodium as a diagnostic reagent and appeared to find replacement of one hydrogen per molecule of ethyl acetate with the reagent. Further study showed, however, that he had brought about a condensation reaction with the sodium, not a simple hydrogen replacement reaction. Even so, a minute amount of the ethyl acetate must have reacted with the metallic sodium to initiate the reaction. Some chemists concluded that Geuther was technically correct and that, although sodium will not completely replace one hydrogen of ethyl acetate, it will replace at least enough to permit the condensation reaction to start.

A contrary point of view soon appeared. Those holding this viewpoint said that sodium must still be looked on as diagnostic for an OH grouping. For ethyl acetoacetate, they said, the reaction could be formulated as follows:

$$CH_3COCH_2COOC_2H_5 \rightarrow CH_3\overset{\displaystyle OH}{\underset{\displaystyle |}{C}}=CHCOOC_2H_5$$

$$CH_3\overset{\displaystyle OH}{\underset{\displaystyle |}{C}}=CCOOC_2H_5 + Na \rightarrow CH_3\overset{\displaystyle O^- Na^+}{\underset{\displaystyle |}{C}}=CCOOC_2H_5 + \tfrac{1}{2}H_2$$

They reasoned that the function of the sodium was to cause the shift of a hydrogen from the ketonic form to the alcoholic form. Since this particular alcohol is attached to an olefinic carbon, the compound was called an *enol*. Thus was born the controversy over so-called "keto-enol tautomerism." The word *tautomer* was originally used by Laar to indicate isomers whose bonding changed with the speed of light, but this usage was replaced by the modern meaning of the word, that is, tautomers are isomers convertible into each other by the shift of at least one atomic center.

To pursue the keto-enol controversy to the case of ethyl acetate, it is possible to argue even in this case that the initial replacement of hydrogen by sodium is preceded by a shift of the hydrogen under the catalytic influence of the sodium metal so that an enol is formed and this reacts with the sodium.

$$
\underset{\substack{\| \\ \text{CH}_3\text{COC}_2\text{H}_5}}{\text{O}} \rightarrow \underset{\substack{| \\ \text{CH}_2{=}\text{COC}_2\text{H}_5}}{\text{OH}}
$$

$$
\underset{\substack{| \\ \text{CH}_2{=}\text{COC}_2\text{H}_5}}{\text{OH}} + \text{Na} \rightarrow \underset{\substack{| \\ \text{CH}_2{=}\text{COC}_2\text{H}_5}}{\text{O}^-\text{Na}^+} + \tfrac{1}{2}\text{H}_2
$$

A tiny quantity of this enolate ion could then react with ethyl acetate.

$$
\underset{\substack{| \\ \text{OC}_2\text{H}_5}}{\overset{\substack{\text{O} \\ \|}}{\text{CH}_3\text{C}}} + \underset{\substack{| \\ \text{CH}_2{=}\text{COC}_2\text{H}_5}}{\text{O}^-\text{Na}^+} \rightarrow \underset{}{\overset{\substack{\text{O}\quad\text{O} \\ \|\quad\|}}{\text{CH}_3\text{C}-\text{CH}_2\text{COC}_2\text{H}_5}} + \text{Na}^+\text{OC}_2\text{H}_5^-
$$

But we have already seen that ethoxide ion reacts completely with ethyl aceto-acetate to form the salt.

$$
\underset{}{\overset{\substack{\text{O}\quad\text{O} \\ \|\quad\|}}{\text{CH}_3\text{CCH}_2\text{COC}_2\text{H}_5}} + \text{Na}^+\text{OC}_2\text{H}_5^- \rightarrow \underset{}{\overset{\substack{\text{Na}^+\text{O}^-\quad\text{O} \\ |\quad\quad\|}}{\text{CH}_3\text{C}{=}\text{CHCOC}_2\text{H}_5}} + \text{C}_2\text{H}_5\text{OH}
$$

Thus ethyl acetoacetate is a much stronger acid than ethyl acetate, and the removal of the insoluble sodium salt would, in this case, provide the driving force which would displace the equilibrium toward the products observed.

14–4 Enolate Anion and Enol

The earlier investigators wrote the sodium salt of ethyl acetoacetate as if the sodium were bonded to the oxygen. Some reactions of the compound, however, caused others to write the compound as if the sodium were bonded to carbon and the structural and diagnostic controversy continued. We can see now that the difficulty lay in the fact that the ionic nature of the salt was not fully appreciated. When recognition of this fact came, it was realized that the salt, like benzene, had more than one formula to represent it and that, also like benzene, neither formula would represent it perfectly.

$$
\underset{}{\overset{\substack{\text{O} \\ \|}}{\text{CH}_3\text{C}-\overset{-}{\text{CHCOOC}_2\text{H}_5}}} \leftrightarrow \underset{}{\overset{\substack{\text{O}^- \\ |}}{\text{CH}_3\text{C}{=}\text{CHCOOC}_2\text{H}_5}}
$$

As with benzene, the existence of two formulas for the same substance whose interconversion requires only that bonds be shifted gives rise to stabilization by *resonance*. The stabilization of the salt form of ethyl acetoacetate and of ethyl malonate by resonance is responsible for the fact that the methylene groups appear to be extraordinarily acidic. This concept will be discussed in detail in Book 2.

It has been found possible to prepare the pure enol of ethyl acetoacetate. This is stable in vessels that are scrupulously free from traces of acid or alkali. The pure ketone has also been prepared. These two substances do differ in the ease of their reactions with various reagents, including alkalis. The enol reacts instantaneously with alkalis, the ketone only slowly, as it is converted to enol. Thus there is an argument that the diagnostic reaction of sodium for the OH grouping is maintained intact. It is clear, however, that this diagnostic reaction cannot be used indiscriminately but must be used with considerably more sophistication than was available to the early investigators who simply wanted to apply it directly and secure results that were immediately intelligible. The resolution of the problem of whether ethyl acetate can yield hydrogen directly from carbon in the presence of sodium or whether it must first rearrange to an enol is one which calls for the highest degree of sophistication of modern instrumentation and is thus not an easy problem to answer.

14-5   The Claisen Ester Condensation

Some years after Geuther's discovery of the formation of ethyl acetoacetate, Claisen found that the reaction could be extended to the condensation of other esters and carbonyl compounds. For example, ethyl acetate and acetone will condense in a parallel reaction.

$$CH_3\overset{O}{\overset{\|}{C}} + H_3C\overset{O}{\overset{\|}{C}}CH_3 + OC_2H_5^- \rightarrow CH_3\overset{O^-}{\overset{|}{C}}{=}CH\overset{O}{\overset{\|}{C}}CH_3 + 2C_2H_5OH$$

$$OC_2H_5$$

$$CH_3\overset{O^-}{\overset{|}{C}}{=}CH\overset{O}{\overset{\|}{C}}CH_3 + H^+ \rightarrow CH_3\overset{O}{\overset{\|}{C}}CH_2\overset{O}{\overset{\|}{C}}CH_3$$

The product, acetylacetone, also has an "active methylene" group. The condensation is usually performed with metallic sodium but will proceed with sodium ethoxide or with sodamide suspended in ether. Such condensations are known as *Claisen ester condensations*.

14-6   Acetoacetic Ester Syntheses

We have seen that the carboxyl in malonic acid causes the easy decarboxylation of the acid. In the same manner, a keto group in the β-position to a carboxyl group will cause easy decarboxylation, so that acetoacetic acid readily loses carbon dioxide to give acetone. Acetoacetic acid salts are normal metabolic intermediates in the breakdown of fats, but ordinarily they do not form in appreciable quantities. Instead they break down to acetates. As performed physiologically, however, this step requires the presence of the hormone insulin. In diabetic patients the insulin is lacking and the normal cleavage does not occur. Instead acetoacetic acid builds up in the blood and is decarboxylated to acetone. This causes the characteristic acetone odor of the breath of a diabetic patient who is not properly controlled with insulin.

In further parallel to the reactions of the malonates, sodioacetoacetic ester, like sodiomalonic ester, can be alkylated on carbon.

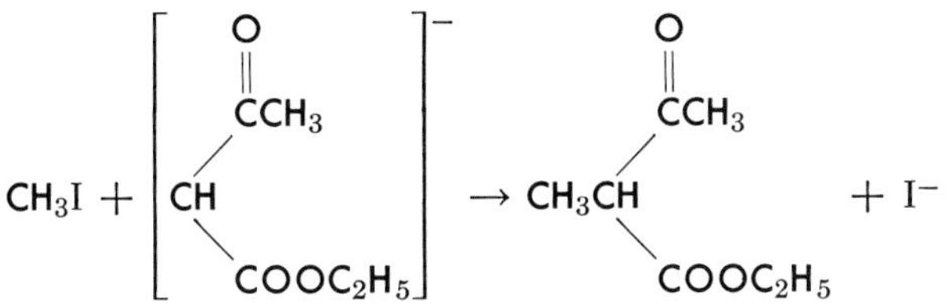

Hydrolysis and decarboxylation of the product yields a monosubstituted acetone.

$$CH_3\overset{\overset{\displaystyle O}{\|}}{C}CH(CH_3)COOC_2H_5 + H_2O \xrightarrow{OH^- \text{ or } H^+} CH_3\overset{\overset{\displaystyle O}{\|}}{C}CH(CH_3)COOH \xrightarrow{\text{heat}} CH_3\overset{\overset{\displaystyle O}{\|}}{C}CH_2CH_3$$

As with ethyl malonate, the alkylation can be repeated.

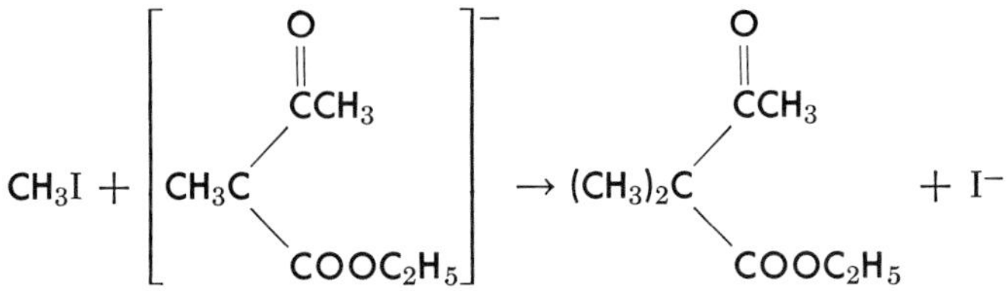

This product, on hydrolysis and decarboxylation, yields a doubly substituted acetone.

$$CH_3\overset{\overset{\displaystyle O}{\|}}{C}C(CH_3)_2COOC_2H_5 + H_2O \xrightarrow{OH^- \text{ or } H^+} CH_3\overset{\overset{\displaystyle O}{\|}}{C}C(CH_3)_2COOH \xrightarrow{\text{heat}} CH_3\overset{\overset{\displaystyle O}{\|}}{C}CH(CH_3)_2$$

Why would it not be possible to prepare $CH_3COC(CH_3)_3$ by this procedure?

The variants on the malonic ester synthesis which were used in the preceding chapter for the synthesis of acids can be applied in the case of the acetoacetic ester synthesis of ketones. How would you prepare

$$CH_3\overset{\displaystyle O}{\overset{\|}{C}}CH_2CH_2\overset{\displaystyle O}{\overset{\|}{C}}CH_3$$

(acetonyl acetone)?

What would you require to synthesize δ-ketocaproic acid from ethyl acetoacetate?

14-7 Keto Acids

The simplest keto acid is pyruvic acid, $CH_3COCOOH$. This can be prepared from acetyl chloride through the nitrile.

$$CH_3COCl + CN^- \rightarrow CH_3COCN + Cl^-$$

The conditions required for the hydrolysis of this particular cyanide are unusual. Dilute acids and alkalies are not satisfactory. Instead, concentrated hydrochloric acid is used.

$$CH_3COCN \xrightarrow{\text{concentrated HCl}} CH_3COCOOH + NH_4Cl$$

Pyruvate, like acetoacetate, is a metabolic intermediate. It is more readily isolated as its dinitrophenylhydrazone than as its bromophenacyl ester. The enol form is called *glucic acid*, $CH_2{=}C(OH)COOH$, and occurs naturally in the form of its phosphate ester.

Pyruvic acid is seldom isolated in the course of an oxidation with acidic dichromate. This is because heating with dilute sulfuric acid causes it to cleave to carbon dioxide and acetaldehyde.

$$CH_3\overset{\displaystyle O}{\overset{\|}{C}}COOH \xrightarrow[\text{dilute H}_2\text{SO}_4]{\text{heat}} CH_3CHO + CO_2$$

Concentrated sulfuric acid, on the other hand, produces still another type of cleavage.

$$CH_3\overset{\displaystyle O}{\overset{\|}{C}}COOH \xrightarrow{\text{concentrated H}_2\text{SO}_4} CH_3COOH + CO$$

Pyruvic acid is not stable to long standing. It polymerizes to form a thick, non-volatile syrup. Acetoacetic acid would also not be isolated during the course of an acidic oxidative degradation, since it would decarboxylate to acetone.

The next higher keto acid is γ-ketovaleric acid, levulinic acid. As the name suggests, it is easily made from levulose, a sugar resulting from the action of acid on cane sugar. Commercially, some levulinic acid is made by the action of acid on starch. Synthetically, it may be prepared from ethyl acetoacetate. (See p. 203.)

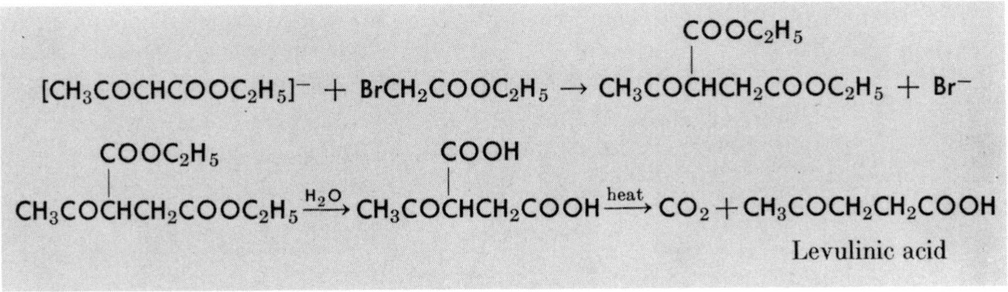

$$[CH_3COCHCOOC_2H_5]^- + BrCH_2COOC_2H_5 \rightarrow CH_3COCHCH_2COOC_2H_5 + Br^-$$

with COOC$_2$H$_5$ branch on the central carbon of the product.

$$CH_3COCHCH_2COOC_2H_5 \xrightarrow{H_2O} CH_3COCHCH_2COOH \xrightarrow{heat} CO_2 + CH_3COCH_2CH_2COOH$$

with COOC$_2$H$_5$ on the left carbon and COOH on the middle product carbon.

Levulinic acid

14–8   Synthesis of Keto Acids

A modification of the malonic ester synthesis can be used to prepare keto acids from levulinic acid. This requires the use of a half-ester, half-acid chloride of a dibasic acid. When the anhydride is available, these may be made simply.

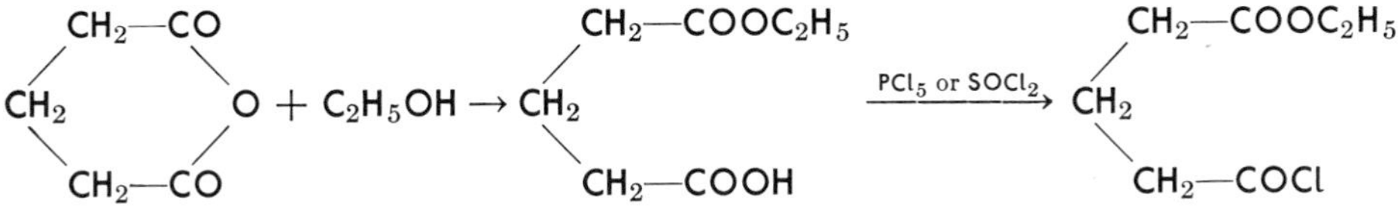

When the anhydride is not readily available, the half-ester may be prepared by partial esterification. Properly conducted, this yields the half-ester as the major product along with some diester and some diacid. The diester can be separated by extraction, the diacid usually by crystallization of the anhydrous sodium or potassium salt. Alternatively, the half-ester can be prepared from the diester by partial hydrolysis, resulting in a similar mixture.

$$HOOC(CH_2)_4COOH + 1C_2H_5OH \xrightarrow{HCl} C_2H_5OOC(CH_2)_4COOH \xrightarrow{SOCl_2}$$
$$C_2H_5OOC(CH_2)_4COCl$$

On treatment with an acid chloride, sodiomalonic ester gives a mixture of the derivative on carbon and that on oxygen. A yield of approximately 50% of the C-acylated derivative can be obtained, however, and this is sufficient to permit the synthesis to proceed.

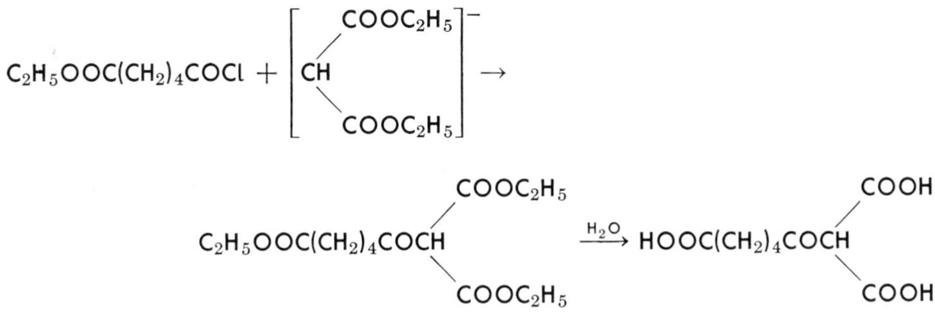

The product of the hydrolysis of the ester has two carboxyl groups attached to a carbon that also has a keto group attached to it. Thus the loss of only one carbon dioxide would leave a substituted β-ketoacid which would then decarboxylate further to give a methyl group.

$$HOOC(CH_2)_4COC\begin{matrix} COOH \\ \\ COOH \end{matrix} \xrightarrow{heat} 2CO_2 + HOOC(CH_2)_4COCH_3$$

ϵ-ketoheptoic acid

How could you prepare ϵ-ketocaprylic acid, $C_2H_5CO(CH_2)_4COOH$?

Through the application of the malonic ester synthesis, the acetoacetic ester synthesis, and the Claisen ester condensation, a wide variety of acids and ketones, dibasic acids, keto acids, and diketones is available for the study of the degradation products of unsaturated cyclic compounds.

PROBLEMS

14-1 (a) How could you prepare ethyl cyclopentan-1-one-2-carboxylate (a) from diethyl adipate, in one step? For which reaction discussed in Chapter 14 is this reaction the cyclic analog?

(b) What product (b) would result if the sodioester of (a) were treated with ethyl acrylate, $CH_2=CHCOOC_2H_5$?

(c) What product would be formed by the hydrolysis (and attendant decarboxylation) of (b)?

(d) Suppose the keto group of (c) were reduced by hydrogen over a platinum catalyst. Would this affect the carboxylic acid group? What would the product be?

(e) When this product is treated with an acid, an internal ester (these are called lactones) is formed, just as an ester is formed from C_2H_5OH and CH_3COOH under these conditions. What is the structure of the ester? How many atoms make up the new ring? Is the formation of a ring of this size favored by analogy with reactions which you have already seen?

14-2 Oil of bergamot yields, after purification procedures, a compound $C_{15}H_{24}$. This material, called bisabolene, gives $C_{15}H_{30}$ on hydrogenation. The double bonds are saturated at different rates, however, and the reaction may be stopped at an intermediate stage, so that tetrahydrobisabolene, $C_{15}H_{28}$, may be isolated.

(a) How many double bonds does bisabolene have? How many rings?

When tetrahydrobisabolene is ozonized, two fragments are obtained, $C_7H_{12}O$ and $C_8H_{16}O$. Chromic-sulfuric acid yields the same fragments.

(b) Are the new compounds aldehydes or ketones?

The compound $C_8H_{16}O$ may be oxidized with sodium hypobromite to give $C_7H_{14}O_2$. (This reaction is analogous to the reaction:

$$CH_3CH_2COCH_3 \xrightarrow[\text{(2) HCl}]{\text{(1) NaOBr}} CH_3CH_2COOH + CHBr_3$$

and is diagnostic for a methyl ketone.)

The compound $C_7H_{14}O_2$ may be carried through the Barbier-Wieland sequence of reactions (Section 12–5) to give $C_6H_{12}O_2$. If this sequence is repeated, $C_5H_{10}O_2$ is found. This compound forms a p-bromophenacyl ester which melts at 68°C.

(c) From this information, reconstruct the formulas for $C_5H_{10}O_2$, $C_6H_{12}O_2$, $C_7H_{14}O_2$, and $C_8H_{16}O$.

The other fragment from tetrahydrobisabolene, $C_7H_{12}O$, forms a semicarbazone which melts at 199°C.

(d) What is $C_7H_{12}O$? What is the structure for tetrahydrobisabolene?

Let us now concern ourselves with the location of the double bonds in bisabolene which were hydrogenated. It is safe to assume that there were no structural rearrangements during the hydrogenation, so that the partial structure we have already assigned is useful. Ozonolysis and reductive cleavage of bisabolene, $C_{15}H_{24}$, yields three fragments, C_3H_6O, $C_5H_8O_2$, and $C_7H_{10}O_3$. The last of these may be oxidized further with chromic-sulfuric acid, but the product, $C_7H_{10}O_4$, is unstable. It loses carbon dioxide readily and the organic product usually isolated is $C_6H_{10}O_2$.

(e) What kinds of acids lose CO_2 readily?

This $C_6H_{10}O_2$ may be prepared by the condensation of α-chloroacetone with sodio-acetoacetic ester and hydrolysis of the condensation product.

(f) What is it?

(g) What was the unstable $C_7H_{10}O_4$ and its predecessor $C_7H_{10}O_3$?

The other fragments are less difficult to identify. The C_3H_6O forms a semicarbazone melting at 187°C.

(h) Identify it.

The $C_5H_8O_2$ may be oxidized to $C_5H_8O_3$ with chromic-sulfuric acid and the product is stable.

(i) What kind of bifunctional ozonolysis product could be oxidized in only one position? A dialdehyde? A ketoaldehyde? A diketone?

(j) What type of compound must the $C_5H_8O_3$ be? Write possible structures fitting this fact. All of these except one can be excluded because they would not be stable under the reaction conditions. What must $C_5H_8O_3$ be?

Now that the fragments have been identified, it is obvious that they could be joined in many ways. We already know the structure of the carbon skeleton from which they were formed, however, because we know the structure of tetrahydrobisabolene. Only one of the fragments from the bisabolene oxidation could form the ring which must be present. Hence we can locate another double bond in bisabolene from the information we can deduce from this fragment. The other fragments must make up the rest of the molecule and thus the remaining unsaturation is located.

(k) What then must the structure of bisabolene be?

(l) What features remain undetermined?

(m) Which is harder to hydrogenate, a triply substituted double bond or a quadruply substituted double bond?

*How can reactions of halogens
be adapted to the purposes of structural proofs?
Which halogen reactions would be useful only in specific cases?
How can halogenations be used to prepare substances
of value as intermediates in synthetic reactions?*

15

HALOGENATIONS AND THEIR USE
IN STRUCTURAL DETERMINATIONS
AND SYNTHESES

15–1 Background

We have now encountered instances in which alkyl halides, acyl halides, and compounds with more than one halogen atom have proved useful in synthetic reactions. Some of the compounds necessary for synthesis can be prepared by addition of halogens or of hydrogen halides to unsaturated compounds. Others, however, are more conveniently prepared by substitution of hydrogen by halogen. In addition to their significance in syntheses, however, halogenation reactions can be used for diagnostic purposes in structural determinations. These synthetic and diagnostic objectives will make a study of halogenation reactions valuable to the reader.

15–2 Chlorination and Bromination in the Presence of Light

The paraffin hydrocarbons are so named because of their low affinity for chemical reagents. Their lack of reactivity extends to the halogens, unless the latter are especially activated. By exposing chlorine or bromine to intense light of the proper wavelength (sunlight is suitable for the purpose) the halogen can be "activated" sufficiently to permit it to react with paraffin hydrocarbons. The reaction is complex, and we shall postpone a discussion of it. The outcome of the reaction can be represented simply, however, as follows:

$$CH_4 + Cl_2 \xrightarrow{\text{light}} CH_3Cl + HCl$$

This reaction is not convenient for the laboratory preparation of alkyl halides. Unless it is controlled carefully, it can lead to explosions. With the higher alkanes, a mixture of the possible products is usually obtained, thus requiring extensive purification before chemical individuals are available. Commercially, on the other hand, the reaction is frequently economical, especially if the various isomers produced can be marketed separately. On a commercial scale, precautions are routinely instituted which make the reaction safe to perform.

In light-catalyzed substitutions, chlorine is more reactive than bromine. Iodine and fluorine differ from chlorine and bromine in their reactivities to alkanes. For iodine, reaction is not possible, even in the presence of light. For fluorine, the uncatalyzed reaction takes place with such violence as to be explosive.

15–3   Fluorinations

Because fluorine and its organic derivatives are assuming increasing industrial importance, a note concerning the reactivity of fluorine is in order. Elementary fluorine is such a powerful reagent that it will react with most materials. Organic chemicals are especially susceptible to its attack, the reactions taking place with violence, often explosive violence. A jet of fluorine directed toward a piece of wood will set it on fire. Thus the material must be handled with the utmost caution. In general, elementary fluorine is not used directly in halogenation reactions. Instead, it is used through an intermediary compound which diminishes the vigor of its attack. For example, antimony pentafluoride may be used to fluorinate alkanes. In the process, it is reduced to antimony trifluoride. The antimony pentafluoride is then regenerated by treatment of the trifluoride with fluorine in a separate operation.

$$CH_4 + SbF_5 \rightarrow CH_3F + HF + SbF_3$$
$$SbF_3 + F_2 \rightarrow SbF_5$$

Unlike most other halogenations, fluorination tends to continue until complete.

$$CH_3F + SbF_5 \rightarrow CH_2F_2 + HF + SbF_3$$
$$CH_2F_2 + SbF_5 \rightarrow CHF_3 + HF + SbF_3$$
$$CHF_3 + SbF_5 \rightarrow CF_4 + HF + SbF_3$$

15–4   Additions to Olefins

Olefins, unlike paraffins, react readily with all the halogens except iodine. Indeed, they are named olefins (that is, oil formers) because of their ability to form oils when reacted with chlorine and bromine. For this reaction, no catalyst is required. The high degree of reactivity to halogens extends even to most substituted olefins.

$$
\begin{array}{ccc}
CH—COOH & & BrCH—COOH \\
\| & \xrightarrow{\text{Br}_2} & | \\
CH—COOH & & BrCH—COOH
\end{array}
$$

Such additions make a wide variety of halogenated compounds available for syntheses. It should be recalled that monohalogenated derivatives can also be secured by an addition reaction.

$$\begin{array}{ccc} CH-COOH & & CH_2COOH \\ \| & \xrightarrow{HBr} & | \\ CH-COOH & & BrCH-COOH \end{array}$$

In this addition reaction, the order of reactivity of the halides is reversed; that is, for the addition of elementary halogens, chlorine is more reactive than bromine, while for the addition of the hydrogen halides, hydrogen bromide is more reactive than hydrogen chloride. For most additions, the reactivity of hydrogen chloride is so low that it is not convenient to react it under ordinary laboratory conditions. Instead, the reaction is usually performed under pressure and at an elevated temperature. Therefore for laboratory reactions, the addition of a hydrogen halide usually means the addition of hydrogen bromide.

15–5 Aromatic Halogenations

Halogenation of benzene rings provides still a third type of reaction. Again the reaction with fluorine is not feasible. Under ordinary conditions chlorine and bromine will not react with benzene, thus pointing to the contrast between the double bond of the ethylenic groups and the type of unsaturation present in benzene and its halogen derivatives. Substitution on the benzene ring can be effected by halogenation in the presence of a catalyst such as ferric chloride or ferric bromide.

$$C_6H_6 + Br_2 \xrightarrow{\text{catalyst}} C_6H_5Br + HBr$$

Iron filings are frequently used for the purpose and tin tetrachloride or tin tetrabromide are also used. The substances that serve for catalysts for the halogenation of "aromatic" substances such as benzene are not capable of bringing about the substitution of the paraffin hydrocarbons.

15–6 Bromine as a Diagnostic Reagent

Bromine constitutes the most useful of the halogens as a diagnostic reagent in most situations. Because it is red and most of the halides formed from it are colorless, decolorization of bromine can be used to establish a positive reaction. As a diagnostic reagent, bromine will distinguish between the three types of hydrocarbon. Uncatalyzed, bromine will react with olefins only. The types unreactive to bromine will usually be either aromatic or paraffinic. To distinguish between these types, reaction in the presence of an iron halide or iron filings could be tried. The *aromatic hydrocarbon* would react with bromine and *iron bromide*, the paraffinic would not. Finally, the *paraffinic hydrocarbon* would react with bromine *in the presence of light* of the wavelengths absorbed by the bromine. Reactivity with chlorine or bromine in the presence of light cannot be used to distinguish between aromatic and paraffinic hydrocarbons. Aromatic hydrocarbons will react with chlorine and bromine in the light to give addition instead of substitution.

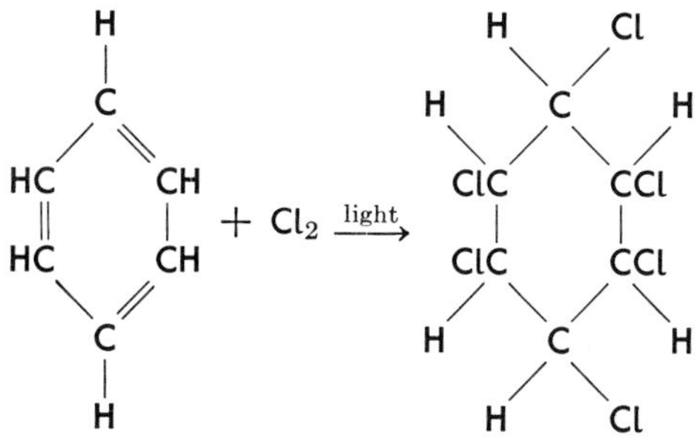

The mixture of stereoisomers of "benzene hexachloride" formed by this chlorination reaction has been used as an insecticide.

15–7 Selective Halogenation

The distinction between the conditions under which methane and benzene are halogenated permits us to control the position of halogenation in alkyl benzenes. Thus toluene can be halogenated either on the ring or on the side chain.

$$C_6H_5CH_3 + Cl_2 \xrightarrow{\text{FeCl}_3} ClC_6H_4CH_3 \quad \text{(mixture of \textit{ortho} and \textit{para} isomers)} + HCl$$

$$C_6H_5CH_3 + Cl_2 \xrightarrow{\text{light}} C_6H_5CH_2Cl + HCl$$

Selectivity of this sort is possible because a suitable catalyst can accelerate a reaction by one pathway while leaving the rate by another pathway unaltered.

The product of the side-chain chlorination is known as *benzyl chloride*. Physiologically it is a lachrymator. It is a reactive chloride and will readily hydrolyze to the alcohol.

$$C_6H_5CH_2Cl + NaOH \rightarrow C_6H_5CH_2OH + NaCl$$

In contrast, *ortho* and *para* chlorotoluenes are very unreactive so that temperatures in the neighborhood of 300°C and very high pressures are required to bring them into reaction.

The side-chain halogenation of toluene can be carried further.

$$C_6H_5CH_2Cl + Cl_2 \xrightarrow{\text{light}} C_6H_5CHCl_2 + HCl$$

This dichloride is known as *benzal chloride*. It is also a lachrymator. Its hydrolysis yields benzaldehyde. This is one of the favored methods for the industrial preparation of benzaldehyde.

$$C_6H_5CHCl_2 + H_2O \rightarrow C_6H_5CHO + 2HCl$$

Finally, the chlorination of the side chain can be completed.

$$C_6H_5CHCl_2 + Cl_2 \rightarrow C_6H_5CCl_3 + HCl$$

This substance, called *benzotrichloride*, is also a lachrymator. It can be hydrolyzed to benzoic acid. It has been postulated by some that the easy hydrolysis of these chlorides to yield HCl is responsible for their lachrymatory action. While this undoubtedly accounts for some irritant action, their potency as lachrymators is much greater than that of HCl. It is more probable that their action in alkylating or acylating, as the case may be, is involved in the physiological reaction. The hydrolysis of benzotrichloride accounts for a small portion of the benzoic acid produced commercially. The product made in this fashion is contaminated by traces of chlorinated by-products which render it inferior for use in perfume and flavoring materials to benzoic acid produced by processes not involving chlorination.

The benzyl ester of benzoic acid, benzyl benzoate, was widely used during World War II in military ointments and sprays as a delousing agent.

15-8 The Hell-Volhard-Zelinsky Reaction

Acetic acid and other monobasic aliphatic acids do not halogenate readily. The esters, anhydrides, and acid chlorides, in contrast, will halogenate, either with chlorine or with bromine.

$$CH_3COOC_2H_5 + Cl_2 \rightarrow ClCH_2COOC_2H_5 + HCl$$
$$(CH_3CO)_2O + 2Cl_2 \rightarrow (ClCH_2CO)_2O + 2HCl$$
$$CH_3COCl + Cl_2 \rightarrow ClCH_2COCl + HCl$$

With chlorine, the reaction can be carried to completion on heating.

$$ClCH_2COCl + Cl_2 \rightarrow Cl_2CHCOCl + HCl$$
$$Cl_2CHCOCl + Cl_2 \rightarrow Cl_3CCOCl + HCl$$

Although there are methods for preparing both dichloroacetic acid and trichloroacetic acid in better yields than this one, the reactions indicate the power of the reagent.

We have already seen that phosphorus chlorides react with acids to form acid chlorides. The preparative chemist can take advantage of this fact to make chloroacetic acid directly from acetic acid by using a little phosphorus as a catalyst.

$$2P + 3Cl_2 \rightarrow 2PCl_3$$
$$3CH_3COOH + PCl_3 \rightarrow 3CH_3COCl + P(OH)_3$$
$$CH_3COCl + Cl_2 \rightarrow ClCH_2COCl + HCl$$
$$ClCH_2COCl + CH_3COOH \rightarrow ClCH_2COOH + CH_3COCl$$

Because chloroacetyl chloride is more difficult to chlorinate than acetyl chloride, the exchange of the halogen on the acid chloride group will take place preferentially, forming more acid chloride. This halogen exchange permits the reaction to go to completion with only catalytic amounts of phosphorus. Water would hydrolyze the acid chloride. As a consequence, acid intended for this reaction must be sharply dried to prevent destruction of the acid chloride formed as an intermediate. The reaction is known as the Hell-Volhard-Zelinsky reaction, after its discoverers. The use of catalytic amounts of phosphorus for halogenation also succeeds for brominations. Again, iodine is not sufficiently powerful to permit halogenations of acids.

The Hell-Volhard-Zelinsky reaction only succeeds in substituting hydrogens on carbon atoms in the α-position to the carboxyl group, as is also true of the halogenation of esters and anhydrides.

$$CH_3CH_2COCl + Cl_2 \rightarrow CH_3CHClCOCl + HCl$$
$$CH_3CHClCOCl + Cl_2 \rightarrow CH_3CCl_2COCl + HCl$$

At this point the reaction stops. Because of this limitation of the reaction to the substitution of α-CH groups, the Hell-Volhard-Zelinsky reaction can be used to distinguish between possible isomeric structures.

$$CH_3CH_2CH_2COOH + Cl_2 \xrightarrow{P} CH_3CH_2CHClCOOH + HCl$$
$$CH_3CH_2CHClCOOH + Cl_2 \xrightarrow{P} CH_3CH_2CCl_2COOH + HCl$$

In contrast
$$(CH_3)_2CHCOOH + Cl_2 \xrightarrow{P} (CH_3)_2CClCOOH + HCl$$

Thus it is possible to prepare α,α-dichlorobutyric acid from n-butyric, but only α-monochloroisobutyric acid from isobutyric acid.

It is probable that the Hell-Volhard-Zelinsky reaction could be used diagnostically for the differentiation of dicarboxylic acids as well as for monocarboxylic acids. These halogenations have not been studied systematically, however, so possible limitations of the reaction are not understood.

15–9 Perchlorination

Acetic acid can also be chlorinated by the use of chlorine and sunlight.

$$CH_3COOH + Cl_2 \xrightarrow{\text{light}} ClCH_2COOH + HCl$$

It will be recalled that chlorine activated by light is a powerful enough reagent to attack aliphatic hydrocarbons. Hence the chlorination of propionic acid by chlorine in the presence of light produces a different result from that in the presence of phosphorus.

$$CH_3CH_2COOH + 2Cl_2 \xrightarrow{\text{light}} ClCH_2CHClCOOH + 2HCl$$

In this reaction the first chlorine goes into the α-position. This makes subsequent halogenation on the same carbon more difficult, so the second halogen then goes on the β-position.

By performing a chlorination with a large excess of chlorine in the presence of sunlight, it is possible to produce "perchloro" compounds, that is, substances in which all the hydrogens have been replaced by chlorines.

$$CH_3CH_2OOCCH_2CH_2COOCH_2CH_3 + 14Cl_2 \xrightarrow{\text{light}}$$

$$CCl_3CCl_2OOCCCl_2CCl_2COOCCl_2CCl_3 + 14HCl$$

15–10 β-Halogenated Acids

The removal of HCl from α-chloropropionic acid by means of alcoholic KOH is successful, just as with the production of an olefinic hydrocarbon from an alkyl halide:

$$CH_3CHClCH_3 + K^+ OH^- \xrightarrow{C_2H_5OH} CH_2{=}CHCH_3 + K^+ Cl^-$$

$$CH_3CHClCOO^- K^+ + K^+ OH^- \xrightarrow{C_2H_5OH} CH_2{=}CHCOO^- K^+ + K^+ Cl^- + H_2O$$

The product is potassium acrylate. Acrylic acid will add HCl or HBr but the reaction takes place with a directive influence opposite to that in the olefins, the COOH group thus causing a reversal of Markovnikov's rule.

$$CH_2{=}CHCOOH + HCl \rightarrow ClCH_2CH_2COOH$$

The reasons for this reversal will be discussed in Book 2.

This reaction completes the possibilities for the monosubstitution of propionic acid by halogens, so that either the α-halo or the β-halo compounds are available, as needed. The addition of chlorine to acrylic acid also provides an alternative and superior method for obtaining α,β-dichloropropionic acid.

$$CH_2{=}CHCOOH + Cl_2 \rightarrow ClCH_2CHClCOOH$$

15–11   The Haloform Reaction

One of the peculiarities of trichloroacetic acid is the ease with which it is decarboxylated by alkalis.

$$Cl_3CCOOH + 2NaOH \rightarrow CHCl_3 + Na_2CO_3 + H_2O$$

We have seen in the foregoing sections that the carbonyl group of an ester, an anhydride, or an acid chloride will activate the CH groups in the α-positions to halogenation. In the same manner, the carbonyl groups of aldehydes and ketones activate the CH groups in the α-positions.

$$CH_3CHO + Cl_2 \rightarrow ClCH_2CHO + HCl$$

This reaction will also proceed to completion.

$$ClCH_2CHO + Cl_2 \rightarrow Cl_2CHCHO + HCl$$
$$Cl_2CHCHO + Cl_2 \rightarrow Cl_3CCHO + HCl$$

The last substance in this series is chloral. On contact with water, chloral forms a hydrate which is an exception to the usual rule that two hydroxyl groups cannot exist on the same carbon atom.

$$Cl_3CCHO + H_2O \rightarrow Cl_3CCH(OH)_2$$

Chloral hydrate has been used in medicine as a hypnotic. It is the drug commonly employed in "knockout drops" or "Mickey Finns."

Like trichloroacetic acid, chloral hydrate undergoes ready cleavage in the presence of strong alkali.

$$Cl_3CCH(OH)_2 + Na^+ OH^- \rightarrow Cl_3CH + HCOO^- Na^+ + H_2O$$

In addition to chloroform, sodium formate is produced.

Acetone can be halogenated by elementary halogens. The halogenated acetones are powerful lachrymators. The speed of the reaction is increased by the addition of either acid or alkali, but since acid is evolved in the halogenation, the reaction soon gains velocity and no added catalyst is necessary. For aldehydes and ketones, the reaction proceeds so readily that even iodine can be used.

$$CH_3COCH_3 + 3I_2 \rightarrow I_3CCOCH_3 + 3HI$$

It will be noted that the halogens build up on the same carbon and are not distributed between the two possible α-positions.

Tri-iodoacetone will also cleave in strong alkali.

$$I_3COCH_3 + Na^+ OH^- \rightarrow CHI_3 + CH_3COO^- Na^+$$

The reaction by which substances with a CH_3 group in the α-position to a carbonyl group are treated with a halogen in the presence of alkali to give cleavage of the C—C bond is called the *haloform reaction*. It constitutes a very useful diagnostic test for a CH_3 group next to a carbonyl or for a group that is readily oxidized to such a system.

$$CH_3CH_2OH + I_2 + 2Na^+ OH^- \rightarrow CH_3CHO + 2Na^+ I^- + 2H_2O$$

$$CH_3CHO + 3I_2 + 4Na^+ OH^- \rightarrow CHI_3 + HCOO^- Na^+ + 3Na^+ I^- + 3H_2O$$

The reaction can be carried out with alkali and chlorine, bromine, or iodine, although the diagnostic utility of the haloform reaction lies in the fact that iodoform is a solid which is relatively easy to crystallize from the alkaline aqueous reaction mixture employed. Iodoform is a slightly yellowish crystalline powder melting at 120°C. It has an "antiseptic" odor that is frequently associated with hospitals, although in recent years its use has diminished because of the creation of more potent antiseptics.

While other halogenated derivatives of carbonyl compounds will sometimes undergo a cleavage similar to those outlined above, it is obvious that there must be three replaceable hydrogens on a single carbon in an α-position to a carbonyl for a haloform to be produced. The reaction thus shows the presence of such a group.

A positive iodoform reaction usually has diagnostic significance. A negative test, however, does not always mean that a methyl group next to a carbonyl is absent. We have already seen that acetic acid will not halogenate under these reaction conditions so in this case a negative reaction would not have diagnostic significance. For ethyl acetoacetate, the presence of two carbonyls adjacent to the central methylene group activates this group to halogenation to the exclusion of halogenation on the terminal methyl group.

$$CH_3COCH_2COOC_2H_5 + Br_2 \rightarrow CH_3COCBr_2COOC_2H_5$$

Strong alkali then cleaves this compound to form carboxylate salts.

$$CH_3COCBr_2COOC_2H_5 + 2Na^+ OH^- \rightarrow CH_3COO^- Na^+ + HCBr_2COO^- Na^+ + C_2H_5OH$$

Still other exceptions to the iodoform rule may occur when a high degree of substitution on one branch of the ketone may act to prevent complete halogenation on the methyl group, especially by iodine, which has less of a tendency to trisubstitute than do the other halogens.

A false positive test may occasionally be obtained when an unsaturated compound is cleaved by alkali to give acetone or another methyl ketone. Such cases are rare, however. Cleavages such as this will be discussed in Book 2.

15-12   Halides in Synthesis

In previous chapters we have found many synthetic reactions that employ halogenated compounds as reaction intermediates and in future chapters we shall add still others. For this reason, the availability of a wide variety of halogenated compounds increases the flexibility of the synthetic processes open to the chemist.

In their reactivities toward substituting reagents such as OH^-, CN^-, ammonia, and the amines and organic anions such as the sodium salts of ethyl acetoacetate and malonic ester, the alkyl halides exhibit the reverse order of reactivity to that of the elementary halogens.

$$F_2 > Cl_2 > Br_2 > I_2$$
$$CH_3I > CH_3Br > CH_3Cl > CH_3F$$

The reasons for these relationships between reactivities will be discussed in Book 2.

In most cases the organic chemist will choose either the iodide or the bromide for laboratory reactions, although the higher temperatures and pressures required to react chlorides are economically desirable industrially to save the extra cost of handling the more expensive bromides and iodides. Under most reaction conditions, fluorides are inert and they are seldom used in synthetic reactions.

PROBLEMS

15–1   Using suitable reagents how could you prepare:

(a) malic acid from maleic acid?

(b) phenacyl bromide from acetophenone?

(c) cyclohexyl chloride from benzene?

(d) nonanoic acid from 2-decanone?

$$\overset{\displaystyle OH}{\underset{\displaystyle }{HOOCCH_2\overset{|}{C}HCOOH}}$$
Malic acid

15–2   A compound has the formula C_8H_7BrO. On treatment with iodine and alkali it forms a slightly yellowish insoluble solid which melts at 60°C and contains only 0.30% hydrogen. When the solution from which the yellowish solid was filtered is concentrated and an ethanolic solution of phenacyl bromide is added, a solid ester is deposited. The ester has a saponification equivalent (that is, an equivalent weight with respect to hydrolysis) of 240, and the acid obtained from the hydrolysis melts at 121°C. What is C_8H_7BrO?

15–3   A liquid hydrocarbon has the formula C_7H_{12}. Oxidation with chromic-sulfuric acid yields $C_7H_{12}O_4$, melting point 127 to 128°C.

(a) To what class of compounds does $C_7H_{12}O_4$ belong?

(b) How many rings has C_7H_{12}? How many double bonds?

When $C_7H_{12}O_4$ is heated with $CaCO_3$, $C_7H_{10}O_3$, melting point 94 to 95°C, is formed.

(c) What type of compound is $C_7H_{10}O_3$?

(d) Write possible structures for $C_7H_{10}O_3$.

When $C_7H_{12}O_4$ is treated with phosphorus and an excess of bromine, a compound with melting point 150°C (dec) is isolated after suitable workup. This material is acidic and has a neutralization equivalent of 159.

(e) How many hydrogens were replaced by bromine?

(f) Are any structures you have drawn excluded by this information?

When the bromo compound is treated with a dehydrating agent, $C_7H_8Br_2O_3$, melting point 94 to 95°, is formed.

(g) Does this add any new information to the solution of the structure?

When $C_7H_{12}O_4$ is refluxed with an excess of dry ethanol in the presence of a little concentrated H_2SO_4, $C_{11}H_{20}O_4$ is formed. This is then added slowly to an excess of phenylmagnesium bromide in ether, and after the usual workup a labile material corresponding to $C_{31}H_{32}O_2$ is obtained. This readily loses water, forming $C_{31}H_{28}$. Reductive ozonolysis of this compound yields a mixture of products. The mixture is reacted with 2,4-dinitrophenylhydrazine and the solid products from this are chromatographed. Among the materials isolated are one melting at 209°C and one melting at 239°C.

(h) What is the material whose 2,4-DNP melts at 239°C? Is this information useful?

(i) What is the structure of the compound whose 2,4-DNP melts at 209°C?

(j) Identify $C_{31}H_{28}$, $C_{31}H_{32}O_2$, $C_{11}H_{20}O_4$, and $C_7H_{12}O_4$.

(k) Identify the hydrocarbon C_7H_{12}.

How can amines be degraded to olefins for the purposes of structural investigation? What additional reactions of amines are useful for these purposes? How can the reactions of amines be used for the synthesis of olefins? How can amines with a variety of substituents be synthesized?

16

AMINES AND THEIR PREPARATION; THE HOFMANN DEGRADATION AND ITS USE IN STRUCTURAL DETERMINATIONS AND SYNTHESES

16–1   Amines and their Occurrence

Amines constitute one group of organic derivatives of ammonia. Just as the two hydrogens of water may be replaced, so may the three hydrogens of ammonia. In the water series, the replacement of one hydrogen with an alkyl group gives an alcohol, while the replacement of two gives an ether. When one of the hydrogens of ammonia is replaced, the derivative is a primary amine, such as methylamine, CH_3NH_2. When two are replaced, the derivative is a secondary amine, such as dimethylamine, $(CH_3)_2NH$. Replacement of all three hydrogens produces a tertiary amine, $(CH_3)_3N$.

The simple aliphatic amines are prototypes of more complicated nitrogen compounds which are of great physiological interest. Several aliphatic amines and some mixed aliphatic-aromatic amines are found as decomposition products of proteins, which are the organic structural substances of muscle, skin, and many other tissue materials. One of the main odoriferous products of stale fish is trimethylamine. Most of the aliphatic amines are unpleasant smelling substances. In general, the naturally occurring amines are formed by bacterial decomposition of amino acids, the building blocks of proteins. We shall study the amino acids in detail later. We might represent the simplest of them as aminoacetic acid, called *glycine*, H_2NCH_2COOH. Putrefactive bacteria have enzymes in them which can cause decarboxylation of amino acids with the formation of amines.

$$H_2NCH_2COOH \xrightarrow[\text{enzyme}]{\text{bacterial}} H_2NCH_3 + CO_2$$

16–2   Ptomaines

In 1870 Selmi found that a group of bases could be isolated from decomposed food. These were called *ptomaines* and it was presumed that the action of bacteria produced these substances, that they were toxic, and that they were responsible for the toxic, often lethal, symptoms of food poisoning. Thus was born the theory of "ptomaine poisoning."

In 1910 Barger, a British chemist, and Dale, a British pharmacologist, collaborated in a study of the field of physiologically active amines with special reference to testing the "ptomaine poisoning" theory. Barger and Dale took "ten pounds of the finest steak and allowed it to putrefy." They then started the chemical isolation of the amines formed. Barger identified a whole series of amines and Dale tested their physiological actions. Most had some activity, being "pressor" substances. That is, they caused an increase in blood pressure. Yet their toxicity was not nearly sufficient to account for ptomaine poisoning. Thus the "ptomaine poisoning" theory was disproved experimentally.

16–3   Bacterial Food Poisoning; Toxins

We know today that food poisoning is usually one of two types. One is due to bacterial infection, the other is due to the production by bacteria of extremely toxic proteins, bacterial toxins. These are much more complicated materials than the amines and will be discussed briefly under the heading of "proteins." By far the most dramatic types of food poisoning are due to the toxin of *Clostridium botulinum*. This organism is an anaerobe which grows in canned food, only in the absence of air. Acid inhibits its growth so that it appears in such foods as canned beans, peas, and meats. The spores from which it grows are common in the earth so that infection of food is easy. Boiling does not destroy the spores. While the organisms will grow in canned food, they will not grow in the body. The toxin which has been produced in the can is still present, however, and is one of the most highly lethal substances known. In spite of this, it is unstable to heat so that thorough boiling immediately before eating will destroy the toxin. The possibility of the infection of food by this organism is one of the hazards of home canning. Periodically, commercial precautions are penetrated and the organism gets into a batch of canned food with grave consequences. So we see that the earlier concept of the formation of a toxic chemical by bacterial action has been demonstrated in actuality by modern studies, even though the chemical is not a "ptomaine" and is tremendously more potent than anything that the chemists of the last century studied.

16–4   Alkaloids

Among the more complicated amines are the so-called *alkaloids*. These include some materials with very potent physiological action. Some alkaloids are used as therapeutic agents, and the investigation of the structures of alkaloids continues to be a field of great activity for organic chemists. Some of the methods of structural investigation used on the simpler amines can be carried over into the field of alkaloid chemistry. In addition, methods of synthesis used for amines can also be carried over into the more complicated field of alkaloid synthesis.

16–5   Hofmann and the Synthesis of Alkyl Amines

The pioneering work in the investigation of the aliphatic amines was performed by A. W. von Hofmann. Hofmann was both an accomplished chemist and an astute chemical politician. He was largely responsible for making the political arrangements which led to German chemical pre-eminence in the latter part of the nineteenth century and the early part of the twentieth century.

In Hofmann's day, pure methyl alcohol was not very readily available. The substance was prepared by the dry distillation of wood, and numerous by-products were present. Purification was tedious and expensive so that the most readily available alcohol was ethyl alcohol. This accounts for the fact that, even today with methanol readily available and cheap, organic chemists still have described far more ethyl derivatives than methyl derivatives. Hofmann made ethyl iodide from ethanol and then studied its action on ammonia. He found that he had difficulty in preparing pure ethylamine.

$$C_2H_5I + NH_3 \rightarrow C_2H_5NH_3{}^+ I^-$$

This equation is not written as Hofmann wrote it. We know today that ammonium iodide and ethylammonium iodide are ionic substances, so we shall write them in this manner:

$$NH_3 + HI \rightarrow H{-}\overset{\overset{\displaystyle H}{|}}{\underset{\underset{\displaystyle H}{|}}{N}}{\overset{+}{-}}H \ I^- \qquad C_2H_5NH_2 + HI \rightarrow C_2H_5{-}\overset{\overset{\displaystyle H}{|}}{\underset{\underset{\displaystyle H}{|}}{N}}{\overset{+}{-}}H \ I^-$$

Ethylammonium iodide reacts with ammonia to form an equilibrium mixture with ethylamine and ammonium iodide.

$$C_2H_5NH_3{}^+ I^- + NH_3 \leftrightarrows C_2H_5NH_2 + NH_4{}^+ I^-$$

The ethylamine made available by this process then reacts with ethyl iodide just as the ammonia does.

$$C_2H_5NH_2 + C_2H_5I \rightarrow (C_2H_5)_2NH_2{}^+ I^-$$

Equilibration then takes place and diethylamine is formed.

$$(C_2H_5)_2NH_2{}^+ I^- + NH_3 \leftrightarrows (C_2H_5)_2NH + NH_4{}^+ I^-$$

This then reacts with ethyl iodide to give triethylammonium iodide.

$$(C_2H_5)_2NH + C_2H_5I \rightarrow (C_2H_5)_3NH^+ I^-$$

Equilibration of this with ammonia makes triethylamine available.

$$(C_2H_5)_3NH^+ I^- + NH_3 \leftrightarrows (C_2H_5)_3N$$

16-6 Quaternary Ammonium Salts

To isolate amines from an alkylation mixture, one would add sodium hydroxide to neutralize the iodide salts present and would then distill the aqueous solution to separate the amines.

$$NH_4{}^+ I^- + C_2H_5NH_3{}^+ I^- + (C_2H_5)_2NH_2{}^+ I^- + (C_2H_5)_3NH^+ I^- + 4Na^+ OH^- \rightarrow$$
$$NH_3 + C_2H_5NH + (C_2H_5)_2NH + (C_2H_5)_3N + 4Na^+ I^-$$

Hofmann did this and found that the mixture of amines which he obtained did not account for all the ethyl iodide taken. Even with modern techniques, the separation of a mixture of this sort, the identification of the constituents, and the quantitative determination of the "material balance" would be a formidable undertaking. When Hofmann performed the task, over a century ago, it was monumental. He identified in his reaction products unreacted ammonia, ethylamine, diethylamine, and triethylamine. Since the sum of the weights of the amines did not account for all the ethyl iodide, Hofmann decided that the remainder must still be in the water solution. So he continued to heat the solution. When most of the water had been removed and the boiling point of the alkaline liquor in the flask began to rise, he found that more triethylamine began to come over. Even this did not account for all the material taken, so he examined the products still more carefully. In addition to the triethylamine, he finally succeeded in isolating ethylene. He reasoned, then, that the water solution contained a soluble base which would decompose on heating to yield triethylamine and ethylene. By treating purified triethylamine with ethyl iodide, he was able to prepare a salt, tetraethylammonium iodide.

$$(C_2H_5)_3N + C_2H_5I \rightarrow (C_2H_5)_4N^+ I^-$$

This crystallized nicely and on treatment with sodium hydroxide yielded an aqueous solution which, on heating, decomposed to give triethylamine and ethylene. Hofmann therefore decided that the base formed was tetraethylammonium hydroxide.

$$(C_2H_5)_4N^+ I^- + Na^+ OH^- \rightarrow Na^+ I^- + (C_2H_5)_4N^+ OH^-$$

This should then decompose according to the scheme.

$$(C_2H_5)_4N^+OH^- \xrightarrow{\text{heat}} (C_2H_5)_3N + C_2H_4 + H_2O$$

To test this scheme, Hofmann decided that the base should be prepared in a more purified form. Silver oxide in aqueous suspension reacts slightly with water to form a small amount of argentous hydroxide.

$$Ag_2O + H_2O \xrightarrow{\Delta} 2Ag^+ OH^-$$

Removal of the silver ion will displace the equilibrium rapidly to generate more hydroxide ion, so that silver oxide can be used to prepare organic bases from their halides. While the reagent employed is Ag_2O, we shall write the equations as if $AgOH$ were taken.

$$(C_2H_5)_4N^+ I^- + Ag^+ OH^- \rightarrow (C_2H_5)_4N^+ OH^- + AgI$$

After filtering off the silver iodide and excess silver oxide, Hofmann had an aqueous solution containing only tetraethylammonium hydroxide. This he purified by removal of the water in a vacuum to avoid heating. The solid which remained turned out to be a very caustic base like sodium hydroxide. It was so hygroscopic that it was difficult to secure an analytical sample, just as is the case with sodium hydroxide. On heating, the base decomposed smoothly to triethylamine, ethylene, and water.

16–7 Decomposition of Quaternary Ammonium Bases

Hofmann's observations on the behavior of tetraethylammonium hydroxide led him to wonder whether or not all tetrasubstituted or "quaternary" ammonium bases would react similarly. He found that tetramethylammonium hydroxide, made by a similar process from ammonia and methyl iodide followed by silver oxide, would decompose, although at a higher temperature than the ethyl compound.

$$(CH_3)_4N^+ OH^- \xrightarrow{\text{heat}} (CH_3)_3N + CH_3OH$$

He investigated other combinations by making tertiary amines and reacting them with various alkyl iodides followed by silver oxide. He found that whenever there was an ethyl group present, ethylene would be formed by the decomposition, no matter whether the other groups were methyls or larger than ethyl. He thus formulated a rule: If the composition of a quaternary ammonium hydroxide makes it possible to form ethylene, then ethylene will be formed on its thermal decomposition. While later investigations have shown that it is possible to construct molecules that will circumvent Hofmann's rule, the rule still holds good for all cases in which the substituting groups on the ammonium nitrogen atom are aliphatic.

Hofmann next prepared a quaternary ammonium compound that could not decompose to ethylene by treating trimethylamine with amyl iodide. The amyl alcohol that Hofmann had available for the iodide preparation was a mixture consisting of about seven parts of isoamyl alcohol, $(CH_3)_2CHCH_2CH_2OH$, with one part of "active amyl alcohol," $C_2H_5CH(CH_3)CH_2OH$. (The reader should clarify for himself why this material is called "active amyl alcohol.") This mixture is very difficult to separate by fractional distillation, and it was not until relatively recently that stills efficient enough to separate the two alcohols were available. We shall write the reaction as if the reagent were all the major component.

$$(CH_3)_3N + (CH_3)_2CHCH_2CH_2I \rightarrow (CH_3)_3\overset{+}{N}C_5H_{11}I^- \xrightarrow{AgOH} (CH_3)_3\overset{+}{N}C_5H_{11}OH^-$$

The decomposition of this compound could yield methanol and dimethylamylamine, or it could give water, amylene, and trimethylamine. Hofmann found that on heating, the latter group of products was formed.

$$(CH_3)_3NC_5H_{11}OH^- \xrightarrow{heat} (CH_3)_3N + H_2O + (CH_3)_2CHCH=CH_2$$

Thus starting with amyl alcohol, Hofmann had, in effect, removed the elements of water to form the corresponding olefin. If we take the alkyl halide as the starting point, we see that trimethylamine followed by silver oxide acts as a "dehydrohalogenating" agent, that is, it removes the elements of a hydrogen halide. In this case, the rearrangements which can accompany the removal of water from alcohols by acids do not occur. Hence investigators interested in preparing pure olefins choose this method for their preparations.

16–8 Hofmann's Rule; Synthesis of Olefins

The implications of Hofmann's discovery with respect to the directive influence at work in olefin formation are interesting with respect to alternative synthetic pathways. Given dimethylethylpropylammonium hydroxide, the formation of ethylene rather than of propylene would be observed.

$$\underset{\underset{CH_3}{|}}{\overset{\overset{CH_3}{|}}{C_2H_5NCH_2CH_2CH_3}}{}^+ OH^- \xrightarrow{heat} CH_2=CH_2 + (CH_3)_2NC_3H_7 + H_2O$$

Considering the hydrogens in the β-positions from the nitrogen, we see that the primary hydrogen was lost in preference to the secondary hydrogen. In the dehydration of alcohols, the Saytzev rule is the opposite: secondary hydrogen is lost in preference to primary. It is true, in general, that the directive influences at work in olefin formation are opposite for the Hofmann degradation from those at work in the acidic degradations usually governed by the Saytzev rule. Thus the degradation of trimethyl-*sec*-butylammonium hydroxide would lead mainly to butene-1

$$\underset{\underset{\displaystyle CH_3CHCH_2CH_3OH^-}{|}}{(CH_3)_3N^+} \xrightarrow{\text{heat}} CH_2{=}CHCH_2CH_3 + N(CH_3)_3 + H_2O$$

while the dehydration of *sec*-butyl alcohol by sulfuric acid would yield mostly butene-2.

$$CH_3CHOHCH_2CH_3 \xrightarrow{H_2SO_4} CH_3CH{=}CHCH_3 + H_2O$$

Reasons for these differences will be discussed in Book 2.

Hofmann's method is still one of the preferred methods for the preparation of olefins. In these reactions a certain proportion of alcohol is formed by a decomposition paralleling that of tetramethylammonium hydroxide (Section 16–7). This proportion is low with lower members of the saturated amine series and rises as the molecular weight of the aliphatic residue increases.

16–9 Olefin Formation in Structural Determinations

Let us now examine the information that can be gained from the Hofmann reaction on a simple unknown. The compound has the analysis $C_5H_{13}N$. This analysis in itself yields information. If we consider the formula for methylamine, CH_3NH_2, we see that it can be considered, formally, as if an NH group were inserted between a C and an H of methane. Thus each nitrogen in an amine carries an additional hydrogen with it and the empirical formula for the saturated amine series is $C_nN_mH_{2n+2+m}$. For methylamine this becomes $C_1N_1H_{2+2+1}$ or CH_5N.

Now we shall return to the discussion of our unknown. Since there is one nitrogen, we may rewrite the formula as $C_5H_{12}NH$. Thus the compound is a saturated amine.

We have seen that treatment with an alkyl iodide will carry an amine all the way to a quaternary salt. To bring this about in the best yield, an excess of methyl iodide is used. Analysis of the product which results will permit us to distinguish between primary, secondary, and tertiary amines. If the amine is primary, analysis will show that the iodide formed from it will contain three more carbons than the starting material. If the amine is secondary, analysis will show the addition of two carbons. If tertiary, only one carbon will be required to form the quaternary.

For our unknown, treatment with excess methyl iodide produced $C_8H_{20}N^+ I^-$. This would be formulated as $C_5H_{13}N + 3CH_3I \rightarrow C_8H_{20}NI + 2HI$. In laboratory practice, a base is added to bind the HI formed and thus permit the reaction to go to completion. The interpretation of the reaction is that three carbons were added in the alkylation reaction, hence the initial amine was primary. On treatment with silver oxide, this will give the quaternary base.

$$C_8H_{20}I + AgOH \rightarrow C_8H_{21}ON + AgI$$

Dry distillation of the base results in the formation of an olefin.

$$C_8H_{21}ON \xrightarrow{heat} (CH_3)_3N + H_2O + C_5H_{10}$$

To complete the structural proof, the olefin is degraded with acid dichromate.

$$C_5H_{10} + CrO_3 \xrightarrow{H_2SO_4} CH_3CH_2CH_2COOH + CO_2$$

This shows that the olefin was 1-pentene. On this basis, two possible formulas can be written for the amine.

$$CH_3CH_2CH_2CH_2CH_2NH_2 \qquad or \qquad CH_3CH_2CH_2CH(NH_2)CH_3$$

Either of these would give 1-pentene as the major product of the degradation. For this reason, distinction between the two possibilities would have to be made by synthesis, one being prepared from *n*-amyl iodide, the other from 2-iodopentane.

16–10 Derivatives for the Identification of Amines; the Schotten-Baumann Reaction

As with acids and alcohols, identification of primary and secondary amines is made by preparing solid derivatives. For this purpose, acid chlorides are usually employed to form amides. Thus methylamine, a gas boiling at $-6°C$, will form solids with the following acid chlorides:

$$CH_3NH_2 + C_6H_5SO_2Cl \xrightarrow{OH^-} CH_3NHSO_2C_6H_5 \quad (m.p.\ 30°C)$$

(Benzenesulfonyl chloride)   (N-methylbenzene-sulfonamide)

$$CH_3NH_2 + C_6H_5COCl \xrightarrow{OH^-} CH_3NHCOC_6H_5 \quad (m.p.\ 80°C)$$

(Benzoyl chloride)   (N-methyl-benzamide)

$$CH_3NH_2 + C_7H_7SO_2Cl \xrightarrow{OH^-} CH_3NHSO_2C_7H_7 \quad (m.p.\ 75°C)$$

(*p*-toluenesulfonyl chloride)   (N-methyl-*p*-toluenesulfonamide)

Benzenesulfonyl chloride, the acid chloride of benzenesulfonic acid, reacts to form benzenesulfonamides. Benzoyl chloride forms benzamides; p-toluenesulfonyl chloride reacts to form p-toluenesulfonamides.

The reaction of an amine with benzoyl chloride in the presence of alkali is known as the Schotten-Baumann reaction. Under the conditions employed, benzoyl chloride will also react with alcohols.

$$C_2H_5OH + C_6H_5COCl \xrightarrow{OH^-} C_6H_5COOC_2H_5$$

The order of reactivity is: amines > alcohols > water.

16-11   The Hinsberg Reaction

Because of the popularity of benzoyl chloride as a reagent during the time that the amines were first being prepared, more substituted benzamides are known than substituted sulfonamides. In recent times, however, the use of p-toluene-sulfonyl chloride has been increasing because of the possibility of distinguishing between primary, secondary, and tertiary amines using it. This reaction will also proceed with benzenesulfonyl chloride. The benzenesulfonamides and p-toluenesul-fonamides of primary amines still have one free NH group. This proves to be sufficiently acidic to react with strong base to form a water-soluble sodium salt, for amines with a moderate number of carbon atoms.

$$C_6H_5NH_2 + C_7H_7SO_2Cl + NaOH \rightarrow C_6H_5\overset{\overset{H}{|}}{N}SO_2C_7H_7 + NaCl + H_2O$$

$$C_6H_5\overset{\overset{H}{|}}{N}SO_2C_7H_7 + OH^- \rightarrow [C_6H_5NSO_2C_7H_7]^- + H_2O$$

With amines of higher molecular weight, the hydrocarbon nature can become so pronounced that the sodium salt is insoluble in water. In this case, the substituted sulfonamide can be dissolved in ether and treated with metallic sodium. If an NH group is present, an insoluble sodium salt will precipitate from the ether.

Secondary amines lack the extra hydrogen, so they do not form alkali-soluble sulfonamides.

$$C_6H_5NHCH_3 + C_7H_7SO_2Cl + Na^+OH^- \rightarrow C_6H_5N(CH_3)SO_2C_7H_7 + Na^+Cl^- + H_2O$$

Tertiary amines do not react with either of the sulfonyl chlorides or with benzoyl chloride in the presence of water.

This method for distinguishing between amines is known as the *Hinsberg reaction*. Not only can it be used for purposes of identification, but it is also valuable for the separation of the three types of amines. Although the regeneration of the original amines from the substituted sulfonamides requires drastic conditions, it can be accomplished.

16-12   Substituted Thioureas

Still another method for the identification of amines has been widely used. This is the reaction with phenyl isothiocyanate.

$$C_2H_5NH_2 + C_6H_5N{=}C{=}S \rightarrow C_2H_5NH\overset{\overset{\displaystyle S}{\|}}{C}NHC_6H_5$$

The derivative formed is a thiourea. Tables of the properties of various substituted benzamides, benzenesulfonamides, toluenesulfonamides, and thioureas of primary and secondary amines are available for the purpose of identifying unknowns. Because we shall have few further instances of obtaining simple amines as unknowns, we shall not reproduce these tables here. We shall rely, instead, on chemical degradations to establish the structures of the more complicated amines that we shall meet.

16-13   Derivatives of Tertiary Amines

Tertiary amines do not react with any of the foregoing reagents under the conditions used for the formation of derivatives of the primary and secondary amines. The best derivatives of tertiary amines for identification purposes are the methiodides, prepared by alkylation with methyl iodide, and the picrates, salts of picric acid.

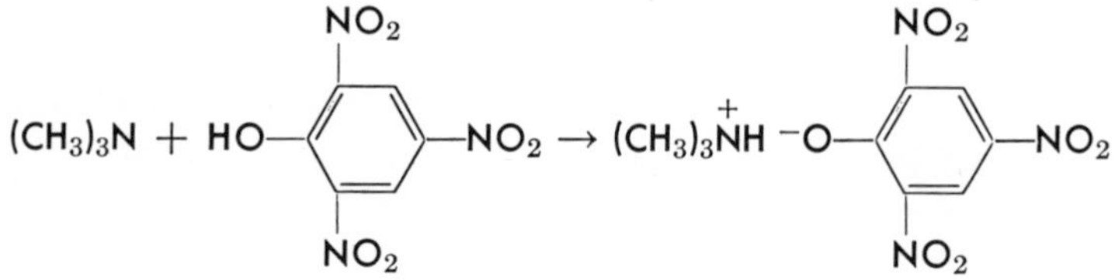

While phenol, C_6H_5OH, is only a little more acidic than water, the substitution of three of the benzene hydrogens with nitro groups increases the acidity of the phenol so that picric acid is comparable to the weaker mineral acids in acid strength. It has the property of forming nicely crystalline salts with a wide variety of organic bases and is thus frequently used in identifications.

PROBLEMS

16-1   Draw structures for the following compounds:
   (a) di-n-butylamine hydrochloride (di-n-butylammonium chloride)
   (b) methyldiphenylamine
   (c) β-aminoadipic acid
   (d) N-propylbenzamide

(e) N,N-dimethylbutyramide

(f) N,N,N',N'-tetramethylglutaramide

(g) N,N-dihexylfumaramide

(h) N,N'-dihexylfumaramide

(i) To what must the prime (') refer? Does the amide related to a dicarboxylic acid by the nomenclature used above contain one or two amide groups?

16-2 Write equations for Hofmann's procedure with CH_3I and Ag_2O with the following amines repeating the reaction until trimethyl amine is obtained. It will pay to write down the empirical formulas for each compound prepared in the procedure and to note how the degree of unsaturation can be determined from the empirical formulas.

(a) $(CH_3CH_2CH_2CH_2)_2NH$ (b) $(CH_3)_2NCH_2CH_2CH_2CH_2CH_2CH=CH_2$

(c) $FCH_2CH_2CHCH_2NH_2$
$\qquad\qquad\quad |$
$\qquad\qquad\ CH_3$

16-3 A compound has the formula $C_8H_{19}N$ (A).

(a) How many hydrogens does it need to correspond to a saturated compound? On treatment with excess methyl iodide it forms $C_{10}H_{24}NI$ (B).

(b) How many carbons were added to the molecule in this step?

(c) What kind of amine must the original compound have been?

(d) What result would have occurred if compound A had been treated with p-toluene-sulfonyl chloride? Would this product have formed a sodium salt?

The following sequence of steps is then carried out:

$$C_{10}H_{24}NI \xrightarrow[H_2O]{Ag_2O} C_{10}H_{25}NO \xrightarrow{heat} H_2O + C_2H_4 + C_8H_{19}N$$
$$\quad (B) \qquad\qquad\qquad (C) \qquad\qquad\qquad\qquad\qquad\quad (D)$$

(e) Since ethylene was produced by heating $C_{10}H_{25}NO$, what alkyl group must have been attached to nitrogen?

(f) Write as much as possible of the formula for $C_8H_{19}N$ (D). How many methyl groups do you know it has?

(g) What reaction would this compound give with benzenesulfonyl chloride?

(h) Write as much as possible of the formula for the *original* $C_8H_{19}N$ (A).

When D is treated with methyl iodide, $C_9H_{22}NI$ is formed. Moist silver oxide converts this to $C_9H_{23}NO$, and pyrolysis of this compound gives H_2O, C_3H_9N, and C_6H_{12}.

(i) What is C_3H_9N?

Ozonolysis of C_6H_{12} followed by reductive workup gives a mixture of two compounds whose semicarbazones are found to melt at 169°C and 191°C.

(j) What is C_6H_{12}?

(k) Where could nitrogen have been attached to the carbon skeleton so that this olefin would have been produced in the pyrolysis step? Is the point of attachment uniquely determined?

(l) Write structures for D, C, B, and A. If their structures are not determined by the degradation, show how you would determine the structure of A.

16–4   An amine is analyzed and found to have the formula $C_6H_{15}N$ (A). Treatment with benzenesulfonyl chloride yields $C_{12}H_{19}NO_2S$ (B), which is found to form a sodium salt on treatment with base.

(a) Is A saturated?

(b) Is A primary, secondary, or tertiary?

When $C_6H_{12}N$ is treated with an excess of methyl iodide, $C_9H_{22}NI$ is formed. Conversion of this to the hydroxide and heating the hydroxide yields C_3H_9N and C_6H_{12}. On closer inspection, however, the C_6H_{12} is not homogeneous. With the most refined techniques of separation it appears to be a mixture of two very similar compounds. The usual laboratory fractionation by distillation appears to be useless.

When a sample of this "C_6H_{12}" is ozonized, and the products characterized by the formation of 2,4-DNP derivatives, three products are found. The 2,4-DNP derivatives melt at 168°C, 154°C, and 122°C.

Oxidation of the "C_6H_{12}" by chromic-sulfuric acid is carried out as a confirmatory test. The acids obtained are characterized by their p-bromophenacyl esters. These are found to melt at 85°C, 63°C and 63°C, respectively. The two with the same melting point depress the melting point of each other.

(c) What two compounds with the formula C_6H_{12}, if they were mixed together, could give rise to this set of products?

(d) Where must the nitrogen have been attached to the carbon skeleton to give this pair of olefins and no others?

(e) What is the structure of A?

Part 5

STRUCTURES OF SOME
NATURAL PRODUCTS

One of the most exciting and rewarding fields in which the organic chemist has engaged is that of the structures of natural products. These products are presumed to have significance to the organisms from which they are obtained, either as structural materials, as active participants in metabolic processes, or as excrement. The investigation of their structures forms the first prerequisite to an understanding of the nature of life processes and is therefore the essential ingredient of mechanistic biochemistry. Synthetic alterations of these structures frequently produce artificial materials which have enhanced physiological or therapeutic value, and the systematic study of these changes is at the basis of modern physiological chemistry and pharmaceutical chemistry. It is mainly through such studies that the great modern developments in chemotherapy have been made possible. Studies on the structures of actively functioning materials have led to a rational basis for the development of pharmacology. Finally, the detailed examination of both structural and functional materials in living organisms gives us our first approach to an understanding of the mechanism of reproduction, the essential key to the difference between animate and inanimate objects. The purpose of Part 5 is to introduce the reader to some of the simpler chemistry involved in these subjects.

*How may the principles developed for determining
the structures of simple amines be applied to the problem
of structural determination in alkaloids?*

17

EXHAUSTIVE METHYLATION

17–1   A Simple Structural Determination

A chemical reduction yielded an unexpected product, requiring a structural investigation. The product was a pungent, basic oil boiling at 88°C which analyzed for C_4H_9N. This analysis is two hydrogens short of that for the saturated amine, $C_4H_{11}N$. Therefore the unknown was either unsaturated or cyclic.

The product obtained on treatment with methyl iodide was $C_6H_{14}NI$. Since this represents the addition of two carbons, the original amine was secondary.

On treatment of the iodide with silver oxide, a base was formed with the formula $C_6H_{15}ON$ which, on heating, gave $C_6H_{13}N$. From the analysis it can be concluded that the original base lost the elements of water on heating.

The thermal decomposition product had two less hydrogens than the saturated amine, $C_6H_{15}N$. The decomposition demonstrates that the original amine, C_4H_9N, contained no ethyl group, since no ethylene was formed in the thermal decomposition.

An amine of the composition $C_6H_{13}N$ must be either unsaturated or cyclic. But this amine was formed by a reaction that is known to give an olefin. For example:

$$CH_3-\overset{\overset{+}{N}(CH_3)_3}{\underset{|}{CH}}-CH_3 \ OH^- \xrightarrow{\text{heat}} CH_3CH{=}CH_2 + H_2O + N(CH_3)_3$$

$$(C_6H_{17}ON)$$

Therefore the amine is unsaturated, not cyclic.

This information enables us to reason back to the essential structural feature of the original amine, C_4H_9N. Had it been unsaturated, it would have had a chain attached to the nitrogen at only a single point. Cleavage of this bond, still present in $C_6H_{15}ON$, would have formed a doubly unsaturated compound which would

231

have been detached from the nitrogen. For example:

$$CH_2\!\!=\!\!CH\!\!-\!\!CH_2\!\!-\!\!CH_2\!\!-\!\!\underset{\underset{H}{|}}{\overset{\overset{CH_3}{|}}{N}}\!\!-\!\!H + 2CH_3I \rightarrow CH_2\!\!=\!\!CH\!\!-\!\!CH_2\!\!-\!\!CH_2\!\!-\!\!\underset{\underset{CH_3}{|}}{\overset{\overset{CH_3}{|+}}{N}}\!\!-\!\!CH_3\ I^- + HI$$

$$(C_5H_{11}N)$$

$$CH_2\!\!=\!\!CH\!\!-\!\!CH_2\!\!-\!\!CH_2\!\!-\!\!\underset{\underset{CH_3}{|}}{\overset{\overset{CH_3}{|+}}{N}}\!\!-\!\!CH_3\ I^- + AgOH \rightarrow$$

$$AgI + CH_2\!\!=\!\!CH\!\!-\!\!CH_2\!\!-\!\!CH_2\!\!-\!\!\underset{\underset{CH_3}{|}}{\overset{\overset{CH_3}{|+}}{N}}\!\!-\!\!CH_3\ OH^- \xrightarrow{\text{heat}}$$

$$(C_7H_{17}ON)$$

$$CH_2\!\!=\!\!CH\!\!-\!\!CH\!\!=\!\!CH_2 + H_2O + N(CH_3)_3$$

But instead of this, a singly unsaturated compound was actually formed, and this was still an amine with the same number of carbons as the quaternary base. Hence the breaking of a C—N bond and formation of an unsaturated compound in the thermal decomposition did not detach the original carbon skeleton from the nitrogen. This means that, after one link had been broken, a link still remained between the original carbon skeleton and the nitrogen; therefore at least two links were originally present. But a carbon skeleton that has two links to nitrogen must be part of a ring; therefore the original compound was cyclic, not unsaturated. For example:

$$\underset{\underset{CH_2}{\diagdown}}{\overset{\overset{CH_2}{\diagup}}{C_2H_4}}\underset{\underset{CH_2}{\diagup}}{\overset{\overset{CH_2}{\diagdown}}{N(CH_3)_2}}\ OH^- \xrightarrow{\text{heat}} \underset{\underset{CH_2}{\diagdown}}{\overset{\overset{CH_2}{\diagup\!\!\diagup}}{C_2H_3}}\underset{\underset{CH_2}{\diagup}}{\overset{\overset{}{\diagdown}}{N(CH_3)_2}} + H_2O$$

To continue the degradation: $C_6H_{13}N$ was treated with methyl iodide to give $C_7H_{16}NI$. This confirms that $C_6H_{13}N$ was a tertiary amine, as expected. Treatment of the methiodide with silver oxide gave $C_7H_{17}ON$. On heating, this gave trimethylamine and C_4H_6. On treatment with an excess of bromine, this hydrocarbon gave a mixture of two tetrabromides, each with the composition $C_4H_6Br_4$. The hydrocarbon had, therefore, two double bonds capable of adding bromine, one formed by each of the thermal decompositions.

It will be found impossible to write a branched-chain structure of the composition C_4H_6 with two double bonds. Two possible straight-chain structures can be written.

$$CH_2\!\!=\!\!CH\!\!-\!\!CH\!\!=\!\!CH_2 \quad \text{and} \quad CH_3CH\!\!=\!\!C\!\!=\!\!CH_2$$

The first of these structures is butadiene, the second methylallene. Treatment of methylallene with excess bromine would give the following reaction:

$$CH_3CH{=}C{=}CH_2 + 2Br_2 \rightarrow CH_3CHBrCBr_2CH_2Br$$

Examination will show that two compounds with different melting points should not be formed from the tetrabromide of methylallene.

Butadiene, on the other hand, should give the reaction

$$CH_2{=}CH{-}CH{=}CH_2 + 2Br_2 \rightarrow BrCH_2CHBrCHBrCH_2Br$$

Examination will show that this compound has two centers of asymmetry, whereas the tetrabromide of methylallene has only one. With two centers of asymmetry, two compounds of different melting points would be formed:

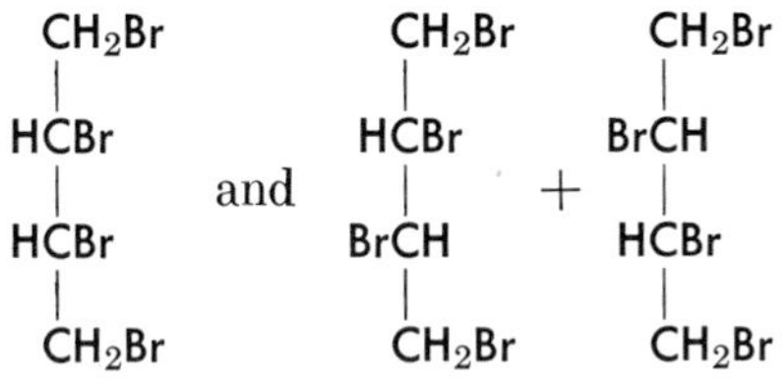

It will be seen that (a) has a plane of symmetry perpendicular to the 2,3 C—C bond. It is therefore internally compensated and not capable of resolution. On the other hand, (b) and (c) are mirror images which are not internally compensated and which, consequently, should be capable of resolution, provided that a means for accomplishing the resolution could be found. Since (a) and the unresolved mixture of (b) and (c) would be separable as compounds of different melting points, then the compound obtained by the thermal decomposition of the base $C_7H_{17}ON$, which gives two tetrabromides, is butadiene.

There are three cyclic compounds that could have the formula C_4H_9N and whose decompositions would follow the path indicated to lead to butadiene. These are

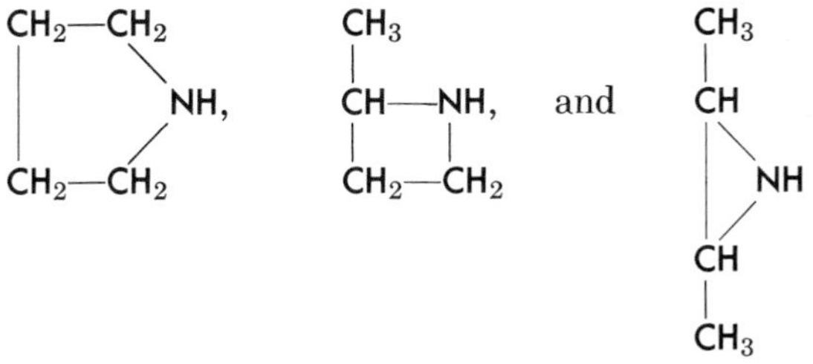

Operation of the rule that primary hydrogens in the β-positions will be removed preferentially would give butadiene after thermal decomposition of each of these

compounds. In this case, however, the unknown compound had been prepared by the reduction of ethylene cyanide, thus making a five-membered ring the more probable formulation.

$$N{\equiv}CCH_2CH_2C{\equiv}N + 4H_2 \xrightarrow{\text{Ni}} \quad \begin{array}{c} CH_2{-}CH_2 \\ | \qquad\qquad \diagdown \\ \qquad\qquad\qquad NH \\ | \qquad\qquad \diagup \\ CH_2{-}CH_2 \end{array} + NH_3$$

Pyrrolidine

In this reduction some of the expected product, tetramethylenediamine, is also produced.

We shall trace the course of the degradation reactions only for pyrrolidine.

$$\begin{array}{c} CH_2{-}CH_2 \\ | \qquad\quad \diagdown \\ \qquad\qquad\quad NH \\ | \qquad\quad \diagup \\ CH_2{-}CH_2 \end{array} + 2CH_3I \rightarrow \quad \begin{array}{c} CH_2{-}CH_2 \\ | \qquad\quad \diagdown \\ \qquad\qquad\quad N(CH_3)_2{}^+ I^- \\ | \qquad\quad \diagup \\ CH_2{-}CH_2 \end{array} + AgOH \rightarrow$$

(C_4H_9N) $(C_6H_{14}NI)$

$$\begin{array}{c} CH_2{-}CH_2 \\ | \qquad\quad \diagdown \\ \qquad\qquad\quad N(CH_3)_2{}^+ OH^- \\ | \qquad\quad \diagup \\ CH_2{-}CH_2 \end{array} \xrightarrow{\text{heat}} \quad \begin{array}{c} CH_2{-}CH_2 \\ | \qquad\qquad \diagdown \\ \qquad\qquad\qquad N(CH_3)_2 \\ CH{=}CH_2 \end{array} + CH_3I \rightarrow$$

$(C_6H_{15}ON)$ $(C_6H_{13}N)$

$$\begin{array}{c} CH_2{-}CH_2 \\ | \qquad\qquad \diagdown \\ \qquad\qquad\qquad N(CH_3)_3{}^+ I^- \\ CH{=}CH_2 \end{array} + AgOH \rightarrow \quad \begin{array}{c} CH_2{-}CH_2 \\ | \qquad\qquad \diagdown \\ \qquad\qquad\qquad N(CH_3)_3{}^+ OH^- \\ CH{=}CH_2 \end{array} \xrightarrow{\text{heat}}$$

$(C_7H_{16}NI)$ $(C_7H_{17}ON)$

$$N(CH_3)_3 + CH_2{=}CH{-}CH{=}CH_2 + H_2O$$

This complete process, in which each of the C—N bonds of an amine is replaced successively with a methyl group, is called *exhaustive methylation* and is a powerful tool for the elucidation of the structures of complex nitrogenous bases such as the alkaloids. It will be seen that the ultimate result of the process is to remove the nitrogen and transform the base into an olefinic derivative. Since we have already dealt with the problem of the structural investigation of olefins, it follows that we shall now be in a position to investigate the structures of more complex nitrogenous bases.

17–2   Exhaustive Methylation in Alkaloid Structural Investigations

The process of exhaustive methylation was applied to the structures of naturally occurring alkaloids as early as the decade of 1870. The great exponent of this process was the German chemist Richard Willstätter who received a Nobel prize for his structural investigations on alkaloids. Because his professorship was held at the University of Munich, Willstätter was one of the first victims of the Nazis. His fate was not so dramatic as that of Lavoisier, a century and a quarter earlier. He resigned his professorship at Munich in 1927 and continued to live in Germany until his death.

We have seen (Section 11–4) that for dehydrations with acid, wandering of a double bond may take place. There is one situation in which a similar uncertainty with respect to structure may arise from the operation of the process of exhaustive methylation. Both chemical studies of the nature of products formed and physical studies on stabilities have established the fact that so-called "conjugated" systems are more stable than "unconjugated" systems. A conjugated system is a series of carbon atoms with alternate single and double bonds, as in butadiene.

$$CH_2{=}CH{-}CH{=}CH{-}CH_3 \qquad CH_2{=}CH{-}CH_2{-}CH{=}CH_2$$

Methylbutadiene (conjugated)   Pentadiene-1,4 (unconjugated)

Benzene is an example of a cyclic conjugated system and is characterized by greater stability (for example, to bromination) than an olefin. If 1,4-pentadiene is heated with alkali, wandering of the double bond to the more stable conjugated position will take place.

$$CH_2{=}CH{-}CH_2{-}CH{=}CH_2 \xrightarrow{K^+OH^-} CH_2{=}CH{-}CH{=}CHCH_3$$

Thus the formation of methylbutadiene under alkaline reaction conditions cannot be taken to exclude the possibility that 1,4-pentadiene might have been the first product formed. Such a reaction sequence was observed by Hofmann in the degradation of N-methylpiperidine.

Pyridine can be hydrogenated to give piperidine. In Hofmann's day this could only be accomplished with sodium and alcohol but today it is readily accomplished by catalytic hydrogenation.

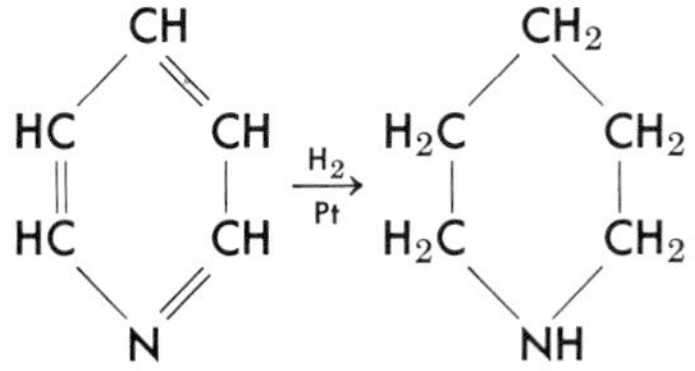

If we assume that we know the structure of pyridine, established in a manner similar to that of benzene, then the structure of piperidine would follow from this.

Treatment of piperidine with one mole of methyl iodide gave the tertiary base, N-methylpiperidine.

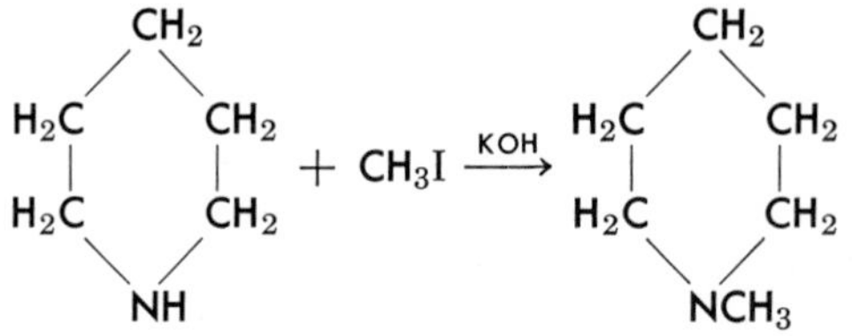

N-methylpiperidine was then subjected to the exhaustive methylation procedure.

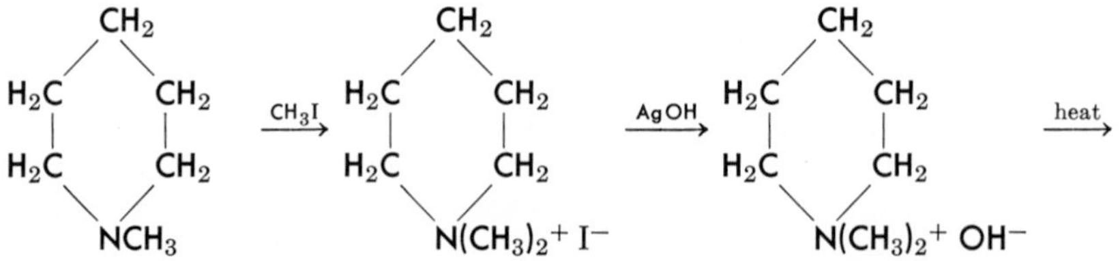

N-methylpiperidine   Dimethylpiperidinium iodide   Dimethylpiperidinium hydroxide

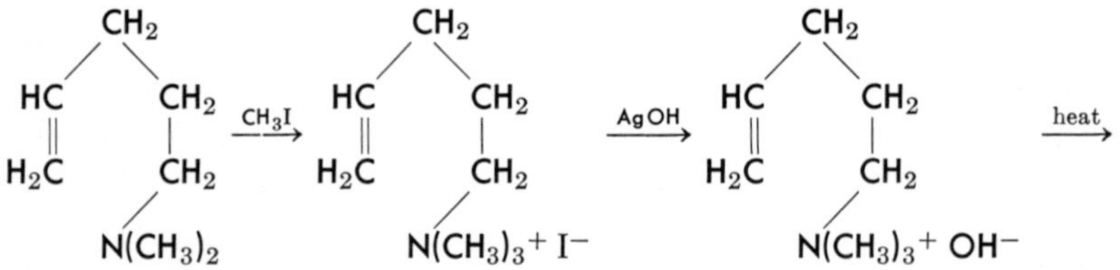

Δ^4-pentenyldi-methylamine

$$C_5H_8 \quad + N(CH_3)_3 + H_2O$$

Piperylene

    In Hofmann's day, investigators believed that piperylene had the structure of 1,4-pentadiene, $CH_2{=}CH{-}CH_2{-}CH{=}CH_2$, which is the formula to be expected from the degradation of piperidine. In 1900, however, Thiele challenged this formulation on the basis of oxidation experiments which he carried out. He found that sodium or potassium malonate was stable in the cold in the presence of permanganate in mildly alkaline solutions and reasoned that if piperylene were 1,4-pentadiene, malonate and formate would be formed by this oxidation.

$$H_2C{=}CH{-}CH_2{-}CH{=}CH_2 \xrightarrow{KMnO_4} HCOO^- + {}^-OOCCH_2COO^- + {}^-OOCH$$

He ran the oxidation in an ice-water mixture with an excess of permanganate. The products isolated were formate and acetate. Oxalate, which might also be expected, is not stable even under these conditions and was not isolated. From his results he reasoned that piperylene was 1,3-pentadiene:

$$H_2C=CH-CH=CH-CH_3 \rightarrow HCOO^- + [^-OOCCOO^-] + {}^-OOCCH_3$$
(not isolated)

Modern research has confirmed Thiele's conclusion with respect to the structure of piperylene. The two dienes can be distinguished by their tetrabromides: piperylene forms a tetrabromide melting at 114°C, while 1,4-pentadiene forms one melting at 86°; 1,4-pentadiene can be made by the pyrolysis of the diacetate of pentamethylene glycol at 600°C.

$$CH_3COOCH_2CH_2CH_2CH_2CH_2OOCCH_3 \xrightarrow{600°} H_2C=CH-CH_2CH=CH_2 + 2CH_3COOH$$
1,5-pentamethylene glycol diacetate

Although the pyrolysis reaction is performed under conditions of rapid flow to minimize the contact of the hydrocarbon with the hot zone, its formation and stability under these conditions shows that the essential condition for the rearrangement into piperylene is the alkali, not the heat alone.

17–3   The Structure of Coniine

The alkaloid coniine is of great historical interest from two points of view. It is a very poisonous liquid occurring in hemlock, especially in the seeds, and is believed to be the poison that was used in the execution of Socrates. In more modern times, it was the first naturally occurring alkaloid whose structural investigation and synthesis was completed. Recently it has received renewed attention because the absolute configurations of naturally occurring substances can be established by means of optical rotatory dispersion.

Coniine has the molecular formula $C_8H_{17}N$ which is two hydrogens less than the saturated amine, $C_8H_{19}N$. On treatment with an excess of methyl iodide, Hofmann found that it gave $C_{10}H_{22}N^+ I^-$. Consequently, it was concluded that coniine is a secondary amine. The shortage of two hydrogens indicates that the compound is either unsaturated or cyclic. This point was solved by exhaustive methylation. The course of the first reaction was as follows:

$$C_8H_{17}N \xrightarrow{CH_3I} C_{10}H_{22}N^+ I^- \xrightarrow{AgOH} C_{10}H_{22}N^+ OH^- \xrightarrow{heat} C_{10}H_{21}N$$

The isolation of a base, necessarily unsaturated, with the same number of carbons as the quaternary established that the starting material was cyclic, not unsaturated. The reasoning is the same as that given at the beginning of the chapter. The process was then repeated.

$$C_{10}H_{21}N \xrightarrow{CH_3I} C_{11}H_{24}N^+ I^- \xrightarrow{AgOH} C_{11}H_{24}N^+ OH^- \xrightarrow{heat} C_8H_{14} + N(CH_3)_3 + H_2O$$
Conylene

Conylene is an octadiene and it follows from this fact that coniine has all its eight carbons attached in a chain, either straight or branched. Since Hofmann had just completed the degradation of piperidine to piperylene, he was quick to note that coniine differs from piperidine by the grouping C_3H_6: piperidine is $C_5H_{11}N$ while coniine is $C_8H_{17}N$. He therefore suggested that coniine might be a propyl or isopropyl piperidine.

Hofmann next undertook a dry distillation with zinc dust in the hope of obtaining a material with more hydrogens than the starting coniine. In this case, however, his technique was not perfect. There is reason to believe that his zinc dust contained zinc oxide, and it is not certain that his precautions to exclude air were adequate. At any rate, conyrine, the product that was obtained, was a *dehydrogenation* product which was easily recognized by its properties as a derivative of pyridine. Pyridine bases are easily distinguishable by their strong tendency to form from saturated compounds, as a result of the conjugation in the pyridine ring, and from their characteristic weak basicity. Piperidine, for example, is approximately a million times as strong a base as is pyridine. These indications were soon confirmed by the oxidation of conyrine to picolinic acid.

$$C_8H_{17}N \xrightarrow{\text{Zn, heat}} C_8H_{11}N \qquad\qquad C_8H_{11}N \xrightarrow{\text{KMnO}_4} C_5H_4NCOOH$$

| Conyrine | Conyrine | Picolinic acid |

The formula for picolinic acid had been established by Skraup as 2-pyridine carboxylic acid.

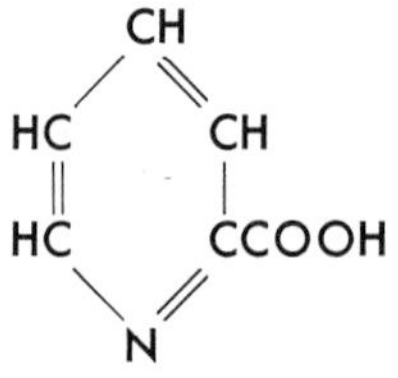

Picolinic acid

These considerations left only two possible structures for conyrine, propyl or isopropyl pyridine. Hofmann finally settled this question by the discovery of a reducing agent powerful enough to convert coniine into a saturated hydrocarbon by the reaction $C_8H_{17}N \xrightarrow{\text{HI}} C_8H_{18}$. The octane obtained by the hydriodic acid reduction of coniine was identified as normal octane by its boiling point and refractive index. This finding required that coniine be the normal propyl derivative.

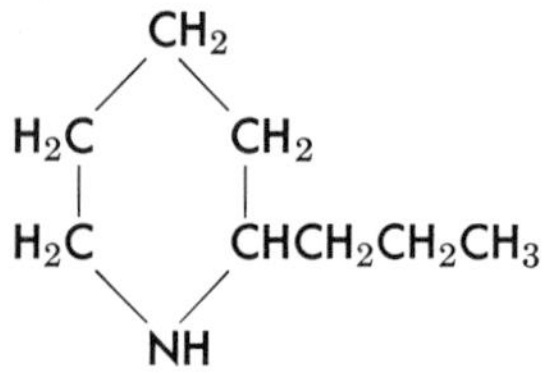

Coniine 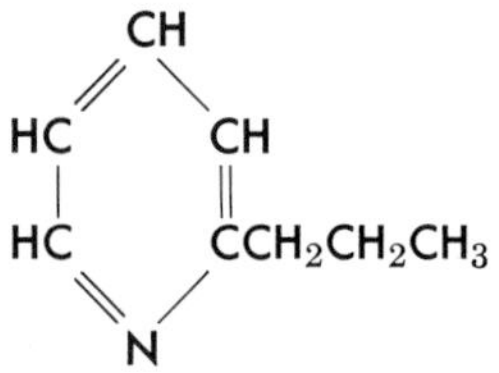   Conyrine

From these facts and the degradation of piperidine, it would follow that conylene is 1,3-octadiene.

$$CH_2{=}CH{-}CH{=}CH{-}CH_2{-}CH_2{-}CH_2{-}CH_3$$

Conylene

17–4   The Synthesis of Coniine

The degradations given above establish the structure of coniine. Confirmation was sought through synthesis. This was accomplished by Ladenburg. This synthesis involves two reactions which we have not encountered previously, a molecular rearrangement and a condensation. The starting point for the synthesis was 2-picoline, which is 2-methylpyridine. It can be obtained from coal tar, and this is the convenient method for preparing it. On the other hand, 2-picoline can also be synthesized from pyridine. This reaction takes advantage of a molecular rearrangement which occurs with some regularity among "aromatic" nitrogen bases. This rearrangement involves a migration of an alkyl group from nitrogen to carbon under high temperatures and pressures.

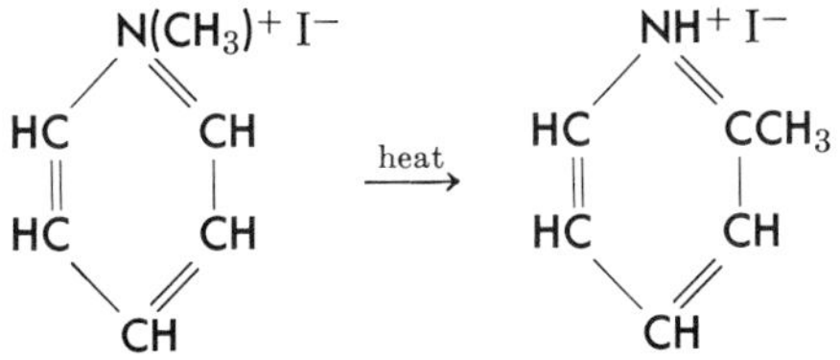

Pyridine methiodide   2-picoline hydroiodide

Neutralization of the hydroiodide yields the free base, 2-picoline. Methyl groups in the 2-position and the 4-position of pyridine are "activated" to condensation with aldehydes. Reasons for this will be discussed in Book 2. In this case, acetaldehyde is used.

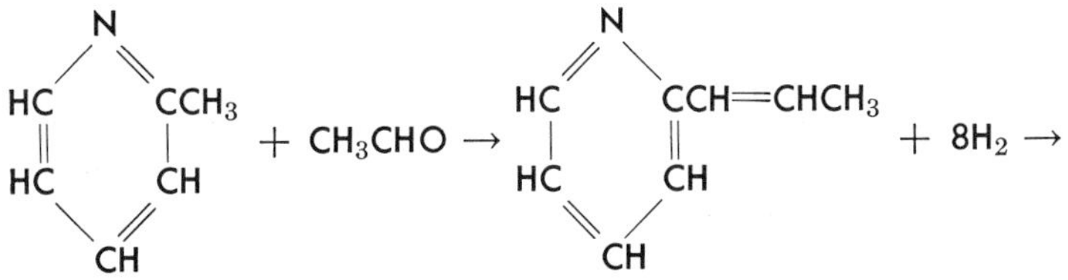

2-propenyl pyridine

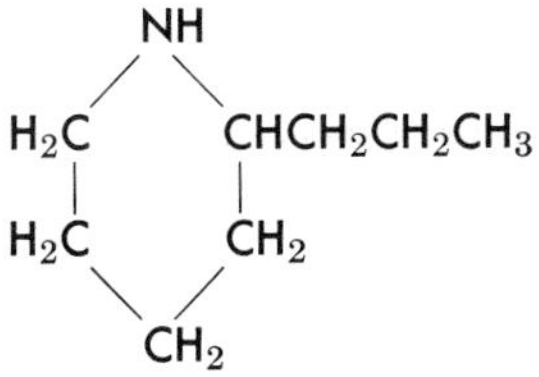

DL-coniine

Ladenburg accomplished the reduction with sodium and alcohol. The contemporary method would be to use catalytic hydrogenation, however.

17–5   Resolution of Synthetic Coniine

Coniine has one asymmetric carbon atom. The naturally occurring alkaloid is dextro-rotatory. The synthetic material is optically inactive. To achieve its resolution, DL-coniine was treated with D-tartaric acid. This yields a mixture of D-coniine-D-tartrate and L-coniine-D-tartrate, which possess different melting points. By fractional crystallization, the resolution was achieved, and the natural D-coniine was liberated by treatment of the tartrate with alkali. After purification, this proved to be identical to the natural product. Thus the first synthesis of a naturally occurring alkaloid was achieved. This was soon followed by many others which opened a whole new field of chemistry, pharmacology and therapeutics.

PROBLEMS

17–1   A number of hemlock alkaloids were isolated at the same time as coniine and are structurally related to it. Some of the names of these compounds contain Greek letters, which, unfortunately, have nothing to do with their structures. A series of isomeric natural products or related compounds are sometimes designated in this fashion in the order in which they are obtained in a study. We have omitted several of the series here.

Conhydrine, $C_8H_{17}NO$, may be oxidized to conhydrinone, $C_8H_{15}NO$, with chromic-sulfuric acid under mild conditions.

(a) What structural group does conhydrine contain?

Conhydrine is converted to β-coniceine, $C_8H_{15}N$, on dehydration with phosphorus pentoxide. (The dehydrating action of this reagent is similar to that of sulfuric acid.) Catalytic hydrogenation of β-coniceine gives coniine.

(b) Write the reactions which take place in this sequence.

When conhydrine is aromatized by dehydrogenation in the presence of palladium (cf., Section 17–3), a pyridine derivative, $C_8H_{11}NO$ is obtained. On mild oxidation with chromic-sulfuric acid, this yields a ketone, C_8H_9NO, but the ketone does not give a positive iodoform test.

(c) Can the alcohol function be located in the ring part of the coniine skeleton and still be oxidized to a ketone containing a pyridine ring? What possibilities for the structure of C_8H_9NO remain?

(d) How does the iodoform test distinguish between these?

(e) What is the structure of the ketone C_8H_9NO by elimination of all other possibilities?

(f) What are the structures of the pyridine derivative $C_8H_{11}NO$ and of conhydrine?

(g) Assuming the applicability of the Saytzev rule in the dehydration step, what would the structure of β-coniceine be? But this is not the structure, because β-coniceine yields acetic acid on chromic-sulfuric oxidation. What must the structure be then? This failure of the rule results from relative instability of olefins connected to six-membered rings this way.

Pseudoconhydrine, $C_8H_{17}NO$, is an isomer of conhydrine, containing the same type of functional group. The iodoform test is negative. It may be dehydrated to yield a material of the composition $C_8H_{15}N$, which is converted to conyrine on dehydration with palladium.

(h) Is the hydroxyl group in the ring or on the chain?

When pseudoconhydrine is treated with methyl iodide, $C_{10}H_{22}NOI$ is formed. This is treated with moist silver oxide and the product heated. A compound $C_{10}H_{21}NO$ is formed and this is catalytically hydrogenated to $C_{10}H_{23}NO$.

(i) Write several possible structures for $C_{10}H_{23}NO$ assuming different positions for the substituent and different directions of Hofmann elimination.

It is found that chromic-sulfuric acid oxidizes this last material to an acid boiling at 224°C, which forms a *p*-bromophenacyl ester melting at 72°C.

(j) What is the acid? Does this eliminate any of your earlier structures by the fact that there must be at least seven unoxidizable carbons in a row? Show that this in itself serves as a partial experimental check on the coniine skeleton.

(k) What positions have now been eliminated for the hydroxyl group?

(l) The full significance of the acid requires some reflection. Given the information that in the oxidation step 1,2-amino alcohols behave like 1,2-glycols, and recalling that 1,2-glycols are not stable under these conditions (cf., permanganate oxidations, Section 10–3), write the structure of $C_{10}H_{23}NO$.

(m) Reconstruct the formula for pseudoconhydrine.

γ-Coniceine, $C_8H_{15}N$, is optically inactive and cannot be resolved. It may be catalytically hydrogenated to DL-coniine.

(n) Write the three possible structures for γ-coniceine. When γ-coniceine is oxidized with chromic-sulfuric acid, no identifiable product boiling below 150°C is found.

(o) What structure does this eliminate?

(p) The Zerevitinov determination on γ-coniceine gives almost no methane; the volume is identical to that of the blank within experimental error. (Piperidine gives a mole of methane under the same conditions.) What is the structure of γ-coniceine?

17–2 Suppose that you treated a sample of ethylpropylbutylamine with methyl iodide. Would the product be optically active? Would you expect it to be resolvable into optically active components? Would compounds with different melting points be expected?

17–3 (a) 2-Picoline is not the only compound we have seen with activated hydrogen. Name some others that we have studied. Show that each of these satisfies a definition for "activated" hydrogen.

(b) Starting from benzaldehyde and other suitable compounds, show how the following could be prepared: (Some steps may require decarboxylation reactions.)

| 2,6-distyrylpyridine | Cinnamic acid | Benzalacetone |

$C_6H_5CH=CH-C$ ... $C-CH=CHC_6H_5$ $C_6H_5CH=CHCOOH$ $C_6H_5CH=CHCOCH_3$

(c) How do you think dibenzalacetone, $C_6H_5CH{=}CHCOCH{=}CHC_6H_5$, would be prepared from acetone? Would it be a good idea to use a stronger base in this synthesis than the one you chose for your proposed synthesis of benzalacetone?

(d) Because of what structural feature could methylmalonic ester,

$$C_2H_5OCOCHCOOC_2H_5$$
$$\overset{|}{C}H_3$$

not be used in a condensation reaction of this sort?

How are the procedures of formula interpretation, exhaustive methylation, and oxidation combined with geometrical principles to arrive at a method for the structural study of polycyclic alkaloids?

18

STRUCTURES OF SOME SIMPLE ALKALOIDS

18–1 Pomegranate Alkaloids

Coniine provides an example of a naturally occurring alkaloid with powerful physiological action whose chemical structure is simple. As a result the bulk of its investigation could be completed relatively early. This accomplishment led organic chemists to attempt the study of slightly more complex alkaloids. Among these, the alkaloids of the pomegranate were early to yield to structural explorations. These alkaloids were discovered by the French chemist, Tanret, in 1877 and named by him in honor of the great early French investigator of alkaloids, Pelletier. We shall confine our attention at present to the structure of one of these, pseudopelletierine, $C_9H_{15}ON$.

18–2 Degradations of Pseudopelletierine

The formula $C_9H_{15}ON$ is short six hydrogens of the saturated oxygenated amine, $C_9H_{21}ON$. Two of these hydrogens are quickly accounted for by the observation that the base gives carbonyl reactions and that, consequently, the C=O group is present. The reduction of a carbonyl group to the corresponding hydrocarbon can be accomplished by the Clemmensen method (Problem 12–4). This was performed and the product was found to be N-methylgranatanine, a base obtained by the methylation of granatanine which, in turn, can be obtained from other pomegranate sources.

$$\underset{\text{Pseudopelletierine}}{C_9H_{15}ON} \xrightarrow[HCl]{Zn(Hg)} \underset{\text{N-methylgranatanine}}{C_9H_{17}N} \xleftarrow[OH^-]{CH_3I} \underset{\text{Granatanine}}{C_8H_{15}N}$$

N-methylgranatanine cannot be hydrogenated in the presence of a catalyst. Since it is four hydrogens short of the saturated amine, it must contain two rings.

Relatively drastic oxidation methods, either with alkaline permanganate or with acidic dichromate, are capable of cleaving a carbon chain at the junction with a carbonyl group. This reaction was performed on pseudopelletierine with the formation of a single dibasic acid, methylgranatic acid.

$$C_9H_{15}ON \xrightarrow[H_2SO_4]{CrO_3} C_9H_{15}O_4N$$

Pseudopelletierine   Methylgranatic acid

The fact that only one such acid was formed suggested the possibility that cleavage on either side of the carbonyl would yield the same product and hence that pseudopelletierine possessed symmetry about the carbonyl group. For example,

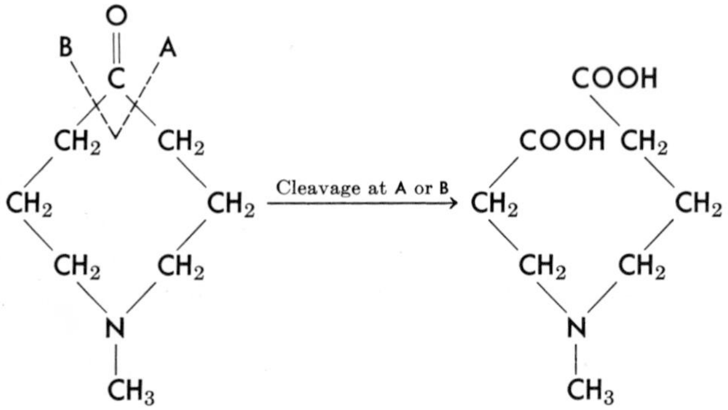

while

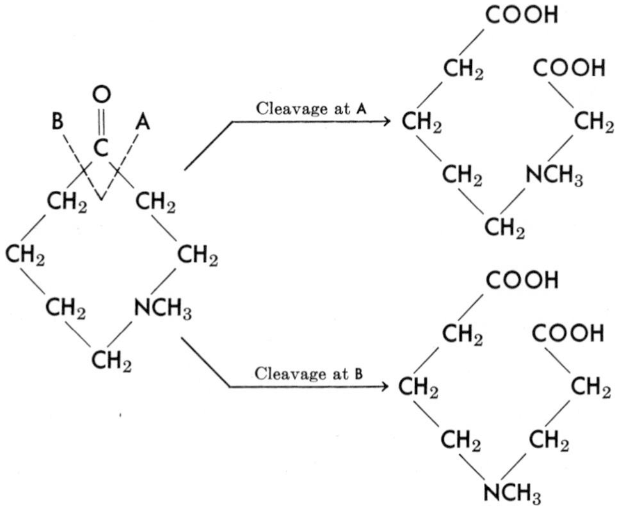

Since methylgranatic acid is six hydrogens short of saturation and four of these are accounted for by the two carboxyl groups, there must be one ring remaining in the molecule, and the oxidation must have broken the other. The ester was then prepared and the nature of the carbon chain determined by exhaustive methylation.

$$C_9H_{15}O_4N \xrightarrow[\text{HCl, then OH}^-]{\text{CH}_3\text{OH}} C_{11}H_{19}O_4N \xrightarrow{\text{CH}_3\text{I}} C_{12}H_{22}O_4NI$$

Methylgranatic   Methylgranatic
ester   ester methiodide

The earlier formation of N-methylgranatanine from granatanine had suggested that granatanine was a secondary base and N-methylgranatanine tertiary. The formation of the methiodide of methylgranatic ester by the addition of a single methyl group established this point. The degradation then continued.

$$C_{12}H_{22}O_4NI \xrightarrow{\text{AgOH, then heat}} C_{12}H_{21}O_4N \xrightarrow{\text{CH}_3\text{I, AgOH, then heat}}$$

Dimethylgranatenic
ester

$$N(CH_3)_3 + H_2O + C_{10}H_{14}O_4 \xrightarrow{\text{OH}^-,\ \text{then H}^+} C_8H_{10}O_4$$

The C_{10} methyl ester obtained from the degradation was hydrolyzed to give the parent carboxylic acid, $C_8H_{10}O_4$, which is eight hydrogens short of the saturated hydrocarbon. Four of these are accounted for by the carboxylic acid groups, and the other four must result from the two unsaturations produced by the two Hofmann degradations. The compound is therefore a doubly unsaturated carboxylic acid. This was hydrogenated to the saturated acid which proved to be suberic acid.

$$C_8H_{10}O_4 + 2H_2 \rightarrow C_8H_{14}O_4, \quad \text{which is} \quad HOOC(CH_2)_6COOH$$

Suberic acid

The identification of suberic acid as a degradation product of pseudopelletierine established the fact that eight carbons of the nine must be in an unbranched arrangement.

18–3   Reconstruction of the Formula for Pseudopelletierine

The facts developed by the foregoing degradations are enough to provide the basis for a reasonable structural formula for pseudopelletierine. Let us review these facts. (1) The compound contains two rings. (2) The carbonyl is symmetrically disposed in one of these rings. (3) Cleavage of this ring by oxidation gives a structure which can ultimately be degraded to an unbranched eight-carbon chain. From this fact it follows that the carbonyl was probably part of an eight-membered carbon ring which was unbranched. (4) Two Hofmann degradations were required to detach the nitrogen. This means that it had two points of attachment and therefore was part of a ring, remaining even after the ring containing the carbonyl had been broken. (5) The carbon not accounted for by the eight-membered ring is an N-methyl.

If we attempt to attach the ring containing the carbonyl to the ring containing the N-methyl by any type of junction which does not include the N-methyl in the second ring, we shall end up with either a branched carbon chain or with a compound which lacks symmetry about the carbonyl. For this reason, we must include the N-methyl in the ring that contains the carbonyl as well as in a ring of its own. This means that the two rings are fused. The symmetry consideration requires that there be an equal number of carbons on each side between the carbonyl and the N-methyl. Possible structures are shown below.

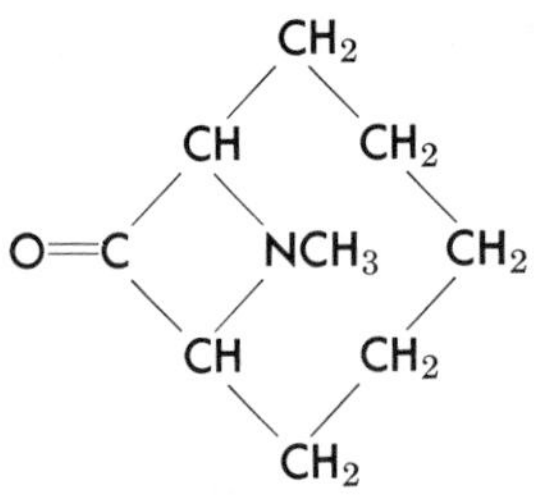

(a) 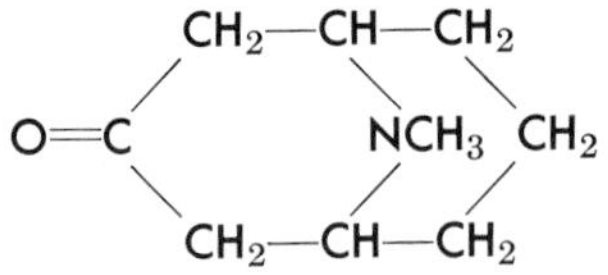   (b) 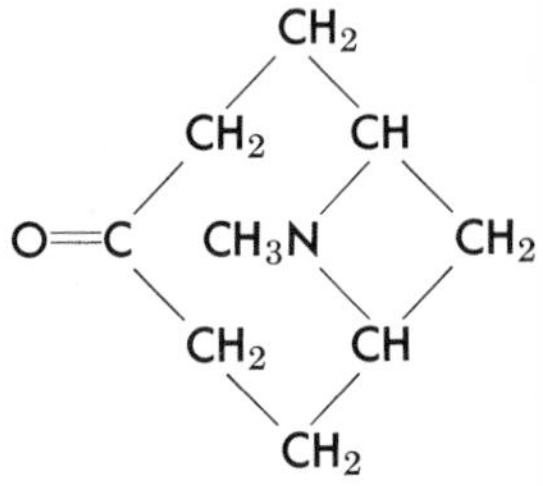   (c)

If we make one further postulate, namely that either five-membered or six-membered rings are probably present, we should reduce the possibilities to formula (b). This postulate is made probable by the resistance of N-methyl granatanine to hydrogenation, an improbable observation for a four-membered ring.

Assuming that formula (b) is correct for pseudopelletierine, write the formula for methylgranatic acid and its ester. Then trace through the exhaustive methylation procedure, writing the formula for each of the intermediates leading to suberic acid.

Confirmation of the structure tentatively assigned was obtained by exhaustive methylation of N-methylgranatanine. We shall follow these reactions using the tentative formula for the compound.

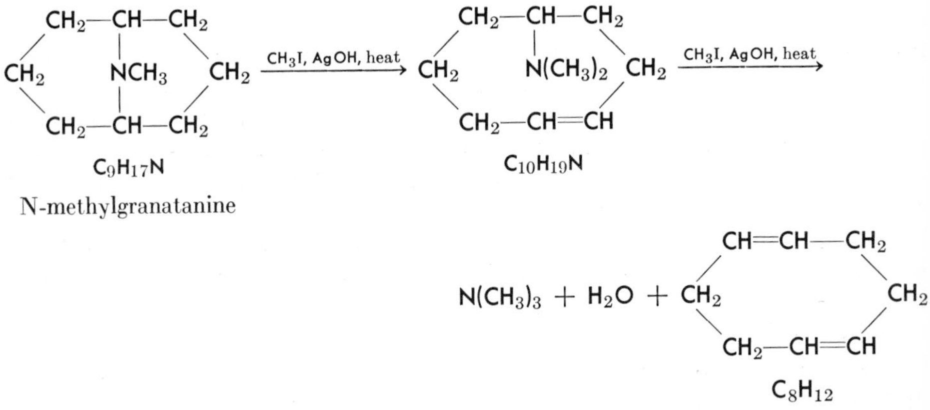

$C_9H_{17}N$

N-methylgranatanine

$C_{10}H_{19}N$

$N(CH_3)_3 + H_2O + $

C_8H_{12}

Cyclooctadiene

Cyclooctadiene was obtained from pseudopelletierine by Willstätter who then submitted the material to Harries for degradation by ozonolysis. The ozonolysis was performed with subsequent hydrolysis but not with a reductive cleavage. As a result, a mixture of aldehyde and acid was obtained.

$$
\begin{array}{c}
CH{=}CH{-}CH_2 \\
\diagup \qquad\qquad \diagdown \\
2CH_2 \qquad\qquad\qquad CH_2 \;+\; O_3 \quad\xrightarrow{\text{then } H_2O}\\
\diagdown \qquad\qquad \diagup \\
CH_2{-}CH{=}CH
\end{array}
$$

$$
\begin{array}{c}
COOH \;+\; HOOCCH_2 \qquad\qquad CHO \;+\; OHCCH_2 \\
\diagup \qquad\qquad\qquad \diagdown \qquad\qquad \diagup \qquad\qquad\qquad \diagdown \\
CH_2 \qquad\qquad\qquad CH_2 \;+\; CH_2 \qquad\qquad\qquad CH_2 \\
\diagdown \qquad\qquad\qquad \diagup \qquad\qquad \diagdown \qquad\qquad\qquad \diagup \\
CH_2COOH \;+\; HOOC \qquad\qquad CH_2CHO \;+\; OHC
\end{array}
$$

Succinic acid   Succinaldehyde

The outcome of the ozonolysis established the structure of cyclooctadiene and from this, the points of attachment of the N-methyl to form the internal ring were determined. This confirmed the formula tentatively assigned on the basis of the first series of degradations.

18–4 Synthesis of Pseudopelletierine

Pseudopelletierine has been synthesized by more than one method. The methods that are most conclusive with respect to establishing the structure consist of a series of stepwise condensations, leading gradually to the desired structure. About forty years ago, Robinson and his colleagues felt that it should be possible to obtain chemical condensations under what he described as "physiological conditions," that is, with the avoidance of strong acids or bases or high temperatures. In his search for mild conditions under which to perform condensations, he was successful in producing a number of relatively complicated substances by synthetic methods which are unrivaled for their elegance. Unfortunately, however, modern investigations have established that the conditions under which Robinson worked were not really "physiological." Most, not all, biosyntheses require enzymes for their completion and turn out to be stepwise syntheses remotely resembling those performed by the organic chemist under his more drastic conditions. The problem of the mechanisms by which enzymes perform their functions is one that is now occupying an increasing amount of attention.

Despite the fact that Robinson's syntheses are not models for biosynthetic processes, they are models of simplicity for the organic chemist to attempt to emulate and, for this reason, the synthesis of pseudopelletierine by Menzies and Robinson will be reproduced here.

The starting materials for the synthesis are glutaric aldehyde, methylamine, and the calcium salt of acetonedicarboxylic acid. These were allowed to stand in aqueous solution for a period of weeks at neutral pH and room temperature and the mixture was then acidified.

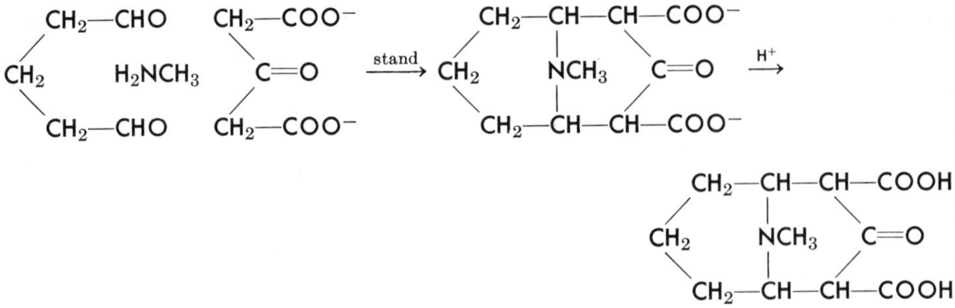

The dicarboxylic acid formed by this condensation is a β-keto acid and therefore decarboxylates readily. Even so, the decarboxylation had to be carried out under nonphysiological conditions. The material was heated in a high vacuum, giving pseudopelletierine (Fig. 18–1).

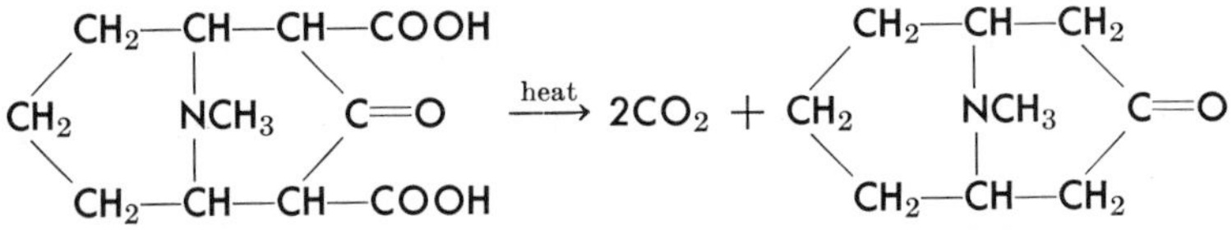

Pseudopelletierine

FIGURE 18–1

The condensation between methylamine and glutaraldehyde resembles somewhat the condensations between ammonia bases and carbonyl compounds which were studied earlier for purposes of identification. Even in these cases, it is possible for condensation to take place with a dicarbonyl compound so as to form a ring instead of the normal product involving a condensation at each carbonyl group. The further condensation with the acetonedicarboxylate is favored by the "activating" effect of the two carbonyls on the methylene group. We have seen earlier how this combined effect alters the reactivity of the methylene group to various reagents. This is a striking example of such an increase in reactivity. By the choice of especially reactive reagents, Robinson was able to avoid the necessity for drastic condensing conditions and thus was successful in achieving the synthesis at low temperature.

18–5 Coca Alkaloids

We shall conclude our study of the simpler alkaloids with a review of the salient features of the structures of atropine and cocaine, obtained from the leaves of the South American coca plant. These two alkaloids are still of considerable interest in medical practice. Atropine acts on the central nervous system and the vagus nerve which controls the heart rate. Cocaine is a valuable local anesthetic. For many purposes it has been supplanted by other drugs which are less dangerous. Cocaine is habit forming, and its medical use has sometimes led to unfortunate cases of habituation. For this reason, its use has been abandoned wherever possible. In eyeball surgery, however, many feel that it is still superior to synthetic materials. The elucidation of the structure of cocaine led immediately to attempts to circumvent its habit-forming properties by an exploration of the part of the molecule responsible for its anesthetic action. This search was largely successful and we now have a variety of relatively safe local anesthetics as a result of these studies. Such studies constitute an important bonus to be gained by the investigation of the structures of substances possessing desirable properties.

18–6 Atropine; Tropic Acid

Atropine has the molecular formula $C_{17}H_{23}O_3N$. On hydrolysis it yields an acid and an alcohol.

$$C_{17}H_{23}O_3N + H_2O \rightarrow C_9H_{10}O_3 + C_8H_{15}ON$$

| Atropine | Tropic
acid | Tropine
(Tropanol) |

Tropic acid has been shown to have the formula

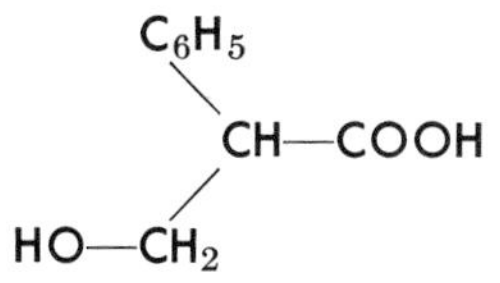

Tropic acid

We shall not pursue the degradation of tropic acid to show how its structure was established; instead we shall give one of the methods by which it has been synthesized. The synthesis starts with one of the standard reactions of carbonyl compounds, the *cyanohydrin reaction*. This is a condensation with HCN in the presence of a little weak base.

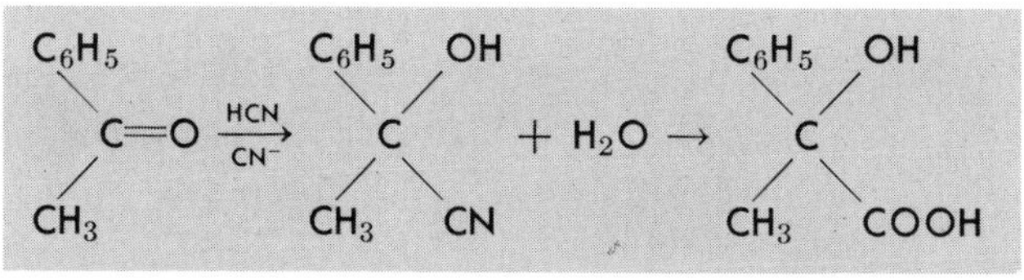

To dehydrate the acid formed in this manner, it is not necessary to add mineral acid as is usually done. Instead, heating the product under reduced pressure is sufficient to bring about the dehydration. The double bond formed is conjugated both to the phenyl ring and to the carbonyl of the carboxyl. This increases the stability of the unsaturated system and makes the dehydration easier.

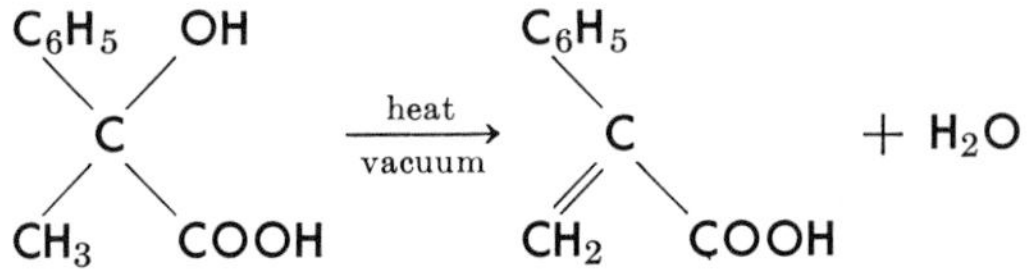

$$\underset{\underset{CH_3 \quad COOH}{}}{\overset{C_6H_5 \quad OH}{\diagdown \diagup C \diagdown}} \xrightarrow[\text{vacuum}]{\text{heat}} \underset{\underset{CH_2 \quad COOH}{}}{\overset{C_6H_5}{\diagdown C \diagdown}} + H_2O$$

Addition of hydrogen chloride in ether solution occurs opposite to the manner predicted by Markovnikov's rule. It should be remembered that this rule was formulated for the addition of reagents to olefinic hydrocarbons. In general, α,β-unsaturated acids add in an "anti-Markovnikov" manner.

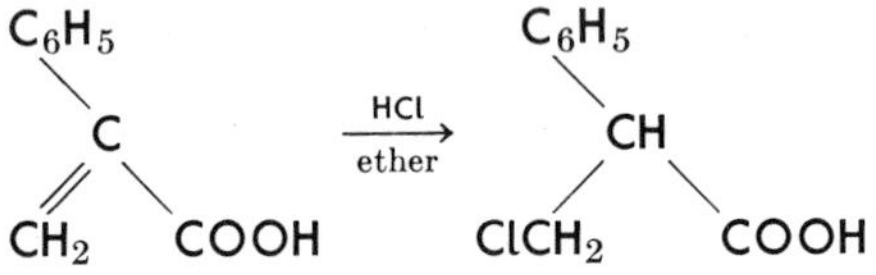

$$\underset{\underset{CH_2 \quad COOH}{}}{\overset{C_6H_5}{\diagdown C \diagdown}} \xrightarrow[\text{ether}]{\text{HCl}} \underset{\underset{ClCH_2 \quad COOH}{}}{\overset{C_6H_5}{\diagdown CH \diagdown}}$$

Tropic acid is then formed by boiling the halide with aqueous sodium carbonate.

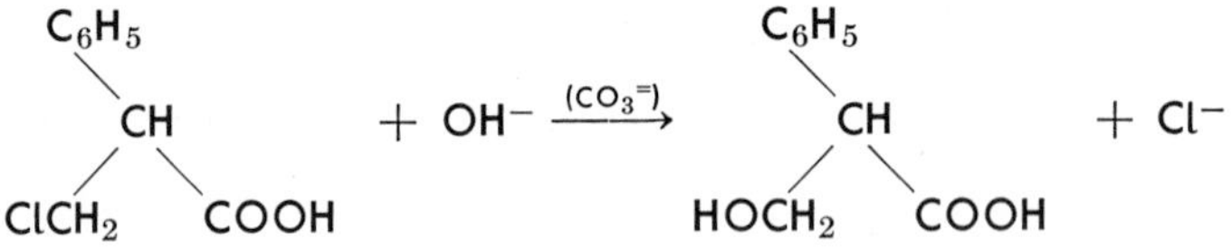

$$\underset{\underset{ClCH_2 \quad COOH}{}}{\overset{C_6H_5}{\diagdown CH \diagdown}} + OH^- \xrightarrow{(CO_3^=)} \underset{\underset{HOCH_2 \quad COOH}{}}{\overset{C_6H_5}{\diagdown CH \diagdown}} + Cl^-$$

18–7 Tropine (Tropanol)

Two structural features of tropine were quickly established. It forms a methiodide by the addition of one mole of CH_3I and is therefore a tertiary base.

$$C_8H_{15}ON \xrightarrow{CH_3I} C_9H_{18}ONI$$

The presence of an alcoholic hydroxyl is inferred from its formation by hydrolysis of an ester. This was confirmed by acidic dehydration to an olefin.

$$C_8H_{15}ON \xrightarrow{H^+} C_8H_{13}N$$

Tropene or Tropidene

Having established the alcoholic nature of tropine, we shall now refer to it by its more systematic name, tropanol. This indicates that the saturated ring compound would be called tropane, the alcohol, tropanol, the unsaturated ring system, tropene, etc.

Tropanol has four hydrogens less than the saturated amine formula. It was quickly inferred that it had two rings, since it lacked the characteristic olefinic reactions. Tropene, on the other hand, added two atoms of bromine. This dibromo derivative gave α-ethylpyridine on zinc dust distillation.

$$C_8H_{13}N + Br_2 \rightarrow C_8H_{13}NBr_2 \xrightarrow{Zn}$$

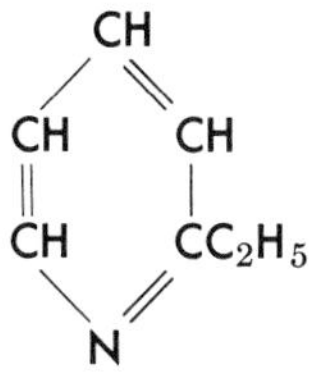

$$C_7H_9N$$

The loss of a carbon in this pyrolytic reaction suggests that there is an N-methyl group present. Degradation to a pyridine ring suggests the presence of a hydropyridine ring in tropanol.

Chromic acid oxidation of tropanol yields a single dicarboxylic acid, tropinic acid.

$$C_8H_{15}ON \xrightarrow[H_2SO_4]{CrO_3} C_8H_{13}O_4N$$

Tropanol   Tropinic acid

Exhaustive methylation of tropinic acid by a series of steps comparable to those used in the degradation of methylgranatic acid yielded an unsaturated acid, $C_7H_8O_4$. On hydrogenation, this yielded pimelic acid.

$$C_7H_8O_4 + 2H_2 \rightarrow C_7H_{12}O_4, \quad \text{which is} \quad HOOC(CH_2)_5COOH$$

Pimelic acid

This established the presence of an unbranched chain seven carbons long. Again, the formation of a single acid with eight carbons in the oxidation indicates the probability that the hydroxyl group of tropanol is symmetrically situated with respect to the nitrogen.

Willstätter found that more vigorous oxidation of tropinic acid yielded an identifiable fragment which permitted him to write a tentative structure for tropanol:

$$C_8H_{13}O_4N \xrightarrow[H_2SO_4]{CrO_3} C_5H_7O_2N, \quad \text{which is}$$

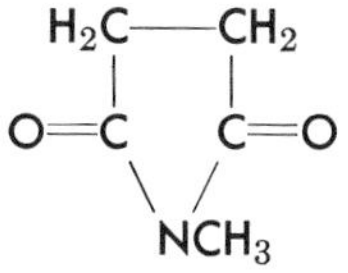

N-methylsuccinimide*

The isolation of N-methylsuccinimide established the presence of the N-methyl grouping and accounted for the eighth carbon. It also showed that the nitrogen

---

* An *imide* is a compound of the amide type with two acyl groups instead of one.

atom is common to both the six-membered piperidine (hydropyridine) ring and the five-membered pyrrolidine (hydropyrrole) ring. With the further fact that the hydroxyl is probably symmetrically situated in the hydropyridine ring, the tentative formula for tropanol would be the following:

$$
\begin{array}{ccc}
CH_2-CH-CH_2 & & \\
| & & \diagdown \\
| & NCH_3 & CHOH \\
| & | & \diagup \\
CH_2-CH-CH_2 & &
\end{array}
$$

Assuming that the tentative formula proposed is correct for tropanol, the reader should write the structure for tropene and the reactions for its conversion to α-ethylpyridine. He should then write formulas for the intermediates in the degradation of tropanol to pimelic acid. Finally, he should show how the oxidation of tropinic acid can yield N-methylsuccinimide.

Confirmation for this tentative structure was drawn from the exhaustive methylation of tropene.

$$C_8H_{15}ON \rightarrow C_8H_{13}N \xrightarrow[\text{methylation}]{\text{exhaustive}} C_7H_8 \xrightarrow{C_7H_8} C_7H_{14}$$

Cycloheptatriene   Cycloheptane

The formula proposed for tropanol is the only one which will accommodate the four structural features found: a piperidine ring, an N-methylpyrrolidine ring, a cycloheptane ring, and symmetrical placement of the hydroxyl in the pyridine ring.

Tropanol was synthesized by Robinson by a modification of the synthesis used for pseudopelletierine. The reader should be able to write the starting materials used and the steps necessary to obtain tropanol after the completion of the condensation.

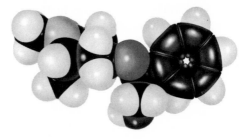

FIGURE 18–2

From the studies outlined above, the formula for atropine (Fig. 18–2) would be:

$$
\begin{array}{ccccc}
CH_2-CH-CH_2 & & O & & C_6H_5 \\
| & & \diagdown & \| & \diagup \\
| & NCH_3 & CHOCCH & \\
| & & \diagup & & \diagdown \\
CH_2-CH-CH_2 & & & & CH_2OH
\end{array}
$$

Atropine

18–8   Cocaine—Ecgonine

Cocaine has the molecular formula $C_{17}H_{21}O_4N$. Hydrolysis yields benzoic acid, methanol, and a base called *ecgonine*.

$$C_{17}H_{21}O_4N + 2H_2O \rightarrow C_7H_6O_2 + CH_3OH + C_9H_{15}O_3N$$

| Cocaine | Benzoic acid | Methanol | Ecgonine |

The presence of both carboxyl and alcoholic hydroxyl groups in ecgonine was soon established. This led to the assumption that the carboxyl of the ecgonine is esterified with methanol, and the hydroxyl with benzoic acid. This was confirmed by the resynthesis of cocaine from ecgonine.

$$C_9H_{15}O_3N \xrightarrow{(C_6H_5CO)_2O} C_{16}H_{19}O_4N \xrightarrow[HCl]{CH_3OH} C_{17}H_{21}O_4N$$

Ecgonine   Benzoylecgonine   Cocaine

Gentle oxidation of ecgonine with chromic acid converts the hydroxyl group into a keto group. This compound turns out to be a β-keto acid which readily decarboxylated to form tropanone, the ketone obtained by the gentle oxidation of tropanol.

$$C_9H_{15}O_3N \xrightarrow{CrO_3} C_9H_{13}O_3N \rightarrow CO_2 + C_8H_{13}ON \xleftarrow{CrO_3} C_8H_{15}ON$$

Ecgonine   Tropanone   Tropanone   Tropanol
                 β-carboxylic
                 acid

These reactions establish the structural relation between the tropane series of alkaloids and the cocaine alkaloids. The easy decarboxylation of the ketone formed from ecgonine establishes the position of the carboxyl group.

```
CH₂—CH—CHCOOH
   |       \
   NCH₃    CHOH
   |       /
CH₂—CH—CH₂
```
$$\begin{array}{c} CH_2{-}CH{-}CHCOOH \\ |\ \ \ \ \ \ \ \ \ \ \backslash \\ NCH_3\ \ \ \ CHOH \\ |\ \ \ \ \ \ \ \ \ \diagup \\ CH_2{-}CH{-}CH_2 \end{array}$$

Ecgonine

From this, the structure of cocaine (Fig. 18–3) can be reconstructed.

$$\begin{array}{c} CH_2{-}CH{-}CHCOOCH_3 \\ |\ \ \ \ \ \ \ \ \ \ \ \ \backslash \\ NCH_3\ \ \ \ CHOOCC_6H_5 \\ |\ \ \ \ \ \ \ \ \ \ \diagup \\ CH_2{-}CH{-}CH_2 \end{array}$$

Cocaine

FIGURE 18–3

The carbon in the alpha position to the carbonyl of tropanone is very slightly acidic and will react with metallic sodium in the presence of anhydrous ether. This sodium salt then reacts with carbon dioxide to give tropanone β-carboxylic acid, from which DL-ecgonine can be prepared by reduction.

$$
\begin{array}{c}
\text{CH}_2\text{—CH—CH}_2 \\
\big| \qquad\qquad \\
\text{NCH}_3 \quad \text{CO} \\
\big| \qquad\qquad \\
\text{CH}_2\text{—CH—CH}_2
\end{array}
\xrightarrow{\text{Na}} \text{Na salt}
\xrightarrow[\text{then H}^+]{\text{CO}_2}
\begin{array}{c}
\text{CH}_2\text{—CH—CH—COOH} \\
\big| \qquad\qquad \\
\text{NCH}_3 \quad \text{CO} \\
\big| \qquad\qquad \\
\text{CH}_2\text{—CH—CH}_2
\end{array}
\xrightarrow[\text{catalyst}]{\text{H}_2}
$$

$$
\begin{array}{c}
\text{CH}_2\text{—CH—CH—COOH} \\
\big| \qquad\qquad \\
\text{NCH}_3 \quad \text{CHOH} \\
\big| \qquad\qquad \\
\text{CH}_2\text{—CH—CH}_2
\end{array}
$$

18–9 Structure and Activity; Novocain

Much of the structural work on cocaine was performed by Einhorn. He followed the structural studies with pharmacological investigations aimed at finding the active grouping responsible for the local anesthetic action mentioned previously. While we cannot undertake to summarize all his findings, the presence of a benzoate ester of an aminoalcohol was found to be one essential feature of this action. Among the many such derivatives synthesized was "novocain." The synthesis of this material starting from simple raw materials may prove instructive:

$$
\text{CH}_3\text{C}_6\text{H}_5 \xrightarrow{\text{HNO}_3} \text{O}_2\text{NC}_6\text{H}_4\text{CH}_3 \xrightarrow{\text{KMnO}_4} \text{O}_2\text{NC}_6\text{H}_4\text{COOH} \xrightarrow{\text{POCl}_3} \text{O}_2\text{NC}_6\text{H}_4\text{COCl}
$$

| Toluene | p-nitrotoluene (separated from mixture) | p-nitrobenzoic acid | p-nitrobenzoyl chloride |

Para-nitrobenzoyl chloride is the first intermediate required for the synthesis. The second is made as follows:

$$
\text{CH}_2\text{=CH}_2 + \text{O}_2 \xrightarrow{\text{Ag}}
\begin{array}{c}
\overset{\displaystyle\text{O}}{\overset{\displaystyle\diagup\ \diagdown}{\text{CH}_2\text{—CH}_2}}
\end{array}
\xrightarrow{\text{NH}_3} \text{HO—CH}_2\text{—CH}_2\text{—NH}_2 \xrightarrow{\text{C}_2\text{H}_5\text{I then OH}^-}
$$

Ethylene   Ethylene oxide β-aminoethanol

$$
\text{HO—CH}_2\text{—CH}_2\text{—N(C}_2\text{H}_5)_2
$$

β-diethylaminoethanol

This is the second intermediate required for the synthesis.

The two intermediates are then combined in a modified Schotten-Baumann reaction.

$$
\text{O}_2\text{NC}_6\text{H}_4\text{COCl} + \text{HOCH}_2\text{CH}_2\text{N(C}_2\text{H}_5)_2 + \text{OH}^- \rightarrow
$$

$$
\text{O}_2\text{NC}_6\text{H}_4\text{COOCH}_2\text{CH}_2\text{N(C}_2\text{H}_5)_2 + \text{Cl}^-
$$

The nitro group is then reduced in hydrochloric acid with iron, giving the hydrochloride of the base, which is the form in which novocain is marketed.

$$O_2NC_6H_4COOCH_2CH_2N(C_2H_5)_2 + HCl \xrightarrow[HCl]{Fe} H_2NC_6H_4COOCH_2CH_2\overset{+}{N}H(C_2H_5)_2 \; Cl^{-}$$

The reader should trace the structural relationship between cocaine and novocain.

PROBLEMS

18–1   There is an isomer of tropine called pseudotropine. Since it is oxidized to tropinone with chromic-sulfuric acid under mild conditions, it must differ only in the arrangement of the alcohol grouping, as in the molecules illustrated in Fig. 18–4.

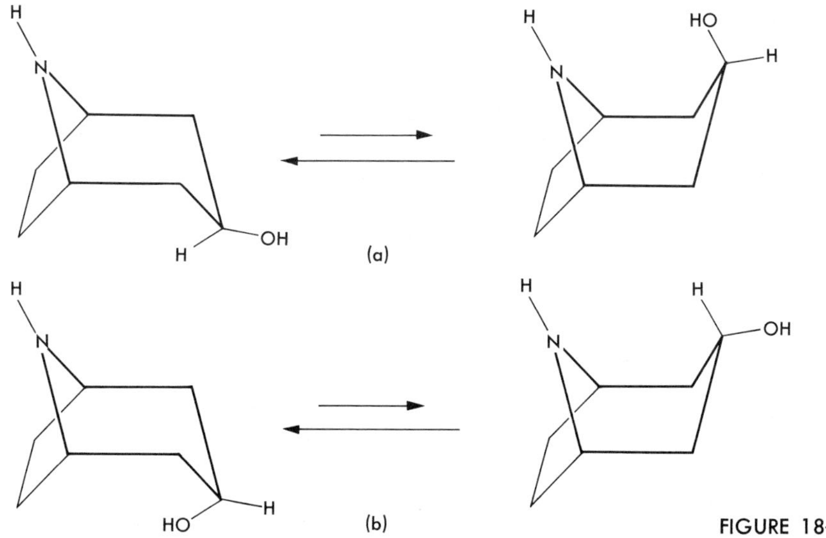

FIGURE 18–4

The compounds corresponding to N-demethylated tropine and pseudotropine are called nortropine and norpseudotropine. In all of these, the piperidine (hydropyridine) ring forms a chair like cyclohexane, with a small amount of the boat form in equilibrium.

When p-nitrobenzaldehyde reacts with norpseudotropine, a ring compound is formed.

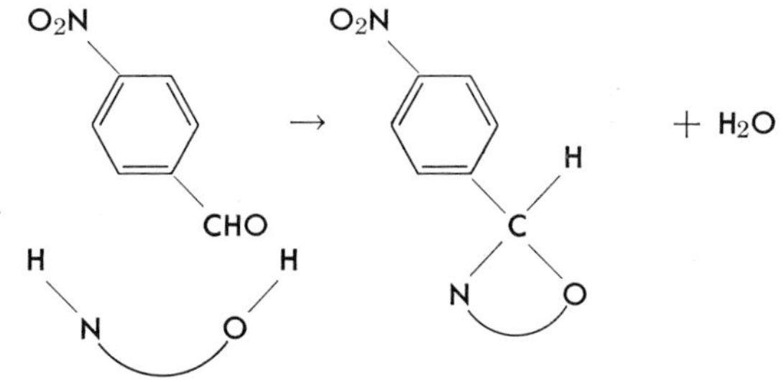

But no reaction occurs with nortropine.

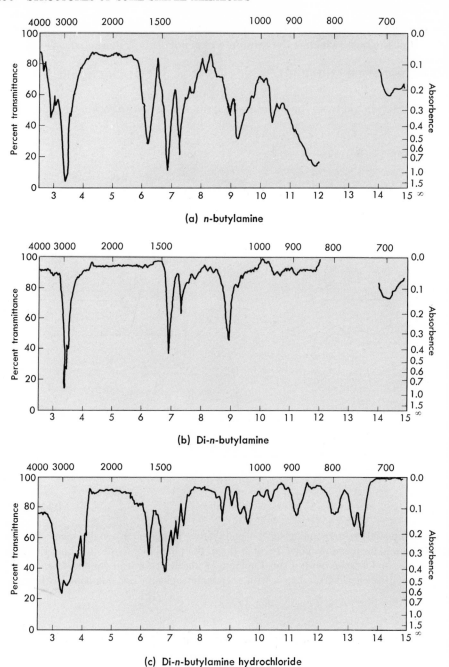

(a) *n*-butylamine

(b) Di-*n*-butylamine

(c) Di-*n*-butylamine hydrochloride

FIG. 18–5.   Infrared spectra of amines.

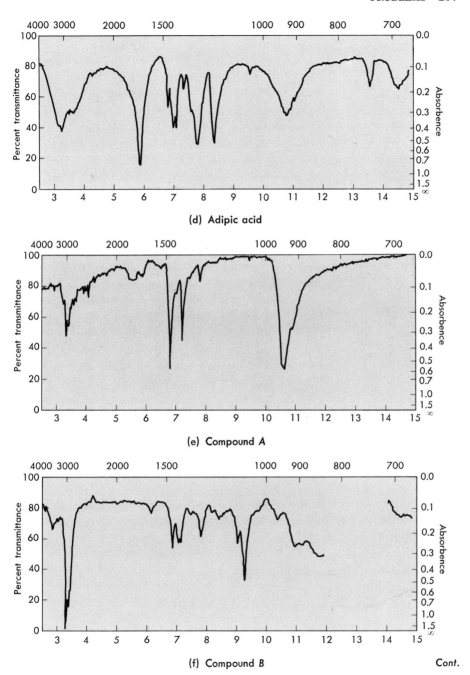

(d) Adipic acid

(e) Compound A

(f) Compound B

Cont.

FIG. 18–5. Infrared spectra of amines. (Cont.)

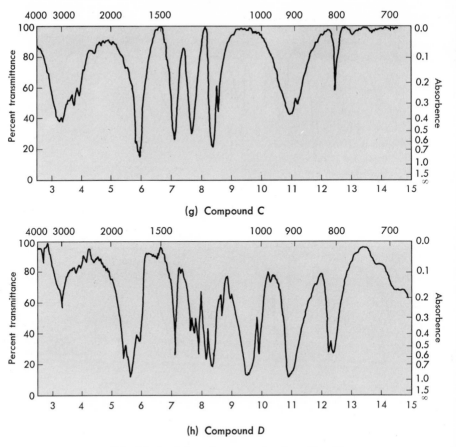

(g) Compound C

(h) Compound D

FIG. 18–5.   Infrared spectra of amines. (Concl.)

The reaction is believed to take place with the boat form, which is removed by reaction as it is formed from the chair, driving the reaction to completion.

Show how the interpretation of this experiment in terms of a proximity effect allows the assignment of structures (a) and (b). Which is nortropine and which is norpseudotropine?

18–2 Devise syntheses for two of Robinson's starting materials:

(a) succinaldehyde from adipic acid

(b) glutaraldehyde from pimelic acid

Reactions in Problem 8–7 and Section 11–5 may be useful.

18–3 The infrared spectra of amines are often useful in structural determinations.   A few illustrative spectra are shown in Fig. 18–5. The N—H stretching in n-butylamine appears at 2.9 microns, between the O—H and C—H regions. In addition, there is a strong absorption characteristic of primary amines at 6.2 microns.   This is attributed to NH_2 torsional deformations.

Di-n-butylamine has only a weak N—H stretching absorption; this would be expected to be weaker relative to the C—H than the N—H in butylamine. Why? A more important observation is the absence of the NH_2 torsion absorption.

Tertiary amines would show no N—H stretching, of course.

Di-n-butylamine hydrochloride shows the characteristic broadening found with amine salts with the group N+—H. The absorption ranges from 3.3 to 4.5 microns and swallows the C—H absorption. Note also the absorption at 6.2 microns. What might this be?

A similar broad envelope from 3.3 to 4.2 microns is found in the spectra of carboxylic acids. These are distinguishable by their carbonyl absorptions near 5.9 microns.

You should be able to identify the unidentified spectra with the following information:

Compound A (spectrum e) has the formula $C_4H_{12}NBr$.

Compound B (spectrum f) has the formula C_4H_9N and is resistant to hydrogenation even under forcing conditions.

Compound C (spectrum g) contains four carbons. On heating with calcium carbonate a crude reaction product is obtained with the spectrum of D (h). Note that a little C still remains in D (5.9 microns). See Problem 13–4 for a review, if necessary.

Spectra with a gap from 12 to 14 microns were recorded as CCl_4 solutions. The rest were taken as dispersions of solids in potassium bromide glasses.

18–4 Hygrine, $C_8H_{15}ON$, is an alkaloid found in Peruvian coca leaves. Treatment with iodine and sodium hydroxide yields iodoform and a carboxylic acid, $C_7H_{13}O_2N$. On Barbier-Wieland degradation this produces $C_6H_{11}O_2N$, which is decarboxylated on dry distillation to $C_5H_{11}N$; $C_5H_{11}N$ reacts with methyl iodide to give $C_6H_{14}NI$.

(a) Is $C_5H_{11}N$ primary, secondary, or tertiary?

Treatment of $C_6H_{14}NI$ with moist silver oxide, followed by heating, yields $C_6H_{13}N$.

(b) Did the nitrogen in $C_5H_{11}N$ have more than one point of attachment to the carbon chain?

The compound $C_6H_{13}N$ reacts with methyl iodide to give $C_7H_{16}NI$. Pyrolysis of the quaternary ammonium hydroxide obtained from this gives C_3H_9N and C_4H_6. The olefin yields formaldehyde and glyoxal on reductive ozonolysis.

(c) What is the olefin?

(d) $C_5H_{11}N$ cannot be hydrogenated. What is its structure?

When the original carboxylic acid $C_7H_{13}O_2N$ is esterified with methanol and the ester subjected to exhaustive methylation, the methyl ester of an unsaturated acid, $C_7H_{10}O_2$, is obtained. When this is hydrogenated with palladium and then hydrolyzed, an acid is obtained which forms a p-bromophenacyl ester melting at 72°C.

(e) How many carbons does the acid contain? What is its structure?

(f) How can the carbon atoms in $C_7H_{13}O_2N$ be arranged to account for the fact that the acid of part (e) can be obtained from it?

(g) What is the structure of hygrine?

Robinson prepared hygrine by the condensation of γ-methylaminobutyraldehyde and calcium acetonedicarboxylate.

(h) Demonstrate the applicability of these starting materials.

Hygroline, $C_8H_{17}ON$, may be oxidized to hygrine with chromic-sulfuric acid under mild conditions.

(i) What is the structure of hygroline?

What are the "building blocks" of proteins?
How were the structures of these building blocks
established? How does their bifunctionality affect their
chemistry?

19

PROTEINS I: THE AMINO ACIDS

19–1 Magnitude of the Structural Problem

The problem of protein structure has intrigued organic chemists because of the tremendous importance of the proteins in all life processes. They are essential constituents of all living matter and it is through them that many of the processes of growth, on the one hand, and disease, on the other, take place.

The problem of protein structure is so complex that at nearly every turn the chemist found his current tools ineffective in dealing with it. Many of the advances in the field have come from the application of new methods designed especially for the problem in hand, and there are few fields in which more ingenuity has been displayed in the application of novel techniques to gather evidence.

As we have seen, in the course of studying the structure of a naturally occurring substance the chemist likes to have the assurance, first, that he is dealing with a pure substance. For proteins, claims have been made to have prepared these materials in a state of purity. In most cases, however, the more accurate statement would be that given samples are pure according to presently available criteria. Past experience has frequently shown, however, that with the introduction of a new method for purification, samples previously thought to be pure turned out to be separable. Thus the preconditions necessary for a chemical structural examination are very difficult to meet in working with proteins.

19–2 Minimum Molecular Weights

One of the first steps in the chemical examination of a substance is, as we have seen, the determination of its molecular weight. For proteins, both physical and chemical methods have been used and both lead to the conclusion that these substances are highly complex, with molecular weights ranging from perhaps as low as 5000 to as high as many millions.

The "protein theory" was advanced in 1839 by a Dutch physiological chemist, G. J. Mulder. It was then supposed that the nitrogenous constituents of animal tissues, seeds, leaves, etc., were all the same. This assumed building block of living matter was called "protein" or "first substance." In 1839 the classical studies of Liebig and Wöhler on the benzoyl radical had just been published. Mulder analyzed various proteins and then plunged. He said that all contained a common protein radical which he wrote as $C_{40}H_{62}N_{10}O_{12}$ and he formulated the composition of egg albumin as $Pr_{20}PS_4$. While later developments showed that Mulder's concept was far too simple, even this formulation presents the complexity of the general problem squarely.

Mulder's theory was slowly abandoned when the researches of the nineteenth century revealed the amino acids as the building blocks of the proteins. Chemists hydrolyzed proteins with acids, alkalies, and enzymes (which are naturally occurring protein catalysts) and obtained a small proportion of the original molecule as amino acids, the rest as noncrystallizing syrup. The big event in protein chemistry came at the end of the century, in 1899, when Emil Fischer began his monumental work on the structure of proteins.

19–3 Isolation of Amino Acids

Fischer was faced with the same difficulty that had stopped previous investigators, that is, the noncrystallizing syrup. Since previous investigators had been able to isolate some amino acids from the hydrolysate, he guessed that it was a mixture of amino acids, so he esterified it. Then, for all practical purposes, he had a mixture of substituted amines which could be separated by fractional distillation. In the course of a few years Fischer was able to isolate nearly all the amino acids occurring in proteins which had not been isolated previously. From his yields he was also able to estimate the amount of each one in a number of different proteins. It follows from these studies that the first step in establishing the constitution of the proteins is the structural examination of the amino acids from which the proteins are built.

When they isolated individual amino acids, the early investigators performed degradations on them to prove their structures. In general, however, we shall omit these studies and emphasize, instead, the synthetic method for establishing structure.

The simplest amino acid possible would be carbamic acid, H_2NCOOH. This substance is incapable of independent existence, although its esters are known. These are the urethanes. Alkaline hydrolysis yields salts of carbamic acid which decarboxylate spontaneously on acidification. Urethanes are prepared from cyanic acid and alcohols.

$$HN{=}C{=}O + CH_3OH \rightarrow H_2NCOOCH_3$$

Urethanes may also be prepared directly from alcohols and urea. This process forms cyanic acid by a reversal of the reaction by which Wöhler first prepared "synthetic" urea in 1828.

$$H_2NCONH_2 \xrightleftharpoons{heat} NH_3 + HN{=}C{=}O \rightleftharpoons NH_4NCO$$

The synthesis of urea from ammonia and cyanic acid has been cited frequently as the first preparation of an organic chemical from inorganic sources. At the time it was accomplished, however, this was not true, since both ammonia and cyanic acid were prepared by Wöhler from organic sources.

Carbamate links have never been established as taking part in protein structure, although indirect evidence for their presence has been recorded.

The simplest amino acid which is known to occur in proteins is aminoacetic acid, glycine. Glycine is prepared from ammonia by alkylation with chloroacetic acid. In the early days, yields of glycine were low because of the intervention of di-alkylation and trialkylation, just as we have seen is the case with methyl iodide. Realizing that this was the source of the difficulty, however, chemists overcame the trouble by the use of a large excess of ammonia. After the reaction has been completed, the ammonia may be recovered by distillation and reused. In practice, approximately 50 moles of ammonia are used to each mole of chloroacetic acid.

$$3NH_3 + ClCH_2COOH \rightarrow NH_2CH_2COO^- NH_4{}^+ + NH_4{}^+ Cl^-$$

19–4   Amino Acids as Dipolar Ions

One might expect that the neutralization of a basic salt of glycine with acid would give the free carboxyl derivative. In fact, however, removal of the ammonia by distillation gives glycine without the necessity for neutralization, and more careful examination establishes the fact that glycine does not have the formula of simple aminoacetic acid, as might be expected. One of the most convincing experiments used to establish the structure of glycine is carried out by potentiometric titration.

The sensing device used for the purpose is a glass electrode, an instrument invented by Fritz Haber for detecting changes in acidity electrically. By the use of pH sensitive glass and a suitable half-cell, usually silver-silver chloride, increases in hydrogen ion concentration are detected by this electrode and can be registered as changes in electrical potential compared to another half-cell, usually calomel, which is insensitive to changes in acidity. The wiring diagram of such a system is shown schematically in Fig. 19–1.

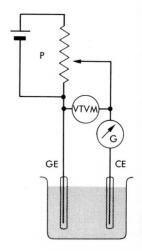

FIG. 19–1. System for the measurement of acidities: G, galvanometer; P, potentiometer; VTVM, vacuum tube voltmeter; GE, glass electrode; CE, calomel electrode.

In use, a solution with the desired proportions of glycine hydrochloride and sodium hydroxide, for example, would be placed in the beaker at a pre-determined temperature and stirred. The slide on the potentiometer circuit would be adjusted until the galvonometer was in balance. At this point the potential developed by the glass electrode-calomel electrode cell would be just balanced by that developed by the potentiometer. This potential could then be read on the vacuum tube voltmeter. Using this system a neutralization curve can be constructed in which the potential developed by the cell, or alternatively the pH, is plotted against the number of milliliters of standard solution used in the titration. The titration curve of glycine is shown in Fig. 19–2.

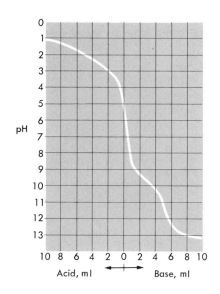

FIG. 19–2. Neutralization curve of glycine.

The neutralization curve shows that glycine has two endpoints in its neutralization, one after the acidic portion of the curve, the other after the basic portion. One of these would correspond to the neutralization of the carboxyl group, the other to that of the ammonium ion. The question to resolve is, which endpoint corresponds to which group? One method of answering the question is by analogy.

We may assume that the neutralization of glycine hydrochloride goes by one of two paths.

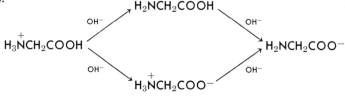

If the upper path is followed, then the neutralization that takes place in acidic solution is the neutralization of an ammonium ion, that in basic solution is the neutralization of a carboxyl group, and glycine would be aminoacetic acid. If the lower path is followed, the reverse is true: the neutralization in acidic solution is that of a carboxyl group, while that in basic solution is that of an ammonium ion, and glycine would be a dipolar ion.

The neutralization that takes place in acid solution corresponds to that of an acid whose acid strength, or pK_a, is 2.35. That in basic solution is that of an acid with pK_a of 9.78. The ammonium ion has an acid strength of 9.25, and the monosubstituted alkylamines are in the neighborhood of 9.50. By analogy, then, we should conclude that the neutralization in basic solution is that of an ammonium ion and that the carboxylate ion attached makes a change in acid strength which shifts the curve from the neighborhood of 9.25 to 9.50 up to the 9.75 observed.

On the acid side, the acid strength of acetic acid is 4.75 as compared with 2.35 observed for glycine. In this case, we must assume that the attached NH_3^+ group shifts the acidity by 2.4 pK units to the observed value for glycine. A chloro substituent on acetic acid shifts the pK_a to 2.85, that is, by 1.9 units. Thus the NH_3^+ would be a somewhat more powerfully acidifying group than the chloro as a substituent. If we add the shift caused by the two groups, that is, 0.53 on the base side and 2.35 on the acid side, we have a total correction of 2.88 units to fit the curve observed on the assumption that the first neutralization is that of a carboxyl group and the second that of an ammonium ion. This would correspond to the second pathway and the dipolar ion intermediate. If, on the other hand, we should insist on following the upper pathway to the uncharged intermediate, the shift for the ammonium ion would be $9.25 - 2.35 = 6.90$, and the shift for the carboxylate ion would be $9.78 - 4.75 = 5.03$. Thus the total shift to fit the curves in this case would be 11.93 units instead of 2.88 units. It is obvious that the formation of the dipolar ion intermediate is a better choice than the alternative pathway. In Book 2 we shall see that the chemical effect of the NH_3^+ group would, in fact, be an acid-strengthening effect instead of an acid-weakening effect which would be required to fit the upper pathway.

Titration curves have been obtained on all the naturally occurring amino acids and in each case it is found that the dipolar ion formula fits the facts better than the uncharged forms. For glycine dissolved in ammonia, the large excess of ammonia used would convert it into the ammonium salt. As the ammonia was removed by evaporation, however, the amino group of the glycine, being a slightly stronger base than ammonia, would compete successfully for the proton, and the dipolar ion would be formed without neutralization during the course of the evaporation.

19–5   Amino Acid Syntheses; Amination and the Strecker Synthesis

All the naturally occurring amino acids of proteins have their amine substituents in the α-position to the carboxyl group. For this reason, the α-halogenation reaction followed by amination, as with glycine, provides a general method for their preparation, if the desired carboxylic acid is available. In some cases, other intermediates are more readily available, so other methods for preparation have been used. One of these is the Strecker synthesis, which employes as starting material an aldehyde with one carbon fewer than the desired amino acid. As an example, we shall outline this method for the synthesis of alanine, the next more highly substituted amino acid. The reaction is analogous to the formation of cyanohydrins from aldehydes and hydrogen cyanide.

$$CH_3CHO + HCN \xrightarrow{\ CN^-\ } CH_3\overset{\displaystyle OH}{\underset{\displaystyle CN}{C}}H$$

Acetone
cyanohydrin

In the Strecker synthesis, ammonium cyanide is substituted for the hydrogen cyanide.

$$NH_4Cl + NaCN \rightarrow NH_4CN + NaCl$$

$$CH_3CHO + NH_4CN \rightarrow CH_3\overset{\displaystyle NH_2}{\underset{\displaystyle CN}{CH}} + H_2O$$

Acid hydrolysis then produces the amino acid.

$$CH_3\overset{\displaystyle NH_2}{\underset{\displaystyle CN}{CH}} + 2H_2O + 2HCl \rightarrow CH_3\overset{\displaystyle NH_3{}^+Cl}{\underset{\displaystyle COOH}{CH}} + NH_4{}^+Cl^-$$

Alanine
hydrochloride

19–6   Reduction of Ketoximes

The amino group may also be formed by the reduction of an oxime or even of a phenylhydrazone. An example is the synthesis of aspartic acid. The first step is a Claisen condensation to form oxaloacetic ester.

$$C_2H_5OOCCOOC_2H_5 + CH_3COOC_2H_5 \xrightarrow{Na} C_2H_5OOCCOCH_2COOC_2H_5 + C_2H_5OH$$

Oxaloacetic ester

The oxime of oxaloacetic ester can then be reduced to aspartic ester which, on hydrolysis, yields aspartic acid.

$$C_2H_5OOCCOCH_2COOC_2H_5 + H_2NOH \rightarrow$$

$$H_2O + C_2H_5OOC\underset{\displaystyle \overset{\|}{NOH}}{C}CH_2COOC_2H_5 + 2H_2 \xrightarrow{Pt} H_2O + C_2H_5OOC\underset{\displaystyle \overset{|}{NH_2}}{C}HCH_2COOC_2H_5$$

$$C_2H_5OOC\underset{\displaystyle \overset{|}{NH_2}}{C}HCH_2COOC_2H_5 + 2H_2O + HCl \rightarrow HOOCCH_2\underset{\displaystyle \overset{|}{NH_3{}^+Cl}}{CH}-COOH + 2C_2H_5OH$$

Aspartic acid
hydrochloride

19–7   Condensations with Diketopiperazine

An intermediate that is useful in the synthesis of amino acids is glycine anhydride, more properly called diketopiperazine. This is made by the self-condensation of glycine ester under alkaline conditions. The reaction is similar to the formation of amides from esters.

$$CH_3COOC_2H_5 + NH_3 \rightarrow CH_3CONH_2 + C_2H_5OH$$

For glycine ester, both of the groups necessary for the condensation are contained in the same molecule, and self-condensation takes place with the formation of a six-membered ring.

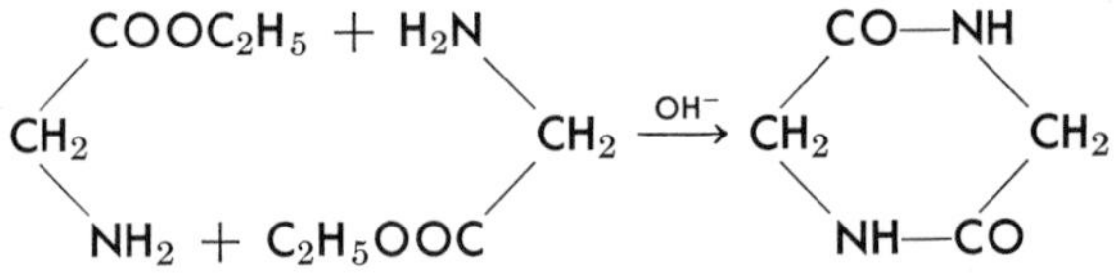

Diketopiperazine

With the use of diketopiperazine, an amino acid can be formed from an aldehyde with two fewer carbons.

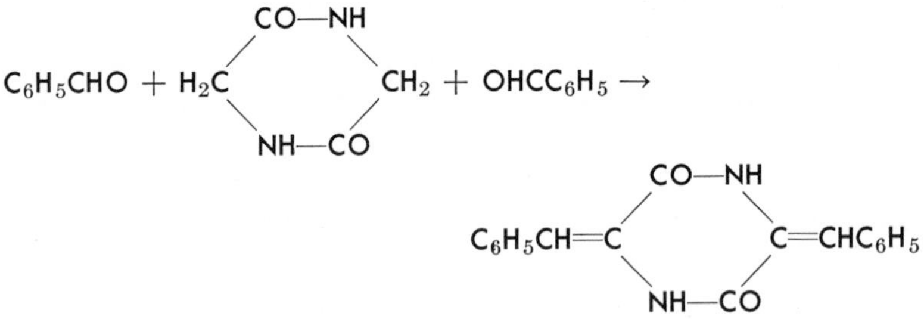

The methylene group in diketopiperazine has been "activated" by the carbonyl and takes part in condensations with aldehydes in a manner similar to malonic ester. Hydrogenation of the product yields the anhydride of phenylalanine which can be hydrolyzed by alkali to the salt of the amino acid.

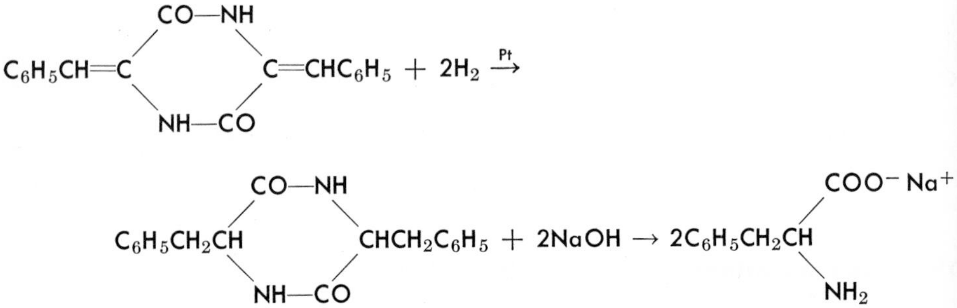

Phenylalanine
sodium salt

19–8   The Gabriel Synthesis

A method that has been used for the preparation of pure primary amines by alkylation is to protect the amine group by forming phthalimide. This is the Gabriel synthesis.

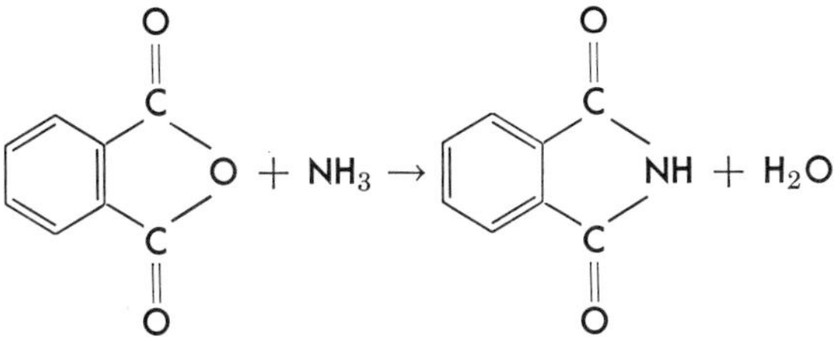

Phthalic
anhydride

Phthalimide

The reaction with ammonia proceeds at the melting point of phthalic anhydride, 131°C, by passing dry ammonia gas through the melt. The phthalimide formed is a much stronger acid than ammonia and will react with potassium hydroxide under anhydrous conditions to form potassium phthalimide.

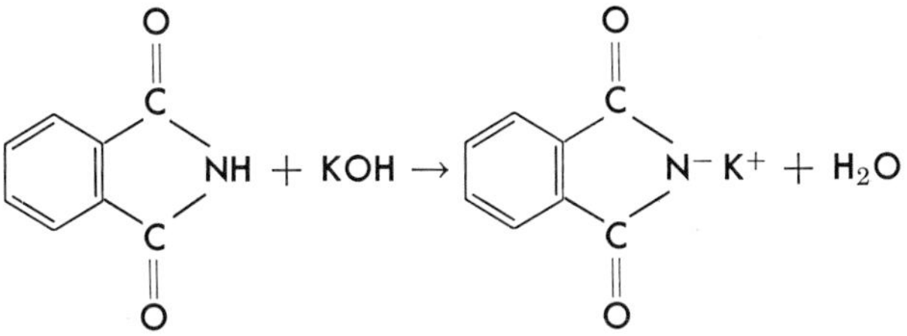

Potassium phthalimide will react with alkyl halides to form alkylated phthalimides, which can be hydrolyzed to the primary amines, and sodium phthalate.

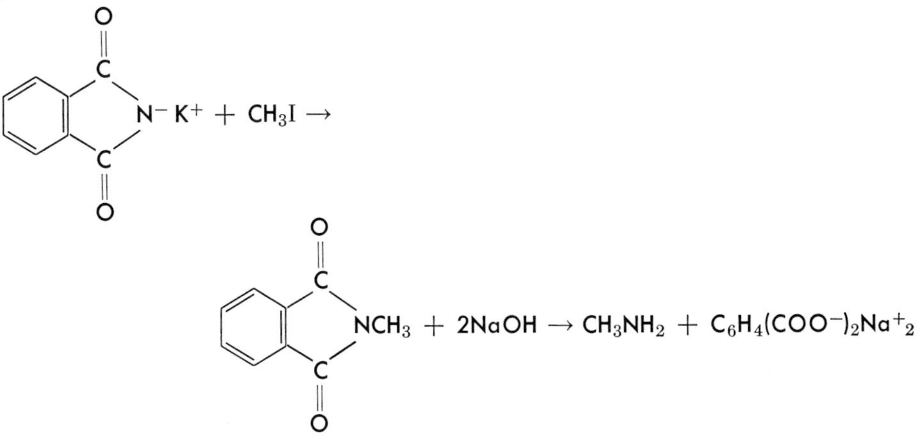

For the formation of arginine by an extension of the Gabriel method, trimethylene bromide is used as the alkylating agent.

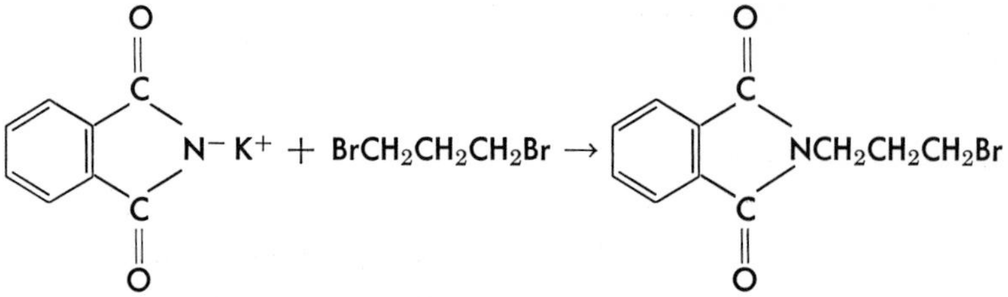

A second reaction with potassium phthalimide is avoided by the use of exactly measured quantities of reagents. The product formed is still an alkyl bromide and may be used in a malonic ester synthesis.

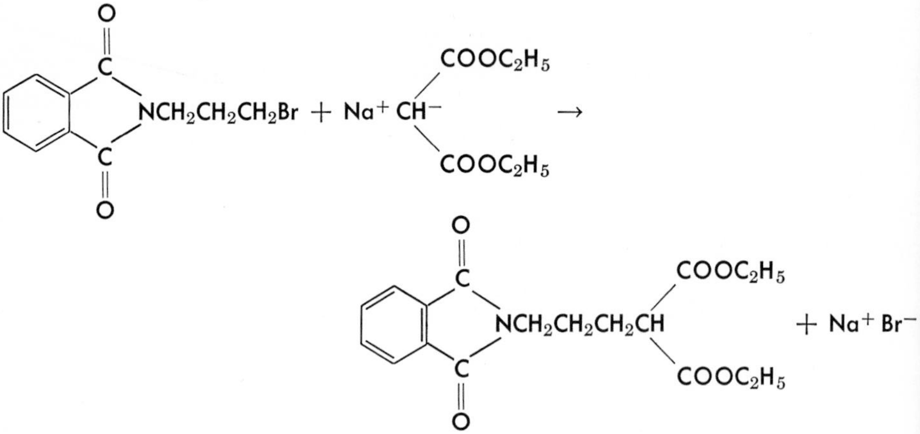

Bromination attacks the α-CH group selectively.

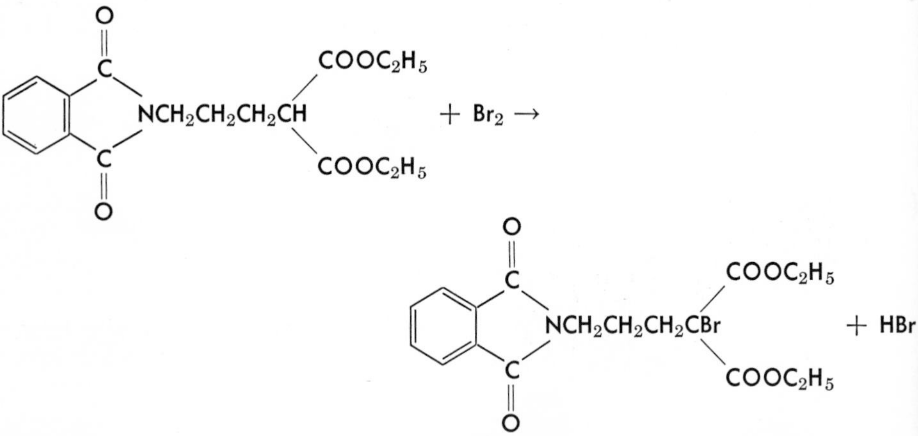

This bromoester can be selectively hydrolyzed because the ester grouping will hydrolyze under milder conditions than either the bromo group or the imide group.

$$C_6H_4 \underset{CO}{\overset{CO}{\diagdown\diagup}} NCH_2CH_2CH_2CBr \underset{COOC_2H_5}{\overset{COOC_2H_5}{\diagdown\diagup}} + 2H_2O \rightarrow$$

$$2C_2H_5OH + C_6H_4 \underset{CO}{\overset{CO}{\diagdown\diagup}} NCH_2CH_2CH_2CBr \underset{COOH}{\overset{COOH}{\diagdown\diagup}} \xrightarrow{heat}$$

$$C_6H_4 \underset{CO}{\overset{CO}{\diagdown\diagup}} NCH_2CH_2CH_2CHBrCOOH + 2NH_3 \rightarrow$$

$$C_6H_4 \underset{CO}{\overset{CO}{\diagdown\diagup}} NCH_2CH_2CH_2\underset{NH_3^+}{CH}COO^- + NH_4^+ Br^-$$

Basic hydrolysis gives ornithine, an intermediate in the synthesis of arginine.

$$C_6H_4 \underset{CO}{\overset{CO}{\diagdown\diagup}} NCH_2CH_2CH_2\underset{NH_3^+}{CH}COO^- + 3OH^- \rightarrow$$

$$C_6H_4(COO^-)_2 + H_2NCH_2CH_2CH_2\underset{NH_2}{CH}COO^-$$

Ornithine salt

Ornithine is found in the excretions of birds. When hens are fed benzoic acid, they excrete ornithuric acid, the dibenzoyl derivative of ornithine. Ornithine is also a physiological intermediate in the formation of arginine. In the laboratory, arginine (Fig. 19–3) is prepared from ornithine by the action of cyanamide, which, in turn, can be formed from thiourea and lead hydroxide.

$$H_2NCSNH_2 + Pb(OH)_2 \rightarrow PbS + H_2NCN$$

$$H_2NCN + H_2NCH_2CH_2CH_2\underset{NH_3}{CH}COO^- \rightarrow$$

Ornithine

$$H_2\overset{+}{N}=\underset{NH_2}{C}-NHCH_2CH_2CH_2\underset{NH_2}{CH}COO^-$$

FIGURE 19–3

Arginine

Table 19–1

COMMON AMINO ACIDS

Name and formula	Abbreviation

GROUP I. NEUTRAL AMINO ACIDS

A. Simple aliphatic amino acids

(1) Glycine, $CH_2(\overset{+}{N}H_3)COO^-$ — Gly

(2) Alanine, $CH_3CH(\overset{+}{N}H_3)COO^-$ (+) — Ala

(3) Valine,* $(CH_3)_2CHCH(\overset{+}{N}H_3)COO^-$ (+) — Val

(4) Leucine,* $(CH_3)_2CHCH_2CH(\overset{+}{N}H_3)COO^-$ (−) — Leu

(5) Isoleucine,* $C_2H_5CH(CH_3)CH(\overset{+}{N}H_3)COO^-$ (+) — Ileu

B. Substituted aliphatic amino acids

(6) Serine, $HOCH_2CH(\overset{+}{N}H_3)COO^-$ (−) — Ser

(7) Threonine,* $CH_3CH(OH)CH(\overset{+}{N}H_3)COO^-$ (−) — Thr

(8) Cysteine, $HSCH_2CH(\overset{+}{N}H_3)COO^-$ (−) — CySH

Cystine, $[SCH_2CH(\overset{+}{N}H_3)COO^-]_2$ (−) — CyS-SCy

(9) Methionine,* $CH_3SCH_2CH_2CH(\overset{+}{N}H_3)COO^-$ (−) — Met

C. Cyclic aliphatic amino acids

(10) Proline

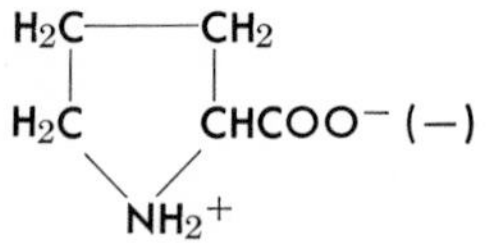

$$\begin{array}{c} H_2C\text{——}CH_2 \\ | \qquad\quad | \\ H_2C \qquad CHCOO^- \ (-) \\ \diagdown \quad \diagup \\ \overset{+}{N}H_2 \end{array}$$

Pro

(11) Hydroxyproline

$$\begin{array}{c} HOCH\text{——}CH_2 \\ | \qquad\quad | \\ H_2C \qquad CHCOO^- \ (-) \\ \diagdown \overset{+}{} \diagup \\ NH_2 \end{array}$$

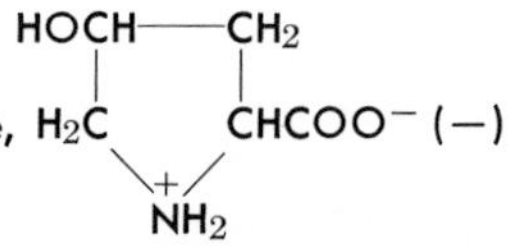

Hypro

The grouping formed by the action of cyanamide is the guanidino group and is so much stronger as a base than the amino group that it removes the proton from the amino group in the α-position. Guanidine in its anhydrous form is difficult to prepare. It is ordinarily isolated as a salt or as the "hydrate" which has the formula of guanidinium hydroxide.

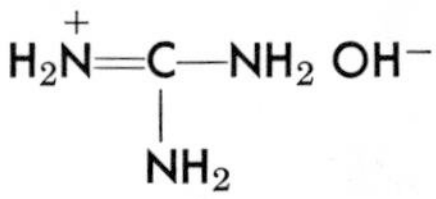

$$H_2\overset{+}{N}\!\!=\!\!C\!\!-\!\!NH_2 \ OH^-$$
$$|$$
$$NH_2$$

This is a base of the same order of strength as sodium hydroxide. It will be seen that all three amino groups in guanidine are equivalent so that the charge and the double bond can shift to any one without changing the compound. This is another

Table 19–1 (*Cont.*)

COMMON AMINO ACIDS

Name and formula	Abbreviation

D. Aromatic amino acids

(12) Phenylalanine,* $C_6H_5CH_2CH(\overset{+}{N}H_3)COO^-$ (−)   Phe

(13) Tyrosine, p-$HOC_6H_4CH_2CH(\overset{+}{N}H_3)COO^-$ (−)   Tyr

(14) Tryptophane,*

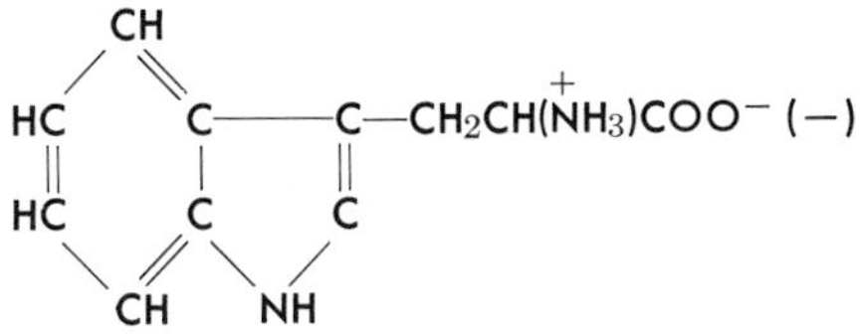

C—CH$_2$CH($\overset{+}{N}$H$_3$)COO⁻ (−)   Try

GROUP II. BASIC AMINO ACIDS

(15) Lysine,* $H_2NCH_2CH_2CH_2CH_2CH(\overset{+}{N}H_3)COO^-$ (+)   Lys

(16) Hydroxylysine, $H_2NCH_2CH(OH)CH_2CH_2CH(\overset{+}{N}H_3)COO^-$ (−)   Hylys

(17) Arginine,* $H_2N\!\!=\!\!CH—NHCH_2CH_2CH_2CH(NH_2)COO^-$ (+)   Arg

$\qquad\qquad\qquad$ |
$\qquad\qquad\quad NH_2$

(18) Histidine,*

—CH$_2$CH($\overset{+}{N}$H$_3$)COO⁻ (−)   His

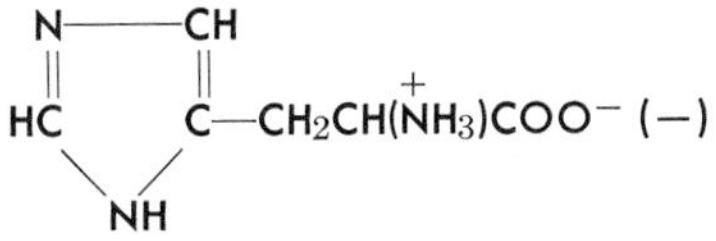

GROUP III. ACIDIC AMINO ACIDS

(19)
Aspartic acid, $HOOCCH_2CH(\overset{+}{N}H_3)COO^-$ (+)   Asp
or
Asparagine, $H_2NCOCH_2CH(\overset{+}{N}H_3)COO^-$ (−)   Asp (NH$_2$)

(20)
Glutamic acid, $HOOCCH_2CH_2CH(\overset{+}{N}H_3)COO^-$ (+)   Glu
or
Glutamine, $H_2NCOCH_2CH_2CH(\overset{+}{N}H_3)COO^-$ (+)   Glu (NH$_2$)

case like that of benzene in which the shift of bonds may be represented as forming more than one structure although only one is found. This type of structure is referred to as a *resonance hybrid*. A full discussion of these will be presented in Book 2. Removal of a proton from guanidine would destroy this symmetry and it is for this reason that guanidium hydroxide retains its proton so tenaciously, creating a strong base.

19–9 The Amino Acids of Proteins

The amino acids commonly isolated from proteins are listed in Table 19–1. They are divided into groups according to their structural characteristics. You should be able to devise syntheses for all but a few of them. It has been found that certain of the amino acids are essential in the diets of laboratory animals. These are marked with an asterisk (*). All of the natural amino acids with the exception of glycine are optically active. The direction of the rotation of each is shown in parentheses. In the last column the common abbreviations are listed.

In addition to these, brominated and iodinated tyrosines are found in certain marine organisms and triiodo and tetraiodothyronine (thyroxine) are found in the thyroid proteins of higher animals.

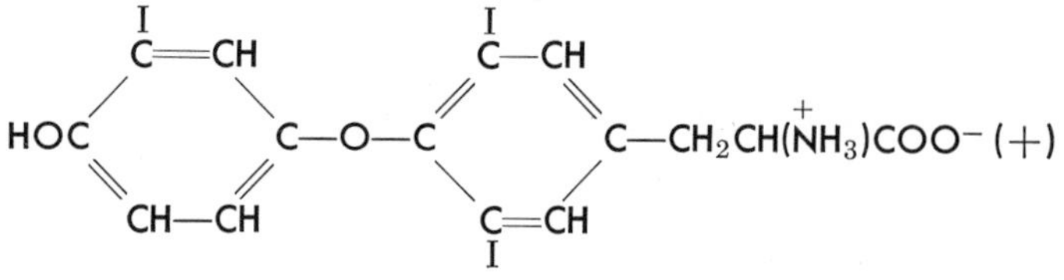

Triiodothyronine

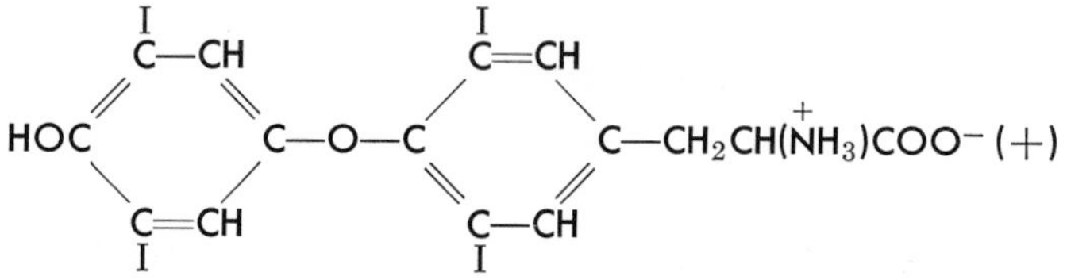

Thyroxine

The essential amino acids must be obtained in the diet of animals from plant sources. Hence they define, in part, our parasitic dependence on the plants.

PROBLEMS

19–1   How would you synthesize isoleucine from 3-methylpentene-1?

19–2   Tyrosine was first isolated by Liebig, who fused fresh cheese with potassium hydroxide. A more elegant preparation is available which uses phthalimide, bromomalonic ester, and p-methoxybenzyl chloride as starting materials.

(a) Work out the proper sequence of steps to arrive at the product.

(b) Why should demethylation of the phenol be reserved until the end?

19–3   Because of their ability to chelate metals, iminodiacetic acid, $HOOCCH_2\overset{+}{N}H_2CH_2COO^-$, and nitrilotriacetic acid, $(HOOCCH_2)_2\,^+NHCH_2COO^-$, are used in analytical chemistry and inorganic chemistry. How might they be prepared? Note the analogy in Section 16–5.

19–4   Betaine, which may be isolated from sugar beets and other sources, can be synthesized from trimethylamine and chloroacetic acid. Its empirical formula is $C_5H_{11}NO_2$ and it is insoluble in organic solvents.

(a) What is its structure?

(b) What characteristic of its structure renders it insoluble in organic solvents? Compounds with this characteristic are usually known as betaines.

When betaine is treated with anhydrous ethanol and hydrochloric acid, it is esterified yielding the chloride salt of betaine ethyl ester. Any ester of betaine may be treated with ammonia to yield the amide.

$$RCOOC_2H_5 + NH_3 \rightarrow RCONH_2 + C_2H_5OH$$

The reaction of esters to form amides is not so vigorous as the preparation of amides from acid chlorides (Section 16–10). Hydrazine, NH_2NH_2, may be used in this reaction to form what may be looked on as a substituted amide, a hydrazide.

(c) Write the reaction which occurs between one mole of hydrazine and one mole of the chloride of betaine ethyl ester.

This product is known as Girard's reagent T. It was developed by the Swiss chemist Girard as a reagent for separating aldehydes and ketones from mixtures with other types of compounds by rendering them water-soluble.

(d) Show how this reagent would be used to separate cyclohexanone from a reaction mixture containing cyclohexanone and cyclohexanol. What kind of derivative is formed by cyclohexanone? What analogies have you seen already?

19–5 Proline has been prepared by a sequence of steps as follows:

(a) $H_2C{=}CH{-}C{\equiv}N + C_2H_5OOCCH_2COOC_2H_5 + Na^+ {}^-OC_2H_5 \rightarrow C_{10}H_{15}NO_4$

(A Michael condensation)

(b) $C_{10}H_{15}NO_4 \xrightarrow[Ni]{H_2} C_{10}H_{19}NO_4$ (Not isolated)

(c) $C_{10}H_{19}NO_4 \rightarrow C_8H_{13}NO_3 + C_2H_5OH$ (cf. Problem 19–4, Part C)

(d) $C_8H_{13}NO_3 \xrightarrow{SO_2Cl_2} C_8H_{12}ClNO_3$ (cf. Use of Cl_2, Section 15–8)

Which hydrogen is α to two carbonyls?

(e) $C_8H_{12}ClNO_3 \xrightarrow{hydrolysis} C_6H_8ClNO_3$

Which must have hydrolyzed more rapidly, the ester or the amide?

(f) $C_6H_8ClNO_3 \rightarrow C_5H_8ClNO$ (Not isolated)

(g) $C_5H_8ClNO \xrightarrow[\text{concentrated HCl}]{\text{further hydrolysis}} C_5H_{10}ClNO_2{\cdot}HCl$

(h) $C_5H_{10}ClNO_2{\cdot}HCl \xrightarrow{NaOH} C_5H_9NO_2$ (cf. Section 16–5)
Proline

Write structural formulas for all of the intermediate products in the synthesis.

(i) As a rule, the proline is purified by formation of proline hydrochloride at this stage, followed by regeneration of proline with a strong organic base. What reason might there be for this?

Is the arrangement of substituent groups in the naturally occurring amino acids random or ordered? By what means was the geometrical relationship between the various amino acids established? How are amino acids joined to each other in protein molecules? How can the nature of their union and their sequence in various fragments be established?

20

PROTEINS II: CONFIGURATIONS OF AMINO ACIDS AND STRUCTURES OF PEPTIDES

20–1 The Configurational Problem

All the amino acids obtained from proteins with the exception of glycine have a center of asymmetry. Accordingly, all of them are optically active, as shown in Section 19–9. The differences in sign of rotation naturally raise the question of whether or not they correspond to differences in configuration. Structurally, if all amino acids had the same configuration, more orderly arrangements would be possible than if the configurations were mixed. For this reason, it became of interest to determine their relative configurations.

20–2 The Walden Inversion

When reactions are performed in which a substitution is carried out at a center of asymmetry, there is always a possibility that the carbon atom may turn inside out on substitution and thus reverse its configuration.

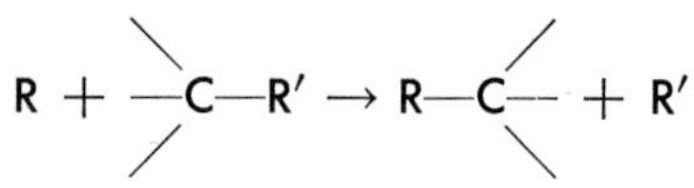

$$R + \overset{\diagdown}{\underset{\diagup}{\text{—C—}}} R' \rightarrow R \text{—} \overset{\diagup}{\underset{\diagdown}{\text{C—}}} + R'$$

FIG. 20–1. Inversion of a carbon atom during substitution.

The possibility also exists that this may not happen. That both possibilities occur in practice was demonstrated by Walden in a series of reactions known as the

274

Walden inversion. The classical example of the Walden inversion is shown below:

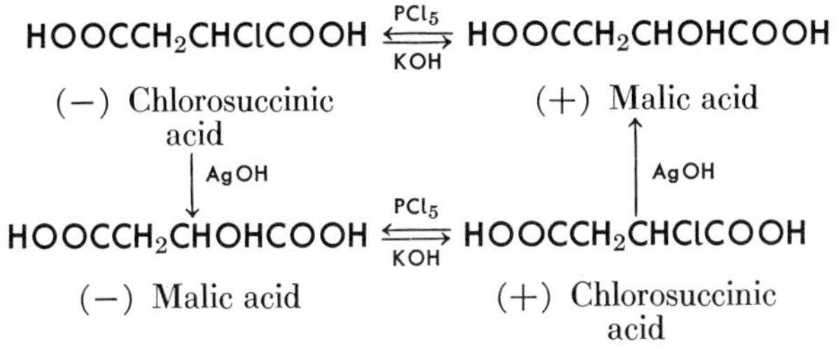
HOOCCH2CHClCOOH
PCl5
KOH
HOOCCH2CHOHCOOH
(−) Chlorosuccinic acid
(+) Malic acid
AgOH
AgOH
HOOCCH2CHOHCOOH
PCl5
KOH
HOOCCH2CHClCOOH
(−) Malic acid
(+) Chlorosuccinic acid

An examination of the course of the reactions will show that either PCl_5 or AgOH, but not both, must produce an inversion, since there is an odd number of inversions in going from D-malic acid to L-malic acid. If AgOH produces an inversion, then KOH must not. On the other hand, if PCl_5 produces an inversion, then KOH must also produce one. In this case, the problem is to identify the step at which the inversion took place. This problem was solved by chemical methods by Kuhn and Wagner-Jauregg, but we shall not give the solution in detail at this time. It is sufficient to state that they found that the inverting agents are KOH and PCl_5. In any given case, however, the possibility that a given reagent may produce an inversion must be submitted to an extensive examination before it can be ascertained whether or not this takes place. To avoid the difficulty about inversion, comparisons can frequently be made between substances by a series of reactions none of which involve the center of asymmetry. In these cases, no change in configuration would take place and relative configurations could be made by simple intercomparisons. This is the method that was used by Emil Fischer in establishing the relative configurations of most of the amino acids.

20–3 Chemical Studies on Configuration

The starting point for the comparison was (−) serine.

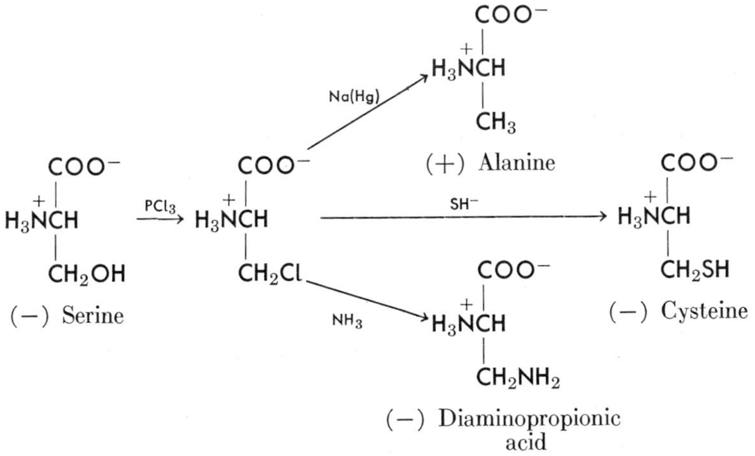
Na(Hg)
(+) Alanine
PCl3
SH−
NH3
(−) Serine
(−) Cysteine
(−) Diaminopropionic acid

This series of reactions has established that serine, alanine, and cysteine, in their natural forms, all belong to the same configurational family, even though the sign of rotation of alanine is opposite to those of the others. This also establishes the point that the sign of rotation, by itself, is insufficient as a guide to configuration. Finally, the reactions provide us with a reference compound, $(-)$ diaminopropionic acid, which can be used for other intercomparisons.

Asparagine can be converted to diaminopropionic acid by another degradation reaction named for Hofmann, the Hofmann amide degradation. As a simple example, let us first examine the Hofmann degradation of acetamide.

$$CH_3CONH_2 + Br_2 \rightarrow CH_3CONHBr$$

On treatment with base, an N-bromoamide rearranges to an isocyanate.

$$CH_3CONHBr \xrightarrow{OH^-} CH_3-N=C=O + Br^-$$

On mild hydrolysis, an isocyanate forms a substituted carbamic acid. This is unstable and will decarboxylate to an amine.

$$CH_3-N=C=O + H_2O \rightarrow (CH_3-NH-COOH) \rightarrow CH_3NH_2 + CO_2$$

This provides a general method for the synthesis of primary amines from the amides with one more carbon atom than the desired product. Hypobromite may be used in one step instead of the separate reactions with bromine and hydroxyl ion shown. The application to the degradation of asparagine follows:

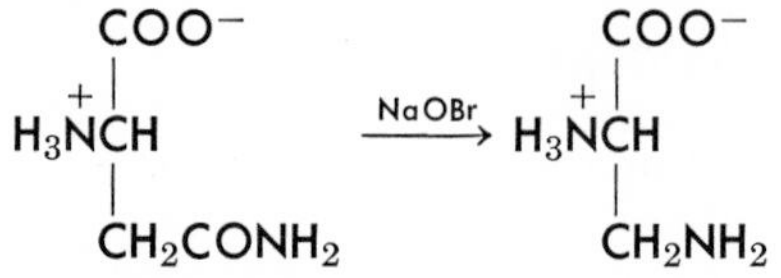

$$
\begin{array}{ccc}
COO^- & & COO^- \\
\overset{+}{H_3}NCH & \xrightarrow{NaOBr} & \overset{+}{H_3}NCH \\
CH_2CONH_2 & & CH_2NH_2
\end{array}
$$

$(-)$ Asparagine $(-)$ Diaminopropionic acid

This reaction establishes the fact that asparagine has the same configuration as serine, alanine, and cysteine.

$$
\begin{array}{ccccc}
COO^- & & COO^- & & COOH \\
\overset{+}{H_3}NCH & + H_2O \xrightarrow{HCl} & \overset{+}{H_3}NCH & + C_6H_5COCl \rightarrow C_6H_5CONHCH \\
CH_2CONH_2 & & CH_2COOH & & CH_2COOH
\end{array}
$$

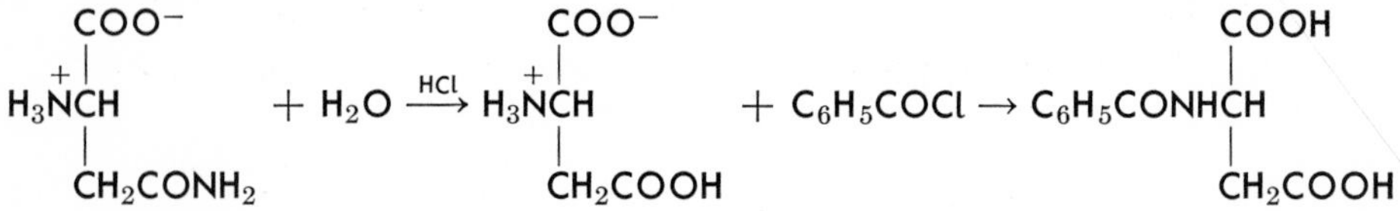

$(-)$ Asparagine $(-)$ Aspartic acid $(-)$ Benzoylaspartic acid

This series shows that asparagine and aspartic acid belong to the same configurational family and provides a further reference compound, $(-)$ benzoyl aspartic acid.

It is possible to prepare a monobenzoyl derivative of histidine from the salt.

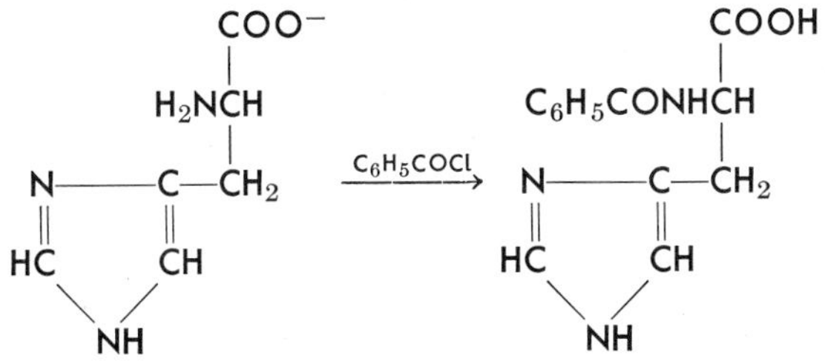

$$\text{(−) Histidine (salt)} \quad \xrightarrow{\ C_6H_5COCl\ }$$

(−) Histidine (salt)

The $C{=}C$ bond of the imidazole ring is then susceptible to ozonolysis.

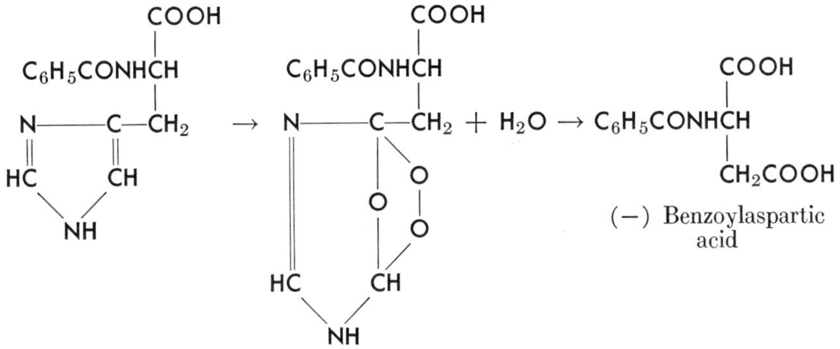

$$\rightarrow \quad + \ H_2O \ \rightarrow \ C_6H_5\text{CONHCH}$$

(−) Benzoylaspartic
acid

This series of transformations interrelates histidine with aspartic acid, asparagine, serine, alanine, and cysteine and shows that all have the same relative configuration.

We shall not complete the interrelationships of the amino acids. The reactions sketched above show how the job can be done and it is sufficient now to say that all the amino acids occurring in proteins have been interrelated and found to have the same relative configuration.

20-4 Absolute Configurations

In the assignment of absolute configurations the reference substance is now taken as (+) glyceraldehyde. This was first arbitrarily assigned the D-configuration. Later, inferences were drawn from mathematical models that the original configurational assignment was correct. Still later the configuration was confirmed by x-ray methods. The projection formula is shown below.

D-(+)-Glyceraldehyde   L-(−)-Glyceraldehyde

The chemical relation of the amino acids to the glyceraldehydes was established by a complex series of degradations starting from glucosamine. We shall not present these in detail, but the conclusion drawn was that the amino acids are related configurationally to L-(−)-glyceraldehyde. In making such an assignment, the choice of the equivalence of groups in transferring from glyceraldehyde to an amino acid is necessarily arbitrary. In both cases, one substituent is hydrogen. A second substituent in each case has a carbonyl group, aldehydic in one case, carboxylic in the other. A third group contains at least one carbon atom in each case, CH_2OH in glyceraldehyde and the amino acid side chain in the other. The last group is OH in one case and NH_2 in the other. This assignment of configuration was also confirmed in 1954 by x-ray analysis.

20-5 Partial Hydrolysis of Proteins; Peptides

The next step taken by Fischer in the structural study of the proteins was partial hydrolysis. By stopping short of the hydrolytic time necessary to produce amino acids, Fischer was able to isolate partial breakdown products of proteins, the peptides. These proved to be amides in which the carboxyl of one amino acid was joined to the amino group of another. The hydrolytic process resembles the production of ammonia or an amine from a simpler amide.

$$CH_3\overset{\overset{\displaystyle O}{\|}}{C}-NHCH_3 + H_2O + HCl \rightarrow CH_3COOH + CH_3\overset{+}{N}H_3 \ Cl^-$$

Amide nitrogens possess only very low basicity, less than that of water, so that normal solutions of strong mineral acids are required to cause appreciable protonation. In hydrolysis, 20% hydrochloric acid is usually employed.

Like the amino acids, the peptides are dipolar ions. We have already seen how diketopiperazine can be prepared from glycine ester. Mild alkaline hydrolysis of diketopiperazine yields the simplest peptide, glycylglycine.

$$O{=}C\underset{\diagdown CH_2-NH}{\overset{NH-CH_2 \diagup}{\Big<}}C{=}O \xrightarrow{\text{OH}^- \text{ then H}^+} {}^-OOC-CH_2-NH-CO-CH_2-NH_3{}^+$$

Because glycylglycine contains residues from two amino acids, it is called a dipeptide. One with residues from three would be a tripeptide and so on until one with many residues would be called a polypeptide. Fischer's concept of protein structure was that these substances are simply long-chain polypeptides. He found methods for the synthesis of peptides, finally producing one with 18 amino acid residues. This compound was disappointing, however, because the increase in chain length did not produce a change in properties corresponding to the observed differences between the short-chain peptides and the proteins. This was ascribed by some to an error in Fischer's basic hypothesis, and one school of investigators took the position that proteins were somehow more complicated than polypeptides. Other investigators took the position that the limitations of the synthetic methods available to Fischer forced him to use simple amino acids in his syntheses and that the proteins themselves contained a good representation of the more complex amino acids. According to this school, the use of a selection of more complex amino acids would yield a product more nearly representative of the natural products.

One property of the proteins, in particular, was not duplicated by Fischer's polypeptide. This was the water solubility. Many proteins are highly soluble in water, more soluble in fact, than the amino acids from which they are made. Fischer's peptide was relatively insoluble with properties approaching those of the silk protein, fibroin. Leuchs, one of Fischer's students had, indeed, succeeded in preparing a polyglycine in 1908 which had properties quite similar to those of silk. Since the hydrolysis of silk yields mainly glycine and alanine, it is reasonable to suppose that the amino acid composition should affect the properties of the protein in a fundamental manner.

20–6   Fischer's Peptide Syntheses

Fischer's peptide syntheses were based on two fundamental discoveries:

(1) it is possible to hydrolyze an ester group in mild alkali at room temperature without simultaneously hydrolyzing the amide linkage of the peptide bond;

(2) it is also possible, under the same conditions, to hydrolyze the ester linkage without simultaneously hydrolyzing an alkyl bromide to the alcohol.

Armed with this information a workable sequence of operations was devised for the preparation of peptides one step at a time. We shall illustrate with a simple example.

$$(CH_3)_2CHCH_2CH\underset{\underset{Br}{|}}{C}OOH \xrightarrow{PCl_5} (CH_3)_2CHCH_2\underset{\underset{Br}{|}}{C}HCOCl$$

This α-bromoacid chloride will condense with an amino acid ester.

$$(CH_3)_2CHCH_2\underset{\underset{Br}{|}}{C}HCOCl + H_2NCH\underset{\underset{CH_3}{|}}{C}OOC_2H_5 \rightarrow (CH_3)_2CHCH_2\underset{\underset{Br}{|}}{C}HCONH\underset{\underset{CH_3}{|}}{C}HCOOC_2H_5$$

If the condensation product, an ester, were treated with ammonia, the ester group would go to an amide group while the bromine was being replaced. To avoid this undesired reaction, the ester group is hydrolyzed at room temperature.

$$(CH_3)_2CHCH_2\underset{\underset{Br}{|}}{C}HCONH\underset{\underset{CH_3}{|}}{C}HCOOC_2H_5 \xrightarrow{OH^- \text{ then } H^+} (CH_3)_2CHCH_2\underset{\underset{Br}{|}}{C}HCONH\underset{\underset{CH_3}{|}}{C}HCOOH$$

At this point, two choices are open. The acid may be treated again with phosphorus pentachloride to form a new acid chloride and continue the synthesis, or the synthesis may be terminated by amination. We shall do the latter:

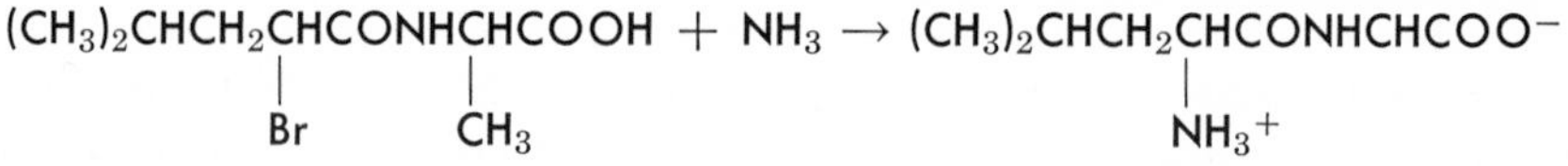

$$(CH_3)_2CHCH_2CHCONHCHCOOH + NH_3 \rightarrow (CH_3)_2CHCH_2CHCONHCHCOO^-$$

with substituents Br and CH_3 on the left structure, and NH_3^+ on the right structure.

Leucylalanine

If desired, the synthesis could be continued on the amino group end of this peptide by esterifying the peptide to protect the carboxyl group and then treating the amine formed with a new acid chloride. Thus the synthesis can be extended in either direction.

20-7 Bergmann-Curtius Peptide Syntheses

Curtius was an investigator in nitrogen chemistry who made a number of contributions to the chemistry of proteins, amino acids, and their derivatives. In fact, he was the person who persuaded Emil Fischer to enter the field. One of the contributions which Curtius made was to devise a method by which an amide could be produced from an ester in good yields without the use of an excess of the amine. The Curtius synthesis is shown below.

$$CH_3COOCH_3 + H_2NNH_2 \rightarrow CH_3CONHNH_2 \xrightarrow{HNO_2}$$

Acethydrazide

$$CH_3CO-N\overset{+}{=}N\overset{-}{=}N \leftrightarrow CH_3CO-\overset{-}{N}-\overset{+}{N}\equiv N$$

Acetazide

The acyl azides can also be prepared from acid chlorides and sodium azide.

$$CH_3COCl + NaN_3^- \rightarrow CH_3CON_3 + Cl^-$$

The azides, like benzene, can be represented by two normal bond formulas. They are quite reactive and condense readily with amines with the elimination of hydrazoic acid.

$$CH_3CON_3 + H_2NCH_3 \rightarrow HN_3 + CH_3CONHCH_3$$

N-Methylacetamide

The Curtius synthesis was not used much until a further discovery was made, this time by Max Bergmann. Bergmann was convinced that peptides containing more complex amino acids must be prepared. In particular, water solubility should be conferred on proteins by their salt-like groups, that is, by COO^- and NH_3^+ groups. Hence he felt it necessary to study means for protecting the carboxyl groups of dibasic acids and the basic groups of the basic amino acids to permit them to be brought into peptide syntheses. The carboxyl groups could be protected by esterification, so the main problem was the protection of the basic groups. The difficulty lay in the fact that most protective groups used were acyl groups and would require hydrolysis to remove them. The required hydrolytic conditions would, however, be drastic enough to break the peptide bonds. Hence it became necessary to invent a protective acyl group that could be removed by a method other than by hydrolysis. Bergmann solved the problem by the use of the "carbobenzoxy" or "carbobenzyloxy" group. The sequence of reactions required for the introduction and removal of this group is shown in a simple example:

$$C_6H_5CH_2OH + ClCOCl \rightarrow C_6H_5CH_2OCOCl + CH_3NH_2 \rightarrow$$

Benzyl	Phosgene	Benzylchloroformate
alcohol		"Carbobenzoxy
		chloride"

$$C_6H_5CH_2OCONHCH_3 + H_2 \xrightarrow{Pt} C_6H_5CH_3 + CO_2 + CH_3NH_2$$

Phosgene is the di-acid chloride of carbonic acid. It readily forms half-esters, the chloroformates, sometimes called chlorocarbonates, which are still acid chlorides and are quite reactive. They will re-act with alcohols and amines just as other acid chlorides will. With methylamine a half-ester, half-amide is formed. This has the unique property of hydrogenating to toluene and carbon dioxide, freeing the amine without hydrolysis.

An example of a peptide synthesis performed by Bergmann using this method of protection is the formation of lysylglutamic acid (Fig. 20–2).

FIGURE 20–2

$$CH_2CH_2CH_2CH_2CHCOOCH_3 + C_6H_5CH_2COCl \rightarrow CH_2CH_2CH_2CH_2CHCOOCH_3$$

NH$_2$	NH$_2$	NHCOCH$_2$C$_6$H$_5$	NHCOCH$_2$C$_6$H$_5$
		‖	‖
		O	O

For convenience, we shall abbreviate the —COOCH$_2$C$_6$H$_5$ group as Cbzo.

$$CH_2CH_2CH_2CH_2CHCOOCH_3 + H_2NNH_2 \rightarrow CH_2CH_2CH_2CH_2CHCONHNH_2 + HNO_2 \rightarrow$$

| | | | |
| HNCbzo | HNCbzo | HNCbzo | NHCbzo |

$$CH_2CH_2CH_2CH_2CHCON_3$$

| | |
| NHCbzo | NHCbzo |

This completes the synthesis of half the molecule. The other half is glutamic ester.

$$\underset{\substack{| \\ \text{NHCbzo}}}{CH_2}CH_2CH_2CH_2\underset{\substack{| \\ \text{NHCbzo}}}{CH}CON_3 \; + \; H_2N{-}\underset{\substack{| \\ \text{COOC}_2\text{H}_5}}{CH}CH_2CH_2COOC_2H_5 \; \rightarrow$$

$$\underset{\substack{| \\ \text{NHCbzo}}}{CH_2}CH_2CH_2CH_2\underset{\substack{| \\ \text{NHCbzo}}}{CH}CONH\underset{\substack{| \\ \text{COOC}_2\text{H}_5}}{CH}CH_2CH_2COOC_2H_5 \; \xrightarrow{\text{OH}^- \text{ then } \text{H}^+}$$

$$\underset{\substack{| \\ \text{NHCbzo}}}{CH_2}CH_2CH_2CH_2\underset{\substack{| \\ \text{NHCbzo}}}{CH}CONH\underset{\substack{| \\ \text{COOH}}}{CH}CH_2CH_2COOH \; \xrightarrow[\text{Pt}]{\text{H}_2}$$

$$\underset{\substack{| \\ \text{NH}_3{}^+}}{CH_2}CH_2CH_2CH_2\underset{\substack{| \\ \text{NH}_3{}^+}}{CH}CONH\underset{\substack{| \\ \text{COO}^-}}{CH}CH_2CH_2COO^-$$

The dipeptide formed by this synthesis is a tetrapolar ion and is appreciably more water soluble than ordinary peptides.

Bergmann's method for the protection of amino groups is widely used by modern investigators. In addition, it also takes advantage of the protective properties of benzyl esters.

$$CH_3COOCH_2C_6H_5 \; \xrightarrow[\text{Pt}]{\text{H}_2} \; CH_3COOH \; + \; CH_3C_6H_5$$

This property is not so widely used because of the relative difficulty of preparing the benzyl esters.

20-8   Modern Peptide Syntheses

In recent years, interest in the synthesis of peptides has been spiraling upward and many new methods for their preparation have been devised. Among the more interesting ones is the reaction with N,N'-dicyclohexylcarbodiimide, introduced by Sheehan and Hess.

$$CbzoNH\underset{\substack{| \\ \text{CH}_3}}{CH}COOH \; + \; C_6H_{11}{-}N{=}C{=}N{-}C_6H_{11} \; + \; H_2N\underset{\substack{| \\ \text{CH}_3}}{CH}COOCH_2C_6H_5 \; \rightarrow$$

$$CbzoNH\underset{\substack{| \\ \text{CH}_3}}{CH}CONH\underset{\substack{| \\ \text{CH}_3}}{CH}COOCH_2C_6H_5 \; + \; C_6H_{11}NH\underset{\substack{\| \\ \text{O}}}{C}NHC_6H_{11}$$

Dicyclohexyl urea

Other di-substituted carbodiimides have also proved useful. Hydrogenation will then produce the free peptide.

$$CbzoNH\underset{\substack{| \\ \text{CH}_3}}{CH}CONH\underset{\substack{| \\ \text{CH}_3}}{CH}COOCH_2C_6H_5 \; \xrightarrow[\text{Pt}]{\text{H}_2} \; H_3\overset{+}{N}\underset{\substack{| \\ \text{CH}_3}}{CH}CONH\underset{\substack{| \\ \text{CH}_3}}{CH}COO^-$$

20–9 The Structures of Peptides

The most valuable tool for the determination of the structures of peptides has been terminal group labeling. The first method for accomplishing this was devised by Fischer, who prepared the β-naphthalenesulfonyl derivatives. Naphthalene sulfonamides are much more resistant to alkaline hydrolysis than are amides so that the cleavage of the peptide bond leaves the terminal nitrogen labeled. An example was the structural determination on a dipeptide obtained from silk fibroin. This had the composition $C_5H_{10}O_3N_2$. Hydrolysis gave glycine and alanine. The peptide could, therefore, be either glycylalanine or alanylglycine. The problem was solved by labeling the terminal amino group.

$$C_{10}H_7SO_2Cl + C_5H_{10}O_3N_2 \xrightarrow{OH^-} C_{15}H_{16}O_5N_2S + H_2O \xrightarrow{OH^-}$$

$$\overset{+}{H_3}NCHCOO^- + C_{12}H_{11}O_4NS$$
$$\underset{CH_3}{|}$$

The compound $C_{12}H_{11}O_4NS$ was found to be identical with β-naphthalenesulfonylglycine, and the isolation of free alanine from the liquor confirmed the structure as glycylalanine. By this method Fischer and his students were able to solve the structural problem for all the dipeptides that they could isolate.

In 1927, Bergmann recommended that phenyl isocyanate be used for the labeling of terminal amino groups. This method was used by Abderhalden and Brockmann in 1930 for the systematic degradation of alanyl-glycyl-leucine. By this method the terminal amino acid which carried the free amino group could be isolated as the phenylhydantoin. Earlier Treat Johnson had studied the formation of phenyl thiohydantoins with the use of phenyl isothiocyanate, but his method was cumbersome. It was applied by Schlack and Kumpf in 1926 to the degradation of peptides, but the cleavages they obtained were not clean. Finally this line of endeavor was brought to a satisfactory outcome by the work of Pehr Edman, who used phenyl isothiocyanate and then, after purification, cleaved the peptide with a cold saturated solution of hydrogen chloride in nitromethane, to avoid hydrolysis of the peptide bonds. The phenylthiohydantoin splits off rapidly at room temperature and can be identified on a paper strip. The peptide which remains can then be subjected to a repetition of the process with the removal of the next amino acid residue, thus providing a systematic stepwise method for degradation. The method was used on alanyl-leucyl-glycine.

$$C_6H_5NCS + H_2NCHCONHCHCONHCH_2COO^- \xrightarrow{\text{pyridine, water}}$$
$$\underset{CH_3}{|} \quad \underset{C_4H_9}{|}$$

$$C_6H_5NHCNHCHCONHCHCONHCH_2COO^-$$
$$\underset{S}{\overset{||}{}} \quad \underset{CH_3}{|} \quad \underset{C_4H_9}{|}$$

Extraction with benzene removes the pyridine and the labeled peptide was dissolved in aqueous acetic acid and precipitated as its silver salt. This was then suspended in nitromethane saturated with hydrogen chloride.

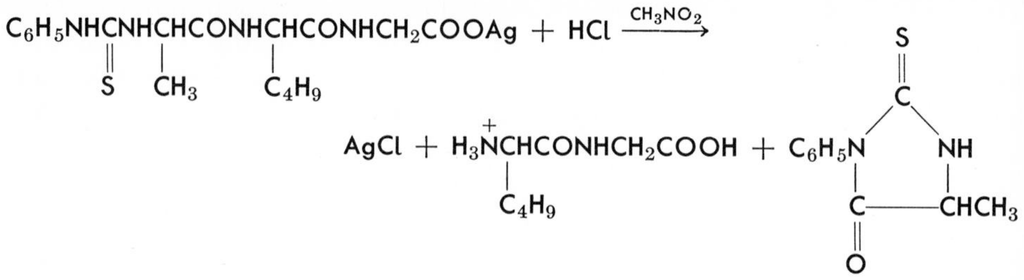

$$C_6H_5NHCNHCHCONHCHCONHCH_2COOAg + HCl \xrightarrow{CH_3NO_2}$$

with structure labels: $\underset{S}{\|} \quad \underset{CH_3}{|} \quad \underset{C_4H_9}{|}$

$$AgCl + \overset{+}{H_3}NCHCONHCH_2COOH + C_6H_5N$$

$$\underset{C_4H_9}{|}$$

(phenylthiohydantoin structure)

$$\begin{array}{c} S \\ \| \\ C \\ \diagup \quad \diagdown \\ C_6H_5N \quad\quad NH \\ | \quad\quad\quad\quad | \\ C\text{————}CHCH_3 \\ \| \\ O \end{array}$$

The identification of the phenylthiohydantoin formed as the derivative obtained from alanine established the fact that the N-terminal amino acid was alanine. The degradation was then repeated and the second phenylthiohydantoin obtained was that from leucine.

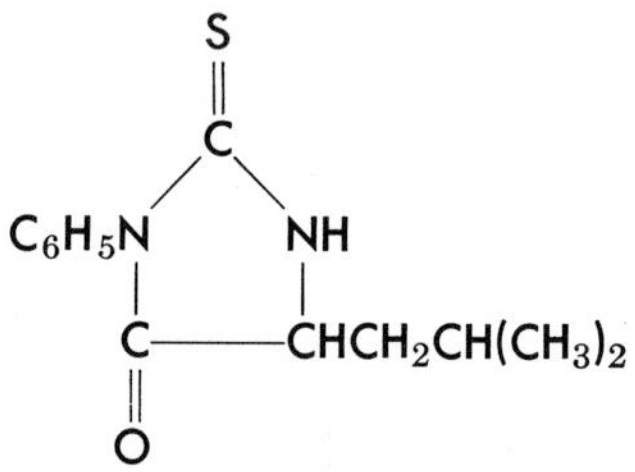

$$\begin{array}{c} S \\ \| \\ C \\ \diagup \quad \diagdown \\ C_6H_5N \quad\quad NH \\ | \quad\quad\quad\quad | \\ C\text{————}CHCH_2CH(CH_3)_2 \\ \| \\ O \end{array}$$

This established leucine in the second position and left only glycine. Therefore the peptide was alanyl-leucyl-glycine.

No thoroughly satisfactory method for degrading peptides from the carboxyl end has been worked out. Enzymatic hydrolysis is usually relied on. In this process a carboxypeptidase, that is, an enzyme that attacks peptides at the carboxyl end, is used and an attempt is made to limit the hydrolysis to the removal of one amino acid.

20–10   The Sanger Method

Another method that has been used widely in the examination of peptide structures is a result of the work of Sanger. In this method, the N-terminal amino acid is labeled with dinitrofluorobenzene by the reaction illustrated on page 285. The dinitrophenyl (DNP) derivatives formed with dinitrofluorobenzene have the advantage that they are colored yellow. This makes their location on chromatographic strips easy. The further refinement employed by Sanger in his work is the recognition of the fact that most peptide bonds are split with approximately equal ease by dilute acid so that the partial hydrolysis of a peptide will produce a mixture of most of the possible partial hydrolysis products. The systematic examination of the DNP derivatives of such a peptide mixture permits the isolation of fragments with one bond intact in one case, and the same bond broken in another case. By the use of enough small fragments, the structure of the complete peptide may be reconstructed. The method employed will be illustrated in the problems.

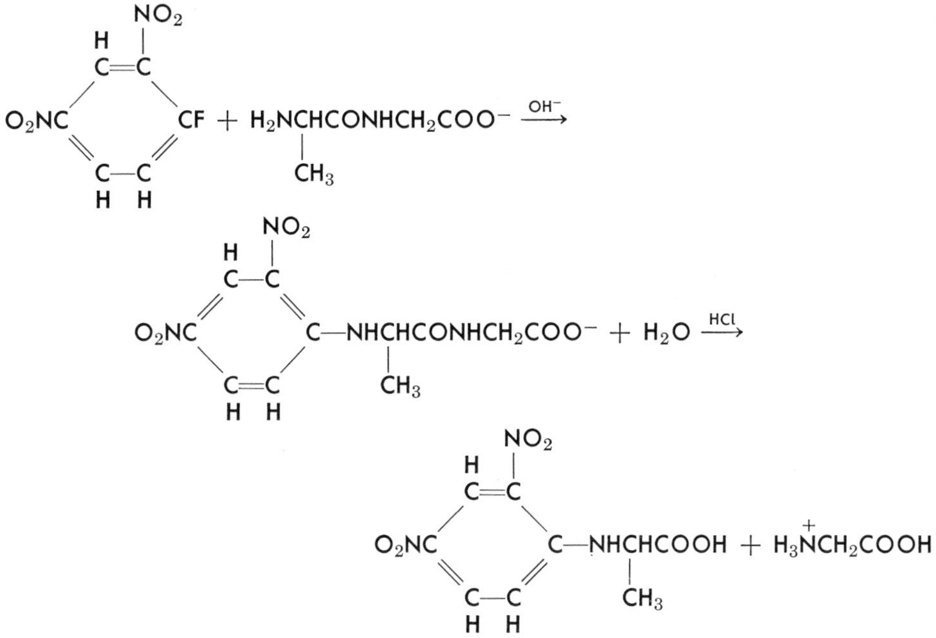

PROBLEMS

20-1 Why could not the Fischer synthesis with racemic α-bromo acids be used effectively in a multistep synthesis of, say, a pentapeptide to be compared with one obtained from natural sources and containing a variety of amino acids?

20-2 Write a suitable sequence of steps for the preparation of L-valyl-L-tyrosyl-L-alanine from the corresponding amino acids.

20-3 One of the peptides obtained from the tryptic hydrolysis of the chain of human hemoglobin may be determined by hydrolysis to have the empirical formula (Ala, Asp, Leu, Lys, Pro, Ser, Val). The enzyme used was specific for cleavage at Lys and Arg; that is, it split the protein into a number of fragments which terminate in Lys-COOH or Arg-COOH.

The peptide under consideration was degraded by the Edman method (phenyl isothiocyanate) in a parallel pair of experiments. After the derivative was prepared, the phenylthiohydantoin was split off. The remaining peptide was divided into two lots; one of these was analyzed by hydrolyzing all the peptide bonds and determining the resulting free amino acids quantitatively. No concurrent analysis of the phenylthiohydantoin was reported. The other portion of the peptide was treated with phenylisothiocyanate again, and in this fashion the molecule was broken down unit by unit.

In Experiment A the material was not chromatographically purified between successive applications of the Edman degradation. The results of these amino acid analyses were found to be as follows at each stage of degradation.

Experiment A

Stage	Ala	Asp	Leu	Pro	Ser	Val
0	1.03	0.99	0.99	1.04	0.98	0.95
1	1.04	0.98	0.98	1.01	0.99	0.10
2	1.00	0.98	0.29	1.00	0.91	0.05
3	1.01	0.91	0.19	0.99	0.36	0.00
4	1.00	0.74	0.15	0.76	0.40	0.00

(a) Write the analysis you would expect for a stepwise degradation of Ala-Asp-Leu-Ser.

(b) Taking a reasonable experimental error into account, how useful is the above table for reconstructing the structure of the hemoglobin fraction?

It is apparent that the intermediates must be purified to make the numbers completely useful. In Experiment B column purification of the remaining peptide was used at each stage of the degradation. Stage 0 remains the same.

Experiment B

Stage	Ala	Asp	Leu	Pro	Ser	Val
1	1.02	1.02	1.03	1.10	0.92	0.05
2	1.02	0.97	0.06	1.04	0.91	0.00
3	1.02	0.94	0.02	1.07	0.08	0.00
4	1.00	0.91	0.00	0.10	0.06	0.00
5	0.12	1.00	0.00	0.04	0.06	0.00

(c) Determine the sequence of amino acids in the peptide.

(d) The origin of the aspartic acid is ambiguous; it could have been either free aspartic acid or asparagine. What would have happened to asparagine under these conditions?

(e) The hydrolysis of the peptide yields less than a mole of ammonia per mole of peptide. (This small amount of ammonia could result from side reaction of the amines.) The peptide is demonstrated to be neutral electrophoretically. Did the aspartic acid in the analyzed amino acids therefore result from the hydrolysis of asparagine during workup, or was it originally present as aspartic acid?

20-4 (a) A peptide isolated from beef insulin was shown to have the empirical formula (Ala, Glu, Leu, Tyr, Val). Conversion of this to its DNP derivative with dinitrofluorobenzene followed by hydrolysis gave DNP-Val, Ala, Glu, Leu, and Tyr. Partial hydrolysis of the original pentapeptide to smaller subunits followed by this procedure gave the following sets of compounds:

DNP-Glu, Leu, Ala
DNP-Leu, Tyr

What is the sequence of amino acids in the pentapeptide?

(b) The preceding method was employed on another peptide from beef insulin, which contains $CySO_3H$ because the original protein was oxidized to break CyS-SCy cross-links between chains, and the following fragments were isolated from pentapeptide-DNP:

DNP-Tyr, CySO₃H, Gly, Leu, Val

The partial hydrolysis technique gave the following sets of fragments:

DNP-Tyr, Leu, Val
DNP-Val, CySO₃H

What is the sequence in this pentapeptide?

(c) A third fragment contained Ala, Val, 2 moles of Ser, and 3 moles of CySO₃H. It gave DNP-CySO₃H, Ala, CySO₃H, CySO₃H, Ser, Ser, and Val. Studies on smaller fragments of it yielded the following combinations:

DNP-CySO₃H, Ala, Ser, Val
DNP-Ser, CySO₃H, Val
DNP-CySO₃H, Ala, CySO₃H

What is the sequence in this heptapeptide?

How can molecular weights of proteins be estimated?
How can the sequence of amino acids in a protein be determined?
What further structural features are of importance in proteins?
How is information concerning these structural features obtained?

21

PROTEINS III: MOLECULAR WEIGHTS; PRIMARY, SECONDARY, AND TERTIARY STRUCTURES

21-1 The Molecular Weights of Proteins

In the early days of organic chemistry, Kekulé determined the molecular weight of methane by serial substitution of the four hydrogens by chlorines, showing that there were four chlorinated derivatives possible and, for this reason, that the alternative formula which represented methane as CH_2 could not be correct. Despite the logically convincing nature of this argument, it was not accepted until it was substantiated by an entirely independent physical means for the determination, based on gas densities. The demonstration by Cannizzaro that Avogadro's hypothesis applied to gas densities would produce the same result as that arrived at by chemical means by Kekulé was instrumental in establishing the modern system of molecular weights.

For proteins, the process of arriving at reliable molecular weights took the opposite course to the one taken with simpler organic substances. Molecular weights were determined by a number of physical methods. Among these, the results obtained by osmotic pressure measurements and diffusion methods were first used, but in later years these were almost entirely displaced by the elegant technique using the ultracentrifuge. By observing the rate of sedimentation of particles in a tremendously high gravitational field, it is possible to calculate particle size with considerable precision. Unfortunately, some chemists have confused particle sizes with molecular weights and, as a result, have been led astray in their interpretations of their results.

21–2   What is a Molecule?

The organic chemist has a conception of a molecule which differs in essential respects from those of some other scientists. For example, the molecule $N{\equiv}C{-}C{\equiv}N$, on heating to 1500°C will decompose into two radicals.

$$NC{-}CN \underset{}{\overset{1500°}{\rightleftharpoons}} 2 \cdot CN$$

Some scientists call these radicals "molecules," but organic chemists would not call them molecules because they do not represent the stable species which is present for examination at room temperature. At the other end of the spectrum, a determination of the vapor density of acetic acid at the boiling point would show that the gas consisted of an associated complex with a vapor density corresponding to a molecular weight of 120. Many chemists would regard 120, then, as the "true" molecular weight of acetic acid. Yet organic chemists will continue to regard 60 as the molecular weight of acetic acid because this is the size of the compound which they must assemble by their synthetic methods to arrive at a substance which will have the properties of acetic acid in bulk. The organic chemist, then, disregards both the processes of molecular dissociation and the processes of molecular association in arriving at his concepts of molecular weights. The ultracentrifugal method gives us an estimate of particle size which frequently does not examine the possible existence of molecular association in arriving at "molecular weights." The most reliable method for examining the possibility of association is to study the behavior of substances with increasing dilution. In many cases, the molecular sizes of proteins are so enormous that it is not feasible to build an ultracentrifuge with rotors sufficiently thick to make optical measurements on a solution of sufficient dilution to meet the necessities for reliable dissociation measurements. As we shall see shortly, there are still other complications standing in the way of a clear concept of protein molecular weights.

21–3   Minimum Molecular Weights

Since each molecule must accommodate at least one atom of each element which makes up its chemical structure, the determination of the percentage composition of proteins with respect to scarce elements was seized on as a possible solution to the problem of molecular weights. Thus the sulfur, phosphorus, or metal analysis of a protein containing these elements could lead to minimum values for the molecular weights. In no case, however, could they be relied on to yield information concerning the size of the particle which must ultimately be synthesized to produce the protein. As amino acid analyses became more precise, it was hoped that the concept of minimum molecular weight could be extended, since the molecule must accommodate integral numbers of each of the amino acids entering into its composition. Even this method could not be relied on to arrive at a reasonable estimate of the size of the synthetic problem facing organic chemists in protein synthesis.

It would always yield a "least common denominator" which could then be multiplied by any given integer to produce the molecular weight. It was obvious that a new approach was required.

21–4 Chemical Molecular Weights

The "new" approach turned out to be disarmingly simple. It was a modern application of Kekulé's "counting" method. This approach was applied by Craig of the Rockefeller Institute (Section 3–7) to the determination of the molecular weight of insulin. The reaction of dinitrofluorobenzene with amino groups produces yellow-colored derivatives. A diamino compound that is allowed to react twice with DNFB will produce a product with twice the color intensity of the same substance allowed to react only once with DNFB. By treating a sample of a diamine with DNFB for a short time, a monodinitrophenyl derivative will be formed. Comparing with a known mono-DNP amine, the color dilution of the substance produced by the remainder of the molecule will permit the molecular weight of the mono-DNP derivative to be estimated.

Applying this technique to a highly purified sample of insulin, a yellow mono-DNP derivative was separated from more highly colored materials and the amount of colorless material attached could be calculated from the color intensity of this most weakly colored of the derivatives. In this manner, the molecular weight of insulin was established as being in the neighborhood of 6500. This was in sharp contrast to the value in the range of 36,000 obtained by the ultracentrifugal method and showed that the ultracentrifuge had been dealing with an associated complex of insulin molecules and not with a molecularly disperse solution. The chemical finding with respect to the molecular weight of insulin has been fully confirmed by subsequent work on the amino acid sequence of the molecule.

21–5 The Hemoglobin Anomaly

For hemoglobin, the situation is more complex. The molecular weight found in the ultracentrifuge is in the neighborhood of 65,000. On treatment with acid or alkali, dissociation takes place into smaller units. Subsequent investigation has shown that these units are not identical, and they have been labeled α and β. The sequence of dissociations found in the ultracentrifuge are as follows:

$$\alpha_2 + \beta_2 \overset{\text{acid}}{\longleftrightarrow} \alpha_2\beta_2 \rightleftarrows 2\alpha\beta \overset{\text{alkali}}{\underset{\longleftarrow}{\longrightarrow}} 2\alpha + 2\beta$$

Hemoglobin

To define a molecular weight under these circumstances is difficult. The chemist would be required to synthesize one α-unit and one β-unit to place both in solution and obtain hemoglobin. These chains possess some kind of "fit" that enables them to interact to form a stable aggregate. This aggregate possesses certain chemical properties that are distinguishable from substances with similar structures that do not have the tendency to form aggregates. Hence the properties of the material in mass cannot be duplicated with isolated α-units or isolated β-units, but only with the associated complexes. Most protein chemists have adopted the concept, then, that the four-chain aggregate is the "molecule" of hemoglobin, even though a strict chemical interpretation would incline to the position that the two-chain αβ aggregate might properly be called a "molecule." It seems obvious that there are situations in which each definition of a molecule leaves something to be desired.

21–6   Amino Acid Sequences of Proteins; Insulin

The primary structure of a protein is defined as the sequence of its amino acid residues. The first protein whose amino acid sequence was worked out in detail was insulin. The feat was accomplished by Sanger and his collaborators at Cambridge. For the purpose Sanger first oxidized insulin, converting the sulfhydryl groups of cystine present to sulfonic acid groups. This broke the molecule into two unequal portions, showing that a linkage was originally present through the R—S—S—R groups of the cystine. The two chains, A and B, obtained by this procedure were then degraded separately. N-terminal residues were identified by making the DNP derivatives, and C-terminal residues by enzymatic hydrolysis with carboxypeptidase. Acid hydrolysis produced a variety of peptides which were separated by chromatography and identified individually by the methods given in the preceding chapter, using DNP derivatives for the identification of N-terminal groups. With these procedures it was possible to reconstruct much of the individual chains by tracing the overlapping patterns of the different peptides isolated. Gaps were found, however, and these were filled by the use of enzymatic hydrolyses, which cleaved the molecule at different sites. In this manner, peptides overlapping each peptide linkage in the chain were obtained, and the complete structure could be reconstructed. The structure for cattle insulin obtained by this method is as follows:

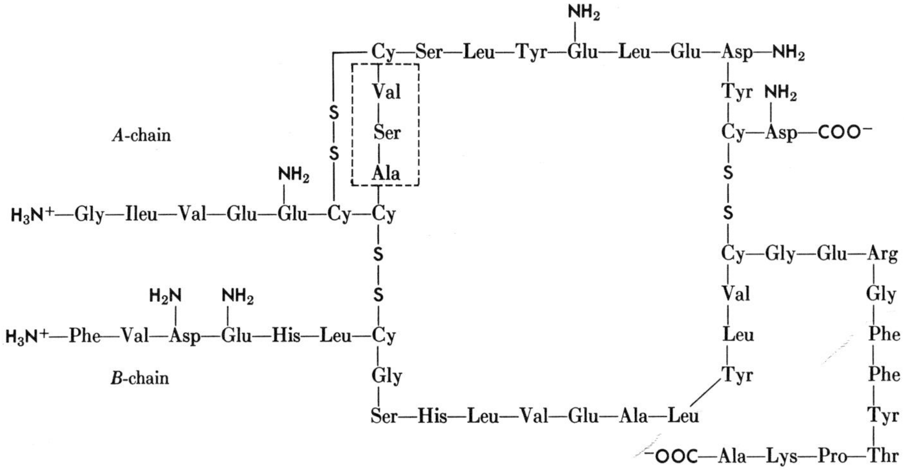

Amino acid sequence of insulin

One of the problems that has interested biologists and chemists for many years is that of species specificity. Proteins obtained from one species are frequently rejected by individuals of another species and, in extreme cases, their repeated injection may lead to serious illness or even to death. The structural differences responsible for these differences in physiological tolerance are of prime importance for an understanding of life processes. With the ability to determine the sequence of amino acids in proteins, answers to some of the problems of species specificity began to appear. In the formula for insulin above, a sequence of three amino acids has been marked with a dashed rectangle. These three amino acids confer the species specificity of beef insulin. Sheep insulin has this grouping replaced by —Ala—Gly—Val—. Thus the substitution of glycine for serine determines the species specificity in this case. Hog insulin has the sequence —Thr—Ser—Ileu— at this point, retaining the serine but replacing alanine with threonine and valine with isoleucine. Horse insulin has the sequence —Thr—Gly—Ileu—, showing the same relation to hog insulin as sheep does to cattle.

The other problem, still unsolved, is how it is possible for a substance consisting entirely of innocuous materials like amino acids to possess powerful physiological action, as insulin assuredly does. How it exerts this action is an intriguing problem that is undergoing intensive investigation.

The smaller A-chain of insulin, shown in the structure above, contains a ring with five amino acid residues and two sulfurs. Since each amino acid residue has three atoms in its chain, this represents a 17-membered ring. Both chains together have a portion of their structure taken up by a larger ring containing 27 amino acid residues. This is thus an 85-membered ring. Its integrity is a precondition for the activity of the hormone. All of the aspartic acid residues of insulin are present as the amide, asparagine. Of the glutamic acid residues, however, only three of the seven are in the form of glutamine, the other four being free. The amino acid sequence determination shows the exact molecular weight of cattle insulin to be 5734.

In 1964, a team at the University of Pittsburgh headed by P. G. Katsoyannis announced the total synthesis of sheep insulin. The synthetic material possessed insulin activity. This was the first synthesis of a naturally occurring protein. It points the way to the syntheses of altered proteins designed to test the critical positions in the molecule for physiological activity and other properties of interest. Thus the field of the relation between chemical structure and activity is now opened to the synthetic chemist.

21-7 Oxytocin and Vasopressin

The problem of the physiological action of polypeptides was given a tremendous impetus by the work of Du Vigneaud on oxytocin and vasopressin. Oxytocin is a hormone obtained from the pituitary which stimulates uterine contractions and initiates the secretion of milk. It has the structure shown on the following page. Replacement of the residues in positions 3 and 8 by phenylalanine and arginine, respectively, gives arginine-vasopressin, while phenylalanine and lysine give lysine-vasopressin. These substances are devoid of the oxytocic property of stimulating uterine contractions and, instead, are weakly antidiuretic and exert a pressor effect, that is, they raise the blood pressure.

$$
\begin{array}{c}
\overset{1}{\text{Cy}}\text{—S—S} \\
\diagup \qquad \diagdown \\
\overset{2}{\text{Tyr}} \qquad \qquad \overset{6}{\text{Cy}}\text{—}\overset{7}{\text{Pro}}\text{—}\overset{8}{\text{Leu}}\text{—}\overset{9}{\text{Gly}}\text{—}\overset{+}{\text{NH}}_3 \\
\mid \\
\overset{3}{\text{Ileu}} \qquad \qquad \diagup \\
\diagdown \qquad \diagup \\
\overset{4}{\text{Glu}}\text{—}\overset{5}{\text{Asp}} \\
\mid \qquad \mid \\
\text{NH}_2 \quad \text{NH}_2
\end{array}
$$

Oxytocin

Numerous other peptides possessing a high degree of physiological activity have yielded to structural studies and some of them have been synthesized. Among the substances whose structures are known are ACTH, glucagon, hypertensin, phalloidin, actinomycin, gramicidins S and J, tyrocidines A and B, polymixin, and bacitracin. Oxytocin was the first of these substances to be synthesized, but now the possibilities of synthesis have been so extended that progress is being made on the investigation of the relationships between structure and activity by the preparation of materials not available in nature.

21–8   Ribonuclease and Hemoglobin

The first protein enzyme whose structure was determined was ribonuclease, studied by Hirs, Moore, and Stein at the Rockefeller Institute. The structure that has been most extensively investigated, however, is that of hemoglobin. The amino acid sequences of both the α-chain and the β-chain have been determined and with them the exact molecular weights of hemoglobin fragments. The special interest in hemoglobin results from the fact that even among human beings, the structures of individual hemoglobins have been shown to differ, as we shall see.

21–9   Electrophoresis of Proteins

Because of the presence of negatively charged carboxylate ions and positively charged ammonium ions and guanidinium ions, proteins, including hemoglobin, will move in an electric field unless the acidity is adjusted precisely to the point at which the positive and negative charges on the molecule just balance. This is called the isoelectric point. With the adjustment of the pH to a value more acidic than the isoelectric point, the protein acquires a positive charge from an excess of ammonium ions and will migrate toward the cathode. In media more alkaline than the isoelectric point, the protein acquires a negative charge and will migrate toward the anode. The rate of migration is controlled by the number of charges in excess of neutrality per unit of molecular weight of the protein. This process of moving charged particles in an electrical field is called *electrophoresis*. Substances with the same mass but with differing charges may be separated by the process, as may substances with the same charge but with differing masses.

One of the major problems in electrophoretic work is to secure migration that is due only to the movement caused by the electrical field and to exclude that caused by convection effects in the medium. The most convenient solution to this problem is to perform the electrophoresis on filter paper where the fibers and the thin layer present prevent convection and permit the migration due to the field to be studied. (See Fig. 21–2.)

21–10 Chemical Disease; Sickle Cell Anemia

A disease of the blood known as "sickle cell anemia" has been known for a number of years and has been shown to be hereditary. In 1949, Pauling, Itano, Singer, and Wells found that the hemoglobin of patients with sickle cell anemia has a different electrophoretic mobility from ordinary hemoglobin. This indicated the possibility that the disease itself might have a molecular basis. In the same year Neel and, independently, Beet traced the inheritance of sickle cell anemia, showing that one gene produces normal hemoglobin A, while a mutant gene produces hemoglobin S, the sickle cell hemoglobin. The presence of this sickling trait can be recognized by a study of the blood cells of an affected individual under conditions of stress due to oxygen deprivation. It will be seen that some of the red cells are warped into the shape of a sickle under these conditions. Curiously, this trait provides its possessor with a degree of resistance to malaria and is found at its greatest incidence in the Negro population of the malaria belt of central Africa. (See the map in Fig. 21–1.)

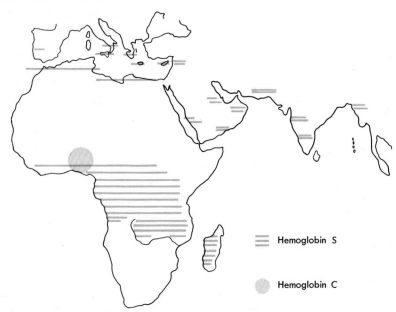

FIG. 21–1. Incidence of sickle cell anemia. [After H. Lehmann, *Brit. Med. Bull.* **15**, 44 (1959).]

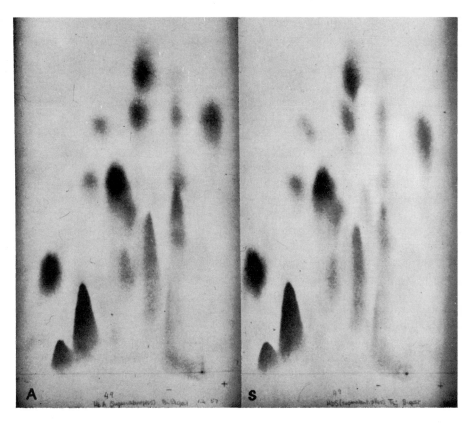

FIG. 21-2.   Fingerprinting of proteins. (Reproduced by permission from V. M. Ingram, *Hemoglobin and Its Abnormalities*, Springfield, Ill.: C. C. Thomas, 1961.)

At first an attempt was made to distinguish between hemoglobin A and hemoglobin S by means of amino acid analysis. The differences proved to be too small and the experimental error too large for a decisive determination to be made. The x-ray crystallographic methods available in 1951 were also inadequate to perceive any difference between the two proteins. Since there was an electrophoretic difference, however, this was investigated with greater care. The original electrophoresis had been performed at pH 8.6 and showed that hemoglobin S had about 2 units less charge per molecular unit of four irons than hemoglobin A. Scheinberg investigated the proteins at pH 3, where all carboxylate ions should be neutralized, and found no difference between them. This indicated that the number of positive charges on the two were the same, but that hemoglobin S had two less negative charges in the alkaline range than hemoglobin A. Hence, it lacked two carboxylate ions from aspartic or glutamic acid residues, that is, one acid residue per "half-molecule."

The method used by Sanger of hydrolyzing the protein by acid to produce essentially random cleavages would have produced an unworkably complex mixture with a chain as long as that present in hemoglobin. Accordingly, enzymatic hydrolysis was used to split the hemoglobin molecule. Hirs, Moore, and Stein, in their work on ribonuclease, exploited the specificity of trypsin, which cleaves a chain only at the peptide bonds involving the lysine and arginine carboxyl groups. By electrophoresis of the resulting hydrolysate, Ingram found it possible to identify about 26 peptides. One of these turns out to be decisively different in the two hemoglobins, A and S. Since the others are the same, this peptide carries the difference between the two proteins. Degradation of this peptide then established that the difference was that a glutamic acid residue in hemoglobin A has been replaced by a valine residue in hemoglobin S. This method is called *fingerprinting* of proteins (Fig. 21–2).

The fingerprinting technique has been used on numerous other naturally occurring variants of hemoglobin, and it has been possible to show that these variants involve single substitutions of one amino acid for another in the chains. For hemoglobin S, the physiological difference responsible for sickling has been shown to be due to a slightly greater tendency of reduced hemoglobin S to crystallize whereas oxyhemoglobin S seems to be essentially as soluble as oxyhemoglobin A. This tendency to crystallize produces a warping of the molecule when it has been deprived of oxygen, and the warping is transmitted to the red cell which contains the abnormal hemoglobin. Thus a seemingly insignificant change in structure can produce a major physiological disturbance.

The study of the abnormal hemoglobins, of which many are now known, has lent new impetus to the study of chemical genetics. It has been shown that other proteins also differ between individuals and, as a result of these investigations, a sound basis has now been created for the study of the chemical differences between individuals.

21–11 Secondary Structures of Proteins

Having found methods for the solution of the problem of the sequence of amino acids in proteins, the next step was to learn the shapes in which these chains are arranged in space. So far, strictly chemical methods have proved powerless to solve this problem. The approach has been physical instead, with prime reliance being placed on x-ray investigations. Two proposals have been made by Pauling to account for two different types of behavior observed in proteins. If we imagine

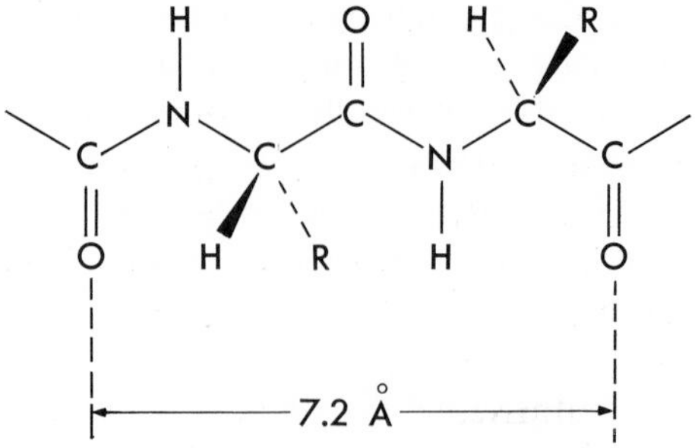

FIG. 21–3. An extended peptide chain.

an extended polypeptide chain, it will form a zig-zag structure such as that shown in Fig. 21–3. Association between two of these chains can take place through *hydrogen bonding* in which a hydrogen bonded to an amide nitrogen tends to be attracted toward an amide carbonyl of an adjacent chain, as in Fig. 21–4. The precise positioning of the side chains in a structure such as that of Fig. 21–4 brings them into spatial opposition and therefore crowds them. To avoid this, it is reasoned that some puckering or "pleating" of the sheets takes place with a slight departure from the expected repeat distance of 7.2 Å. The value observed for silk fibroin, 7.0 Å, is thus accounted for. This is called the beta arrangement of peptide chains to form fibrous proteins. Approximately 84% of the side chains of silk fibroin are either glycine, with no side chains, or alanine or serine, with small side chains. Thus steric accommodation should be easy with these groups.

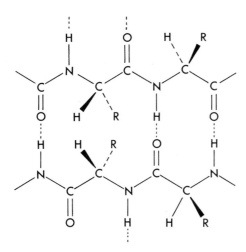

FIG. 21–4.   Flat sheet structure for a protein such as silk fibroin.

21–12   The Alpha Helix

Many other proteins have entirely different types of physical properties from those of fibroin. Pauling reasoned that these are caused by a different secondary structure, the alpha helix (Fig. 21–5), in which the peptide chain is wound into a helix which will contain 3.6 residues per turn. In this type of structure, the stereochemistry of the amino acids determines that all the side chains protrude from the helix, thus causing no crowding. Pauling found such a structure in a synthetic peptide that was submitted to careful x-ray examination and reasoned from this that the structure would form spontaneously. Deviations from such a

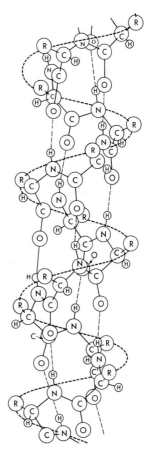

FIG. 21–5.   The alpha helix originally   proposed   by Pauling.

structure would be forced wherever a proline or hydroxyproline residue was found in the chain, since proline could not fit into the helix structure. Some have reasoned that the placement of these residues determines folding points in proteins. The alpha helix structure has been widely used to explain the x-ray findings on complex protein structures. This constitutes the second type of secondary structure proposed for proteins.

21–13 Tertiary Structures of Proteins

If the helices formed from long-chain peptides were folded or coiled in different manners, various generalized shapes could be made from them. These shapes made from helices are referred to as the *tertiary* structures of proteins (Fig. 21–6). Again no chemical means for their investigation has proved reliable. The insertion of proline residues at certain points might well cause certain folding patterns to

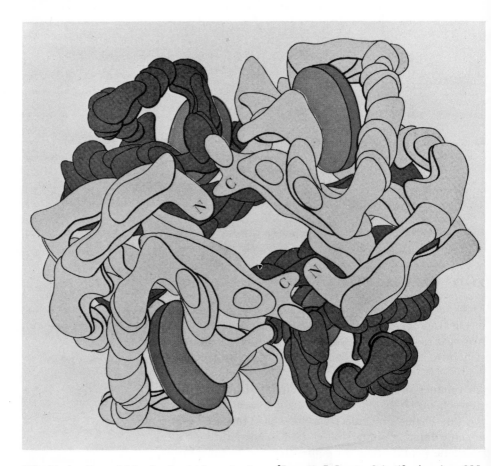

FIG. 21–6. Hemoglobin, showing tertiary structure. [From M. F. Perutz, *Scientific American* **211**, 5 (Nov. 1964).]

emerge spontaneously in proteins with predetermined amino acid sequences. Evidence exists which suggests, however, that the story may ultimately turn out to be more complex than this.

One of the types of specificity which is encountered is immunological specificity. That is, the injection of a foreign protein into the blood stream of an animal causes the animal to form an "immune body" or "antibody" which is specific for that particular foreign protein. Landsteiner has shown that the ability of the body to recognize chemical structures in the formation of antibodies is quite discriminating. He made artificial foreign proteins or "antigens" which consisted of natural proteins to which specifically substituted benzene rings had been attached. The body was able to recognize and respond to differences between *meta* and *para* substitutions of the same side chain on the benzene ring.

The amino acid sequences of specific antibodies have not yet been investigated to learn whether or not the host organism responds to *meta-* and *para*-substituted antigens by producing different amino acid sequences. All present evidence indicates that it does not, however, but responds by taking the same protein in each case and folding it differently. If this should turn out to be the case, then the forces that determine the geometry of the folding of proteins would remain mysterious.

PROBLEMS

21-1 One of the polypeptides elaborated by *Bacillus brevis* is tyrocidine A. Hydrolysis of this material yields amino acids in the following ratio: $Asp_{0.93}Glu_{0.89}Leu_{0.95}Orn_{1.00}Pro_{1.16}$ $Tyr_{0.94}Val_{0.90}$. Treatment with dinitrofluorobenzene yields one colorless derivative and two yellow derivatives. Both of the yellow derivatives have the same intensity, but the elementary analyses indicate that one of them has gained two dinitrophenyl residues. The absorption of one of these latter corresponds to a molecular weight of 1620, the other to 1840.

(a) These molecular weights might be accurate to 10 or 20%. Do they indicate that the analysis above corresponds to the actual composition, or is the molecule a dimer or trimer of this analysis?

It has been found that the dinitrophenyl ether of tyrosine is colorless.

(b) Assume that all possible products of the DNFB reaction were obtained. The yellow DNP derivatives obviously each contain one *normally* substituted amino group. How does this derivative of tyrosine explain first, why a colorless derivative is formed, and second, why the compound containing two dinitrophenyl residues has such a low intensity?

(c) Consider the structure of an ornithine unit in a peptide, neither NH_2-terminal nor COOH-terminal. Would it form a DNP derivative with DNFB?

(d) Does this now account for all the derivatives formed with DNFB? Can there be a terminal amino group in tyrocidine A?

During the hydrolysis of tyrocidine A, approximately two moles of ammonia are evolved. The peptide has one excess basic group over neutrality; indeed, it is found to contain no carboxylic acid group. But it is soluble in sodium hydroxide.

(e) In what form are Asp and Glu present?

(f) How many amino groups are free in the molecule? Which one must this be?

(g) If the peptide chain has no terminal position, what type of structure is it? Note that the titration data support the deduction from the color intensity analysis.

(h) Why is the peptide soluble in sodium hydroxide? (See Problem 5–3.)

When the amino acids obtained from the hydrolysis are analyzed, most of them are found to have about the same rotation as the common naturally occurring amino acids. But the phenylalanine has a rotation of $+8°$. (α_D for natural L-phenylalanine is $-35°$.)

(i) Account for this on a molecular basis, noting that three moles of phenylalanine are generated from one mole of polypeptide. Assume that a slight amount of racemization might have occurred in workup.

A number of small peptides are obtained from the partial hydrolysis of the natural product. These have the following composition:

Phe, Phe	Glu, Tyr, Val
Phe, Phe, Pro	Orn, Tyr, Val
Phe, Phe, Pro	Leu, Orn
Leu, Phe	Asp, Phe
Asp, Glu, Phe	Glu, Tyr
Orn, Val	

The following facts are also observed about the different amino acids: Only one of the Phe, Phe, Pro's has a terminal NH2-group.

(j) How does this determine the sequence of four of the amino acids? Look at the structures of phenylalanine and proline. Asp, Phe, when treated with DNFB and hydrolyzed, gives DNP—Phe.

If Phe, Phe is hydrolyzed, the solution is optically inactive. But if the DNP derivative is made, and then the dipeptide is hydrolyzed, the optical rotation of the yellow compound corresponds to that of the DNP derivative of L-phenylalanine.

(k) Write the structure of tyrocidine A and specify to which family (D or L) each of the amino acids belongs.

How were the details of the
structural formula for glucose established?
How was the geometrical configuration
of the groups determined?

22

CARBOHYDRATES
I: THE CONFIGURATION
OF GLUCOSE

22–1   Research on Carbohydrates

The four great classes of organic substances from which living matter is built are the proteins, the fats, the nucleic acids, and the carbohydrates. We have had an introduction to the chemistry of the proteins. We shall now consider the carbohydrates. We shall examine the structure of glucose, as the prime representative of this class.

Carbohydrates occupied the attention of Emil Fischer and his collaborators between 1885 and 1900. The elucidation of the structure of glucose by this study constitutes one of the milestones of organic chemical research. It is a triumph of the application of geometrical logic to the solution of a problem in organic chemistry. It is one of the classics of organic chemistry and has led the way to many similar achievements.

In a limited space it is possible to present only a brief abstract of the work done by Fischer. As with any search into the unknown, he did not know when he started which of many paths might lead to the desired result. He was forced to run many reactions that did not contribute to his progress for each that did. In a presentation such as this, it is necessary to cull from the literature the reactions which led to usable answers. Because only a few reactions are presented, the reader should not get the idea that these are all that were performed. When working with the unknown, the investigator always has to follow some false leads. It might require only a few weeks or months in the laboratory to duplicate results which took years in the first instance because the productive trails were not clear

301

in advance. After the trail has been blazed, it is easy to see which path is productive and which unproductive.

The solution to the problem of the structure of glucose is important as an example of the classical methods of carbohydrate chemistry. In addition, however, it is important in its own right because glucose is a most important biological substance: it is blood sugar. It occurs in numerous places in the plant and animal kingdoms, in both free and combined form. Its metabolism is important as a source of energy and of chemical alteration products for use in building other substances.

22-2 Chemical and Structural Features of Glucose

The molecular formula for glucose is $C_6H_{12}O_6$. The superficial formulation $(C \cdot H_2O)_6$ is responsible for its early classification as a "carbohydrate." Generic names are given to simple sugars according to the number of carbons they contain: Those with five carbons are pentoses; with six, hexoses; with seven, heptoses. Structurally, it will be seen that the formula has two hydrogens less than a saturated alcohol and must, therefore, have a double bond or a ring. The fact that glucose will react with carbonyl reagents indicates that it has a $C{=}O$ double bond, but later evidence showed Fischer that the carbonyl structure had to be modified (see Chapter 23). Despite this, we shall treat glucose as a carbonyl compound in the initial stage of the structural studies.

The reaction of glucose with bromine water oxidizes the glucose to an acid, gluconic acid. The reaction is buffered with $CaCO_3$.

$$C_6H_{12}O_6 + Br_2 + H_2O \xrightarrow{\ CaCO_3\ } C_6H_{12}O_7 + 2Br^- + 2H^+$$

Glucose   Gluconic acid

Gluconic acid titrates as a monobasic acid. Since it is an acid with the same number of carbons as glucose, the carbonyl must be aldehydic and not ketonic. This establishes glucose as an aldohexose.

Treatment of glucose with HI in the presence of phosphorus produced some n-hexyl iodide, some secondary hexyl iodide, and some n-hexane. This establishes that there is a six-carbon chain and that it is not branched.

The foregoing reactions account for six carbons and one oxygen. As a first approach to the structure, we may write an aldehyde group at the head of a six-carbon chain. We must now find how to place the other oxygens. Since there is no ether linkage in the chain and no more carbonyls are compatible with the analysis, we must write the remaining oxygens as hydroxyls. Confirming this, glucose forms a penta-acetate. It is not immediately apparent whether the hydroxyls are to be distributed among all five remaining carbons or are to be concentrated with two on some carbons. In analogy to the situation that usually, but not always, prevails, glucose was written with the hydroxyls distributed. Subsequent reactions, given below, confirm this initial assignment.

22–3 The Problem of the Configuration of Glucose

If we write a six-carbon chain with an aldehyde group at one end and a CH_2OH group at the other end and distribute the hydroxyls one to a carbon, this leaves four $CHOH$ groups in the chain, each of which must be asymmetric. The major problem which Fischer had to face was the determination of the configurations of the intermediate $CHOH$ groups. With four centers of asymmetry, sixteen isomers are possible. The problem was to assign the correct one of the sixteen structures to glucose. The solution to the structural problem would be greatly facilitated if all sixteen isomers were available for intercomparison. At the beginning of systematic sugar chemistry, however, they were not. One of the time-consuming researches that Fischer undertook was to search for as many as possible of these isomers to speed his structural intercomparisons. He examined as many plant and animal sources as possible, found many sugars more complex than glucose, and was able to hydrolyze some of them to produce aldohexoses other than glucose. By interconversions, Fischer was able to prepare samples of most of the aldohexoses. The last of the sixteen was not produced until many years later.

22–4 The Osazones

The availability of aldohexoses other than glucose was put to a variety of uses. One of the first was in the study of osazones. Glucose, in common with other α-hydroxy aldehydes, undergoes a reaction with phenylhydrazine that is different from those of aliphatic aldehydes. A condensation product, the osazone, is formed with two moles of phenylhydrazine instead of one. This involves an oxidation of the α-hydroxy group to a keto group. The oxidation takes place at the expense of a mole of phenylhydrazine, which is reduced to aniline and ammonia.

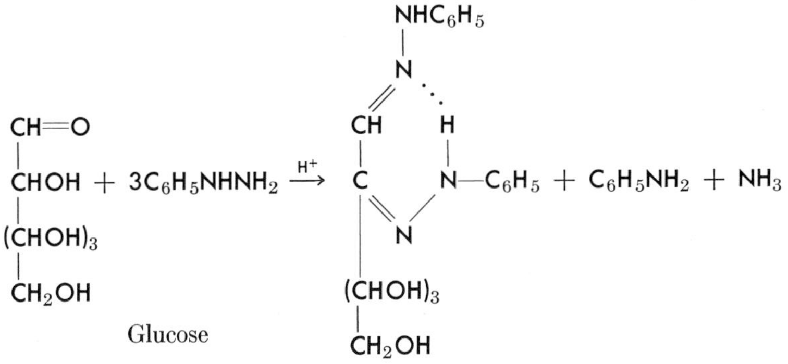

Glucosazone

On examining his samples of aldohexoses, Fischer found that each one of them would form an osazone and that one of them, and only one, formed an osazone identical with that formed by glucose. This substance was mannose, obtained from manna. Mannose is demonstrably different from glucose, being readily distinguishable by its different optical rotation. The formation of an osazone destroys any differences which may exist at the second carbon, but leaves the rest of the molecule intact.

Therefore we can conclude that mannose is identical with glucose in the last four carbons, but differs from glucose at the second carbon. More precisely, the optical configurations of the three active carbons in mannosazone are identical to those in glucosazone, since the two osazones are identical. This means that the difference between glucose and mannose lies in the optical configuration at C-2.

22-5 The Kiliani Synthesis

Before Fischer could proceed with the solution to the problem of the relative configurations of the carbons, he needed to acquire a point of reference. After studying the possibilities, he decided that the logical choice for an arbitrary assignment of configuration as a point of reference would be C-5, next to the CH_2OH group, instead of C-2, next to the aldehyde group. His reason for using this as the point of reference was that he conceived of the possibility that glucose might be built stepwise by a series of cyanohydrin condensations. Starting with glycollic aldehyde, it might be possible to prepare glyceric acid by a series of reactions discovered by Kiliani.

$$\underset{\overset{|}{CH_2OH}}{CH{=}O} + HCN \rightarrow \underset{\overset{|}{CH_2OH}}{\overset{CN}{\overset{|}{CHOH}}} + H_2O \rightarrow \underset{\overset{|}{CH_2OH}}{\overset{COOH}{\overset{|}{CHOH}}}$$

If it were then feasible to reduce this to the aldehyde, a systematic means for building sugars one step at a time would be available.

22-6 The Configurational Reference Point

The next problem was to choose which arbitrary configurational assignment to make. Fischer chose to assign a D-configuration to the fifth carbon of dextro-rotatory glucose, using the following scheme for the projection of the spatial arrangement:

$$\underset{\overset{|}{CH_2OH}}{\overset{\overset{\displaystyle CH{=}O}{\overset{|}{\underset{\overset{|}{H\underline{C}OH}}{(CHOH)_3}}}}{}}$$

This assignment reduced the number of formulas to be examined from sixteen to eight. Later it was found possible to relate this carbon to the optically active carbon of (+)-glyceraldehyde and it was found that both belonged to the same configurational family. Hence both were assigned the D-configuration. Still later, as discussed in the chapters on optical activity, it was found that the arbitrary configurational assignment adopted by Fischer was the correct one. Because it is relatively easy to compare with D-glyceraldehyde and relatively difficult to compare with D-glucose, the new standard of configuration has been taken as glyceraldehyde. It is obvious that this involves no change in assignments.

22–7   The Relation Between Glucose and Arabinose

Having given an arbitrary spatial assignment to C-5 of glucose, it follows that mannose has the same configuration at its C-5. The next step was to relate both glucose and mannose to a simpler sugar. For this purpose he chose the aldo-pentoses. There are eight of these possible. In his studies, Fischer had succeeded in preparing all eight, either from natural sources or by artificial means from other sugars. We have seen that glucose can be oxidized to gluconic acid. In the same way mannose can be oxidized to mannonic acid. If all eight of the aldopentoses were subjected to the cyanohydrin reaction, one of them was bound to yield a mixture of mannose and glucose. This would identify it as the sugar having the same "tail" as glucose and mannose and would simplify the structural problem.

The eight aldopentoses are $(+)$- and $(-)$-arabinose, $(+)$- and $(-)$-xylose, $(+)$- and $(-)$-ribose, and $(+)$- and $(-)$-lyxose. The sugar yielding the desired cyanohydrin is $(-)$-arabinose, obtained later from aloes. The reactions are:

$$
\begin{array}{ccccc}
 & \text{CN} & \text{CN} & \text{COOH} & \text{COOH} \\
 & | & | & | & | \\
\text{CH}{=}\text{O} & \text{HCOH} & \text{HOCH} & \text{HCOH} & \text{HOCH} \\
| & | & | & | & | \\
(\text{CHOH})_3 + \text{HCN} \rightarrow (\text{CHOH})_3 + & (\text{CHOH})_3 \rightarrow (\text{CHOH})_3 + & (\text{CHOH})_3 \\
| & | & | & | & | \\
\text{CH}_2\text{OH} & \text{CH}_2\text{OH} & \text{CH}_2\text{OH} & \text{CH}_2\text{OH} & \text{CH}_2\text{OH} \\
(-)\text{-Arabinose*} & & & \multicolumn{2}{c}{\text{Mixture of gluconic}} \\
 & & & \multicolumn{2}{c}{\text{and mannonic acids}}
\end{array}
$$

This acid mixture is separable, and the individual acids were identified. The identification enabled Fischer to conclude that $(-)$-arabinose belongs to the D-configurational family. Any information gained concerning its structure was then immediately transferrable to glucose and mannose.

22–8   The Configuration at C-3

The difference between the aldehyde group of arabinose and the primary alcoholic group at the other end can be destroyed by oxidizing both groups to carboxyls. Such dicarboxylic acids are called "aldaric" acids because of their similarity in structure to tartaric acid.

$$
\begin{array}{c}
\text{COOH} \\
| \\
\text{CHOH} \\
| \\
\text{CHOH} \\
| \\
\text{COOH}
\end{array}
$$

A tartaric acid

---

* Note. When the reaction was first performed, only $(+)$-arabinose was available to Fischer. This yielded the enantiomorphs of gluconic and mannonic acid.

The oxidation can be accomplished by hot nitric acid. Fischer's genius became apparent at this point when he appreciated that this reaction could be used for the assignment of the configuration of the carbon at C-2 of D-arabinose, which corresponds to C-3 of glucose. Regardless of the structure at C-3 of arabinose, a decision with respect to the configuration of C-2 is possible. Two formulations can be drawn at C-2 as follows:

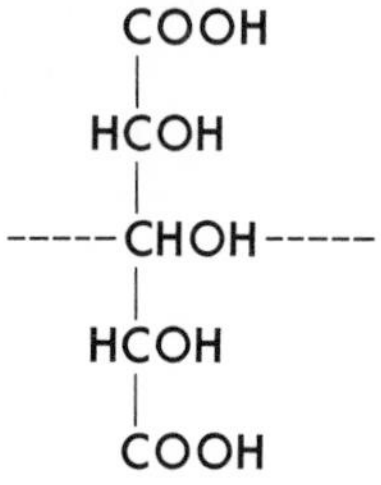

$$
\begin{array}{ccc}
\text{COOH} & & \text{COOH} \\
| & & | \\
\text{HCOH} & & \text{HOCH} \\
| & & | \\
-----\text{CHOH}----- & \text{and} & -----\text{CHOH}----- \\
| & & | \\
\text{HCOH} & & \text{HCOH} \\
| & & | \\
\text{COOH} & & \text{COOH} \\
(1) & & (2)
\end{array}
$$

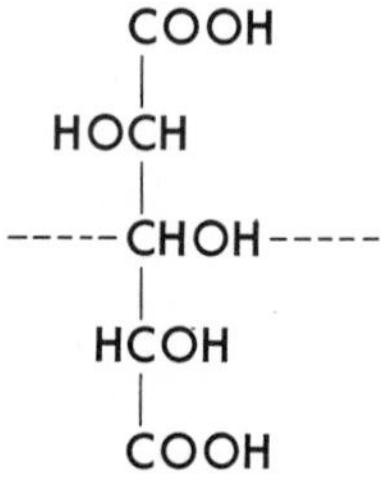

Formula (1) has a plane of symmetry through the center of the chain, regardless of the configuration of C-3. Formula (2) has no symmetry and must therefore be optically active, again regardless of the configuration of C-3. The aldaric acid obtained from arabinose proved to be optically active and for this reason, formula (2) must represent it. This gave a partial formula for D-arabinose as follows:

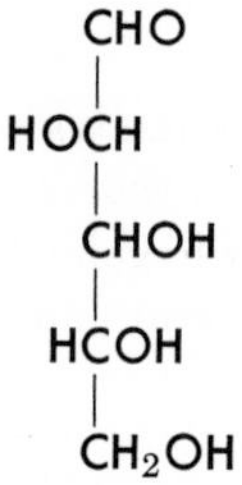

$$
\begin{array}{c}
\text{CHO} \\
| \\
\text{HOCH} \\
| \\
\text{CHOH} \\
| \\
\text{HCOH} \\
| \\
\text{CH}_2\text{OH}
\end{array}
$$

This argument made use of the arbitrarily assigned configuration of C-2 as a point of reference and showed the utility of the approach.

Reference to the Kiliani synthesis then established the corresponding assignments for glucose and mannose.

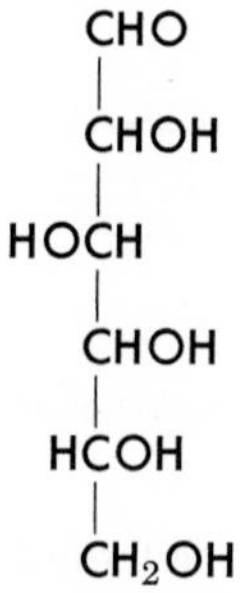

$$
\begin{array}{c}
\text{CHO} \\
| \\
\text{CHOH} \\
| \\
\text{HOCH} \\
| \\
\text{CHOH} \\
| \\
\text{HCOH} \\
| \\
\text{CH}_2\text{OH}
\end{array}
$$

22–9   The Configuration at C-4

The next step was to assign the configuration of C-4. Again a simplification was achieved by oxidation to the aldaric acids. Since only two centers of asymmetry remained unassigned, only four formulas were possible.

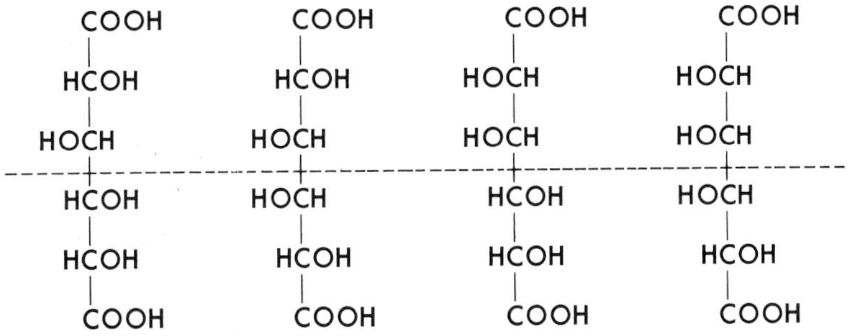

COOH	COOH	COOH	COOH
HCOH	HCOH	HOCH	HOCH
HOCH	HOCH	HOCH	HOCH
HCOH	HOCH	HCOH	HOCH
HCOH	HCOH	HCOH	HCOH
COOH	COOH	COOH	COOH
(I)	(II)	(III)	(IV)

The pair (I) and (II) has one configuration about C-2 and the pair (III) and (IV) has the opposite configuration. One of these pairs represents the two possible formulas derived from glucose, the other the two derived from mannose.

    A plane perpendicular to the chain at a point between C-3 and C-4 of formula (II) is a plane of symmetry. Neither formula (I), (III), or (IV) has a plane of symmetry. Therefore formula II is a key. The pair of acids (I) and (III) might be obtained by the oxidation of glucose and mannose, in which case both aldaric acids would be optically active. The alternative is that the pair (II) and (IV) might be obtained, and of these only one would be optically active, the other inactive. Examination shows that both saccharic acid, the aldaric acid obtained from glucose, and mannosaccharic acid, obtained from mannose, are optically active. It is concluded that formula (II) represents neither and that consequently formulas (I) and (III) must represent saccharic and mannosaccharic acids. A partial formula can be written as follows:

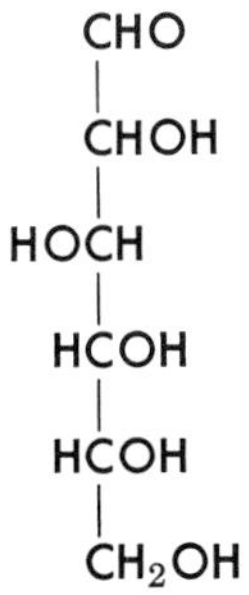

$$
\begin{array}{c}
\text{CHO} \\
|\\
\text{CHOH} \\
|\\
\text{HOCH} \\
|\\
\text{HCOH} \\
|\\
\text{HCOH} \\
|\\
\text{CH}_2\text{OH}
\end{array}
$$

Thus the configuration at C-4 is established for glucose and mannose.

22–10   The Configuration at C–2

The final point to be determined is the differentiation between glucose and man-nose at C-2. This was also achieved through reference to properties of the aldaric acids. To understand the process, it is necessary to explain the use of the con-vention with respect to projection formulas. If we were to have a four-carbon sugar of the formula

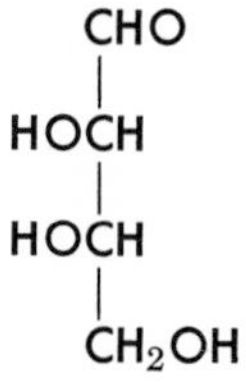

$$
\begin{array}{c}
\text{CHO} \\
| \\
\text{HOCH} \\
| \\
\text{HOCH} \\
| \\
\text{CH}_2\text{OH}
\end{array}
$$

(a)

it could be rotated in the plane of the paper through 180° and it would still be the same. The resulting formula would be (a′), shown on the left below. If, on the other hand, we leave the formula alone and simply interchange the aldehyde and primary alcohol groups, we have a different sugar. (See (b) below.)

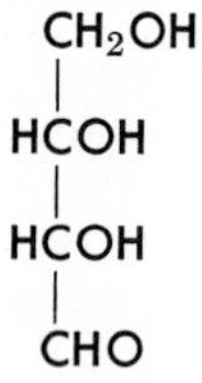

$$
\begin{array}{c}
\text{CH}_2\text{OH} \\
| \\
\text{HCOH} \\
| \\
\text{HCOH} \\
| \\
\text{CHO}
\end{array}
\qquad\qquad
\begin{array}{c}
\text{CH}_2\text{OH} \\
| \\
\text{HOCH} \\
| \\
\text{HOCH} \\
| \\
\text{CHO}
\end{array}
$$

(a′) Rotated (identical with a) 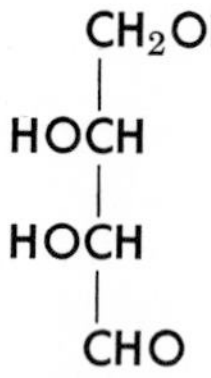   (b) (Different from a)

The aldaric acid with formula (I) is formed from the structure (A) on the left below. Interchange of the aldehyde and primary alcohol groups of (A) gives (B), shown on the right below.

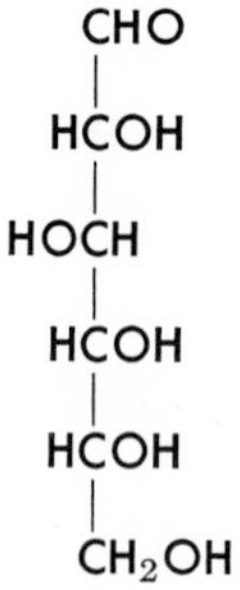

$$
\begin{array}{c}
\text{CHO} \\
| \\
\text{HCOH} \\
| \\
\text{HOCH} \\
| \\
\text{HCOH} \\
| \\
\text{HCOH} \\
| \\
\text{CH}_2\text{OH}
\end{array}
\qquad
\begin{array}{c}
\text{COOH} \\
| \\
\text{HCOH} \\
| \\
\text{HOCH} \\
| \\
\text{HCOH} \\
| \\
\text{HCOH} \\
| \\
\text{COOH}
\end{array}
\qquad
\begin{array}{c}
\text{CH}_2\text{OH} \\
| \\
\text{HCOH} \\
| \\
\text{HOCH} \\
| \\
\text{HCOH} \\
| \\
\text{HCOH} \\
| \\
\text{CHO}
\end{array}
$$

(A) 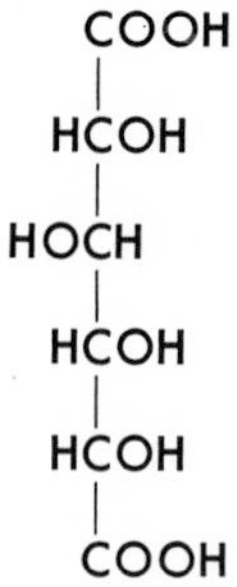   (I) 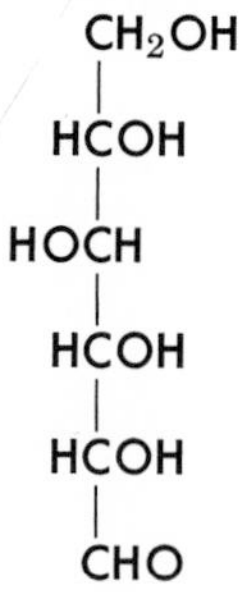   (B)

Examination will show that (B) is a different sugar from (A), just as (b) is a dif-ferent sugar from (a).

The aldaric acid formula (III) is formed from (C). (See left below.) Unlike (a) and (A), however, reversal of the aldehyde and primary alcohol groups on (C) produces no change in the sugar, because of its symmetry. (See right below.)

$$
\begin{array}{cccc}
\text{CHO} & \text{COOH} & \text{CHO} & \text{CH}_2\text{OH} \\
\text{HOCH} & \text{HOCH} & \text{HOCH} & \text{HOCH} \\
\text{HOCH} & \text{HOCH} & \text{HOCH} & \text{HOCH} \\
\text{HCOH} & \text{HCOH} & \text{HCOH} & \text{HCOH} \\
\text{HCOH} & \text{HCOH} & \text{HCOH} & \text{HCOH} \\
\text{CH}_2\text{OH} & \text{COOH} & \text{CH}_2\text{OH} & \text{CHO} \\
\text{(C)} & \text{(III)} & \text{(C)} & \text{(C)}
\end{array}
$$

is identical with

For formula (A), then, another sugar will exist which will be different from (A), but which will oxidize to the same saccharic acid, since this oxidation destroys the differences between the two ends. For formula (C), no other sugar can exist which will oxidize to the same saccharic acid.

Although Fischer did not have all the possible aldohexoses, he oxidized the ones that he had and found one sugar, gulose, which was different from glucose but which, on oxidation, gave the same saccharic acid. The positive result in the case of gulose established the point that glucose had the formula represented by (A). From this it followed that mannose had the structure represented by (C). This completed the configurational assignments of the carbons of glucose and mannose and established the structure of arabinose as well.

$$
\begin{array}{cccc}
\text{CHO} & \text{CHO} & \text{CHO} & \text{CHO} \\
\text{HCOH} & \text{HOCH} & \text{HOCH} & \text{HCOH} \\
\text{HOCH} & \text{HOCH} & \text{HCOH} & \text{HOCH} \\
\text{HCOH} & \text{HCOH} & \text{HCOH} & \text{HOCH} \\
\text{HCOH} & \text{HCOH} & \text{CH}_2\text{OH} & \text{CH}_2\text{OH} \\
\text{CH}_2\text{OH} & \text{CH}_2\text{OH} & \text{D-(-)-arabinose} & \text{L-(+)-arabinose} \\
\text{D-(+)-glucose} & \text{D-(+)-mannose} & & \text{(common arabinose)}
\end{array}
$$

This work was published in 1891; in 1902 Fischer received the Nobel Prize for it.

PROBLEMS

22–1 Apiose, $C_5H_{10}O_4$, is obtained by the hydrolysis of apiin, a glycoside occurring in parsley and celery. Oxidation under mild conditions (bromine water) yields apionic acid, $C_5H_{10}O_5$. When apionic acid is reduced with hydriodic acid, isovaleric acid is obtained.

(a) Write as much of the structure of apiose as you can from this information and the reasonable assumption that there is only one hydroxyl group on each carbon bearing them.

(b) How many optically active centers does this compound have?

22-2 Human blood may be divided into four main groups, which are well known because of their importance in blood transfusion. The groups are distinguishable by the presence or absence in the red blood cells of structures called blood group A, B, and H substances. These are very similar materials, and their analytical differences are mainly in the amount of the sugar fucose which they contain.

Blood group substance fucose has a negative rotation. Its formula is found to be $C_6H_{12}O_5$, and it may be oxidized to the corresponding acid, $C_6H_{12}O_6$. This is the only six-carbon acid that is formed by any of the usual methods of oxidation.

(a) What kind of carbonyl function does fucose contain?

(b) How many carbons carry hydroxyl functions?

A similar substance has been prepared from D-galactose, $C_6H_{12}O_6$, an isomer of glucose. The optical rotation of this artificial fucose is equal and opposite to that of blood substance fucose. This isomer is also a naturally occurring substance. To prepare it from galactose, use is made of the ability of acetone to form a cyclic acetal as shown at the right.

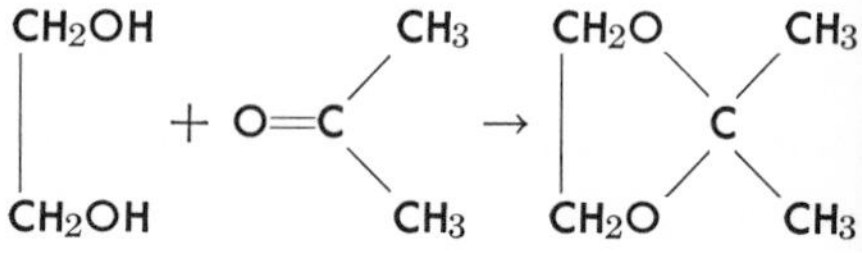

Ethylene glycol   Acetone   o-isopropylidene ethylene glycol

The reaction sequence involves treatment of galactose with two moles of acetone as a blocking reagent; one hydroxyl function remains and the tosylate ester of this is prepared by reaction with p-toluenesulfonyl chloride. Sodium iodide converts the tosylate to an organic iodide and p-toluenesulfonate ion, and reduction of the organic iodide with sodium replaces I by H. Hydrolysis of the isopropylidene groups yields artificial fucose.

$$C_5H_{11}O_5\text{—COH} \xrightarrow{(CH_3)_2C=O} C_{11}H_{19}O_5\text{—COH} \xrightarrow[\text{chloride}]{\text{p-toluene sulfonyl}} C_{11}H_{19}O_5\text{—COSO}_2C_7H_7 \xrightarrow{NaI}$$

$$C_{11}H_{19}O_5\text{—CI} \xrightarrow{Na} C_{11}H_{19}O_5\text{—CH} \xrightarrow[H^+]{H_2O} C_5H_{11}O_5\text{—CH}$$

$$\text{D-(+)-fucose}$$

The oxidation of fucose by basic permanganate yields potassium acetate. Under these conditions potassium malonate is stable.

(c) What carbon did not bear a hydroxyl group in fucose?

(d) Which carbon in galactose was affected by the transformation outlined above?

D-galactose is characterized by the following considerations. The aldaric acid obtained by nitric acid oxidation of D-galactose, called mucic acid, is optically inactive.

(e) Write the two possible formulas for mucic acid and for D-galactose which this information permits.

D-galactose is treated with hydrogen cyanide and hydrolyzed. The mixture of acids obtained is then oxidized to a mixture of dibasic acids which is separated and both are found to be optically active.

(f) What is the structure of D-galactose?

(g) What is the structure of the fucose present in blood group substance A?

*Why was it concluded that glucose is not an open-chain aldehyde?
How were the details of the ring structure of glucose established?
How can the three-dimensional aspects of the glucose molecule
be represented on paper? How do conformational changes
affect the chemistry of hexoses? What is the nature of the
junction between sugars and "aglycones" in glycosides?*

23

CARBOHYDRATES II: PROPERTIES OF CYCLIC CARBOHYDRATES; GLYCOSIDES

23-1 Is Glucose an Aldehyde?

Most samples of glucose, including so-called "Chemically Pure" and "U.S. Pharmacopoeia" grades, give positive tests for aldehydes. Purification over active charcoal will remove the substance responsible for this reaction. Exposure to acid or alkali regenerates it. Examination of the charcoal shows that the aldehyde which causes the reaction is hydroxymethyl furfural, formed by the dehydration of glucose.

$$\underset{\text{Glucose}}{\begin{array}{c}\text{CHOH—CHOH}\\ |\qquad\quad|\\ \text{HOCH}_2\text{HCOH}\quad\text{CHOH—CHO}\end{array}} \rightarrow 2\text{H}_2\text{O} + \underset{\text{Hydroxymethyl furfural}}{\begin{array}{c}\text{HC———CH}\\ \|\qquad\quad\|\\ \text{HOCH}_2\text{C}\qquad\text{C—CHO}\\ \diagdown\quad\diagup\\ \text{O}\end{array}}$$

Because of the ready formation of hydroxymethyl furfural, it has been erroneously concluded that glucose contains a small percentage of open-chain aldehyde, such as Fischer first formulated. In fact, by 1895 Fischer had concluded that the open-chain formula which he first proposed required modification. The first evidence of this was the failure of purified specimens of glucose to respond to certain characteristic aldehyde reagents.

The dye fuchsin is reduced by sulfur dioxide to form a colorless aqueous solution, which on treatment with an aldehyde, undergoes a complex reaction to form a new colored compound. This test is called the *Schiff test*. Purified glucose gives a negative Schiff test.

Another characteristic reaction of aldehydes is the addition of sodium bisulfite.

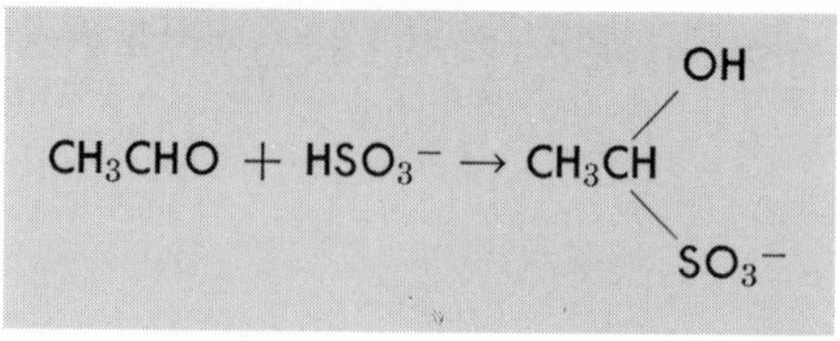

$$CH_3CHO + HSO_3^- \rightarrow CH_3CH \Big\langle \begin{array}{l} OH \\ SO_3^- \end{array}$$

Bisulfite addition products convert many initially insoluble aldehydes into water-soluble derivatives and are therefore useful in the purification of the aldehydes. Purified glucose fails to add bisulfite.

23-2 Mutarotation

The most detailed evidence against the assumption of an open-chain aldehyde was the discovery that D-glucose can be obtained in two different forms. When D-glucose is crystallized from cold water, a product with optical rotation of +112°, α-D-glucose, is obtained. After the product stands in solution, the rotation gradually drops to an equilibrium value of +52.7°. When glucose is crystallized from hot water or more readily from hot pyridine, a product with optical rotation of +18.7°, β-D-glucose, is obtained. After it stands in solution, this product also gradually assumes the equilibrium value of 52.7°. The change from high or low rotation to the equilibrium value is called *mutarotation*. The isolation of two materials with the formula of D-glucose indicates the existence of an additional center of asymmetry in the molecule. That the asymmetry actually exists is shown by the fact that the two materials have different optical rotations. This shows the contribution of a dextro carbon in one case and a levo carbon in the other.

23-3 Acetals and Hemiacetals

In the presence of a trace of acid, aldehydes react with alcohols to form acetals.

$$CH_3CHO + 2CH_3OH \xrightarrow{NH_4Cl} CH_3CH(OCH_3)_2 + 2H_2O$$
Acetaldehyde   Dimethylacetal

Acetals are quite stable to base but are readily reconverted to the aldehydes by the action of an excess of acid.

$$CH_3CH(OCH_3)_2 + 2H_2O \xrightarrow{H^+} CH_3CHO + 2CH_3OH$$

Ketones do not form acetals nearly as readily as aldehydes. When structural conditions are favorable, intermediates between the free aldehydes and the acetals may be isolated. These are called *hemiacetals*. When isolated, they prove to be unstable to either acid or base. A curious example of a hemiacetal is formed when attempts are made to prepare cyclopropanone in methanol:

$$\begin{array}{ccc} CH_2 & & OH \\ & \diagdown & \diagup \\ & C & \\ & \diagup & \diagdown \\ CH_2 & & OCH_3 \end{array}$$

We may distinguish between acetals, on the one hand, and hemiacetals, on the other, by the stability of acetals to base, but not to acid, and the instability of hemiacetals to both base and acid.

Treatment of glucose with methanolic HCl does not yield a dimethyl acetal, as might be expected if glucose were an open-chain aldehyde. Instead, it yields a monomethyl derivative, methyl glucoside. Methyl glucoside is stable to alkali but not to acid, indicating that it is an acetal, not a hemiacetal. The mutarotation of glucose, on the other hand, is strongly catalyzed by both acids and bases, showing the instability of the substance to both agents and indicating the probability that the material is a hemiacetal.

A crude representation of the cyclic hemiacetal forms of α- and β-D-glucose can be made using the geometrical form of the projection formulas which Fischer proposed:

$$
\begin{array}{ccc}
\text{HCOH} & & \text{HOCH} \\
| & & | \\
\text{HCOH} & & \text{HCOH} \\
| & & | \\
\text{HOCH} & \text{and} & \text{HOCH} \\
| & & | \\
\text{HCOH} & & \text{HCOH} \\
| & & | \\
\text{HC} \!-\!\!-\! \text{O} & & \text{HC} \!-\!\!-\! \text{O} \\
| & & | \\
\text{CH}_2\text{OH} & & \text{CH}_2\text{OH} \\
\text{(I)} & & \text{(II)}
\end{array}
$$

23–4 The Principle of Optical Superposition

The choice of a six-membered ring may be considered arbitrary until it is established. These two formulas differ in the configuration at the first carbon, called the *anomeric* carbon, and the isomers are called *anomers* for this reason. The problem is to assign configurations to the alpha and beta forms. An initial solution to the problem was reached by the use of the principle of *optical superposition*.

The principle of optical superposition was proposed by van't Hoff, and used by Hudson to aid in the assignment of ring sizes on the basis of optical activity. It was shown to be reliable for this purpose only when applied to certain groups of substances and, as a consequence, it fell into disrepute. When used properly, however, it can be of great assistance. Its use is based on an understanding of the relative contributions of various substituents to the observed degree of optical activity of a compound. In general, the rule may be stated that the optical activity at an asymmetric center is controlled by the configuration of the substituent whose ultraviolet absorption lies nearest to the wavelength used for measurement. For sugars, this group is the hydroxyl group.

According to the principle of optical superposition, the total rotation of a sugar molecule may be regarded as made up of the sum of the rotations induced at the individual carbon atoms. In the application to glucose, we may take the sum of the rotations of the groups from C-2 to C-5 as being a constant, A, and the rotation at C-1 as being a variable, x. The variable x will have only two values in our example, $+x$ and $-x$. It is assumed, further, that the rotation due to a D-configuration is $(+)$, in line with observations on the total rotation of D-glucose. We may then write the equations for the rotation of alpha and beta glucose as

$$A + x = +112°, \qquad A - x = +18.7°.$$

Solving, we find that $A = +65.35°$ and $x = +46.65°$. According to this interpretation, the configuration which would add would be D, and α-D-glucose should have formula (I), while β-D-glucose should have formula (II). It may be replied that this result is implicit in the assumption that the rotation caused by a D-configuration is $(+)$. This assumption certainly requires independent confirmation. Recently this confirmation has come through x-ray and NMR analysis which substantiates these assignments.

23–5 Determination of the Ring Size

Having established that glucose is a hemiacetal and methyl glucoside is an acetal, it follows that a ring exists and the next problem is to determine its size. This problem was solved by Haworth. Methyl glucoside was first prepared, giving an alkali-stable compound. This was then methylated by dimethyl sulfate in strong alkali. The product formed was tetramethyl-methyl glucoside. Treatment of this acetal-ether with hydrochloric acid opened the acetal linkage with the formation of tetramethylglucose. It might be assumed that either a five-membered or a six-membered ring was present. This would give two possible formulas for Haworth's tetramethylglucose:

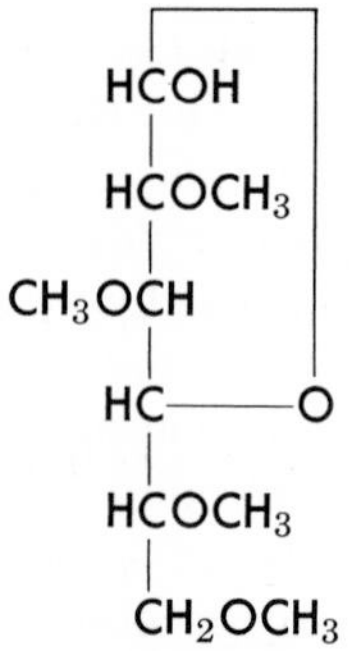

(III)   or   (IV)

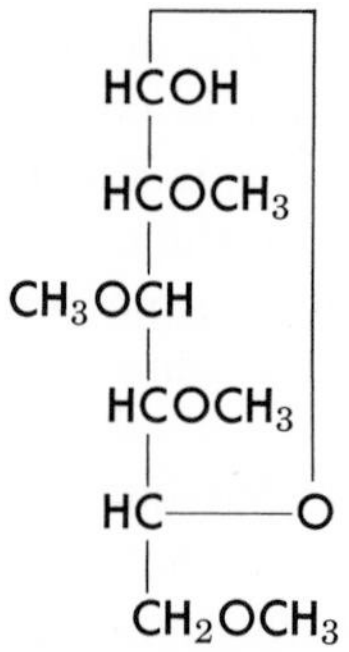

Acid would open the ring, exposing the hydroxyl in the C-4 or C-5 position to oxidative attack. Nitric acid oxidation would then produce a carboxyl group at C-1 and a keto group at C-4 or C-5. If the oxidation were continued, cleavage of the chain on each side of the keto group would take place. Formula (III) would then lead to the following cleavage products:

$$
\begin{array}{c}
COOH \\
| \\
HCOCH_3 \\
| \\
CH_3OCH \\
| \\
CO \\
| \\
HCOCH_3 \\
| \\
CH_2OCH_3
\end{array}
\xrightarrow{\text{HNO}_3}
\begin{array}{c}
COOH \\
| \\
HCOCH_3 \\
| \\
COOH
\end{array}
\; + \;
\begin{array}{c}
COOH \\
| \\
HCOCH_3 \\
| \\
CH_2OCH_3
\end{array}
\quad \text{and} \quad
\begin{array}{c}
COOH \\
| \\
HCOCH_3 \\
| \\
CH_3OCH \\
| \\
COOH
\end{array}
\; + \;
\begin{array}{c}
COOH \\
| \\
CH_2OCH_3
\end{array}
$$

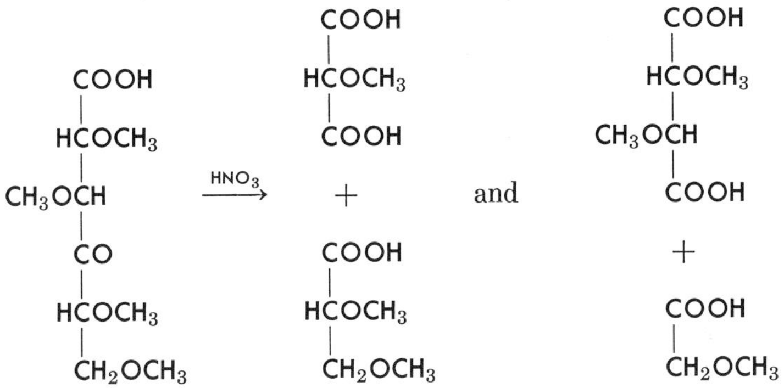

Formula (IV) would lead to the following cleavage products:

$$
\begin{array}{c}
COOH \\
| \\
HCOCH_3 \\
| \\
CH_3OCH \\
| \\
HCOCH_3 \\
| \\
CO \\
| \\
CH_2OCH_3
\end{array}
\xrightarrow{\text{HNO}_3}
\begin{array}{c}
COOH \\
| \\
HCOCH_3 \\
| \\
CH_3OCH \\
| \\
COOH
\end{array}
$$

Dimethoxysuccinic acid

$$
+
\begin{array}{c}
COOH \\
| \\
CH_2OCH_3
\end{array}
$$

$$
+ \;
\begin{array}{c}
COOH \\
| \\
HCOCH_3 \\
| \\
CH_3OCH \\
| \\
HCOCH_3 \\
| \\
COOH
\end{array}
$$

Trimethoxyglutaric acid

$$
+ \;
CO_2
$$

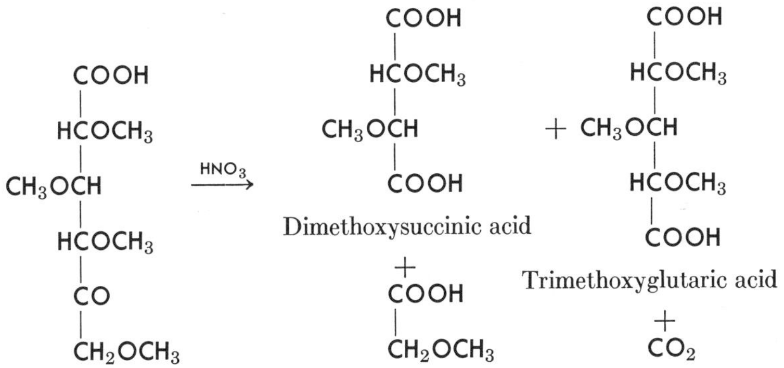

The dibasic acids resulting from the nitric acid oxidation were isolated and proved to be a mixture of dimethoxysuccinic acid and trimethoxyglutaric acid. This showed that the keto group must have been formed at C-5 and thus that glucose has a six-membered ring.

Six-membered rings with a single oxygen and five carbons are called *pyranes* and from this the sugars with six-membered rings are referred to as *pyranoses*. Five-membered rings with a single oxygen and four carbons are called *furanes* and the corresponding sugars are called *furanoses*. Using this system of nomenclature, α-D-glucose would be referred to as "α-D-glucopyranose."

23–6 Geometrical Representation of Carbohydrate Rings

Knowing that glucose has a six-membered ring, we are in a position to represent it with a formula, introduced by Haworth, more closely related to its geometry. For this purpose, the aldehyde formula is first laid on its side and curled, as shown in (a) below. By convention, the three groups attached to C-5 are then rotated through a 120° angle to give the representation shown in (b) below.

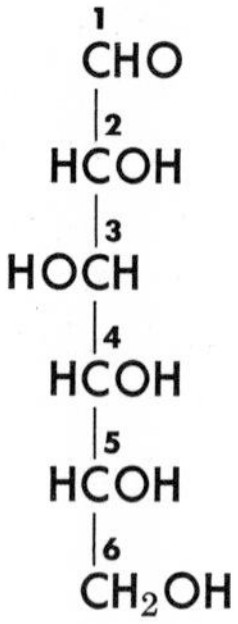

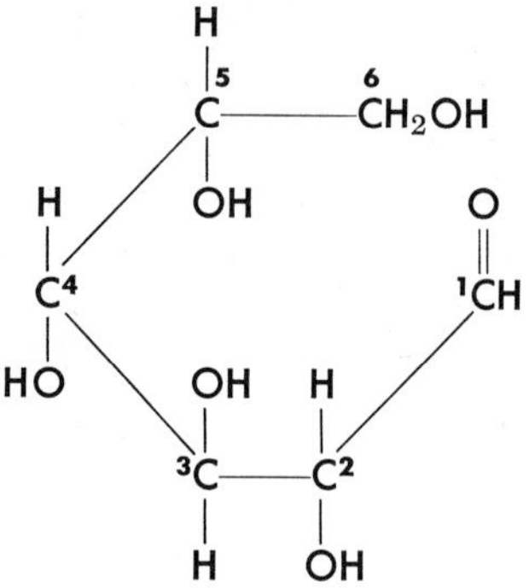

(a) 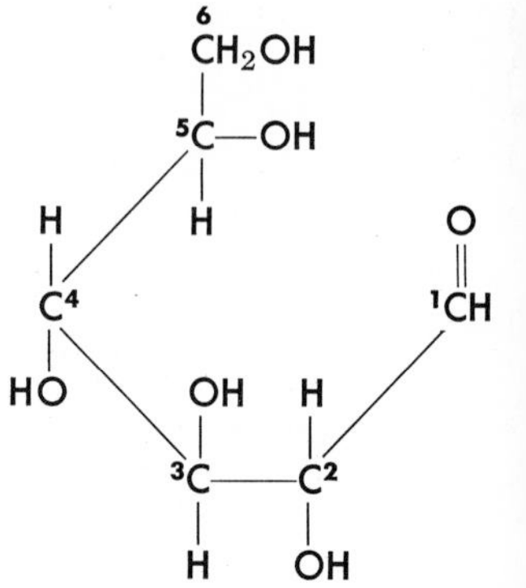   (b)

Finally, from this position, the acetal ring is closed.

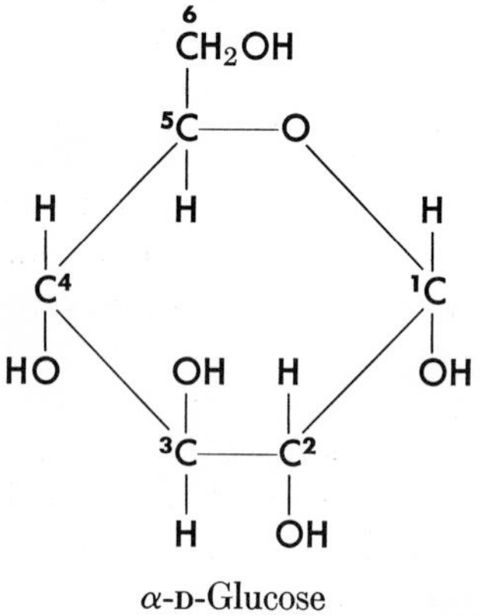

α-D-Glucose β-D-Glucose

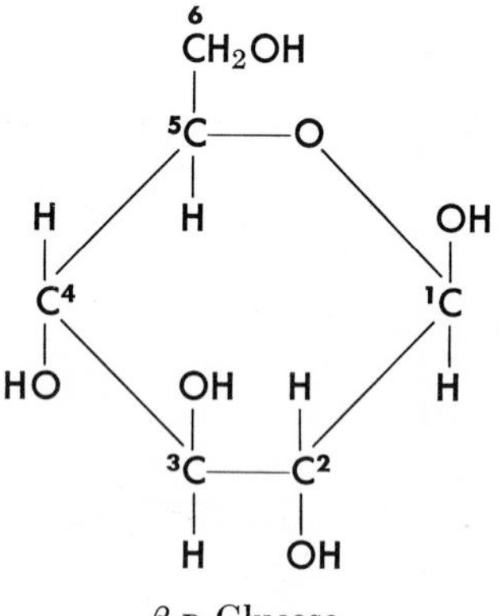

FIGURE 23-1

In these formulas the α-form has the OH group down; the β-form has it up as illustrated in Fig. 23-1. The reader should practice drawing the formulas for various sugars in the cyclic representation until the correspondence between the Fischer projections and the geometrical projections becomes clear.

23–7 The Conformations of Hexoses

Even more useful than the geometrical projections of the preceding section are the conformational skeletons of the hexoses. Like cyclohexane, these might conceivably exist in either boat or chair conformations.* Again like cyclohexane, we should expect the chair conformations to be more stable. Unlike cyclohexane, however, the hexoses have more or less bulky substituents at each position except the oxygen in the ring. We have seen that bulky substituents in axial positions tend to be relatively more crowded than the same substituents in equatorial positions. Since the bulkiest substituent of all is the CH_2OH group, its tendency to become equatorial will ordinarily determine the conformation of the molecule as a whole as shown in Fig. 23–2. In some cases, however, strong dipole effects may stabilize axial groups. (See Chapter 32.)

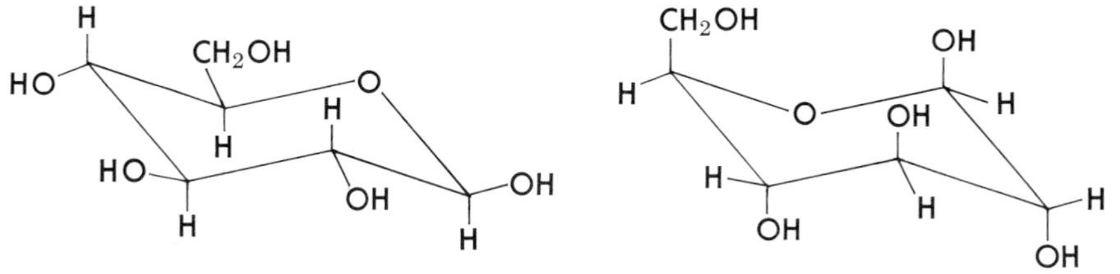

β-D-Glucose (equatorial)   FIGURE 23–2   β-D-Glucose (axial)

The formula on the left in Fig. 23–2, labeled equatorial, has the CH_2OH group and all the hydroxyls in equatorial positions. The formula on the right, labeled axial, has all of these groups in the axial positions. Because of steric repulsions, the "equatorial" conformation of glucose is more stable than the "axial" and x-ray studies show that it is the form actually present in the molecule.

We have seen that the change from glucose to mannose entails the reversal of configuration of C-2. This brings with it a conformational change as well, as shown in Fig. 23–3. It can be seen from Fig. 23–3 that changing C-2 from D to L in going from glucose to mannose changes the hydroxyl group from the equatorial position in glucose to the axial position in mannose. This indicates that mannose should be slightly less stable than glucose.

Another sugar of great interest in human nutrition is galactose. As a result of a hereditary trait, some infants are unable to tolerate galactose, which is formed by

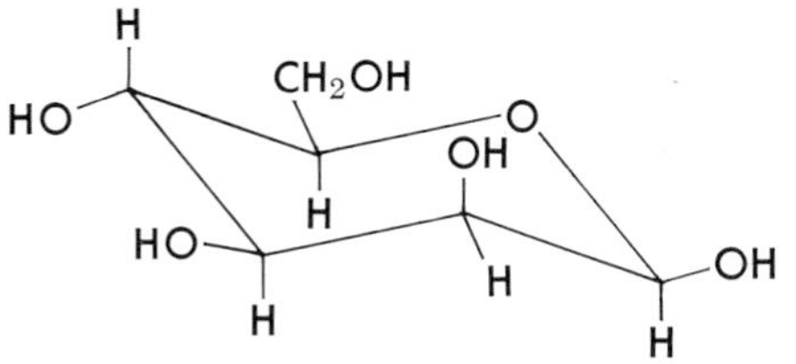

FIG. 23–3. β-D-Mannose. 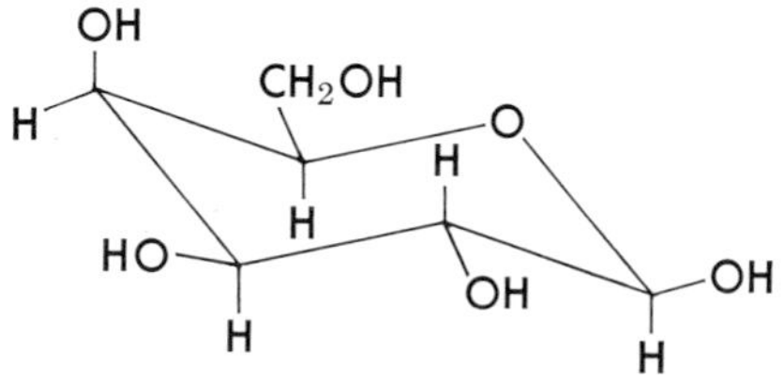   FIG. 23–4. β-D-Galactose.

---

* Note. Because of the absence of substituents on the oxygen, an intermediate or "skew" form may exist in pyranose sugars.

the enzymatic hydrolysis of lactose, milk sugar. These infants suffering from "galactosemia," find their mothers' milk poisonous and if it is not removed from their diets, they will die. Galactose differs from glucose only in the configuration of C-4 (see Fig. 23-4).

Again we see that the change from glucose to galactose has been accompanied by an unfavorable change in conformation from the point of view of stability. Indeed, any change at all that is made from the configuration of β-D-glucose forces some group into a sterically unfavorable axial conformation. This is even true with respect to alpha glucose. The equilibrium mixture formed by mutarotation of glucose has a rotation of 52.7° instead of the value of 65.35° which would be expected of a 50/50 mixture of alpha and beta forms. Calculation shows that this mixture is approximately 65% beta and 35% alpha, indicating that the beta form is more stable than the alpha by approximately 186 calories per mole. It has been speculated that the fact that derivatives of β-D-glucose occur more frequently than those of any other sugar is due to this conformational bias.

23-8   Glycosides

Glucose is capable of forming acetals with a wide variety of alcohols in addition to methanol. These derivatives are the glucosides. Since other sugars form similar compounds, however, a more general name is needed to refer to the category of acetal condensation products of the sugars. Chemists have fixed on the term *glycosides* to indicate the whole category.

Glucosides, both natural and synthetic, fall into two classes distinguished in practice by their reactions to the enzymes maltase and emulsin. Maltase has been found to hydrolyze only α–D glucosides, and emulsin hydrolyzes only β–D glucosides.

23-9   Hydrolysis of Salicin

Salicin, a bitter-tasting principle, occurs in the bark of the willow (*Salix*) and the poplar. This was prized in earlier times as a treatment for rheumatism and as a tonic. The material is a colorless, crystalline substance with the analysis $C_{13}H_{18}O_7$. Hydrolysis is accomplished by emulsin to yield glucose and saligenin.

$$C_{13}H_{18}O_7 + H_2O \xrightarrow{\text{emulsin}} C_6H_{12}O_6 + C_7H_8O_2$$

Salicin   Glucose   Saligenin

A "genin" is a material which combines with a sugar to form a glycoside. The generic term for genins is "aglycones." Accordingly, the aglycone of salicin is saligenin.

23-10   The Structure of Saligenin

The formula $C_7H_8O_2$ suggests that saligenin is a derivative of benzene. A diacetate can be formed, suggesting the presence of two hydroxyl groups. Solubility in alkali suggests that one of the hydroxyl groups is phenolic. A high degree of reactivity to acids suggests that the other hydroxyl group is similar to that of benzyl alcohol, that is, aliphatic. The structure was established by the synthesis of saligenin. Salicylaldehyde was first made from phenol:

$$C_6H_5OH + CHCl_3 \xrightarrow{KOH} \text{o-HOC}_6H_4CHO$$

Salicylaldehyde

This reaction for the introduction of an aldehyde group into a phenol is called the *Reimer-Tiemann reaction*. The aldehyde was then hydrogenated:

$$\text{o-HOC}_6H_4CHO + H_2 \xrightarrow{Pt} \text{o-HOC}_6H_4CH_2OH$$

Salicylaldehyde   Saligenin

Saligenin possesses both mild antiseptic and mild anesthetic properties.

23-11 The Synthesis of Salicin

The formation of saligenin and glucose from salicin by emulsin shows the presence of a β-D-glucosidic linkage. The structure was confirmed by synthesis. For this purpose a derivative of glucose is necessary in which the hydroxyl groups are protected by a group which subsequently can be removed. The glycoside to be formed has a C—O—C linkage so that a modification of the Williamson ether synthesis should be suitable. This would require that the glucosidic carbon have a halogen substituent. The requisite conditions are met by tetra-acetylbromoglucose (c), formed by the reactions indicated (a and b) from glucose.

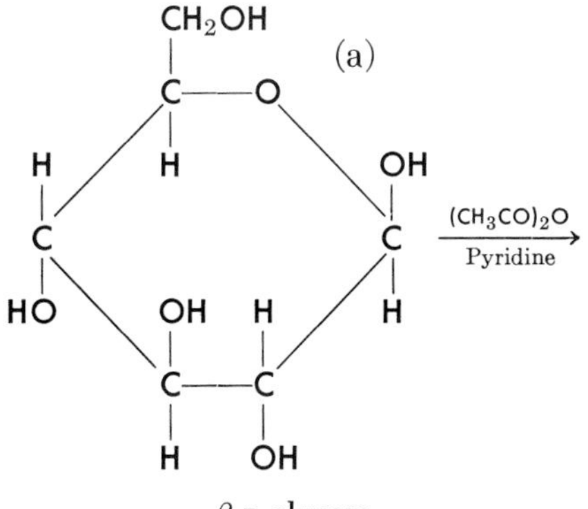

(a)

β-D-glucose

(b)

Penta-acetyl-β-D-glucose

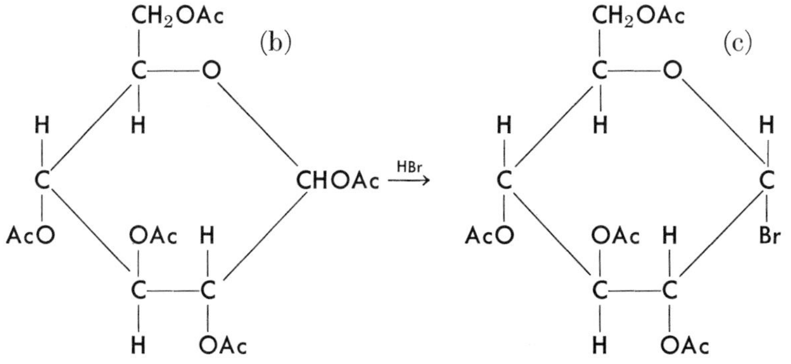

(c)

Tetra-acetylbromo-D-glucose
(Tetra-O-acetyl-α-D-glucopyranosyl bromide)

The treatment of penta-acetyl glucose with **HBr** brings about a reaction which is confined to the glycoside carbon because of its great reactivity. The bromide is stabilized in the α-position (axial) by polar forces. A subsequent inversion will bring about the formation of the desired configuration. The bromide is reacted with the sodium salt of saligenin to form a mixed phenolic acetal:

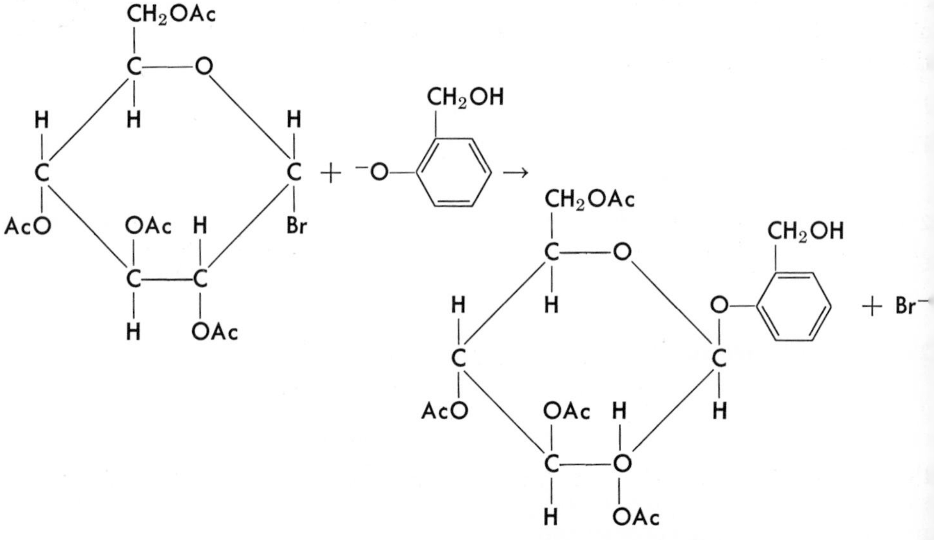

Tetra-acetyl-salicin

Since the glycosidic linkage is stable to alkali, the acetyl groups may be removed by alcoholysis:

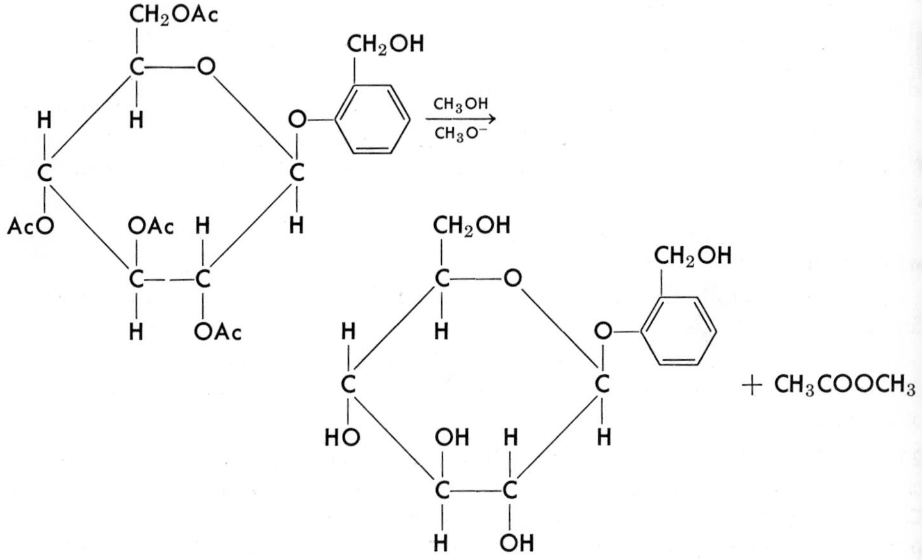

Salicin

Synthetic salicin, prepared by this method, is identical in all respects to the natural product.

The simple example of the synthesis of salicin illustrates the principles that are used in more complex carbohydrate syntheses. In general, it is necessary to prepare one part of the molecule in a reactive form with all groups except the center of reaction covered with a removable protective grouping. The other portion of the molecule, also suitably protected, is then brought into reaction. Finally, the protective groups are removed.

PROBLEMS

23-1 Periodic acid, HIO_4, and its salts react with compounds containing hydroxyl groups on consecutive carbons. Cyclohexane-1,2-diol, for example, gives adipaldehyde.

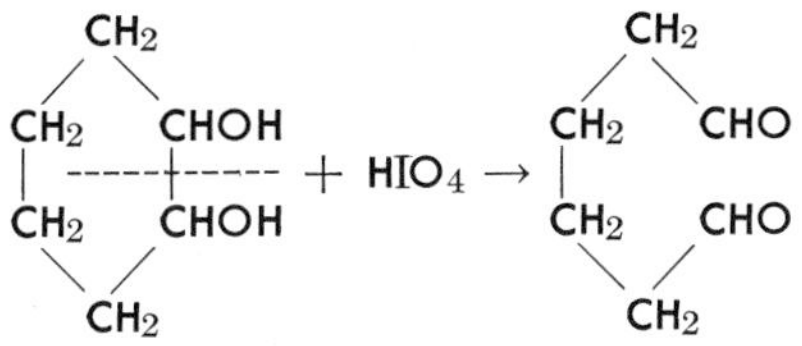

Cyclohexane-1,2,3-triol yields one mole of formic acid and one mole of glutaraldehyde:

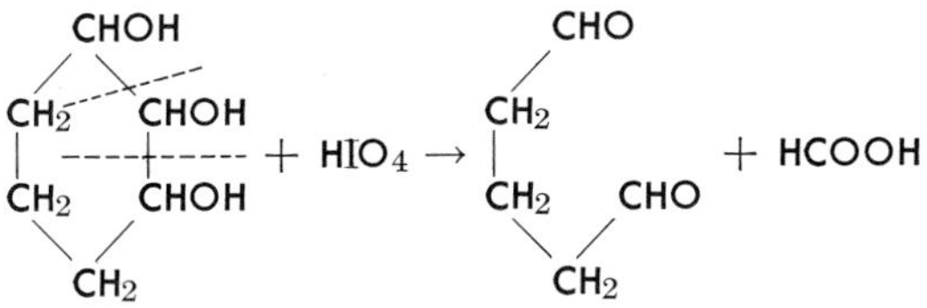

If ethers are prepared as derivatives of these alcohols so that no 1,2-glycol linkage is present, no reaction takes place.

(a) What would be the analogous oxidation product from ethylene glycol (ethane-1,2-diol)?

(b) Could this reaction distinguish between the five-membered and six-membered ring forms of methyl glucoside by quantitative determination of the amount of volatile acid formed?

(c) Could it distinguish between the four-membered and the six-membered ring forms with this much information?

(d) Would determination of the amount of volatile aldehyde formed add further information in either case?

(e) How much information is necessary to distinguish between the various ring structures for glucose itself? It is reasonable to assume that 1,2,3,4-tetraols would produce two moles of formic acid.

23-2 Arbutin, $C_{12}H_{16}O_7 \cdot H_2O$, is a product occurring in the leaves of the bearberry and cranberry, and some varieties of pears. It is hydrolyzed by emulsin to yield glucose and $C_6H_6O_2$. This latter compound, hydroquinone, is aromatic and forms a diacetate but is peculiarly oxidizable by acidic dichromate to yield quinone, $C_6H_4O_2$, which forms a derivative with two moles of semicarbazide. Hydroquinone cannot be used to form an acetal of formaldehyde, but an isomer of it, catechol, does form an acetal of formaldehyde if it is heated with methylene chloride and sodium ethoxide.

(a) What is the structure of catechol?

(b) What are the structures of hydroquinone and quinone?

(c) What is the structure of resorcinol, the remaining isomer of hydroquinone and catechol?

(d) What is the full structure of arbutin?

23-3 The optical rotation of α-D-galactose is $\alpha_D = +150.7°$. That of β-D-galactose is $+52.8°$. Both of these mutarotate to an equilibrium value of $+80.2°$. (Refer to Sections 23-4 and 23-7.)

Calculate the equilibrium constant, $K_{eq} = [\alpha]/[\beta]$, for D-galactose.

23-4 The formation of a bisulfite addition compound is fairly general for aldehydes. Methyl ketones in which the other α-carbon is not part of an aromatic ring also form bisulfite compounds, and a few special ketones in which the alkyl substituents are "pinned back" (for example, cyclohexanone) are known to also give a positive bisulfite test.

Identify each of the compounds in the following sequence of reactions:

$$C_9H_{10}O + NaHSO_3 \longrightarrow \text{no reaction}$$
$$C_9H_{10}O + I_2 + NaOH \longrightarrow CHI_3 + C_8H_7O_2Na$$
$$C_8H_7O_2Na + KMnO_4 + NaOH \longrightarrow C_8H_4O_4Na_2$$
$$C_8H_4O_4Na_2 + H_2O + HCl \longrightarrow C_8H_6O_4$$
$$C_8H_6O_4 \xrightarrow{heat} C_8H_4O_3$$

How are the structures of disaccharides, oligosaccharides, and polysaccharides demonstrated?

24

CARBOHYDRATES III: DISACCHARIDES; GENTIOBIOSE, AMYGDALIN, MALTOSE

24–1 Amygdalin

Condensation products of sugars containing two sugar residues are called *disaccharides*, those containing a few residues, such as two, three, four, or five, are called *oligosaccharides* and those containing many residues are called *polysaccharides*. Both oligosaccharides and polysaccharides occur widely in nature in the free state and bound with other substances. An instructive example of a bound disaccharide is amygdalin, the glycoside of bitter almonds and of other seeds, leaves, and bark, such as laurel leaves and wild cherry bark. Amygdalin has found very limited use in medicine and is introduced into cough syrups and certain liqueurs, such as maraschino, as a flavoring material.

24–2 Degradations of Amygdalin

Amygdalin has the molecular formula $C_{20}H_{27}NO_{11}$. Acidic hydrolysis or hydrolysis with the enzyme of the almond, emulsin, produces benzaldehyde, HCN, and two moles of glucose.

$$C_{20}H_{27}NO_{11} + 2H_2O \xrightarrow[\text{emulsin}]{H^+ \text{ or}} \underset{\text{Benzaldehyde}}{C_6H_5CHO} + HCN + \underset{\text{Glucose}}{2C_6H_{12}O_6}$$

Susceptibility to the action of emulsin shows that the glycosidic linkage is β-D.

Careful purification of the hydrolytic enzymes of the almond produces two distinct substances, amygdalase and prunase. The action of amygdalase on amygdalin produces prunasin and glucose.

$$C_{20}H_{27}NO_{11} + H_2O \xrightarrow{\text{amygdalase}} C_{14}H_{17}NO_6 + C_6H_{12}O_6$$

Prunasin   Glucose

Prunasin is a glucoside present in the pits of plums and prunes, as well as in the leaves and bark of the same species. The structure of prunasin was established by Fischer, but the more complex problem of the structure of amygdalin waited twenty years longer for the discovery of methods capable of dealing with the problem of the oligosaccharides. Attempts to perform a partial hydrolysis of amygdalin to isolate the disaccharide combined in it were unavailing and the structural investigation and synthesis were completed before this was accomplished. Freudenberg finally solved the problem of the direct preparation of a disaccharide from amygdalin by hydrogenation. In this reaction, the accompanying products were not isolated. The reaction is reminiscent of the hydrogenation of the carbobenzyloxy derivatives used for the protection of amino groups in peptide synthesis.

$$C_{20}H_{27}NO_{11} + 4H_2 \xrightarrow{\text{Pt}} C_6H_5CH_2OH + CH_3NH_2 + C_{12}H_{22}O_{11}$$

Gentiobiose

Gentiobiose, obtained from amygdalin, is identical with that prepared by fermentation from gentianose, a trisaccharide which can be extracted from the roots of the gentian and the iris.

Amygdalin does not reduce Fehling's solution and therefore has no free hydroxyl on the anomeric carbon. Instead, both glucose units must have acetal structures. This results in stability of these portions of the molecule to alkali. Alkaline hydrolysis does hydrolyze the cyano group to a carboxyl group, however, with the formation of amygdalinic acid.

$$C_{20}H_{27}NO_{11} + 2H_2O \xrightarrow{\text{OH}^-} C_2O\,H_{28}O_{13} + NH_3$$

Amygdalin   Amygdalinic
acid

When an alkaline solution of amygdalinic acid is treated with an excess of dimethyl sulfate, the methyl ester is formed and seven additional methyl groups are introduced to form methyl ethers.

$$C_{20}H_{28}O_{13} + 8(CH_3)_2SO_4 + 8OH^- \rightarrow C_{28}H_{44}O_{13} + 8CH_3SO_4^- + 8H_2O$$

Amygdalinic   Heptamethyl-
acid   amygdalinic
methyl ester

Acid hydrolysis of heptamethylamygdalinic methyl ester breaks the acetal links and gives a mixture of methylated glucose derivatives, along with mandelic acid rom the acidic portion of the molecule.

$$C_{28}H_{44}O_{13} + 3H_2O \xrightarrow{H^+} C_{10}H_{20}O_6 + C_8H_{18}O_6 + C_6H_5CHOHCOOH + CH_3OH$$

	Tetramethyl-glucose	Trimethyl-glucose	Mandelic acid	

The tetramethylglucose was isolated and found to be identical with 2,3,4,6-tetramethylglucose obtained from the methylation of glucose. This, therefore, represents the terminal glucose residue, whose anomeric carbon must have been joined to the second glucose residue in a glycosidic linkage. The absence of methylation in the 5-position shows that the ring structure is a six-membered or pyranose ring.

The structure of the trimethylglucose obtained from amygdalin was established by nitric acid oxidation. This yielded inactive trimethoxyglutaric acid by the reaction shown at the right. This trimethoxyglutaric acid is inactive because of the plane of symmetry perpendicular to the molecule at the central carbon atom. The sequence of stereochemical configurations necessary to achieve this inactivity corresponds to that found in the 2-, 3-, and 4-positions of glucose, but not to any other sequence in the glucose molecule. Hence the trimethylglucose must have been the 2,3,4-trimethyl derivative.

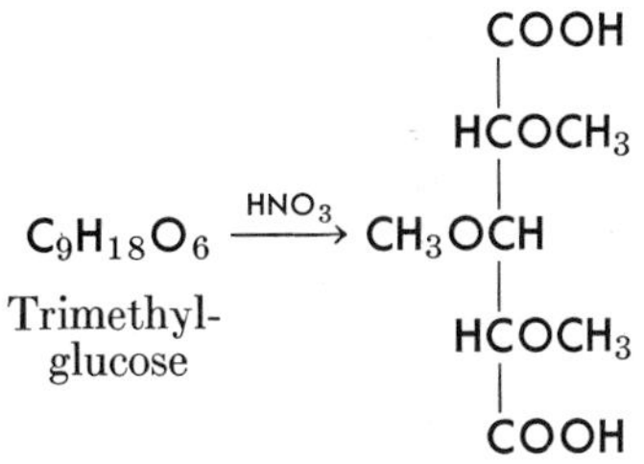

$$C_9H_{18}O_6 \xrightarrow{HNO_3} \begin{array}{c} COOH \\ | \\ HCOCH_3 \\ | \\ CH_3OCH \\ | \\ HCOCH_3 \\ | \\ COOH \end{array}$$

Trimethyl-glucose

Inactive trimethoxyglutaric acid

(Tri-O-methylxylaric acid)

The 5- and 6-positions in 2,3,4-trimethylglucose are open. Either of these could be the point of attachment of the glycosidic link and the other would then be the atom to which the ring was attached. The two possible ring sizes on this basis would be a six-membered ring and a seven-membered ring. The size of the ring was established by a method which will be given below in connection with the structure of maltose. Anticipating this result, we may say that the ring is a six-membered ring closed to C-5. From this it would follow that the glycosidic linkage is attached to C-6. The complete formula for amygdalin is, then, as follows:

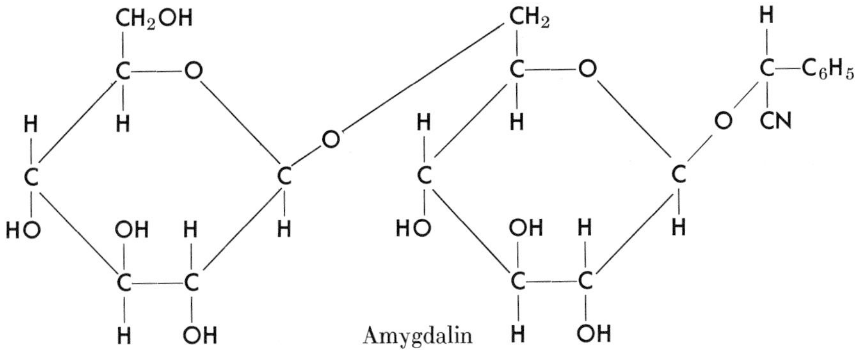

Amygdalin

24–3   The Synthesis of Amygdalin

The structural study on amygdalin and gentiobiose furnishes an example of the general method used for the determination of the structures of disaccharides. Methylation establishes the ring size and the identity of the terminal sugar residue. It also gives most of the information needed to establish the ring size and point of attachment of the other residue. The remaining information can be secured by an oxidative degradation, illustrated later. The final step in the structural investigation is the synthesis. For amygdalin, the synthesis of the glycosidic linkage was easy; the difficulty arose in the introduction of the cyano group. This was accomplished indirectly by a number of investigators almost simultaneously. The synthesis starts with acetobromogentiobiose, prepared by the method used for acetobromoglucose:*

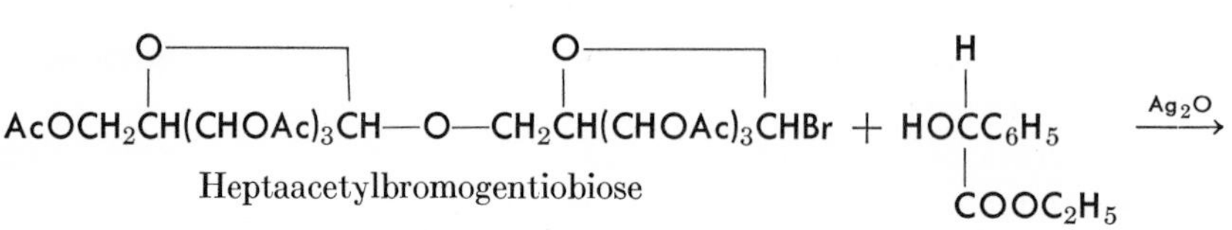

$$AcOCH_2CH(CHOAc)_3CH-O-CH_2CH(CHOAc)_3CHBr \; + \; HOCCH_6H_5 \xrightarrow{Ag_2O}$$

Heptaacetylbromogentiobiose

DL-ethyl mandelate

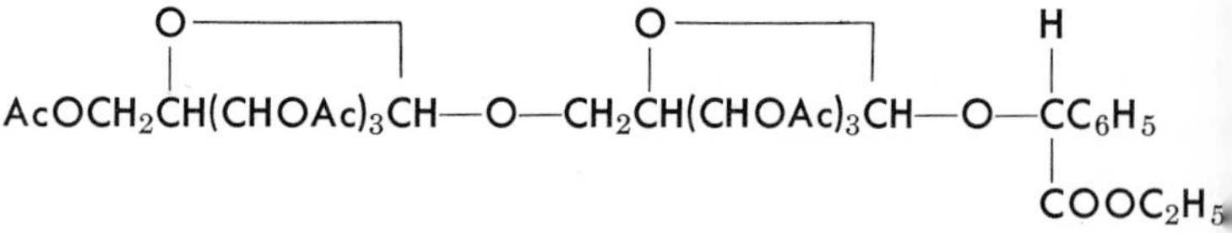

$$AcOCH_2CH(CHOAc)_3CH-O-CH_2CH(CHOAc)_3CH-O-CC_6H_5$$

DL-heptaacetyl ethyl amygdalinate

The use of methanolic ammonia under mild conditions replaces the ethyl ester group with an amide linkage without reacting with the acetate ester groups.

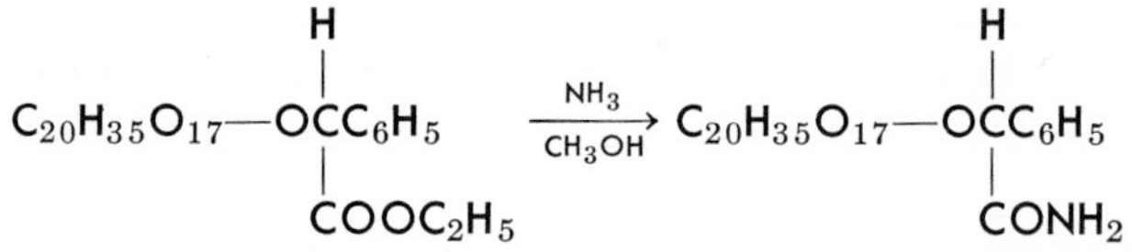

$$C_{20}H_{35}O_{17}-OCC_6H_5 \xrightarrow[CH_3OH]{NH_3} C_{20}H_{35}O_{17}-OCC_6H_5$$

DL-heptaacetyl
ethyl amygdalinate

DL-heptaacetylamygdalinic
amide

The properties of the amide are suitable for resolution. Since a new asymmetric center has been added to a previously resolved sugar residue, two compounds of different melting points and solubilities are formed, the D-amide and the L-amide. Both of these have negative rotations because of the sugar residue, but the one with the smallest negative rotation was arbitrarily assigned the D-configuration. It is

---

* In these formulations, we shall abbreviate acetyl as Ac.

identical with material prepared from amygdalin. The synthesis then continued
as follows:

$$\underset{\substack{\text{D}(-)\text{-heptaacetyl-} \\ \text{amygdalinic amide}}}{\underset{\displaystyle \overset{\displaystyle \text{H}}{|}}{C_{20}H_{35}O_{17}\text{—O}\overset{\displaystyle |}{\underset{\displaystyle \text{CONH}_2}{\text{C}}}C_6H_5}} \xrightarrow{P_2O_5} \underset{\substack{\text{D}(-)\text{-heptaacetyl-} \\ \text{amygdalin}}}{\underset{\displaystyle \overset{\displaystyle \text{H}}{|}}{C_{20}H_{35}O_{17}\text{—O}\overset{\displaystyle |}{\underset{\displaystyle \text{CN}}{\text{C}}}C_6H_5}}$$

This dehydration reaction of amides to give nitriles is a reversal of the hydrolysis
of nitriles to give amides (Section 4–4), an intermediate step in the formation of
acids from nitriles. The seven acetyl groups in heptaacetylamygdalin are in ester
linkages, and it is known that esters readily form amides on reaction with ammonia. Therefore the acetyl groups can be removed to free the alcoholic groups by
reaction with alcoholic ammonia.

$$C_6H_7O(OAc)_4\text{—O—}C_6H_7O(OAc)_3\text{—O—}\overset{\displaystyle \overset{\text{H}}{|}}{\underset{\displaystyle \underset{\text{CN}}{|}}{\text{C}}}\text{—}C_6H_5 + 7NH_3 \xrightarrow{CH_3OH}$$

$$\underset{\text{Amygdalin}}{C_6H_7O(OH)_4\text{—O—}C_6H_7O(OH)_3\text{—O—}\overset{\displaystyle \overset{\text{H}}{|}}{\underset{\displaystyle \underset{\text{CN}}{|}}{\text{C}}}\text{—}C_6H_5 + 7CH_3CONH_2}$$

24–4   The Synthesis of Gentiobiose

To retrace the complete synthesis of amygdalin, it is now only necessary to find
how to produce gentiobiose synthetically. It is obvious that this can be accomplished by the methods previously used for the synthesis of glycosides, provided
that a means can be found for covering all except the 6-position of one glucose
residue. This problem was solved by Helferich, who showed that triphenylmethyl
chloride (trityl chloride) reacts preferentially with primary alcoholic groups. For
glucose, this means preferential reaction with the 6-position.

$$\underset{\text{Glucose}}{\overset{\overset{\displaystyle O\text{————}}{|}}{HOCH_2\text{—CH(CHOH)}_3\text{—CHOH}}} + (C_6H_5)_3CCl \rightarrow$$

$$(C_6H_5)_3C\text{—O—}\overset{\overset{\displaystyle O\text{————}}{|}}{CH_2\text{—CH(CHOH)}_3\text{—CHOH}} \xrightarrow{(CH_3CO)_2O}$$

$$\underset{\text{Tetraacetyltritylglucose}}{(C_6H_5)_3C\text{—O—}\overset{\overset{\displaystyle O\text{————}}{|}}{CH_2\text{—CH(CHOCOCH}_3)_3\text{—CHOCOCH}_3}}$$

That the 6-position was the one involved in the ether formation was established earlier from other starting materials.

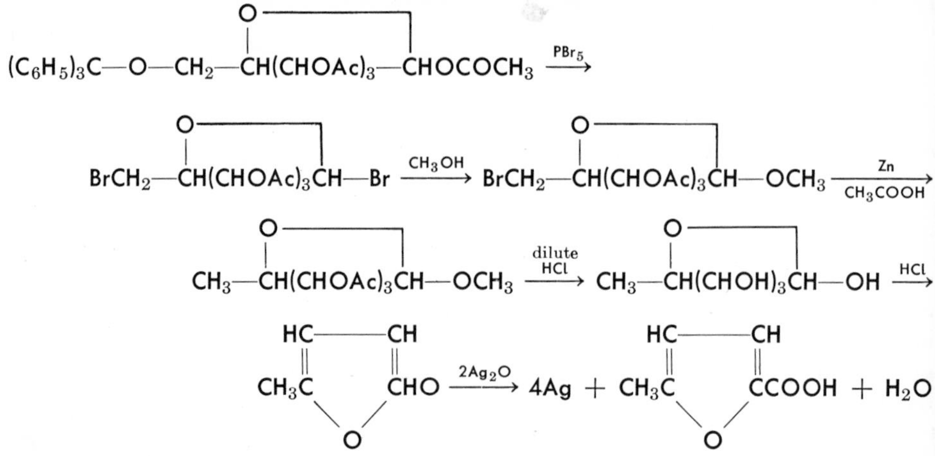

$$(C_6H_5)_3C—O—CH_2—\overset{\overset{\displaystyle O\text{——————}}{|}}{CH(CHOAc)_3—CHOCOCH_3} \xrightarrow{PBr_5}$$

$$BrCH_2—\overset{\overset{\displaystyle O\text{———————}}{|}}{CH(CHOAc)_3CH—Br} \xrightarrow{CH_3OH} BrCH_2—\overset{\overset{\displaystyle O\text{———————}}{|}}{CH(CHOAc)_3CH—OCH_3} \xrightarrow[CH_3COOH]{Zn}$$

$$CH_3—\overset{\overset{\displaystyle O\text{————————}}{|}}{CH(CHOAc)_3CH—OCH_3} \xrightarrow[HCl]{dilute} CH_3—\overset{\overset{\displaystyle O\text{————————}}{|}}{CH(CHOH)_3CH—OH} \xrightarrow{HCl}$$

HC———CH
‖ ‖
CH₃C   CHO $\xrightarrow{2Ag_2O}$ 4Ag + CH₃C   CCOOH + H₂O
\   /   \   /
O   O

5-methylfuroic acid

The identification of the methyl group on a derivative of furoic acid shows that the bromine that was reduced by the zinc was on a methylene group and hence that the trityl group was also on a methylene group. This establishes that the 6-position was the one attacked.

On treatment with dry gaseous hydrogen bromide, trityl ethers are readily split to form trityl bromide and the free alcohol.

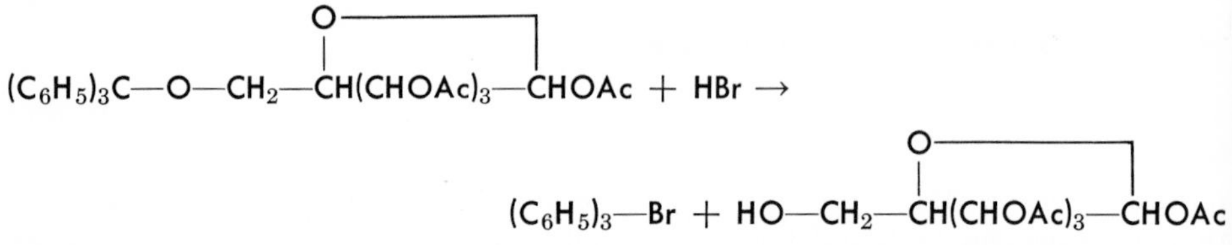

$$(C_6H_5)_3C—O—CH_2—\overset{\overset{\displaystyle O\text{————}}{|}}{CH(CHOAc)_3—CHOAc} + HBr \rightarrow$$

$$(C_6H_5)_3—Br + HO—CH_2—\overset{\overset{\displaystyle O\text{————}}{|}}{CH(CHOAc)_3—CHOAc}$$
1,2,3,4-tetraacetylglucose

In 1,2,3,4-tetraacetylglucose all the OH groups except the one in the 6-position are protected. It is therefore suitable for the formation of glycosides involving linkages at this position.

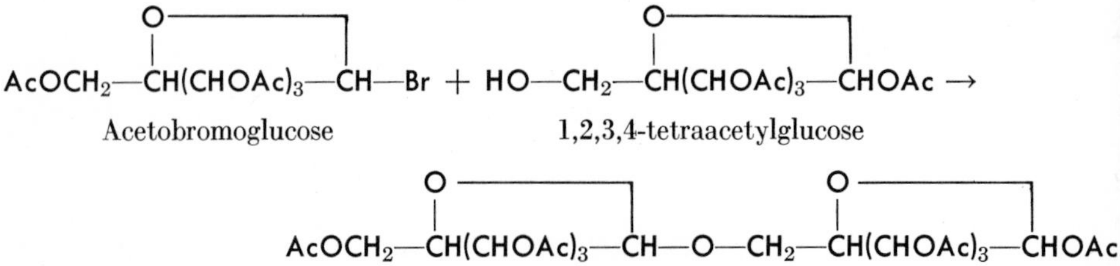

$$AcOCH_2—\overset{\overset{\displaystyle O\text{————}}{|}}{CH(CHOAc)_3—CH—Br} + HO—CH_2—\overset{\overset{\displaystyle O\text{————}}{|}}{CH(CHOAc)_3—CHOAc} \rightarrow$$

Acetobromoglucose   1,2,3,4-tetraacetylglucose

$$AcOCH_2—\overset{\overset{\displaystyle O\text{————}}{|}}{CH(CHOAc)_3—CH—O—CH_2}—\overset{\overset{\displaystyle O\text{————}}{|}}{CH(CHOAc)_3—CHOAc}$$
Octaacetylgentiobiose

For purposes of identification by melting points, the fully acetylated compounds are superior to the free sugars. Hence the first identification with the natural product was obtained at this point. Treatment with methanolic ammonia then converted the acetate into the free sugar.

$$AcOCH_2-CH(CHOAc)_3-CHOCH_2CH(CHOAc)_3-CHOAc + 8NH_3 \xrightarrow{CH_3OH}$$

$$HOCH_2CH(CHOH)_3CHOCH_2CH(CHOH)_3CHOH + 8CH_3CONH_2$$

Gentiobiose—6-O-(β-D-glucopyranosyl)-D-glucopyranose

24-5   Maltose; The Structure of 2,3,6-Trimethylglucose

Complete acid hydrolysis of starch produces glucose. If the hydrolysis is performed with the enzyme diastase, however, the reaction is incomplete and an intermediate sugar, maltose, which has the molecular formula $C_{12}H_{22}O_{11}$, is obtained. Further hydrolysis by acid or by the enzyme maltase produces two molecules of glucose. Maltose is not hydrolyzed by emulsin. It is thus concluded that the glycosidic linkage in maltose is alpha.

Maltose is a reducing sugar and exhibits mutarotation. From this it is concluded that it has the hemiacetal structure with a ring. It forms an octaacetate.

The position of the glycosidic linkage was established by methylation, as in earlier cases. Methylation of maltose gave an octamethyl derivative which on hydrolysis gave 2,3,4,6-tetramethylglucose and 2,3,6-trimethylglucose.

$$C_{12}H_{22}O_{11} \xrightarrow[NaOH]{(CH_3)_2SO_4} C_{20}H_{38}O_{11} \xrightarrow{HCl} C_{10}H_{20}O_6 + C_9H_{18}O_6$$

Maltose	Heptamethyl-methylmaltoside	2,3,4,6-tetramethyl-glucose	2,3,6-trimethyl-glucose

The tetramethylglucose must have been formed from the terminal glucose residue. The trimethylglucose must have had a glycosidic linkage to one of the carbons, C-4 or C-5, and the ring closure to the other. To establish this point, it is first necessary to show that the trimethylglucose obtained from maltose really is the 2,3,6-trimethyl derivative. This was accomplished by a systematic investigation of its properties. Methylation converts it into 2,3,4,6-tetramethylglucose. This shows that one of the unmethylated positions is the 5-position. The problem is to establish the position of the remaining open hydroxyl. This trimethylglucose does not form an osazone, indicating that the 2-position is occupied. Oxidation with nitric acid produces a dimethylsaccharic acid, with six carbons in the chain, but with the loss of one of the methyl ether groups. Since the anomeric carbon was necessarily free, the production of a carboxyl group with no diminution in chain length but with loss of a methyl group must mean that the 6-position had the methyl ether linkage which was lost in this oxidation.

$$C_9H_{18}O_6 \xrightarrow{HNO_3} HOOC(CHOH)_2(CHOCH_3)_2COOH$$

Trimethyl-
glucose

Dimethylsaccharic acid

Since it has now been established that the 2- and 6-positions are occupied, the other free position must be either 3 or 4. Evidence that the 3-position is occupied, and therefore that the 4-position is the one that is free, was obtained by reference to the disaccharide lactose, which is milk sugar. Lactose is a glycoside of galactose and glucose. On methylation and subsequent acid hydrolysis, lactose yields the same trimethylglucose as that obtained from maltose. Lactose is a reducing sugar and therefore has a free anomeric carbon. Reducing sugars, in general, can be degraded by a method discovered by Ruff, using hydrogen peroxide and ferric ion. As an example, glucose can be degraded to arabinose by this method.

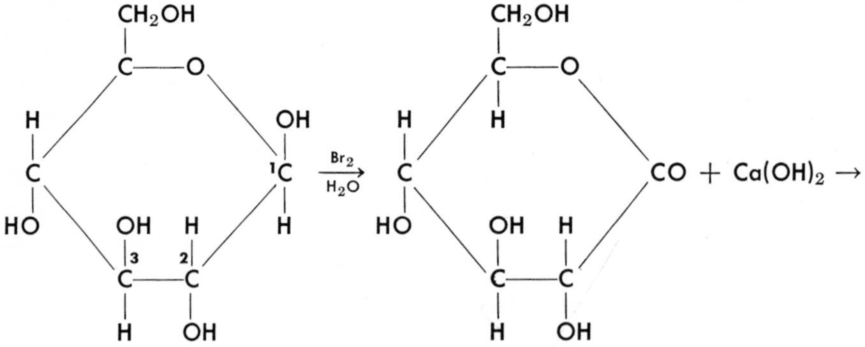

Glucose

Gluconolactone

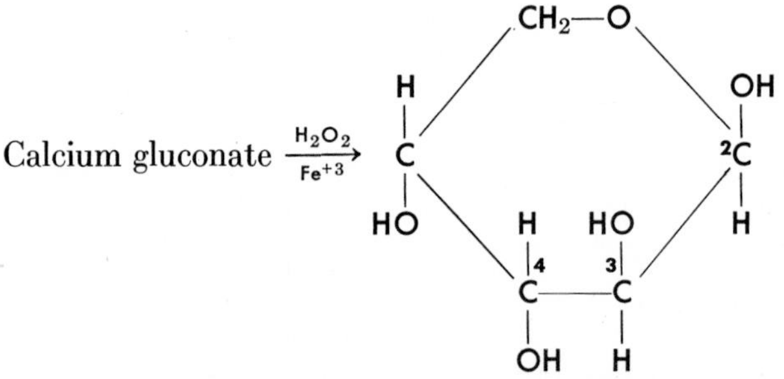

β-D-arabinose

This degradation removes the anomeric carbon of glucose and moves C-2 of glucose into the anomeric position of arabinose.

The Ruff degradation was performed on lactose. The resulting disaccharide still had the galactose residue intact but the glucose residue had been degraded to an arabinose residue. The degraded sugar still forms an osazone, showing that C-2 is free. But C-2 of the degraded sugar was C-3 of lactose. Hence we can conclude that C-3 of lactose is free and not occupied in the linkage with galactose. Because of this, lactose will methylate in the 3-position. But we have already seen that lactose methylates so as to give on hydrolysis the trimethylglucose obtained from maltose. This trimethylglucose therefore has the 3-position methylated.

24–6   Maltose; The Point of Glycosidic Attachment

Step by step, then, it has been established that positions 2, 3, and 6 are methylated in this glucose derivative, leaving carbons 4 and 5 free. This means that one of the two was involved in ring formation, the other in the glycosidic linkage of maltose. On this basis, we shall write a tentative formula for maltose, using a six-membered ring, and then show how the point of attachment of the glycosidic link was differentiated from the point of attachment of the ring.

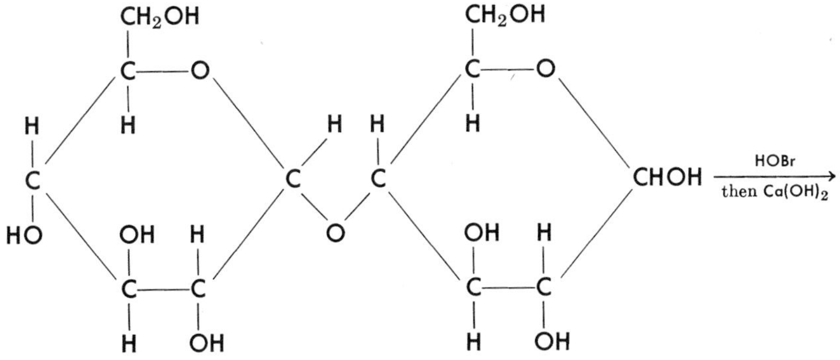

Maltose
4-O-(α-D-glucopyranosyl)-D-glucopyranose

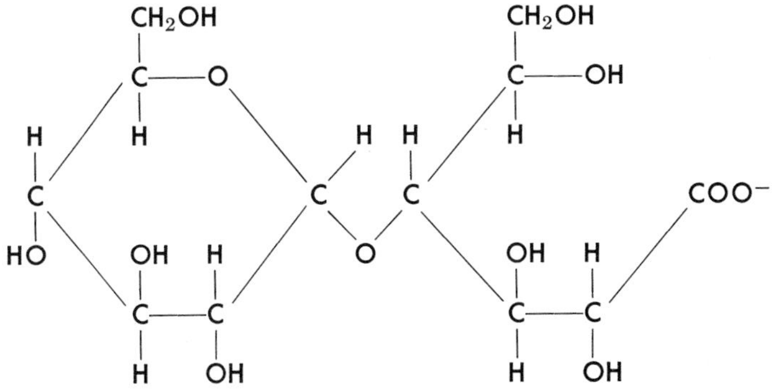

Calcium salt of maltonic acid

Oxidation of the anomeric carbon of maltose opens the ring, freeing the hemiacetal hydroxyl for subsequent methylation. Hence the only hydroxyl from the ring of maltonic acid that remains bound is the one that holds the glycosidic link. This is subsequently identified:

Calcium salt of maltonic acid $\xrightarrow[\text{NaOH}]{\text{(CH}_3)_2\text{SO}_4}$

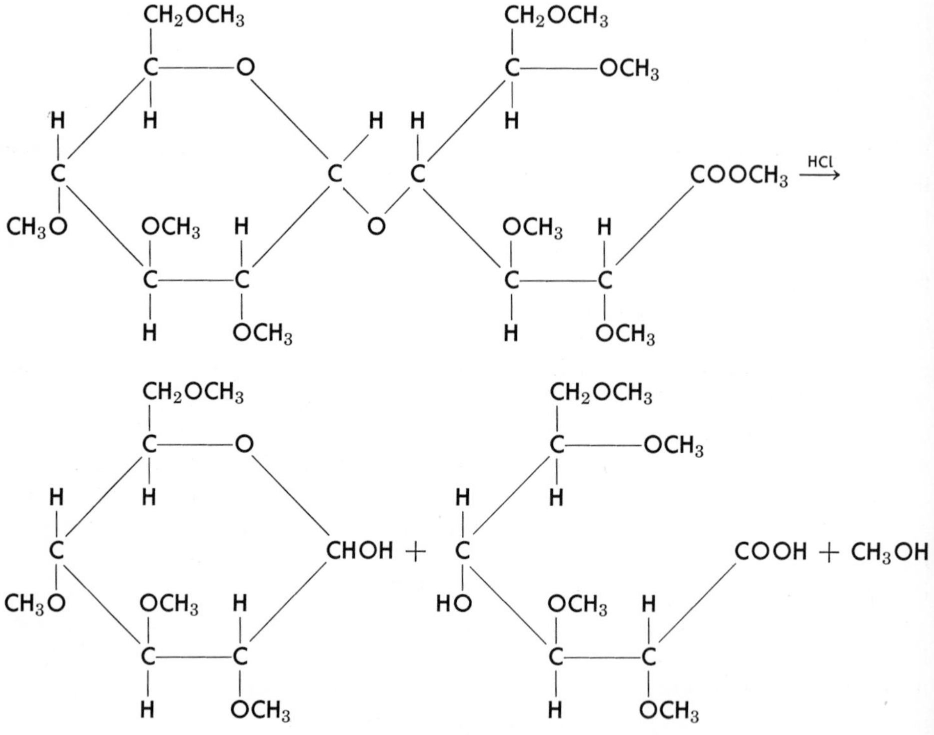

2,3,4-tetramethylglucose   2,3,5,6-tetramethylgluconic acid

Oxidation of the tetramethylgluconic acid obtained by this degradation process yields active 2,3-dimethoxysuccinic acid and no 2,3,4-trimethoxyglutaric acid, showing that the 4-position is the one that is free and therefore open to oxidative attack.

2,3,5,6-tetramethylgluconic acid $\xrightarrow{\text{HNO}_3}$

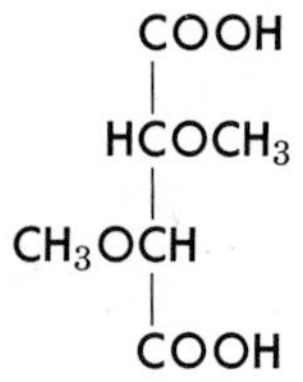

$$\begin{array}{c} \text{COOH} \\ | \\ \text{HCOCH}_3 \\ | \\ \text{CH}_3\text{OCH} \\ | \\ \text{COOH} \end{array}$$

Active dimethoxy-
succinic acid

These degradations establish the 4-position as being the one holding the ether group of the glycoside. From this, it follows that the 5-position held the ring oxygen in maltose. In the earlier work on amygdalin, the same type of degradation was used to establish the 5-position as being the one holding the ring. All of these sugars are thus shown to be pyranose derivatives.

24–7   Cellobiose

The incomplete hydrolysis of cellulose yields a disaccharide, cellobiose, that can be hydrolyzed further to give two moles of glucose. All chemical degradations of cellobiose are identical with those of maltose. Enzymatically, however, cellobiose is hydrolyzed by emulsin while maltose is hydrolyzed by maltase. It may be concluded, therefore, that cellobiose has a β-D-glucosidic link while maltose has an α-D-glucosidic link and is therefore 4-O-(β-D-glucopyranosyl)-D-glucopyranose.

24–8   Starch and Cellulose

Two polysaccharides have been isolated from starch: amylose, a water-soluble material precipitated by butanol, accounting for about 20% of the weight of the starch, and amylopectin, accounting for the remainder of the starch. Both amylose and amylopectin have been degraded by diastase to yield only the single disaccharide, maltose. From this it is assumed that the chains of each consist of α-glucosyl links. Methylation of amylose, followed by hydrolysis, yields nearly all 2,3,6-trimethylglucose. Less than 0.5% of 2,3,4,6-tetramethylglucose is also formed, indicating its presence at the ends of the methylated chains. From this it is concluded that amylose has an "unbranched" chain of α-glucosyl groups. Amylopectin, on the other hand, gives approximately ten times as much 2,3,4,6-tetramethylglucose, indicating the presence of many more terminal glucose links in the chain. This is accompanied by an almost equivalent amount of 2,3-dimethyl-glucose, whose presence could be accounted for by "branching" of the chains with glucose units attached to some residues at both the 3- and the 4-positions.

Cellulose, on hydrolysis, yields only the disaccharide cellobiose. Hydrolysis of methylated cellulose gives a very high yield of 2,3,6-trimethylglucose, indicating practically no branching of the chain.

PROBLEMS

24–1   A cyanogenetic glycoside may be obtained from the seeds of the wild vetch, *Vicia angustifolia*. This material is called vicianin, and hydrolysis with emulsin yields one mole of L-arabinose, one mole of D-glucose, one mole of HCN, and one of benzaldehyde.

(a) Are the glycosidic linkages in vicianin alpha or beta?

Partial hydrolysis of vicianin yields HCN, benzaldehyde, and a disaccharide called vicianose. The structure of this material was demonstrated by synthesis in the following way:

$$\text{L-arabinose} \xrightarrow{\text{(CH}_3\text{CO)}_2\text{O}} C_{13}H_{18}O_9$$

(b) How many acetyl groups have been added to the sugar?

(c) What is the structure of the derivative? (See Section 24–5.)

$$C_{13}H_{18}O_9 \xrightarrow{\text{dry HBr gas}} C_{11}H_{15}O_7Br$$

(d) Which acetyl group has been replaced?

$$\text{D-glucose} \xrightarrow{(C_6H_5)_3CCl} C_{25}H_{26}O_6 \xrightarrow{(CH_3CO)_2O} C_{33}H_{34}O_{10} \xrightarrow{HBr} C_{14}H_{20}O_{10}$$

$$C_{11}H_{15}O_7Br + C_{14}H_{20}O_{10} \rightarrow \text{heptaacetylvicianose}$$

(e) Which position is free in $C_{14}H_{20}O_{10}$?

(f) Which carbon in the arabinose unit and which carbon in the glucose unit are linked?

(g) Write the systematic name for vicianose.

(h) Is vicianose a reducing sugar?

(i) Draw the structure for vicianin.

24–2 Trehalose, a nonreducing sugar, is obtained from various fungi and yeasts. On prolonged hydrolysis it yields two moles of glucose. When trehalose is methylated octamethyltrehalose is obtained; when this is hydrolyzed, the same tetramethylglucose is obtained as is obtained by direct methylation of D-glucose.

(a) What carbons are linked in trehalose?

(b) Draw several possible structures for trehalose which differ in the configuration at the anomeric carbons.

The treatment of trehalose with periodic acid yields two moles of formic acid. The other product, which is aldehydic, may be oxidized to an acid which is characterized as its distrontium salt. Further hydrolysis and oxidation of this salt yields oxalic acid and D-glyceric acid (Section 22–5).

(c) Show that this evidence confirms the previous evidence regarding the ring size in the glucoside links in trehalose.

24–3 (a) What is the minimum number of glucose units in the amylose chain?

Ignoring the substituents in the ring, we see that the skeleton and connecting bonds have the geometry shown in Fig. 24–1 (a).

(b) Link a few (five or six, say) units together keeping the geometry of the unit above in mind. Will they form a linear chain or a helix?

The familiar dark blue color obtained by the interaction of iodine and starch is believed to result from a complex whose geometry involves encirclement of the smaller species by the larger. Such complexes are called clathrates. For the iodine-starch complex, assumption of helical geometry would allow the interpretation of the geometry of the complex as in the diagram shown in Fig. 24–1 (b).

A variety of such complexes is known. Crystalline urea forms clathrate compounds with normal paraffins, apparently because the crystal structure of urea contains similar cylindrical apertures. It is of interest that on the basis of studies with molecular models, branched-chain paraffins, because of their greater cross section at the branch carbon, would not be expected to form complexes. They do not in fact form complexes, and this observation has been used to separate n-alkyl compounds from the branched-chain isomers.

The action of *Bacillus macerans* on amylose produces a series of compounds known as Schardinger dextrins, after their discoverer. The α-dextrin has been shown to contain six of the same units as amylose, but there is no terminal unit.

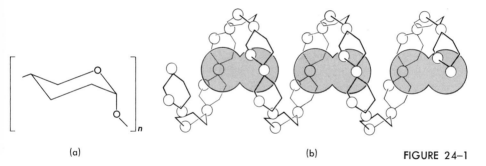

(a)   (b)   FIGURE 24-1

(c) Write an abbreviated structure to account for the information given about α-dextrin.

The solubility of α-dextrin in water is 14.5 g/100 ml. If enough benzene is brought into contact with this solution to form a separate layer, the solubility of the dextrin drops to 0.8 g/100 ml. The precipitate which forms contains about one mole of benzene for each mole of dextrin.

(d) Draw a 1:1 structure for this complex as a clathrate compound. The complex is apparently favored by geometry, and no bonds seem to be formed.

If bromobenzene is used as the precipitant, the precipitation is not so efficient; the final solubility of the dextrin in water in contact with bromobenzene is 2.4 g/100 ml.

(e) Can you suggest a reason for this similar to that proposed for the selectivity of urea clathrates?

(f) Draw a few possible abbreviated structures for amylopectin. One would be a randomly organized molecule. Branching in others would follow definite geometrical arrangements.

(g) Show that the polysaccharide chain in cellulose is approximately linear, not curved.

What special techniques were used to establish the structure of sucrose?

25

CARBOHYDRATES IV: THE STRUCTURE AND SYNTHESIS OF SUCROSE

25–1 The Nature of the Linkages in Sucrose

To the layman, the term "sugar" is synonymous with cane sugar or, perhaps, beet sugar, that is, sucrose. Sucrose is found widely distributed in the plant kingdom and was the object of early chemical investigations. The essential points of its structure were clear soon after adequate methods for the structural investigations of sugars were found. Despite this, the synthesis of sucrose lagged because of the difficulties encountered, and it was only recently that these difficulties were overcome to give the first, although low-yield, synthesis of sucrose. It is a commentary on the clumsiness of our synthetic methods that this substance which is formed so readily by a host of plants remains a synthetic curiosity.

Sucrose is a disaccharide, $C_{12}H_{22}O_{11}$. Hydrolysis with either acid or with the enzyme invertase, produces one mole of glucose and one of fructose. Fructose has a high negative rotation, in contrast to the positive rotations of both sucrose and glucose, so that the process of hydrolysis produces an inversion in the sign of rotation. Fructose is, therefore, sometimes called "levulose" and the hydrolysis is called the inversion of sucrose. The catalysts which bring about inversion have been carefully studied. Since fructose is sweeter than either sucrose or glucose, invert sugar is believed by many to be sweeter than sucrose, although this is a matter of individual perception. In investigating the structure of sucrose, the first point to be established is the structure of fructose.

Fructose is not oxidized to an acid by hypobromite and, consequently, does not have a potential aldehyde group. On the other hand, treatment of fructose with phenylhydrazine forms glucosazone. From this it can be concluded that carbons

3,4,5, and 6 of fructose are identical with those carbons on glucose. The differences must lie on carbons 1 and 2. Since fructose is a nonaldehydic isomer of glucose it must be a ketose sugar. Methylation has established the fact that it has a pyranose ring. The formula, therefore, is

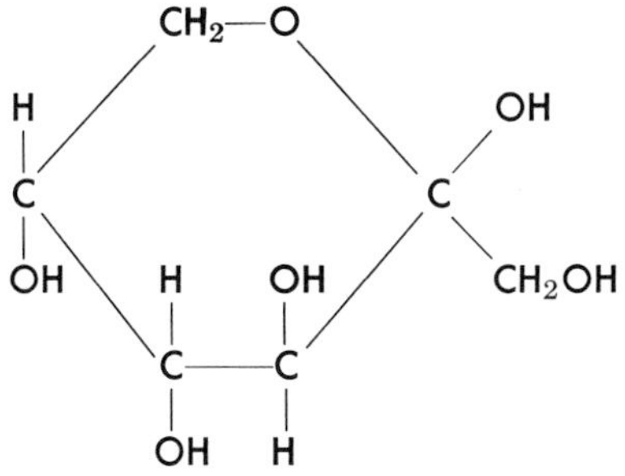

β-D-fructose

Fructose undergoes mutarotation to form a mixture of α- and β-isomers. Despite the lack of an aldehyde group, fructose reduces Fehling's solution. This has been shown to occur because the alkali used in Fehling's solution causes an isomerization between glucose, fructose, and still other sugars.

Sucrose is a nonreducing sugar. This information makes this assignment of the points of condensation on each of the hexose molecules apparent. Both glycosidic carbons must be involved. This gives the following partial formula for sucrose:

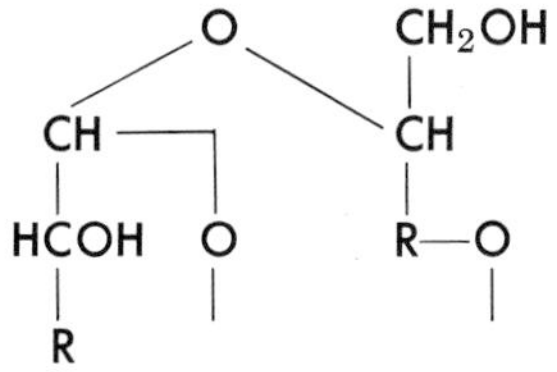

Glucose Fructose
residue residue

Sucrose is hydrolyzed by maltase, showing the glucosidic linkage to be alpha. Independent studies have shown that invertase, sometimes referred to as sucrase, is specific for certain types of beta-glycosidic links. It was therefore concluded that the fructose linkage is β-D. Polarimetric studies by the method of optical superposition support the conclusion that the linkage to glucose is α-D, and that to fructose is β-D.

25–2 Ring Sizes

The next problem is that of the sizes of the two rings. It was found easy to methylate seven of the hydroxyls in sucrose but methylation of the eighth proceeds with difficulty. By patient work, however, octamethyl sucrose was obtained.

Hydrolysis yielded 2,3,4,6-tetramethylglucose, which was readily identified. This established the ring in the glucose residue as pyranoid. Cleavage of heptamethyl-sucrose showed that the unmethylated hydroxyl was in the glucose residue, so fully methylated fructose can be obtained from heptamethylsucrose. This product was used for the further investigation of structure.

It was found that the tetramethyl fructose obtained from sucrose is different from that obtained by direct methylation of fructose. Since this was shown to be 1,3,4,5-tetramethylfructose, indicating a pyranoid ring, the presumption was that the tetramethylfructose from sucrose would be the 1,3,4,6-isomer, indicating a furanoid ring. This assumption was established as correct by the work of Avery, Haworth, and Hirst. The first step in the degradation was oxidation with nitric acid. This attacked the primary carbon next to the potential keto group, which may well be an actual keto group under these highly acidic conditions.

$$
\begin{array}{ccc}
\text{CH}_2\text{OCH}_3 & & \text{COOH} \\
| & & | \\
\text{HOC}\text{---} & & \text{HOC}\text{---} \\
| & & | \\
\text{CH}_3\text{OCH} & + \text{HNO}_3 \rightarrow & \text{CH}_3\text{OCH} \\
| & & | \\
\text{HCOCH}_3 & & \text{HCOCH}_3 \\
| & & | \\
\text{HCO}\text{---} & & \text{HCO}\text{---} \\
| & & | \\
\text{CH}_2\text{OCH}_3 & & \text{CH}_3\text{OCH}_3
\end{array}
$$

This oxidation has removed one methyl ether group to form the carboxylic acid. For purposes of identification, the acid was converted to its methyl ester, which was converted to the amide. The amide formed good crystals with a reversible melting point.

It was next found possible to remove the carboxyl group by a reaction similar to the Ruff degradation. In this instance, the oxidizing agent employed was barium permanganate in acidic solution.

$$
\begin{array}{ccc}
\text{COOH} & & \\
| & & \\
\text{HOC}\text{---} & & \text{O}=\text{C}\text{---} \\
| & \xrightarrow[\text{Acid}]{\text{Ba(MnO}_4)_2} & | \\
\text{CH}_3\text{OCH} & & \text{CH}_3\text{OCH} \\
| & & | \\
\text{HCOCH}_3 & & \text{HCOCH}_3 \\
| & & | \\
\text{HCO}\text{---} & & \text{HCO}\text{---} \\
| & & | \\
\text{CH}_2\text{OCH}_3 & & \text{CH}_2\text{OCH}_3
\end{array}
$$

The acid formed by this oxidation readily forms an inner ester, a lactone. The lactone can be oxidized by nitric acid to yield active dimethoxysuccinic acid:

O=C ——┐
|
CH₃OCH
|
HCOCH₃   + HNO₃ →
|
HCO ———┘
|
CH₂OCH₃

COOH
|
CH₃OCH
|
HCOCH₃
|
COOH

(−)-Dimethoxysuccinic acid
(2,3-di-O-methyl-D-threonic
acid)

The dimethoxysuccinic acid was converted to the ester, and the ester into the amide. Again, the amide was found to be suitable for purposes of identification.

This stepwise degradation established the presence of two methoxy groups between the unmethylated hydroxyls, and the optical activity of the product further identified these two carbons as those from the 3- and 4-positions of fructose. These oxidations established the structure of the tetramethylfructose from sucrose as the 1,3,4,6-derivative. From this it follows that the ring connects the 2- and 5-positions and must be furanose. The formula for sucrose is therefore as shown below. The model of sucrose is shown in Fig. 25–1.

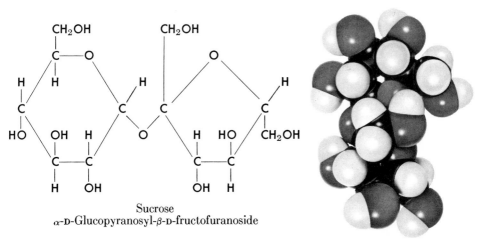

Sucrose
α-D-Glucopyranosyl-β-D-fructofuranoside

FIGURE 25–1

25–3   Preparation of the Fructose Group

Two problems in synthesis created the difficulty in the production of synthetic sucrose. The first was that acetobromoglucose gives beta glycosides in its condensations. The problem of the formation of alpha glycosides is a difficult one. The second is that many derivatives of fructose which might be suitable as starting materials in the synthesis have pyranose rings. Hence it was necessary to find a method of obtaining a condensable derivative with a furanose ring. The latter problem was solved earlier by Irvine, but the formation of the alpha linkage remained a problem until recently.

Furanose sugars have been referred to as gamma sugars. Irvine found that he obtained a gamma derivative of fructose when he dissolved it in hot absolute ethanol and then treated it with anhydrous hydrogen chloride.

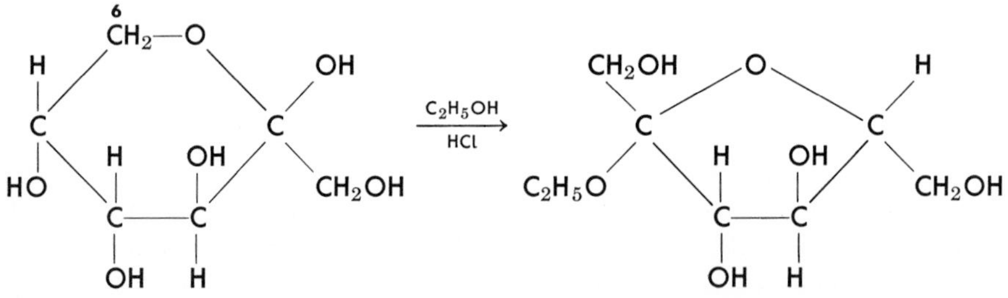

Fructose   γ-ethylfructoside

The structure of γ-ethylfructoside was established by methylation and subsequent hydrolysis of the glycosidic group to 1,3,4,6-tetramethylfructose.

Acetylation of γ-ethylfructoside was accomplished with acetic anhydride and sodium acetate.

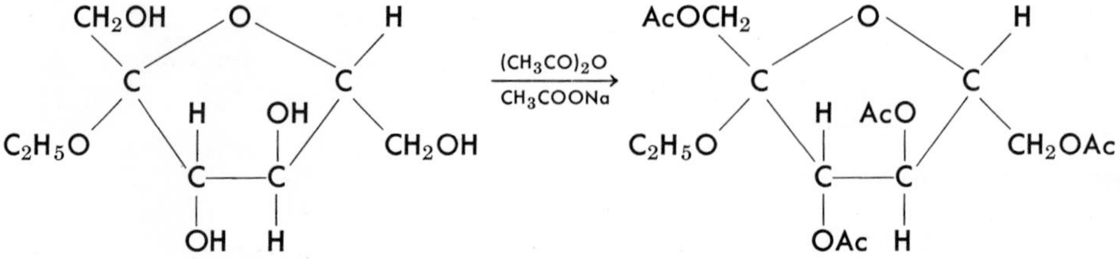

Tetracetyl-γ-ethylfructoside

As in the production of acetobromoglucose, treatment with anhydrous hydrogen halides will replace the glycosidic group. In this case, acetyl chloride was chosen as the solvent and dry hydrogen chloride was used as the reagent.

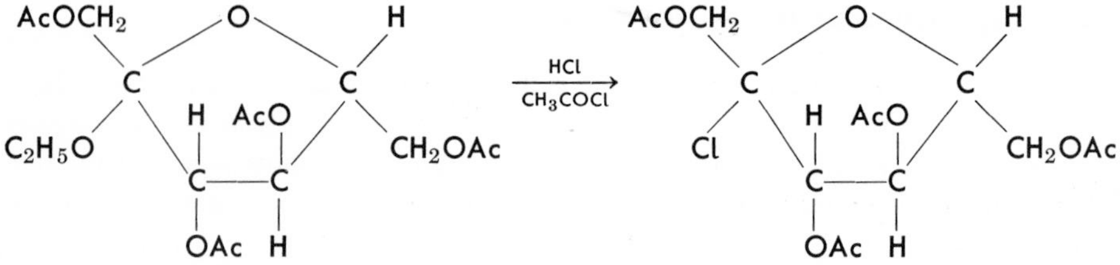

Finally the chlorine atom was replaced by the hydroxyl group by the action of moist silver oxide.

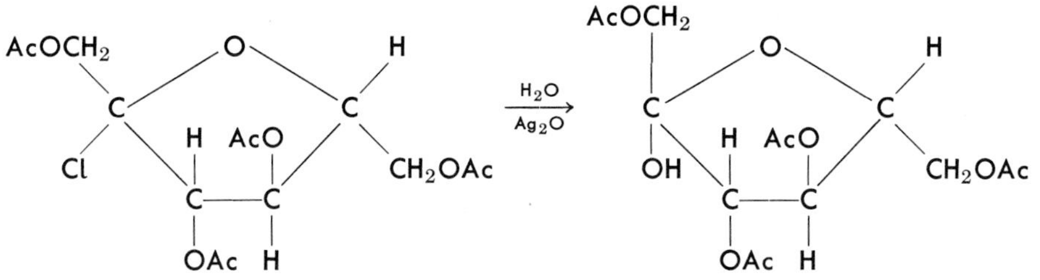

1,3,4,6-tetraacetylfructose

The product, 1,3,4,6-tetraacetylfructose, has both the furanose ring and the free hydroxyl in the 2-position, which is necessary for the condensation to sucrose. In the intermediates formulated above, configurations at the anomeric carbons have not been definitely established, so the only assumption made is that the final product is beta, as required to give sucrose.

25-4   Preparation of "Brigl's Anhydride"

The glucose derivative required for the synthesis of sucrose was prepared in 1921 by Brigl, but its significance was only recognized recently. Brigl observed that the action of phosphorus pentachloride on pentaacetylglucose not only replaced the acetyl group on the anomeric carbon by chlorine, as expected, but also attacked the acetyl group on the 2-position to give chlorination to the trichloroacetyl derivative. While phosphorus pentachloride had been observed previously to give chlorinations in a few unusual situations, this reaction was strikingly novel. Its mechanism remains to be explained. (In the remaining formulations, we shall write only the carbon skeletons instead of the complete formulas used previously.)

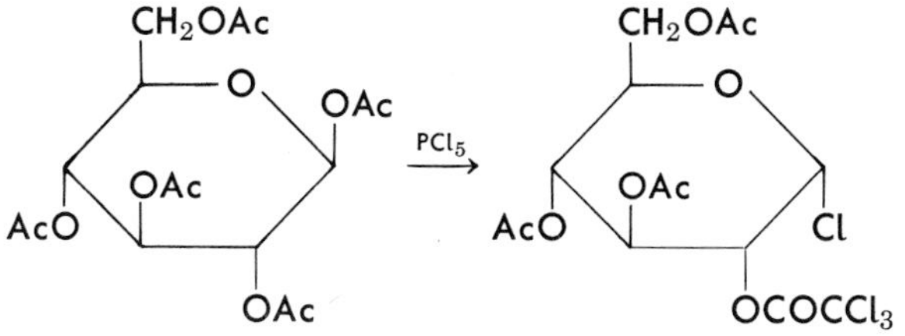

β-D-glucopyranose   3,4,6-tri-O-acetyl-2-O-(trichloroacetyl)-
pentaacetate   α-D-glucopyranosyl chloride

Because of the high reactivity of the trichloroacetyl group, treatment of the product in cold ether solution with dry ammonia gas removed the trichloroacetyl group as an amide, as shown below:

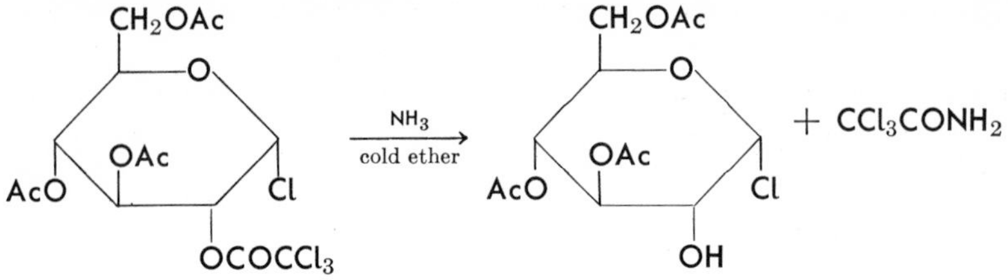

The product spontaneously mutarotates, giving a mixture in which the beta form predominates.

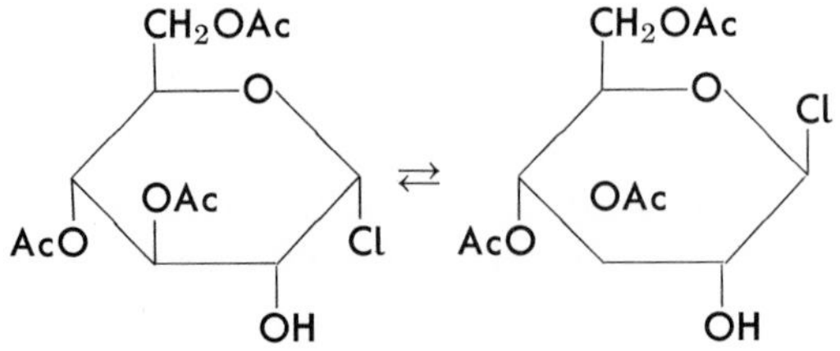

Treatment of this substance with ammonia in benzene solution at a somewhat higher temperature yields a derivative of ethylene oxide, a so-called "epoxy" compound.

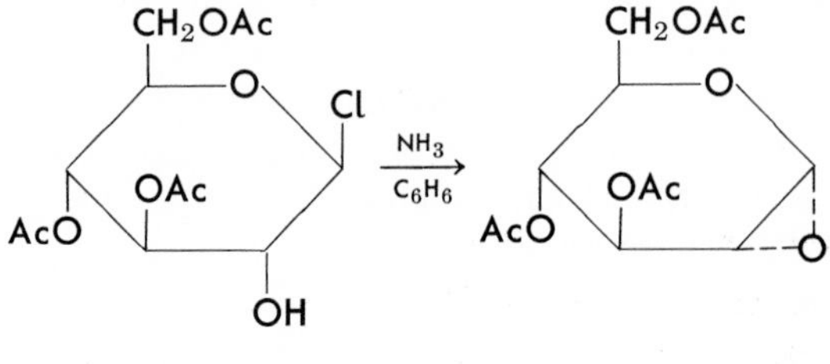

This triacetyl 1,2-anhydro-α-D-glucose has been called "Brigl's anhydride."

25–5   The Formation of Levoglucosan

When Brigl's anhydride is reacted with methanol, a β-D-glucoside is formed.

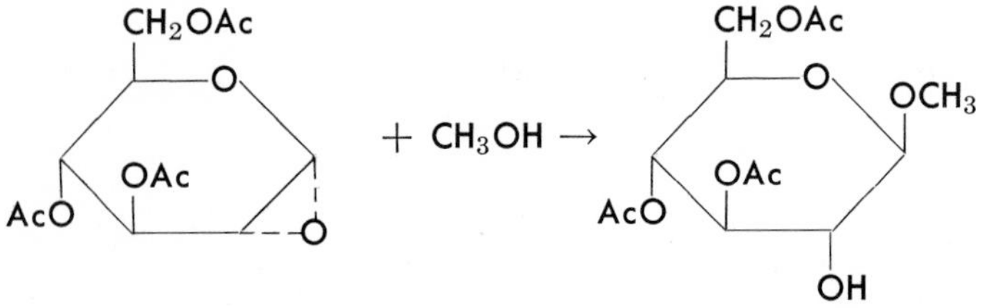

Methyl 3,4,6-tri-O-acetyl-β-D-glucopyranoside

This is the wrong configuration for sucrose and it was because of this reaction course that Brigl's anhydride was long considered unsuited to the synthesis of sucrose. It is believed that the course of the reaction of methanol with the epoxy ring involves a "backside" approach to the ring in the manner of a Walden inversion. The attacking reagent is believed to be a small amount of methoxide ion normally present in methanol, just as a small amount of hydroxide ion is normally present in water.

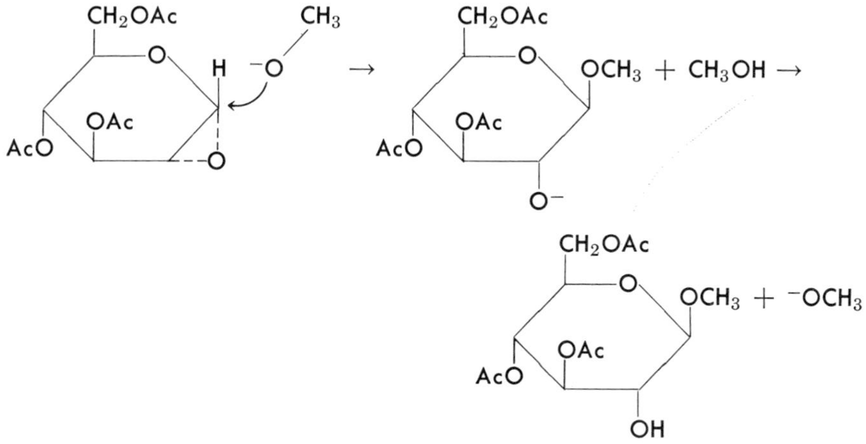

A peculiarity of the reactions of Brigl's anhydride was discovered in observing its reaction with aqueous alkali to form levoglucosan.

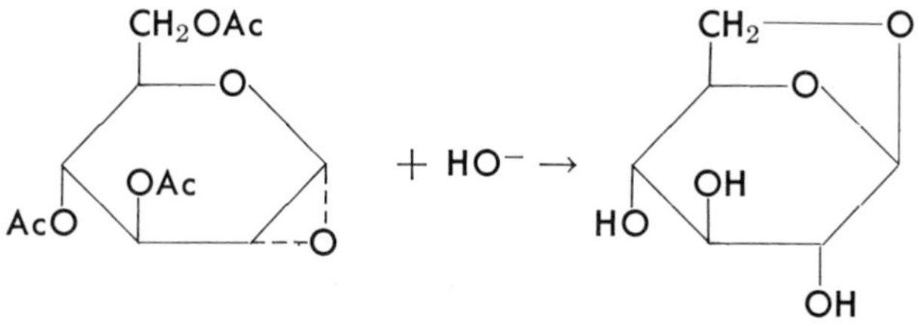

Lemieux, who completed the synthesis of sucrose, reasoned that the mechanism of this hydrolysis involved a preliminary hydrolysis of the acetyl group on the primary alcohol in the 6-position with the formation of an alkoxide ion which then attacked from the backside in much the manner that methoxide ion is believed to attack.

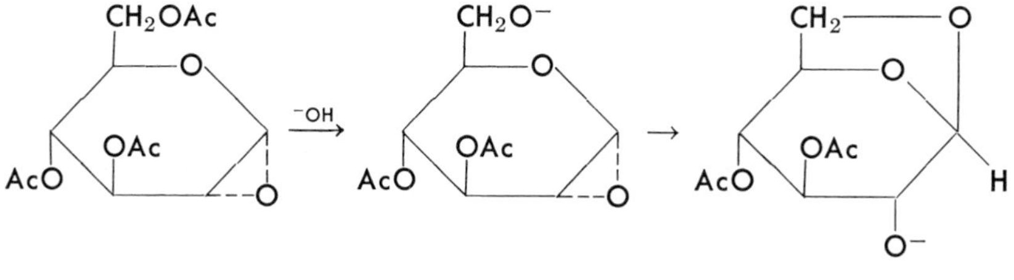

This five-membered ring formation was then followed by completion of the hydrolysis of the acetyl groups to form levoglucosan. The proximity of the oxygen on the primary alcohol group in the 6-position to the anomeric carbon is brought out more forcefully by writing the conformational diagram for levoglucosan.

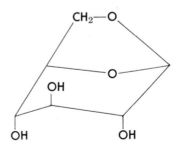

The energy required to force the three hydroxyls into the axial positions is supplied by the opening of the three-membered epoxide ring.

25–6   The Synthesis of Sucrose

When Brigl examined the reaction of his anhydride with alcohols, he noted that phenol reacts to give mainly the α-D-glucoside. Later, other investigators found that secondary alcohols of high molecular weight also give mixtures of alpha and beta isomers. Lemieux reasoned that these high molecular weight alcohols had large steric requirements and that, being secondary, they would not react as readily as primary alcohols and would, consequently, require higher reaction temperatures. He reasoned further that under these conditions the acetyl group in the 6-position would participate in the reaction, forming a transient inter-mediate which would resemble levoglucosan. A proton from the secondary alcohol might open the epoxide ring, leaving the secondary alcohol free to attack into the alpha configuration.

Whether or not this is the mechanism, the fact is that on prolonged heating in a bomb tube in concentrated benzene solution at a temperature above 100°C, the mixture of Brigl's anhydride and Irvine's 1,3,4,6-tetraacetylfructose gave hepta-acetylsucrose in yields from 2% to 9%:

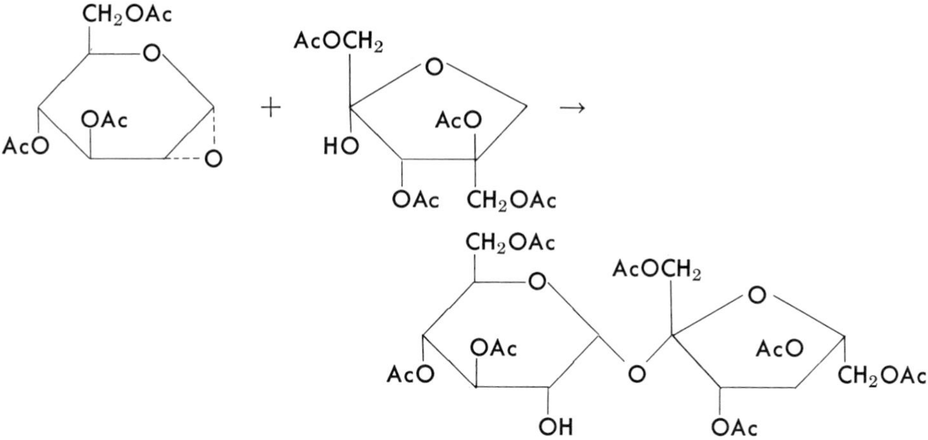

Sucrose heptaacetate

For purification, the material was acetylated to the octaacetyl derivative.

The synthesis of sucrose was finally completed in 1953 by Lemieux and Huber. The materials used for the purpose had been available for nearly twenty-five years before the logic of reaction mechanisms impelled their use. In spite of this, it is doubtful that the synthesis would have been completed successfully very many years before it was actually tried. This is because the purification of the reaction product was accomplished by means of chromatographic techniques which had not been perfected very long before they were used in this purification. Two different chromatographic techniques were used in the purification. One, on the deacetylated material, was preparative paper chromatography. The other, on the fully acetylated material, was column chromatography on magnesium silicate and diatomaceous earth. Techniques such as these have enabled the modern organic chemist to deal effectively with noncrystallizing syrups that used to baffle investigators.

PROBLEMS

25-1   One of the intermediates in photosynthesis is sedoheptulose, which was first obtained from *Sedum spectabile*. It is a seven-carbon sugar, $C_7H_{14}O_7$, and can be reduced to a pair of heptaalcohols, sedoheptitols, with sodium amalgam. Nitric acid may be used to oxidize these to dicarboxylic acids. One or both of these dicarboxylic acids may also be prepared by the sequential treatment of D-altrose, L-gulose, and D-mannose with HCN, hydrolysis to the mixture of monocarboxylic acids in each case, and oxidation of these to the dicarboxylic acids. Not all of the acids produced by this procedure correspond to those made from sedoheptulose, of course.

```
 CHO       CHO       CHO       CHO       CHO       CHO       CHO       CHO
 |         |         |         |         |         |         |         |
HCOH      HOCH      HCOH      HOCH      HCOH      HOCH      HCOH      HOCH
 |         |         |         |         |         |         |         |
HCOH      HCOH      HOCH      HOCH      HCOH      HCOH      HOCH      HOCH
 |         |         |         |         |         |         |         |
HCOH      HCOH      HCOH      HCOH      HOCH      HOCH      HOCH      HOCH
 |         |         |         |         |         |         |         |
HCOH      HCOH      HCOH      HCOH      HCOH      HCOH      HCOH      HCOH
 |         |         |         |         |         |         |         |
CH2OH     CH2OH     CH2OH     CH2OH     CH2OH     CH2OH     CH2OH     CH2OH
```

D-(+)-allose	D-(+)-glucose	D-(−)-gulose	D-(+)-galactose
D-(+)-altrose	D-(+)-mannose	D-(−)-idose	D-(+)-talose

(a) Show that certain pairs of the acids synthesized for comparison define the stereochemistry of four of the carbons in the acids from sedoheptulose.

(b) These acids differ in the stereochemistry of one carbon. Since sedoheptulose gave two alcohols on reduction, this must be the carbon that was reduced. Is the sugar a ketose or an aldose? The insertion of -ul- in the name is part of a generic system which designates this fact.

(c) What is the linear formula for sedoheptulose?

It is found that sedoheptulose is easily dehydrated by mineral acids to yield a crystalline compound, sedoheptulosan, $C_7H_{12}O_6$, which is stable to base. Methylation of this compound with methyl iodide and silver oxide yields a tetramethyl derivative. Oxidation of this material yields optically active trimethoxyglutaric acid.

(d) Is sedoheptulosan furanose or pyranose? Write the partial structure indicating which carbons are linked by oxygen.

(e) What kind of carbonyl protecting function is stable to base, a hemiacetal or an acetal?

(f) What two possible structures may be drawn involving remaining hydroxyl functions?

(g) Derivatives of ethylene oxide (epoxides) are unstable to base; they open to give 1,2-glycols if the base is hydroxide, for example. How does this eliminate all but one structure for sedoheptulosan? What is it?

(h) Compare this structure to that for levoglucosan. What might have been the structure for sedoheptulose?

25-2   Gentianose may be isolated from many species of gentian. Mineral acid hydrolysis yields fructose and twice as much glucose. Sucrase acts on gentianose to give fructose and gentiobiose, and emulsin produces sucrose and glucose.

(a) What is the structure of gentianose?

(b) Develop a synthesis of gentianose hendecaacetate. You may wish to use levoglucosan as a starting material, or you may want to look for a better synthesis than the one this suggests, after noting the possible flaw in the scheme.

25-3   Show that the easiest synthesis for trehalose yields the wrong isomer at the anomeric carbons.

How were synthetic methods used to establish the structures of the basic components of nucleic acids?

26

NUCLEIC ACIDS I: THE STRUCTURES OF PYRIMIDINES AND PURINES

26–1 "Aromatic" Heterocyclic Compounds

Cyclic compounds which contain only carbon atoms in the ring are called carbocyclic or isocyclic compounds. Those containing atoms other than carbon are heterocyclic. We have seen that benzene is an isocyclic compound which, although originally formulated with double bonds, does not undergo the typical addition reactions of olefins. Its tendency to undergo substitution reactions instead of addition reactions is at the basis of so-called "aromatic" chemistry. Numerous heterocyclic compounds are known whose chemistry is also typically aromatic. Special attention may be called to certain of these, shown below, which are of great importance in natural product chemistry.

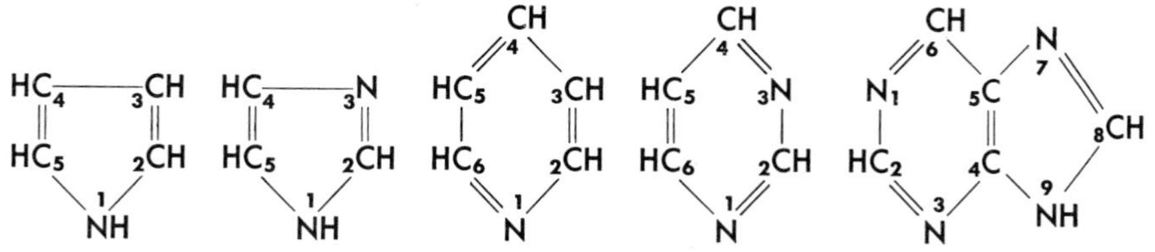

Pyrrole Imidazole Pyridine Pyrimidine Purine

The nucleic acids constitute a group of materials which are critical in the growth and reproduction of all living organisms. Complete hydrolysis of nucleic acids produces phosphoric acid, carbohydrates, and pyrimidine and purine bases. For this reason, we shall now examine the chemistry of pyrimidines and purines with greater care.

26-2   Pyrimidine Syntheses

The most convincing proof of the structures of the pyrimidines lies in their syntheses. Most of these syntheses are variants of the fundamental one used in the production of barbituric acid.

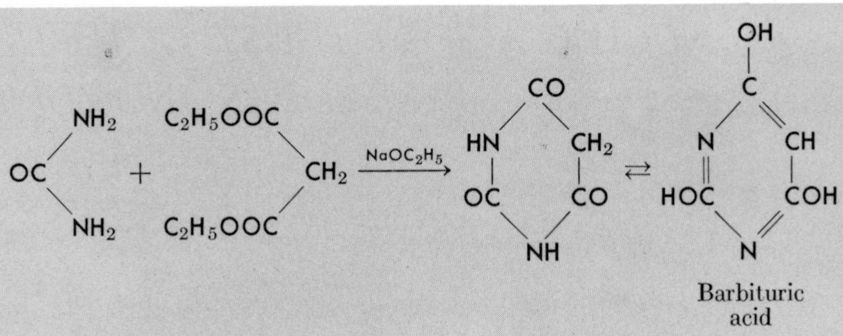

This condensation may be considered as the formation of a cyclic amide from an ester. Barbituric acid may be assigned either of the two tautomeric forms shown, just as keto and enol forms of acetoacetic ester may be formed.

The most convenient method for preparing unsubstituted pyrimidine is from barbituric acid.

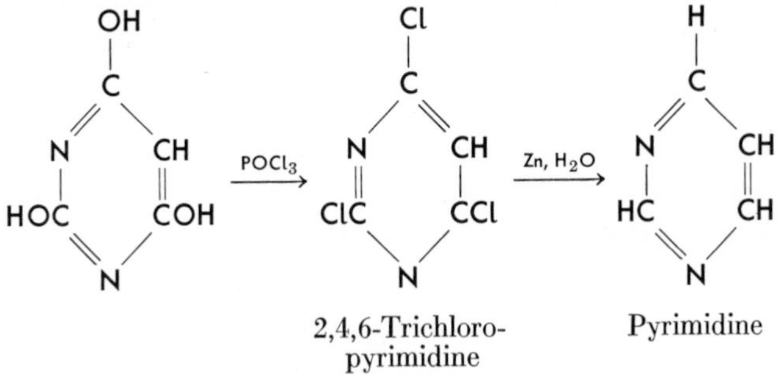

2,4,6-Trichloro-
pyrimidine   Pyrimidine

This reaction sequence establishes the fact that barbituric acid is a derivative of pyrimidine.

By using disubstituted malonic ester derivatives in the barbituric acid condensation it is possible to prepare a wide variety of hypnotic drugs which are disubstituted barbiturates. The widespread abuse of these drugs has brought about a serious problem of addiction and requires state and federal controls to prevent criminal misuse. Their cheapness and ready availability on prescription has also led to the substitution of pill-taking for the natural induction of sleep.

26–3 Pyrimidines from Nucleic Acids;
Synthesis of Uracil and Cytosine

Pyrimidine bases which have been isolated from nucleic acids are uracil, cytosine, thymine, 5-methylcytosine, and 5-hydroxymethylcytosine:

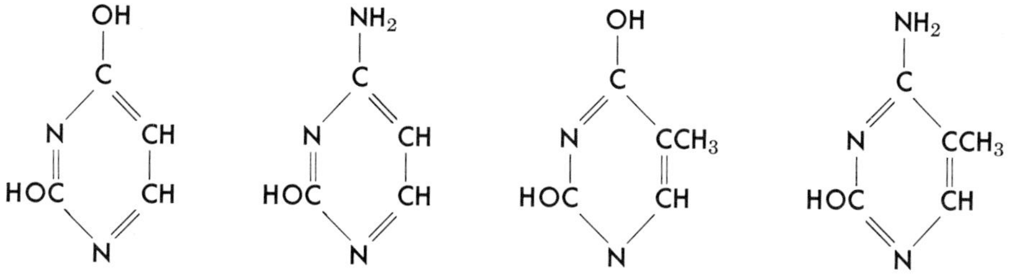

Uracil   Cytosine   Thymine   5-Methylcytosine

We shall outline the syntheses of uracil and cytosine first. The starting point is thiourea instead of urea. This may be prepared from cyanamide and hydrogen sulfide.

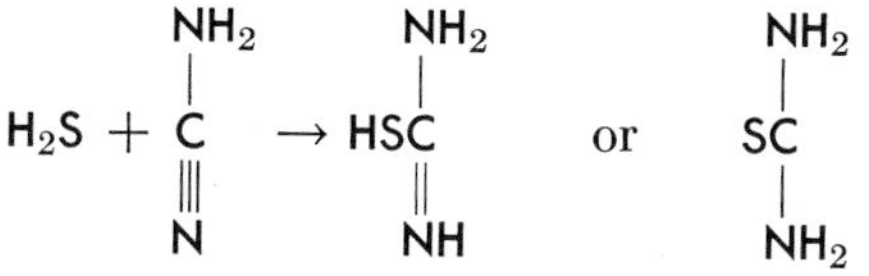

Thiourea   Thiourea
(written as
thioenol)

Alkyl iodides readily react with thiourea. The point of greatest reactivity is the sulfur atom so the reactions produce derivatives of the thioenol.

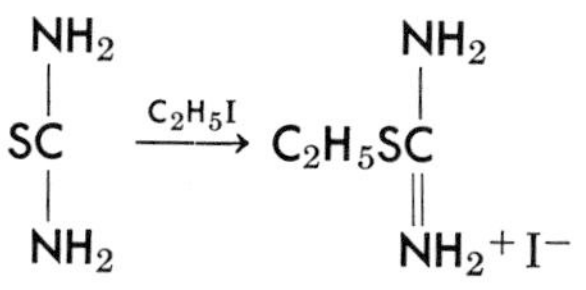

Thiourea   S-ethylthiourea
hydroiodide

The other starting material required for the synthesis is formylacetic ester. This is formed by a Claisen condensation between ethyl acetate and ethyl formate. The product of the condensation is the sodium enolate, which is always used directly in synthesis without isolation of the relatively unstable formyl ester.

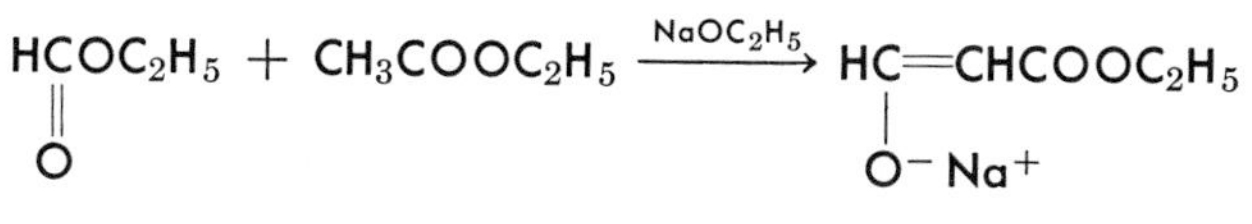

$$HCOC_2H_5 + CH_3COOC_2H_5 \xrightarrow{NaOC_2H_5} HC{=}CHCOOC_2H_5$$
$$\underset{O}{\|} \qquad\qquad\qquad\qquad\qquad\qquad \underset{O^- Na^+}{|}$$

S-Ethylthiourea and sodioformylacetic ester are then condensed with sodium ethoxide as in the preparation of barbituric acid.

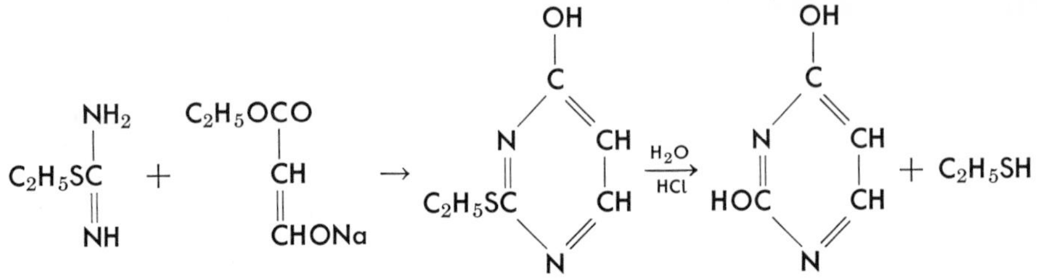

2-ethylthio-4-hydroxypyrimidine   Uracil (2,4-dihydroxy-pyrimidine)

The 2-ethylthio-4-hydroxypyrimidine formed in the preceding reactions can be converted into cytosine by a different sequence of reactions.

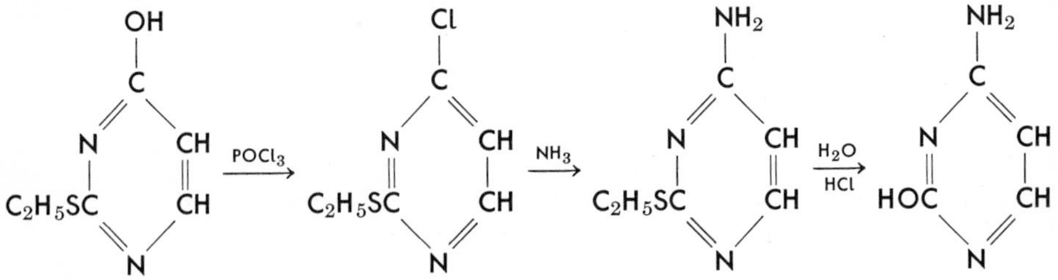

Cytosine (2-hydroxy-4-aminopyrimidine)

26–4 The Importance of Sequence in Synthesis

The planning of the foregoing syntheses should be carefully noted. As we saw in the production of pyrimidine from barbituric acid, phosphorus oxychloride replaces pyrimidine hydroxyls with chlorines. Chlorines on pyrimidine rings may then be reduced, aminated, hydrolyzed back to hydroxyls or treated with hydrogen sulfide to give thiol groups. The ethyl-thiol group, on the other hand, is not replaced by the action of phosphorus oxychloride so that it serves to protect a position at which a later reaction may be desired. While the replacement reactions in the pyrimidine series proceed much more readily than those on benzene, they usually require elevated temperatures so that the hydrolyses and aminations are frequently performed in sealed tubes under pressure. By using these reactions in different sequences, it is possible to secure a variety of different reaction products.

26–5 Thymine and 5-Methylcytosine

Thymine is 5-methyluracil. A small change in the starting materials permits the same reaction sequences to be used for the production of thymine and 5-methyl-

cytosine as were used in the production of uracil and cytosine.   The required
starting material is formylpropionic ester (a).

CH₃ │ HC═CCOOC₂H₅ │ O⁻ Na⁺	OH │ C (ring)	NH₂ │ C (ring)
Sodioformyl- propionic ester (a)	Thymine (5-methyluracil) (b)	5-methyl- cytosine (c)

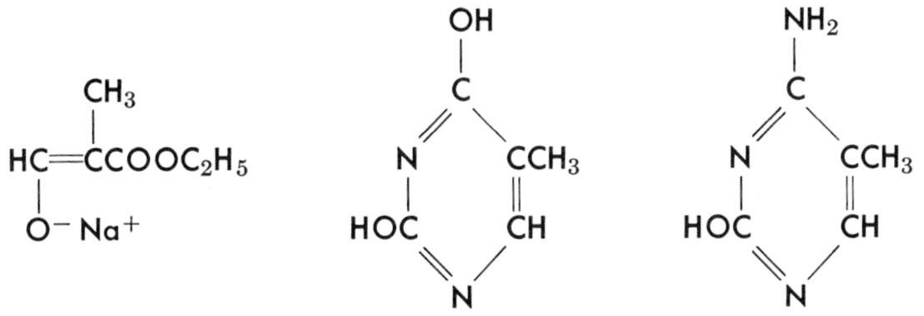

The reader should suggest a method for preparing this starting material and
outline the steps required for the synthesis of thymine (b) and 5-methylcytosine (c).

26–6   Purine Structures

The first of the purines to be isolated was uric acid, prepared in 1776 by Scheele
from urinary stones.   It is known to be one of the end products of protein metabolism.   The monosodium salt forms sharp needlelike crystals which deposit in the
joints in cases of gout and cause intense pain.   The analysis and empirical formula
for uric acid were completed in 1834 before the introduction of the Dumas procedure
for nitrogen analysis.   Uric acid, along with some similarly constituted compounds,
gives grossly erroneous analytical results with the Dumas procedure, so this is a
fortunate circumstance.   The empirical formula was established by Liebig and
Mitscherlich as $C_5H_4N_4O_3$.   The structure is indicated by the nature of the oxidation products obtained with nitric acid.

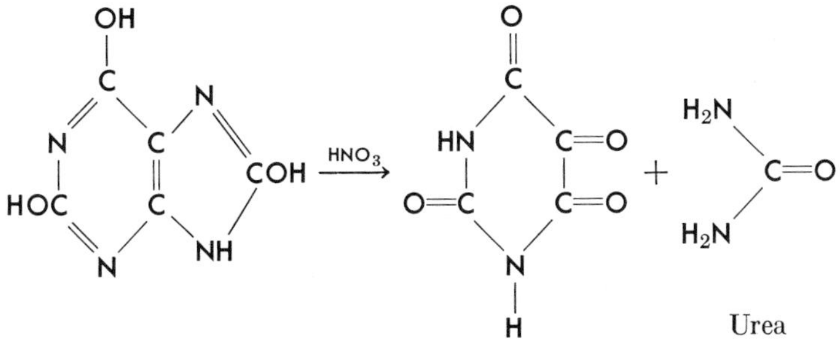

Alloxan

Urea

Alloxan is of interest because its ingestion causes the production of artificial
diabetes.

26-7   The Synthesis of Uric Acid

The methods used for the synthesis of purines are, in general, a result of the studies of Traube. The plan is to produce a suitably substituted diaminopyrimidine and then condense the amino groups with a derivative of formic acid to give the imidazole ring. Following this scheme, uric acid can be prepared from urea and cyanoacetic ester.

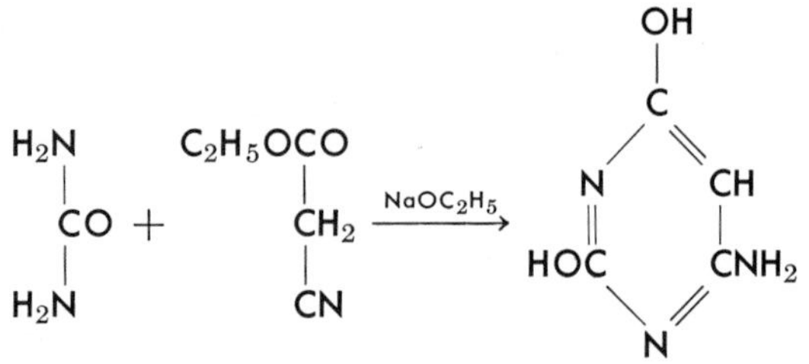

2,3-dihydroxy-6-
aminopyrimidine
(6-aminouracil)

The normal reaction of an aliphatic amino group with nitrous acid is a deamination reaction.

$$CH_3NH_2 + HNO_2 = CH_3OH + N_2 + H_2O$$

In the aromatic series, the normal reaction is diazotization.

$$C_6H_5NH_2 + HNO_2 + HCl \rightarrow C_6H_5N_2{}^+ Cl^- + 2H_2O$$

In the pyrimidine series, neither of these reactions occurs readily. It is a peculiarity of pyrimidines, including aminopyrimidines, that *substitution* on the 5-position takes place more readily with nitrous acid than any other reaction. As a result, nitrosation can be used as a preliminary step to the introduction of an amino group.

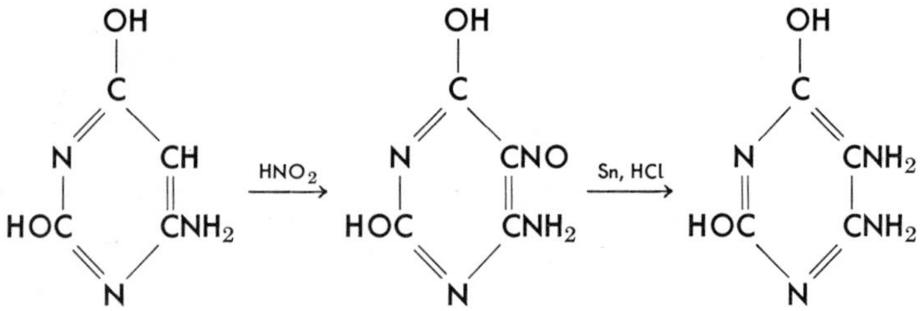

5,6-diaminouracil

Condensation of 5,6-diaminouracil with ethyl chloroformate gives a urethane whose sodium salt, on heating, is converted to uric acid:

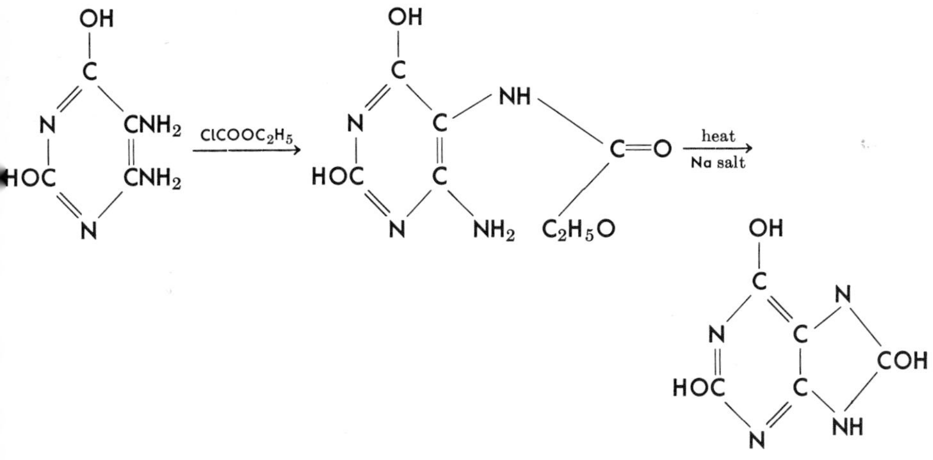

Uric acid

26–8 Caffeine

The use of 5,6-diaminouracil as a valuable intermediate in the synthesis of other purine bases is of general interest. For example, caffeine, the stimulating drug present in coffee, can be prepared from it. The purpose of the bromination is to direct the methylation to the 7-position. In the absence of the bromine, methylation would take place on the 9-position.

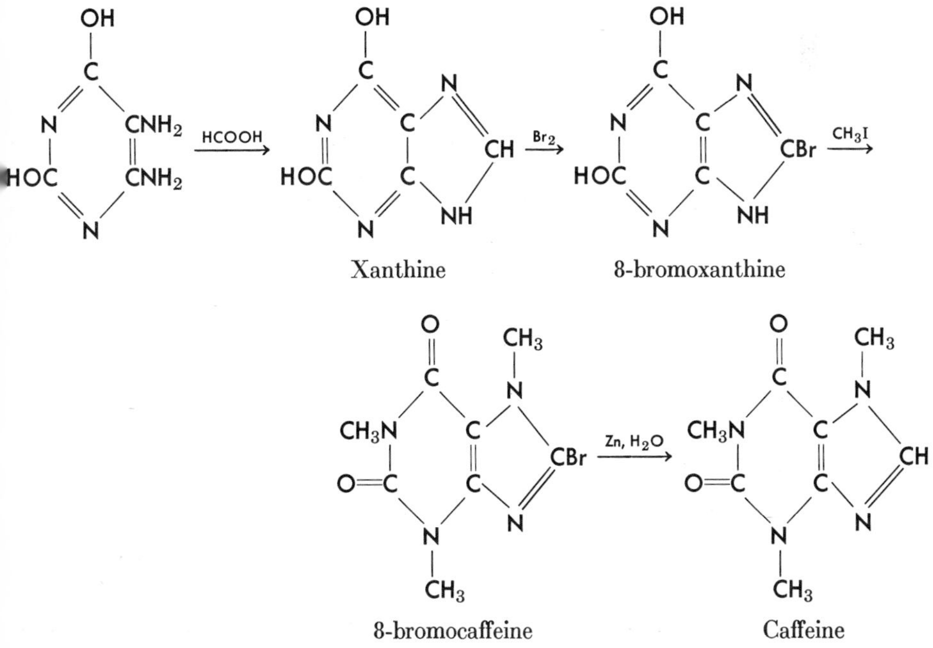

Xanthine   8-bromoxanthine

8-bromocaffeine   Caffeine

26–9 Purines from Nucleic Acids; Synthesis of Adenine and Guanine

The two purines which occur in nucleic acids are adenine and guanine. A mode of adenine is shown in Fig. 26–1.

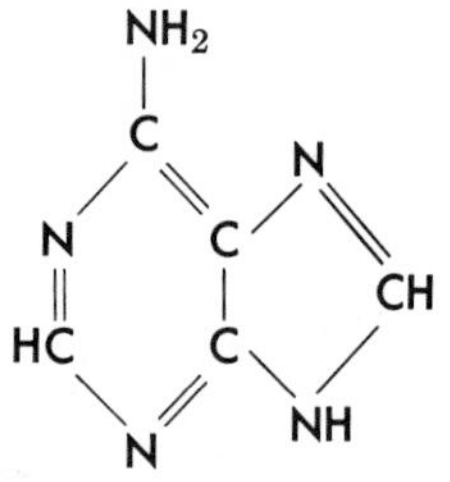

Adenine 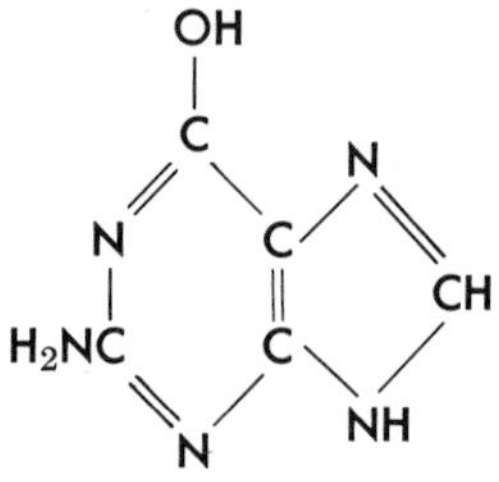   Guanine

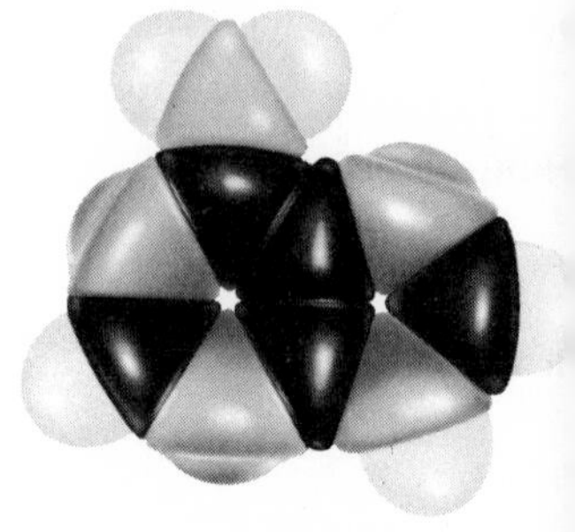

FIGURE 26–1

The structure of adenine is established as 6-aminopurine by the synthesis, starting from thiourea and malononitrile.

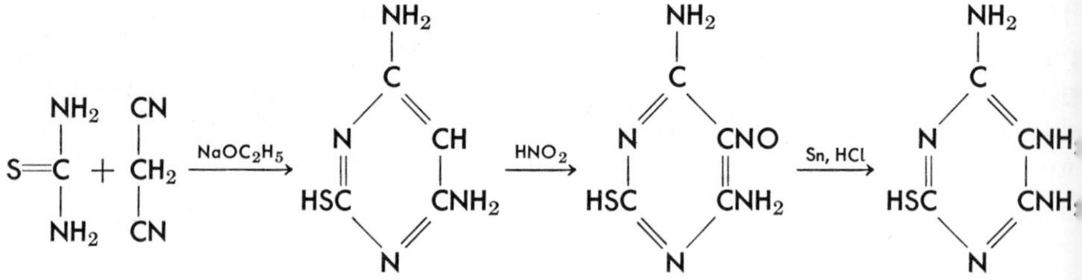

2-thio-4,6-diamino-
pyrimidine

2-thio-4,5,6-tri-
aminopyrimidine

The next step in the synthesis is the condensation with formic acid. Since 2-thio-4,5,6-triaminopyrimidine is a symmetrical molecule, it does not matter whether the condensation is represented as taking place between the amino groups in positions 4 and 5 or between those in positions 5 and 6, the product will be the same. By convention, this is represented as a condensation between positions 4 and 5.

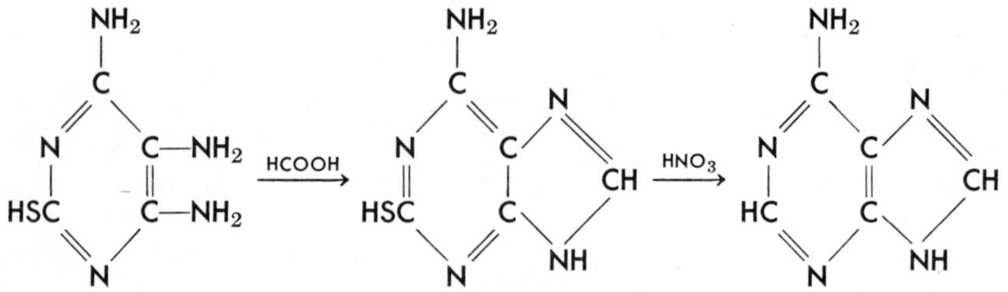

2-thioadenine   Adenine

Guanine is 2-amino-6-hydroxypurine. Its structure can also be confirmed by reference to its synthesis. This starts with guanidine and cyanoacetic ester. Since the condensing agent used in the synthesis is sodium ethoxide, an even more powerful base than sodium hydroxide, the proton giving the guanidinium ion a positive charge is removed in this highly basic medium.

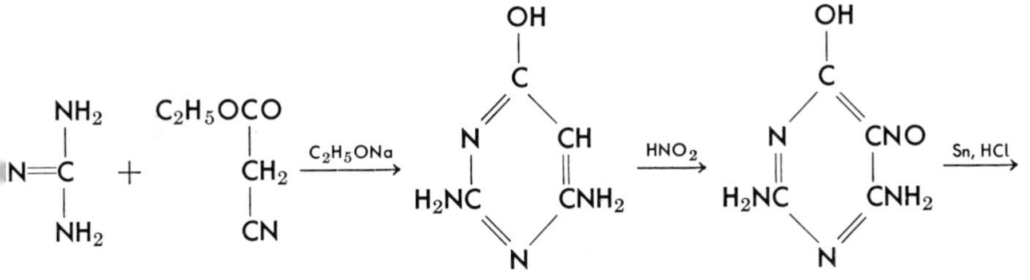

2,4-diamino-6-
hydroxypyrimidine

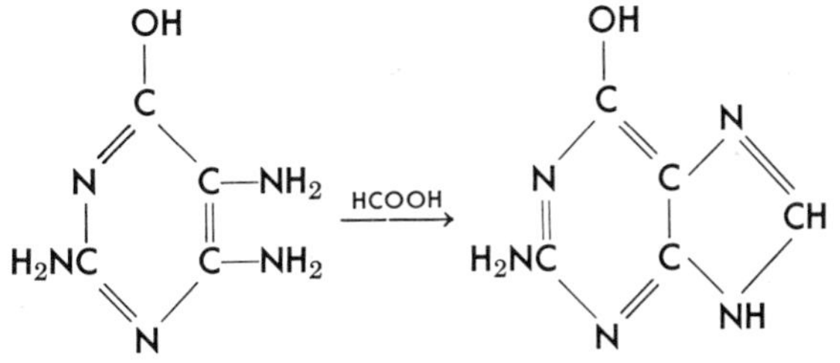

Guanine

6-10   Identification of Pyrimidines and Purines

Some of the most interesting pyrimidines and most of the purines do not possess reversible melting points. The usual criteria of identity and purity used by the organic chemist fail in these cases and reliance must be placed on other methods. Some of these are less conclusive than the use of melting points, especially with respect to purity. For example, elementary analysis is widely used for identification in this field. As we have pointed out, nitrogen analyses of purines in particular are not reliable and, in general, the analytical methods used are not of sufficient discrimination to detect impurities which may be present. Gulland has found that identifications may frequently be secured by a comparison of the crystal forms of the perchlorates. This is one of the quickest and most convenient methods for the identification of purines. It must be used with caution, however, since perchlorates are notorious for their tendency to explode on heating. In general, only the tiny samples actually needed for comparisons are converted to the perchlorates. More recently, infrared spectra have been used for comparisons between samples of these substances. These leave something to be desired, however, because of the difficulties which are encountered in the interpretation of the infrared spectra of the naturally occurring hydroxy and amino purines and pyrimidines.

In the foregoing presentation, we have represented the pyrimidines and the purines as though they were fully "aromatic" structures with cyclic conjugated systems. While this system fits the prejudices of the organic chemist, it is by no means certain that it is in accord with the facts. Evidence exists favoring each of the alternative tautomeric forms. A substance like caffeine, which cannot have an aromatic structure, appears to be quite as stable as xanthine, which can. Infrared spectra, which might be expected to settle the question, have proved to be inconclusive, with one set of investigators disagreeing with the interpretations of another set.

26–11 The Point of Sugar Attachment in Nucleosides

Incomplete hydrolysis of nucleic acids may be conducted so as to yield pyrimidine and purine glycosides. These substances are called *nucleosides*. For the purine nucleosides, the point of attachment of the sugar residues was in doubt for a long period of time. It was known that the point of attachment must be either the 7- or the 9-position but means for deciding between the two proved elusive. The problem was finally solved by the use of ultraviolet absorption spectra. Reference compounds were prepared in which the method of preparation established 7-substitution in one case and 9-substitution in the other. On examination it was found that the two types of reference compounds had characteristically different absorption spectra.

26–12 Structure of 7-Methyladenine

We shall first study the evidence that is used to establish the position of the methyl group in 7-methyladenine. The first reference compound is uramil, prepared from alloxan.

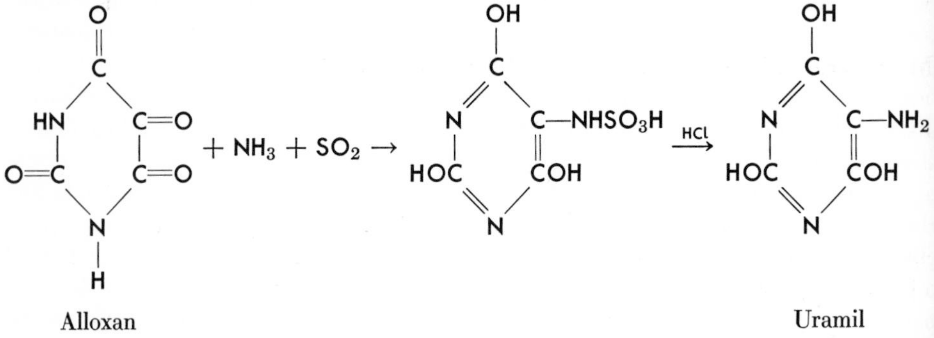

Alloxan   Uramil

The synthesis from alloxan does not establish the position of the amino group in uramil. This was established by an alternative synthesis from barbituric acid:

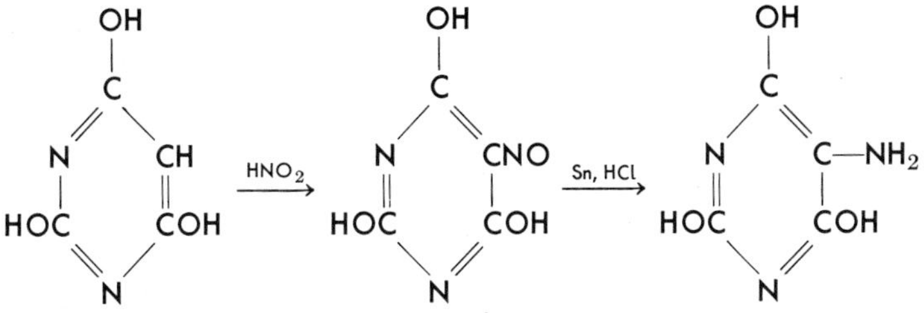

Barbituric
acid

Uramil

The condensation with alloxan can now be used on methylamine instead of ammonia to introduce a methylamino group for the reference compound for 7-methyladenine.

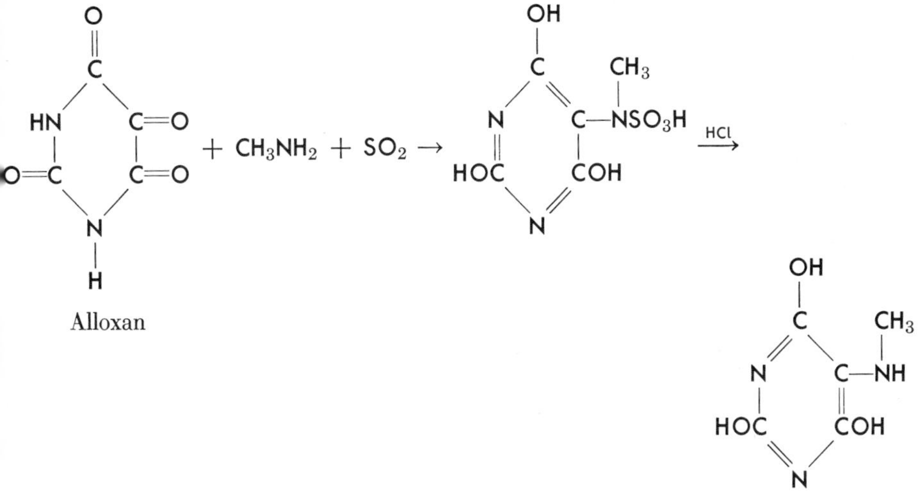

$+ CH_3NH_2 + SO_2 \rightarrow$

Alloxan

Methyluramil

Methyluramil is now converted into 7-methyluric acid.

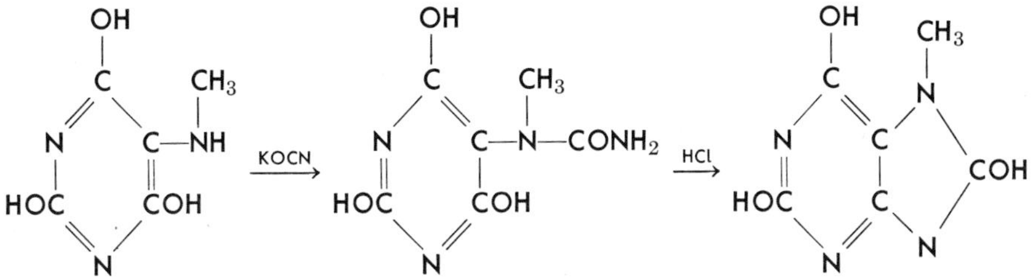

7-methyluric acid

Theobromine, the characteristic stimulating drug of cocoa, can be converted to 7-methyluric acid, thus establishing the 7-substitution in theobromine.

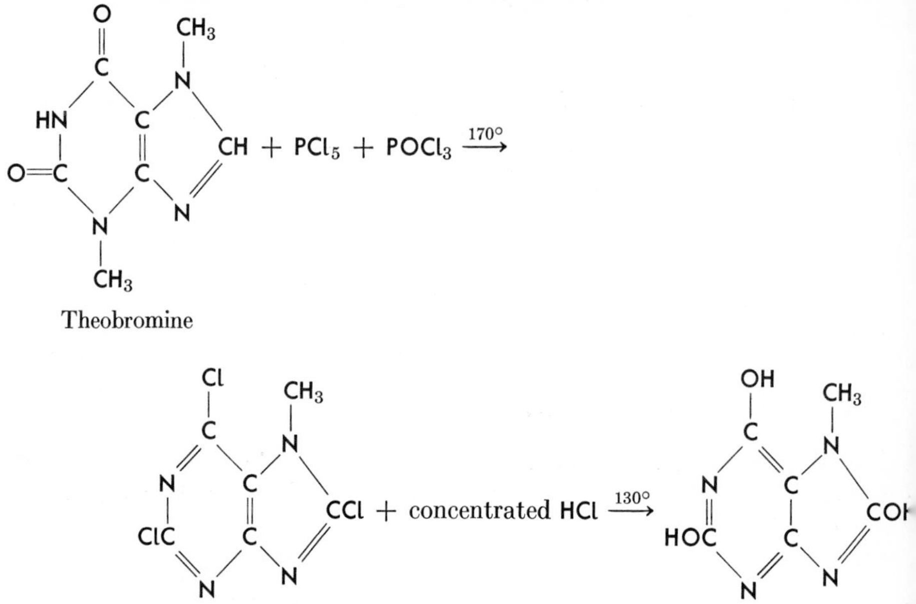

Theobromine

7-methyluric acid

Finally, theobromine can be converted into 7-methyladenine.

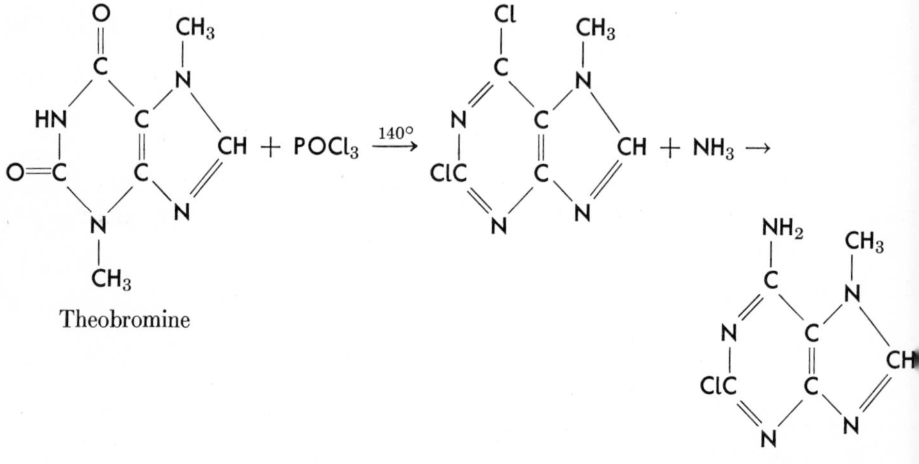

Theobromine

2-chloro-6-amino-
7-methylpurine

Characteristically, the chloro substituent in the 6-position is more reactive than that in the 2-position.   Reaction under more drastic conditions could replace both. Reduction of the remaining chloro substituent gives 7-methyladenine:

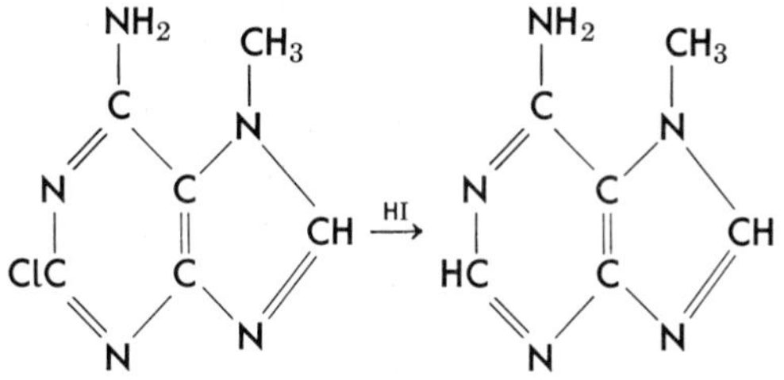

7-methyladenine

The synthetic intercomparisons establish the fact that the methyl group is in position 7.

26–13   Structure of 9-Methyladenine

The other reference compound needed for the structural comparison is 9-methyladenine. This can be prepared directly from adenine by methylation with methyl iodide.

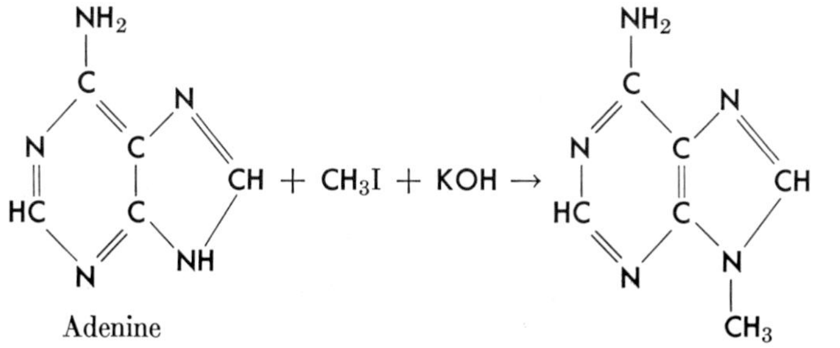

Adenine   9-methyladenine

This method of synthesis does not establish the structure of the compound. Structural comparisons were made with 9-methyluric acid as the reference compound. This was also prepared by direct methylation.

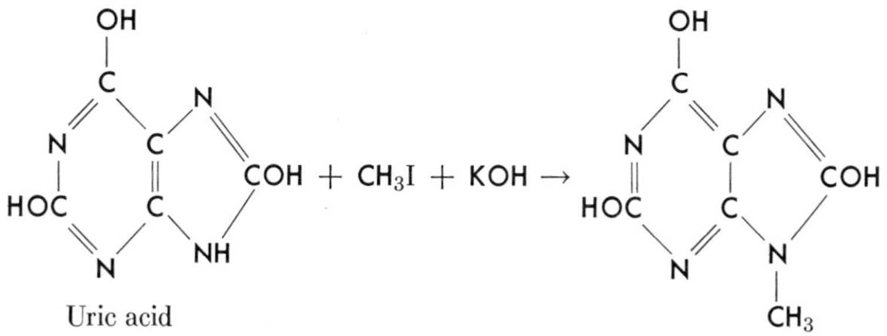

Uric acid

9-methyluric acid

Oxidation of 9-methyluric acid with chlorine water gives alloxan and mono-methyl urea.

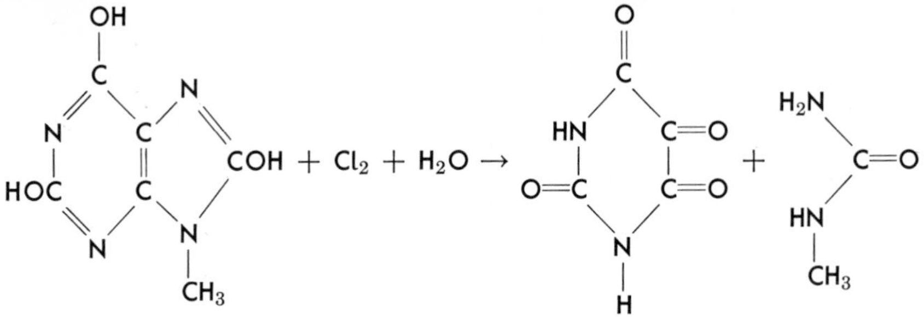

9-methyluric acid   Alloxan   Methylurea

The formation of methylurea shows that the methyl group added by direct alkylation went into the imidazole ring. Since 7-methyluric acid has already been prepared and this substance is different, it must be 9-methyluric acid. The final step in the comparison is the preparation of 9-methyladenine from 9-methyluric acid.

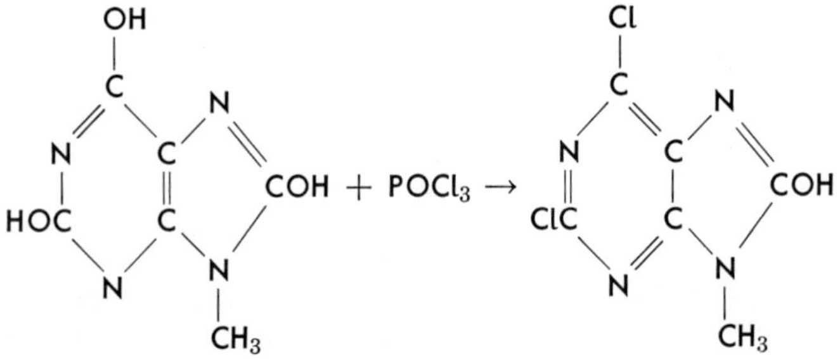

9-methyluric acid   2,6-dichloro-8-hydroxy-9-methylpurine

The hydroxyl group in the imidazole ring is characteristically more difficult to replace with chlorine than are those in the pyrimidine ring. By using minimum reaction conditions, a selective reaction can be achieved. The greater reactivity of the 6-position is used to introduce the amino group at the desired position.

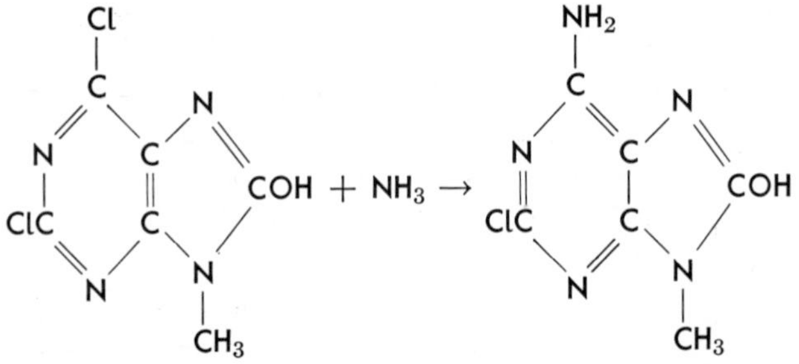

2-chloro-6-amino-8-hydroxy-9-methylpurine

The next step is to replace the 8-hydroxy by a chloro substituent, so that both protective chloro substituents can be removed.

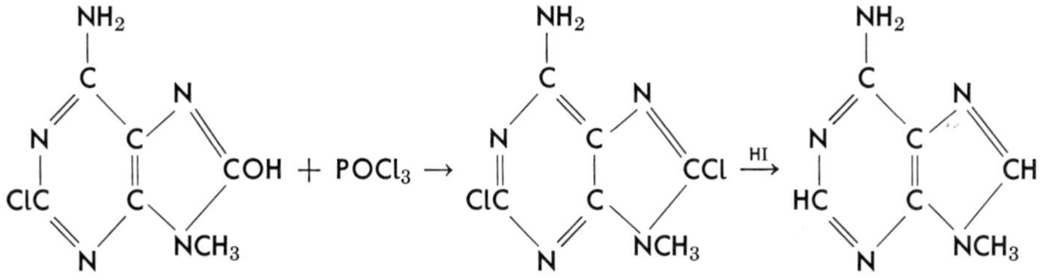

9-methyladenine

With both 7-methyladenine and 9-methyladenine available as reference compounds and with their structures established, intercomparisons could be instituted. It was found that adenosine, one of the nucleosides obtained by partial hydrolysis of nucleic acids, had an ultraviolet absorption spectrum identical to that of 9-methyladenine and differing markedly from that of 7-methyladenine. On this evidence, the linkage of the sugar residue in adenosine was assigned to the 9-position.

PROBLEMS

26–1   Derivatives of barbituric acid with two substituents in the 5-position have been used as depressants for the central nervous system. The first of these, 5,5-diethylbarbituric acid, has been superseded by 5-ethyl-5-phenylbarbituric acid and other derivatives as a sedative and for treatment of epilepsy.

An example of a drug of intermediate duration is 5-ethyl-5-n-butylbarbituric acid. One which is cleared rapidly by the body is 5-ethyl-5-α-methylbutyl-2-thiobarbituric acid, whose sodium salt is the standard drug for intravenous induction of general anesthesia, sodium pentothal.

Show how each of these could be synthesized, starting with urea or thiourea and other materials available in the laboratory, such as malonic ester and alkyl halides.

26–2   Theophylline is found together with caffeine in tea leaves. It has a structure similar to that of caffeine except that it lacks a methyl group in the 7-position. Develop a synthesis of this material, using 1,3-dimethylurea, $CH_3NHCONHCH_3$, as a starting material.

26–3   Hypoxanthine, 6-hydroxypurine, has been found in vegetable and animal tissue, and is a growth factor (vitamin) for some unicellular organisms. Develop a synthesis for it making use of a desulfurization reaction with nitric acid.

26–4   Vicine is a glycoside found in vetch (*Vicia sativa*) and other leguminous plants. Hydrolysis of vicine yields D-glucose and divicine, a substituted pyrimidine believed to be responsible for the toxicity of vetch to chickens. Divicine has the empirical formula $C_4H_6O_2N_4$ and resisted attempts at synthesis until the proper protective groups were used.

The final synthesis began with glycollonitrile, $HOCH_2C{\equiv}N$, which was protected by the use of dihydropyran as shown below.

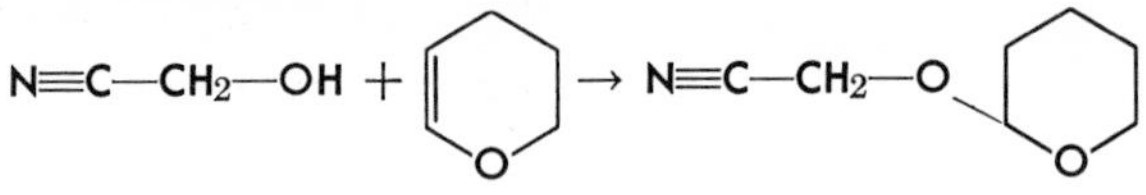

$$N{\equiv}C-CH_2-OH + \text{(dihydropyran)} \rightarrow N{\equiv}C-CH_2-O\text{(tetrahydropyranyl)}$$

(a) What kind of link is formed in the protecting group?

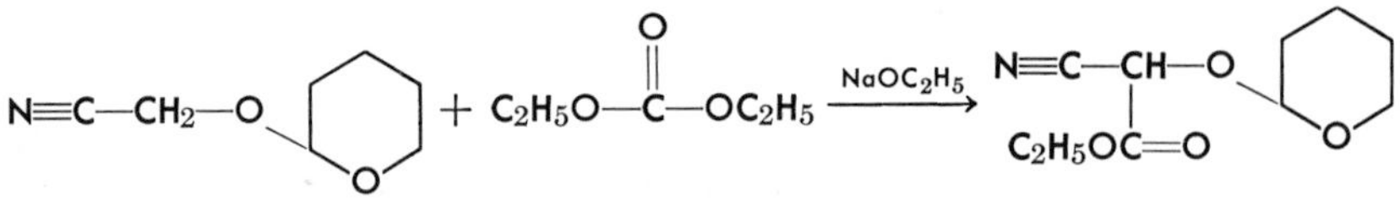

$$N{\equiv}C-CH_2-O\text{(pyranyl)} + C_2H_5O-\overset{\overset{O}{\|}}{C}-OC_2H_5 \xrightarrow{NaOC_2H_5} \begin{array}{c} N{\equiv}C-CH-O\text{(pyranyl)} \\ | \\ C_2H_5O\overset{}{C}{=}O \end{array}$$

Ethyl carbonate

(b) How could ethyl carbonate have been prepared from phosgene?

(c) Show that this condensation resembles other condensations of active methylene groups.

The product was then condensed with guanidine in the same reaction mixture.

(d) What was the structure of the product?

The protecting group was removed with aqueous acetic acid to yield divicine, a diamino-dihydroxypyrimidine.

(e) What is the structure of divicine?

(f) Other syntheses failed because the protecting group (an alkyl group in these cases) could not be hydrolyzed. Why was the group used in this synthesis useful? Cite analogies from previous chapters.

(g) What other protecting group, removable by catalytic hydrogenolysis, might have been used in the synthesis?

Methylation of vicine and hydrolysis yields 2,3,4,6-tetramethylglucose. A beta linkage was supported by the data from other tests.

Vicine is hydrolyzed by emulsin; treatment with periodic acid consumes two moles of the reagent and produces about one mole of formic acid, but no formaldehyde. The ultra-violet spectrum of vicine indicates that the 5-position is "blocked," that is, the H of this substituent is replaced by another group.

(h) What is the structure of vicine?

How may the nature of the linkages in the larger fragments
of nucleic acids be demonstrated? What chemical
evidence exists for the structures of the nucleic acids
themselves? What other types of evidence
contribute to our knowledge of these structures?

27

NUCLEIC ACIDS II: THE STRUCTURES OF NUCLEOSIDES, NUCLEOTIDES, AND NUCLEIC ACIDS

27–1 The Nucleosides

The characteristic sugars found in nucleic acids are ribose and 2-deoxyribose. Hydrolysis of nucleic acids at elevated temperatures under pressure, slightly on the alkaline side, yields the ribosides of the pyrimidine and purine bases whose structures were examined in the preceding chapter.

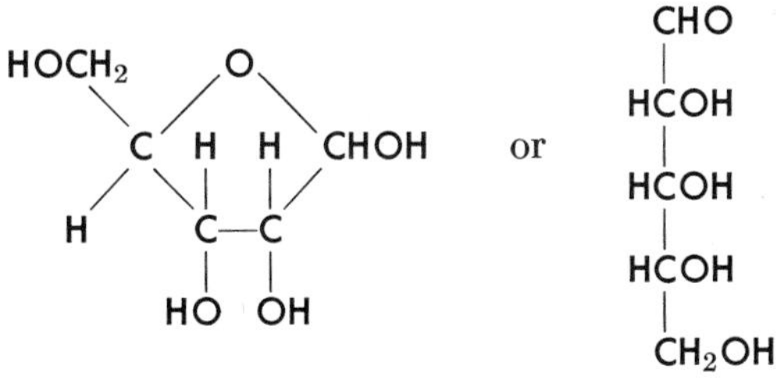

D-(−)-ribose

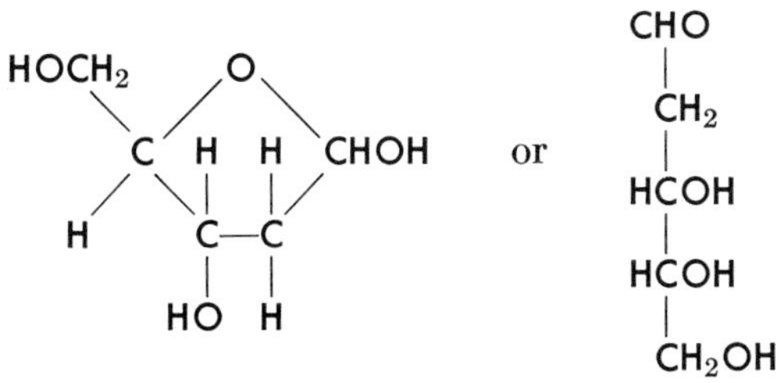

D-(−)-2-deoxyribose

Deoxyribose is not stable under these conditions and the deoxyribosides must be isolated by enzymatic hydrolyses. These base-sugar compounds from nucleic acids belong to the category of *nucleosides*.

27–2   Structures of the Nucleosides

Treatment of ribosides or deoxyribosides with triphenylmethyl chloride gives trityl derivatives in each instance, so that all the nucleosides formed by the degradation of nucleic acids have their primary alcohol groups free. This, in turn, implies that the rings are furanose rings. That they are not four-membered rings was established by methylation procedures. Levene and his collaborators, for example, showed that adenosine (Fig. 27–1), on methylation and subsequent oxidation, gave dimethoxysuccinic acid. It was found that an aqueous solution of adenosine was not suitable for the methylation procedure but that fully acetylated adenosine could be dissolved in acetone and, on treatment with a large excess of dimethyl sulfate and alkali, replacement of the acetyl groups by methyl groups could be accomplished without hydrolysis of the sugar to base linkage. Tetramethyladenosine was formed by the methylation and isolated as its hydrochloride. This was then hydrolyzed by acid to give trimethyl-ribose, as shown on p. 365.

FIGURE 27–1

Earlier work had established that the methylation of ribose gives 2,3,4-trimethyl-ribose, after hydrolysis of the glycosidic methyl group. This establishes the fact that ribose normally is a pyranose sugar. The trimethylribose obtained from the methylation of adenosine, however, proved to be different from that obtained directly from ribose. Oxidation of the 2,3,4-trimethylribose obtained from ribose gave exclusively trimethoxyglutaric acid. The oxidation of the other trimethyl-ribose, obtained from adenosine, was carried out in stages as shown below.

$$CH_3OCH_2 \xrightarrow{Br_2/H_2O} CH_3OCH_2 \xrightarrow{HNO_3} COOH$$

Trimethylribose   Trimethylribonolactone   Dimethoxysuccinic acid

No trimethoxyglutaric acid was formed in this reaction and the dimethoxysuccinic

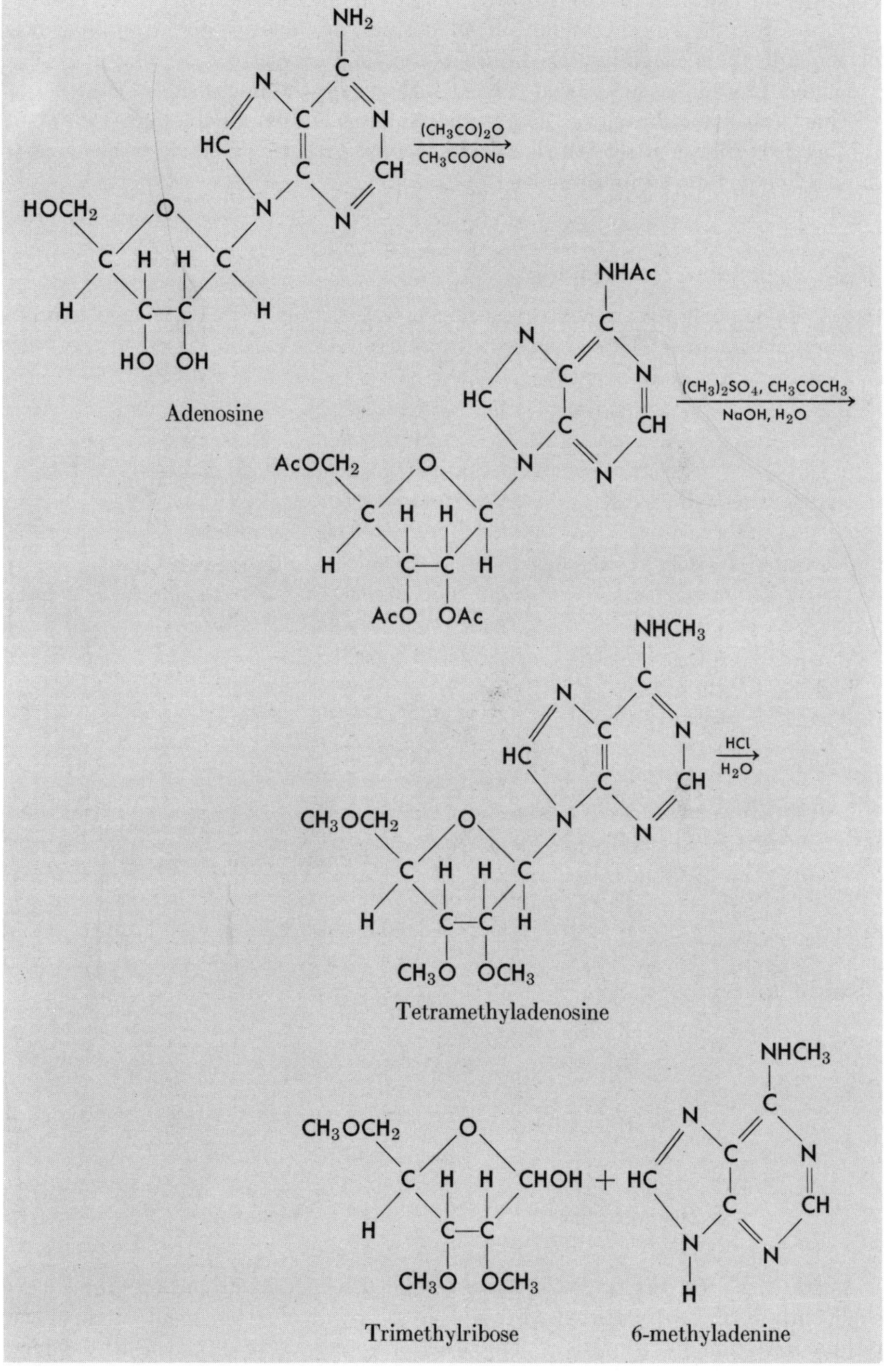

Adenosine

$$\xrightarrow[\text{CH}_3\text{COONa}]{(\text{CH}_3\text{CO})_2\text{O}}$$

$$\xrightarrow[\text{NaOH, H}_2\text{O}]{(\text{CH}_3)_2\text{SO}_4,\ \text{CH}_3\text{COCH}_3}$$

$$\xrightarrow[\text{H}_2\text{O}]{\text{HCl}}$$

Tetramethyladenosine

Trimethylribose + 6-methyladenine

acid was the expected inactive isomer. These circumstances establish the furanose structure for the ribose residue on adenosine and identify the trimethylribose obtained in the methylation procedure as the 2,3,5-derivative.

Similar procedures have been carried through on the nucleosides from each of the purine bases and each of the pyrimidine bases and on all the nucleosides containing deoxyribose instead of ribose. In each case, the sugar residue was found to have a five-membered furanose ring.

27–3   Pyrimidine Nucleosides

The most important pyrimidine nucleosides are cytidine, uridine, deoxycytidine and thymidine.

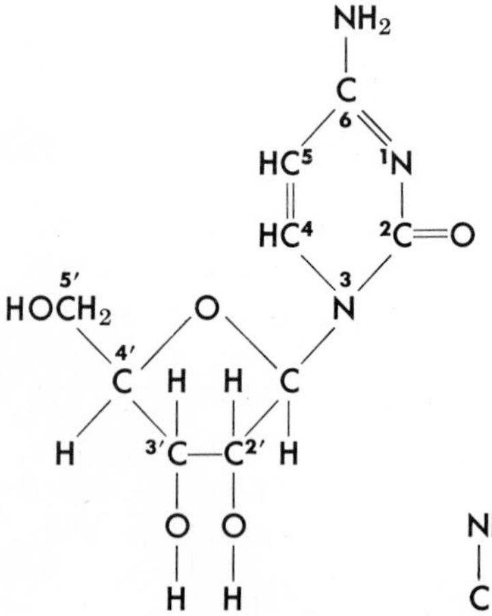

Cytidine

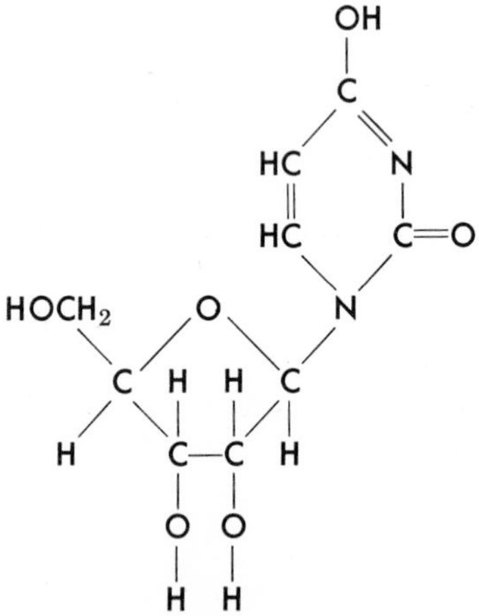

Uridine

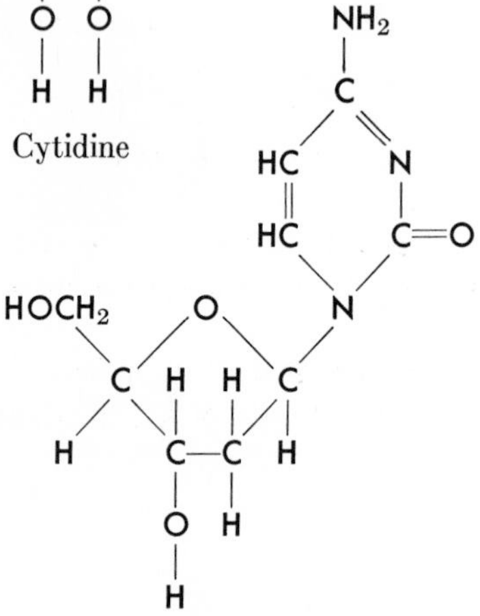

Deoxycytidine

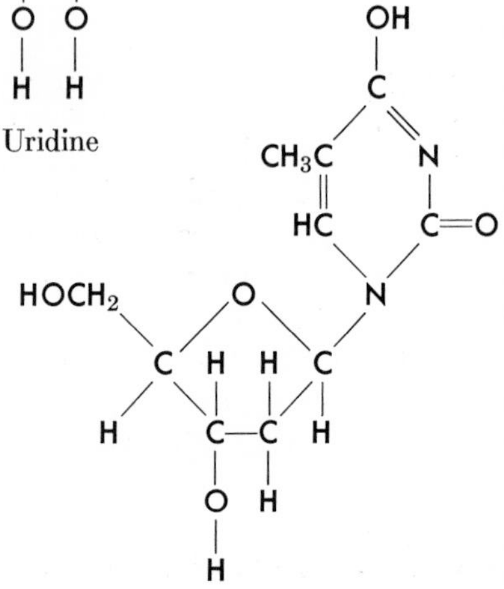

Thymidine

As stated above, the ring size was established by methylation procedures. We shall outline the method used to establish the point of attachment of the sugar residue in cytidine and uridine. The other structures were established by similar methods.

Reaction of cytidine with nitrous acid gives deamination to uridine.

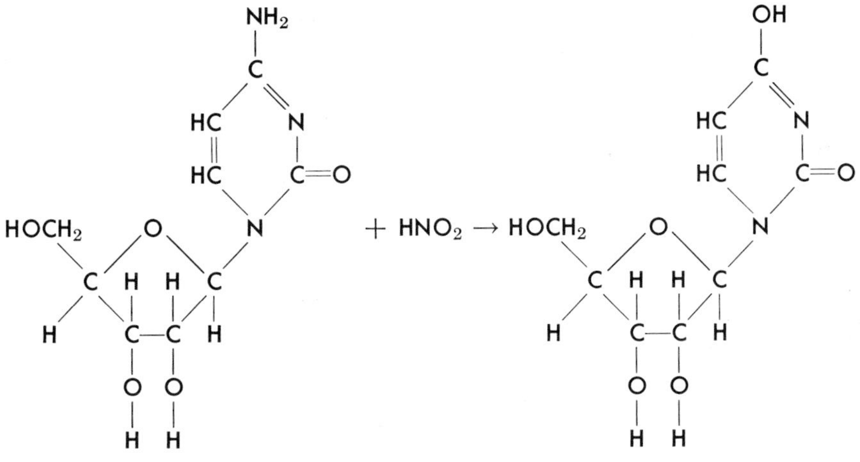

Cytidine   Uridine

This shows that both cytidine and uridine are similarly constituted with respect to both the position and the nature of the sugar substituent. It also shows that the sugar is not attached to the nitrogen in the 6-position, which was lost in the deamination reaction.

Methylation of uridine yields an N-methyluridine which can be hydrolyzed to 1-methyluracil, whose structure was established by synthesis. This eliminates the 1-position from consideration for the attachment of the sugar residue. Nitration of uridine can be conducted to give 5-nitrouridine and bromination gives 5-bromouridine. In each case, subsequent hydrolysis yields the corresponding 5-substituted uracil, showing that the sugar is not attached to the 5-position. Bromination of uridine followed by treatment with phenylhydrazine leads to a uridine derivative with both the 4-position and the 5-position substituted by phenylhydrazine groups. This eliminates the 4-position from consideration. The only position remaining is the 3-position. For this reason, both uridine and cytidine are assigned the structures of 3-glycosides.

It should be pointed out that for the pyrimidines, substitution on one of the nitrogens forces the oxygen into a keto form. X-ray studies of the bond distances in these compounds substantiate this conclusion.

27–4   Structures of Nucleotides

Hydrolysis of nucleic acids at elevated temperatures produces the nucleosides whose structures have just been discussed. If, however, hydrolysis is conducted either with acid or with alkali at room temperature, a less degraded series of products is obtained, the nucleotides. These substances are base-sugar-phosphoric acid derivatives. Nucleotides may also be prepared by enzymatic hydrolysis of nucleic acids. This is the method chosen for the preparation of nucleotides containing deoxyribose, since the glycosidic linkage to the deoxy sugar is very labile to acid and much too stable to alkalis for satisfactory hydrolysis.

The ribose nucleotides have three hydroxyl groups on which esterification with phosphoric acid could take place. Only two positions are available in deoxyribose nucleotides, however, the 3'- and 5'-positions. Adenylic acid, a nucleotide, can be obtained from muscle by means indicating that it is not a nucleic acid degradation product. The structure of this compound was shown to be the 5'-phosphoric ester of adenosine. Adenylic acid obtained from the nucleic acid of yeast was shown by Levene and Harris to be different from muscle adenylic acid. They undertook a systematic degradation of this substance and established its structure. The first step was the deamination of the 6-position with nitrous acid, yielding a 6-hydroxy compound, called inosinic acid. Acid hydrolysis of inosinic acid gave hypoxanthine and a ribose phosphate. Catalytic reduction of the ribose phosphate gave a ribitol phosphate.

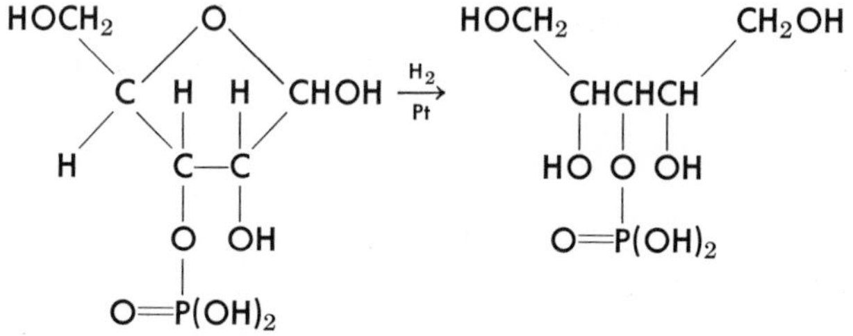

$$\text{Ribose-3-phosphate} \xrightarrow[\text{Pt}]{H_2} \text{Ribitol-3-phosphate}$$

The observation that the ribitol phosphate formed in this manner is optically inactive established the fact that the substitution is in the 3'-position.

27–5 Interconversion of Phosphates

Later work on the hydrolysis of nucleic acids has shown that adenylic acids substituted in either the 2'-position or the 3'-position can be obtained. This discovery was followed by the disturbing observation that the 2'-phosphate is converted to the 3'-phosphate in acid solution, and vice versa. Brown and Todd suggested that this interconversion could proceed through a cyclic phosphate, shown below, which they proceeded to synthesize. The R-groups used in the syntheses were such that cyclic nucleotides of adenosine, cytidine, and uridine were produced. It is easy to see how this complication could cause confusion concerning the possible position of esterification of the sugar in the nucleotides. Fortunately, however, enzymatic hydrolysis is not subject to the same complication, and the enzyme used in most of this work, ribonuclease, is unable to hydrolyze the cyclic esters. By repeating the work on enzymatically produced nucleotides, it was established that the 3-position originally assigned by Levene and Harris is the correct one.

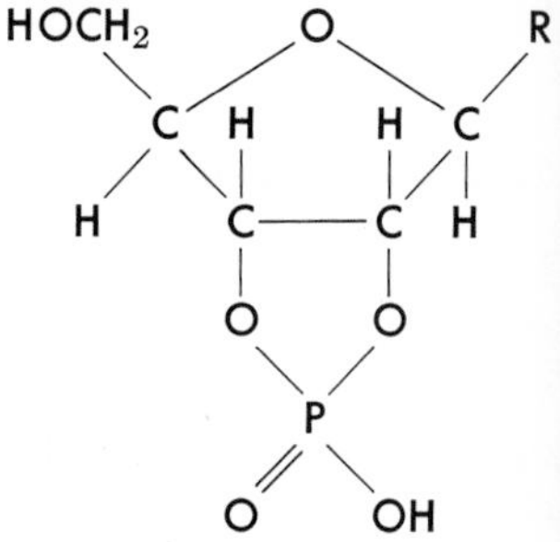

27-6   Linkages Present in Nucleic Acids

By the substitution of enzymes purified from snake venoms, nucleic acids may be hydrolyzed to produce 5′-phosphates, substituted similarly to muscle adenylic acid. These linkages are ordinarily broken in the chemical hydrolyses and in hydrolyses by ribonuclease. Their production by snake venom enzymes, however, shows that they are present in the nucleic acid molecules and leads to the formulation of the nucleic acid chain as one in which successive sugar residues are joined by phosphoric acid residues from the 3′-position of one sugar to the 5′-position of the next and so on. This leads us to a further consideration of the structures of nucleic acids.

27-7   Structural Evidence from Analysis

Nucleic acids are of two types, those containing only ribose as the sugar, the ribose nucleic acid group, called RNA, and those containing only deoxyribose as the sugar, the deoxyribose nucleic acid group, called DNA. On complete hydrolysis, the RNA group yields the purine bases adenine and guanine and the pyrimidine bases cytosine and uracil. The DNA group, on the other hand, yields the same two purines but the pyrimidines are cytosine and thymine, together with some 5-methylcytosine. Quantitative analysis has shown that for each base there is one sugar and one phosphoric acid residue, within the limits of error of the analytical methods employed. The hydrolytic methods which have been reviewed have shown that each sugar is attached to two phosphate groups and each phosphate to two sugars and that phosphates do not attach to the bases. Finally, examination by the usual physical methods establishes the fact that the nucleic acids are substances of extremely high molecular weight. Taken together, this indicates that the repeating unit in the chain making up the nucleic acids is (sugar-phosphoric acid)$_n$. This repeating unit then has base groups attached as substituents, one base to each sugar.

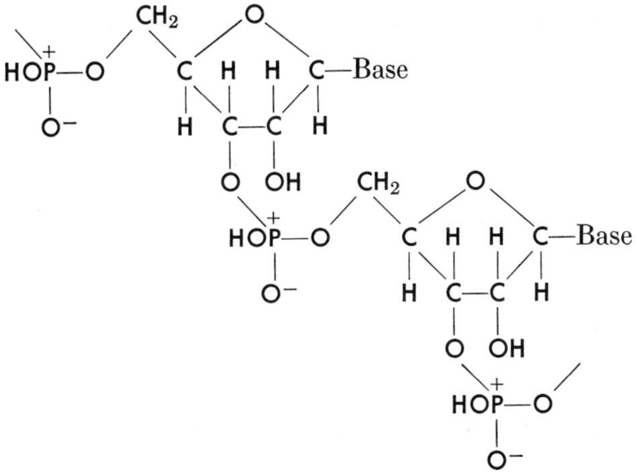

Section of nucleic acid chain

Chemical analysis for the exact amounts of the various bases present produced an unexpected result. In a series of thirty analyses, the value for adenine ranged from a low of 13.4% to a high of 31.2%, but the ratio of adenine to thymine ranged only from a low of 0.94 to a high of 1.08. The values for guanine ranged from a low of 17.0% to a high of 23.5%, but the ratio of guanine to the sum of cytosine and 5-methylcytosine ranged only from a low of 0.95 to a high of 1.15. On this basis, it has been postulated that for every adenine there is one thymine, and for every guanine there is either a cytosine or a 5-methylcytosine. Analyses by Bendich and his collaborators on fractions obtained by the degradation of calf thymus, however, showed much wider variations in these ratios than the whole acids. The ratio of adenine to thymine varied from a low of 0.99 to a high of 1.14 and the ratio of guanine to cytosine from 0.75 to 1.00. The exact significance of the fractionation which took place has yet to be determined.

27–8 Structural Evidence from Partial Hydrolysis

By allowing pancreatic deoxyribonuclease to act on DNA for a time insufficient to bring about complete hydrolysis, Sinsheimer and Koerner were able to obtain dinucleotides, in much the same way that Fischer earlier had obtained dipeptides from proteins. The dinucleotides were separated and purified by ion-exchange chromatography. Representing the five possible deoxyribonucleosides by their initials: A for deoxyadenosine, G for deoxyguanosine, C for deoycytidine, T for thymidine and M for 5-methyldeoxycytidine, we see that fifteen dinucleotides are possible, if we consider only the bases present and not their sequences. These are: MM, MC, MT, MA, and MG; CC, CT, CA, and CG; TT, TA, and TG; AA and AG; and GG. Since there is only a small amount of M, all the combinations of M with other nucleosides are present in small amounts and MM was not found. All the other combinations were found in the nucleic acid from wheat germ. In the nucleic acid from calf thymus, MT and MA were not found, but all others were present.

After the isolation of dinucleotides was completed, the method was extended to include trinucleotides. Thus the groundwork is being laid for systematic chemical investigation of the sequence of base residues on nucleic acid chains, similar to that performed on proteins.

The dinucleotides isolated by ion-exchange chromatography consist of mixtures of isomers with different base sequences. If we allow the letter p to stand for the phosphate link, these may be represented as pXpY and pYpX. Analysis for the individual components of these mixtures has been carried out as follows: (pXpY + pYpX) is hydrolyzed with phosphomonoesterase obtained from prostate glands to give (XpY + YpX). This mixture of monophosphate diesters can be separated by ion-exchange chromatography to give the individual components (XpY) + (YpX). The individual components can then be hydrolyzed by venom phosphodiesterase, (XpY) → (X + pY) and (YpX) → (Y + pX). The resulting mononucleotides with phosphates in the 5-positions can be separated by ion-exchange chromatography:

$$(X + pY) \rightarrow (X) + (pY)$$

and

$$(Y + pX) \rightarrow (Y) + (pX)$$

The molar ratios of the two can then be calculated. Table 27–1 shows a comparison of the amounts of some of the isomers found by Sinsheimer in calf thymus, calculated on the basis of the percentage of phosphorus in each.

Table 27–1

MOLAR PROPORTIONS OF DINUCLEOTIDE ISOMERS IN CALF THYMUS DNA

pGpM	0.00	pMpG	1.03
pTpC	0.78	pCpT	2.34
pApC	0.00	pCpA	3.22
pGpC	0.75	pCpG	0.12
pApT	0.10	pTpA	1.36
pGpT	0.16	pTpG	2.61
pGpA	0.97	pApG	0.20

It will be observed that definite biases exist in favor of certain sequences over their isomers. The significance of these biases has not yet been fully assessed. With one exception, pGpC, it will be observed that the terminal phosphate of the more abundant isomer is on the pyrimidine residue, not the purine. This bias may result from a peculiarity of the mechanism of action of deoxyribonuclease or from a regularity in the structure of the nucleic acid.

The isolation of dinucleotides containing only purines and others containing only pyrimidines shows that an alternate purine-pyrimidine sequence is not the rule in nucleic acids. Purely random arrangements of these bases might be assumed. Shapiro and Chargaff have made a careful study of the rates of acid hydrolysis of some dinucleotides. They conclude that pyrimidines flanked by purines hydrolyze rapidly to give pyrimidine nucleoside diphosphates, while pyrimidines flanked by pyrimidines hydrolyze only slowly to give pyrimidine nucleoside diphosphates. By studying the analyses of the products of nucleic acid hydrolyses carried on for varying lengths of time, they conclude that it is probable that regions of polypyrimidine chains and regions of polypurine chains exist within the larger nucleic acid chain. This has been confirmed, at least partially, by the isolation of "apurinic" acids, that is, polynucleotides containing only pyrimidines.

Hope for even more extensive knowledge of base sequences is given by the discovery that venom diesterase degrades a synthetic pentanucleotide one step at a time from the end bearing the free 3-hydroxyl group, while the diesterase from calf spleen degrades the same molecule in stepwise fashion from the other end, that is, from the free 5-hydroxyl end.

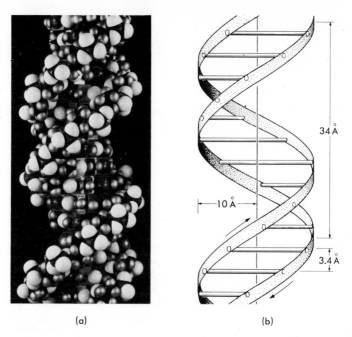

(a)   (b)

FIG. 27–2. The Watson-Crick model of DNA or RNA. (Courtesy of Dr. M. H. F. Wilkins.)

27–9 X-ray Evidence; the Watson-Crick Model

By the x-ray study of nucleic acid "crystalloids" produced by special techniques, Watson and Crick concluded that these preparations have a helix composed of two strands intertwined in parallel configurations like the banisters of a spiral staircase. The junction between the two strands is thought to consist of opposite pairs of purine and pyrimidine bases, in the positions of the stair steps. (See Fig. 27–2.)

27–10 Genetic Evidence; Application of the Watson-Crick Model

Geneticists have shown by their methods that the hereditary properties of cells reside in the genes, which make up the chromosomes in the nuclei of cells. In the process of *mitosis* or cell division, it is possible to produce sequential photographs showing the division and replication of the chromosomes in the nuclei. The chromosomes consist largely of nucleic acid materials, so it has become customary to regard the nucleic acid as the bearers of the "information" that makes the replication of a cell possible. It is assumed from this that any chemical structure adopted for a nucleic acid must be capable of accounting for the possibility of replication.

The Watson-Crick nucleic acid model, taken with the close approach of the adenine-thymine and guanine-cytosine ratios to unity, provides a ready explanation for the phenomenon of replication. According to this explanation, the distance between the two strands is too small to accommodate two purines, too large for two pyrimidines, but is just right for one purine and one pyrimidine. A special chemical "fit" between the basic amino group of adenine and the acidic hydroxyl group of thymine can be postulated and a similar "fit" between the basic amino group of cytosine and the acidic hydroxyl of guanine should exist. Attraction between the acidic group of guanine and that of thymine or between the basic group of adenine and that of cytosine would not be expected. Thus the "pairing" can be based on chemical grounds. The Watson-Crick model, then, assumes that one strand is the purine-pyrimidine reverse of the other. Where strand 1 has an adenine, strand 2 has thymine, where strand 1 has a thymine, strand 2 has an adenine, and likewise for guanine and cytosine. Because of their large number, the links between the strands are firm but because of the fact that none is covalent, they can be easily separated. When they are separated by uncoiling, strand 1 replicates by "growing" a new strand 2' whose base sequence is predetermined by the existing purine-pyrimidine sequence of strand 1. Strand 2 then also "grows" a new strand 1' on the same model. The nature of the synthetic process which permits this growth to take place is not understood at present.

27–11 Structural Evidence from Cryptography

According to this picture, a nucleic acid is a long "memory tape" with information coded into it in the form of purine-pyrimidine base sequences. It has been postulated, further, that the particular information encoded has to do with the amino-acid sequences in proteins formed under the genetic control of the nucleic acids. During the past few years a great deal of effort has gone into the attempt to unravel the "genetic code." Most of the attempts have been based on nonchemical principles and will, therefore, not be examined in detail here. The most common assumption made is that the identities of twenty amino acids are capable of being encoded, and attempts have been made to fit the list of amino acids within the limit of twenty to accommodate this supposed limitation of the code. In fact, however, more than twenty amino acids occur in proteins, since aspartic acid and asparagine are individually placed, as are glutamic acid and glutamine. In addition, the iodinated and brominated derivatives of tyrosine also have their peculiar places, as do serine and acetylserine. It is possible that the apparent interchangeability of cytosine and 5-methylcytosine on attachment to guanine may not be real and that each of these pyrimidines has its own place in the code.

One way to secure complete flexibility with a code would be to include punctuation after each bit of information. Such a code would contain a series of "commas" which could be obtained chemically by omitting one base from attachment to a sugar at the appropriate positions. Such a situation does not exist, however, since the analyses of the base-to-sugar ratio and of the sugar-to-phosphorus ratio establish that the nucleic acid molecule has these materials in the ratio of $1:1:1$. For this reason, it is argued that the code must be a "comma-less" code. Using four "letters," A, C, G, and T, in groups of three, it is possible to secure 64 bits of information. Strung out along a chain, however, these could lead to many ambiguities, if some means were not taken to distinguish between groups in a sequence.

One method to secure this in the absence of punctuation would be to use only certain combinations for commands. The remaining combinations, which might otherwise cause ambiguity, would, instead, be nonsense and therefore not interpreted as commands. On accepted principles of cryptography, it is possible to form just twenty distinct pieces of information from four letters by arranging them in sequences of three and avoiding the sequences in which overlap could lead to ambiguity. If, for each three letters, one and only one amino acid would fit, then the arrangements of twenty amino acids could be encoded.

It seems reasonably certain that further research will show that such a picture is oversimplified. In spite of this, this picture, grounded in experiments in diverse fields, constitutes the first soundly based attempt to correlate the facts of chemistry with those of genetics and thus opens broad vistas to chemical and biological experimentation on the most fascinating problem of all, the chemical basis of heredity.

FIG. 27–3. The Watson-Crick scheme for reproduction. Reproduced by permission from W. D. McElroy and B. Glass, *The Chemical Basis of Heredity*, Baltimore, Md.: The Johns Hopkins Press, 1957.

PROBLEMS

Coenzymes were originally considered as simple organic compounds which could combine with the proper protein groups, called apoenzymes, to form enzymes. These, in turn, catalyze biochemical reactions. This interpretation was later revised when it became clear that some coenzymes themselves undergo reaction at the same time and must be continually regenerated in a multienzyme pathway.

27–1 Adenosine triphosphate (ATP) is a so-called transphosphorylating agent; it is important in cell metabolism as a means of transferring chemical energy. Alkaline hydrolysis yields a phosphate of adenosine and pyrophosphate. (Note the anhydride P—O—P link.)

$$\text{HO}-\overset{\overset{\displaystyle \text{OH}}{|}}{\underset{\underset{\displaystyle \text{O}}{||}}{\text{P}}}-\text{O}-\overset{\overset{\displaystyle \text{OH}}{|}}{\underset{\underset{\displaystyle \text{O}}{||}}{\text{P}}}-\text{OH}$$

Pyrophosphoric acid

Acid hydrolysis gives adenine, a ribose phosphate and two molecular equivalents of phosphoric acid. ATP consumes one mole of periodic acid and gives a dialdehyde.

(a) At a minimum, how many hydroxyls in the sugar must be free?

(b) Since these must be adjacent, on which carbon must the phosphate be in the ribose phosphate, and therefore in the adenosine phosphate?

ATP may be deaminated with nitrous acid without loss of any phosphate, and therefore the adenine cannot carry a phosphate group. This leaves only one type of linkage available for the connection of the pyrophosphate to the rest of the molecule.

(c) What type of link is this?

Titration experiments on ATP indicate that it contains one secondary and three primary acidic groups. By comparison, pyrophosphoric acid contains two primary and two secondary acidic groups; these figures are concerned with the ionization of protons in hydroxyl groups bound to the same phosphorus atom.

(d) Show that this information confirms your structure for ATP.

27–2 Diphosphopyridine nucleotide (DPN or NAD) is important as a coenzyme in hydrogen transport in living systems. Acid hydrolysis yields adenine, nicotinamide, two moles of ribose, and two moles of phosphoric acid.

Nicotinamide

When nicotinamide is reacted with triacetyl-chloro-ribose, a compound containing a quaternary nitrogen is produced; a similar compound may be prepared from ethyl nicotinate. This material may be deacetylated with ammonia in methanol to give a glycoside which has been obtained from enzymatic hydrolysis of DPN as well. Optical rotation studies indicate that the link is β.

(a) Write a structure for this material as its chloride.

(b) This material consumes one mole of periodate at $0°C$. Show that this confirms the furanose structure of the sugar.

The action of phosphoryl chloride on this glycoside to form a phosphate ester is surprisingly clean. The phosphate thus formed is purified by ion exchange chromatography. It is completely hydrolyzed by snake venom 5′-nucleotidase and still consumes one mole of periodate at $0°C$.

(c) What is the structure of the synthetic nucleotide? This material is itself called nicotinamide mononucleotide (NMN).

This material is coupled with adenosine 5′-phosphate in the presence of dicyclohexylcarbodiimide to yield DPN by elimination of a molecule of water to form an anhydride. DPN is subject to the action of a specific pyrophosphatase, which cleaves it to the starting materials for this synthesis.

(d) Write partial formulas for the starting materials and reaction products at the phosphate links.

(e) DPN is a dipolar ion in neutral form; betaine has the same characteristics. Why is this so?

(f) Write the structure for DPN.

(g) Show that it has only one primary acidic group on titration.

An enzyme has been isolated from yeast and liver which catalyzes the following reaction:

$$NMN + ATP \rightleftharpoons DPN + \text{pyrophosphate}$$

(h) Do your structures fit the stoichiometry of this equation?

BOOK 2

How do we learn about the processes which take place between the disappearance of the reagent and the formation of the product in an organic chemical reaction?

Part 1

ELEMENTS OF CHEMICAL BONDING

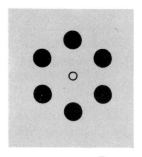

When an organic chemical reagent disappears, bonds are broken. When a new substance is formed, new bonds are formed. To understand the processes taking place in a chemical reaction, it is essential to have certain information concerning the character of chemical bonds, their relative strengths, and the varying conditions under which they may be broken or formed. A brief survey of these subjects is given in Part 1.

*How may a coulombic model be used to
give information concerning the problem of atomic structure?
What are the limitations of such a model?*

28

INTRODUCTION TO ORGANIC REACTION MECHANISMS

28-1 The Problem of Direct Observation of Structures and Mechanisms

In Book 1 we examined the powerful "microscope" which the organic chemist has invented to permit him to reconstruct logically the arrangements of atoms in molecules. This instrument is static in nature, permitting the chemist to examine structures at his leisure to secure the necessary degree of "resolution" to arrive at fine structural differentiations.

The *processes* of chemistry embrace chemical change from one structure to another. These processes are believed to proceed through definite pathways. Very shortly after chemists began to understand chemical structures, they started to wonder about chemical processes and to formulate hypothetical pathways through which the atoms in a reacting molecule might move to be transformed into a product molecule. We now know that the time involved in such a transformation is of the general order of 10^{-10} to 10^{-12} second. Experts in high-speed photography have succeeded in photographing events taking place in 10^{-6} to 10^{-7} second. It is evident that, even if we had a microscope with sufficient magnifying power to see and resolve atomic dimensions, we should be a long way from visualizing chemical transformations because of the time factor. What is needed is a peculiar dynamic microscope, capable of over a millionfold magnification in space and over a ten billionfold slowing down in time. An instrument for accomplishing this directly seems quite remote at the present time. Nevertheless, the logical processes of the organic chemist have again succeeded in making substantial progress in the desired direction.

28-2   The Mechanistic Problem

The structures of organic chemistry represent a logical approximation of the first order, requiring quasigeometrical reasoning to substitute for our lack of a suitable magnifying instrument. Studies of organic reaction mechanisms represent logical approximations of the second order, requiring the grafting of a quasitemporal argument to the quasispatial argument of structural chemistry. Because of the greater order of difficulty, progress in understanding mechanisms has been slower than that in determining structures. The field of organic reaction mechanisms is an extraordinarily active one at the present time, and concepts are in a state of constant flux. For this reason, presentations of mechanisms cannot be made with the same degree of conviction and finality as those in structural chemistry. Many of the concepts are still the subjects of active polemics in the chemical literature. This presentation will attempt either to avoid the more controversial aspects of reaction mechanisms or to show the bases of the controversy and thus to label open questions as such.

In any process in which a chemical reaction has taken place, either a new bond must be formed, an old bond broken, or both must occur. For this reason, it is appropriate that we begin our discussion of the organic chemist's "high-speed high-resolution microscope" with an introductory account of the nature of the chemical bond.

28-3   The Phenomenon of Periodicity; The Value of Models

The first and most basic information required for an understanding of organic reaction mechanisms is an appreciation of the nature of the periodic table of the elements. The forces responsible for the periodic table are complex and cannot yet be described mathematically with precision. The most refined mathematical methods used so far for treating the problem rely on quantum mechanics. When it was found that application of classical mechanics—the laws governing the physical relationships between objects of our everyday world—could not explain basic phenomena at the atomic level, physicists were obliged to abandon their approach to atoms as particles which were merely smaller than oranges and ball bearings but obeyed the same laws as these common objects. A method of approaching the problem was derived some years later and forms the basis of quantum mechanics. In this new mechanics, the forms of the natural laws governing relations between particles have great similarity to the older classical expressions. A fundamental distinction between the two approaches results from the following law: there is a limit to the accuracy with which the position and momentum of an object can be defined. In the classical realm, a ball bearing is so large that this lower limit is of no practical importance. At the atomic level, however, it is of extreme importance; we simply cannot state exactly where an electron is. We may be able to define a general volume inside of which it may often be found, but it is useless to attempt to pinpoint its location. Quantum mechanics, then, must take account of this indeterminacy as it applies the natural laws to very small systems, and all mathematical models constructed for the study of atomic particles must be based on this principle.

Methods exist, then, utilizing mathematical models to represent the charged particles of the atom. Other types of models have also been used. None that has yet been invented is capable of giving answers closely resembling the experimental situation for any but the simplest atoms and molecules. Yet this is the very purpose for which we wish to develop our model, to learn more about the nature of the forces in the more complicated atoms and molecules which are of interest to the organic chemist.

Suppose that a chemist chooses to examine the electrical fields in an atom to understand more precisely the causes of the chemical behavior of that element. If he wishes to study hydrogen by a mathematical approach, he will have to examine the quantum-mechanical properties of a system containing a heavy positively charged particle and a light particle of opposite charge. The mathematical devices used in the solution to this problem are relatively simple and so the problem of the hydrogen atom was one of the first problems solved by quantum mechanics. The agreement between these answers and experimental data was extraordinary and paved the way for the acceptance of quantum mechanics as a useful tool of the theoretical chemist.

When the chemist turned to more complex problems than the hydrogen atom, he encountered difficulties of great importance. Suppose, for example, that he chose to calculate the properties of the carbon atom. As a problem involving charged species, this would call for solution of the interactions between one positively charged heavy particle and six negatively charged particles. No method for the exact solution of a problem involving so many particles and the many interactions between them has been perfected yet. The worker cannot solve his problem with the available mathematical tools.

If the chemist cannot solve the problem exactly, he can be content with an approximation to the right answer—provided it is a good enough approximation. He might carry out his study by neglecting certain terms in his mathematical expressions, by combining certain expressions for similar interactions, by adding terms in his new expression to counterbalance the absence of the terms he neglected previously, and so forth. He is rewarded by the extent to which his mathematical model agrees with fundamental atomic values calculated from experimental data. An active area of investigation in theoretical chemistry at the present time is the study of new mathematical expressions to approximate more closely the actual case in atoms and molecules; to be useful, a model must be reasonably accurate in its predictions and must also be capable of use in systems of interest. One presently known expression for the helium atom involves more than a thousand terms in its mathematical expansion; it predicts values for certain constants with extreme accuracy, but, of course, the utility of a similar expression for examining methane (or merely carbon, for that matter) is limited.

It is not our purpose to explore mathematical models for atoms and molecules in any detail in this book. We shall be guided by the same criteria of reasonable accuracy and applicability in the physical model we are about to employ.

28-4 A Coulombic Model

The great difficulty with the mathematical model lies in its inability to take account of the interactions of the several electrons in the atom; thus the applicability of this sort of model to explain periodicity in the elements is restricted insofar as precise calculations are concerned. In 1878 a physicist, A. M. Mayer, invented a demonstration of periodicity using magnets, but it was not until 1905 that Sir J. J. Thompson first pointed out the parallelism with the periodic table. Its impact on early pictures of the nature of the atom is evident, although the realization that the atom could not be described classically led to substantial revision of this picture. It is of interest that the model also has been used to illustrate periodicity in other fields, notably the interactions of columnar vortices in meteorology.

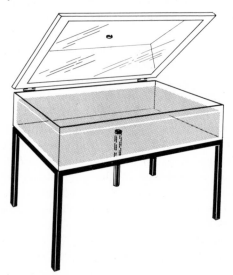

FIG. 28–1. Coulombic atomic model.

As we have stated, the forms of the laws governing relations between particles are similar in quantum mechanics and classical mechanics, except that the un-certainty principle enters into considerations of small systems. It is not surprising, then, that outwardly similar phenomena should be encountered on the two scales. For example, coulombic interactions still depend basically on the charges involved, and the magnitude of the interaction is formally still derived from the same radial law at the smaller level. Thus a classical coulombic model might be expected to shed some light on the nature of multiple coulombic interactions at the atomic level, those interactions which have not yet been treated successfully by mathe-matics and which underlie the periodic table. Restriction of our attention to the appropriate portion of the results of the experiment reflects the attitude of the quantum mechanician who chooses a model to represent portions of the behavior of electrons in a given system; both cases involve the most convenient rough estimations available.

The coulombic model consists of a number of particles free to move when change in an equilibrium situation disturbs them; they are attracted to a central particle of opposite sign and they repel each other. The central particle is a large powerful cylindrical magnet suspended from the bottom of a diamagnetic tank with its north pole up. After the tank is filled with water, a marker magnet in a cork float attached to a submerged bar magnet is placed over the powerful core and then other magnets mounted in floats with their north poles up are added one by one. They do not collide, because the fields of force are powerful enough to repel them before contact. An illustration of the coulombic atomic model is shown in Fig. 28–1.

It is apparent that there are several limitations to the analogy between the physical systems we are comparing, even if we applied only classical mechanical arguments to both: (1) the model is two-dimensional, the atom is three-dimensional; (2) the model is static, the atom is dynamic; (3) mass distributions differ greatly in the two systems; (4) interactions between fewer types of forces are present in the model than in the atom. It is not difficult to make allowance for these dissimilarities in our interpretation of the model, however.

28–5   Periodicity in the Coulombic Model

The sequential addition of magnets about the central magnet produces a series of geometric figures as shown in Fig. 28–2. Particular attention should be paid to several occurrences in these figures.

First, it is apparent that a certain periodicity results from these classical coulombic interactions. Closed shells occur at figures including six or ten magnets; addition of further magnets begins a new period. We might have guessed first that the addition of magnets would result in a single, ever-widening circle. A moment's reflection, however, would show that such a situation should be unstable; the increasing size of the circle would tend to diminish the force of attraction more rapidly than that of repulsion. Magnetic fields obey an inverse square law, so that forces between two magnets in close proximity are relatively much greater than those at a larger distance. As magnets are added progressively, the distance between adjacent magnets on the circumference tends to become smaller, increasing the force of repulsion. At the same time, the radius tends to increase, diminishing the force of attraction holding the magnets together. As a result, a point will come at which one magnet will be forced out of the first ring, starting a second one. The first ring then is able to contract from the radius that it would have had if the circle had increased. All the remaining magnets are drawn to the center until the repulsion of the marker and the other magnets stops them. This problem, complicated by the simultaneous interactions of so many forces, is difficult to solve mathematically; the physical model gives a rapid graphical solution.

The precise geometric figure at which the change occurs can be calculated by making the approximation that because of the inverse square law, magnets not adjacent to each other may be neglected in calculating repulsions. In addition, the distance between two magnets at vertices of the figure must be greater than the radial distance from the nucleus to any vertex, if the repulsive forces are not to

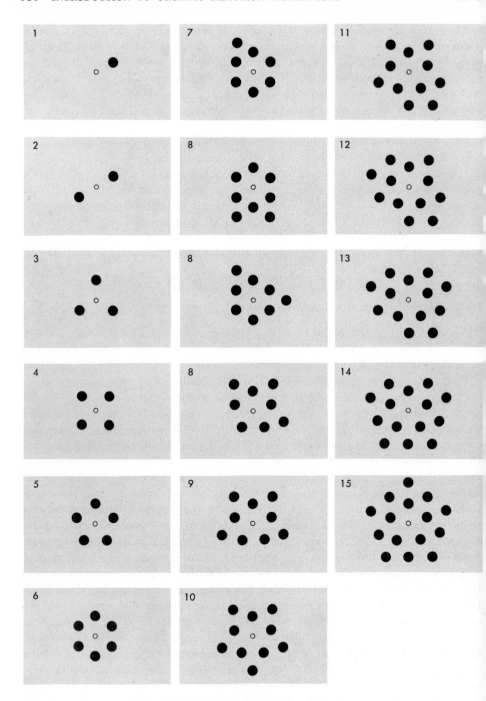

FIG. 28-2.   Patterns of coulombic interactions.

overcome the attractive force. Thus the side of the figure must be greater in distance than the distance from the center of the vertex. Representing the distance along a side as S and that from the center to the vertex as R, the ratios for the several regular geometric figures observed are as follows:

Figure	S/R
Triangle	1.73
Square	1.414
Pentagon	1.176
Hexagon	1.000

Thus the hexagon is just at the balance point between attraction and repulsion, and any figure with more vertices will have a greater repulsive force than the attractive force.

28–6　Analogy to the Three-Dimensional Case

It is interesting to note that in a three-dimensional model, the corresponding figures are:

Figure	S/R
Tetrahedron	1.937
Octahedron	1.414
Cube	1.154

Thus the cube is the last regular figure satisfying the necessary relationship, and a three-dimensional model would have a "magic number" of eight.

28–7　Further Analysis of the Patterns

In the largest figure, the radial distances to the magnets of the outer ring are more than twice the radius of the inner ring. This is partly the result of the inverse square law. An additional factor is at work, however. Exterior magnets undergo repulsion from the interior, but none from the exterior. Interior magnets undergo repulsion from both the interior and the exterior. The exterior repulsion tends to balance the repulsion from the interior so that they are held more tightly in place. Hence the binding force on the interior magnets is appreciably greater than that on the exterior ones.

When the ninth magnet is added to the figure containing eight, a major reorganization of the system occurs. The inner shell collapses from six to five. There is a degree of stability, then, in both the pentagonal and the hexagonal arrangements, and they are in delicate balance.

There are several cases in which more than one configuration is stable. The configuration attained depends on the direction of the introduction of the last magnet. Some of these configurations, such as the one in which the lower figure contains ten magnets, cannot be disturbed without rearrangement; that is, they are metastable.

The value of these observations will be seen as we attempt to refine the simple mathematical model we mentioned earlier.

28-8 The Preliminary Mathematical Model

The purpose of any model of atomic structure is to form a foundation by which physical phenomena actually measured in the laboratory can be correlated so that a deeper insight into structure may be gained. As we have noted, a mathematical model for the hydrogen atom was constructed using quantum mechanics very early in the development of the field. It is important to review the physical phenomena which made it necessary to develop explanations of such complexity.

One of the most valuable means for obtaining information about the nature and magnitude of the forces at work in chemical bonding has been spectroscopy. By studying the absorption and emission of light in the visible, infrared, and ultraviolet, physicists have been able to secure a vast number of highly precise measurements which they have succeeded in correlating into an essentially unified deductive science.

In 1885, Balmer discovered the law which governs the distribution of the lines which had been observed in the spectrum of hydrogen filling a space between two electrodes. This was the beginning of modern spectroscopy. Other physicists found other series of lines which could be correlated by using a generalization of Balmer's law. Rydberg and others showed that with suitable modifications, this new generalized law could be applied to the emission spectra of many elements subjected to the conditions of electrical discharge. The generalized law for all the series of emission lines for the hydrogen atom was the simple formula

$$\nu = R(1/m^2 - 1/n^2),$$

where R is a constant named for Rydberg, m and n are integers, and ν is the frequency of the emitted light, measured in cm^{-1}. The frequency is directly proportional to the energy.

Although these equations were useful in correlating large collections of data, the reason for their existence was not successfully demonstrated for several decades. As a result of the work of numerous investigators, including especially Rutherford, Planck, and Bohr, it was demonstrated that light corresponding to one of these energies, ν, results when an electron, which has been previously excited to a high energy level, makes a transition from a higher to a lower energy level, as in Fig. 28-3.

The fact that there are discrete lines, exactly reproducible in position in the spectrum, shows

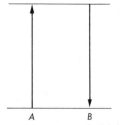

FIG. 28-3. Transitions of electrons between energy levels; A = absorption of energy and B = emission of energy.

that the energy levels related to the lines are fixed. Thus electrons in atoms may exist only at certain energies—the energy levels are quantized. From similar studies, most of them made with a high degree of precision, it has been possible to assign energy levels for the electrons surrounding the nuclei of most of the atoms of the periodic table. Figure 28–4 is a diagram showing the energy levels of hydrogen.

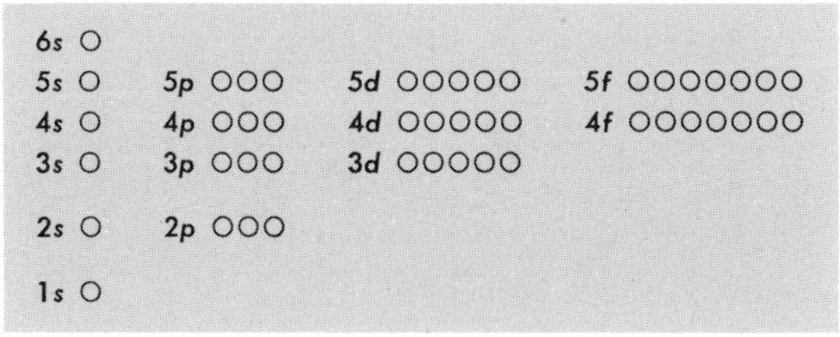

FIG. 28–4.   The energy levels of hydrogen.

The letters s, p, d, and f are a throwback to the early days of physics before the energy levels had been explained by a comprehensive theory. They represent the trivial names of the physicist and arose from the names of certain series of lines in the spectra of some elements: s stands for "sharp," p for "principal," d for "diffuse," and f for "fundamental."

Application of a simple quantum-mechanical model accurately described the energy levels found by the experimental spectroscopists. The only energy level which is occupied in the case of the hydrogen atom is the $1s$ level, which contains a single electron. All the higher energy levels may be considered as present but unoccupied. The process of excitation, for the hydrogen atom, consists of adding the proper amount of energy to the electron so that it undergoes transition to one of these higher levels. As we noted, this excitation results from the electrical energy supplied in a discharge tube. The electron then falls back to a lower level, and the energy difference is lost in the form of light. The several combinations of transitions from certain levels to others causes the series of lines in the hydrogen discharge spectrum.

28–9   Extension of the Simple Mathematical Model to the Periodic Table

The mathematical model we have illustrated was so successful in rationalizing the spectrum of hydrogen that chemists soon turned to it as a means for correlating facts concerning the periodic table in general. Before we attempt to review their progress, let us note briefly which other experimental and theoretical factors have a bearing on the problem.

In 1913 Bohr suggested that electrons must be in motion to explain the phenomena of spectroscopy. In 1923, G. N. Lewis proposed that the chemical phenomena which he had associated with *pairs* of electrons could be best explained if one assumed a cause for the pairing similar to the one in the following physical analogy: The motion of an electric current around a closed ring is known to produce a magnetic field perpendicular to the ring. If the motion is clockwise, the magnet will have its north pole upward; if counterclockwise, the south pole will be up. Lewis proposed that the pairing of the electronic motions caused the neutralization of the two magnetic fields resulting from the two electrons, as in Fig. 28–5.

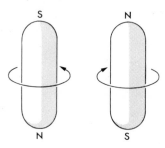

FIGURE 28–5

Such explanations of chemical properties had their counterparts in explanations of atomic spectra by the physicists. In 1925, Uhlenbeck and Goudsmit postulated electron spin to interpret certain features in the spectra of the elements. It was recognized later that pairing of electrons occupying the same orbital occurs so that the spins are antiparallel, even though the electromagnetic analogy suggested by Lewis is not exact. It is useful to the extent that it predicts the repulsion of electrons with the same spin, just as the magnets would repel each other. Likewise, it predicts the attraction of electrons with antiparallel spin, so that they occupy the same orbital. It was not immediately obvious how this phenomenon could be accounted for by the mathematical model but within a few years Dirac had demonstrated that the inclusion of relativity within the framework of the theory gave a satisfactory explanation.

To build up the periodic table, then, we would hope to take the energy levels found for our model of hydrogen, and into each orbital add a total of two electrons. Since we would gain more energy from filling the lower orbitals, these would be filled first and the order of filling should proceed from the lowest-lying orbital to the highest.

H																	He
Li	Be											B	C	N	O	F	Ne
Na	Mg											Al	Si	P	S	Cl	Ar
K	Ca	Sc	Ti	V	Cr	Mn	Fe	Co	Ni	Cu	Zn	Ga	Ge	As	Se	Br	Kr

FIG. 28–6. The beginning of the periodic table.

Reference to Figs. 28–4 and 28–6 indicates that at the beginning, our simple mathematical model does indeed predict a first period of two elements and a second of eight. The third period, however, contains only eight elements, but the model requires that there be a total of eighteen elements in this period. The disagreement between the simple model and experimental fact becomes worse and worse as we proceed further along the table.

28–10   Combination of the Two Models

We are faced with the choice of two possibilities: either our assumption about filling lower orbitals first was incorrect, or our model for the energies of the levels is wrong. The first alternative seems much less reasonable than the second, and we shall attempt to modify our model of the atom accordingly.

To do this, let us note one point of extreme importance which we have not taken into account in our presentation: we have added electrons to our system without allowing for the fact that the electrons will interact with each other because of their charge. As we noted before, the expansion of a mathematical model in this direction rapidly leads to uncontrollable numbers of terms. However, our physical model of periodicity has drawn our attention to a number of effects of the interactions of several electromagnetic forces. Let us see what qualitative results obtained from this model should be applicable.

First, we noted that periodicity resulted from the interactions of two sets of forces. Beyond that point, it is not of much value to comment on the quantitative aspects of periodicity in the model because of the limitation of analogy, as we noted in Section 28–4. We note, however, that the same cause—interaction of two forces—gave rise to periodicity of an improper sort as well in the mathematical model we used.

Second, we saw that the binding force on interior charges is greater than that on exterior charges. Here is an effect we have not taken into account yet; it implies that inner electrons tend to "screen" the full effect of the nucleus from the outer electrons and that the outer electrons compress the volume of space available to the inner electrons. Surely this should have some effect on electrons nominally at different distances from the nucleus, and we should not be surprised that the $6s$ electron, at a great distance from the nucleus, is held much more loosely than the $1s$ electron. Of course it would be held more loosely simply because it is farther

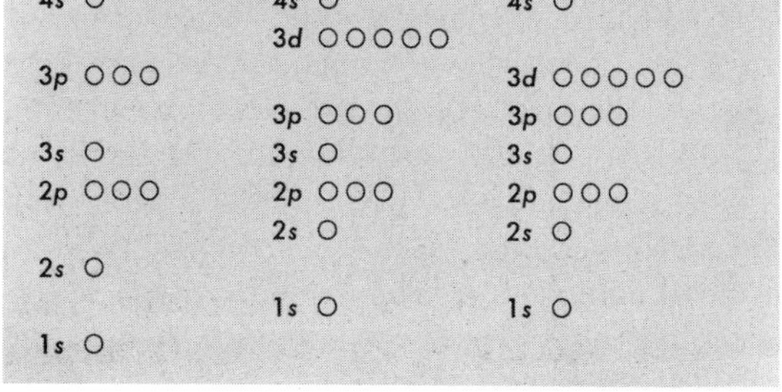

FIG. 28–7.   Possible arrangements of orbitals at three points in the periodic table.

away, but there is an added factor resulting from the electronic interactions. Of greater importance for our purposes is the fact that, within any level, the s-, p-, d-, and f-electrons are affected differently by these interactions. We have not yet mentioned the fact that the mathematical model may be used to generate pictures for the volumes of space in which these electrons usually move. In a given level, the s-electrons are, in general, a little closer to the nucleus than the p-electrons; these in turn are closer than the d, and these closer than the f. Since this is so, our physical model would predict that s-electrons at some general level would be compressed more by other electrons in the same level. Hence s-electrons should be more tightly bonded to the nucleus than p-electrons, p more than d, and d more than f. This effect should be dependent on the number of outer electrons that are available to compress the inner ones, so that at various points in the periodic table, the different orbitals would have different relative energies, as indicated in Fig. 28–7.

Thus the nature of the electronic interactions really involves a different energy-level diagram for every element of the periodic table. However, a generalized energy-level diagram can be prepared which holds qualitatively for most of the elements. Such a diagram is illustrated in Fig. 28–8.

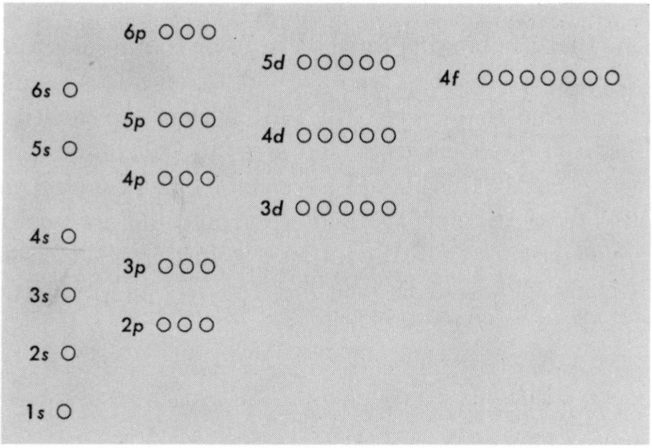

FIGURE 28–8

The reader should be certain that he understands the general reasons for the various amounts by which levels have been displaced in order from the original diagram for hydrogen and then should verify that such an explanation can now be used to demonstrate the origin of the periodic table.

We also noted that there would sometimes be cases in our physical model in which there would be arrangements with nearly the same stability. Such cases may also be found in the periodic table. Slight changes in the environment of certain transition metal compounds cause reorganization of the electron arrangements; arguments similar to those presented above have been used to explain these phenomena.

28–11   Perspectives in the Use of Models

In retrospect, neither a simple physical model nor a simple mathematical model does an adequate job of explaining the periodic table. Since they were designed so that certain important features of elementary particle interactions were ignored in each one, this is not surprising. It is clear, however, that what one model ignores, the other accentuates. They are, therefore, complementary. The quantitative failure of either requires us to review the merits of the other, and the picture which results from consideration of the two taken together presents a reasonably satisfactory picture for our purposes. Neither can be ignored, nor should either be treated as holding the complete answer to the problem.

28–12   Molecules

Now that we have reviewed the nature of the periodic table, let us proceed to a discussion of the forces that hold atoms together in molecules. As we might expect, description of the properties of the covalent bond by a mathematical model involves ever-increasing approximations and neglect of interactions. Those factors constituting the covalent bond which may vary from compound to compound and thus influence reactivity may very well be overlooked in a simple mathematical approach. We shall therefore put increased emphasis on the nature of the interactions shown by our physical model.

PROBLEMS

28–1   Periodicity results from the interaction of two forces. What two forces or constraints cause the periodicity resulting from the mathematical model of the hydrogen atom?

28–2   In electronic notation, the number of electrons in an orbital in a given instance is represented by a superscript following the orbital designation. Thus $2p^6$ indicates that there are six electrons in the $2p$ orbitals.

Explain the following results for the electronic structures of the designated elements found by the interpretation of the emission spectra of the metals.

Ca	$1s^2 2s^2 2p^6 3s^2 3p^6 4s^2 3d^0$		Fe	$1s^2 2s^2 2p^6 3s^2 3p^6 4s^2 3d^6$
Sc	$1s^2 2s^2 2p^6 3s^2 3p^6 4s^2 3d^1$		Co	$1s^2 2s^2 2p^6 3s^2 3p^6 4s^2 3d^7$
Ti	$1s^2 2s^2 2p^6 3s^2 3p^6 4s^2 3d^2$		Ni	$1s^2 2s^2 2p^6 3s^2 3p^6 4s^2 3d^8$
V	$1s^2 2s^2 2p^6 3s^2 3p^6 4s^2 3d^3$		Cu	$1s^2 2s^2 2p^6 3s^2 3p^6 4s^1 3d^{10}$
Cr	$1s^2 2s^2 2p^6 3s^2 3p^6 4s^1 3d^5$		Zn	$1s^2 2s^2 2p^6 3s^2 3p^6 4s^2 3d^{10}$
Mn	$1s^2 2s^2 2p^6 3s^2 3p^6 4s^2 3d^5$			

(Note that the $3d$ shell is not filled regularly.)

28-3   Making use of the concept of periodicity, explain why many of the reactions of organic sulfur compounds are similar to those of the corresponding oxygen compounds Show the basis of your reasoning on an energy-level diagram.

(a) How would you prepare a thioacid chloride?

(b) How would you prepare a thioamide?

(c) How would you prepare a dialkylselenium, R—Se—R?

28-4   (a) In an analogy to which compounds would you expect $(C_6H_5)_3P$ to exist?

(b) How would you prepare $(CH_3)_4P^+ I^-$ from $(CH_3)_3P$?

28-5   A very stable type of compound was discovered accidentally when cyclopentadiene was heated with iron, producing $(C_5H_5)_2Fe$, called "ferrocene," shown in Fig. 28-9. X-ray studies indicated that the molecule exists as a sandwich. An explanation for its stability was advanced. Iron has 26 electrons and 5 should be added to this number from each cyclopentadienyl unit (one from each carbon in the ring) to make 36 electrons surrounding iron.

(a) In analogy to which element should a 36-electron configuration be expected to produce stability?

(b) Why is a 36-electron configuration more "stable" than one containing 35 or 37 electrons? Explain what you mean by stability. Is there analogy for this in the physical model we employed?

(c) Would you expect to find that the compounds listed below are stable by this criterion?

Ruthenocene, $(C_5H_5)_2Ru$,
Osmocene, $(C_5H_5)_2Os$,
Dibenzenechromium, $(C_6H_6)_2Cr$,
(Cyclopentadienyl)-(cycloheptatrienyl)molybdenum, $(C_5H_5)(C_7H_7)Mo$

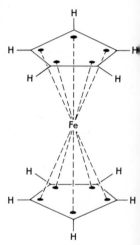

FIGURE 28-9

How do coulombic forces affect bond distances, bond angles, and the types of bond cleavage?

29

BOND DISTANCES, BOND ANGLES, AND A COULOMBIC MOLECULAR MODEL

29-1 Isoelectronic Radii

With one of the figures containing more than one ring, it is easy to use the magnetic atom model for an experimental demonstration of the "isoelectronic series" of the elements. If the number of floating magnets is kept constant and the magnetic field is increased by raising the central magnet toward the tank, it will be observed that the radii of the rings decrease (Fig. 29–1). This corresponds to the atomic situation in which the number of electrons is maintained constant while the

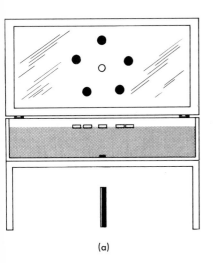
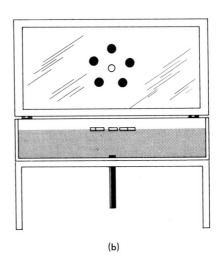

(a)   (b)

FIG. 29–1.   Floating magnet patterns: (a) with weak central attraction; (b) with stronger central attraction.

395

Table 29–1

RADII OF ISOELECTRONIC IONS

			H^-	He	Li^+	Be^{++}	B^{3+}	C^{4+}	N^{5+}	O^{6+}	F^{7+}
			2.08	(0.93)	0.60	0.31	0.20	0.15	0.11	0.09	0.07
C^{4-}	N^{3-}	$O^=$	F^-	Ne	Na^+	Mg^{++}	Al^{3+}	Si^{4+}	P^{5+}	S^{6+}	Cl^{7+}
2.60	1.71	1.40	1.36	(1.12)	0.95	0.65	0.50	0.41	0.34	0.29	0.26

nuclear charge is increased by moving along a row of the periodic table. The isoelectronic radii of the first two rows of the periodic table, as observed or calculated
by Pauling, are given in Table 29–1.

29–2 Bond Distances

Examination of the table of isoelectronic radii will show that the radii do indeed
diminish as the nuclear charge increases. Thus it is easy to remember qualitatively
the relationship between position in a row of the periodic table and the isoelectronic
radius. It is qualitatively what would be predicted from the operation of Coulomb's
law. The relationship in a bonding series, as distinguished from an isoelectronic
series, is not simple to predict, however. In this case, as in the isoelectronic case,
the attractive force is increasing, but it might be argued that the force of repulsion
between the added bonding electrons would act sufficiently in the opposite direction to cancel the increased attraction of the nucleus. Because of the nature of the
electron distribution in covalent bonds, however, the cases of the isoelectronic
series and the covalent bond series are qualitatively identical, though differing
somewhat quantitatively. To appreciate this fact, let us examine the series ethane,
methylamine, methanol, and methyl fluoride.

```
   H  H            H  H            H                H
   ·· ··           ·· ··           ··  ··           ··  ··
 H : C : C : H   H : C : N : H   H : C : O : H    H : C : F :
   ·· ··           ·· ··           ··  ··           ··  ··
   H  H            H               H                H
```

In the bonded series, as contrasted to the isoelectronic series, it will be seen that
the cores of carbon, nitrogen, oxygen, and fluorine are all surrounded by the same
number of electrons, eight. These electrons comprise a three-dimensional cloud
surrounding the cores and attracted to them by increasing nuclear charges as we
go from left to the right. The attractive forces may be thought of as acting radially
on the electrons. In methylamine, for example, the distance from the carbon core
to the center of the electron cloud is smaller than that between the carbon nucleus
and the nitrogen nucleus. For this reason, the repulsive forces between the two
atomic nuclei act at a greater distance and are, therefore, relatively less important
than the attractive forces between nuclei and electrons in determining bond
distances. Similar situations prevail in each case. Hence the overall result is

Table 29–2

COVALENT BOND RADII, ANGSTROMS

B, 0.88	C, 0.77	N, 0.70	O, 0.66	F, 0.64
	Si, 1.17	P, 1.10	S, 1.04	Cl, 0.99
	Ge, 1.22	As, 1.21	Se, 1.17	Br, 1.11
	Sn, 1.40	Sb, 1.41	Te, 1.37	I, 1.33

qualitatively the same as in the isoelectronic series, that is, bond radii diminish on going from carbon to nitrogen to oxygen to fluorine. Because of the great nuclear charge and the lack of screening electrons, the fluorine nucleus exerts a greater electron-attracting force than any other element in the periodic table.

Pauling has shown that it is possible, to a first approximation, to divide the total distance between two atoms into two portions, the two radii characteristic of the individual atoms. While the bond radius of a covalently bound element varies appreciably depending on the molecule in which it is found, the variations are minor with respect to the radii themselves. For this reason, the organic chemist will find that for most purposes, average values of bond radii are sufficiently accurate for his purposes. The radii of the elements which will interest us most in the following discussions are given in Table 29–2. These are taken from values given by Pauling.

29–3   Bond Angles

In covalent bonding, electrons with antiparallel spins act in pairs. To set up a magnetic analogy, a single floating magnet may be used to represent an electron pair. Two floating magnets tend to orient themselves on a straight line intersecting the nucleus when the center of attraction is brought to the surface of the tank by placing a second attracting magnet above the tank at a distance equal to that of the first below the tank. This illustrates the fact that repelling electrons seek to maintain a maximum distance between themselves in space. Where a central atom has only two other atoms bonded to it and there are no unshared

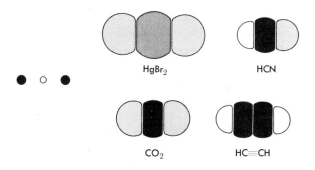

FIG. 29–2. 180° bond angles.

electron pairs, this repulsion assures an angle of 180° between the two radii connecting the two outer atoms to the inner one. Thus the bond angle is 180° (Fig. 29–2). An example of a compound with bond angles of 180° is Br—Hg—Br, mercuric bromide. In organic compounds, this angle is found in acetylene, H—C≡C—H, as the H—C—C angle in each case. To rationalize this angle, it is only necessary to think of the hydrogen as seeking a position as far as possible from the carbon to which it is not bonded. The same situation will prevail in H—C≡N or in R—C≡N.

FIG. 29–3. 120° bond angles.

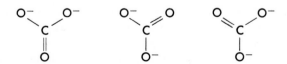

BF₃

When we add a third floating magnet, the figure formed is a triangle. This represents the regular figure with three vertices as far as possible from each other in space. The angle between the radii in this case is 120° (Fig. 29–3). An example of a compound with six bonding electrons which assumes this shape is BF_3. Organic compounds with 120° bond angles are numerous, representing many substances with multiple bonding. The simplest carbon-containing compound of this type is the carbonate ion, $CO_3^=$, in which the three oxygens are attached to the central carbon atom and their bonding electrons repel each other to assume an angle of 120°. Carbonate ion is a hybrid between three possible structures differing only in the assignment of electrons.

As a consequence, all bonds are exactly equivalent and an angle of 120° would be expected. Another example is benzene. In this case, the hexagonal symmetry of the ring combined with the hybrid nature of the C—C bonds determines that the C—C—C bond angles shall be 120°. The hydrogen then assumes the position farthest from the two closest carbons to which it is not bonded. This makes all angles 120°.

29–4   Bond Angles in Three Dimensions; Symmetrical Molecules

At this point, the two-dimensional limitation of our magnetic experiment makes the results obtained with it deviate from those to be expected in three dimensions. Geometrically, however, it is easy to see that four equally repelling particles bonded equally to a central attractive force would assume positions as far apart

FIG. 29–4. Tetrahedral angles.

Tetrahedron in a sphere

CH_4

as possible in space on the surface of a sphere. This is the essence of the factor that is responsible for the tetrahedral angle of carbon, since a tetrahedron is the regular figure with four vertices as far apart as possible on the surface of a sphere. The internal radial angles of a tetrahedron are 109°28′ (Fig. 29–4). Consequently, this is the bond angle in methane. On the other hand, it should not be expected that all derivatives of methane would have bond angles of exactly 109°28′. As we shall see later, substitution by atoms with different electron-attracting powers, such as halogens, nitrogen, or oxygen, should create fields of different magnitudes and alter bond angles slightly as a result.

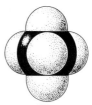

FIG. 29–5. Five vertices maximally separated on a sphere.

Triangular biprism in a sphere

PCl_5

There is no regular geometrical figure with five vertices equally spaced on the surface of a sphere (Fig. 29–5). The closest approach is a triangular bipyramid. This may be thought of as a figure with two vertices at opposite poles and three in an equilateral triangle on the equator. If an attracting nucleus were placed at the center of this sphere, five bonds to equally bonding atoms with equal repulsive forces would assume this configuration. This is the structure of gaseous PCl_5.

The next regular figure is the octahedron. This consists of eight equilateral triangles intersecting in six vertices, all equidistant on the face of a sphere. This is the figure assumed by a symmetrical compound with twelve bonding electrons. Examples are SF_6 and ferro- and ferricyanide ions, $Fe(CN)_6^{4-}$ and $Fe(CN)_6^{3-}$. Many other examples are to be found among the coordination compounds of organic substances with metals. The radial bond angles are 90° (Fig. 29–6).

FIG. 29–6. Octahedral angles.

Octahedron in a sphere

SF_6

FIG. 29-7.   Seven vertices maximally separated on sphere.

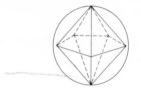

There is no regular figure with seven vertices equidistant on a sphere (Fig. 29-7). The closest approach is a pentagonal bipyramid with vertices at the two poles of the sphere and five vertices equally spaced on the equator.

Pentagonal biprism in a sphere

The regular figure with eight vertices as far apart as possible on a sphere is a cube. This is the figure which should be assumed by a symmetrical compound with sixteen bonding electrons. While substances with sixteen bonding electrons are known, none of them has all bonds equivalent so that the cubic coordination system has not yet been found. An alternative arrangement of eight vertices which does appear in coordination compounds is the "Archimedean antiprism" (Fig. 29-8). In addition to unsymmetrical substitution, another factor which frequently prevents perfect symmetry in these higher coordination compounds is an unsymmetrical distribution of electrons among the available orbitals.

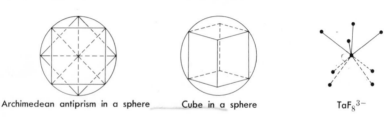

Archimedean antiprism in a sphere   Cube in a sphere TaF_8^{3-}

FIG. 29-8.   Eight vertices on a sphere.

It can hardly be an accidental coincidence that the bond angles of mercuric chloride, carbonate ion, methane, phosphorus pentachloride, and ferricyanide all fit those calculated on the basis of the geometry of regular figures inscribed in a sphere. It should be emphasized, however, that each of these substances is symmetrically substituted. The bond angles of unsymmetrically substituted substances would be much more difficult to calculate with any precision. Fortunately, this is not necessary for the organic chemist. He will know that gross deviations from the symmetrical bond angles are not to be expected and that the small deviations which do occur will, as a rule, not be of serious concern to him. As we shall see, however, small deviations can yield useful information concerning details.

29-5   Bond Angles; Molecules with Unshared Pairs

Perhaps the greatest deviations from the regular figures should be expected to occur in the cases where one substituent is entirely lacking. Thus we might compare the bond angles in methane and ammonia. As a first approximation, we may consider the repulsions of the four electron pairs in ammonia to produce separations of the bonds to something approaching the tetrahedral angle. The repelling forces of three of the pairs will, however, be less than that of the fourth because of the fact that their negative charges are partially neutralized by the attraction of the positive charges of the hydrogen nuclei associated with them. Since the repelling forces of the hydrogen nuclei will be acting on each other at distances larger than the repelling forces of the electrons, those of the electrons will have the greater weight. So we emerge with a qualitative picture of three weakened repelling forces of electron pairs attached to hydrogens and one full repelling force of an electron pair that is unshared. The greater repelling force should thus be expected to prevail, forcing the hydrogens closer together than the tetrahedral angle. Measurement by means of infrared and Raman spectra shows that the H—N—H bond angle in ammonia is 106°47'. The deviation from the tetrahedral angle of methane forced by the unshared electron pair in ammonia is 2°41'.

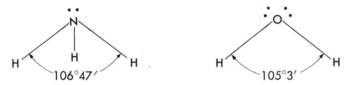

FIG. 29–9. Bond angles of ammonia and water.

Repeating the process of vacating a bond, we may compare the bond angles of ammonia and water (Fig. 29–9). Using the same argument, we should expect the H—O—H angle in water to be still smaller than that of ammonia. However, since the crowding of charges becomes increasingly difficult as they get closer together, we should expect the decrement in angle to be something less for the change from ammonia to water than that found in the change from methane to ammonia. Comparison shows that the H—O—H angle of water is 105°3'. The decrement from the ammonia angle is 1°44', as against 2°41' from methane to ammonia.

29–6   Bond Angles Beyond the First Row of the Periodic Table

We may pursue the electrostatic analogy into the second row of the periodic table. As might be expected, the bond angles of silane, SiH_4, are tetrahedral. With phosphine, as with ammonia, we should expect the repelling force of the unshared pair to reduce the H—P—H bond angle. We have seen from the floating magnets that the action of the inverse square law substantially weakens the attractions exerted on the second ring of electrons and that the screening effect weakens it still more. Hence we should expect to find that the H—P—H angle is easier to bend than the H—N—H angle. From this we should reason that the repelling force of the unshared pair would cause the H—P—H angle to be smaller than the H—N—H angle. Infrared observation shows that the angle is approximately 99°. Thus the decrement from silane to phosphine is over 10°, quite substantially greater than that from methane to ammonia. Arsine, on the other hand, shows an H—As—H angle of 97.5°, indicating that the greatest increase in bond flexibility occurs on going from the first to the second row of the periodic table. Continuing in the second row, the decrement in bond angle on going from phosphine to hydrogen sulfide is from 99° to 92°16′, a change of not quite 7°. Again the decrement produced by a second unshared pair is less than that produced by the first.

In attempting to calculate bond angles of molecules containing elements beyond the first row of the periodic table, quantum mechanicians have frequently found it convenient to approach the problem from the point of view of an unoccupied orbital system which is then progressively filled with electrons. Since the unoccupied orbitals have 90° angles, the argument starts by assuming these angles as "standard" and then calculating deviations from the standard introduced by the multiplicity of electrons and their hybridization. While this approach is more convenient for certain types of calculation, it does not lend itself as readily to qualitative understanding as does the approach presented above which starts with all bonding positions occupied.

29–7   A Simple Molecular Model

While the interactions of protons and electrons in atoms to form molecules is more complex than simple coulombic attractions and repulsions between electrostatic charges, nevertheless an understanding of the outcome of such interactions provides a sound base on which to build the more complex concepts. Experimentation with the forces of magnetic fields provides an accurate means for assessing many-centered coulombic interactions and thus will repay further study. As an approach to the visualization of the interactions of two polycentered fields, we may prepare two atom models consisting of nuclear markers and four floating magnets each, as in Fig. 29–10(a). Since the pentagonal arrangement is the most stable, atoms with four electrons may be thought of as the two-dimensional analogs of halogen atoms. On allowing these centers to approach each other, interactions of their fields will be observed. Finally, a new figure will form with one side shared between two pentagons, as in Fig. 29–10(c).

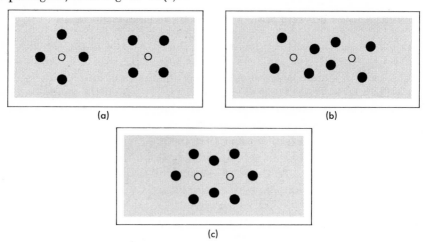

FIG. 29–10.   Interactions of two equal polycentered fields.

29-8 Homolytic Cleavage

Careful separation of the two magnetic nuclei will result in the restoration of the original two square figures. The combined figure, represented by Fig. 29–10(c), may be thought of as analogous to a halogen molecule, Cl—Cl, and the process of separation may be likened to the chemical process of *homolytic cleavage* which can be accomplished in the case of chlorine by the thermal dissociation of the molecule into two chlorine atoms:

$$Cl_2 \underset{}{\overset{heat}{\rightleftarrows}} 2Cl\cdot$$

29-9 Heterolytic Cleavage

In a homolytic cleavage, a bond is broken symmetrically, with one electron going to each atom. Homolytic cleavages are of interest to organic chemists because some organic reactions proceed by radical mechanisms. On the other hand, the majority of organic cleavages belong to a second category, *heterolytic cleavages*. Heterolytic cleavages may be illustrated using the same model by placing one of the stationery magnets closer to the tank than the other. This magnet will draw the floating magnets closer to it than will the more remote magnet, creating two centers with unequal attracting powers. On allowing these centers to approach each other, it will be observed that a figure similar to Fig. 29–10(c) is formed but that the new figure is not symmetrical. This model may be thought of as analogous to Cl—I. Since the bonding electrons of iodine are at a greater distance than those of chlorine and are screened by intervening layers of electrons, they are less strongly held and may be compared to the atom model with the more remote stationary magnet. The atom model with the stronger field is the analog of the chlorine atom. Because the centers of electric charge are displaced from each other, such a molecule is called a *dipole*.

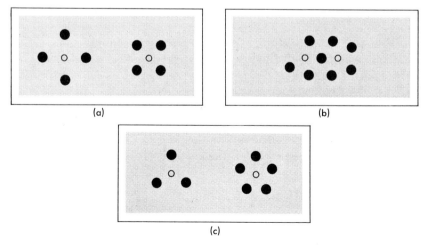

FIG. 29–11.   Interactions of two unequal polycentered fields.

On separating the two nuclei of the new figure, it will be observed that five magnets accompany the magnet with the stronger field, while only three accompany that with the weaker field (Fig. 29–11). The atom with the five magnets may be likened to the negative ion and that with three magnets to the positive ion in the equation:

$$Cl\text{—}I \rightarrow Cl^- + I^+.$$

This is an example of heterolytic cleavage, a reaction type which occurs with moderate frequency in organic chemistry. It will be noted that the atom with the greater electron-attracting power is the one which captures the electron from the shared bond on cleavage. For this reason, such atoms are frequently referred to as *electronegative*. The most highly attracting entity would be one with a positive charge, leading to the confusing concept that the most electronegative entity is one with a positive charge. While this nomenclature is widely used in the literature, it can lead to misunderstanding and we shall continue to refer to such atoms as *electron attracting*. Atoms such as the iodine atom in Cl—I we shall refer to as *electron releasing*. It should be noted that in CH_3I iodine is electron attracting and carbon is electron releasing. Thus the terms "electron attracting" and "electron releasing" are relative.

29–10   The Displacement Reaction

A third type of reaction, one which occurs with even greater frequency than either of the foregoing, is the so-called *displacement reaction*. An example of the displacement reaction is the reaction of hydroxide ion with methyl iodide:

$$HO^- + CH_3I \rightarrow CH_3OH + I^-.$$

In this reaction, methyl iodide is a dipole. Because of its position at the right of the periodic table, the iodine atom is electron attracting, and the carbon is electron releasing, creating an excess of negative charge in the vicinity of the iodine and a deficiency in the vicinity of the carbon. For this reason, the approach of the hydroxide ion will be oriented in favor of the carbon. This would be true even if the electron-attracting group bore a full positive charge as in —$^+N(CH_3)_3$. This principle can also be illustrated magnetically by observing the approach of a polar particle resembling the ion to a dipole resembling the molecule. Such particles can be constructed by lashing magnets together as shown in Fig. 29–12. It will be observed that the approach of the "ion" to the "dipole," on receiving a kinetic impetus, will be strongly oriented by the magnetic fields of the dipole (Fig. 29–13).

Ion

Dipole

FIGURE 29–12

FIG. 29–13. Magnetic analogy to the collision of an ion and dipole.

In the same manner, the fields surrounding the methyl group influence the approach of the hydroxide ion. We shall discuss this point in greater detail in a later chapter.

As we progress, we shall find other experiments which can be performed with the floating magnets to illustrate the role played by coulombic forces in atomic and molecular structures. It will be useful next, however, to turn our attention to some experiments which do not fit classical electrostatic theory.

PROBLEMS

29-1   What approximate bond angles would you expect in the compound shown below?

$$CH_3—\overset{\overset{\displaystyle O^-}{|}}{\underset{\displaystyle \cdot\cdot}{S^+}}—CH_3$$

29-2   On the basis of the arguments we have used to explain electron-attracting ability and its effect on the type of bond cleavage observed, which compound in each of the following pairs would be more likely to cleave homolytically? Which would be more likely to cleave heterolytically under the same conditions?

$$RS—H \quad or \quad RO—H$$
$$R—F \quad or \quad R—I$$
$$I—Cl \quad or \quad I—I$$

29-3   One of the known sites of x-ray damage in proteins is the mercapto group of cysteine. No similar process occurs in alanine, for example, or serine. What primary step for a homolytic photodegradation process does this information suggest?

29-4   Spectroscopy in the microwave region of the spectrum has yielded information leading to the assignment of the following H—C—H bond angles.

CH_3F	109°59′
CH_3Cl	110°31′
CH_3Br	111°14′
CH_3I	111°25′

To rationalize this information, it is necessary to consider the relative magnitudes of the electrostatic attractions and repulsions operating, since these are the major factors responsible for distortions from the tetrahedral form.

(a) Remember that charges interact according to the inverse square law. Which would be the predominating force between atoms A and B (Fig. 29–14):
   (1) Repulsion between the nuclei of A and B?
   (2) Attraction between the electrons of A and the nucleus of B and vice versa?
   (3) Repulsion between the electrons of A and B?
(b) Do the observed H—C—H angles correlate with the relative sizes of the halogen atoms?

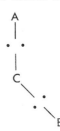

FIGURE 29-14

(c) Do the observed angles correlate with the lengths of the C—X bonds?

(d) Do the angles correlate with the electronegativities of the C—X bonds?

(e) What effect would you expect if the unshared electron pairs of the halogens had the predominant repulsive role? What if the bonding electrons had the major role? Which do you think is the more probable?

(f) Consider the shielding of the outer valence shell electrons by inner shell electrons. Will the outer shell electrons in larger atoms be more or less easily influenced by external electrostatic forces: In the interaction of a halogen with electrons on hydrogen which would be distorted more, the electrons of fluorine or those of iodine? This deformability is also known as polarizability.

(g) Recall the relative repulsions between the nonbonding electron pairs of oxygen and those of the O—H bond in water. What does a diminution in the "effective charge" of an electron pair by shielding by a nucleus do to the bond angle? What would be the effect of shielding by a strongly electron-attracting group in contrast with a weakly electron-attracting group?

(h) On the basis of your answers to the foregoing questions, can you rationalize the relative bond angles of the four alkyl halides given?

(i) Can you explain the difference in bond angles between methane and methyl fluoride? We shall have an opportunity for another argument based on a different line of reasoning in Chapter 32.

What major factor in addition to coulombic attractions and repulsions must be taken into account in the rationalization of the relative strengths of chemical bonds? How can this factor be illustrated by analogy? How can it be represented in chemical formulas?

30

THE COVALENT BOND; RESONANCE

30–1 The Wave Theory of Light

During the eighteenth and nineteenth centuries the ancient concept of the infinite divisibility of matter was finally laid to rest. The collaboration between chemists and physicists brought about a realization of the atomic and molecular nature of matter.

During the same period, our knowledge of the nature of radiant energy was also increasing. As early as 1678, Huygens had definitely enunciated the wave theory of light. This was put on an essentially modern basis in 1860 by Clerk Maxwell who showed that the waves were electromagnetic in nature and who formulated wave equations capable of wide application in the treatment of the phenomena of radiant energy.

30–2 The Corpuscular Theory of Energy

In 1901, Max Planck, as a result of studies on the distribution of energy in black-body radiation, came to the conclusion that Maxwell's classical equations were not sufficient to explain the phenomena that concerned him. He concluded that energy, like matter, must be regarded as corpuscular in nature, that is, that energy like matter is characterized by discontinuity. He could interpret his experimental results only on the assumption that electromagnetic radiation is quantized in extremely tiny units which can be measured by multiplying their frequency by a factor now universally called *Planck's constant*, 6.6256×10^{-27} erg·sec.

30-3 The Equivalence of Matter and Energy

In 1905, Einstein laid the physical and philosophical basis for the release of atomic energy with his statement of the equivalence of matter and energy. He formulated it in precise terms: energy is equal to mass times the square of the velocity of light,

$$E = mc^2.$$

30-4 The Wave Theory of Matter

Chemists and even many physicists took refuge behind a wall of incredulity for many years. However in 1923 de Broglie brought the argument to its logical conclusion with his formulation of the wave theory of matter. Up to that time an electron had been looked on as a charged particle of matter. De Broglie stated that it must also be considered as having a definite wavelength, λ, given by the expression

$$\lambda = h/mv,$$

where h is Planck's constant and mv is the product of the mass and velocity and therefore equal to the momentum of the electron. De Broglie proposed this relationship to correlate data previously in the literature, and it was soon verified by an experiment of Davisson and Germer who used a surface as a diffraction grating for electrons and found that the "spectrum" that resulted from this diffraction could be treated just like a spectrum of ordinary light if the relationship of de Broglie were utilized. It is by the utilization of "light" consisting of a beam of electrons that the electron microscope functions to give resolving power sufficient for the visualization of heavy atoms and approaching the diameters of the lighter atoms which interest the organic chemist. These experiments established the wave nature of matter and lent further support to Einstein's thesis concerning the equivalence of matter and energy.

30-5 Quantum Mechanics

During the succeeding five years a group of physicists, Heisenberg, Schrödinger, Born, Dirac and others formulated and developed the field of quantum mechanics which permitted calculations to be made concerning the nature of matter based on the wave theory.

Using the quantum-mechanical approach, a number of investigators turned to the problem of cataloging and estimating the extent of the forces responsible for chemical bonding. The simplest case was that of hydrogen and by a process of elimination, one after another of the factors affecting the stability of the bonding of two nuclei to form a hydrogen molecule has been evaluated.

30-6 Hydrogen in an Electric Discharge

When hydrogen is sealed into a tube between electrodes and subjected to an electrical discharge, physicists have been able to identify among the substances present an ionized species which is the molecule of hydrogen less one electron, H_2^+. This species is not properly referred to as a molecule in the chemical sense because it is a high-energy form, considerably less stable than the hydrogen molecule. Yet it has definite stability with respect to its possible decomposition products, a hydrogen atom and a stripped proton:

$$H \cdot + H^+ \rightarrow (H \cdot H)^+ - 57{,}000 \text{ cal.}$$

The energy of H_2^+ has been estimated as a function of the distance of separation between the two hydrogen nuclei. This is shown in Fig. 30–1.

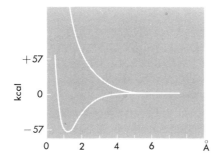

FIG. 30–1. Stability of H_2^+ with separation of nuclei.

Figure 30–1 shows that a hydrogen atom and a proton when separated to an infinite distance exert neither attraction nor repulsion on each other. This is the zero reference level of energy. The lower of these curves shows what happens when the single electron between the two nuclei is allowed to fall into a "bonding" orbital. Under these conditions attraction between the nuclei takes place and at a distance of approximately 1.1 Å, the position of greatest stability is reached with a bond strength of approximately 57 kcal. This compares with 103 kcal for the bond in H_2. Closer approach between the nuclei results in repulsion. If the single electron is allowed to go into an "antibonding" orbital, the result is shown in the upper curve. Repulsion between the nuclei takes place as soon as they approach close enough to affect each other.

Since H_2^+ does not possess an electron pair, it can be concluded that a bond can be formed even in the absence of an electron pair. The strength of this bond can be measured by the amount of electrical energy which must be added to it in the discharge tube to break it up. This strength turns out to be different from that which would be calculated on the basis of the coulombic attraction of two positively charged nuclei for one electron. Hence there must be some other factors contributing to its stability. For reasons whose validity are questioned by some, one of these additional factors was named "resonance," and the name has persisted in spite of its shortcomings. We shall now attempt to secure an understanding of the nature of resonance by analogies to mechanical and molecular phenomena. As usual, we cannot expect such analogies to be exact but, within limits, they should help to clarify the nature of the subatomic phenomena under study.

30–7 Entropy

First, let us consider a gas-tight container with a partition in the middle, filled with gas on one side and empty on the other, as in Fig. 30–2. If a pinhole were drilled into the partition, it would be easy to predict the result: gas would flow from A to B until the pressure on both sides became equal. Evidently, the system is more stable when the gas is spread over both parts of the container than when it is confined to one side. Nearly everyone recognizes that gas flows from a system at higher pressure to one at lower pressure, which was the case in this example. Now let us consider a second case in which this pressure differential does not exist. This is illustrated in Fig. 30–3.

FIGURE 30–2   FIGURE 30–3

In Fig. 30–3 we have represented two gases which are as nearly alike as is feasible and which are confined in the container at equal pressures. A pinhole is now drilled into the partition and the container allowed to stand. In spite of the fact that no pressure differential exists, it will be found that the two gases distribute themselves evenly in the two compartments rather than remain in the ones which originally held them. Even in this case, the system is more stable when both gases are spread over both parts of the container than when each remains on one side.

The factor which stabilizes a system in a large volume with respect to the same system in a smaller volume is called *entropy*. Entropy may be thought of as a measure of disorder. One of the basic laws of nature which governs energy is the second law of thermodynamics. It follows from this law that spontaneous changes tend to take place in the direction in which entropy increases. This says that spontaneous changes go in the direction which creates an increase in disorder.

Most persons rebel at the concept that the disorder in the world is constantly increasing. They cite the obvious fact that man has built great cities and is busily engaged in rearranging the countryside to secure greater order. Energy measurements show, however, that the energy required to rearrange objects to secure this order is more than sufficient to offset the measure of order gained. The result is that the apparent increase in order which man gains is made only at the expense of the creation of an even greater amount of insensible disorder in the form of energy degraded for the tasks undertaken.

The great French philosopher, Henri Bergson, has summarized the second law of thermodynamics nonmathematically:

> The law of the degradation of energy does not bear essentially on magnitudes—it is the most metaphysical of the laws of physics since it points out without interposed symbols, without artificial devices of measurements, the direction in which the world is going. It tells us that changes that are visible and heterogeneous will be more and more diluted into

changes that are invisible and homogeneous, and that the instability to which we owe the richness and variety of the changes taking place in our solar system will gradually give way to the relative stability of elementary vibrations continually and perpetually repeated.*

The British physicist, Clerk Maxwell, tried to imagine a process by which the second law of thermodynamics might be reversed. He thought of two gas containers, such as those in Fig. 30–3, with a pinhole between them. Stationed at the pinhole was to be a small intelligent being, "Maxwell's demon." Whenever the demon saw a fast gas molecule approaching from the right, he would open the pinhole and allow it to pass through. If it came from the left, he would keep the hole closed. However, if a slow molecule came from the left he would allow it to pass through. By this process, the left container would ultimately have all the fast molecules and the right container all the slow ones. Thus a temperature differential would be established and order would be created from disorder. The fallacy in this argument is that energy would be required even to open and close the pinhole, without considering that necessary to gauge the relative velocities of the gas molecules. The amount of energy required to perform these necessary tasks would outweigh the gain recorded in the temperature differential of the final system.

We may summarize by saying that whenever men have studied *complete* systems instead of *isolated* systems, they have concluded that spontaneous changes take place in the direction that is accompanied by an increase in entropy. Hence a system with high entropy is more stable than one with low entropy.

30–8　Entropy and Resonance

While the analogy of these large-scale phenomena with those of subatomic particles is not a perfect one, it is true even in the realm of electrons that a system in which an electron or electron pair can occupy a large volume is more stable than one in which it can occupy only a small volume. For $H_2{}^+$, the application of this principle leads to the conclusion that the system will be more stable when the single electron is free to wander about the whole of the volume between the nuclei than when it is confined to the central point. This extra stabilization obtained through the electron's utilization of the whole volume available to it instead of its confinement to the central position is called *resonance stabilization*.

The classical formulas of organic chemistry are not well adapted to the representation of bonds stabilized by resonance. New formulations must be sought. None that has been devised so far is free from possible criticism. The most expressive of these are the most cumbersome. A compromise is usually sought by writing a formula according to a convention and reading into this conventional symbolism more than is explicit in the symbol itself. Alternative schemes of symbolism have been based on alternative methods of analysis of the details of the bonds which are being represented.

---

*Henri Bergson, *Creative Evolution*, translated by Arthur Mitchell. London: Macmillan and Co. Ltd., 1911.

30-9 The Valence-Bond Approach

The first quantum-mechanical analysis of the chemical bond was performed in 1927 by Heitler and London. They utilized the so-called "valence-bond" analysis, which corresponds more closely to the usual chemical picture of a bond than to some of the later representations. According to the valence-bond description, two atoms are first considered when separated at a considerable distance. Changes in energy are then calculated as they approach close enough to interact. This corresponds to the process illustrated in Fig. 30–1.

The formation of the coulombic molecular model, illustrated by the approach of two nuclei with four floating magnets each, Fig. 29–1 (a) and (b), corresponds quite well to the hypothetical process of interaction whose results are calculated by the valence-bond method. If we imagine the diatomic molecule as being formed by the approach of two atoms in the manner shown, analysis shows that the main forces holding the molecule together are electrostatic attractions between protons and electrons. Spin pairing permits coalescence of the atoms instead of repulsion and resonance stabilization also contributes to the stabilization of the bond. Using this system, we may represent the delocalization of the electron pair which results in resonance stabilization by the following symbolism:

$$H—H \leftrightarrow H^+H^- \leftrightarrow H^-H^+$$

We may consider a double bond as being formed by the addition of a second bond to one already existing. Because of the strength of a double bond, its rupture does not take place in a single step, as was shown in the systematic degradation of ethylene to oxalic acid and finally, to carbon monoxide and carbon dioxide. Accordingly, we may treat the first bond as fixed and the second as the bond of particular interest for chemical study. The resonance stabilization of the first bond is thus conventionally ignored and attention is concentrated on that of the second bond, thus simplifying the symbolism. The conventional representation of the carbon-to-carbon double bond would then be as follows.

It will be noted that in this representation, only electron pairs are delocalized. An additional delocalization can be conceived as follows.

In this hypothetical form, an electron pair has been broken and the spins are no longer paired; thus the formula implies more than it states explicitly, just as we saw that the formula for benzene implies more than it states. To unpair the electrons would cost the energy resulting from electron pairing. Accordingly, this would be a high-energy form and would not be capable of contributing to the lowering of energy by resonance. Such separations of electrons have been observed in the study of the spectra of organic molecules and it is known that when separated, unpaired electrons tend to pair again only relatively slowly. Such a slow recombination would not meet the requirements for resonance stabilization. The change from an electron pair to two unpaired electrons is said to involve a change in *multiplicity*. The name results from the fact that in similar cases in atomic spectra, the number of spectral lines within a short distance under certain conditions changes, in this case from one to three, when the electronic multiplicity changes. Thus the change from paired to unpaired electrons is a "singlet-triplet" transition. Because of the energy and time relationships involved in a change in multiplicity, it is a rule of resonance that only those forms are included in a representation which involve no change in multiplicity.

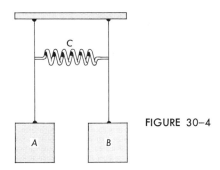

FIGURE 30–4

30–10   Resonating Pendulums

The name "resonance" was applied to the phenomenon of delocalization of electrons in analogy to mechanical and acoustical resonance in physics. Mechanical resonance may be illustrated readily by the use of coupled pendulums. Figure 30–4 shows such a pair of pendulums. In this experiment, the two pendulums, A and B are adjusted so that their periods are equal, and a light spring is used to couple them. Pendulum A is then raised along its arc to the maximum excursion desired while pendulum B remains at rest. Pendulum A is then allowed to fall through its arc, thus starting it in motion 90° out of phase with pendulum B. The motion of A will be weakly transmitted through the spring, and it will be observed that B gradually picks up in oscillation, while A simultaneously dies down. A stage will be reached in which B is exactly 90° out of phase with A and in which all the motion is concentrated in B, and A is at rest. The process will then reverse itself and the motion will be retransmitted to A. Two coupled pendulums performing in such a manner are said to exhibit *resonance*. As an alternative, we might imagine a hypothetical condition in which the energy would remain in A without being transmitted to B. Such a condition may be approximated by exerting a constraint on pendulum B that prevents it from moving. The more stable of the two conditions may be defined as being that observed to eventuate when all restraints are removed. Removal of the restraint on pendulum B is seen to cause the system to assume the condition in which energy interchanges between the two pendulums. If the hypothetical system were the more stable, it would be the one observed. It may be concluded that this interchange of energy over a larger volume than that swept out by the pendulum *A* alone causes a stabilization of the system as a whole. Thus we may say that the condition in which energy is being interchanged between the two pendulums is "stabilized by resonance," while the two hypothetical conditions in which the pendulums are coupled but in one of which *A* would oscillate without affecting *B* and in the other of which *B* would oscillate without affecting *A* are not resonance-stabilized.

Coupled pendulums may also be used to illustrate still further principles of resonance. Suppose that *A* is appreciably shortened so that it oscillates much more rapidly than *B*. The pendulums are then coupled by the spring and, as before, *A* is drawn out of phase by 90° and then allowed to start oscillating. It will be observed that the transfer of energy between the two systems is now quite imperfect: *A* slows down some but never stops completely, *B* speeds up some but never attains maximum excursion. Each pendulum has some tendency to slow down and speed up but the "resonance interaction" is much smaller than in the case of the two pendulums which were initially of the same energy. This experiment illustrates another principle which has been observed at the molecular level. When estimations of the magnitude of resonance stabilization of bonds are attempted, it is found that the greatest stabilization is achieved between those bonds in which the hypothetical extremes are identical. In cases in which they differ greatly, resonance stabilization is greatly diminished.

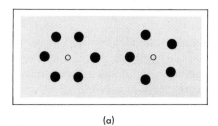 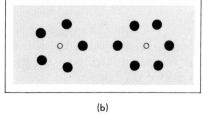

(a)   (b)

FIGURE 30–5

30–11 "Resonance" in a Coulombic System

The principle involved in symmetrical resonance may also be illustrated with the floating magnets. If two atoms are made on the central track of the tank, one with five "electrons," the other with six, it can be seen that the sixth electron can be displaced from the hexagon to the pentagon and back with no difficulty (Fig. 30–5). If, however, we attempt to displace an electron from the pentagon to the hexagon, the experiment will not work. Energy exchange of the type represented by the motion of electrons does not take place readily between two systems of widely differing energies.

30–12 Estimation of Resonance Energy

Several methods have been used to estimate the extent of resonance stabilization. One of these is spectroscopic. Its consideration will be deferred until we reach a more detailed discussion of color and constitution. Another method relying on a simpler principle is that from so-called "thermochemical" measurements. This may be illustrated by the example of benzene.

Benzene can be thought of, as Kekulé did originally, as being made up of two extreme structures, (a) and (b).

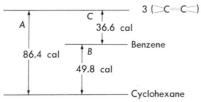

(a)   (b)

These would correspond to the hypothetical cases of pendulums A and B in Fig. 30–4 in which no interchange of energy between the two forms occurred. Each of these would have the same energy. The energy evolved on hydrogenation to cyclohexane could be calculated by assuming that each $C=C$ bond would evolve the same amount of heat on hydrogenation as ethylene would. The heat of hydrogenation of ethylene is 28.8 kcal/mole. Since there are three double bonds, the expected heat of hydrogenation of benzene would be 86.4 kcal. When the experiment was performed by Kistiakowsky, the heat of hydrogenation observed was only 49.8 kcal. Since less heat was evolved than expected, the benzene must have been more stable than the three ethylenic bonds by the difference in energy, that is, by 36.6 kcal. The relationships are illustrated in the energy diagram in Fig. 30–6. In this diagram, A (86.4 kcal) is the heat which would be expected from the hydrogenation of three ethylenic bonds, B (49.8 kcal) is that observed in the hydrogenation of benzene, and C (36.6 kcal) is distance on the energy diagram by which benzene lies below three ethylenes. This distance represents an estimate of the resonance stabilization of benzene.

FIG. 30–6. Energy diagram illustrating the relationship between the heat of hydrogenation of three ethylene bonds and of benzene.

PROBLEMS

30-1   Three principles which have emerged from the discussions on electronic behavior will be of value in the estimation of the relative energies of different electronic arrangements in molecules, the so-called "canonical structures" used in formulating resonance possibilities. These principles are (1) octets are more stable than sextets; (2) it requires energy to separate charges; (3) it costs energy to stretch bonds. We may review electronic structures about nitrogen, since resonance involving nitrogen atoms is of common occurrence.

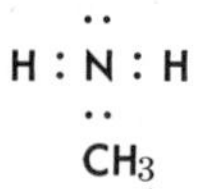

$$\overset{..}{\underset{..}{H : N : H}}$$
$$CH_3$$

Methylamine

N has an octet. In its outer shell N has two unshared electrons and the equivalent of $\frac{6}{2}$ or 3 electrons in bonds. The total is 5. This matches the 5 positive charges on the nucleus. Therefore N is neutral. The formulation on the left below has a sextet. The charge is +1. Why?

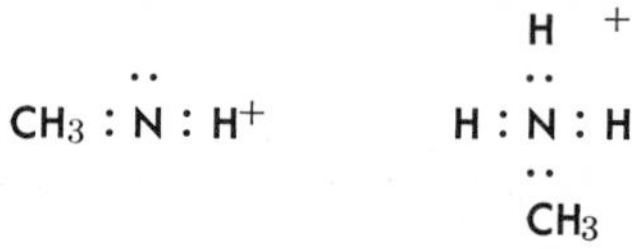

$$CH_3 : \overset{..}{N} : H^+ \qquad \overset{H \quad +}{\underset{CH_3}{\overset{..}{H : N : H}}}$$

Methylammonium ion

In methylammonium ion N has an octet. It has no unshared electrons and $\frac{8}{2}$ or 4 electrons in bonds. Therefore it has a charge of +1. The formulation below has a sextet. There is no charge. Why?

$$\overset{..}{: N : H}$$

(a) Which would contribute most to the resonance stabilization of benzene?

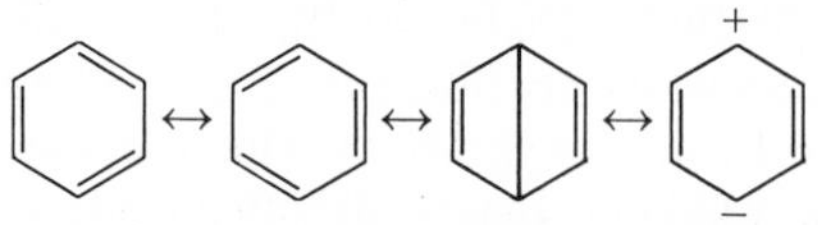

(a)   (b)   (c)   (d)

(b) Which would contribute more to the stabilization of methyl isocyanide?

$$CH_3—\overset{+}{N}\equiv\overset{-}{C} \qquad CH_3—N=C$$
(a)   (b)

How many electrons has the isonitrile carbon in (a)? In (b)?

(c) For nitromethane:

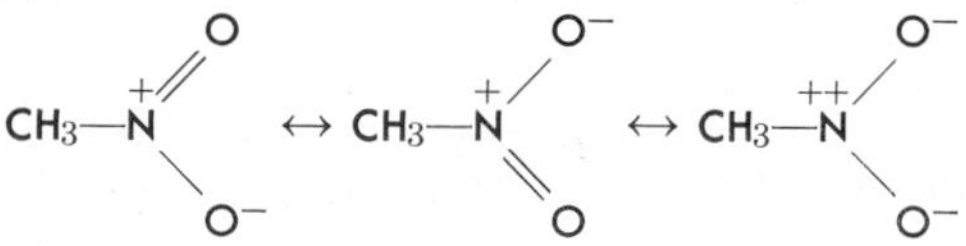

(a)   (b)   (c)

(d) For acetamide:

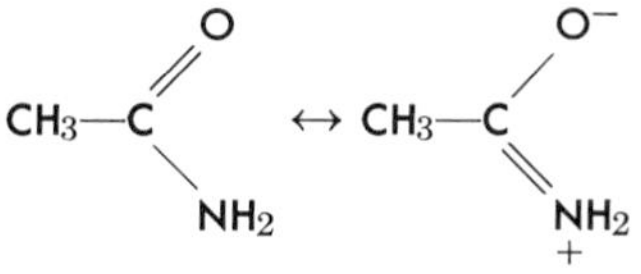

$$CH_3-C \begin{smallmatrix} O \\ \\ NH_2 \end{smallmatrix} \leftrightarrow CH_3-C \begin{smallmatrix} O^- \\ \\ \overset{+}{NH_2} \end{smallmatrix}$$

$$(a) \qquad\qquad (b)$$

30–2 Resonance structures should be anticipated in systems containing alternating double bonds or in systems which can produce double bonds by utilization of unshared electron pairs on electronegative atoms. For example, we should expect a minor contribution to the structure of butadiene from the ionic structures derived as follows:

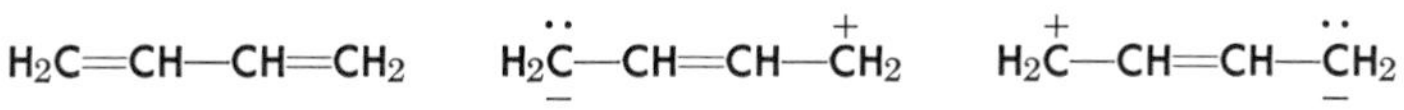

$$H_2C=CH-CH=CH_2 \qquad H_2\overset{\cdot\cdot}{\underset{-}{C}}-CH=CH-\overset{+}{CH_2} \qquad H_2\overset{+}{C}-CH=CH-\overset{\cdot\cdot}{\underset{-}{CH_2}}$$

(a) To keep account of the structures, organic chemists often use an arrow to indicate movement of an electron pair. Show how these may thus be derived from each other. Note the use of ethylene as an example.

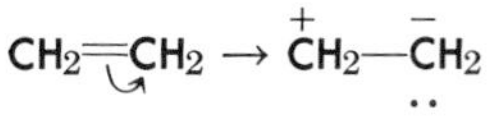

$$CH_2=CH_2 \rightarrow \overset{+}{C}H_2-\overset{-}{\underset{\cdot\cdot}{C}}H_2$$

Likewise, aniline will be stabilized through structures of the type shown below.

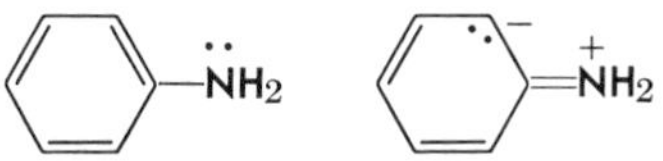

$$\bigcirc-\overset{\cdot\cdot}{N}H_2 \qquad \bigcirc\overset{\cdot\cdot}{\underset{-}{=}}\overset{+}{N}H_2$$

(b) Write two other resonance structures for aniline. Use the electrons on the 2-position to form a new double bond and displace the double bond to avoid a pentavalent carbon.

(c) Can you write similar structures for the cation I formed by adding a strong mineral acid to aniline?

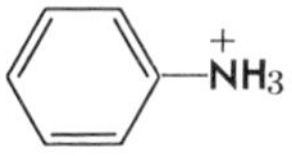

$$\bigcirc-\overset{+}{N}H_3$$

$$I$$

(d) Write the important resonance structures for pyrrole. Is nitrogen ever negative, or always positive? One of these situations is excluded because it would destroy all bonding between two atoms in the molecule.

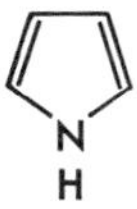

Pyrrole

(e) Choose several more conjugated molecules from earlier chapters and practice writing structures if you think you need more practice. At this point you should recognize that most resonance structures in neutral molecules *separate* charge. In ions—which we shall see are often intermediates in reactions—resonance structures *distribute* an already existing charge.

(f) Write the structures you would expect for the benzhydryl cation II. What other systematic name would you give this as a derivative of methane (or methyl cation)?

II

(g) Will resonance be more important in stabilizing neutral molecules or the ions derived from them in the course of a reaction? Keep this point in mind for later chapters.

30–3   Because Dewar was the first to suggest the importance of long-bond structures such as III for benzene resonance, such forms with *para* positions connected are called Dewar structures. The actual preparation of "Dewar benzene" was effected recently; this material is demonstrably different in its spectra, but may be converted into benzene quantitatively by heating it at 90°C for 30 minutes.

III

(a) Since long bonds are unlikely, this material will have bonds of reasonable length. Considering the distorted 120° and 109°28′ angles involved, draw a perspective view of this molecule.

(b) Would you expect a molecule corresponding to the structure you have drawn to be thermally stable, considering the bond strain in it? What other fact helps to explain the ready rearrangement of the molecule to benzene?

(c) The molecule has been described as an isomer of benzene, not a resonance structure. Because the nuclei cannot move with the same speed as the electrons, the bonds are not directed to the same angles as in benzene, and the nuclei are in different positions in space. Since nuclei do not move at the speed of light, there can be no "equilibration" with the usual Kekulé resonance structures. Consider now that no molecule corresponding exactly to everything that only one Kekulé structure by itself implies (a simple cyclohexatriene, with no resonance at all) has been prepared. Would this molecule—if it had been prepared—be a resonance structure of benzene? The answer to this question implies that when we use Kekulé forms as resonance contributors to benzene, we read more into them than they actually represent in classical formulation. What extra fact is that?

30–4   Keeping in mind where single and double bonds absorb in the infrared, rationalize the following facts.

(a) Acetone absorbs at about 5.80 microns in the infrared, but acetophenone absorbs at about 6.12 microns.

(b) 1-acetyl-2-methylcyclohexene-1 absorbs at 5.94 microns; 1-acetyl-2-methylcyclohexene-2 at 5.85 microns.

(c) In D_2O sodium acetate absorbs at 6.41 microns; on the addition of DCl this band is replaced by one at 5.78 microns. This shift can be reversed by the addition of NaOD. In this study H_2O could have been used except for technical reasons; it absorbs in this region. It would help to consider the carbon-carbon bonds in benzene as averages of single and double bonds and apply this approach to the resonating systems above.

How can the orbital concept of atomic spectra
be extended to include organic molecules?

31

ATOMIC AND MOLECULAR ORBITALS

31–1 Molecular Orbitals

In the preceding chapter we saw the approach to the formulation of a mathematical model of the covalent bond through the "valence-bond" method, the first to be invented for the purpose. Essentially, this model is constructed by imagining two atomic nuclei with their associated electrons to be far apart in space and then allowing them to approach and calculating the interactions which would result when the nuclei are separated by the distance of the bond in question. The other sequence of operations which might be adopted has also been applied to the solution of the same problem. In this approach, the two nuclei are imagined as being stripped of all their electrons and then are arbitrarily set at the intermolecular distance. Electrons are then added and the nature of the interactions calculated on completion of this different sequence of events. This sequence may be illustrated with the floating magnets, using two separated centers at interaction distance and adding magnets to distribute between them. This approach is called the "molecular-orbital" approach. It is simpler for the mathematical solution of certain problems and consequently has its place in the chemical literature.

31–2 Valence-Bond and Molecular-Orbital Approaches

Some controversy has arisen in the literature over which of the two views, the valence bond or the molecular orbital, is "correct." Since the molecular-orbital approach is a later one, some have even imagined that just for this reason it must

419

be the only correct approach. It will be seen, however, that neither of these approaches can be considered to be "correct" in an absolute sense. Each is a mathematical model designed for the simplification of the solutions to a particular series of problems. Since they are models, we should expect the extent of the analogies to be obtained with either to be limited. In his own work, the organic chemist will find that the solutions to many problems in reaction mechanisms are reached more easily with the valence-bond approach and that the solutions to others are more readily grasped from the molecular-orbital point of view. The latter statement is particularly true for the solution to problems involving inter-actions of matter with electromagnetic radiation, that is, spectroscopic and photo-chemical problems. For this reason, we shall now consider briefly some of the main points of the molecular-orbital theory.

31-3   Atomic Orbitals

Since the promulgation of the Bohr model for the hydrogen atom in 1913, spectro-scopists have used the atomic-orbital approach to the rationalization of atomic spectra. They have been rewarded by a very high degree of precision in the calcu-lation of atomic spectra. It is natural, then, that the general approach used in the simpler problem of atomic spectra should be modified in an attempt to apply it to the more complex problem of molecular spectra. The resultant theory is the molecular-orbital theory. Obviously, some understanding of atomic orbitals should precede a study of molecular orbitals because of the historical sequence of the development of the field.

Since the term "orbital" was first applied in an imagined analogy to the orbits of celestial mechanics, this analogy is one which is frequently assumed to be applicable by the beginning student. In fact, gravitational fields obey the inverse square law that is also followed by electrostatic and magnetic fields. In spite of this, there are profound differences between the three types of field. The concept of polarity is lacking in gravitational fields. All masses attract each other, and a gravitational force comparable to the repulsive force between similarly charged particles has not yet been discovered. In celestial mechanics, the force that balances gravitational attraction is centrifugal, a kinetic manifestation relying on different principles from the positive and negative charges in electrostatics.

A second distinction between celestial orbits and atomic orbits lies in the relative geometries of the two systems. Planets are distinct and discrete bodies which rotate about the sun. Electrons, on the other hand, are sometimes described mathematically as though they behave similarly, while for purposes of other calculations, they must be treated as diffuse charge clouds engulfing the nucleus. The geometry of the hydrogen atom may be thought of as resembling a solar system for some purposes, but the Li_2 molecule is best described as two bonding electrons which because of their spins, have coalesced into a cloud and have positively charged nuclei *external* to the electron cloud, a situation which would be impossible to achieve in a solar system controlled by gravitational and centrif-ugal forces.

31–4   The Hydrogen Atom

The picture of the hydrogen atom which best describes its quantitative behavior can be represented, as an approximation, as though the charge function being studied is the probability that an electron will be found at a given instant at a certain position with respect to the nucleus. We may suppose that the means for locating the position of an electron could exist and that we should be able to locate the electron at any given instant. We should then repeat this observation perhaps millions of times until we could state the probability of finding the electron at any given distance from the nucleus. The probability-distribution function would then appear as shown in Fig. 31–1. The mathematical equation describing this function is known. In this figure, the vertical distance represents the probability of finding an electron, and the horizontal distance represents the radial distance from the nucleus. The distance a_0 is the radius of greatest electron density and corresponds to the radius of the hydrogen atom under the original Bohr theory. This is the distance from the nucleus at which the electron was supposed to remain in its circular "orbit." In fact, the energy relations of hydrogen are better described by the function represented by Fig. 31–1 which shows that the electron may be found with moderately high frequency (i.e., 60% of the time) at distances from the nucleus greater than the atomic radius.

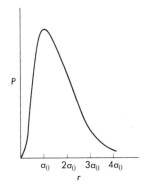

FIG. 31–1.   Probability of electron density.

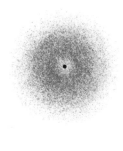

FIG. 31–2.   Representation of electron distribution in the hydrogen atom.

Alternative representations of the geometry of the atom may be presented pictorially. One which has received wide currency is a series of dots surrounding a nucleus in which an attempt is made to equate the density of the dots with the probability function, as shown in Fig. 31–2. This is difficult to do with any acceptable degree of precision. Another scheme which is easier for the draftsman and arrives at excellent precision is to prepare a contour map. For the hydrogen atom, this would be a circular target, as shown in Fig. 31–3 with the rings labeled according to the numbers to be approximated from the probability function. The convention most frequently adopted, however, is the use of cross-sectional drawings with only the boundary surfaces used to represent the whole figure. Such a representation of the hydrogen atom is given in Fig. 31–4. This type of representation should be understood in terms of physical symbolism. The drawing is not meant to represent a negatively charged shell of a given radius removed from the positively charged nucleus, nor a surface within which the electrons are confined. Instead, it represents a sphere whose charge-density distribution varies with the distance from the center in the manner shown in Fig. 31–1. As indicated above, the Bohr radius of the hydrogen atom is the radius of a sphere encompassing approximately 40% of the electron density. We shall use boundary surfaces in representing other orbitals later. In each case, these should be understood in the symbolic sense rather than in the literal sense.

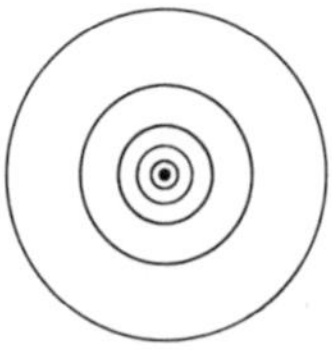

FIG. 31–3. Contour representation of electron distribution in the hydrogen atom.

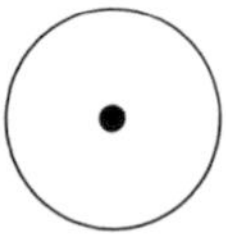

FIG. 31–4. Boundary surface of the hydrogen atom.

31–5 Atomic Spectra

In the early days of spectroscopy, as we saw in Chapter 28, it was discovered that lines could be found in the emission spectrum of hydrogen whose frequencies corresponded to relatively simple whole number relationships. These will be discussed in more detail later when we study absorption spectra. Several such series were found in the hydrogen spectrum. After the advent of the Bohr theory, it was realized that these series corresponded to electronic transitions taking place between higher and lower energy levels of the hydrogen atom. Since the frequencies of spectral lines could be measured with high precision, this permitted the energy differences between various levels in the hydrogen atom to be measured with corresponding precision. These studies were extended to other elements. It was then found that corresponding energy levels exist in the other elements but that the spacing between levels in different elements is different. Hence it is possible

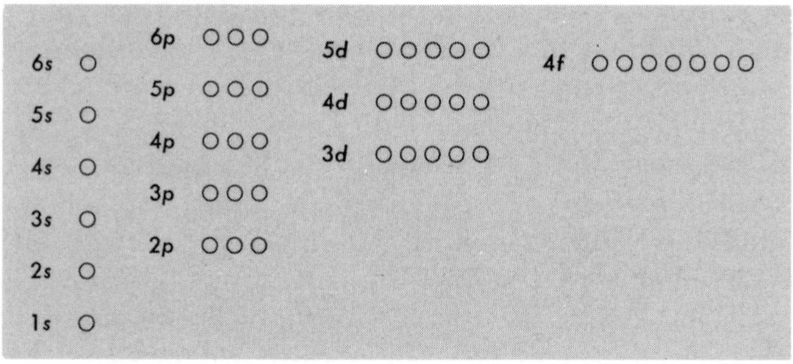

FIG. 31–5. General energy levels for atoms.

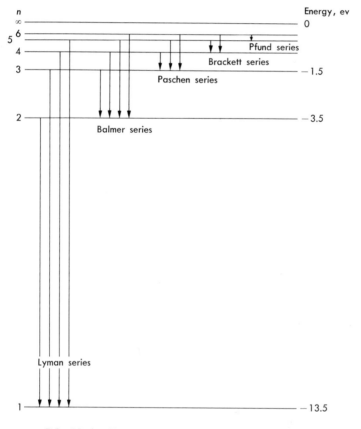

FIG. 31–6.   Major transitions of the hydrogen spectrum.

to draw general energy-level diagrams whose outlines will be similar for all the elements, but whose details will vary from element to element. These variations may be sufficient to alter the relative positions of levels bearing the same designation in some cases. A generalized energy-level diagram is given in Fig. 31–5. In the hydrogen spectrum, transitions from the 2-, 3-, 4-, and 5-levels to the 1-level form the Lyman series, those from the 3-, 4-, 5-, and 6-levels to the 2-level form the Balmer series, those from the 6-, 5-, and 4-levels to the 3-level form the Paschen series, and so on, as shown in Fig. 31–6.

31–6   Atoms Beyond Hydrogen in the Periodic Table

Each of the "cells" in Fig. 31–5 represents an orbital and is able to hold two electrons. Spectroscopists have determined that in building atoms, a lower energy level is filled with two electrons, as a rule, before a higher one is started. Thus beryllium would have two electrons in the 1s-level and two in the 2s-level. In 1930, Hund discovered that electrons tend to avoid being in the same orbital, so

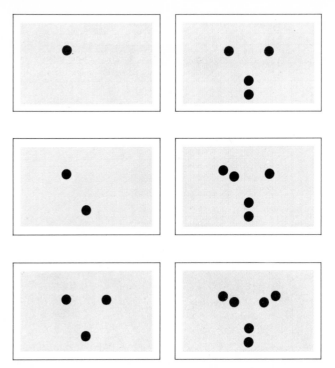

FIG. 31–7. Progressive addition of six floating magnets to three attracting centers. Illustration of Hund's rule.

far as possible. Accordingly, in the nitrogen atom, electrons would be paired in the 1s- and 2s-levels, but only single electrons would be present in each of the three orbitals of the 2p-level. This principle can also be illustrated by the floating magnets. Distribution of three magnets among three attracting centers results in one going to each before pairing begins (Fig. 31–7).

The presence of electrons in lower levels conditions the patterns which can be assumed by those added to higher levels. We have already seen this principle illustrated by experiments with the floating magnets and, although the geometry of the three-dimensional system differs from that of the floating magnets, the general principle still holds true. Atomic orbitals higher than the s-levels no longer possess spherical symmetry. The p-orbitals are dumbbell shaped with nodes, that is, points of zero electron density, at the nucleus and two lobes, one on either side of the nucleus. For convenience, these are represented on cartesian coordinates, one orbital on the x-axis, one on the y, and one on the z. The opposite lobes are conventionally marked $+$ and $-$ to distinguish opposite parity, that is, a change in sign of the mathematical function on passing through the origin. As a rule, coupling between orbitals occurs only with orbitals of like parity. With six charged lobes in space, the angles found between them are $90°$, as would be expected. For convenience in visualization, the three p-orbitals have been separated according to their spatial orientations in Fig. 31–8.

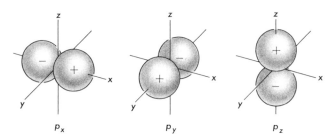

Boundary surfaces of p-orbitals   FIGURE 31–8

31–7   Molecular Orbitals; the Hydrogen Molecule

When spectroscopists had learned enough about the nature of the orbitals to permit the calculation of atomic energy levels with precision, it was a logical extension for them to use the same approach in the formulation of molecular energy levels. If we imagine two identical hydrogen atoms separated to a considerable distance, each will have a nucleus and an electron; in the ground states, each will have its electron in the 1s-orbital. Hence there will be two identical orbitals. If we now imagine these two atoms combined into a hydrogen molecule, then, on analogy with the hydrogen atom, there should be only one orbital at the lowest level, corresponding to the 1s-level. To distinguish this from the atomic case, this is called a sigma orbital, represented by the Greek letter σ. However, when two atomic orbitals are combined, two molecular orbitals result. One of these is a bonding orbital, that is, an orbital in which the approach of electrons produces an energy minimum and resulting attraction. The other is an antibonding orbital, in which the approach of electrons produces repulsion. The antibonding orbital is represented by the notation σ^*. The splitting is represented in Fig. 31–9. Figure 30–1 showed the energy diagrams for the H_2^+ species when the single bonding electron was placed in the σ orbital and in the other case in which it was placed in the σ^* antibonding orbital. In the latter case there is only increasing repulsion between the atoms as they approach. A hydrogen molecule with two bonding electrons in the sigma orbital may have one of them promoted to an antibonding orbital in a higher energy level by the absorption of light. The resulting repulsion is not so great as the attraction in the case of the sigma electron, especially since the electron in the higher energy level may continue to be spin-paired with that in the lower level. The result is an "excited" hydrogen molecule with a weak bond whose length would be greater than that of the ground state molecule. This is a qualitative representation of the process of light absorption by a molecule which gives the measurements necessary to calculate the difference in energy between the various levels of the molecule.

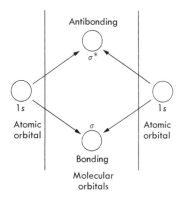

FIGURE 31–9

The preceding discussion should make it clear why the spectroscopist finds it convenient to cast molecules into the conceptual framework which has proved to be fruitful in the calculations of atomic spectroscopy. While we shall find this approach convenient in the discussion of molecular spectroscopy, we shall also find that the qualitative picture presented in this manner is very useful in approaching certain portions of the study of reaction mechanisms.

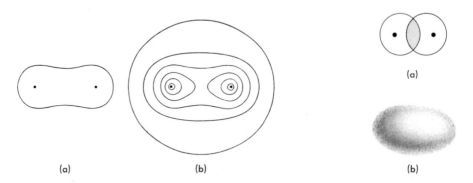

(a)   (b)   (a)

(b)

FIGURE 31–10   FIGURE 31–11

While the electron cloud surrounding a hydrogen atom has spherical symmetry, study of the radial energy distribution in the hydrogen molecule shows that the coalescence of the two clouds produces a new shape in the sigma cloud. The boundary surface of this cloud may be represented as in Fig. 31–10(a). The contour diagram is given in Fig. 31–10(b). In the contour diagrams, each continuous curve represents the cross-sectional contour of a solid at the distance of equal probability of electron density. This process of coalescence of the two electron clouds of the atoms into a single cloud of a sigma bond is commonly referred to as *overlapping* and is frequently pictured as mutual sharing of space by two atomic boundary surfaces as in Fig. 31–11(a). This representation suffers from the disadvantage that it does not convey the essence of the contour representation of Fig. 31–10(b), which is what should be read into the symbolism of Fig. 31–10(a). The electron-cloud picture is given in Fig. 31–11(b).

31–8   Orbitals of the First-Row Elements

After the σ and σ^* orbitals, the next higher orbitals are made by combinations of the $2s$ and then the $2p$ atomic orbitals. The relative positions of the resulting molecular orbitals are shown in Fig. 31–12.

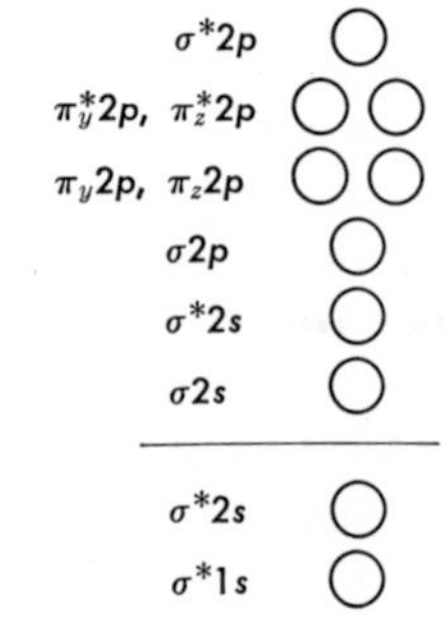

σ^*2p

$\pi_y^*2p,\ \pi_z^*2p$

$\pi_y2p,\ \pi_z2p$

$\sigma2p$

σ^*2s

$\sigma2s$

σ^*2s

σ^*1s

FIG. 31–12.   Relative positions of first-row molecular orbitals.

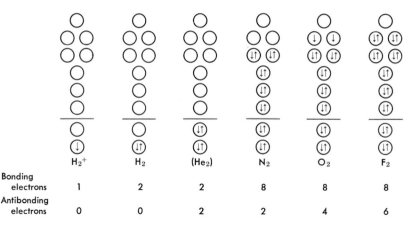

H_2^+	H_2	(He_2)	N_2	O_2	F_2
Bonding electrons					
1	2	2	8	8	8
Antibonding electrons					
0	0	2	2	4	6

FIG. 31–13.   Electronic structures of molecules in the first row.

The molecular-orbital representations of the electronic structure of some selected symmetrical molecules of the first row are shown in Fig. 31–13.

31–9 The Orbitals of Methane

Physical evidence such as the measurement of the moment of inertia of the methane molecule by means of infrared spectroscopy and chemical evidence of the type discussed in Book 1 both lead to the conclusion that the four C—H bonds in methane are equivalent. Yet the carbon atom on which methane is constructed has four orbitals in the 2-level, one $2s$ and three $2p$. How are these facts to be reconciled?

To rationalize the fact that methane has four identical C—H bonds, it is assumed that each of these bonds is composed of hybrid orbitals having some s-character and some p-character. These orbitals are called sp^3 hybrid orbitals, since each of them is formed from one s-orbital and three p-orbitals. The boundary surfaces of these orbitals, arranged at tetrahedral angles, are represented in Fig. 31–14. As in the hydrogen molecule, the electron pair bonding each hydrogen to the central carbon engulfs the hydrogen nucleus creating an external negative field around the whole of the molecule.

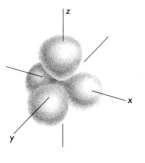

FIGURE 31–14

31–10 The Orbitals of Ethylene

The carbon-carbon bond of ethane resembles the C—H bonds of methane in many respects. For ethylene, however, a new factor is introduced by the double bond. Spectroscopic studies, as well as the chemical studies which we reviewed in Book 1, show that one C—C bond of ethylene is quite different from that of ethane. Chemically, this is responsible for the "unsaturation" of ethylene. Spectroscopically, ethylene absorbs light of much lower frequency, and therefore of much lower energy, than does ethane. This means that the electrons in the second bond of ethylene are less tightly held than those of a sigma bond. For this reason, it is customary to represent ethylene as having two different types of bond, a sigma bond, as in ethane, and another bond with looser electrons, called a π-bond because it is formed from p-electrons instead of s-electrons and has the same relation to its nodal plane as a p-orbital. The bonding skeleton of each carbon in ethylene, then, consists of one s-orbital and two p-orbitals, so that each carbon is surrounded by three sigma orbitals instead of four. Hence these orbitals are called "sp^2" hybrids. If all three were equivalent, it would be expected that their bond angles would be 120°. In fact, they are not precisely equivalent so that the C—C—H bond angle of ethylene is a few minutes greater than 120°.

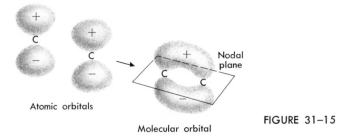

Atomic orbitals

Molecular orbital

FIGURE 31–15

The π-bond of ethylene is formed from the remaining p-orbitals on the carbons of ethylene. These coalesce in much the same way that the s-orbitals of hydrogen atoms coalesce. Since each is two-lobed with a nodal plane at the atomic center, the resulting figure is a double sausage, as shown in Fig. 31–15. It should be noted that only lobes of like parity will couple, as shown.

Chemical evidence for the existence of the pi cloud was presented by Lucas who found that silver ion forms a complex with ethylene in which the silver ion is equidistant from the two carbons:

$$\overset{\displaystyle Ag^+}{H_2C=\!\!=\!\!CH_2}$$

This does not represent covalent bonding of the silver to the carbons since it is a weak compound with the silver above the plane of the H—C—H triangle. This is taken to indicate that the silver is bonded to one lobe of the pi bond above this plane. For this reason, the compound is called a *pi complex*.

31–11   The Orbitals of Acetylene

Acetylene has two bonds that are unlike the C—C bond of ethane. Thus it is conventionally represented as having only one sigma bond between the carbons and one to each of the hydrogens. The two sigma bonds on carbon, then, will involve an s atomic orbital and a p atomic orbital and will be sp-hybrids. Since the H—C—C bond has only two sigma orbitals repelling each other in space, it would be expected to assume a bond angle of 180°, the value found by infrared observations.

FIG. 31–16. Molecular orbital of acetylene.

Since there are now four p-electrons remaining, we shall have four p atomic orbitals to coalesce to form the molecular orbitals. These would be expected to form two sets of double sausages, like those of Fig. 31–15, with their nodal planes at right angles, since this is the distribution that permits the lobes to be as far apart as possible in space. In the usual model, these coalesce into a cylinder, as in Fig. 31–16.

31–12 The Orbitals of Benzene

If benzene were correctly represented by one of the Kekulé structures, we should expect to find three ethylenic orbitals in the ring. The other structure, however, would give three new ethylenic orbitals at the positions alternate to those of the first Kekulé structure. Since benzene is not properly represented by either of these but behaves like a hybrid, we should expect hybridization of the six sets of ethylenic orbitals to form a single large benzene orbital encompassing the entire ring. This would have one lobe above the ring and one below with a nodal plane in the plane of the benzene carbons. This is the picture used by spectroscopists in their approach to the formulation of the ground state of the benzene ring. It is shown schematically in Fig. 31–17.

We shall discuss the chemical and spectroscopic implications of the molecular-orbital formula for benzene at the appropriate points in the succeeding chapters.

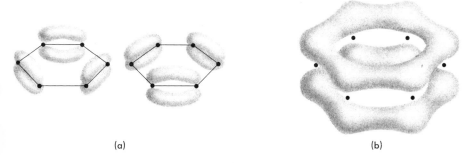

(a)   (b)

FIG. 31–17. (a) Ethylenic orbitals of Kekulé structures; (b) a molecular orbital of benzene.

31-13   The "Reality" of Orbitals

It should be emphasized again that the orbital picture, like the valence-bond picture, is a convenient concept for spectroscopic calculations and for energy estimations of interest to the reaction chemist. The organic chemist should use the one that he finds more convenient for his purposes. The method used in quantum mechanics for the visualization of a certain definite picture within a general conceptual framework is to make repetitive calculations, using many different models. The model associated with the calculation which gives the closest approach to the figures observed is taken as the most probable model. It is by these means that the models sketched in the foregoing section were arrived at. They are subject to correction whenever someone can conceive of a new model which fits better than the ones that have been used until then. It has been estimated that all the matter in the universe would not furnish enough paper to record the results of a computer calculation embracing all the possibilities for models for the benzene molecule. Whether or not we accept this estimation, we are forced to the conclusion that the difficulties in the way to a rigorous demonstration of the correspondence of any of the models to "reality" are tremendous. For this reason, we accept these models on a pragmatic basis realizing that they may conceivably be replaced later by something which has an even firmer pragmatic basis. As indicated, the methods used to arrive at the models are not chemical but are mathematical. To ground them thoroughly would require a text as large as the present one devoted solely to the subject of quantum mechanics. It is enough for the purposes of the beginning organic chemist to transfer to his kit of tools the best that the spectroscopists and other theorists have devised, provided he realizes that the base on which they are built is not as solid as rock.

PROBLEMS

31-1   It has been found possible in some cases to separate mixtures of olefins (and di-olefins) by chromatography over crushed silver nitrate. Explain this method.

31-2   The valence-bond theory predicts stabilization of molecules and ions for which several resonance forms can be written. Each form is considered to contribute a certain percent of the actual structure of the molecule. We have seen earlier how to write possible resonance forms and how to judge their effectiveness in contributing to the actual structure and thus increasing the stabilization. A chemist interested in the hypothetical stability of various small ions might consider the imaginary processes shown in Fig. 31–18. The new ions

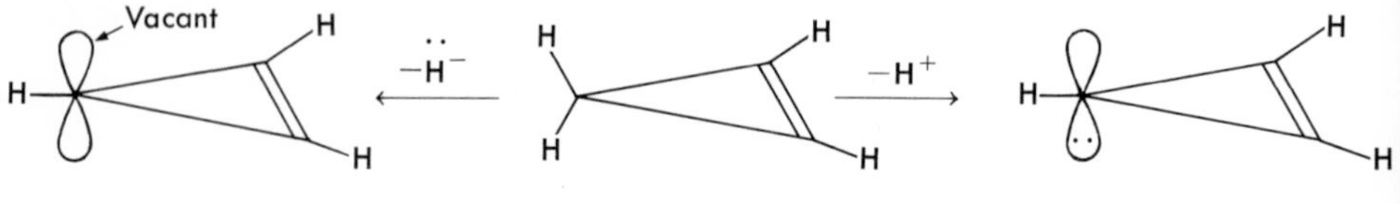

FIGURE 31–18

have orbitals with a different geometry; we may consider them more like sp^2- and p-orbitals, while the original molecule had orbitals more like sp^3. (Note that we say "like," because the bond angles in this molecule are not at all correct for pure sp^2- and sp^3-hybridization.) Therefore they are in proper positions for resonance to take place.

(a) What should the proper bond angles for sp^2- and sp^3-hybridization be?

(b) Draw a picture of the ions to show that there is proper geometry between orbitals for resonance to be effective.

(c) We can simplify our drawings of these ions (see right) and read this new geometry into them. Show now that valence-bond theory predicts that these ions will both be stabilized by resonance; that is, write the important resonance forms and comment on their contributions to the real picture of the molecule.

(d) Do the same for cyclobutadiene, cyclopentadienyl cation, cyclopentadienyl anion, benzene, cycloheptatrienyl cation, cycloheptatrienyl anion:

Valence-bond theory predicts special stability for each of these molecules.

Molecular-orbital theory takes a greatly different approach to these problems. Fundamentally, what valence-bond calculations do is to begin with several hypothetical molecules and find the best way to combine them:

In contrast, molecular-orbital theory starts with one molecule—in fact, not even a molecule but just the nuclei arranged in the proper geometry. Then electrons are added one by one until the right number is reached, and one calculates by a more or less complicated procedure the energy of the system and the positions in space of the volumes the electrons occupy. With certain assumptions this becomes very simply a matter of calculating the *energy levels* of the molecule, just as calculations for the hydrogen atom produced the chart. We will not carry out these calculations, but the very simplest method (called the Hückel method after its inventor) gives the following molecular energy levels of the pi systems for the geometries of three-, four-, and five-membered rings; note that some orbitals have the same energy, just as for hydrogen:

three-membered ring   four-membered ring   five-membered ring

six-membered ring   seven-membered ring

Just as the picture in Fig. 31–5 says nothing about the shapes of *s*-, *p*-, *d*-, and *f*-orbitals, so these diagrams say nothing about the shapes of molecular orbitals.

(e) Count the number of electrons (remember charges!) in each pi system in the eight structures shown below. (The pi system includes all atoms covered by resonance from the valence-bond approach.)

(f) Add the appropriate number of electrons for each case to the appropriate orbital diagram, filling the orbitals of lowest energy first. Remember that Hund's rule (Section 31–6) applies here for orbitals of equal energy, just as it does for the atomic case.

(g) This operation will tell which molecules and ions will be diradicals (2 unpaired electrons in different orbitals) and which will have all their electrons paired. According to this theory, which of the five have their electrons paired and which are diradicals?

(h) Organic diradicals are known to be reactive molecules; simple radicals alone are destroyed by oxygen and cause polymerization. Diradicals might be expected to be at least as reactive in this sense. If we interpret stability to mean lack of chemical reactivity, which of the molecules or ions above are stable, and which are not stable? Contrast this result with that from the valence-bond theory.

Experimental details are far from complete in this area. What has been done so far indicates that in this case the molecular-orbital approach does a somewhat better job of explaining at least the known facts.

For most of this course, valence-bond figures allow a more direct and easier method of determining stabilities of ions in reactions, and we shall not find ourselves in situations where the two theories predict different results, as in the case above. We will adopt the valence-bond approach until Chapter 51, when the molecular-orbital theory will be more useful. At that time we will also develop the pictures of the shapes of orbitals which we did not need here.

(i) Organic chemists often state that the Hückel rule implies special stability for cyclic species containing $4n + 2$ pi electrons. What is the basis for this rule of thumb?

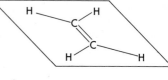

31–3 (In answering the following questions, all orbitals should be drawn.)

(a) Ethylene has a geometry as shown in Fig. 31–19(a), not Fig. 31–19(b). Both of these forms have all 120° angles. Why should all *six* atoms be in one plane?

(b) Would you expect the tendency in biphenyl to be toward nearly coplanar rings or rings at about 90° to each other?

Biphenyl

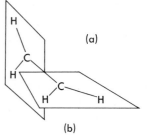

FIG. 31–19. (a) All one plane; (b) two planes.

What are the relationships between
the position of an atom in the periodic
table and its covalent radius, its van der Waals radius,
its relative polarity, the ease of its cleavage from a molecule,
and its bond strength in various molecules?

32

CORRELATIONS BETWEEN VARIOUS
PHYSICAL PROPERTIES OF INTEREST
TO THE CHEMIST

32–1 Van der Waals Radii

In Chapter 29 we saw that the increase in electron-attracting power of the nucleus on passing from the left to the right in the periodic table causes a decrease in the covalent bonding radius. In Chapter 31 we saw that the electron clouds surrounding most substances with sigma or pi bonds create negatively charged fields around the molecules. With the aid of these two principles it is possible to rationalize the main facts concerning van der Waals radii.

The equation of state for gases, put forth by van der Waals on empirical grounds (Chapter 8), is:

$$(P + a/V^2)(V - b) = RT.$$

In this equation P is the pressure, V is the volume, R is the gas constant, and T is the absolute temperature. When van der Waals first used the equation, the parameters a and b were simply empirical constants. Analysis will show, however, that a is the measure of an attractive force between molecules whose importance increases as V is diminished, that is, at high pressures. The parameter b, on the other hand, measures a force of repulsion which also becomes of greater importance as the pressure increases. We shall not deal further with the parameter a. The parameter b is a correction subtracted from the volume which is sufficiently close to the liquid volume to suggest its cause. After careful study, it has been deduced that this parameter represents the extreme limits of compressibility of the gas, that is, the volume occupied by the molecules of the gas. On this assumption, it is

433

Table 32-1

	N	O	F
Covalent radius	0.70	0.66	0.64
Van der Waals radius	1.50	1.40	1.35
Ratio	2.15	2.13	2.11

possible to calculate the interference radii of molecules and from these to derive interference radii of the atoms which compose the molecules. These radii are commonly referred to as the van der Waals radii. They may also be estimated by observing the closest approach of nonbonded atoms in crystals.

The forces of nuclear attraction which hold the molecule together also obviously act, at a greater distance, on the electron clouds surrounding the molecules. It would be expected, then, that an increase in the nuclear attractive force which diminished the covalent radius would also diminish the interference radius. How this works out in practice is shown by Table 32-1. (All measurements in this chapter are given in angstroms unless otherwise specified.) It will be seen that as the radius diminishes, the attraction of the charge becomes slightly more effective in reducing the van der Waals radius.

As we add rings of electrons between the nucleus and the valence electrons, we should expect the size of the interfering field on the exterior to be a smaller proportion of the whole than in the first row of the table. This effect is shown in Table 32-2.

Table 32-2

	P	S	Cl	As	Se	Br	Sb	Te	I
Covalent radius	1.10	1.04	0.99	1.21	1.17	1.14	1.41	1.37	1.33
Van der Waals radius	1.9	1.85	1.80	2.0	2.00	1.95	2.2	2.20	2.15
Ratio	1.7	1.78	1.82	1.7	1.71	1.71	1.6	1.61	1.61

Again we see that van der Waals radii diminish as covalent radii diminish. Scrutiny of the ratios in Table 32-2 shows, however, that these do not move in the same direction as in the first row. This may be ascribed to increasing ease of mechanical penetration of the van der Waals radii in the larger elements, resulting in interference radii which are smaller than might be expected for denser and more tightly bound fields.

It will be noted that no interference radii have been given for carbon. In aliphatic compounds, carbon is buried in the surrounding fields, as we have seen in the preceding chapter. In olefins and benzenoid derivatives, however, collisions with the fields surrounding carbon do take place. The half-thickness of the benzene ring, according to Pauling, is 1.7. The C—C bond distance in benzene is smaller than in ethane because of the multiple bonding. The interatomic distance has been found to be 1.39, giving a radius of 0.695. The ratio is 2.66, showing that the π-cloud above the benzene ring interferes at a relatively large distance from the plane of the ring. This leads to the conclusion that the benzene ring is extraordinarily thick.

As we saw in Book 1, it is because van der Waals radii are larger than covalent-bond radii that models must be constructed as truncated spheres to reflect true interferences in molecules.

32–2   Dipole Moments and Bond Polarities

We have seen that the fundamental force whose change alters bond radii is the charge on the atomic nucleus. As the charge increases on going toward the right in the periodic table, bond radii diminish because of increasing attraction on the bonding electrons. In a covalent bond, such a change will also affect other fundamental properties of the bond. One of these which is important in determining the course of a chemical reaction is the polarity of the bond.

Our magnetic model has shown how unequal attractions on the floating magnets determine the distribution of magnets in the figures resulting from the separation of two nuclei. In the cleavage of a covalent bond, unequal attractive forces exerted by unequally charged atomic nuclei exert a similar effect. Thus bond cleavages fall into two general classes, *homolytic*, in which the electrons constituting the covalent bond being broken are equally distributed between the separated particles, and *heterolytic*, in which one particle separates with one more electron pair than the other. We shall now examine in more detail the structural features responsible for a hypothetical changeover from one type of reaction to the other.

Differences between bonds with respect to their internal electronic distributions can be estimated by means of measurements of their dipole moments. In a symmetrical molecule, the center of positive charge coincides with the center of negative charge. In a dipole, the center of positive charge is moved in one direction and the center of negative charge in a different direction by the unequal nuclear attractions, with the result that the two no longer coincide. Thus the dipole moment may be regarded as two units of charge, one positive, the other negative, separated to a fraction of the distance between the two nuclei. The largest possible dipole moment for a single bond would result if the two charges were separated to the full bond distance. The equation for the dipole moment can be written in the form used for mechanical moments:

$$\mu = ec, \tag{1}$$

where μ is the dipole moment, e is the electrostatic charge on either center (in esu), and c is the distance of charge separation (in angstroms). We shall be interested in the ratio of the actual charge separation to the maximum possible charge separation. We may write:

$$c = pd, \tag{2}$$

where c is the distance of charge separation, d is the bond distance or internuclear distance, and p is the fraction of the bond distance to which the charges have been separated. Thus p will be a direct measure of bond polarity. This simple calculation will usually not give more than an approximation to the bond polarity, however, because the line of the charge separation sometimes forms an angle to the line connecting the nuclei. This angle may be estimated but cannot always be determined with high precision. In the data which follow, it will be neglected.

In Eq. (1) e is 4.8×10^{-10} for a covalent single bond, that is, the charge on an electron. Hence we may combine Eqs. (1) and (2) to give Eq. (3) after multiplying the charge by 10^{-10}; that is, the bond polarity is the dipole moment divided by the product of the bond distance and the charge on an electron,

$$p = \mu/4.8d. \tag{3}$$

32–3 Measurement of Dipole Moments

Dipole moments may be measured by separating two charged plates by the medium to be measured and finding the dielectric loss or charge leakage between the two plates. A part of the dielectric loss is due to dipoles induced on the molecules by the mere fact of their presence in an electrostatic field. These induced dipoles are essentially independent of the orientation of the molecules and as a consequence, their effect does not change when the molecule turns over. Hence, their magnitude will not be dependent on the rate of rotation of the molecules. The permanent dipoles of the molecules, on the other hand, will affect the dielectric loss differently as the dipoles increase their rate of rotation. Hence this portion of the dielectric loss will be temperature dependent. By separating the dielectric loss into its temperature-dependent and temperature-independent portions, it is possible to estimate the contributions of the permanent dipoles and thus the magnitude of the dipole moments.

32–4 Dipole Moments of Paraffins

It would not be expected that the C—H bond would be symmetrical and, in fact, it turns out that it is not. On the other hand, ethane is a symmetrical molecule and has no dipole moment. Methane is also a symmetrical molecule with no dipole moment. If we analyze these two propositions, it is seen that the moment of the C—H bond is exactly equal to that of the CH_3 group. If we imagine a methane molecule perched on three of its hydrogens, then the fourth hydrogen will stand vertically above the carbon. If we place a plane parallel to this C—H bond and project the other three onto it, it will be seen that each C—H bond contributes one-third of a bond distance, so that the three charges separated by one-third of a bond distance from the center are equaled by one charge separated by a full bond distance. This is the symmetry of a tetrahedron, shown in Fig. 32–1. The net effect of this symmetry is that any C—H bond may be replaced by a CH_3 group without affecting the dipole moment of the hydrocarbon and, therefore, all paraffin hydrocarbons have zero permanent dipole moment.

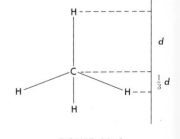

FIGURE 32–1

Table 32–3

	CH$_3$NH$_2\downarrow$	CH$_3$OH$\downarrow$	CH$_3$F
μ	1.23	1.66	1.81
d	1.47	1.43	1.41
p	0.17	0.24	0.27

32–5   Bond Polarity and Position in the Periodic Table

The dipole moments of methylamine, methanol, and methyl fluoride have been measured and are given in Table 32–3 together with the other pertinent data for the estimation of values of p. The arrows following methylamine and methanol are to remind us that these two dipoles are at an angle to the C—X bond. It will be seen, however, that the bond polarity increases as we move to the right in the periodic table, as would be expected from the increased electron-attracting power of the nuclei to the right of carbon.

Table 32–4

	CH$_3$F	CH$_3$Cl	CH$_3$Br	CH$_3$I	HCl	HBr	HI
μ	1.81	1.86	1.82	1.65	1.03	0.78	0.38
d	1.41	1.76	1.91	2.10	1.28	1.43	1.62
p	0.27	0.22	0.20	0.16	0.17	0.11	0.05 ($r_H = 0.29$)

We have seen that the attractive power of nuclei for electrons with more than a single ring of electrons diminishes as the number of rings increases. This is due both to screening and to the increased distances of the electrons from the center of the atoms. These relationships can be formulated more precisely in terms of the dipole moments of the bonds involved. The figures are given in Table 32–4.

32–6   Polarity and Bond Cleavage

Since the C—C bond in hydrocarbons has no dipole moment, its cleavages would be expected to be homolytic, that is, with one bonding electron going to each particle:

$$H_3C—CH_3 \rightleftarrows 2CH_3 \cdot$$

This is the reaction that actually takes place when sufficient heat is applied to break the bond. Cleavage takes place with moderate speed at temperatures above 600°C, producing methyl radicals. Since these reaction conditions are not those ordinarily encountered in organic reactions, we shall postpone discussion of such radical reactions until later in the course.

Most reactive substances that the organic chemist deals with are polar in nature as we shall see in examples as we progress. Hence it is of interest to learn the

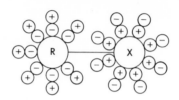

FIGURE 32–2

conditions that favor heterolytic cleavages of bonds. In general, ionization, the extreme form of heterolytic cleavage, takes place most readily in solvents that are highly polar. The ability of solvents to promote ionization is measured by their dielectric constants. These, in turn, are closely related to the molecular dipole moments. Solvents of high dielectric constant prevent homolytic cleavages. On the other hand, they promote ionization or heterolytic cleavage. It is easy to rationalize this behavior on the assumption that the dipoles of the polar solvents line up with respect to those of the reacting molecule so that they force themselves in between the two reacting atoms and thus separate them. In Fig. 32–2, R is a group with a partial positive charge, induced by the electron-attracting properties of X, which, in consequence, has a partial negative charge. The solvent molecules are represented by their dipoles, shown below.

32–7 Limiting Dielectric Constants for Heterolytic Cleavage

As the polarities of bonds increase, the tendency to heterolytic cleavage will naturally be expected to increase so that progressively lower dielectric constants will be effective in bringing about heterolytic cleavages. Waters has calculated the lower limits of the dielectric constants at which heterolytic cleavages of various types of bonds would be expected. These are given in Table 32–5.

One of the most valuable developments of the postwar years from the point of view of laboratory technique has been the production of a wide variety of new solvents, many of them possessing extraordinarily high dielectric constants. The dielectric constants of a number of commonly available solvents are given in Table 32–6.

The first group of solvents has dielectric constants low enough to permit radical reactions, even when other conditions may be favorable to heterolytic cleavages.

Table 32–5

Bond	Limiting D	Bond	Limiting D	Bond	Limiting D
C—I	44	C—H	64	S—H	20
C—Br	22	C—N	55	N—H	7
C—Cl	15	C—OH	18	O—H	6
C—F	5				

Table 32–6

Low dielectric constant
Permit radical reactions

Hexane	D = 1.9
Cyclohexane	2.1
Carbon tetrachloride	2.2
Benzene	2.3
Tetrachloroethylene	2.3
Toluene	2.4
Carbon disulfide	2.6
Octene	4.1
Ethyl ether	4.3

Intermediate dielectric constants

Chloroform	D = 4.7
Amyl acetate	5.0
Chlorobenzene	5.7
Ethyl acetate	6.4
Tetrahydrofuran	7.4
Phenol	9.7
Acetic acid	9.7
Ethylene chloride	10.7
t-butanol	10.9

Moderate dielectric constants
Permit ionization

Pyridine	D = 13
Sulfur dioxide	14
Ammonia	17
n-butanol	18
Acetophenone	19
Acetic anhydride	20
Acetone	21
Ethanol	25

Higher dielectric constants
Favor ionization

Methanol	D = 31
Nitrobenzene	36
Nitromethane	36
N,N-dimethylformamide	37
Acetonitrile	38
Ethylene glycol	42
Dimethyl sulfoxide	45
Hydrazine	53
Formic acid	59

High dielectric constants
Promote ionization

Water	D = 78
Hydrogen fluoride	84
Formamide	110
Sulfuric acid	ca 110
Hydrogen cyanide	115
N-methylformamide	182

In some of these cases, the reagents necessary to bring about a desired reaction may alter the polarity of the solvent. Thus ether acts as a weak base, and the addition of HCl tends to form an etherate salt which is more polar than the ether itself.

We may conclude that the influence exerted by increasing nuclear charges on substituent atoms has a profound effect on the course of organic reactions and that this effect may be rationalized, once one has an understanding of the effect of increasing nuclear charge on the attracting power of the nucleus for the bonding electrons.

32–8   Bond Strengths

In addition to its polarity, the strength of a bond is a critical factor in the ease with which it will undergo chemical reaction. Bond strengths are also determined by the electron-attracting properties of the nuclear charges, but the relationships are not so simple as those of the bond polarities. While the bond polarities increase regularly on moving from left to right in the table and the bond radii diminish in the same direction, the bond energies, that is, the energies required to separate compounds into the corresponding atoms homolytically, diminish from carbon to nitrogen before turning up. As would be expected, however, bond energies are lower in the higher periods of the table. Both these relationships are illustrated in Table 32–7. It is apparent that in most cases, as the bond polarity increases, the bond strength also increases. This may be attributed to the increased attraction of the nucleus for the bonding electrons. The exceptions in the cases of carbon and silicon have been ascribed to greater resonance interaction in these cases, since the bonds are composed of atoms which are closer to the same energies than is the case with bonding farther to the right in the table. As we move to the right in the table, resonance energy would be expected to diminish and energy arising from coulombic attraction would be expected to increase.

Table 32–7

ENERGIES OF COVALENT BONDS, kcal/mole

C—H	N—H	O—H	F—H		C—C	C—N	C—O	C—F
99	93	111	135		83	70	84	105
Si—H	P—H	S—H	Cl—H				C—S	C—Cl
70	76	81	103				62	79
	As—H	Se—H	Br—H					C—Br
	59	66	88					66
			I—H					C—I
			72					57

A common error is to assume that in organic compounds with two adjacent positive charges, the overall effect is one of repulsion. While it is true that positive charges in space would repel, bonded positive charges are bonded by electrons which have the opposite charges. Hence the force of attraction between nucleus and electron acts at roughly half the distance of the force of repulsion between the two positive charges, and the attractive force outweighs the repulsive force. This is illustrated by the difference between hydrazine, $H_2N—NH_2$, and hydrazinium ion, $H_3N^+—^+NH_3$. Bond distance measurements have shown that the distance in hydrazine is greater than that in the hydrazinium ion. This means that the two adjacent charges have the effect of shortening the bond, and from this we may safely deduce that the N—N bond has been strenthened by the adjacent positive charges.

We may summarize by stating that covalent bond radii, van der Waals radii, bond polarities, and bond energies all correlate with the attractive forces exerted by the nuclei and that the directions of their changes within the periodic table may easily be remembered, even if the precise values for these constants are not.

32–9 Conclusions

We have now completed a brief review of some of the principles on which a study of reaction mechanisms must be based. We have learned something about the relationship between the nuclear charges of the elements and their positions in the periodic table. At the same time, we have seen how the steady increase in nuclear charge brings with it the phenomenon of periodicity, when successive electrons are added to the outer shell. We have seen how these changes affect the chemical properties of the elements in their combinations with other elements. We have reviewed briefly the relationships between nuclear charge and bond distance as well as bond angle. Two ways of regarding covalent bonds have been presented, both of which will be used in specific applications during the remainder of the course. Since all these properties have a common electromagnetic basis, it is not surprising that many correlations between them should exist. Some of the possible correlations have been examined briefly. Throughout this presentation of basic materials, we emphasized the selection of physical facts and ideas which will prove of value in the study of reaction mechanisms. The next group of tools that we shall need in the study of reaction mechanisms is chemical in nature. These chemical tools for the investigation of reaction mechanisms will form the subject of the next section.

32–10 General References for Reaction Mechanisms

The reader who wishes to study the subject of reaction mechanisms more deeply than is possible within the scope of an introductory course will find useful material in the following references.

G. E. K. BRANCH and M. CALVIN, *The Theory of Organic Chemistry*, Englewood Cliffs: Prentice-Hall, 1941.

C. A. COULSON, *Valence*, London: Oxford University Press, 1961.

E. S. GOULD, *Mechanism and Structure in Organic Chemistry*, New York: Henry Holt and Co., 1959.

L. P. HAMMETT, *Physical Organic Chemistry*, New York: McGraw-Hill, 1940.

J. HINE, *Physical Organic Chemistry*, New York: McGraw-Hill, 1962.

C. K. INGOLD, *Structure and Mechanism in Organic Chemistry*, Ithaca, N.Y.: Cornell University Press, 1953.

M. S. NEWMAN, *Steric Effects in Organic Chemistry*, New York: John Wiley and Sons, 1956.

L. PAULING, *The Nature of the Chemical Bond*, Ithaca, N.Y.: Cornell University Press, 1960.

P. SYKES, *A Guidebook to Mechanism in Organic Chemistry*, New York: John Wiley and Sons, 1965.

G. W. WHELAND, *Resonance in Organic Chemistry*, New York: John Wiley and Sons, 1955.

K. WIBERG, *Physical Organic Chemistry*, New York: John Wiley and Sons, 1964.

PROBLEMS

32-1 (a) What would be the relative lengths and dipoles of C—N and B—N bonds?

(b) What would be the direction of the C—B dipole?

(c) Is carbon always electron-releasing in a single bond?

(d) Suppose that it were possible to describe adequately a bond between Li and F as covalent. What would be the order of magnitude of its dipole moment?

(e) Would Li be electron accepting or electron releasing with respect to other elements of the first row?

32-2 From the data given in Table 32–4, which would you expect to be more electron attracting in the C—H bond, C or H?

32-3 Why would it be expected that bonds in the second row of the periodic table would be weaker than those in the first row?

32-4 We have used methyl iodide as a methylating agent many times in our earlier discussions. It might be argued that methyl fluoride should be a much better methylating agent because of the high polarity of the C—F bond, which promotes heterolytic cleavage. Yet methyl fluoride is a very poor methylating agent, and methyl iodide is often the reagent of choice. Can you explain this apparent contradiction?

32-5 Since electrons are constantly in motion, the dipole moments that we measure are average figures. At any given instant, even a nonpolar molecule such as an alkane will have a fleeting dipole moment simply because the position of the center of negative charge will not coincide with the center of nuclear charge. This is another way of describing a dipole. This transitory dipole induces a dipole in neighboring molecules, so that a net attraction between molecules results because of these effects, sometimes called London forces.

n-Pentane boils at 37°C and neopentane at 9.5°C. Show that the greater symmetry of one of these molecules (that is, its closer approximation by a sphere) may be combined with the preceding argument to rationalize the order in boiling points.

32-6 Other factors beside transitory and induced dipoles are important in intermolecular attraction. For example, the boiling points of a series of substituted methanes with nearly the same molecular weight are as follows:

	Boiling point, °C
CH_3CH_3	−88.3
CH_3NH_2	−6.5
CH_3OH	64.65
CH_3F	−23.65

Note that the boiling point of methyl fluoride is above that of ethane but below that of methylamine.

(a) Will a suitable explanation of this order be found on the basis of dipole-dipole attraction alone?

The intermolecular forces in methylamine and methanol are obviously of a different order of magnitude; what distinguishes these compounds from the others is the presence of both an electronegative atom with unshared electron pairs, the electron donor, and hydrogen, the electron acceptor, bonded to this atom. The same situation obtains, therefore, as in water; the increase in boiling point is enough to warrant the description of the phenomenon in terms of the formation of a new bond called a hydrogen bond. Hydrogen bonds are weak by the usual standards, that is, they are of the order of $\frac{1}{20}$ of the strength of a C—C bond. One bit of evidence in favor of such an interpretation is a shift in infrared absorption spectrum.

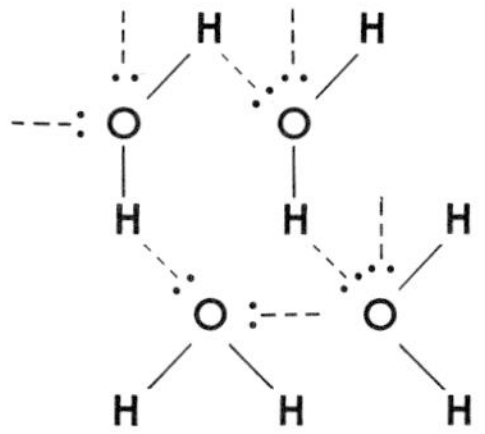

(b) Using this explanation, explain the difference in boiling point patterns given above.

(c) Why does methanol boil at a lower temperature than water?

(d) Consider the redistribution of the electrons around hydrogen in water: if the hydrogen bond becomes stronger, what happens to the covalent O—H bond at the same time?

(e) Would you find your answer in agreement with the fact that a typical alcohol has an absorption at 2.75 μ in the gas phase or in very dilute CCl_4 solution, but more concentrated solutions absorb at 2.90 μ?

(f) If such concentration-dependent behavior is indicative of hydrogen bonds forming between molecules, how would you interpret the spectrum of a compound which absorbs at the longer wavelength regardless of concentration? Consider what would happen in the case of $HOCH_2CH_2CH_2OH$ or a sugar.

(g) In terms of valence-bond theory a hydrogen bond might be described as a resonance hybrid of two forms. Crystallographic studies definitely indicate that the hydrogen is not symmetrically disposed between the two electronegative atoms. What does this mean in terms of the various contributing structures?

32-7 Intermolecular attractive forces may be considered in mixed systems as well. Explain the following observations.

(a) When water is added to a mixture of methanol and dibutyl ketone, it turns cloudy briefly and then separates into two phases. On the other hand, a mixture of acetone and methanol is entirely miscible with water.

(b) Dimethyl ether is about twenty times as soluble in water at room temperature as methyl fluoride.

32-8 Arrange the following according to increasing solubility in water:

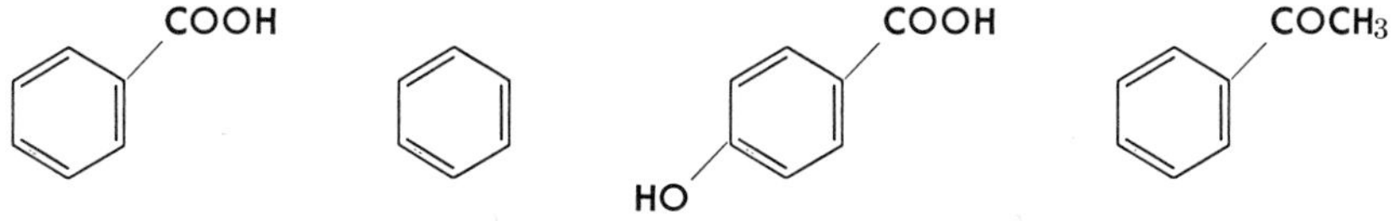

32-9 Can you propose another argument for the bond angles of the methyl halides based on bond strengths in heterolytic cleavage and resonance effects (Problem 29-4)?

Part 2

CHEMICAL TOOLS FOR THE INVESTIGATION OF REACTION MECHANISMS

Knowing the elements of chemical bonding, the organic chemist is in a position to examine a list of organic substances undergoing a chemical reaction and to reason how structural changes affect reactivity and why. He can measure the factors which affect the rate of a reaction and reason from these as to the underlying causes of the changes. In particular, he can draw much information from the relationship between the rate of a reaction and the concentrations of the reagents producing the reaction. Combining this information with the physical picture of the changes in bond energies with distance, he is able to construct a mental image of the highly transitory states which exist at the instant of bond exchange. From these concepts, he can proceed to more complete reaction mechanisms. The basic methods and concepts which permit this type of reasoning are the subject of Part 2.

How can the physical properties based on electron attraction by nuclei be correlated with acidities of organic compounds? How can acidities be correlated with reactivities, both with respect to rates and with respect to the positions of equilibria?

33

ACIDITIES AND THEIR CORRELATION WITH REACTIVITIES

33–1 Acidities

In the preceding chapters we have found how it is possible to correlate various physical properties of interest to the chemist with the varying powers of nuclei to attract bonding electrons. We shall now turn to a chemical application of this information, the application to the problems of variations in acidity.

Brønsted defined an acid as a substance capable of donating protons. While there are situations in which a less restrictive definition will prove of value, for many purposes of the organic chemist this definition is satisfactory. An increase in ability to donate protons, then, would be characteristic of an increase in acidity.

33–2 The Acidity of Methane

Methane can be classed as probably one of the weakest hydrogen-bearing acids possible. The position of the equilibrium constant for the reaction of methane with sodium to form sodium methide, a reaction which cannot be performed directly, has been estimated by comparing the base strength of sodium methide with that of other very powerful bases. Acidity measurements are expressed in pK units. The pK is the negative logarithm of the equilibrium constant. For water, the equilibrium is usually written:

$$H_2O \rightleftarrows H^+ + OH^-,$$

even though it would be more accurate to write it as

$$2H_2O \rightleftarrows H_3O^+ + OH^-.$$

Using the first form, the equilibrium constant would be

$$K = (H^+)(OH^-)/(H_2O) = 10^{-14}/55.5.$$

This value is just under 10^{-16}. The corresponding pK, then would be 16. On the usual scale in which water is assigned a pK of 16, methane would be assigned a pK of 44. This means that the ratio between the two acids is a factor of 10^{28}. Insertion of an oxygen between the carbon and the hydrogen of methane to form methanol strengthens the acidity a tremendous amount, since methanol is within a power of ten of being as strong an acid as water. Even though the O—H bond is substantially stronger than the C—H bond, its polarity permits its ionization in water solution. It should be realized that this ionization is a transfer of a proton from one oxygen to another, so that the energy of the O—H bond is not lost in the process.

$$CH_3OH + HOH \rightleftarrows CH_3O^- + H_3O^+$$

or

$$CH_3OH + HOH \rightleftarrows CH_3OH_2^+ + OH^-$$

The increased ease of this transfer tells us that the electron-attracting power of the oxygen has facilitated a heterolytic cleavage of the O—H bond so that the O retains the electron pair.

33–3   Acidities and Polarities

We may examine the effect on acidities of moving to the right in the periodic table. As stated, methane is an extremely weak acid. Ammonia, with the greater electron attracting power of the nitrogen, should be expected to be stronger. It turns out to be an acid with a pK roughly estimated to be 32, that is, a factor of 10^{12} stronger than methane. Water, as we have seen, has a pK of approximately 16, indicating a factor of 10^{16} by the change from nitrogen to oxygen. Finally, HF is the strongest acid in the row, with a pK of approximately 4, and hence is another factor of 10^{12} stronger than water. Thus we see that the increasing polarity of the X—H bond has a powerful effect in increasing the ease of heterolytic cleavage of the bond and that the direction of the change can be rationalized on the same basis as the changes of radii, polarities, and bond energies.

33–4   Acidities of the Halogen Acids

A word of caution is in order at this point. In water, the halogen acids HCl, HBr, and HI all appear about equally strong, although means for showing differences do exist. The reason that these acids appear to be about equally strong is that only an infinitesimal amount of the undissociated acid exists in equilibrium with the ions in water solution. The water is such a powerful base that it degrades all of these acids to H_3O^+, and we usually measure the relative strengths of three samples of H_3O^+ derived from different sources. By using a weaker base as solvent, differences between these acids can easily be detected. It is then found that the order of their acidities is $HCl < HBr < HI$. This is the reverse order to that which might be predicted on the basis of bond polarities and demonstrates that bond polarities do not necessarily outweigh all other factors in determining acid strength. In this case, the ionization is not a symmetrical operation, as it was for methanol. Instead, weaker and weaker bonds are being broken to form, for example, O—H bonds of constant strength. Thus more and more energy is gained by the bond break, and the cleavage of the very weak H—I bond yields enough energy to favor this cleavage over all the others, making H—I the strongest acid of the group.

33–5   Acidities and Resonance

To continue the argument concerning the change from methane to methanol, it seems reasonable to suppose that other groups attached to the carbon, which would increase the electron-attracting power of the oxygen, would still further increase the acidity of the compound. One means for increasing the electron-attracting power of the carbon attached to the O—H bond of methanol would be to substitute another oxygen. The stable compound with an O—H bond intact but with another oxygen attached to the carbon is formic acid. Because of the presence of the second oxygen, the formyl group is a stronger electron-attracting group than the methyl group, and we should expect formic acid to be a stronger acid than methanol. In fact, the ratio is a factor of approximately 10^{12}. Since the second oxygen is not so directly attached to the ionizing hydrogen as the first, its effect would not be expected to be so large. Careful studies on many types of acid have shown, as we shall see later, that a portion of the difference in acidity between methanol and formic acid is to be ascribed to another cause than the increased electron-attracting power of the group. This is the fact that the formate ion, formed when formic acid is ionized, is stabilized by resonance.

$$
\begin{array}{ccc}
\text{O} & & \text{O}^- \\
\parallel & & | \\
\text{H}\!-\!\text{C}\!-\!\text{O}^- & \leftrightarrow & \text{H}\!-\!\text{C}\!=\!\text{O}
\end{array}
$$

The net effect of this is to increase the stability of the ion with respect to the acid, thus tending to shift the equilibrium toward greater ionization. This means that the resonance of the ion increases the strength of the acid.

$$
\begin{array}{cc}
\text{O} & \text{O} \\
\parallel & \parallel \\
\text{HCOH} + H_2O \rightleftarrows \text{HCO}^- & + H_3O^+
\end{array}
$$

Summarizing, we see that there are two major factors which affect the acidities of hydrogen atoms: first, the electron-attracting power of the atom to which the hydrogen is attached and, second, the possibility of stabilization of the ion (in some cases the acid) by resonance.

33–6   The Inductive Effect

If we confine our attention for the moment to derivatives of acetic acid, we may formulate this relationship in more precise terms.

$$X—CH_2COOH + CH_3COO^- \rightleftarrows X—CH_2COO^- + CH_3COOH$$

If the equilibrium in the equation lies to the right, then the substituted acid will be a stronger acid than acetic acid.

We have seen that fluorine is the strongest electron-attracting atom. When attached to carbon, as in methyl fluoride, it causes an electron displacement to occur with the formation of a dipole. The net result of this drift of electrons is that the carbon in methyl fluoride will, in its turn, attract electrons from the hydrogens more strongly than would a carbon in ethane, for example. If we transfer our attention to fluoroacetic acid, the fluorine atom would attract electrons from the carbon, causing the carbon to attract electrons more strongly from the carbonyl group. However, part of the increased electron-attracting effect of the carbon would be dissipated on the two hydrogens, which are also attached to it, so that the influence of the $F—CH_2—$ group on the carbonyl would not be as great as would be the effect of an F directly attached to the carbonyl. Thus there would be a transfer of the effect of the F to the carbonyl with some loss in passing through the methylene group. The carbonyl group, in its turn, would transmit a portion of the increased electron-attracting power of the fluorine on to the hydroxyl group. The net effect of this drift of electrons caused by the substitution of F for H in acetic acid would be to increase the electron-attracting power of the substituted acetyl group over that of acetic acid. But we have seen that an increase in electron-attracting power of all substituents on the OH makes the ionization of the hydrogen proceed more readily. Hence fluoroacetic acid would be a stronger proton donor than acetic acid and, by definition, a stronger acid. In fact, it is approximately 122 times as strong an acid as acetic acid. The type of electron drift induced by the fluorine atom as a substituent is called the *inductive* effect of the substituent.

We may extend the reasoning to include the other halogens. Since chlorine produces less polarization, as measured by dipole moments, than fluorine, we should expect its effect to be smaller. The halogens should then form the following series with respect to the magnitudes of their inductive effects:

$$F > Cl > Br > I$$

Measurements of the acidities of the halogenated acetic acids have been carried out. The results obtained are shown in Table 33–1.

Table 33–1

	F	Cl	Br	I	H
10^5K, XCH_2COOH	217	155	138	75	1.8
K/K_{acetic}	122	86	77	42	1

33-7   Branch and Calvin's Equation

Branch and Calvin studied a large group of acids, most of them inorganic, which would be regarded as derivatives of water having the general formula X—OH. By correlating the effects of the acids in increasing the acidity of water, these investigators were able to construct a table which summarizes briefly the inductive effects of the various atoms. These effects are used in calculating acidities in an equation which is widely used in estimating inductive effects in organic compounds. The equation, as applied to water, is

$$\log K = -16 + \sum I_a \alpha^i + \sum I_c \alpha^i + \log n/m$$

The meanings of the various terms are as follows: $\log K$ is the logarithm of the equilibrium constant of the acid in question. The term -16 is the value for the equilibrium constant for the ionization of water. This value takes into account three factors, the usual dissociation constant, the molarity of pure water (55.5), and the statistical correction resulting from the fact that water can donate either of two protons, whereas X—OH can donate only one. The term $\sum I_a \alpha^i$ breaks down into two portions: I_a stands for the inductive constant of an individual atom (these constants are obtained from the table), and α^i is a modifying factor to correct for the number of bonds intervening between the atom being considered and the OH bond. For each bond that the atom is removed from OH, the effect diminishes by a factor of $(1/2.8)$ or 0.357. If the atom is two bonds removed, the factor will be $(1/2.8)^2$ or 0.1277. If three bonds removed, the factor will be $(1/2.8)^3$ or 0.0455. Hence i is the number of bonds intervening between the atom under consideration and the OH group. The product of $I_a \alpha^i$ is found for each atom in the compound and the sum of these products is the term $\sum I_a \alpha^i$. The next term $\sum I_c \alpha^i$ is arrived at by a similar process, but the operations are performed on the inductive effects of the charges on the atoms instead of on the atoms themselves. This indicates that the total inductive effect of a charged atom, —NH_3^+, for example, would be the sum of the inductive effect due to the atom and the inductive effect of the charge. The final term of the equation, $\log n/m$, is the statistical correction. If an acid has two ionizable hydrogens which are entirely equivalent, then it will be a stronger acid than a similar acid with only one such ionizable hydrogen by a factor of 2, and the logarithm of the equilibrium constant must be corrected by $\log 2$. If the base formed by the ionization of the acid in question has two equivalently charged RO^- groups, then it will be a stronger base than the hydroxide ion by the factor of 2, and the logarithm of the equilibrium constant would be corrected by $\log \frac{1}{2}$. Thus n/m is the number of equivalent ionizable hydrogens divided by the number of equivalent negatively charged oxygens. An example would be sulfuric acid, written as follows.

In this formulation, n, the number of equivalent ionizable hydrogens, is 2 while m, the number of equivalent negatively charged oxygens in the bisulfate ion, is 3. Hence the statistical correction would be log $\frac{2}{3}$.

The inductive constants found for the various atoms and charges are given in Table 33–2.

Table 33–2

I_c	±12.3	I_{Se}	+2.7
I_F	+ 9.0	I_{Te}	+2.4
I_{Cl}	+ 8.5	I_N	+1.3
I_{Br}	+ 7.5	I_P	+1.1
I_I	+ 6.0	I_{As}	+1.0
I_O	+ 4.0	I_H	0.0
I_S	+ 3.4	I_C	−0.4

Adapted from G. E. K. Branch and M. Calvin, *The Theory of Organic Chemistry*, Englewood Cliffs, N.J.: Prentice-Hall, 1941.

33–8   Use of the Equation and the Table

An example will illustrate the use of the equation and the table.   Let us choose sulfurous acid, written as:

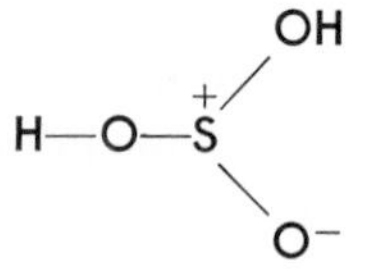

We shall consider the effects on the ionizable **OH** group of the sulfur, the two oxygens, the positive charge, and the negative charge.   The sulfur is directly attached to the ionizable **OH** group.   Hence, from the table, its contribution will be +3.4.   In addition to the ionizable **OH** under consideration, there are two more oxygens attached to the sulfur and therefore each is removed one bond from the ionizable **OH** group.   From the table, the value to be assigned for oxygen is +4.0. But since these are one atom from the group under consideration, they will be multiplied by the factor α^i or 1/2.8 or 0.357.   The sum of the three terms, one for sulfur, one each for the oxygens, $[(3.4) + (4.0)(0.357) + (4.0)(0.357)]$, is $I_a\alpha^i$ for sulfurous acid.

Since there is a positive charge on the sulfur, its contribution will be +12.3. The contribution of the negative charge will be diminished by the factor (0.357), since it is one bond removed from the ionizable **OH**.   Hence the algebraic sum of these two terms will be $I_c\alpha^i$.   This will be $[(12.3) − (12.3)(0.357)]$.

Since there are two equivalent ionizable hydroxyls, $n = 2$.   In the ion resulting from the ionization, there will be two equivalent —O^- atoms.   Hence $m = 2$.

Consequently, the statistical correction will be log $\frac{2}{2}$ or zero. The calculation will then be:

$$\log K_{H_2SO_3} = -16 + [(3.4 + (4)(0.357) + (4)(0.357)] + [12.3 - (12.3)(0.357)]$$
$$= -16 + (6.25) + (7.91) = -16 + 14.2$$
$$= -1.8$$

Found: -1.8.

33–9   General Implications of the Equation

This equation illustrates the manner in which the inductive electron drift falls off with the distance from the substituent which initiates it. The effectiveness of a substituent diminishes by roughly one-third for each bond that separates it from the point at which its action is measured. This information, as well as the relative magnitudes of the effects of different substituents, will be of value later in estimating the outcome of competitive inductions on a reacting center.

To visualize the relative effects of various substituents, recourse has frequently been had to a so-called *electronegativity scale*. In such a scale, relative electronegativities are plotted against the position in the periodic table. Such a scale for the values determined by Branch and Calvin is given in Fig. 33–1.

A modified form of the equation is used to deal with the electronegativities of carboxylic acids. This may be found in the original work.

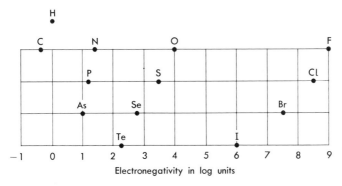

Electronegativity in log units

FIGURE 33–1

33–10   The Hammett Equation

One of the most extensive attempts to correlate chemical reactivity with acidity was initiated by Hammett. Hammett pointed out that *meta* and *para* substituents in the benzene ring exert effects on a variety of reactions which can be related to the influence of these substituents on the acidity of benzoic acid. *Ortho* substituents do not correlate simply because varying portions of their effects involve distortions of the electron clouds of the carboxyl group by the substituent due to proximity and size instead of simply nuclear attraction. These effects are classed as *steric*, and special techniques are required to separate them from the influences due to electron-attracting or electron-releasing effects of the nuclei. The equation which correlates the effects in the *meta* and *para* positions is

$$\log (K/K^0) = \rho\sigma.$$

In this equation, K is the equilibrium constant for a reaction with the given substituent. The corresponding constant for the same reaction with hydrogen as a substituent is K^0.

33–11   The Determination of Rho Values

The characteristic reaction constant is ρ, which is measured by the slope of a straight line which gives the best fit to a number of different substituent constants for the same reaction. The standard slope is taken as that of the substituted benzoic acids, and this is arbitrarily assigned a value of 1 (Fig. 33–2); that is, it is a straight line at a 45° angle to the coordinates and passing through the origin.

33–12   The Determination of Sigma Values

By plotting the experimental values for $\log K$ on the 45° line at distances determined on the vertical axis, the horizontal coordinates of these same points define the values of σ. These substituent constants are then arbitrarily used on other reactions as the substituent constants for these reactions. The value for H is arbitrarily set equal to 0. It then follows that substituents with a positive value of

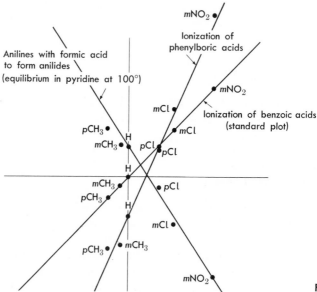

FIGURE 33–2

sigma are electron attracting and those with a negative value of σ are electron releasing.

There is no reason, *a priori*, why the use of the same set of substituent constants for other reactions should plot out to straight lines. The fact that they do, however, establishes the validity of the correlation. Sample Hammett plots of some reactions are shown in Fig. 33–2.

33–13   The Sign of Rho

The reaction of benzoic acid with water is that involved in the standard reaction. Thus the acid undergoing the change of substituents is being attacked by the base, water, in this reaction. Accordingly, it would ordinarily be expected that attack by a base on the molecule to which the substituents are attached would give a reaction with a positive slope, that is, a positive value for ρ. On the other hand, attack by an acid on the molecule to which the substituents are attached would give a negative ρ.

The attack of water on phenylboric acids to ionize them, like the attack of water on benzoic acids, has a positive value of ρ. The attack of formic acid on anilines to form an equilibrium mixture containing substituted formanilides,

$$XC_6H_4NH_2 + HCOOH \rightleftarrows XC_6H_4NHCHO + H_2O,$$

has a negative ρ, as would be expected from the change in nature of the attacking reagent in relation to the compounds bearing the substituents. As will be seen by an examination of Fig. 33–2, in each plot the same substituent falls on the same vertical line. The point at which this vertical line crosses the horizontal axis is the value of σ for this substituent.

33–14   The Magnitude of Rho

Major changes in the magnitude of the value of rho are brought about by differences in the ease of transmission of polar effects from the point of substitution to the point of reaction. For example, the insulating effect of a single bond, brought to light in the consideration of the Branch and Calvin equation, will make a polar effect less easy to transmit to the point of reaction. Thus the effect of substituents on the ionization of phenols is greater than their effect on the ionization of carboxylic acids because it is transmitted through a shorter distance in the case of the phenols:

$$X-C_6H_4\!-\!\overset{\longleftrightarrow}{O\!-\!H} \quad \text{is less than} \quad X-C_6H_4\!\overset{O}{\underset{\parallel}{C}}\!-\!\overset{\longleftrightarrow}{O\!-\!H}$$

As a consequence, rho for the ionization of phenols in water is $+2.008$, while for the ionization of benzoic acids, also in water, it is $+1.000$.

33-15   Extent of the Hammett Correlation

Hammett presented data on 52 reactions and 44 substituents. Since his original publications, many more reactions and substituents have been added. In addition, Taft has studied the extension of the equation to correct for steric effects, so that applications can be made to *ortho* positions and to aliphatic reactions. These extensions of Hammett's concept make it far and away the most ambitious attempt to correlate a wide variety of reactions and substituents into a single conceptual framework. It should be noted that the basis for the whole organization of these data is the measurement of acidities, which form the point of departure for all the remaining correlations. Since acidities correlate with the electron-attracting and electron-releasing properties of atoms, these fundamental concepts can be extended to embrace a tremendous amount of information concerning relative reactivities of organic compounds.

The majority of the reactions included by Hammett, Taft and others in the scope of the Hammett equation and its modifications are irreversible reactions in which the measurements which are correlated with acidities are measurements of the rates of the reactions instead of measurements of their equilibrium constants. Again, there seems to be no reason, *a priori*, why rates and equilibria should correlate and, indeed, many cases are known in which they do not. To analyze the cases which do correlate and those which do not, it is necessary to go more deeply into the subject of the rates of chemical reactions. This will be the subject of the next chapter.

PROBLEMS

33-1   Which would be a stronger base, water or ethanol? Ethanol or *t*-butanol? Water or acetic acid? Acetic acid or benzene? Which might be the best solvent to study the relative ionizations of the halogen acids?

33-2   Why is the formate ion favored by resonance over the formic acid molecule?

33-3   Which will be the stronger acid, toluene or ethane? Triphenylmethane or diphenylmethane?

33-4   When acetone is dissolved in strong acid, it accepts a proton. Will this add to the oxygen or to the carbon of the carbonyl group? Keeping in mind the relative importance of inductive and resonance effects,

(a) which will be a stronger base, acetone or phenyl benzyl ketone and

(b) which will be a stronger acid, acetone or phenyl benzyl ketone?

33-5   Which should be the stronger acid:

(a) FCH_2COOH or $F_2CHCOOH$?

(b) $CH_3CHFCOOH$ or FCH_2CH_2COOH?

(c) $HOCH_2COOH$ or H_2NCH_2COOH?

(d) How do you account for the fact that glycine is a much stronger acid than glycollic acid?

33–6 Nitromethane is an acid, $K_a = 6 \times 10^{-11}$.

  (a) What makes a compound an acid?

  (b) What is the anion formed by simple ionization of nitromethane?

  (c) Why should this ion be stable?

  (d) Does the nitro group withdraw electrons by induction?

  (e) By resonance?

33–7 Which will ionize in base more readily, *p*-cresol, phenol, or *m*-hydroxyacetophenone?

33–8 Which will protonate in acid more readily, *p*-toluidine (*p*-methylaniline), aniline, or *m*-aminoacetophenone?

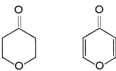

33–9 Which of these compounds would be protonated more easily in acid solution? Which oxygen would bear the proton in that compound? What kind of effect predominates in stabilization of the cation?

33–10 Acetophenone absorbs at 5.91 microns in dilute CCl_4 solution; the *p*-nitro compound at 5.88 and the *p*-amino compound at 5.96.

  (a) Explain these shifts.

  (b) On the basis of the usual correlations, where would you expect the carbonyl absorption of *p*-methylacetophenone to occur?

*How can critical reagents in an organic
reaction be identified through the use of chemical kinetics?
How does this information aid in securing
knowledge about reaction mechanisms?*

34

THE LAW OF MASS ACTION;
CHEMICAL KINETICS

34–1   The Law of Mass Action

Experience in the study of reaction mechanisms has shown that one of the most useful principles in the determination of the course of a reaction is the Law of Mass Action. The origins of the Law of Mass Action can be traced back to the time of the American Revolution, when, in 1777, C. F. Wenzel stated that chemical reaction was proportional to the amount of substance taking part in the reaction. At that time, however, proper methods for the measurement of the critical quantities, molar concentrations, were not available. In 1799, C. L. Berthollet made sufficiently accurate measurements of the rates of chemical reactions to permit the the use of differential equations in representing the rates. He stated his opinion that the velocity of a chemical reaction was proportional to the mass of the substance taking part in the reaction. Other investigators carried the work forward sporadically during the first half of the nineteenth century. However, it remained for two Norwegian chemists, Guldberg and Waage, to establish in 1867 that the critical factor in reaction velocity is not the quantity of matter but its concentration. They studied the solution of metals in acids and the reaction of potassium sulfate with barium carbonate with great care and clearly enunciated the principle known as the Law of Mass Action. Unfortunately, however, their publication was not widely circulated because it was written in Norwegian. Some time later it was republished in German and its importance was stressed by van't Hoff in his book on chemical dynamics in 1883. Meanwhile, methods for the measurement of reaction velocities and their mathematical representation were placed on a firm basis by the work of Harcourt and Essen in 1880 on the reaction of permanganate with oxalic acid. These investigators studied the interactions of concurrent and consecutive reactions and succeeded in formulating them by methods which have remained valid until the present.

34–2 Chemical Kinetics

To follow the operation of the Law of Mass Action, the chemist studies the velocities of chemical reactions as functions of the concentrations of various reagents and catalysts, as well as of changes of solvent and temperature. These studies constitute the field of chemical kinetics.

The most general method for following the rate of a chemical reaction is to devise a method of analyzing either reagents or products and then to follow the changes in this analysis with time. A convenient method frequently employed is the use of absorption spectra. In favorable cases, it may be possible to analyze spectrophotometrically for both reagents and products, thus permitting complete study of the reaction. In most cases it is only possible to follow one or two components of the reaction mixture, but this frequently proves sufficient for the purposes of mechanistic studies. Other methods which are used in the studies of reaction rates will be mentioned as examples arise.

34–3 Reaction Order

The velocity of a chemical reaction may be defined by the equation

$$V = kA^n B^m \ldots,$$

where V is the velocity of the reaction, k is the constant of proportionality, called the *rate constant*, and A, B, etc. represent the concentrations of the reagents whose concentrations affect the reaction velocity. It sometimes happens that one reagent may affect the velocity as the square or even a higher power of its concentration. The superscripts n and m are used to provide for these possibilities. In reactions with simple kinetics, these superscripts have integral values. Fractional values for the superscripts indicate complexity in the reaction mechanism.

The reaction order is defined as the sum of all the superscripts on all the reagents whose concentrations affect the reaction velocity proportionately in the kinetic equation.

34–4 Zero-Order Changes

The organic chemist will seldom deal with a zero-order reaction, that is, one whose velocity is independent of the concentrations of all reagents.

The most familiar example of a zero-order change, however, is the standard for all kinetic measurements, the movement of the hands of a clock. The angles swept by the hands of a properly functioning clock are independent of the length of time which has elapsed previous to the reading, and the change is zero order.

In mathematical terms, the velocity of the movement of any hand is the derivative of the angle with respect to time, and the equation for the action of a clock is

$$V = d\theta/dt = k,$$

where θ is the angle swept by the hand, and k is the proportionality constant whose magnitude indicates the type of hand, second, minute, hour, or day, which is governed by the equation.

34-5   First-Order Reactions

Many reactions are known whose velocities obey the mathematical formulation for a first-order reaction. We shall show later that this does not necessarily mean that only a single reagent enters into the reaction. For a hydrolysis reaction in which water is used as the solvent, the velocity would be proportional to the concentration of the material being hydrolyzed and to that of the water. However, the water is present in such overwhelming excess that its consumption during the reaction does not measurably affect the remaining concentration. Hence its concentration will remain sensibly constant and the order of the reaction will be determined only by variations in the concentration of the substance being hydrolyzed. Such a reaction is called a pseudo first-order reaction and is the usual type of reaction whose kinetics are described by first-order mathematics.

The expression for the velocity of a first-order reaction is

$$V = dA/dt = kA.$$

This relation states that the velocity of the decrease in concentration of the reagent is proportional to the concentration of the reagent raised to the first power. The dimensions of k are sec^{-1}.

The processes of integral calculus permit the concentration of A at any time to be calculated. The relationship is

$$2.303 \log (A/A_0) = -kt,$$

where A_0 is the initial concentration of A and t is the time elapsed from beginning of the reaction until the desired concentration of A is measured. The plot of the concentration of the reagent against time in a first-order reaction is shown in Fig. 34-1. If the concentration of A is plotted on the logarithmic scale of semilogarithmic paper and the time is plotted on the plain scale, the resulting plot will be a straight line, if the reaction is first order. The slope of this line will be the rate constant. In standard kinetic practice, time is measured in seconds.

It is characteristic of a semilogarithmic plot that equal fractions of the reagent disappear in equal time intervals. A quick way of checking for first-order kinetics is to use two standards for comparison with the reacting material. The first should be diluted to half the original concentration, the second to a quarter. The time

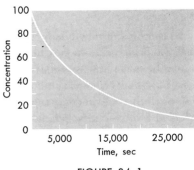

FIGURE 34–1   FIGURE 34–2

required for the sample to go from full concentration to half concentration is measured, then the time from half concentration to quarter concentration. If the two times are equal, the reaction is following first-order kinetics.

The first-order equation with positive k describes the normal growth conditions of a large variety of organisms, enterprises, and even whole economies, provided that crippling restraints are not introduced.

34–6 Second-Order Reactions

The simplest case of a second-order reaction is that in which the concentrations of both the reagents involved are initially identical. In this case, the velocity of the reaction is given by the equation

$$V = dA/dt = -kAB.$$

This states that the rate of decrease in concentration of A is proportional to the product of the concentrations of A and B. The dimensions of k are 1/mole-sec. Where both concentrations are initially identical, the equation becomes

$$dA/dt = kA^2.$$

Again use of the methods of integral calculus permits the calculation of the concentration of A after the lapse of any period of time. This is given by the equation

$$1/A_0 - 1/A = -kt.$$

From this, it can be seen that if the reciprocals of successive values of A are plotted against successive values for t, the result will be a straight line, if the reaction is second order. This plot may also be made on special paper which is ruled for reciprocals in one direction and for plain values in the other. Such a reciprocal plot is shown in Fig. 34–2.

In cases in which initial values for A and B are not identical, the relationship found is somewhat more complex but the reciprocal plot is still valid.

34–7 Higher-Order Reactions

The organic chemist will seldom encounter reactions of an order higher than the second, although many instances of such reactions are known. Special methods for dealing with such reactions exist and should be consulted when the need arises.

34–8 Reversible Reactions

In the preceding examples, it has been assumed that any reverse reaction which might have taken place was so small as to be negligible. In many cases, however, this assumption is not true, and the reverse reaction must be taken into account. Such a case, for example, is found in the esterification of acetic acid. The water formed in the reaction definitely slows down the reaction of esterification until finally the reaction appears to come to a halt short of completion. In such a case, the apparent cessation of activity is due to the fact that both forward and reverse reactions are taking place but at equal rates. The measurement of the concentrations at this equilibrium point gives the equilibrium constant, which is the ratio of the forward to the reverse reaction rate constant.

In reversible reactions, it is sometimes possible to choose the concentrations of two of the reagents, one on each side of the reaction, so that these two remain sensibly unchanged during the course of the reaction. In this case, both forward and reverse reactions become pseudo first order and it is possible to formulate the kinetic equations governing them simply:

$$A \rightleftarrows B$$

$$V_f = dA/dt = -k_f A + k_r B, \qquad V_r = dB/dt = -k_r B + k_f A.$$

At equilibrium, $V_f = V_r$ so that

$$-k_f A + k_r B = -k_r B + k_f A.$$

Solving, we find that

$$k_f/k_r = B/A = K_{eq}.$$

In these expressions, k_f is the forward rate constant, k_r is the reverse rate constant, and K_{eq} is the equilibrium constant for the reaction.

The methods of differential equations permit a solution to this problem. The solution is:

$$\frac{KA_0}{KA_0 - B(K+1)} = e^{(k_f + k_r)t}$$

where K is the equilibrium constant, A_0 is the initial concentration of A, the initial concentration of B is assumed to be zero, and e is the base of natural logarithms; B is then the concentration of B at time t.

A similar expression can be found for the case in which each side of the equation is second order and the reaction is reversible.

34–9   Consecutive Reactions

In most of the reactions which interest the organic chemist, products are formed as a result of a series of consecutive reactions. The simplest such case is that in which there is a single intermediate and the two consecutive reactions are irreversible:

$$A \xrightarrow{k_1} B \xrightarrow{k_2} C.$$

In this reaction the rate of increase of B is the difference between the rate of its formation from A and that of its consumption in the formation of C. Its rate of formation is the rate of disappearance of A with the sign reversed:

$$-dA/dt = k_1 A.$$

Its rate of consumption is the rate of formation of C with the sign reversed:

$$-dC/dt = k_2 B.$$

Its overall rate of increase is then

$$dB/dt = k_1 A - k_2 B.$$

According to the definitions of calculus, dB/dt will be zero when B reaches a maximum. It follows that at this point, the expression

$$B/A = k_1/k_2$$

will be true. If it becomes possible to measure k_1 and k_2, the value for B/A will be known at the time at which B reaches a maximum. After this point, B diminishes in value. Hence, calculation of this point would permit the isolation of the maximum yield. The actual value for B at this point is a complex function of the ratio k_1/k_2, which has been calculated by the methods of differential equations. As the ratio k_1/k_2 increases, the value of B at the maximum increases so that it is sometimes possible to isolate reasonable yields under these conditions. It is also characteristic of this system that as the ratio k_1/k_2 increases, the time at which B is a maximum also increases. The converse of both these propositions is also true, so that if k_2 becomes very large, the maximum amount of B formed is very small and the time required to reach this maximum is very small. Some of these relationships are plotted in Fig. 34–3. In this plot k_1 is maintained constant. In the curves with continuous lines $k_2 = k_1$. In the dashed curves $k_2 = 10k_1$.

    Further complications ensue when either the first or the second reaction is reversible. Finally, in the usual case, most of the reactions in any sequence are at least second order. In these cases, the complexity of the computations involved increases rapidly. Frequently it is possible to simplify these computations greatly by various chemical or mathematical devices. The greatest simplifications result

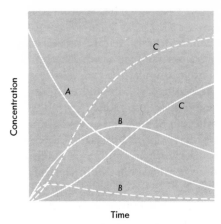

FIG. 34-3.   Relationship between concentration and time for consecutive reactions. (Adapted by permission from G. E. K. Branch and M. Calvin, *The Theory of Organic Chemistry*, Englewood Cliffs, N.J.: Prentice-Hall, 1941.)

when the intermediates are consumed more rapidly than they are formed, so that their concentrations never become large.   Under these conditions it may be assumed that all the material introduced into the reaction is in the form of the initial reagents or of the final products at any time.   This greatly simplifies the mathematics required for the calculations.

As might be imagined, the introduction of computers has entirely changed the possibilities in working with kinetic equations.   Instead of seeking an "analytical" solution to the problem of the general algebraic type illustrated in the preceding examples, it is possible to obtain a series of numerical solutions, varying the reaction rate constants at will and also varying the amounts of the reagents which it is assumed will enter into the reaction.   For rapid exploration of kinetic possibilities, electronic analog computers have been widely used where a high degree of precision is not required.   Where greater precision is desired, digital computers have been used.   With either of these types of computer it is possible to explore rapidly kinetic systems of greater complexity than it is possible to work with conveniently by analytical methods.

34-10   The Use of Chemical Kinetics in the Investigation of Reaction Mechanisms

We have seen that the order of a chemical reaction may be determined by an analysis of the mathematics that governs the equation describing the formation of products or the disappearance of reagents.   By determining the dependence of the rate of a reaction on the concentration of each of the reagents going into the reaction, it is possible to learn which reagents are critical in rate determination. In a series of consecutive reactions, the slowest reaction forms the bottleneck which determines the overall rate of progress of the reaction.   All reagents which take part in the reaction before this bottleneck is reached will be critical in their effect on the reaction velocity. Reagents which enter into the reaction after the bottle-neck has passed will not affect the reaction velocity. For example, if we formulate a reaction as

$$A + B \underset{k_2}{\overset{k_1}{\rightleftharpoons}} C + D \xrightarrow{k_3} E + F \xrightarrow{k_4} G + H$$

and find that the slowest reaction is that governed by k_3, that is, k_3 is the smallest of the rate constants, then the rate of the forward reaction will be $k_1 k_3 / k_2$, but k_4 will not enter into the rate expression. In this case, the conversion of C and D into E and F will be the "bottleneck" of the reaction. Hence a determination of the rate dependence of the reaction on each of the reagents will enable these to be sorted out into those that enter before the slow, or rate-determining, reaction and those that enter after the rate-determining reaction. This is valuable information in the investigation of reaction mechanisms.

More subtle points can also be learned by the investigation of the rate dependence of a reaction on change in solvent. If the rate-determining reaction is one which involves an ionization, then a change to a solvent of higher dielectric constant will speed the reaction, although not in the same manner as a change in the concentration of a reagent.

As this study progresses, we shall see illustrations of these uses of reaction kinetics in the determination of chemical mechanisms, as well as other examples which will arise in special cases. In general, it can be stated that the various types of application of the Law of Mass Action make it one of the most powerful tools at the disposal of the investigator of reaction mechanisms.

PROBLEMS

34–1 Is it possible to predict the orders of any of the following reactions on the basis of the stoichiometry given and no other prior information? If so, decide which of the following should be characterized by zero-order kinetics; first-order kinetics; second-order kinetics.

(a) $NH_4^+ + CNO^- \rightarrow H_2N-\overset{\overset{\displaystyle O}{\displaystyle \|}}{C}-NH_2$

(b) $CH_3COOC_2H_5 + HO^- \xrightarrow{\text{pyridine}} CH_3COO^- + C_2H_5OH$

(c) $R_3N + RI \rightarrow R_4N^+ I^-$

(d) $C_2H_4 + H_2 \xrightarrow{Ni} C_2H_6$

(e) $\alpha\text{-glucose} \xrightarrow[H_2O]{H^+} \beta\text{-glucose}$

34–2 Consider a set of chemical reactions governed by the interactions given in the diagram shown below.

$$A + B \underset{k_2}{\overset{k_1}{\rightleftharpoons}} C + D \underset{k_4}{\overset{k_3}{\rightleftharpoons}} E$$
$$k_5 \downarrow \uparrow k_6$$
$$F$$

Case I: Suppose that

$$A_0 = B_0; \quad k_1 = 10k_2; \quad k_3 = k_4; \quad k_5 = 10k_6; \quad k_1 = k_3 = k_5.$$

(a) Sketch the concentration of A as a function of time.

(b) Sketch the concentration of E as a function of time.

(c) Sketch the concentration of F as a function of time.

Case II: Suppose that

$$A_0 \neq B_0; \quad k_1 = 10k_2; \quad k_4 = 0; \quad k_5 = 10k_6; \quad k_1 = 100k_3 = k_5.$$

(d) Sketch the concentration of E as a function of time.

(e) Sketch the concentration of F as a function of time.

Suppose that the initial quantity of B is increased by a factor of ten.

(f) What changes would you expect in the curves for parts (a), (b), (c), (d), and (e)?

34-3 Using the data given, deduce the order of each of the following reactions.

(a) When ethylbenzene is nitrated with $7M$ nitric acid using acetic acid as the solvent, the data shown below are obtained.

Time, min	0	5	10	15	20	25	30
$C_6H_5C_2H_5$	0.093	0.075	0.055	0.037	0.020	0.002	0

(b) A sample of glucose, crystallized at a low temperature, was found to have a rotation of 112°. A solution was acidified and the rotation measured at exactly one minute intervals. The readings were as shown below.

Time	Rotation, degrees
0	112
1	106.1
2	101.4
3	97.2
4	93.4
5	90.0
next morning	59.0

What fraction of the reaction was completed after each time interval? What is the order of the reaction? What is this reaction called?

How did the qualitative consideration of the nature of the reacting
species and the dependence of rates on the concentration of these species
lead to the understanding of the course of simple addition and
displacement reactions? What is the nature of a transition state?
How are displacement reactions examined to determine it?

35

SIMPLE REACTION MECHANISMS;
TRANSITION STATES

35–1 First Applications of the Law of Mass Action to Mechanisms

Rates of chemical reactions were being measured during the entire nineteenth century. During the latter part of the century, many organic reactions of interest were investigated kinetically. In spite of this, the implications of the Law of Mass Action with respect to reaction mechanisms were not perceived clearly until after the beginning of the twentieth century. A pioneer in this work was A. Lapworth, a British chemist who succeeded in establishing the essentials of the mechanisms of several reactions a couple of decades ahead of the general appreciation of the significance of these methods.

35–2 The Cyanohydrin Reaction

In 1903, Lapworth published a study of the cyanohydrin reaction. For acetone, organic chemists wrote this reaction as $(CH_3)_2CO + HCN \rightarrow (CH_3)_2C(OH)CN$. Lapworth discovered that pure HCN and pure acetone react very slowly at room temperature. The time required for the reaction to proceed halfway to completion is in the neighborhood of three to four hours. If sodium cyanide is used instead of hydrogen cyanide, the reaction is effectively complete in two minutes. Lapworth saw that this meant that the reagent which was critical in the reaction was the cyanide ion. Hence the reaction should be formulated as:

$$(CH_3)_2CO + CN^- \rightarrow (CH_3)_2\overset{\displaystyle O^-}{\underset{|}{C}}CN$$

In the reaction of acetone with pure HCN, it may be assumed that the self-ioniza-
tion of the HCN produces a tiny amount of CN$^-$, which would be sufficient to account
for the slow reaction observed. As a preparative procedure, it is convenient to take
advantage of Lapworth's discovery by catalyzing the reaction of HCN with acetone
by adding a crystal of sodium or potassium cyanide to the reaction mixture.
This greatly speeds the reaction, which may then be assumed to proceed according
to the sequence:

$$(CH_3)_2CO + CN^- \rightarrow (CH_3)_2\overset{\overset{\displaystyle O^-}{\displaystyle |}}{C}CN + HCN \rightarrow (CH_3)_2\overset{\overset{\displaystyle OH}{\displaystyle |}}{C}CN + CN^-$$

The HCN thus liberates the free cyanohydrin from its sodium salt and regenerates
the cyanide ion to continue the reaction. Before the introduction of Pyrex, the
usual catalyst was one of moderate alkalinity because soft glass was used.

The cyanohydrin reaction did not require a careful rate determination to permit
the perception of the applicability of the Law of Mass Action because the rate
differences were so large as to be noticeable qualitatively. In other cases, more
precise work was necessary to appreciate the relationships.

35-3   The Hydrolysis of Methyl Iodide

In earlier days it was customary to write the reaction for the hydrolysis of methyl
iodide as:

$$CH_3I + H_2O \rightarrow CH_3OH + HI$$

Investigation of the rate dependence of the reaction, however, showed that the
reaction is first order in methyl iodide but that it does not proceed readily in the
presence of hydriodic acid, as would be necessary for the reaction presented to go
to completion. Experimentation showed that the rate of the reaction is proportional
to the concentration of hydroxide ion, a reagent not appearing in the classical
equation. The reaction is second order, its rate being dependent on the first power
of the methyl iodide and the first power of the hydroxide ion concentration. Consequently, we may rewrite the reaction as

$$CH_3I + OH^- \rightarrow CH_3OH + I^-$$

35-4   The Displacement Reaction

As formulated, the reaction between methyl iodide and hydroxide ion typifies a
large group of organic reactions which may be represented by the equation

$$A + BC \rightarrow AB + C$$

This type of reaction is called the *displacement reaction*. Since the reaction does
not proceed in the absence of base, it is obvious that the separation of the iodide

ion from the carbon is not a spontaneous ionization process. Instead, it must be a process in which the iodide ion is released while the methyl carbon is strongly under the influence of the hydroxide ion. As a first approximation, we may assume that the entrance of the hydroxyl group and the exit of the iodide ion occur simultaneously.

To get a still closer insight into the interactions which occur, we may inquire as to the possible angles of approach of the hydroxide ion. We have already seen that methyl iodide is a dipole with the iodine atom attracting electrons from the carbon atom. The consequence of this will be that the carbon will be at the positive end of the dipole and the iodine at the negative end. This is conventionally represented as

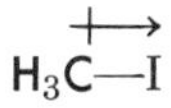

$$\overset{\longmapsto}{H_3C-I}$$

As indicated in Section 29–10, we should expect the hydroxide ion to approach the electron-deficient end of the molecule more readily than the electron-attracting end. For this reason we should expect the geometry of the approach of the hydroxide ion to be as shown in Fig. 35–1.

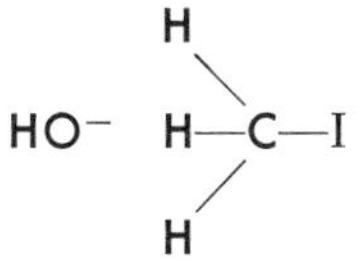

$$HO^-\quad \overset{\displaystyle H}{\underset{\displaystyle H}{H-C}}-I$$

FIGURE 35–1

The process of approach of the hydroxide, simultaneous attachment of hydroxide, and release and departure of iodide may then be represented as in Fig. 35–2. This, of course, is a diagram of the course of a Walden inversion, and the frequency with which Walden inversions occur when substitution takes place on an aliphatic carbon constitutes independent evidence for the correctness of the hypothesis concerning the mechanism of substitution in this type of displacement reaction.

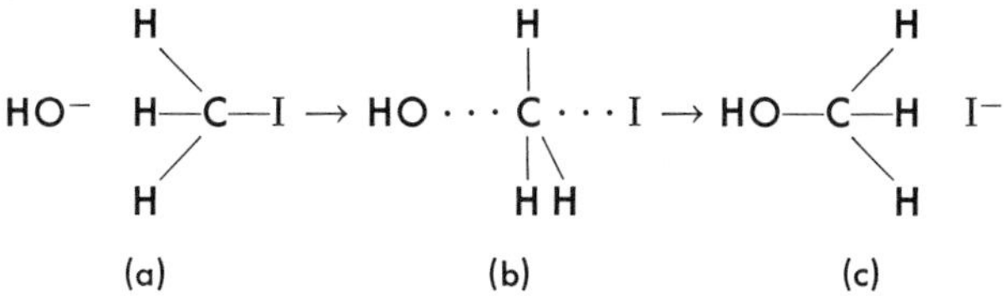

$$HO^-\quad \overset{H}{\underset{H}{H-C}}-I \to HO\cdots\overset{H}{\underset{H\,H}{C}}\cdots I \to HO-\overset{H}{\underset{H}{C}}-H \quad I^-$$

(a)   (b)   (c)   FIGURE 35–2

Structure (b) in Fig. 35–2 represents a special entity in which five groups are within the sphere of influence of the carbon atom on which substitution is occurring. The hydroxyl group is entering and interacting with the bonding electrons of the carbon, and the iodide ion is leaving but is still interacting with the bonding electrons of carbon. Such a structure is usually referred to as a *transition state* or occasionally as an *activated complex*. The characteristic of a transition state is that it usually has more groups associated with it than would be normal and that it has forming bonds and breaking bonds. Another manner of representing the electron drifts in such a reaction was introduced by British mechanists.

$$HO^{\curvearrowright}\quad \overset{\frown}{C}H_3\overset{\frown}{\text{—}}I$$

The first curved arrow indicates that the electron pair of the hydroxide ion is moving to make a new bond with carbon. The second curved arrow indicates that the electron pair constituting the bond between carbon and iodine is moving to become the negative charge on the iodide ion.

35-5   The Reaction of Hydrogen with Iodine

The displacement reaction, as pictured, represents a two-center collision. Chemists have frequently represented reaction mechanisms as taking place by simultaneous exchange of partners in a four-center collision. Such mechanisms turn out to be rare in organic chemistry. The most carefully studied case is that of the reaction of hydrogen and iodine. This was studied by Bodenstein who established that the rate of the reaction is proportional to the concentration of each of the reagents and that no preliminary dissociation of the hydrogen or of the iodine takes place. Trautz proposed that the reaction be formulated as a four-center collision as illustrated in Fig. 35-3. In this reaction, the structure (b) represents the transition state.

H—H   H · · · H   H   H
    $\rightarrow$:   : $\rightarrow$ | |
I—I   I · · · I   I   I

   (a)   (b)   (c)   FIGURE 35-3

35-6   The Nature of the Transition State

As we progress, we shall find experimental methods which throw more light on the details of the transition states of a variety of reactions. For the displacement reaction, certain general considerations are apparent from the fact that these reactions are quite common. In the first place, the fact that such reactions occur frequently must mean that this type of reaction path meets with a lower energy barrier than alternative pathways. The fundamental picture attempting to clarify the existence of the low energy barrier was presented by London in 1929. Essen-

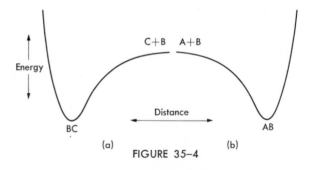

FIGURE 35-4

tially it is based on interactions between two molecules with potential energy curves like those pictured in Fig. 30–1. If the separation between these molecules were great, then there would be no interaction, and the height of the barrier which would have to be surmounted to bring about reaction would be equal to the dissociation energy, as shown in Fig. 35–4. Collision between **A** and **BC** brings the three centers into a configuration in which **A** is closer to **B** than the dissociation distance represented by Fig. 35–4(b), and **C** is closer to **B** than the dissociation distance represented by Fig. 35–4(a). This might be represented by the top of the barrier in Fig. 35–5.

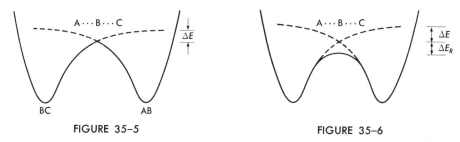

FIGURE 35–5   FIGURE 35–6

In Fig. 35–5, the interval marked ΔE is the gain in energy over the dissociation energy which the system enjoys as a result of the close approach of **A** to **BC**. London assumed, however, that a still further gain would be enjoyed by this system as a result of delocalization of electrons or resonance. This may be represented by the valence-bond formulation for the transition state.

$$\underbrace{A \cdots BC \leftrightarrow AB \cdots C}_{\text{Transition state}}$$

It will be seen that for the instant that the transition state exists, the bonding electrons of the bond **BC** have a greater volume in which to move than they do before or after. Hence, it is argued, there will be resonance stabilization of the transition state with respect to the two possible systems which compose it and the resultant energy diagram would be expected to be like that of Fig. 35–6. The total energy gain enjoyed by the system, then, is that which results from the close approach on collision and the extra energy decrement due to resonance, ΔE_R, in Fig. 35–6. It is reasoned that the sum of these two quantities is great enough to account for the frequency of occurrence of displacement reactions.

35–7 $S_N 2$ Mechanisms

Ingold has introduced a reaction symbolism which has been widely adopted in the classification of organic reaction mechanisms. The picture of the transition state presented in the preceding sections is largely a theoretical one based on analogy and on the reasonable course of action of the particles under consideration. The search during the years intervening between the proposal of these ideas and the present has been concerned with the discovery and refinement of experimental methods for the investigation of the concepts first based purely on theoretical grounds. Many such experimental methods have been found and in the succeeding chapters we shall examine some of them at appropriate points in the discussion. The reaction of methyl iodide with hydroxide would be classed as a *nucleophilic substitution* reaction. The term *nucleophilic* is easily rendered as having affinity for a nucleus. A term distinctive from the word *basicity* is required, however, because nucleophilic activity and basicity do not always run parallel. This is a description of the class of reagents to which the hydroxide ion belongs. The designation is independent of charge type. Thus ammonia and the amines are nucleophiles, since they readily react with protons to form ammonium ions. The opposite type of reagent is designated as electrophilic. The simplest example of an electrophile would be a solvated proton. Again, the designation is independent of charge type. Thus the singly protonated species of a diacid base could be either a nucleophile or an electrophile. For example, $NH_2NH_3^+$ can be attacked by a base to form hydrazine. In this case it would be acting as an electrophile. On the other hand, it could react with acid to form the doubly protonated species. In this case it would be acting as a nucleophile. In like manner, the bisulfate ion can act either as an electrophile or as a nucleophile.

For methyl iodide, the substitution at the carbon takes place in a second-order reaction. Hence the designation S for substitution, subscript N for nucleophilic, and 2 for second order. This reaction is then classified as an S_N2 reaction. Ingold has attempted to define the concept of *molecularity* in such a manner as to have it coincide, as a rule, with the kinetically determined order of the reaction. This definition is strained, however. The straightforward idea to be associated with the word molecularity would have to do with the number of molecules taking part in the reaction up to the rate-determining step. The increase in energy necessary to bring about chemical reactions has been found to result from collisions with fast-moving molecules. Since we cannot conceive of a reaction taking place chemically without a collision, it would follow that there is no reaction with molecularity less than two. A photochemical reaction involves a collision between a molecule and a photon. In the mass sense, this would be unimolecular. In the broadest sense, however, such a reaction would involve a collision between two packets, one a packet of matter, the other a packet of energy. Hence it would be unimolecular in the mass sense, but second order in the sense of the number of packets involved in the reaction. For most purposes, it is sufficient to designate the kinetically determined order of the reaction when assigning mechanistic symbols.

35–8 S_N1 Mechanisms

If we study the hydrolysis of tertiary butyl chloride instead of methyl iodide, we find that the reaction proceeds equally well in alkali or in acid. It is evident from a superficial qualitative examination that the reaction is not dependent on hydroxide ion concentration and, for this reason, does not belong to the same mechanistic category as the hydrolysis of methyl iodide. Measurement of the rate dependence of the reaction shows that it is first order in tertiary butyl chloride and independent of hydroxide ion concentration. Since it is still a nucleophilic substitution reaction, the mechanism is represented by the symbol S_N1, indicating that it is a first-order nucleophilic substitution.

A great deal of effort has gone into the study of the mechanism of the S_N1 reaction. We shall not attempt an exhaustive treatment of these studies but will point out a few of the critical experiments. In general, these reactions proceed more rapidly in media of high dielectric constant than in media of low dielectric constant. In spite of this, it cannot be argued that the dielectric constant is the sole determining factor in the rate change. An example is furnished by the substitution of benzhydryl chloride in alcohol, a reaction studied by several groups and interpreted by Hammett. In this reaction benzhydryl ethyl ether is formed according to the following equation:

$$(C_6H_5)_2CHCl + C_2H_5OH \rightarrow (C_6H_5)_2CHOC_2H_5 + HCl$$

The reaction is independent of alkoxide ion concentration. Raising the dielectric constant by the addition of nitrobenzene slows the reaction. Raising the dielectric constant by the addition of water, however, speeds the reaction while exerting little influence on the product composition. It is argued that this effect is due to the specific affinity of the water for the chloride ion which must be solvated for the reaction to proceed. The logical conclusion from these experiments is that water solvates the chloride ion best, while alcohol solvates it better than nitrobenzene. From these experiments we must also conclude that the participation of solvent in the reaction is not zero order but is of an order higher than one. For this reason, the reaction has been called *solvolytic.*

35–9 Rate-Determining and Composition-Determining Steps

The addition of water to an ethanol solution of benzhydryl chloride does not produce a rise in the formation of benzhydrol commensurate with the amount of water but leaves the reaction with alcohol to form the ethyl ether essentially intact, although speeding it. This fact leads to the conclusion that the reaction must be considered in two steps, (1) the rate-determining step, which is affected by water, and (2) the product-determining step, in which the action of the alcohol predominates. The rate-determining step is one in which the C—Cl bond is broken and the product-determining step is one in which the C—OEt bond is formed. This contrasts with the case of the hydrolysis of methyl iodide. The evidence is, then, that in the S_N1 reaction, bond breaking and bond formation are not simultaneous processes but are successive steps. Further support is lent to this concept by the observation that the addition of a relatively large amount of chloride ion slows the reaction, while a similar concentration of azide ion, N_3^-, exerts no effect on the reaction velocity. This is interpreted to mean that the reaction of bond breaking is reversible but that the rate constant of the reverse reaction is quite small. Since we should expect the cleavage of a C—Cl bond to be heterolytic, because of the strong electron-attracting property of the Cl, it would follow that the species formed by the heterolysis of benzhydryl chloride or of tertiary butyl chloride would be one in which the carbon bears a positive charge. Such a species is called a *carbonium ion*.

35-10   The Stereochemistry of the Displacement Reaction

As we have formulated the S_N2 mechanism for the displacement reaction, we should expect a Walden inversion to take place. The first case in which this was definitely established was found in 1923. Later other examples were added. For instance, D-*sec*-octyl iodide can be converted into L-*sec*-octyl iodide by the action of potassium radioiodide in acetone solution. In this reaction, it is possible to follow the rate of uptake of the radioactive iodine by the octyl iodide and, simultaneously, to follow the rate of inversion polarimetrically. It was found that the two rates are identical, thus showing that the displacement of iodine by radioiodide is accompanied by Walden inversion:

$$C_6H_{13}CHICH_3 + \overset{*}{I}{}^- \rightarrow C_6H_{13}CH\overset{*}{I}CH_3 + I^-$$

$$(\text{D}) \qquad\qquad\qquad (\text{L})$$

We may conclude that the examples in which inversion has been established provide support for the mechanism of the displacement reaction as formulated.

For S_N1 reactions, we should expect the separation of a carbonium ion to be accompanied by complete loss of stereochemical identity, since such a trigonal structure would be flat with 120° angles, in accordance with the principles discussed in Chapter 29. In fact, however, it is found that most of the substance racemizes, but that proportions which vary with the nature of the substituents undergo inversion instead of racemization. This shows that all the stereochemical bias is not lost in the formation of a carbonium ion. The conclusion seems inescapable that in those cases in which there is some residual optical activity, the carbonium ion cannot have been entirely free. While the C—Cl bond must have broken, the hydration of the resultant carbonium ion must have taken place before the halogen ion had moved far enough away in space to lose its shielding effect entirely. This gives us a means of estimating the survival time of carbonium ions. While such estimates are probably not highly accurate, it is suggested that the survival times must be in the neighborhood of 10^{-8} sec to account for the phenomena observed.

35-11   Mechanism of Solvolysis

Sodium chloride in its solid form exists in an ionic lattice. When it dissolves in water, the electrostatic forces binding it into the lattice are dissolved by polar attractions of the water for the sodium and chloride ions. In water molecules, the

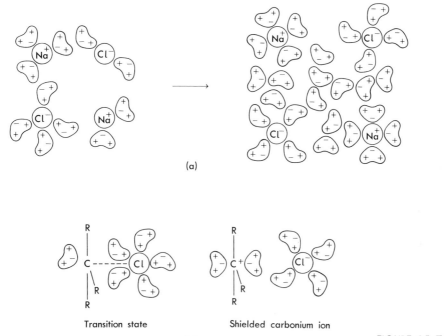

(a)

Transition state   Shielded carbonium ion

(b)   FIGURE 35–7

oxygen is electron attracting and thus forms the negative pole. The two hydrogens are positive poles. We may represent the process of dissociation of the ionic lattice, that is, the physical separation of the pre-existing ions, as in Fig. 35–7(a).

We must imagine the process of formation of a carbonium ion as being one in which both ionization and at least partial separation of the ions take place simultaneously. The carbonium ion will be surrounded by a water shell but the strong polar attraction of water will take place mainly at the positive center of the ion. Insinuation of water molecules into the space between the chloride and the carbon will provide the main ionizing force of the reaction. The top of the energy barrier, that is the transition state, will be the point at which the C—Cl bond is stretching and the solvent cage is just being formed around the nascent chloride ion. In the "fully developed" ion as distinct from the transition state, the solvent cage around the chloride will be complete, but the chloride will not yet have left the vicinity of the carbonium ion. These steps may be sketched as in Fig. 35–7(b). The shielded carbonium ion will be more susceptible to attack by an energetic nucleophile from the side away from the chlorine than from the side on which the chlorine interposes. This condition will rapidly pass, permitting racemization of any ions which were not attacked while shielded.

We see thus that the interpretation of a variety of experiments can lead us to present a picture of the events taking place at the time of bond breaking and immediately thereafter. The elaboration and refinement of sequences such as these constitute the objectives of the study of reaction mechanisms.

35–12   Conclusions

This completes a brief general survey of the physical and chemical tools and concepts used in the study of reaction mechanisms in organic chemistry. We shall now turn to the application of these principles to the study of the major reactions of aliphatic chemistry, supplementing them, as necessary, with further principles that prove useful in understanding the course of chemical events.

PROBLEMS

35-1   Consider a reaction sequence of the following steps:

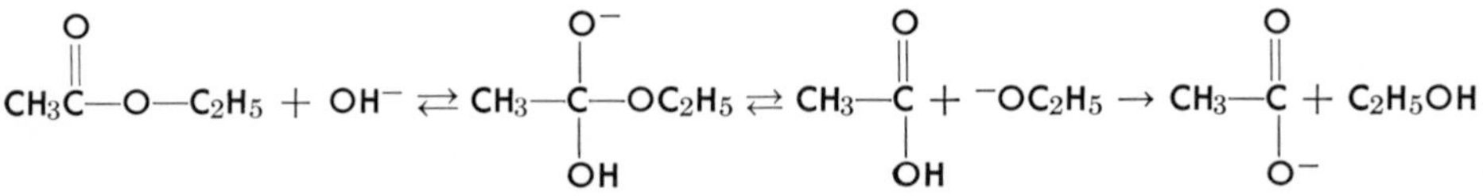

$$
\underset{A}{CH_3C(=O){-}O{-}C_2H_5} + OH^- \rightleftarrows \underset{B}{CH_3{-}\overset{O^-}{\underset{OH}{C}}{-}OC_2H_5} \rightleftarrows CH_3{-}\overset{O}{\underset{OH}{C}} + {}^-OC_2H_5 \rightarrow CH_3{-}\overset{O}{\underset{O^-}{C}} + C_2H_5OH
$$

(a) Is B a reaction intermediate or a transition state?

(b) Draw all the transition states occurring in this process.

(c) Suppose the first step were the slowest in the sequence. Draw the energy profile of the reaction (*cf.* Section 35–6).

(d) Suppose the second step were rate-determining. How would the reaction profile appear in this case?

(e) What would be the kinetic dependence of the reaction if the first step were rate determining?

(f) What would the kinetic dependence of the reaction be if the second step were rate determining? Could these two mechanisms be distinguished by simple measurement of the kinetic law governing the reaction?

(g) Suppose the rate in water were compared with that in a less polar solvent. Would this distinguish between the alternatives?

(h) Why is the last step essentially irreversible?

(i) Is OH^- a nucleophilic or electrophilic reagent in this reaction?

(j) Is there any similarity between this proposed mechanism and Lapworth's cyanohydrin reaction mechanism? Why should an analogy exist?

35-2   (a) Show that each of the following reactions, which we have seen before, is a nucleophilic substitution reaction.

$$Na^+\ {}^-OCH_3 + CH_3I = CH_3OCH_3 + Na^+I^-$$

$$CH_3I + N(CH_3)_3 = (CH_3)_4N^+I^-$$

$$(C_2H_5OOC)_2CH^-\ Na^+ + CH_3CH_2CH_2Br = (C_2H_5OOC)_2CHCH_2CH_2CH_3 + Na^+Br^-$$

(b) Will the reagents listed below be electrophilic or nucleophilic?

$$Br_2,\ I^-,\ (CH_3)_2SO_4,\ H_2O_2,\ AlCl_3,\ Zn,\ HCl,\ NaOH,\ NH_3$$

Note that in some cases it is necessary to define the reaction under consideration.

35-3 When optically active α-phenylethanol is reacted with HBr under various conditions different sets of products are obtained.

(a)

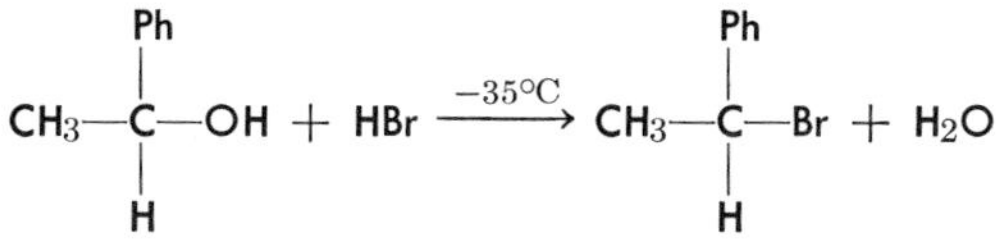

$$\underset{\text{L-}\alpha\text{-phenylethanol}}{\text{CH}_3\text{—}\overset{\displaystyle \text{Ph}}{\underset{\displaystyle \text{H}}{\text{C}}}\text{—OH}} + \text{HBr} \xrightarrow{-35^\circ\text{C}} \underset{\substack{\text{Racemic mixture of} \\ \text{D- and L-phenylbromoethane}}}{\text{CH}_3\text{—}\overset{\displaystyle \text{Ph}}{\underset{\displaystyle \text{H}}{\text{C}}}\text{—Br}} + \text{H}_2\text{O}$$

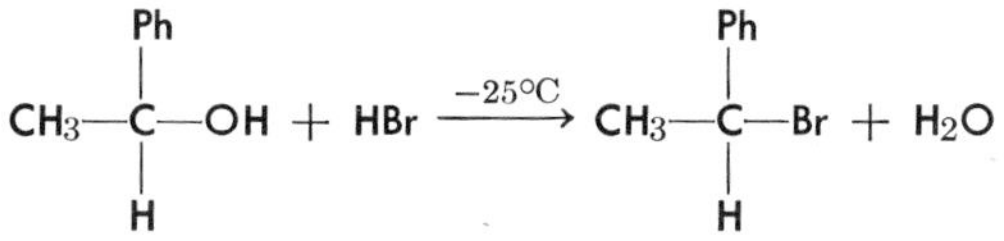

(b)

$$\underset{\text{L-}\alpha\text{-phenylethanol}}{\text{CH}_3\text{—}\overset{\displaystyle \text{Ph}}{\underset{\displaystyle \text{H}}{\text{C}}}\text{—OH}} + \text{HBr} \xrightarrow{-25^\circ\text{C}} \underset{\substack{\text{Mainly D-phenylbromoethane} \\ \text{somewhat contaminated} \\ \text{with L-bromide}}}{\text{CH}_3\text{—}\overset{\displaystyle \text{Ph}}{\underset{\displaystyle \text{H}}{\text{C}}}\text{—Br}} + \text{H}_2\text{O}$$

Interpret these results in terms of suitable reaction mechanisms, showing structural formulas for transition states involved. Explain why the product from reaction (b) is somewhat impure.

Part 3

SOME SPECIFIC MECHANISMS
IN THE ALIPHATIC SERIES

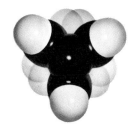

The general experimental methods for investigating reaction mechanisms, which rely on the use of the Law of Mass Action, the study of rates and equilibria and their correlation with electronic effects, the theoretical methods relying on the concept of the transition state, and the details of bond formation and bond breaking are all useful in most mechanistic studies. When individual reactions are examined, however, it is frequently found that individual problems arise which require the invention of new methods designed to fit the cases at hand. For this reason, an understanding of the reasoning underlying mechanistic studies requires the study of a group of more or less typical reactions in several fields of chemistry. Part 3 deals with the mechanisms of a selection of reactions widely used in preparative aliphatic chemistry.

How can electronic effects be differentiated from
steric effects in the displacement reaction?
How do changes in the nature of the
entering and leaving groups affect the reactions?

36

STRUCTURAL EFFECTS ON THE DISPLACEMENT REACTION

36–1   The S_N2 Reaction in Homologs

Ingold and his collaborators have studied extensively the effects of changes of structure on the course of the displacement reaction. One of their early observations was that increasing alkyl substitution on the carbon at the reacting center would cause a decrease in the velocity of the S_N2 reaction. We have already seen that in a carbon-to-halogen bond, the electron-attracting power of the halogen causes an electron drift, making the carbon the positive end of the dipole and the halogen the negative end. It will be of interest to compare the changes in velocity with the changes in dipole moment. Table 36–1 gives the comparison between second-order rate constants and dipole moments of the same halides. The rate constants were measured in 80 volumes of ethanol and 20 of water at 55°C. The figures given should be multiplied by 10^{-5}. The dipole moments were determined in benzene solution. The rate constant is thus accompanied by a change in dipole moment. It remains to rationalize the directions of the two changes.

Table 36–1

	CH_3Br	C_2H_5Br	$(CH_3)_2CHBr$	$(CH_3)_3CBr$
Second-order rate constants, 1/mole-sec	2140	170	4.7	–
Dipole moments in benzene, D*	1.82	1.88	2.04	2.21

* Debye units $= 10^{-18}$ esu

36–2   Rates and Dipole Moments

According to the view which we have advanced previously, the diminution in rate of the S_N2 reaction should be caused by a diminution in the magnitude of the positive charge on the carbon end of the dipole. Yet the increase in dipole moment might be interpreted as being due to an increase in the positive charge on the carbon accompanied by an increase in the negative charge on the bromine. How are we to reconcile these apparently contradictory possibilities?

In the Branch and Calvin equation for acidity, we found a tool for estimating the extent of electron drift toward or away from an electron-attracting center, in this case the hydroxyl group. For purposes of qualitative estimation, this equation may be used to weigh the relative electron drifts toward other electron-attracting centers. For methyl bromide, the electron-attracting power of halogen has caused a drift of electrons away from the carbon, leaving the carbon in a state which would be electron attracting with respect to a carbon in ethane. Hence we may assume that this carbon will cause a further electron drift to take place from additional carbons attached to it. Such a drift would have two effects: (1) It would cancel a portion of the positive charge existing on the carbon of the C—Br bond. (2) It would move the center of gravity of the positive charge farther away from the bromine. These are precisely the two conditions that are needed to correlate the second-order rate constants and the dipole moments. (1) The diminution of the positive charge at the carbon of the C—Br bond would diminish the rate of the second-order reaction. (2) The migration of the center of positive charge away from the bromine would increase the dipole moment. We thus see that the rate changes and the dipole moment changes are both consistent with the inductive effect. Additional explanations of the rates have been offered in the literature, based on the concept of increased delocalization of the σ-electrons with this type of substitution and based on steric considerations. In accordance with a general rule of parsimony of causes, however, we may content ourselves at present with the explanation based on the inductive effect.

36–3   The S_N1 Reaction in Homologs

The measurements cited in Table 36–1 were made in 0.01-N NaOH. If the specific rate constants are calculated by the rates at which the alkali is consumed by the reaction, the values obtained differ from those given in the table. The values of the specific rate constants are as follows: CH_3Br, 21.4; C_2H_5Br, 1.7; $(CH_3)_2CHBr$, 0.29; $(CH_3)_3CBr$, 1010. It will be seen that the first two of these values are identical with those of the table, after correction for the value of the normality of the base, 0.01. The value for isopropyl differs slightly from the corrected value, however, and that for tertiary butyl bromide differs tremendously. The explanation lies in the fact that the value for tertiary butyl bromide is found to be independent of the hydroxide ion concentration and therefore cannot be included in the second-order rate constant. Careful examination shows that a portion of the reaction of isopropyl bromide is also independent of the hydroxide ion concentration, so that this rate is separated into a second-order portion and a first-order portion. The first-order portion of the two bromides is, then, $(CH_3)_2CHBr$, 0.24; $(CH_3)_3CBr$, 1010. How can we correlate these with structure?

36–4   The Mechanistic Discontinuity

Ingold has presented the data from the two series in graphic form to emphasize the mechanistic change which takes place. The graph is reproduced in Fig. 36–1. Examination of Fig. 36–1 makes it strikingly clear that a continuation of the process of substitution with alkyl groups at the reacting carbon slows down the second-order reaction, speeds up the first-order reaction, and produces a mechanistic discontinuity.

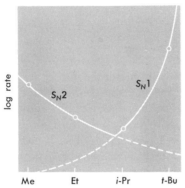

FIG. 36–1.   Graphical representation of data from S_N1 and S_N2 reactions. [From J. L. Gleave, E. D. Hughes, and C. K. Ingold. *J. Chem. Soc.* 238 (1935).]

36–5   Ionization and the Inductive Effect

One rationalization offered for the increase in velocity of the first-order, or solvolytic, reaction is essentially an extension of the reasoning used in correlating acidities with electron-attracting powers. In the case of acidities, we argued about the effects of electron-attracting groups in increasing the ease of ionization of positively charged particles, protons, from O—H bonds. Now we must argue about the effects of electron-donating groups in increasing the ease of ionization of negatively charged groups, halide ions, from C—halogen bonds. One would immediately predict that the two arguments would run parallel, that is, that an increase in electron-donating power should secure an increase in ease of ionization of the C—halogen bond. We saw in the last chapter that the rate-determining step in the S_N1 reaction is this ionization. Hence we should expect a direct relationship between an increase in electron-donating power and ease of ionization of a C—halogen bond. This is what is found in the series of displacement reactions studied by Ingold and his collaborators.

36–6 Ionization and Hyperconjugation

An alternative explanation for the electron drift responsible for the increased ease of ionization of tertiary halides in contrast to primary halides has been based on the concept of sigma-bond delocalization. In this case the delocalization responsible for the stabilization of the tertiary butyl ion would be represented as follows:

$$H^+ CH_2\!=\!C(CH_3)_2 \leftrightarrow (CH_3)_3C^+ \leftrightarrow (CH_3)_2C\!=\!CH_2 H^+$$

This type of sigma-bond delocalization has been referred to as *hyperconjugation*. Its contribution to the stabilization of any given species is difficult to assess because the general contributions of sigma-bond delocalizations have not been systematically investigated by independent physical methods in organic systems. Whatever the mechanism, investigators are in agreement that the tertiary butyl radical is more strongly electron donating than the methyl radical when attached to a halogen and that this is fundamentally the factor that is responsible for the increased ease of ionization.

Reasoning of the type advanced in the preceding paragraph is not properly classed as predictive. The mechanistic change in the displacement reaction was not predicted but was observed experimentally and then rationalized. Having once found such a series, however, it is reasonable to look for it again in other reactions and, indeed, numerous examples of such mechanistic inversions are now known. All that the present state of our knowledge permits, however, is recognition of the fact that such inversions may occur. Prediction of the exact point in substitution at which they are to be expected would require much more precise information than we now possess.

36–7 Steric Effects in the S_N2 Reaction; Alpha Substitution

In our discussion of conformational effects on the relative stabilities of hydrocarbons and of sugars, we found that the space-occupying properties of groups could be important with respect to their stabilities. Such effects are classed as steric. In much the same manner as space-occupying effects can influence stabilities of normal molecules, they can also influence stabilities of transition complexes. If substitution makes the formation of transition complexes increasingly difficult because of crowding, we should have a steric effect on reaction velocity.

For the series progressing from methyl to tertiary butyl, it might be argued that the progressive decrease in rate with increased alkyl substitution could be the result of a steric effect. Examination of the models of the transition states permits an estimation of the magnitude of this effect. In each case, the groups surrounding the carbon are relatively close together when held at the tetrahedral angle and move farther apart when they go into the transition state. This is so because in the transition state the angle separating them will be 120° while in the initial state, they are closer together at $109\frac{1}{2}°$. It is true that calculation shows that the compression of the transition state increases with increasing alkyl substitution. The important consideration, however, is the *increase* in energy on going from the initial state to the transition state. The energy due to crowding in the normal state would always be decreased by relief of crowding as the molecule goes to the transition state because of the increase in angles separating the groups and the decrease in the coefficient of repulsion as groups separate. The difference is shown in Fig. 36–2(a) and (b).

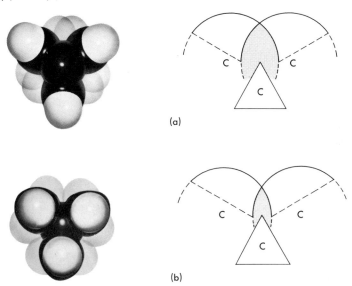

(a)

(b)

FIG. 36–2. (a) Normal state of the tertiary butyl group, showing the projection of the volume of overlap between two van der Waals radii of hydrogens on adjacent methyl groups. (b) Tertiary butyl carbonium ion, showing the projection of the volume of overlap between two van der Waals radii of hydrogens on adjacent methyl groups.

For this reason, the process of activation in each case involves a loss of crowding energy, and the amount of this loss increases as substitution is increased. Consequently, we should not expect an important contribution of steric crowding to be the diminution in reaction rate.

We learned from the Branch and Calvin equation that equal changes in inductive effects should be expected to produce equal changes in the logarithms of the acidities. Assuming that similar factors are at work in reactivities, we might expect equal changes in inductive effect to produce equal changes in the logarithms of rate constants. In Table 36–1, the ratio of the rate constants CH_3Br/C_2H_5Br is 12.6. Consequently, we should expect the next change, from ethyl to isopropyl to be of the same order of magnitude. This would lead to diminution in the rate constant from 170 to 13.5 instead of to 4.7 as observed. This calculation indicates that the major portion of the change in rate can be accounted for consistently on the basis of an inductive effect, with only a minor remainder to be accounted for on other grounds.

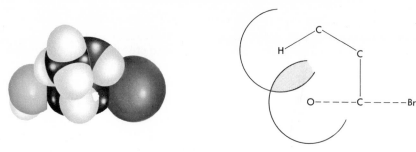

FIGURE 36–3

36–8   Steric Effects in the S_N2 Reaction; Beta Substitution

The situation is different for substitution around the β-carbon of an alkyl halide. For example, we may consider the change on going from ethyl to normal propyl bromide. Here the normal curving of the molecule, caused by the tetrahedral angles of the substituents, brings the hydrogens of the terminal methyl group into the line of motion of an entering group. The general outlines of the transition state may be visualized by reference to Fig. 36–3. It will be seen that there is serious interference with the oxygen if we insist on having it approach on an angle of 180° from the leaving bromine. As we have seen, to have it approach from any other angle will cost relatively more energy; if it approaches on the 180° angle, it will also cost more energy because of the necessity for overcoming the repulsive force of the terminal group. The result will be that any angle of approach will require more energy than is required for ethyl bromide. For normal propyl bromide, two alternatives exist, involving rotation of the methyl group away from the position of interference so that a hydrogen attached to the α-methylene group may be in the path of the entering group instead of the terminal methyl group. Substitution of another β-methyl group to make isobutyl bromide, $(CH_3)_2CHCH_2Br$, should reduce but not eliminate this possibility. Finally, the use of neopentyl bromide, $(CH_3)_3CCH_2Br$, should eliminate the possibility of avoiding the blockage of the path of approach taken by the entering hydroxyl group.

We may also argue the case for a decrease in reaction velocity of substitution due to an inductive effect from the β-position. Having seen from the Branch and Calvin equation that the effect of a group falls off approximately one-third on passing through a single bond, we should expect the inductive effect of three groups in the β-position to be approximately equivalent to that of one in the α-position. This can be evaluated directly from Table 36–1. From this table we can see that the inductive effect of substituting should cause at most approximately

Table 36–2

	CH_3Br	C_2H_5Br	$CH_3CH_2CH_2Br$	$(CH_3)_2CHCH_2Br$	$(CH_3)_3CCH_2Br$
Second-order rate constants	34.4	1.95	0.547	0.058	0.000,008,26
Ratio, C_2H_5Br/RBr	0.057	1.00	3.57	33.6	23,600

a thirty-six-fold decrease on going from ethyl to neopentyl. Constants actually observed are given in Table 36–2. This reaction differs slightly from that recorded in Table 36–1, since the reagent is ethoxide ion instead of hydroxide ion, and the medium is anhydrous ethanol. Second-order constants are given. These should be multiplied by 10^{-3} to secure the true constants.

It seems evident from the figures that the magnitude of the decrease in the second-order velocity constant in going from ethyl to neopentyl is quite incommensurate with any possible inductive effect. If we take the factor of 3.57 on going from ethyl to propyl as being due to an inductive effect, we should expect an approximately equal decrement in the logarithm of the constant to occur on going from ethyl to isobutyl. This would give a calculated ratio of approximately 13 instead of the value of 33.6 observed. On these grounds, we should expect the value for neopentyl to be approximately 46 or $(3.57)^3$, which agrees reasonably well with the value of 36 calculated earlier from Table 36–1. Instead we find a factor of nearly 24,000. The substantial drop on going from isobutyl to neopentyl is in line with the rationalization made on the basis of a steric effect. It will be recalled that both propyl and isobutyl could avoid the full steric effect by rotation around the bond connecting the α-position to the β-position. However, this possibility does not exist for neopentyl. On all counts, then, the explanation of the effects of β-substitutions appears to agree with the expectations based on steric grounds and to be incompatible with the expectations based on inductive grounds alone.

36–9   Influence of the Leaving Group

In the second-order displacement reactions that have been measured, the rates of substitution of bromides are of the order of 30 to 40 times as fast as those of chlorides and those of iodides are 2.0 to 2.5 times as fast as those of bromides. The order of rates, $I > Br > Cl$, is the order of decreasing bond strengths, $I < Br < Cl$. This indicates that the controlling factor in differences in the rate of the S_N2 reaction in these cases is the ease of the breaking of the C—halogen bond rather than the polarity of the bond. It is of interest to note that the acidities of the halogen acids have been compared in nonbasic solvents. In acetic acid, for example, the series is $HI > HBr > HCl$. Again we see that the controlling factor is the change in bond strength rather than the change in polarity. We may extend the series to include positively charged groups. Reference to Branch and Calvin's table shows that the effect of a positive charge in increasing bond strength should be greater than that of changes within any row of the periodic table, since the electron-attracting power of a positive charge is greater. We should expect, therefore, that bonds to positively charged groups should be stronger than those to neutral groups and hence that their displacement should be slower. This is the observed order. In addition, we should expect that a positively charged group in the second row of the periodic table should be less strongly bound than one in the first row. Hence we should expect to find NR_3^+ to be more firmly held than SR_2^+. Again this is the order observed. From this we may construct the reactivity series:

$$I > Br > Cl > SR_2^+ > NR_3^+$$

A consideration of leaving groups based on bond strengths alone, however, is not completely reliable. The hydroxyl group and the amino group, when uncharged, form weaker bonds than the OH_2^+ and NR_3^+ groups yet are poorer leaving groups. This effect may be rationalized by assuming that in these cases the polarity of the bonds is insufficient to promote the displacement reaction strongly. This explanation has not been independently verified. At the other end of the reactivity series, the toluenesulfonyl group, $-OSO_2-C_6H_4CH_3$, is a better leaving group even than iodide, yet it would seem reasonable to suppose that the $C-O$ bond strength in this case is greater than for the $C-I$ bond.

A similar study can be made for the S_N1 reaction. It has been found that tertiary butyl fluoride hydrolyzes with a very slow but measurable rate and that tertiary butyl chloride hydrolyzes about 10^5 times as fast. Bromides hydrolyze with rates of the order of 25 to 60 times as great as chlorides, and iodides 1.5 to 4.5 times as fast as bromides. Thus the same reactivity series occurs with respect to the leaving groups in S_N1 reactions as in S_N2 reactions. Since the order of magnitude of the increase in rate in the first-order series is quite comparable to that in the second-order series, it follows that the mechanistic change from second order to first order should take place at about the same point with respect to increasing aliphatic substitution in the chloride, bromide, and iodide series. This is also in accord with the experimentally observed results.

Measurements have been made of the displacement of H_2O by bromide ion in a series of alcohols. This is the familiar reaction of alcohols to produce alkyl halides. It was studied kinetically in 90% aqueous phenol. The reaction of methanol with hydrogen bromide may be formulated as

$$Br^- + CH_3OH_2^+ \rightarrow CH_3Br + OH_2$$

While the mechanistic conclusions which could be reached on the basis of the kinetic data were not conclusive, it is shown that the reaction passes through a rate minimum at ethyl and that the rates for the formation of the isopropyl and tertiary butyl bromides are progressively greater. This rate relationship is similar to that found for the displacement of bromide ion by hydroxyl ion and suggests that the same mechanistic discontinuity is at work in this displacement series.

36–10   Influence of the Nucleophile

Reference to Tables 36–1 and 36–2 will show that there is a significantly higher rate of attack by ethoxide ion than by hydroxide ion in the displacement of bromide ion by the second-order mechanism. Because of the electron-releasing property of alkyl groups attached to oxygen, we should expect ethanol to be a weaker acid than water. It would follow that the conjugate base of ethanol, that is, ethoxide ion, should be a stronger base than the conjugate base of water, that is, hydroxide ion. This also is the observed relationship. These observations lead to a tentative conclusion that the reactivity series in the S_N2 reaction might be expected to follow the order of increasing basicities of the nucleophiles. More extensive examinations show that this rule is generally true for nucleophiles which are in the same row of the periodic table but that it does not hold on going from one row to the next. Thus experiments with rates establish that the order of decreasing nucleophilic power for oxygen bases is

$$OH^- > OC_6H_5^- > CO_3^= > OCOCH_3^- > CH_3C_6H_4SO_3^-$$

$$> BrC_6H_4SO_3^- > H_2O > ClO_4^-$$

This is precisely the order of diminishing base strength. A similar series for nitrogen bases may be constructed, and base strengths and nucleophilic powers will again correlate. Finally, if the charge type is kept constant, the following series represents diminishing base strength and diminishing nucleophilic power:

$$R_3C^- > R_2N^- > RO^- > F^-$$

These correlations indicate that the electron density of the attacking species is an important variable in the control of the rate of the reaction. These electron densities may be correlated with changes in polarity. Hence we may conclude that changes in polarity do affect the rate of the displacement reaction on the side of bond formation, while bond strengths are more important on the side of bond breaking.

As indicated above, the correlation between base strength and nucleophilic power breaks down when we go from one row of the periodic table to another. Thus the order of decreasing nucleophilic power of the halides is

$$I^- > Br^- > Cl^- > F^-$$

This is the order of increasing basicities instead of the order of decreasing basicities. The complete explanation for this inversion has not been firmly established. One rationalization is that this is the order of diminishing deformability or *polarizability* of the electron clouds associated with the nucleophilic groups. This suggests the possibility that an important consideration in establishing a new bond may be the ease of deformation of the electron cloud under the influence of the electron-attracting center at which the new bond is to be formed.

The series presented above is important with respect to the practical conduct of organic reactions. Organic chemists have known for the better part of a century that the addition of iodine or iodide ion would frequently permit a recalcitrant reaction to proceed. The explanation for the displacement reaction is that iodide ion is one of the best nucleophiles and also one of the best leaving groups. In a reaction involving methyl chloride as a nucleophile, for example, the addition of a trace of iodide ion, because of its high nucleophilic power, would permit the conversion of some methyl chloride to methyl iodide. This would then attack the other reactant more powerfully than the methyl chloride because of the excellent leaving-group characteristics of the iodide ion. Finally, the iodide ion, having been set free, would reenter the reaction. Thus it would serve as a catalyst.

We have seen that the rate-determining step of the S_N1 reaction takes place prior to the entrance of the nucleophile into the molecule. Accordingly, there should be no effect of change of nucleophile on the rate of the S_N1 reaction. In a variety of first-order displacements, it has been found that bicarbonate, acetate, carbonate, bromide, and chloride all substitute at the same rate in these reactions. This is in accord with the sequence of events in the first-order mechanism which has been developed. We may conclude that this furnishes still another verification of the hypothesis used to account for these reactions.

PROBLEMS

36–1 The second-order rate constants for the reactions of various tertiary amines and alkyl halides have been measured for the following cases at 25°C:

	CH$_3$I	**C$_2$H$_5$I**	**(CH$_3$)$_2$CHI**
Triethylamine	3.29×10^{-2}	1.92×10^{-4}	1.13×10^{-6}
Quinuclidine	1.88	4.87×10^{-2}	7.97×10^{-4}

The structure of quinuclidine is shown below.

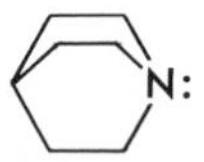

Quinuclidine

Calculate the ratios of rate constants for triethylamine and quinuclidine for the three iodides. Is there any evidence of a steric effect? How would you rule out an explanation on inductive grounds alone?

36–2 The rates of reaction of iodide ion in acetone with alkyl bromides have been measured. Some examples are given below of relative bimolecular rate constants at 25°.

		Relative rate
(1)	(CH$_3$)$_3$CCH$_2$Br	1
(2)	(CH$_3$)$_3$C—C≡C—CH$_2$Br	7.6×10^5
(3)	CH$_3$C≡C—CH$_2$Br	1.4×10^6

(a) How does this information indicate the importance of the steric effect in S_N2 reactions?

(b) Does this information allow the derivation of a quantity representative of the inductive effect of the t-butyl group? If so, determine this quantity and compare its value to the theoretical value found by application of (say) the Branch-Calvin equation, as was done in the text.

(c) Would you expect to find a small difference in rates between neopentyl bromide and ethyl bromide? Could you predict roughly (from other data, perhaps) what the relative rate for ethyl iodide would be?

(d) Would it be proper to ascribe all the difference in the rates of compound 1 and compound 2 solely to removal of a steric effect? Before answering this, draw the molecular-orbital picture for the transition state of the carbon in question in the two cases. Is there any overlap with a pi system in the second case? Do you think this delocalization would raise or lower the energy of the transition state? Would there be any difference if the charge on the attacking atom were different?

36–3 Which would you expect to be hydrolyzed by base more rapidly, chloride I or chloride II? Bromide III or bromide IV? Assume that the conformations are locked in the positions shown. All other factors, such as the expected kinetics of the reaction, proper angle of entry of the attacking group, etc., should be included in your answer.

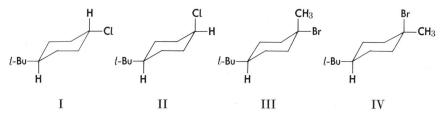

| I | II | III | IV |

36–4 We have noted the expected steric effects of alpha substitution. Do you think we would expect different steric influences if the leaving and entering groups were at greater or smaller distances from the trigonal carbon in the transition state? Compare your predictions for the following cases (Å = angstrom unit):

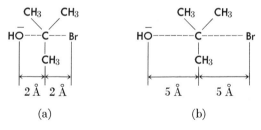

(a)   (b)

*Is the addition of bromine to double bonds a
one-step or two-step process?
How is the answer determined?
How do changes in structure affect the rates of these reactions?*

37

THE ADDITION OF BROMINE
TO DOUBLE BONDS

37–1 The Four-Center Collision Theory

From the equation for the addition of bromine to an ethylenic double bond, one might assume that the reaction would involve a four-center collision.

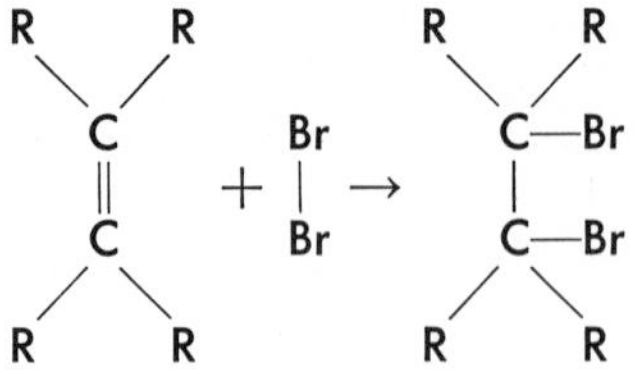

The instinctive assumption of organic chemists that this was the correct mechanism delayed the development of an understanding of the reaction for about a quarter of a century. In 1911 McKenzie found that the addition of bromine to maleic acid takes place by the introduction of the two bromines in *trans* positions on the double bond. We shall examine the interpretation of this finding shortly. For the moment, it is sufficient to point out that the four-body collision theory would require the bromines to add in the *cis* position and, consequently, this theory must be abandoned in cases in which stereochemical evidence conflicts.

37–2 Evidence for a Two-Step Process

The next steps in the systematic development of our knowledge of the mechanism of addition of bromine were taken in 1925 by Terry and Eichelberger and by Francis. Terry and Eichelberger showed that the addition of bromine to maleate or fumarate in aqueous medium results in the formation of bromohydrin,

$$^-OOC—CHOH—CHBr—COO^-,$$

but that the amount of this is limited by a high concentration of bromide ion. Addition of bromide ion brings about the formation of a relatively greater proportion of the dibromide. The natural interpretation of this observation would be that bromide ion is necessary for the formation of the dibromide and that in its absence the stronger nucleophile, hydroxide ion, reacts to form the bromohydrin. Such a reaction sequence would be possible if the nucleophile were assumed to add to a pre-existing carbonium ion in which one bromine had already formed a bond.

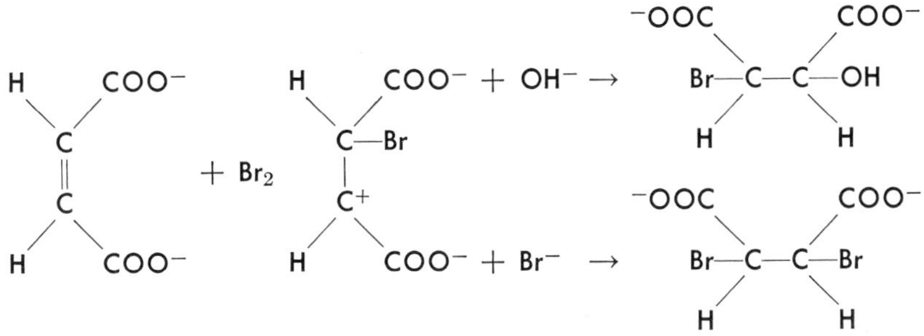

This reaction sequence would require a two-step reaction instead of the single step assumed in the four-body mechanism.

37–3   Is Bromohydrin Formed from HOBr?

The contribution of Francis was to carry the implications of the two-step mechanism to their logical conclusions. Earlier chemists had assumed that the formation of bromohydrin was due to the reaction of HOBr with the double bond. Francis showed that in 4 N sulfuric acid where the concentration of HOBr is negligible, the reaction of bromine with maleic acid yields as much bromohydrin as it does in alkaline media. In both cases the product consists of 35 to 90% bromohydrin and only 10 to 15% dibromide. The reaction of bromine and water with silver sulfate to remove the bromide ion which reverses the formation of the hypobromous acid can be used to prepare HOBr. Reaction of maleic acid under these conditions merely slows the reaction materially without altering the product ratio. The reaction in 4 N sulfuric acid is 1000 times as fast as in the absence of sulfuric acid, yet the product ratio is unchanged. It is highly unlikely that the acceleration would be so precisely the same for both Br$_2$ and HOBr. Hence we may assume that there is only one reagent at work. It has frequently been assumed that this reagent is Br$^+$, but the facts can probably be explained equally well by the assumption that the reagent is bromine but that, under the attack of a nucleophile, the cleavage of the bromine molecule is heterolytic. Either mechanism would lead to the formation of the same positively charged intermediate containing one bromine atom.

37–4   Other Products from the Bromination Reaction

Francis also showed that the addition of bromine to maleate in the presence of an excess of potassium chloride leads to the formation of the chloro-bromo compound.

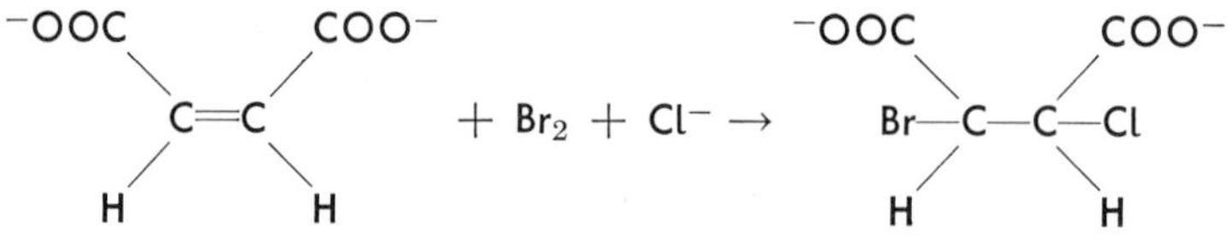

$$
\begin{array}{ccc}
{}^-OOC \quad\quad COO^- & & {}^-OOC \quad\quad COO^- \\
\diagdown \quad\quad \diagup & & \diagdown \quad\quad \diagup \\
C = C & + Br_2 + Cl^- \rightarrow & Br - C - C - Cl \\
\diagup \quad\quad \diagdown & & \diagup \quad\quad \diagdown \\
H \quad\quad H & & H \quad\quad H
\end{array}
$$

In this reaction, no dichloride is formed. This identifies the chloride ion as the second reagent in the series of reactions. In like manner, Francis found that the reaction of bromine with ethylene in neutral sodium chloride solution leads to the formation of 1-bromo-2-chloroethane but no ethylene chloride, 1,2-dichloroethane. The reaction of iodine with ethylene in the presence of neutral sodium chloride gives 1-iodo-2-chloroethane but no ethylene chloride. Finally, the addition of bromine to ethylene in the presence of sodium nitrate yields $BrCH_2CH_2{-}ONO_2$, the nitrate ester of the bromohydrin. We thus have overwhelming evidence that a nucleophile in solution during the course of the halogenation is capable of reacting with the reaction intermediate. This means that the reaction intermediate itself is an electrophilic reagent. The natural assumption would be that this reagent is a carbonium ion of the type assumed in our tentative two-step scheme for the reaction mechanism. We shall see how a full consideration of the experiments of McKenzie led Roberts and Kimball to modify this view.

37–5   The Stereochemistry of Halogen Addition

If we imagine bromine to add to maleic acid in the *cis* position, the product formed would be *meso*-dibromosuccinic acid.

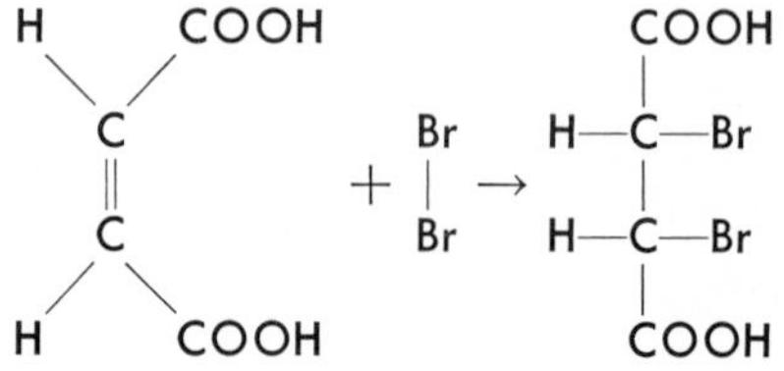

$$
\begin{array}{ccc}
H \quad\quad COOH & & COOH \\
\diagdown \quad\quad \diagup & & | \\
C & Br & H - C - Br \\
\| & + \; | \; \rightarrow & | \\
C & Br & H - C - Br \\
\diagup \quad\quad \diagdown & & | \\
H \quad\quad COOH & & COOH
\end{array}
$$

Meso-dibromosuccinic acid

The *trans* addition would lead to the opposite product, that is, racemic dibromosuccinic acid.

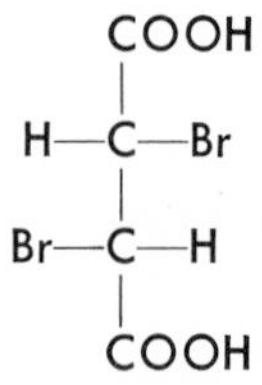

$$
\begin{array}{c}
COOH \\
| \\
H - C - Br \\
| \\
Br - C - H \\
| \\
COOH
\end{array}
$$

Following the same type of logic, *trans* addition to fumaric acid would yield *meso*-dibromosuccinic acid. McKenzie's experiment showed that the product actually formed from maleic acid is the racemic acid, and that from fumaric acid is the *meso* acid. This establishes that the addition of bromine is *trans*.

In our tentative mechanism for the two-step addition of bromine to an ethylenic bond, the intermediate was assumed to be a carbonium ion. Since a carbonium is planar with bond angles of approximately 120°, this would be expected to react with a nucleophile equally well on either side and hence to yield an equimolar mixture of the *meso* and racemic acids. Since the experiment shows that this is not the observed course of the reaction, the mechanistic hypothesis must be modified to take the stereochemical observations into account. This modification was the contribution of Roberts and Kimball.

37–6   Nature of the Intermediate in Bromine Addition

According to the reasoning of Roberts and Kimball, we are required to visualize an intermediate which has a positive charge and which retains the power to control the stereochemical course of the reaction; that is, the intermediate must itself have a stereochemical bias based on the original bias of the olefin from which it was formed. They pointed out that these conditions could be met by assuming that the intermediate is a three-membered heterocyclic ring containing bromine.

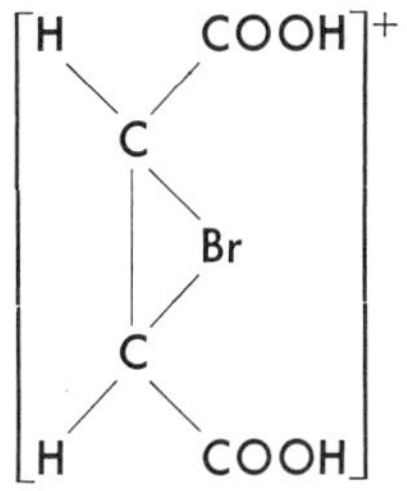

Such a ring would preserve the stereochemical bias of the maleic acid. If we then assume that nucleophilic attack on the ring is the usual backside attack, the entering nucleophile would bring about a Walden inversion of the group on which the attack took place, effecting an overall *trans* addition.

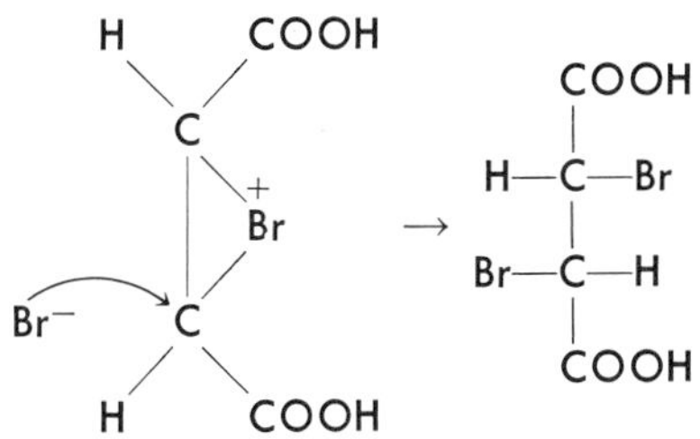

A Newman projection indicating this is given in Fig. 37–1. Thus by adding the

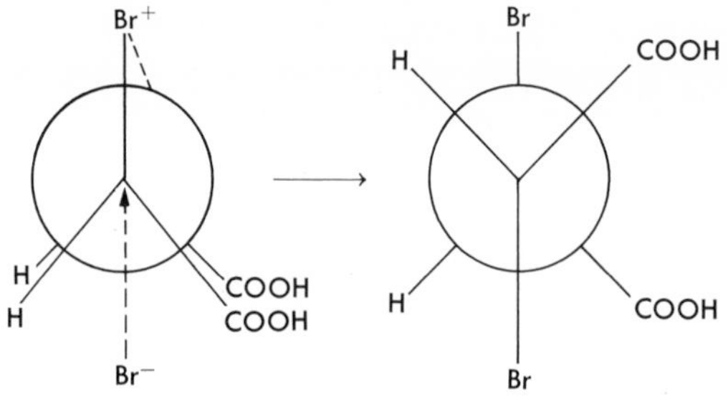

FIG. 37-1.   Course of *trans* addition.

hypothesis of a three-membered ring to the generally accepted mechanism for a Walden inversion, we arrive at a reasonable mechanism for the addition of bromine to double bonds which takes into account a variety of observations.

37-7   Stability of the Three-Membered Ring

We may next inquire about the limits of the stability of the three-membered ring. One experiment that has been performed places a strict limitation on its stability. It has been observed that maleate ion and fumarate ion in solution both yield the same product on bromination in polar solvents. The product is *meso*-dibromosuccinic acid. This is the product to be expected from the fumarate but not from the maleate. Roberts and Kimball accounted for this on the assumption that the two carboxylate ions, because of their like charges, exert a repulsion on each other in solution and rotate into the fumaroid configuration after rupturing the ring. This explanation based on electrostatic repulsions seems reasonable. More refined tests of the bond strength are not available, however.

37-8   Kinetic Studies on Bromine Addition

The reaction of bromine with stilbene in methanol was studied by Bartlett and Tarbell. This provides further substantiation for the mechanism postulated. As in the brominations in water, two products are formed. In methanol, the second product is the methyl ether of the bromohydrin.

$$C_6H_5CH{=\!\!=}CHC_6H_5 + Br_2 \xrightarrow{CH_3OH}$$

$$C_6H_5CHBrCHBrC_6H_5 + C_6H_5CHBrCH(OCH_3)C_6H_5$$

If we were to assume first that the methyl ether is formed from methyl hypobromite, then the rate of its formation should be proportional to the concentration of the hypobromite. But hypobromite is formed in equilibrium with bromine according to the equation:

$$Br_2 + 2CH_3OH \rightarrow CH_3OBr + Br^- + CH_3OH_2^+$$

In stronger acid, the increasing concentration of the protonated species would tend to reverse the reaction with the destruction of hypobromite. Hence the rate of the reaction should decrease with increasing acidity. In fact, experiment shows that the rate is independent of acidity and that, in consequence, the hypobromite does not take part in the rate-determining step. We may assume, as an alternative, that the three-membered ring is formed as an intermediate and that it then may react either with bromide ion to form the dibromide or with methanol to form the methyl ether. If so, increasing the amount of bromide ion should increase the proportion of dibromide formed. This was actually observed to be the case. Hence, we may conclude that the composition of the mixture obtained is dependent on the bromide ion concentration, as would be expected from the postulated mechanism.

37–9   The Rate-Determining Step

We may next inquire whether the formation of the three-membered ring or its collapse is the rate-determining step. The studies of Bartlett and Tarbell also provide an answer to this question. If the collapse of the three-membered ring were rate determining, then we should expect that an increase in bromide ion concentration would increase the rate of the reaction. On the other hand, it is known that bromide ion can react with bromine to form the tribromide ion.

$$Br_2 + Br^- \rightarrow Br_3^-$$

Because of its negative charge, we should expect the tribromide ion to be a much weaker electrophile than bromine. Consequently, if the attack of bromine on the stilbene were the rate-determining step, we should expect that the addition of bromide ion would slow the reaction. Experiment shows that the addition of bromide ion slows the reaction by an amount consistent with the assumption that tribromide ion reacts with 1% of the rate of free bromine. This provides clear-cut evidence that the rate-determining step in the bromination reaction is the attack by the bromine, not the collapse of the three-membered ring.

37–10   Further Evidence for the Three-Membered Ring

In a later paper, Tarbell and Barlett procured independent evidence for the course of the bromination reaction. They found that dimethylmaleate ion and dimethylfumarate ion each react with aqueous bromine to give one of two stereoisomeric lactones.

Both the dibromide and the bromohydrin were prepared, and it was found that neither of these would give the lactone under the conditions of the reaction. Hence neither of these substances can be an intermediate in the formation of the lactone. The intermediate must be a substance in which one bromine has added to one carbon of the double bond. Again this suggests the three-membered ring. The formation of the lactone from the ring would be an example of an internal nucleophilic-substitution reaction.

$$
\begin{array}{c}
\text{COO}^- \\
|\\
\text{CH}_3\text{—C} \\
\diagdown \\
\quad\quad \text{Br} \rightarrow \\
\diagup + \\
\text{CH}_3\text{—C} \\
|\\
\text{COO}^-
\end{array}
\qquad
\begin{array}{c}
\text{Br} \\
|\\
\text{CH}_3\text{—C—CO} \\
|\quad\quad| \\
\text{CH}_3\text{—C—O} \\
|\\
\text{COO}^-
\end{array}
$$

We may conclude that the evidence which has been accumulated concerning bromination of double bonds is consistent with the assumption of the three-membered ring intermediate in a two-step bromination reaction.

37–11   Structural Effects on Rates

We should expect that the effect of an electron-releasing group on the rate of a bromination reaction would be to speed it. Since bromine is an electrophilic reagent, the greater availability of electrons should lead to an increase in reaction rates. In fact, Ingold found that the relative rates of the bromination of ethylene and unsymmetrical dimethylethylene are as 1:5.5, that is, the introduction of two methyl groups on one carbon speeds the reaction more than fivefold. The case of tetramethylethylene is not so clearly explained. This compound reacts fourteen times as fast as ethylene. One theory advanced by Ingold is that the addition of further methyl groups increases the availability of electrons to the attacking reagent. This is an effect on *polarizability*. An alternative explanation, advanced later, is that the intermediate is stabilized by delocalization of the electrons of the three-membered ring.

$$
\overset{+}{\text{Br}} \qquad\qquad \text{Br} \qquad\qquad \text{Br}
$$

$$
\text{CH}_3\text{—C}\!\!\diagup\!\!\diagdown\!\!\text{C—CH}_3 \leftrightarrow \overset{+}{\text{H}}\ \text{CH}_2\text{=C}\diagdown\text{C—CH}_3 \leftrightarrow \text{CH}_3\text{—C}\diagup\text{C=CH}_2\ \text{H}^+
$$
$$
\ \ |\quad\quad\ |\qquad\qquad\qquad\quad |\quad\quad\ |\qquad\qquad\quad |\quad\quad\ |
$$
$$
\text{CH}_3\ \ \text{CH}_3\qquad\qquad\qquad \text{CH}_3\ \ \text{CH}_3\qquad\qquad \text{CH}_3\ \ \text{CH}_3
$$

At present it appears that no method capable of settling the question exists.

   Ingold has classified substituent groups by the type of electronic effects that they can exert on a carbon atom to which they are attached. One that releases electrons to a carbon inductively is classed as exerting a $+I$ effect. One that attracts electrons inductively is classed as exerting a $-I$ effect. In the nomenclature that we have adopted, Ingold's $+I$ effect would be an inductive electron-releasing effect. The $-I$ effect would be an inductive electron-attracting effect. A group that releases electrons by the movement of bonds is classed as a $+T$ substituent, the T standing for *tautomeric*. This is the resonance effect that we mentioned earlier and shall return to again. A group that attracts electrons by a tautomeric effect is classed as a $-T$ group. Nearly all groups that exert a tautomeric effect also exert an inductive effect which may be either in the same direction or in the opposite direction. As examples of these effects, we may cite the following:

(1) $+I$, $=C{\leftarrow}CH_3$

(2) $-I$, $=C{\rightarrow}\overset{+}{N}(CH_3)_3$

(3) $-I-T$, $\equiv\!C{\rightarrow}COOH\ (-C{=}\underset{|}{\overset{O^-}{C}}OH)$

(4) $-I+T$, $=C{\rightarrow}Br\ (-C{=}\overset{+}{Br})$

(5) $+I-T$, $=C{\leftarrow}O^-$

(6) $+I-T$, $\equiv\!C{\leftarrow}COO^-$

(7) $\pm T$, $\equiv\!C{\rightarrow}C_6H_5$

Interpreting the preceding table shows that the methyl group activates for bromination. The trimethylamino group should deactivate. Later, we shall give examples showing that it does. The carboxyl group should deactivate because both effects are in the same direction. Experimentally, acrylic acid brominates less than 0.03 times as fast as ethylene. In case (4), one cannot predict which effect would be expected to be larger, since they work in opposite directions. Experimentally, bromoethylene brominates less than 0.04 times as fast as ethylene, showing that bromine deactivates in this case. Case (7) is of particular interest. Since bromine is electrophilic, it would be predicted from the scheme that the phenyl group would activate. In fact, styrene brominates 3.24 times as fast as ethylene. The scheme would also predict that the phenyl group would activate to a nucleophilic agent. To release electrons to the ethylenic carbons by means of a "tautomeric" effect, it would be necessary for a phenyl group to form a double bond to the ethylenic carbon, illustrated with stilbene:

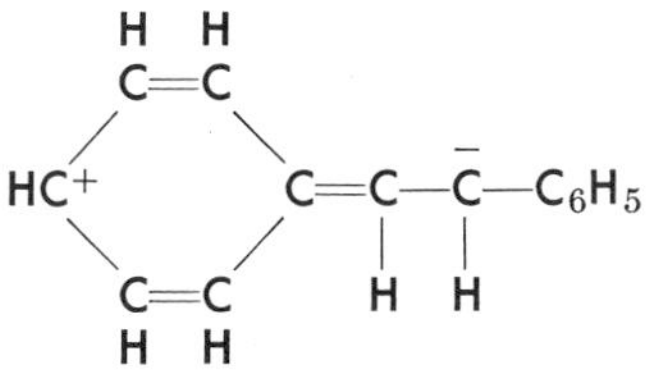

Because of steric interference, it will be found that a model of tetraphenylethylene (Fig. 37–2) does not readily assume such a configuration. In fact, tetraphenylethylene brominates more slowly than ethylene.

FIGURE 37–2

We may conclude that, in most cases where the dielectric constants of the solvent are sufficiently high, the effects of substituents on the rates of bromination of double bonds are consistent with the electrophilic character of the initial attack of bromine on the double bond.

37–12   Chlorinations

Chlorinations and iodinations have not been examined with nearly the care that brominations have. For chlorinations, two reactions are known in which the course of chlorohydrin formation is not entirely consistent with the picture that we have drawn. The first is the chlorination of propylene. In this reaction, we should expect the three-membered ring to be:

$$
\begin{array}{c}
\overset{+}{\text{Cl}} \\
\diagup \diagdown \\
\text{CH}_3\text{—C———C—H} \\
| \quad\quad | \\
\text{H} \quad\quad \text{H}
\end{array}
$$

Attack on this ring by water should yield 2-chloropropanol-1, because the methyl group would be expected to slow a nucleophilic attack. In fact, a small amount of the expected product is formed, but the major product is 1-chloropropanol-2. In similar fashion unsymmetrical dimethylethylene should be expected to form 2-chloro-2-methylpropanol-1. Instead, the product is 1-chloro-2-methylpropanol-2. Again the directive influence of the methyl groups seems reversed.

PROBLEMS

37–1   It has been mentioned that the addition of bromine to maleic acid and fumaric acid produces a different isomer in each case. On the other hand, sodium maleate and sodium fumarate give the same product on bromination.

(a) How stable is the three-membered ring intermediate, then, with respect to a charge in a molecule?

(b) What would you expect to happen if the structure shown below were brominated? Do you think that the repelling charges would interact as much as in sodium maleate?

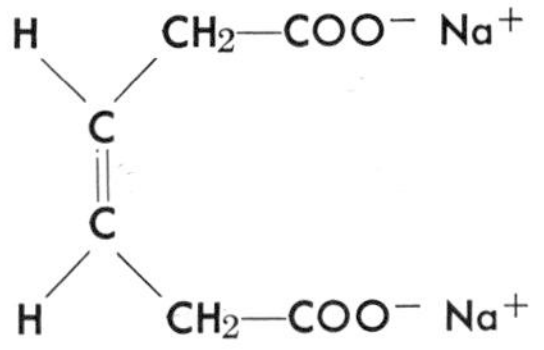

$$
\begin{array}{c}
H \qquad CH_2-COO^- \ Na^+ \\
\diagdown \qquad \diagup \\
C \\
| \\
C \\
\diagup \qquad \diagdown \\
H \qquad CH_2-COO^- \ Na^+
\end{array}
$$

Sodium dimethylmaleate and sodium dimethylfumarate, on treatment with bromine water, give stereoisomeric lactones in poor yield; that formed from dimethylmaleate anion has m.p. 94 to 95° and that from dimethylfumarate anion melts at 148 to 150°C.

(c) Are the three-membered rings broken before the lactones form?

(d) Compare the stereospecificity of this pair of reactions with that found in the unsubstituted ions.

(e) Would you expect a trend in the observed direction on the basis of inductive effects? Would the data suggest that other kinds of effects may be important in this situation?

37-2 In acetic acid solution I_2 is found to react with a set of olefins slower than IBr, which in turn is slower than ICl. Similarly, BrCl is found to react faster than Br_2. Rationalize these facts.

37-3 We have seen that substituent effects can be applied to rates of reactions as well as equilibria.

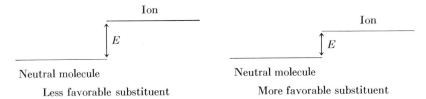

Previously we related substituent effects to equilibria by observing whether electron donation or withdrawal made production of an ion easier; we could then rationalize the relative stability of sets of analogous ions in this way.

We can extend this argument to the rationalization of rates. Let us look at the intermediate whose formation is rate determining. If the intermediate has a charge, then that charge is developing in the molecule in the transition state. Depending on whether a substituent stabilizes or destabilizes this charged intermediate, the transition state for the rate-determining step is affected similarly. That is, if the energy of the critical intermediate is lowered by a substituent, so is the energy of the transition state (or barrier to reaction) also lowered, and the reaction should proceed more rapidly. (See Fig. 37-3.)

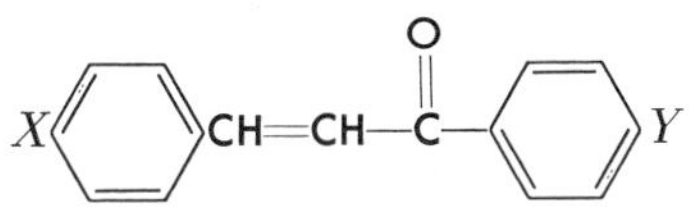

$$X\!-\!\!\bigcirc\!\!-\!CH\!=\!CH\!-\!\overset{\overset{\displaystyle O}{\|}}{C}\!-\!\!\bigcirc\!\!-Y$$

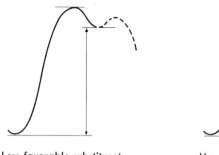

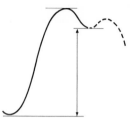

Less favorable substituent   More favorable substituent

FIGURE 37–3

When various substituents were placed in position X in this molecule, it was found that the second-order rate constants for chlorine addition to the double bond gave a fairly good Hammett plot (using $K_{forward}$ in place of K_{eq} as we have done previously) with $\rho = -4$ to -5.

(a) Draw the transition state of the rate-determining step for the reaction under discussion.

(b) Why is ρ negative? Is the order of increasing stabilization in agreement with what you found in Problem 37–1?

(c) Suppose that $X = $ H only, and various substituents are placed in position Y. Would the slope of the Hammett plot be positive or negative? Would its magnitude be greater or less than that found with X substitution? That is, based on induction, will a substituent at Y have more or less effect than one at X on the transition state?

37–4 Suppose that the three-membered ring ions formed in the chlorination of propylene and unsymmetrical dimethylethylene would rearrange to simple carbonium ions before attack of the negative species.

(a) Which carbonium ion would be more stable in the case of propylene? In the case of dimethylethylene?

(b) Show how this hypothesis would explain the formation of the products actually obtained (Section 37–12).

37–5 In the addition of hydrogen halides to olefins, there is assumed to be a sequence of steps beginning with an electrophilic attack on the double bond. The initial complex rearranges to a carbonium ion, and reaction of this species with halide ion completes the process.

(a) What part of the molecule performs the electrophilic attack?

(b) Show that this sequence of steps accounts for Markovnikov's rule (Section 11–4) when it is applied to some suitable olefins.

What is the evidence on which the mechanism for the halogenation of ketones is based?
What evidence is there for acidic and basic properties of ketones?
How do these properties affect their chemistry?

38

HALOGENATION OF KETONES

38–1 The Rate Paradox in Acetone Halogenation

General observations on the reactivity of the halogens with organic compounds have been made frequently. Fluorine is so active that unless special precautions are taken, fire or explosion results from its action on most organic substances. Chlorine is quite powerful in its attack. Bromine is weaker than chlorine and its action is easily controlled. Iodine is the weakest of the group and does not react with many compounds that are attacked by the others. These relationships were summarized in Chapter 15.

Because of these general relationships, we should expect that the rate of action of the common halogens on acetone, for example, would be in the order, chlorine > bromine > iodine. When the reaction was tried experimentally by Lapworth, however, it was found that the prediction did not hold true. All three halogens react with acetone at the same rate.

38–2 Exploratory Kinetic Observations

Let us consider the reaction of bromine with acetone. The stoichiometric equation for the reaction is:

$$CH_3COCH_3 + Br_2 \rightarrow CH_3COCH_2Br + H^+ + Br^-$$

According to this equation, it would be expected that the rate of the reaction would be proportional to the concentration of the acetone and to that of the bromine. Experiment shows, however, that the rate is proportional to the concentration of the acetone but is independent of the concentration of the bromine. Even a large increase in the bromine concentration leads to no increase in the rate of reaction.

If bromine and acetone are mixed in a solution suitable for kinetic measurements, another peculiarity of the kinetics soon is observed. The rate "constant" shows an accelerating drift with elapsed time. The reaction begins slowly and as time passes, its speed picks up.

Initial kinetic observations, then, give us three unexpected rate relationships: (1) The rate is independent of the identity of the halogen; (2) the rate is independent of the concentration of the halogen; (3) the reaction is autocatalytic. Any mechanism proposed for the reaction must reconcile these three observations.

38-3 The Discovery of Acid Catalysis of the Reaction

The fact that the reaction is autocatalytic gives an excellent tool for further investigations. The interpretation of this observation is that one of the products of the reaction must accelerate it. A trial soon establishes that neither bromide ion nor bromoacetone has the observed effect but that acidity, introduced by means of any acid, does have a catalytic effect. This leads us to the still more surprising conclusion that one of the *products* of the reaction can participate in the reaction before the rate-determining step.

38-4 The Discovery of Base Catalysis

The observation that acid from any source catalyzes the reaction would induce an experimenter to try the action of base on the rate. It is soon found that base is an even more effective catalyst for the reaction than is acid. We shall examine the base-catalyzed reaction in more detail before returning to the acid reaction.

38-5 Acidic Properties of Acetone

Preparative chemists have found that under suitably controlled conditions, acetone behaves as a very weak acid. If acetone is cooled below $-20°C$ and treated with sodium amide, a solid sodium salt of acetone can be prepared according to the following equation:

$$CH_3COCH_3 + NaNH_2^- \rightarrow NH_3 + (CH_3COCH_2)^- Na^+$$

Ordinarily, the structure for this salt would be written:

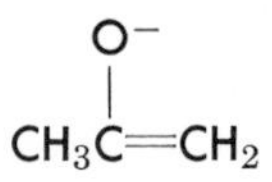

$$\underset{\underset{CH_3C=CH_2}{|}}{O^-}$$

but it should be recognized that there would also be a small but real contribution of the form shown below:

$$CH_3\overset{\displaystyle O}{\overset{\|}{C}}-CH_2{}^-$$

and thus the salt is slightly stabilized by resonance. It can be used for introducing substituents into the 1-position of acetone, that is, at the carbon represented in the latter formula as having a negative charge.

38-6   Proposed Mechanism for the Base-Catalyzed Reaction

The extraordinary effectiveness of bases in catalyzing the bromination of acetone suggests the possibility that base converts a tiny amount of acetone into the salt and that this, because of its strongly nucleophilic character, attacks bromine with great rapidity. Certainly, it is observed that the isolated sodium salt of acetone reacts with halogens rapidly and violently. This makes the assumption of its presence in very small amounts as an intermediate an attractive hypothesis. Thus we may write a tentative reaction sequence:

$$CH_3COCH_3 + B \xrightarrow{\text{slow}} CH_3COCH_2{}^- + BH^+$$

$$CH_3COCH_2{}^- + Br_2 \xrightarrow{\text{fast}} CH_3COCH_2Br + Br^-$$

where B is any base capable of extracting a proton from acetone. It is not necessary to assume that B is uncharged. The transition state in the conversion of acetone into its enolate ion would then be formulated as follows:

$$CH_3COCH_2 \cdots H \cdots B$$

38-7   Proposed Mechanism for the Acid-Catalyzed Reaction

The next step is to find whether or not the acid-catalyzed reaction can be brought into a scheme which is consistent with that formulated for the base-catalyzed reaction. One hypothesis which would permit this would be to assume that acid is capable of catalyzing the reaction of acetone to form the enol instead of the enolate ion. This would be formulated:

$$CH_3COCH_3 + H_3O^+ \xrightarrow{\text{fast}} CH_3\overset{\displaystyle OH^+}{\overset{\|}{C}}CH_3 + H_2O \xrightarrow{\text{slow}} CH_3\overset{\displaystyle OH}{\overset{|}{C}}{=}CH_2 + H_3O^+$$

On this assumption, the transition state for the acid-catalyzed reaction would strongly resemble that for the base-catalyzed reaction.

$$CH_3\overset{\displaystyle OH^+}{\overset{\|}{C}}CH_2 \cdots H \cdots OH_2$$

The final assumption would be the reasonable one that the enol, with its double bond, would react with bromine faster than the ketone. With these assumptions, the mechanism for the acid-catalyzed bromination would be:

$$CH_3COCH_3 + H_3O^+ \xrightarrow{fast} CH_3\overset{\overset{\displaystyle OH^+}{\|}}{C}CH_3 + H_2O \xrightarrow{slow} CH_3\overset{\overset{\displaystyle OH}{|}}{C}=CH_2 + H_3O^+$$

$$CH_3\overset{\overset{\displaystyle OH}{|}}{C}=CH_2 + Br_2 \xrightarrow{fast} CH_3\overset{\overset{\displaystyle OH^+}{\|}}{C}CH_2Br + Br^-$$

$$CH_3\overset{\overset{\displaystyle OH^+}{\|}}{C}CH_2Br + H_2O \xrightarrow{fast} CH_3\overset{\overset{\displaystyle O}{\|}}{C}CH_2Br + H_3O^+$$

38-8 Bromination of an Enol

The chemical behavior of enols was investigated by the actual isolation and study of these substances. The first substance to be separated into both enol and keto forms was the one which had been studied most intensively, ethyl acetoacetate. In 1911, Knorr and his collaborators succeeded in isolating the two substances by crystallization at −80°C. Subsequently, in 1920, Kurt Meyer found that the isomers could be separated quite conveniently by distillation. Ordinary soft glass, in wide use at the time in laboratories, contains enough alkali to catalyze the equilibration of the enol with the ketone. Quartz, on the other hand, does not do this. By distillation from quartz, Meyer found that the more volatile enol could be removed, leaving the less volatile ketone as the still residue. Examination of the two showed that the enol would react rapidly with bromine, and the ketone would not react. In 1911, Meyer invented a method for the volumetric titration of the enol content of an equilibrium mixture. In this method, the enol is brominated and beta-naphthol is quickly added to destroy excess bromine. Beta-naphthol is used because of its rapid reaction with bromine. This will be discussed in greater detail in a later chapter. The bromination reaction is then reversed by the addition of acid, and the bromine liberated is used to oxidize iodide ion to iodine. Finally, the iodine is titrated with thiosulfate.

$$CH_3\overset{\overset{\displaystyle OH}{|}}{C}=CHCOOC_2H_5 + Br_2 \rightarrow CH_3\overset{\overset{\displaystyle O}{\|}}{C}CHBrCOOC_2H_5$$

$$CH_3\overset{\overset{\displaystyle O}{\|}}{C}CHBrCOOC_2H_5 + H^+ + 2I^- \rightarrow CH_3\overset{\overset{\displaystyle O}{\|}}{C}CH_2COOC_2H_5 + I_2 + Br^-$$

Meyer's titration showed that the equilibrium mixture of ethyl acetoacetate contains 7.5% enol, while acetylacetone, $CH_3COCH_2COCH_3$, contains 80.4% and benzoylacetone, $C_6H_5COCH_2COCH_3$ contains 98%.

38–9 The Effect of Alkyl Substituents

According to the picture which we have drawn for the base-catalyzed bromination reaction, ionization of the proton is made possible by the strong electron-attracting power of the oxygen of the carbonyl group. This makes the carbon which donates the proton much more positive than the carbons of hydrocarbons. This effect is reinforced by the resonance stabilization of the ion to produce small but detectable acidity in the ketone. Accordingly, substitution by electron-releasing groups should diminish the ease of ionization. This concept was tested experimentally by Evans and Gordon who followed the rates of bromination of a series of phenyl alkyl ketones of the general structure, C_6H_5—CO—CHRR'. The relative rates were:

R,R'	H, H	CH_3, H	C_2H_5, H	$(CH_3)_2CH$, H	CH_3, CH_3
Rate	100	15.4	12.0	5.9	3.0

Thus we see that the effect of the electron-releasing alkyl groups is consistently to diminish the rate of bromination, which is taken to be a measure of the relative rates of enolization.

For acid-catalyzed bromination, the selectivity of the reagent is not nearly so great as for base-catalyzed bromination. In methyl ethyl ketone, halogenation of the ethyl branch is approximately three times as rapid as that of the methyl branch. We may compare the formation of an enol in acid solution to the olefin-forming elimination reaction in acid which is governed by the Saytzev rule. (See Sections 11–4 and 16–8.) The forces at work in this situation have not been as sharply defined experimentally. We have seen that bond breaking in the case of C—halogen bonds is probably governed by bond strength. If we consider the great increase in bond strength caused by the introduction of a positive charge, this will be more effective in strengthening the CH bond of the methyl side than of the ethyl side, because of the electron-donating effect of the methyl groups. Hence, if bond strength were the determining factor in the acid bond cleavage, the ethyl side would be preferred. Because of the lack of a clear-cut rationalization of the forces behind the Saytzev rule, the observations with respect to the structural influences on the acid-catalyzed reaction neither support nor contradict the proposed mechanism. (See Sections 39–8 and 39–9.)

38–10 Stereochemical Test of the Mechanism

A more decisive test of the mechanism was based on the comparison between rates of racemization and bromination of optically active carbonyl compounds. The first such compounds employed were carboxylic acids. In 1934 Ramberg and Mellander resolved the acid shown below.

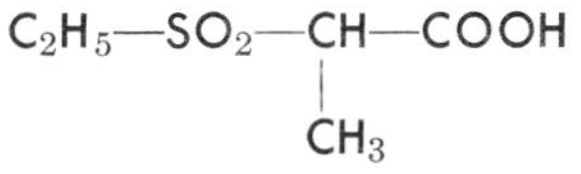

$$C_2H_5—SO_2—CH—COOH$$
$$|$$
$$CH_3$$

They then compared the rate of acid-catalyzed bromination with that of acid-catalyzed racemization under identical conditions. The sulfonyl group in this compound should promote enolization in the same manner that carbonyl groups in ketones do. According to the mechanism advanced, the formation of the enol should destroy optical activity; since this is assumed to be the slow step in the bromination, the rate of destruction of optical activity should be identical with that of halogenation, if the mechanism is sound. Ramberg and Mellander found that within experimental error, the two rates are the same. This provided an independent check on the proposed mechanism. In the same year, Ingold and Wilson studied the rates of racemization and bromination of the following ketone:

$$\text{(indanone ring)}\ \overset{\displaystyle CH_2}{\underset{\displaystyle CO}{CH}}-CH_2-\text{C}_6\text{H}_4-COOH$$

The next year Bartlett and Stauffer compared the rates of racemization and iodination of

$$\overset{\displaystyle C_2H_5}{\underset{\displaystyle CH_3}{CH}}-CO-C_6H_5$$

In both cases the rates of racemization and halogenation were identical within experimental error.

38–11 Test of the Mechanism by Isotopic Labeling

The commercial availability of isotopes for labeling made possible another critical test of the proposed mechanism. In 1937, Reitz showed that the rate of bromination of acetone in deuterium oxide under acid catalysis is equal to the rate of uptake of deuterium by the acetone in the absence of bromine. For the experiments with racemization, the observations establish that the breaking of the C—H bond takes place at the same rate as the halogenation. For the deuterium exchange, the experiment establishes that the breaking of the C—H bond is part of the reversible process involving exchange with the solvents and that this also takes place at the same rate as does halogenation. This establishes the reversibility feature of the proposed mechanism. This work was still further substantiated by Hsu, Ingold, and Wilson who studied both the rates of racemization and deuteration of Bartlett's phenyl isobutyl ketone under base catalysis and found them equal to the rate of halogenation. The work was also extended to the acid catalysis, and all three rates were found equal. Thus the independent methods of racemization and deuterium exchange substantiate the assumption that the rate-determining step in halogenation is the formation of enol in acidic solution and of enolate ion in basic solution. This evidence furnishes excellent verification for the proposed mechanism.

Table 38–1

pK$_a$ VALUES FOR WEAK BASES IN SULFURIC ACID SOLUTION

2,4-dinitroaniline	−4.38	p-bromoacetophenone	−6.40
p-methylacetophenone	−5.35	6-bromo-2,4-dinitroaniline	−6.59
Benzalacetophenone	−5.61	i-butyrophenone	−6.72
β-benzoylnaphthalene	−5.92	Benzoic acid	−7.26
Acetophenone	−6.03	Phenylacetic acid	−7.59
p-benzoyldiphenyl	−6.19	Anthraquinone	−8.15
n-butyrophenone	−6.21	2,4,6-trinitroaniline	−9.29
Propiophenone	−6.28		

38–12   Basic Properties of Ketones

The mechanism which we have proposed for the acid-catalyzed halogenation or enolization of ketones requires that these substances exhibit weakly basic properties, just as the mechanism for the base-catalyzed reaction requires that they exhibit weakly acidic properties.   Since we are not accustomed to regarding carbonyl compounds as bases, we may logically inquire whether or not there is any justification for this view.

Sulfuric acid is a substance capable of attaining a wide variety of acid strengths. By dilution of 100% sulfuric acid with varying amounts of water, intermediate acidities may be obtained which are measurable and which can be used for the examination of the base strengths of very weak bases.   The technique was exploited by Hammett and his collaborators. Acidities in sulfuric acid solutions are measured in pK units, just as in aqueous media. The acidities of ordinary aqueous solutions are positive, since the pH and pK values are negative logarithms and the concentrations are fractional.   Once we have passed the point at which hydrogen ion concentration is molar, however, pH and pK values become negative.   In strongly acidic solutions, departures from ideality are great so that the activities are not linearly dependent on concentrations.

By dissolving ketones and even carboxylic acids in sulfuric acid solutions, Hammett learned that the typical absorption peak in the ultraviolet spectrum is altered when the acidity is sufficiently high.   Thus these substances behave as indicators in sulfuric acid solution, even though it requires photoelectric means to reveal the color change. We may assume that the change that takes place in the absorption spectrum is due to protonation of the carbonyl group. On this assumption, the positions of the equilibria involved may be measured and the base strengths of the carbonyl compounds calculated.   Hammett and his collaborators have measured the basicities of a number of carbonyl compounds and weak nitrogen bases. The results of some of their measurements are given in Table 38–1.

Not all the substances listed in Table 38–1 are colorless, so it is possible to use some of them as visual indicators in sulfuric acid solutions.

It can be calculated that a solution of acetophenone in 0.1 N aqueous hydrochloric acid is converted into its conjugate acid only to the extent of one part in ten million. In spite of this 0.1 N hydrochloric acid exerts an appreciable catalytic effect on the halogenation of acetophenone. This indicates that the conversion is adequate to permit enolization to proceed to the extent necessary for halogenation to take place.

We see from those studies of the basicity of ketones that the assumption made in our proposed mechanism for the acid-catalyzed enolization and halogenation is in accord with the chemical facts determined by entirely independent methods.

From all these studies, we may conclude that the mechanism for the halogenation of ketones in acid and alkaline solutions is established on reasonably firm grounds.

PROBLEMS

38-1   It is a general rule that alcohols have higher boiling points than ketones of similar molecular weight. For example, acetone boils at 56.5°C, while i-propyl alcohol boils at 82.3°C.

(a) How can this be rationalized?

It has been demonstrated that the enol form of ethyl acetoacetate has a *lower* boiling point than the keto form.

(b) Explain this exception, which is fairly general. Note that hydrogen bonds in one form permit strong attractive forces *within* one molecule, while the attractive forces in the other form must occur *between* molecules. To determine what sort of structure is favored for the hydrogen-bonded case, see ring formation of cycloalkanes (Section 8–3) and test analogous structures for favorable properties; note what ring sizes are most favored geometrically.

38-2   Explain the relative percentages of enol content in ethyl acetoacetate, acetylacetone, and benzoylacetone (Section 38–8). What factors affect the stability of the enol form in each case and allow a rank with respect to stability to be made?

38-3   (a) Which would brominate in basic solution faster, acetone or bromoacetone? Reformulate this question in terms of the ease of occurrence of the rate-determining step. On what, in turn, is that dependent?

(b) Which carbon in bromoacetone would be substituted more rapidly in basic solution, the one bearing only hydrogens or the one carrying a bromine? How does this question differ from part (a)? Are your answers for both parts similar?

(c) Write a mechanism for the iodoform reaction (see Section 15–11). The last few steps involve nucleophilic attack of the carbonyl by OH^- [cf. attack by CN^- (see Section 35–2 and Problem 35–1)], followed by formation of the conjugate base of iodoform, CI_3^-. To complete the mechanism:

(1) Why is this anion more stable than CH_3^-?

(2) Is it more stable than the conjugate base of the carboxylic acid form? That is, which is a stronger acid, iodoform, or (say) acetic acid? Your answer calls for one last step in the mechanism (Problem 35–1).

38-4   Write a mechanism for the formation of ethyl acetoacetate from ethyl acetate (see Section 14–3). This is analogous to the other exercises to the extent that an anion is formed. The rest of the reactions involved depend on the nucleophilicity of the anion toward the carbonyl group of another molecule of ethyl acetate.

*What are the most important factors determining the
course of elimination reactions?
How can adjustment of these factors secure
control over the course of the elimination?*

39

THE ELIMINATION REACTION;
STEREOSPECIFICITY

39–1 The Importance of Stereochemical Effects

Students of the chemistry of complex natural products have long known of the importance of stereochemical effects. Among the alkaloids, isomers differing only stereochemically occasionally display markedly different reactivities under identical reaction conditions. Similar situations occur among the steroids and among still other substances composed of fused ring systems. Such differences occur particularly in physiologically active materials: for example, one sugar may taste sweet, and the inversion of a single carbon atom may cause its stereoisomer to taste bitter. Amino acids of the L-configuration are of overwhelming importance in nature, while those of the D-configuration are seldom encountered. This is another example of stereospecificity of processes carried on by living organisms. Students of enzyme reactions are well aware of the fact that most enzymatic reactions are highly stereospecific; reactivities of stereoisomers differ frequently by factors of tens or hundreds. Only comparatively recently has it been possible to rationalize these huge differences in reactivity on mechanistic grounds. Now mechanisms involving stereochemical control are known in a variety of fields of organic chemistry. As illustrations, we shall choose examples from the field of elimination reactions in this chapter.

Eliminations are, in general, of two types, olefin-forming eliminations and carbonyl-forming eliminations. An example of an olefin-forming elimination is

$$CH_3—CH_2OH \xrightarrow{H_2SO_4} CH_2{=}CH_2 + H_2O$$

An example of a carbonyl-forming elimination is the reversal of the cyanohydrin reaction:

$$OH^- + CN-C(CH_3)_2-OH \rightarrow H_2O + (CH_3)_2C=O + CN^-$$

In this presentation, we shall confine our attention to olefin-forming eliminations.

39–2 Eliminations in Cyclic Systems

The first problem that must be solved is that of the stereochemical requirements for elimination. Is the reaction usually *cis* or *trans*? This can be solved most conclusively by the study of cyclic compounds. For example, Cristol examined the isomeric hexachlorocyclohexanes produced by the chlorination of benzene in sunlight. One of these, the beta isomer, has been shown by x-ray diffraction to have the all-*trans* configuration:

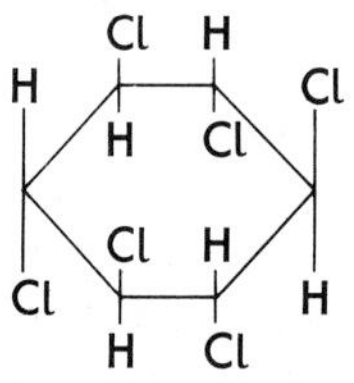

β-isomer   or β-isomer

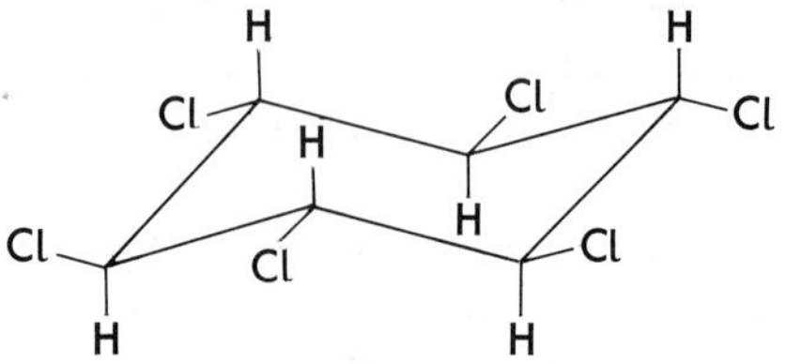

Cristol showed that the action of alcoholic sodium hydroxide on this isomer proceeded from 1/7000 to 1/24,000 times as fast as the elimination from any of the other isomers, each of which must have at least one *cis* configuration. The fact that the beta isomer has all the chlorines in *trans* positions means that each Cl has a hydrogen in a *cis* position to it on either side so that *trans* elimination of HCl is not possible. With two chlorines in *cis* positions, *trans* elimination becomes possible and the rate is increased by a factor of at least 7000.

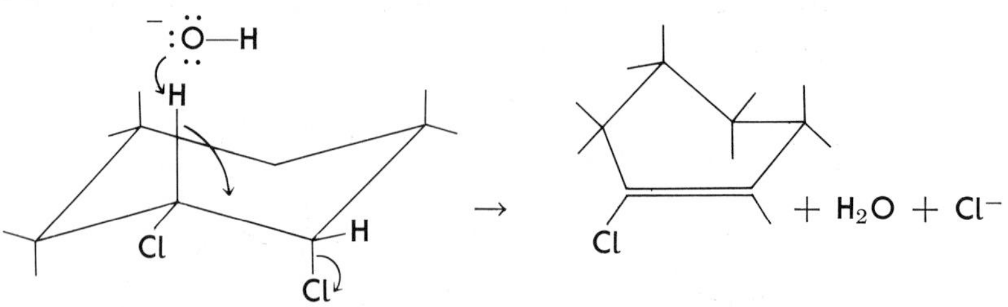

trans elimination with chlorines in *cis* positions

If the reaction were taking place in a straight-chain derivative, rotation about the bond would permit the compound to assume the favorable *trans* position. In a ring compound, this type of rotation is blocked by the second attachment of the reacting group. It is for this reason that stereochemical considerations become overriding in cyclic compounds when the reaction mechanism demands a precise stereochemical relationship in the transition state. The single example given above may be extended to the chemistry of terpenes, steroids, alkaloids, and other cyclic systems. In these compounds unfavorable stereochemistry can block addition and elimination reactions.

39–3 Dehalogenation

For purposes of identifying olefins, their property of adding halogens is sometimes the most convenient method of preparing a definable product. Having prepared and identified the dibromide, for example, the chemist may then wish to regenerate the olefin. To do this, he ordinarily uses debromination, typically with zinc. In studying this reaction in the steroid series, Barton and Miller found that it may be seriously limited if the rings present constrain the two bromine atoms from becoming coplanar with the two carbons to which they are attached during the course of the debromination reaction. Again, the course of the reaction is most clearly shown by examining cyclic compounds. In this case, however, less dramatic stereochemical effects can be demonstrated in open-chain compounds. The reactions involved may be illustrated with a simple example, the debromination of 2,3-dibromobutane. This was studied by Young, Pressman, and Coryell in 1939. Three stereoisomers of 2,3-dibromobutane are possible, D, L, and *meso*. We may first use Fischer projection formulas to represent them.

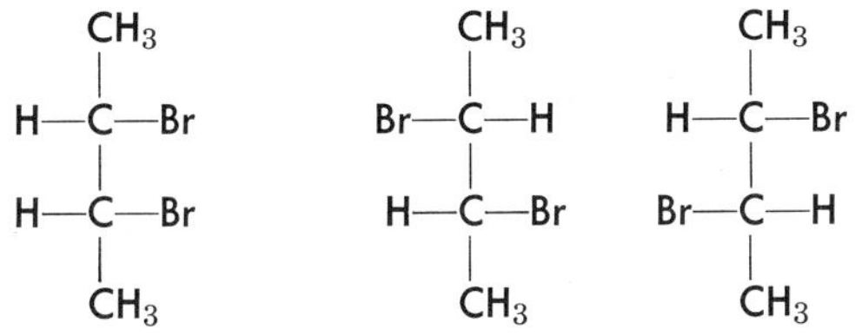

meso   D and L

The Newman projections of these two configurations, arranged with bromines in the *trans* positions, are shown below.

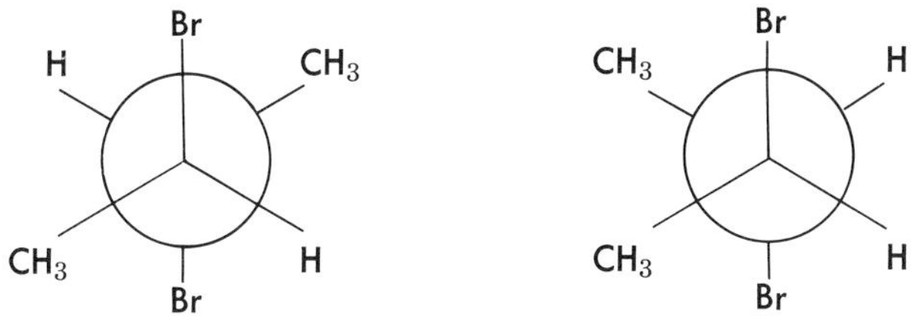

meso   DL

The *meso* configuration permits a conformation in which each methyl is between a bromine and a hydrogen on the adjacent carbon, while in the DL-configuration, the methyl on one carbon is between a methyl and a bromine on the other carbon.

As the reaction proceeds to the transition state, the substituents will be drawn into the same plane, since they must be coplanar in the resulting olefin. For the *meso* configuration, this will bring a methyl and a hydrogen into opposition on each carbon. For the DL-configuration, this will bring the two methyls into opposition in the transition state. The situation may be represented in Newman projections as shown below:

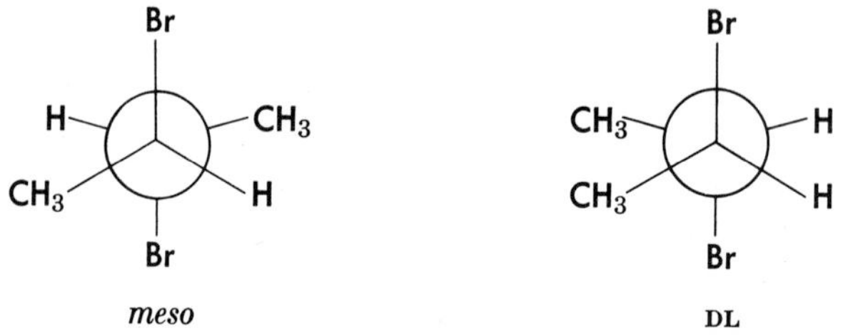

meso   DL

As we saw in Book 1 (Chapters 9 and 23) bringing bulky groups into opposition costs energy. For this reason, we should expect the transition state associated with the DL form to be a higher energy form than the transition state associated with the *meso* form. Consequently, we should expect the debromination of the DL form to be slower than that of the *meso* form. Measurement showed that this is the case: the debromination of the DL form is only half as fast as that of the *meso* form. Thus even in a straight-chain compound, a stereochemical difference accounts for a twofold difference in reactivity.

39–4   E1 Reactions

In the solvolysis of alkyl halides, the substitution reaction is usually accompanied by some elimination with olefin formation. For example, the reaction of *t*-butyl bromide in ethanol yields 81% ethyl *t*-butyl ether and 19% isobutene. The olefin is represented as being formed from proton elimination from the *t*-butyl cation:

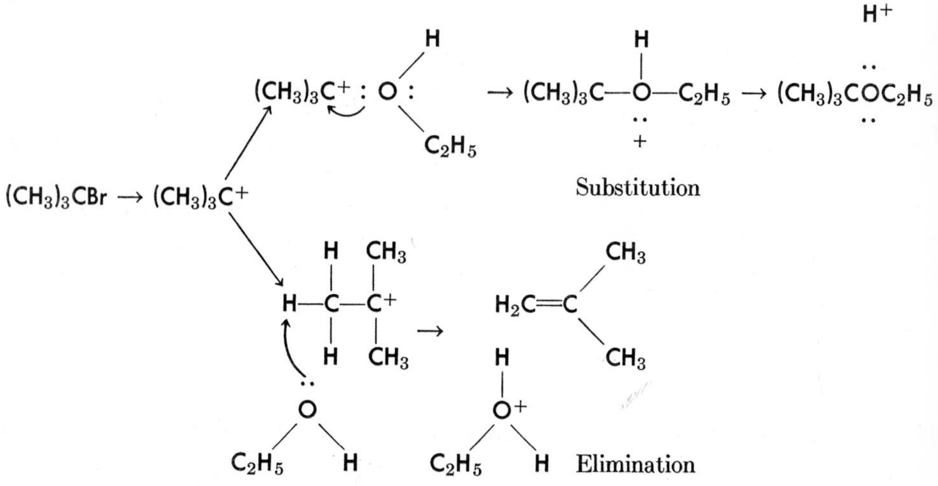

$(CH_3)_3C^+ : O :$ $\rightarrow (CH_3)_3C—O—C_2H_5 \rightarrow (CH_3)_3COC_2H_5$

Substitution

$(CH_3)_3CBr \rightarrow (CH_3)_3C^+$

$H_2C=C$

Elimination

Table 39–1

(1)	CH_3—$C(CH_3)_2Cl$	16
(2)	CH_3CH_2—$C(CH_3)_2Cl$	34
(3)	$(CH_3)_2CH$—$C(CH_3)_2Cl$	62
(4)	$(CH_3)_3C$—$C(CH_3)_2Cl$	61
(5)	$(CH_3)_3C$—$C(C_2H_5)_2Cl$	90

The reason for this conclusion is that, within wide limits, factors, such as the temperature and the dielectric constant of the solvent, which affect the rate of ether formation, affect the rate of olefin formation identically so that the product ratio remains constant. Reactions of this sort are termed $E1$ reactions, that is, first-order eliminations.

The amount of olefin formed from carbonium ions is a function of the structure of the carbonium ion. Differences in the ease with which olefin formation takes place have been ascribed both to stereochemical effects and to electronic effects. Brown found that branching at the beta carbon, from which the proton is eliminated, favors elimination. Under identical reaction conditions (80% aqueous ethyl alcohol at 25°C) the olefin percentages in the total product that are listed in Table 39–1 were obtained. In these reactions, ethanol serves as the nucleophile.

Table 39–2

	Olefin	Structures	Yield
(1)	CH_2=$C(CH_3)_2$	6	16
(2)	CH_3CH=$C(CH_3)_2$	9	34
(3)	$(CH_3)_2C$=$C(CH_3)_2$	12	62
(4)	$(CH_3)_3C$—C=CH_2 　　　　 | 　　　　CH_3	3	61
(5)	$(CH_3)_3C$—C=$CHCH_3$ 　　　　 | 　　　　C_2H_5	5	90

39–5 The Role of σ-bond Delocalization

Compound (4) is of special interest, since the chain branching was not at the carbon which must lose the proton; the percentage of olefin remains high nevertheless. This indicates that the mere fact that branching occurs is more important than the effect of branching on the beta hydrogen. It is known from thermochemical measurements that branched-chain olefins are more stable than straight-chain olefins. This has been ascribed by some to sigma-bond delocalization or hyperconjugation. The formulation would be:

$$CH_3CH=CH_2 \leftrightarrow H^+ \; CH_2=CH-\overset{-}{C}H_2$$

The products formed by the eliminations from the halides of Table 39–1 are listed in Table 39–2, with the number of equivalent structures that each could have in sigma-bond delocalization in the second column and the yields in the third. While sigma-bond delocalization might be assumed to account for the increase in yield in the series (1) to (3), it cannot account for the increase of the series (2), (4), (5).

39–6   The Steric Argument

Brown argues that the essential factor in determining the outcome of the competition between substitution and elimination is that the carbonium ion has 120° angles, the substitution product (alcohol or ether) has 109° angles, and the olefin has 120° angles. Since there will be less crowding in substances with 120° angles than in those with 109° angles, the introduction of an increasing number of substituents will favor the olefin with its 120° angles over the substitution product with its 109° angles.

39–7   *E2 Reactions*

Since the first-order eliminations referred to in the preceding section are dependent only on the concentration of the halides, it follows that they are unaffected by the addition of bases. Many olefin-forming reactions behave differently, however, their rates being strongly dependent on base concentration. Such eliminations are usually found to be second order with rates proportional to the concentrations of halides and base. They are consequently designated as *E2* reactions or second-order eliminations.

It might be argued that a second-order elimination would proceed in two steps. The first step would be attack by the base with removal of a proton. This would form an anion. The second step would be the elimination of the halide ion from the anion to give the olefin. For phenylethyl bromide, this mechanism would be as follows:

$$C_6H_5CH_2CH_2Br + OH^- \rightleftarrows C_6H_5\overset{-}{C}HCH_2Br \rightarrow Br^- + C_6H_5CH{=}CH_2$$

If the carbanion designated in the preceding equation were formed, it would be stabilized by resonance interaction with the benzene ring. Consequently, it would exist long enough for appreciable interchange with the starting material to take place. The competition reaction was carried out in D_2O with the idea that unreacted bromide and the styrene formed by the elimination would both contain deuterium.

$$C_6H_5CH_2CH_2Br + OD^- \rightleftarrows DOH + C_6H_5\overset{-}{C}HCH_2Br \overset{D_2O}{\rightleftarrows} C_6H_5CHDCH_2Br + OD^- \rightleftarrows$$

$$C_6H_5\overset{-}{C}DCH_2Br \rightleftarrows Br^- + C_6H_5CD{=}CH_2$$

When the experiment was performed, it was found that no deuterium incorporation had taken place, either in the unchanged halide or in the styrene. It was concluded, as a result, that the reaction does not take place in two steps. Several other eliminations from halides were carried out with the same results. Hence it is concluded that the elimination reaction from halides probably does not proceed by a two-step mechanism.

The alternative to a two-step mechanism is simultaneous withdrawal of the proton and the bromide ion. This would be a so-called "concerted" mechanism. For phenylethyl bromide, it would be formulated as follows:

$$HO^- \; H-CH-CH_2-Br \rightarrow H_2O + CH=CH_2 + Br^-$$
$$\qquad\qquad \underset{C_6H_5}{|} \qquad\qquad\qquad\quad \underset{C_6H_5}{|}$$

In the present state of our knowledge of the elimination reaction, a concerted mechanism seems the most reasonable way to account for the experimental facts.

39–8   Orientation of Elimination Reactions

During the course of our structural studies on olefins, it was found that two different orientation rules would act in elimination reactions. The Hofmann rule is operative for eliminations from quaternary ammonium compounds, and the Saytzev rule is operative for elimination from alcohols. Brown has argued that the difference can best be explained on steric grounds. As an example, let us consider the elimination reaction of 2-amyl derivatives. With these, formation of 1-pentene would result from Hofmann-type elimination, while formation of 2-pentene would result from Saytzev-type elimination:

$$\underset{CH_3CH_2CH_2\overset{|}{C}HCH_3}{\overset{\overset{X}{|}}{}} \nearrow CH_3CH_2CH_2CH=CH_2 \quad \text{(Hofmann type)}$$
$$\searrow CH_3CH_2CH=CHCH_3 \quad \text{(Saytzev type)}$$

Brown found that the proportion of Hofmann-type product formed increased as the size of the leaving group, —X, increased:

Ratio $\dfrac{\text{1-pentane}}{\text{2-pentane}}$	—X =	—Br	$-\overset{+}{S}(CH_3)_2$	$-SO_2CH_3$	$-\overset{+}{N}(CH_3)_3 \cdot$
		0.45	6.7	7.7	50

Not only is the ratio dependent on the size of the leaving group but it is also dependent on the degree of branching of the hydrocarbon residue in the halide being treated. In the group of bromides given below, formation of a 1-olefin takes place according to the Hofmann rule, while 2-olefins are formed according to the Saytzev rule.

$$\underset{CH_3}{\overset{CH_3}{\underset{|}{\overset{|}{C_2H_5CBr}}}} \quad \underset{CH_3}{\overset{CH_3}{\underset{|}{\overset{|}{CH_3CH_2CH_2CBr}}}} \quad \underset{CH_3}{\overset{CH_3}{\underset{|}{\overset{|}{CH_3CHCH_2CBr}}}} \quad \underset{CH_3 \; CH_3}{\overset{CH_3 \; CH_3}{\underset{|\quad|}{\overset{|\quad|}{CH_3CCH_2CBr}}}}$$

Ratio $\dfrac{\text{1-olefin}}{\text{2-olefin}}$	0.45	1.00	1.17	6.1

Thus by increasing the branching of the olefin formed, it is possible to reverse the Saytzev rule for an alkyl bromide.

Finally, the effect of the attacking base is important in determining the orientation of the elimination reaction. Using a single alkyl bromide but varying the size of the base gave the following results:

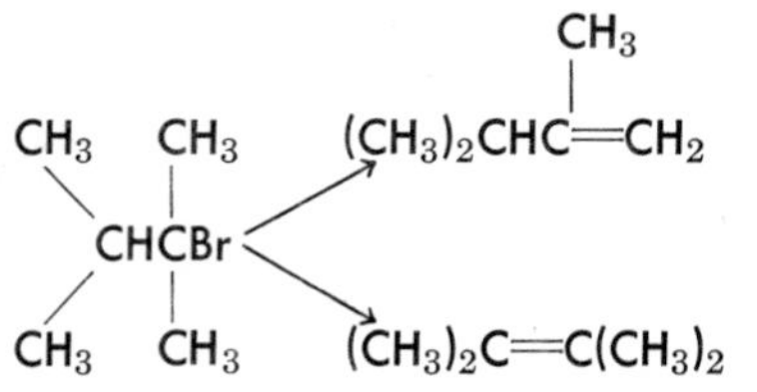

$$
\begin{array}{c}
\text{CH}_3 \\
| \\
\text{(CH}_3)_2\text{CHC}=\text{CH}_2 \quad \text{(Hofmann type)}
\end{array}
$$

$$
(\text{CH}_3)_2\text{C}=\text{C(CH}_3)_2 \quad \text{(Saytzev type)}
$$

Ratio $\dfrac{\text{1-olefin}}{\text{2-olefin}}$	Base =	$C_2H_5O^-$	$(CH_3)_3CO^-$	$(CH_3)_2\overset{\underset{\displaystyle|}{C_2H_5}}{C}O^-$	$(C_2H_5)_3CO^-$
		0.25	2.7	4.3	11.4

Again we see that it is possible to reverse the Saytzev rule by the proper choice of reagent used for the reaction.

39–9   The Steric Argument in Orientation

Re-examination of the results shows that the shift from Saytzev-type to Hofmann-type orientation was secured in each instance as the degree of crowding increased, regardless of whether the crowding was in the leaving group, the alkyl bromide, or the attacking base. A stereochemical picture to account for these facts must show the influence of each of these three factors on the transition state for the elimination reaction. We have already seen that the reaction is best accounted for on the assumption that the removal of the proton and the leaving group is a concerted action. Using the usual additional assumption that the elimination is a *trans* reaction, an explanation embodying all the foregoing facts may be presented. In this picture, the subsequent formation of the olefin would make it energetically cheapest for the two carbons, the proton, and the leaving group all to be in the same plane. If we assume, additionally, that the attacking base attacks in this plane, as shown below,

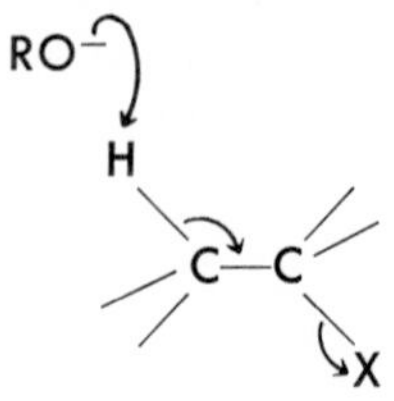

then the reaction requirement would be for five atoms to be coplanar.

Let us assume that elimination is taking place from

$$CH_3$$
$$|$$
$$(CH_3)_2CHCBr$$
$$|$$
$$CH_3$$

A Newman projection of the Saytzev reaction complex is shown in Fig. 39–1 (a and b).   See also the model in (c).

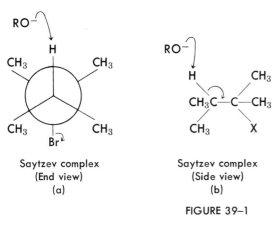

Saytzev complex
(End view)
(a)

Saytzev complex
(Side view)
(b)

FIGURE 39–1   (c)

The Newman projection of the Hofmann complex is shown in Fig. 39–2 (a and b).   See also the model in (c).

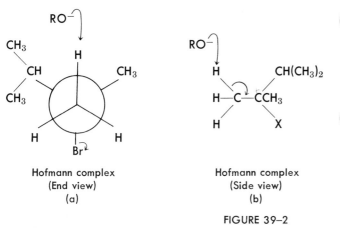

Hofmann complex
(End view)
(a)

Hofmann complex
(Side view)
(b)

FIGURE 39–2   (c)

Examination of the two complexes will show that bulky groups of any type, that is, leaving groups, attacking base groups or branched hydrocarbon groups on the halide, will fit the Hofmann-type projection with less crowding than they will the Saytzev-type projection.   In the Hofmann-type projection, each of the bulky groups has an opportunity to fit between hydrogens, while in the Saytzev complex, the bulky groups must fit between the bulky alkyl groups, a factor which will cost more energy and therefore proceed more slowly. It appears, then, that the factors which influence the orientation in elimination reactions are the bulkiness of the groups involved and that the picture of the transition state having five atoms in a plane is adequate to account for the observed facts.

FIGURE 39–3

It should be noted especially that mere bulk is not enough to be decisive in these reactions. The critical factor is the space requirement in the volume in which interference can take place. At greater distances from the reacting centers, the addition of more bulk would be a matter of indifference in determining the outcome of the reactions. Thus the p-toluenesulfonyl group is heavier than the other groups which we have discussed, yet, as a leaving group, its steric requirements are not great. This is because it is not branched at the point of attachment but one atom farther away: $-O-SO_2-C_6H_4-CH_3$. This should be compared with $-^+N(CH_3)_3$. Models of these groups attached to the 1,2-dimethylpropyl group are shown in Fig. 39–3.

39–10   Conclusions

Our brief survey of the mechanisms of displacement reactions, addition to double bonds, halogenation of ketones, and the elimination reaction constitutes a preliminary survey of some of the major reaction types of the aliphatic series. The survey illustrates the reasoning involved in arriving at mechanisms. From the point of view of the organic chemist and of those who will use the materials and methods of organic chemistry, however, the survey will indicate how an understanding of mechanisms increases the chemist's control over the course of reactions and how the modification of conditions or structures may bring about entirely different results from those initially envisaged.

Our next step will be to extend this type of reasoning to reactions in the aromatic series.

PROBLEMS

39-1   According to the description in Section 39-4, which reaction proceeds more rapidly, formation of *t*-butyl ethyl ether or that of isobutylene? Or do they proceed at the same rate? If you stopped this reaction after only 10% of the initial *t*-butyl bromide had disappeared, would you expect the ratio of *t*-butyl ethyl ether to isobutylene to be greater than, less than, or equal to 81:19?

39-2   Which would you expect to form an olefin more rapidly in ethanolic potassium hydroxide, cyclopentyl bromide, or cyclohexyl bromide?

39-3   (a) Which would form an olefin more rapidly, *cis*-4-methylcyclohexyl bromide or its *trans* isomer?

(b) Which would form an olefin more rapidly, *cis*-3-methylcyclohexyl bromide or its *trans* isomer?

39-4   The Hofmann elimination of quaternary ammonium hydroxides may be considered to proceed by a mechanism similar to the eliminations of alkyl halides that we have illustrated in this chapter.

(a) Write a mechanism for the Hofmann elimination performed on tetraethylammonium hydroxide, paying particular attention to the geometry of the transition state.

(b) Write the structure of the product of the reaction of quinuclidine and methyl iodide.

(c) The quaternary hydroxide corresponding to this iodide does not undergo the usual elimination to form an olefin. Why might such a reaction not be favored?

(d) Instead, the products are methyl alcohol and quinuclidine. Write a mechanism for this. What sort of reaction is it?

39-5   The structure of α-benzene hexachloride is given below. When the DL-mixture was allowed to stand with half an equivalent of brucine, one of the isomers was selectively destroyed as judged by the fact that the remaining mixture had a rotation of $-14.6°$. Brucine hydrochloride was isolated in an amount somewhat less than equivalent to the α-benzene hexachloride destroyed. The discrepancy was presumably due to losses in workup.

α-benzene hexachloride   Brucine

(a) What type of reaction would account for the formation of the brucine hydrochloride?

(b) What would the isolation of the optically active residue of the starting material show about the dependence of the rate of the reaction on the shapes of the reacting molecules?

Part 4

SOME SPECIFIC MECHANISMS
IN THE AROMATIC SERIES

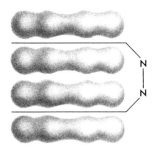

The change from aliphatic to aromatic structures brings with it a major change in the course of chemical reactions. While many of the general methods of attack on the mechanistic problem which are useful in the aliphatic series can be used to advantage in the aromatic series as well, the different course of most aromatic reactions requires a different approach to the problem of mechanistic interpretation. Part 4 deals with the investigation of some of the fundamental mechanisms of the aromatic series.

Why do different groups on a benzene ring orient the attack
of an entering group to different positions?
What is the precise nature of the reagent active in aromatic nitration?
How can the study of orientation effects, rates, and reagents be related to a
consistent mechanism for aromatic nitration?

40

ELECTROPHILIC AROMATIC SUBSTITUTION I: GENERAL CONSIDERATIONS

40–1   Importance of the Study of Benzene Substitution

Probably the most fruitful discovery of the early organic chemists was that of the ease of substitution of the benzene ring. By combining substitutions in varying sequences with subsequent reactions on the substituents, a tremendous variety of useful industrial products was made available. This, in turn, stimulated an increasing amount of research into the nature of organic chemical processes. It is only natural that a portion of this research resulting from useful discoveries in the field of aromatic substitution should be directed toward understanding the process itself. It is probable that as much effort has gone into the study of the mechanisms of aromatic substitution as into any similarly restricted field in organic chemistry.

40–2   Course of the Development of Substitution Theory

Körner's method for the absolute determination of the positions of substituents in the benzene ring was published in 1874. Within two years, three investigators including Körner, working independently, had arrived at the conclusion that the significant property of a substituent in exerting its directive influence on an entering group was its "electronegative" or "electropositive" character. These concepts were based on the ideas of Berzelius concerning the electrochemical character of atoms and groups as substituents on organic molecules. We shall see shortly that these first ideas, though incomplete, were essentially correct. It is interesting to note here another example of the time lag in the development of chemical ideas. Organic chemists in general were not prepared to accept electrochemical ideas at this stage of development. As a result numerous more or less irrelevant alternatives were proposed to account for aromatic substitution during the next fifty years and it was not until 1926 that electronic theory had developed sufficiently for a well-grounded explanation of the facts of aromatic substitution to be offered.

40–3   The Inductive Effect in Substitution

Early investigators found that there were two general types of orientation effects exerted by substituents on the benzene ring: one set of groups directed *ortho* and *para*, and the other set directed *meta*. Körner in 1874 and Hübner and Noelting in 1875 and 1876 stated their belief that "electronegative" groups such as NO_2, would direct *meta*, and "electropositive" groups, such as CH_3, would direct *ortho-para*. Ingold has pointed out that this electronegativity argument is parallel to a modern argument based on the inductive effect.

40–4   The Resonance Effect in Substitution

In 1887 Armstrong stated that groups attached to benzene which were multiply bonded were *meta* directing. In 1892, Crum Brown and Gibson stated that the substituent X would be *meta* directing if HX could be directly oxidized to HOX. An example would be $H\!-\!NO_2 \rightarrow HO\!-\!NO_2$. Again Ingold has pointed out that this rule foreshadows the "mesomeric" or resonance effect in orientation. While the rule is not always obeyed, the parallel to the mesomeric effect of Ingold results from the fact that the presence of nonbonded electrons on an atom such as the nitrogen of $H\!-\!NO_2$ permits oxidation. This oxidation is facilitated by electron-accepting groups, such as the oxygens of $H\!-\!NO_2$ so that ultimately nitric acid has a greater degree of resonance stabilization than nitrous acid. It is these same electron-accepting groups which permit electron withdrawal from the benzene ring, thus making the ring *meta* directing, as we shall see below. Either of these rules is incomplete, however, because both inductive and resonance effects play a part in determining orientation and, as in the case of halogenation of a double bond, their effects may be in opposite directions.

40–5   The Determination of Isomer Ratios

In 1910 the field of aromatic substitution was given a tremendous impetus by the publication of Holleman's book on the subject. Holleman presented refined methods for the determination of the ratio of the isomers formed in a substitution reaction. Many of his methods are in use, with modifications, even today. He also pointed out the importance of the determination of reactivities of the compounds being substituted. Generally speaking, *ortho-para* directing groups facilitate substitution, while *meta* directing groups retard substitution. We shall see that this rule is not without exceptions but its use, where valid, does much to throw light on the mechanisms involved.

40–6   The Effect of a Positive Charge

A critical set of observations was published by Vorländer and Siebert in 1919. These investigators stated that groups with a permanent positive charge, such as the $-N(CH_3)_3{}^+$ cation, are *meta* directing while it had been known for some time that groups with a permanent negative charge, such as the $-O^-$ anion, are *ortho-para* directing. Recent work has shown that Vorländer's observation that the trimethylamino group is 100% *meta* directing is erroneous; the figure should be 89%. In spite of this, the significance of its very strong directive influence is still real.

40–7   Modern Development of the Theory of Aromatic Substitution

In 1926 the laboratories of Robinson and of Ingold advanced an electronic interpretation of the course of aromatic substitution which has served as the basis for modern developments in the field. This was based at first on attempts to correlate existing data with the electronic interpretations which were just then being exploited in organic chemistry. A mass of new data, mostly from Ingold's laboratory, designed to test the electronic interpretations in detail soon followed. We shall review a portion of this evidence.

The first and most important question which must be answered is that of the nature of the attacking reagent in aromatic substitution. Holleman's observation that *ortho-para* substitution is usually easier to accomplish than *meta* substitution, coupled with the identification of the groups which cause this (such as the groups from methyl to $-O^-$) as electron-releasing groups, suggests that substitution takes place most readily at an electron-rich center. The converse observation that *meta* directing groups retard substitution, coupled with the observation that *meta* directing groups, such as nitro and trimethylammonio, are electron attracting, suggests that diminishing the electron density at the position being substituted slows the reaction. These observations tend to reinforce the concept that the process of substitution takes place most readily at an electron-rich center. If these are to be accepted, it would follow that the process involved is attack by an electrophilic reagent. This, in essence, is the argument of Robinson and of Ingold.

40–8   Identification of the Reagent in Nitration

As early as 1903, Euler proposed that the active species in nitration is the $NO_2{}^+$ ion. The means for establishing this experimentally were published by Hantzsch in 1908. In spite of this fact, however, clear evidence that this species exists in sulfuric acid solution was not obtained until 1946. This was based on revisions of the technique of Hantzsch published by Hammett and his collaborators in the period from 1933 to 1937.

The method of investigation used by Hantzsch was to dissolve the material to be studied in 100% sulfuric acid and then observe the depression of the freezing point caused by the solute. The cryoscopic method is relatively convenient because pure sulfuric acid melts at approximately 10.5°C. Using this technique,

Hantzsch found that the freezing point of the sulfuric acid was depressed by an amount corresponding to the solution of three moles of material for every mole of nitric acid added. This ratio of the moles found to the moles added is called the van't Hoff i value. For nitric acid, there was difficulty in interpreting the i value, particularly because there seemed to be some difficulty in reproducing the measurements.

40–9   The Conductivity of Sulfuric Acid

Curiously, the key to the solution of the problem was published in the same year, 1908, by Lichty in the United States. Lichty showed that 100% sulfuric acid, like water, retains a small but measurable conductivity when pure. This is ascribed to an equilibrium of the same type that occurs in water:

$$2H_2SO_4 \rightleftarrows H_3SO_4^+ + HSO_4^-$$

Addition of water increases the conductivity by the reaction:

$$H_2O + H_2SO_4 \rightleftarrows H_3O^+ + HSO_4^-$$

Addition of SO_3 also increases the conductivity, presumably by the reaction:

$$SO_3 + 2H_2SO_4 \rightleftarrows H_3SO_4^+ + HS_2O_7^-$$

It follows from these observations on conductivity that the minimum number of particles in sulfuric acid solution occurs at precisely the 100% point in the composition curve. On either side of this point, more particles would be in solution and a freezing point lower than the maximum would be observed.

40–10   The Freezing Point of Sulfuric Acid

The deduction concerning the existence of a freezing-point maximum was confirmed by Hammett in 1933, twenty-five years after the critical conductivity measurements were performed. Hammett took a solution containing an indeterminate amount of dissolved SO_3 and titrated water into it, reading the freezing point as a function of the composition. The curve obtained is shown in Fig. 40–1. Thus the increase in conductivity on the SO_3 side in composition is matched by a lowering of freezing point from the maximum, and that on the H_2O side is matched by a similar but steeper lowering in freezing point. This locates the source of the error in Hantzsch's work and shows how to correct it.

Let us assume that the molar freezing-point depression of a sample of sulfuric acid whose composition is that shown at point A were to be determined by the addition of 0.05 moles of water. The freezing point would be lowered to the point C and the line AC would be taken as having the proper slope to represent the freezing-point depression. Let us suppose that, in another laboratory or at another

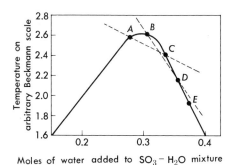

FIG. 40–1. Freezing point of sulfuric acid as a function of composition. [Adapted from L. P. Hammett and A. J. Deyrup, *J. Am. Chem. Soc.* **55**, 1902 (1933).]

time, a sample with composition represented by B were taken for the same determination. The new freezing-point depression would be represented by the slope of the line BD. It is obvious that both these conclusions are erroneous. This is the source of the error. Hammett pointed out that the correct value for the freezing-point depression is to be found by starting at the point C and is represented by the slope of the line CE. Since water is usually one of the products in any equilibrium involving solutes in sulfuric acid, then all studies must be performed slightly on the water side of the maximum.

40–11   The Dissociation of Nitric Acid in Sulfuric Acid

The experiments of Hammett laid the foundation for more reliable determinations of freezing-point lowering of solutions in sulfuric acid and thus for the calculation of the correct number of moles of material dissolved in it. Using the revised cryoscopic technique, Gillespie, Ingold, and their collaborators remeasured the freezing-point depression of nitric acid dissolved in sulfuric acid and found that the addition of one mole of nitric acid produces four moles of dissolved material. This is interpreted as showing that nitric acid dissociates in sulfuric acid according to the equation:

$$HNO_3 + 2H_2SO_4 \rightleftarrows NO_2^+ + 2HSO_4^- + H_3O^+$$

If this equation is to be accepted, then in sulfuric acid approaching 100%, nitric acid would be completely dissociated into the nitronium ion, NO_2^+. As water is added to such a solution, the formation of additional H_3O^+ and HSO_4^- would drive the equilibrium farther to the left and diminish the proportion of nitronium ion present in the solution. Ultimately, a composition would be reached in which the amounts of this ion would be small but, according to equilibrium laws, it would approach but never reach zero. Thus even in solutions much weaker than 100% sulfuric acid, some nitronium ion would be present which could act as a nitrating agent.

40–12   Spectroscopic Observation of the Nitronium Ion

The existence of the nitronium ion was confirmed by the identification of a frequency in the Raman spectrum at 1400 cm^{-1} as resulting from it. Raman frequencies and infrared frequencies are related to each other by certain rules of symmetry. Application of these symmetry rules and the use of reasonable force constants in the interpretation of the Raman spectrum of nitric-sulfuric acid indicated that this frequency could be assigned only to a species which was diatomic, such as CO, or else triatomic and linear, such as CO_2 but not H_2O. The frequency is found on mixing sulfuric and nitric, nitric and perchloric, or nitric and selenic acids. Since NO_2^+ is triatomic and should be linear, like CO_2, the spectroscopic observation provides strong experimental evidence for its existence.

40–13   X-ray Observation of the Nitronium Ion

Still further confirmation of the existence of the nitronium ion was obtained by an x-ray examination of solids first discovered by Hantzsch in 1925. One of these is formed by the reaction of nitrogen pentoxide with perchloric acid:

$$N_2O_5 + 3HClO_4 \rightarrow 2NO_2^+ + H_3O^+ + 3ClO_4^-$$

The solid obtained from this is a mixture of nitronium perchlorate and hydronium perchlorate. The nitronium perchlorate can be purified by crystallization from nitromethane. Its x-ray analysis shows the nitrogen atom in line with two oxygens and this group removed in space from the perchlorate ion.

40–14   The Rate Paradox in Nitration

The problem of investigating the rate of the nitration of benzene was a difficult one. Most of the techniques that had been used previously were found unsuitable. A general method for the study of rates is the use of a dilatometer. In principle, this is an apparatus with a bulb and stem like a thermometer. A sample of the reaction mixture to be studied is trapped in the bulb, and the expansion or contraction during the course of the reaction is measured as a function of time. The usual method for trapping the reacting solution is with a stopcock. Alternatively, the bottom of the bulb may be adjusted to a mark with mercury. However, neither of these strategems would work for the nitration of benzene. The stopcock could not be properly greased because the solution would attack the greases. Mercury would also be attacked by the nitric acid. Ingold solved the problem by the use of a "tapless" dilatometer. This is an instrument with *two* stems of equal size and a single bulb. The use of a second stem loses half of the sensitivity of the instrument but permits rapid filling of the bulb. A diagram of such a dilatometer is given in Fig. 40–2.

With the introduction of stopcocks with polytetrafluoroethylene taps, it is probable that the extra precision available with a stopcock could be obtained for these studies.

With a dilatometer, Benford and Ingold measured the rate of the nitration of benzene in nitromethane, using a constant excess of nitric acid. To their surprise, the reaction turned out to be of zero order, that is, the reaction proceeded at a constant rate, independent of the concentration of benzene, until the benzene was exhausted, when it came to a sudden stop. The same situation was found to apply with toluene, ethylbenzene, p-xylene, mesitylene, and p-chloroanisole. Under identical conditions, each of these substances nitrates at exactly the same rate as all the others.

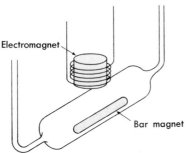

Electromagnet

Bar magnet

FIG. 40–2.   "Tapless" dilatometer with internal bar magnet for stirring.

According to Holleman, however, the alkyl benzenes all nitrate more readily than benzene. Ingold set about to test the correctness of this view. A competitive reaction was run in which equimolar quantities of benzene and toluene were allowed to compete for a small amount of nitric acid. After completion of the reaction, the mixture of nitrobenzene and the nitrotoluenes was separated by distillation. It was found that the rate of nitration of toluene was approximately 30 times as great as that of benzene. These findings confronted the investigators with a major paradox: The rate of nitration of toluene is 30 times as great as that of benzene when the two are allowed to compete directly, yet when measured individually, both rates are identical. How can the paradox be resolved?

40–15   Resolution of the Paradox

Reflection will show that the two measurements performed are quite different. For the experiment with the dilatometer, the overall rate of the reaction was being measured. This rate is governed by the slowest step in the whole process, the rate-determining step. For the competitive reaction, we are determining a product ratio, that is, the relative rates of reactions which may have taken place after the rate-determining step. This composition-determining step need not be governed by the same rate law as that which governs the rate-determining step. The very fact that the two measurements disagree establishes the point that the composition-determining step must have taken place subsequent to the rate-determining step. Hence the paradox is resolved by assuming that the reaction takes place in at least two steps, the first of which is rate-determining, the second composition-determining.

From the fact that different hydrocarbons perform differently in the composition-determining step, we can identify this step as the one at which the hydrocarbon participates. This must be the reaction of the hydrocarbon with an active nitrating agent. Hence the zero-order nitration is one in which the aromatic hydrocarbon takes no part. It follows that this step must involve the nitric acid alone. Further study shows that this step is temperature dependent, showing that it has an activation energy and must proceed over an energy barrier. This indicates that the process involves breaking a bond in nitric acid. Two observations indicate that the process is heterolytic. The first is that the rate of the process is dependent on the polarity of the solvent. Solvents of higher polarity give a greater rate constant than those of low polarity. The second observation is that cited earlier, that is, the fact that the reagent formed must be electrophilic, that is, electron deficient. What electrophilic reagent can be formed by the heterolytic cleavage of a bond of nitric acid? The reasonable assumption is that the reagent is the nitronium ion:

$$HO\text{—}NO_2 \rightarrow HO^- + NO_2{}^+$$

or

$$H_2\overset{+}{O}\text{—}NO_2 \rightarrow H_2O + NO_2{}^+$$

This assumption is consistent with all the studies cited above and has now come to be generally accepted.

40–16   Mechanism of the Composition-Determining Step

One possibility with respect to the mechanism of the composition-determining step, which we shall call path 1, is that the introduction of the nitro group and the abstraction of the proton are simultaneously accomplished. This would involve the following transfers:

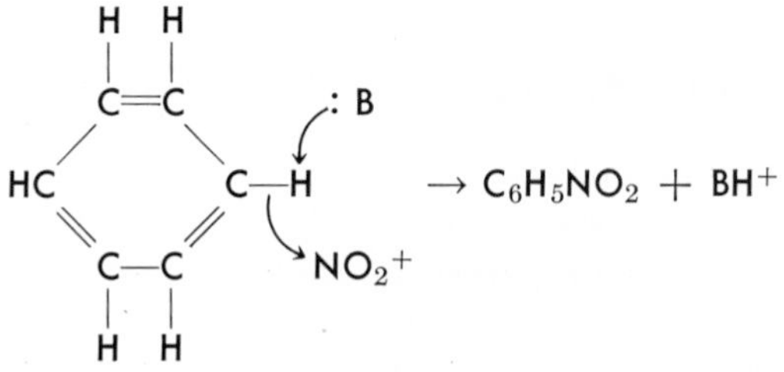

Path 1

In sulfuric acid, the base, B, would be the bisulfate ion, which would usually be present in an amount sufficient to make the possibility of a termolecular process at least theoretically tenable.

An alternative pathway for the reaction is to assume that this, too, is a two-step reaction involving a slower addition of the nitronium ion to the aromatic hydrocarbon followed by a faster abstraction of the proton by the base, path 2:

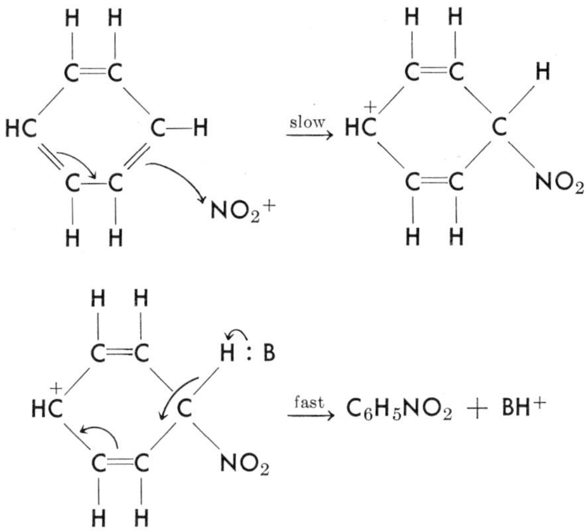

Path 2

There are several considerations which make the two-step mechanism preferable to the termolecular process. A clear-cut decision between them was obtained by the work of Melander, using the kinetic isotope effect.

40–17 The Effect of Isotopic Substitution on the Nitration

It has been experimentally established that ordinary hydrogen, which we shall call protium, and deuterium are separated from the same element in identical compounds at widely different rates, when the rate-determining step involves the breaking of an X—H or X—D bond. This, in the final analysis, is the method used to separate these substances commercially. In general, the rate of breaking of an X—H bond is found experimentally to be 3 to 12 times greater than the rate of breaking of an X—D bond. The corresponding factors for protium and tritium are from 5 to 30. This information may be used in reverse to determine whether or not a process involving the cleavage of an X—H bond is rate determining. If it is, there will be a difference in rates with deuterium or tritium substitution. If it is not, the rates will be the same.

In both the termolecular reaction, path 1, and the stepwise bimolecular reactions, path 2, only a small fraction of the collisions with the nitronium ion will result in reaction. This fraction will be larger for toluene than for benzene, so that differences in rate will exist for this portion of the reaction by either path 1 or path 2, even though neither of these paths is rate determining with respect to the overall nitration reaction. The composition-determining part of the reaction, then, has its own slow or rate-determining step and the problem is to find whether or not breaking of the C—H bond is involved in this step.

In the termolecular process for nitronium ion attack during the composition-determining step, path 1, the breaking of the C—H bond participates in the slow step. In the two-step process, path 2, the attack by nitronium ion is slow, the abstraction of the proton by the base is fast. Hence this case is an ideal one for examination by the kinetic isotope effect.

When the experiment was performed by Melander, it was found that, using tritium, there was no selectivity in product composition between the C—H bonds and the C—T bonds. From this experiment, we may conclude that the breaking of the C—H bond is not the slow step and, consequently, that the termolecular mechanism is not supported by the experimental evidence.

40–18 Mechanistic Conclusions

The experiments summarized, then, lead us to the conclusion that the nitration of aromatic hydrocarbons in organic solvents takes place in at least three steps: (1) formation of an active nitrating species, NO_2^+; (2) addition of the nitronium ion to the hydrocarbon to form an organic cation; (3) abstraction of the proton from the cation by a base to give the nitrated hydrocarbon. In stronger nitrating solvents, such as sulfuric acid, the increase in speed of the reaction is due to the larger proportion of the nitronium ion present in these better ionizing media.

PROBLEMS

40–1 It is found experimentally that under conditions fairly similar to those used for the kinetic studies with benzene, the nitration of ethyl benzoate is first order with respect to ethyl benzoate. While this might at first suggest a different mechanism from that for benzene, further reflection indicates that this datum can be reconciled with the mechanism for benzene. Recall that electron drift is caused by the carbethoxy ($—COOC_2H_5$) substituent. Note that the electronegativity of oxygen and resonance effects will place a charge in the ring. What result will this produce as far as attack by nitronium ion is concerned? Justify the statement that a new mechanism is not needed to explain the change in kinetic order.

40–2 (a) Remembering the order of bond strengths in the hydrogen halides, what would be the order of X—O bond strengths in HOI, HOBr, and HOCl assuming that the situations are analogous?

(b) Experimentally it is found that HOI is a better iodinating agent than I_2, while HOCl and HOBr are poorer halogenating agents than Cl_2, and Br_2. Rationalize this finding. Note also that a solution of HOI in water is slightly basic.

(c) Phenol brominates very readily to form 2,4,6-tribromophenol. Is this product an *addition* product or a *substitution* product? This is one of the useful distinctions between the chemistry of aromatic double bonds and that of aliphatic double bonds.

(d) What would be the inorganic side product in the formation of tribromophenol? Write a mechanism based on the hints given earlier for the reaction of one mole of bromine to demonstrate your point.

(e) Devise an experiment to distinguish between Br^+ and Br_2 as the active brominating agent in this reaction.

(f) A catalyst is required for the bromination of benzene itself; often $FeBr_3$ is used. The utility of this component has been explained by the fact that it is a Lewis acid, i.e., an electron acceptor. How might its acidity influence the Br_2 molecule or the benzene molecule to effect reaction?

40–3   Suppose that a variety of substituted benzenes is nitrated and the rates of the reactions measured by competitive substitution methods. When the data are correlated by Hammett sigma constants, would you anticipate that rho would be positive or negative? (It turns out that another set of constants gives a better correlation than Hammett's original values in this case, but the similarities of the two sets of values are sufficient for our present purposes.)

40–4   Suppose that we were trying to determine the time sequence of steps between the addition of NO_2^+ and the loss of H^+ in the steps involving the aromatic compound.

(a) Show why a study of the rate of nitration of C_6D_6 and comparison of this result with that found for C_6H_6 does not add any information to our knowledge of the mechanism of nitration.

(b) Would the following experiment help to determine the mechanism: competitive nitration of C_6D_6 and C_6H_6 (that is, in the same reaction vessel at the same time)?

(c) It was found that when a sample of monodeuterobenzene (C_6H_5D) of 91.5% purity (the remainder being ordinary benzene) was nitrated, the nitrobenzene formed contained 74.9% monodeuteronitrobenzene. The m-dinitrobenzene formed by further reaction contained 60.9% monodeuterodinitrobenzene. Show that this result is in accord with the mechanism proposed for nitration.

40–5   In addition to paths 1 and 2, Section 40–16, there is a third possible pathway which might have been considered for the nitration of benzene, involving a fast attack of NO_2^+ on benzene followed by slow loss of H^+ from the intermediate ion. What piece of experimental data excludes this possibility?

41

ELECTROPHILIC AROMATIC SUBSTITUTION
II: SUBSTITUENT EFFECTS

41–1 Energy Profiles

We have seen that experimental evidence from the kinetic isotope effect shows that the process of nitration of a hydrocarbon must be at least a two-step reaction. A mechanism embracing this concept had been proposed in 1928, even before this evidence was available, by Pfeiffer and Wizinger who assumed that the intermediate in aromatic nitration could be formulated as:

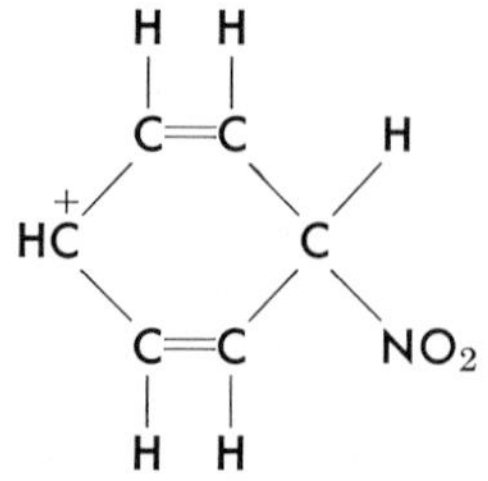

$$
\begin{array}{c}
\text{H} \quad \text{H} \\
| \quad\; | \\
\text{C}=\text{C} \quad\; \text{H} \\
\overset{+}{\text{HC}} \qquad\quad \text{C} \\
\text{C}=\text{C} \quad\; \text{NO}_2 \\
| \quad\; | \\
\text{H} \quad \text{H}
\end{array}
$$

It will be evident that this is a resonating structure with the relative instability of the six-electron carbon partially compensated by delocalization of the charges to the *ortho* positions, resulting in a broad positive-charge distribution throughout the ring.

The information that a metastable intermediate exists in nitration, coupled with the fact that the rate-determining step is the formation of this intermediate, not its destruction, allows us to draw an energy profile for the reaction. In this profile, the slowest reaction is represented as having the highest energy barrier, and energy barriers, in general, are inversely proportional in height to the speed of the reactions they represent. A stable compound is represented as existing in an energy trough. The distance along the x-axis represents an arbitrary concept termed the "reaction coordinate" by Eyring. In one sense, it may be regarded as representing the fraction of completion of the reaction. As will be shown shortly, however, it has significance in terms of the distance of separation of atoms in the process of forming the transition state which exists at the top of the energy barrier. As an old bond stretches on the way to the top, the reaction coordinate measures the amount of this stretch. As the new bond shortens on the way down the hill after passing the summit, the reaction coordinate measures the distance of bond shortening. According to these principles, the energy profile for the reaction of benzene with the nitronium ion may be represented as in Fig. 41–1.

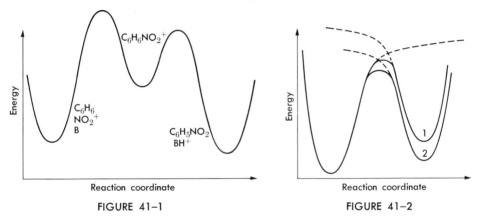

FIGURE 41–1   FIGURE 41–2

41–2 Resonance Effects

Rationalization of the experimental results concerning directive influences of substituents due to resonance are ordinarily attempted by means of energy profiles. If *ortho-para* substitution is faster than *meta* substitution, this means that the path to the *ortho-para* substitution has a lower energy barrier than that to *meta* substitution. To rationalize these facts, we require information about the reasons for one energy barrier being lower than another. When comparing widely diverse reactions, such rationalizations are difficult and sometimes impossible. When comparing two reactions as similar as *para* substitution and *meta* substitution, however, the reactions are so similar that it has been found possible to argue the case for changes in the height of the energy barriers with some assurance, even in cases where the answer is temporarily unknown.

We saw in Chapter 35 how the processes of bond breaking and bond formation can be allowed to overlap to produce an energy profile for the formation of a transition state. If two such diagrams were constructed, both starting from the same mixture of reagents but ending with metastable states with different energies, then the very fact that the metastable states had different energies would produce intersections at different heights on the energy scales. Allowing for similar stabilizations of the transition states by resonance, the resulting diagrams would appear somewhat as in Fig. 41–2. The figure shows that the reaction path forming the more stable intermediate would be expected to have a lower energy barrier than that forming the less stable intermediate. This is essentially the argument advanced by Wheland to permit the correlation of stabilities of reaction intermediates with the rates of their formation in aromatic-substitution reactions. In the final analysis, then, the problem reduces to that of finding which path of substitution would give the more stable intermediate.

41–3   *Meta* and *Para* Substitution Contrasted

As an example of the reasoning that may be used, we may consider the case of the substitution of phenol by the electrophile **X**. We shall assume that it enters the *meta* position for path 1 and the *para* position for path 2. The intermediates would be formulated as:

Path 1

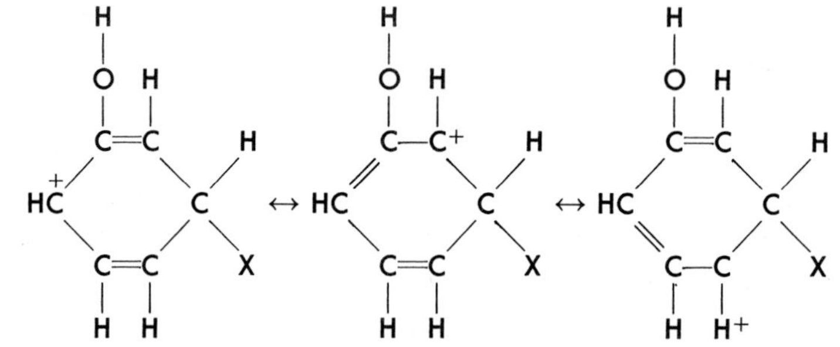

Path 2

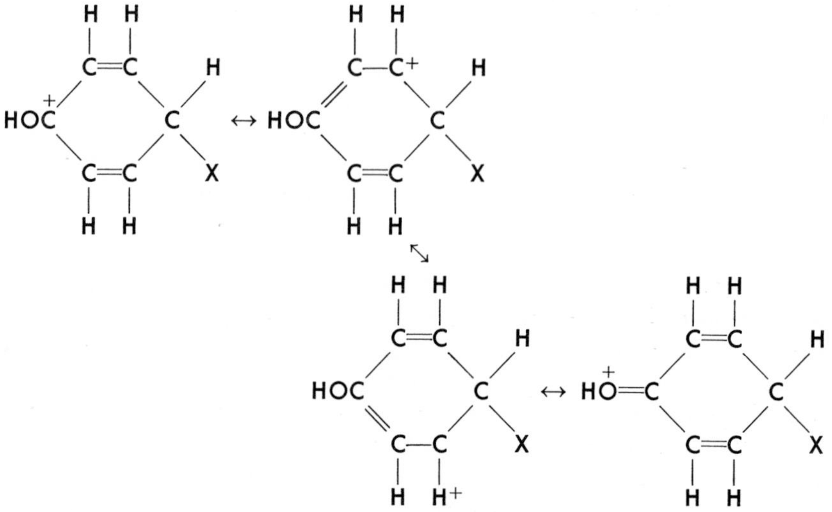

The intermediate in path 1 is stabilized by delocalization of the electrons between the two *ortho* and one *para* positions to the entering group. The intermediate in path 2 is stabilized by the same types of structures plus delocalization to the oxygen. All the forms with positive charges on carbon have sextets of electrons and are therefore less stable than those with octets. The one form with the positive charge on oxygen has a stable octet and thus will substantially stabilize the intermediate. From this argument, we should expect that phenol would substitute more readily in the *para* position than in the *meta*. Thus we have a rationalization of the fact of the easy substitution of phenol, which was known approximately a century before the modern explanation was offered. Reasoning of this sort, while of limited predictive power because of the huge number of cases that has already been investigated, is useful to the organic chemist as an aid to the memory. It is usually easier to reason out the result than to remember it. There are many pitfalls in the way of a pure reasoning process in correlating the facts of aromatic substitution, however. One of these is the effect of the medium in altering the nature of the material being substituted.

41–4   Medium Effects

Gillespie and Norton investigated the effect of changing water content on the rate of nitration in strong sulfuric acid solutions. Earlier investigators knew that concentrated sulfuric acid, that is, 94% acid, is a better nitrating medium than 100% sulfuric acid. The objective of the later investigation was to learn what the cause of the difference was.

Table 41–1

RATE CONSTANTS, $k(1/\text{mole-min})$

	90%	100%	$\dfrac{k(90\%)}{k(100\%)}$
Phenyltrimethylammonium ion	2.08	0.55	3.8
Nitrobenzene	3.22	0.37	8.7
Anthraquinone	0.248	0.0053	48

In strong sulfuric acid solutions, as we have seen, the concentration of nitronium ion is quite high and, for this reason, its rate of formation is not rate determining. Instead, the nitration reaction under these conditions is second order, being dependent on the concentrations of the nitronium ion and of the species being nitrated. We shall select three substances from those studied by Gillespie and Norton to illustrate their results. They are the phenyltrimethylammonium ion, nitrobenzene, and anthraquinone, shown at the right. The rates were studied in 90% sulfuric acid and in 100% sulfuric acid. Comparative rate constants are given in Table 41–1.

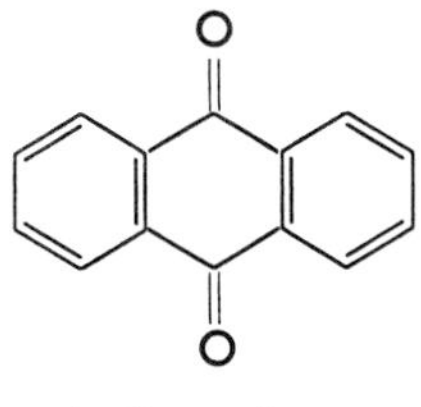

Anthraquinone

41–5   Hypothesis of Reaction with Bisulfate Ion

Orienting experiments showed that the rate of nitration increased up to a concentration of 90% sulfuric acid. This can be attributed to increasing formation of nitronium ions. Above this point, however, the concentration of nitronium ions continues to increase, but the reaction reaches a maximum in velocity and then slows down. The first hypothesis which was used to explain the decrease in rate was that bisulfate ions speed the reaction by removing the protons from the intermediate. The work of Melander on kinetic isotope effects, however, disposed of this argument by showing that the rate of removal of the proton is not critical in determining the rate of the reaction.

41–6   Hypothesis of Solute Protonation

The next hypothesis that was tested was that the very strong sulfuric acid was capable of reacting with the material being substituted. This was tested by measuring the degree of protonation of these substances in sulfuric acid. The results obtained are shown in Fig. 41–3. The curves in Fig. 41–3 are plotted so that increasing protonation is shown by a down curve. It is evident that the protonation of anthraquinone is sufficient to account for the decrease in reactivity on going from 90% sulfuric acid to 100% sulfuric acid. Nitrobenzene, on the other hand, is not readily protonated until this range is exceeded. Experiment shows that the rate of nitration of nitrobenzene continues to diminish after this point is passed so that the additional decrease in the rate of nitration beyond that at 100% sulfuric acid may be accounted for by increased protonation. No protonation of the phenyltrimethylammonium ion takes place, even in SO_3 solutions. After passing the point of 100% sulfuric acid, the rate of nitration of this species again increases. The minimum of the nitration rate of the phenyltrimethylammonium ion at 100% sulfuric acid corresponds to the minimum in conductivity at 100% sulfuric acid, which we have already learned about in connection with its cryoscopic properties. It is postulated that the presence of dissolved ions increases the reactivity of materials dissolved in sulfuric acid by their effect on its dielectric constant. While this seems reasonable, it is difficult to establish experimentally. It is obvious, however, that the change in the medium produced an increase in rate up to 90%

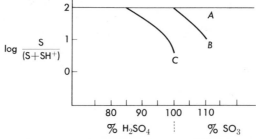

FIG. 41–3. A = phenyltrimethylammonium ion; B = nitrobenzene; C = anthraquinone; S = solute. (Reproduced by permission from P. B. D. de la Mare and J. H. Ridd, *Aromatic Substitution*, London: Butterworths, 1959.)

sulfuric acid by increasing the amount of nitronium ion present. Beyond this point, a part, at least, of the diminution in reactivity of anthraquinone is due to its protonation. Above 100%, part of the decrease in reactivity of nitrobenzene is due to its protonation. Between 90% and 100%, the diminution in rate with nitrobenzene and phenyltrimethylammonium ion is due to some general solvent effect, possibly its decrease in dielectric constant. The complexity of these changes and interactions should serve to warn the organic chemist that he should not be surprised if his predictions in a new situation turn out to be erroneous. It is frequently difficult to anticipate all the factors which may be critical in any given situation.

41-7 Inductive Effects: On Addition to Double Bonds

In Chapter 37 we saw that in addition to resonance effects, inductive effects are important in determining the course of the addition of bromine to a double bond. This is also true with respect to the directive effects of substituents in electrophilic aromatic substitution. Since we have seen that the addition of bromine is also an electrophilic reaction, parallels between the two reactions should prove instructive. To draw these parallels more clearly, we shall choose an electrophilic reagent for double bonds which is unsymmetrical. Thus the direction of the electronic effect will be clear. Such a reagent is hydrogen bromide. The directive influence of substituents on double bonds on the addition of hydrogen bromide serves as an excellent model for reasoning concerning the directive influences of the same substituents on aromatic substitution.

The rate-determining step in the addition of bromine to a double bond is the electrophilic attack of the bromine. It has been found by rate studies that the rate-determining step in the addition of hydrogen bromide is the addition of the proton. This will naturally go to the point of greatest electron density. In a succeeding fast reaction, the halide ion will go to the other side of the double bond. The analysis of the course of an addition reaction which is primarily affected by an inductive mechanism must be conducted differently from the analysis of the course of a reaction primarily controlled by resonance. For resonance-controlled reaction, the directive influence can be assumed on the basis of the intermediate which is the more stable, as we saw in the case of *meta* and *para* substitution in phenol. For a reaction controlled by an inductive mechanism, the course is analyzed on the basis of the electron density of the initial state, rather than the stabilities of the possible intermediates.

We have seen that a halogen atom will cause an electron drift with the formation of a dipole:

$$\overset{\longleftarrow +}{F-CH_3}$$

On attachment to a double bond, a strongly electron-attracting group would perform a similar function:

$$(CH_3)_3\overset{+}{N}-CH\overset{\longleftarrow +}{=\!\!=}CH_2$$

This indicates a drift of electrons toward the positively charged nitrogen. This is sometimes represented symbolically as:

$$(CH_3)_3\overset{+}{N}{\leftarrow}CH{=}CH_2$$

In the case of the double bond, the electron-attracting power of the positive pole may even displace the pi-electrons:

$$(CH_3)_3\overset{+}{N}{-}\overset{-}{C}H{-}\overset{+}{C}H_2$$

This effect is sometimes represented symbolically by:

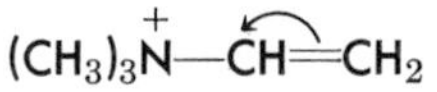

$$(CH_3)_3\overset{+}{N}{-}CH{=}CH_2$$

Experimentally, it is found that the hydrogen goes to the carbon next to the positively charged nitrogen. Symbolically, this might be represented:

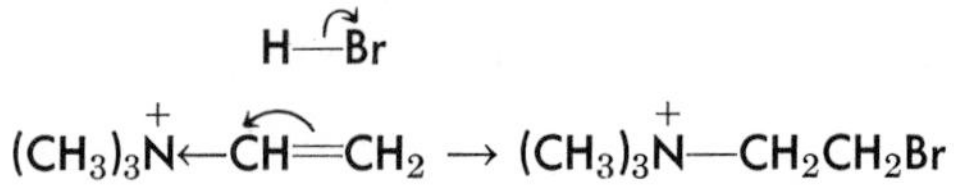

$$H{-}Br$$

$$(CH_3)_3\overset{+}{N}{\leftarrow}CH{=}CH_2 \rightarrow (CH_3)_3\overset{+}{N}{-}CH_2CH_2Br$$

This symbolism indicates polarities that determine orientation, but it does not imply a reaction mechanism.

We would also expect that the CF_3 group is a strong electron-attracting group because of the presence of three powerful attracting fluorine atoms on a single carbon. It directs in the same manner as the trimethylammonium ion:

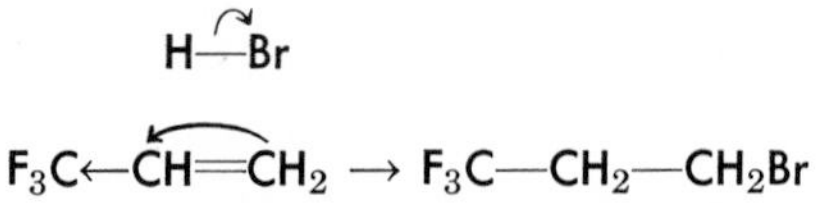

$$H{-}Br$$

$$F_3C{\leftarrow}CH{=}CH_2 \rightarrow F_3C{-}CH_2{-}CH_2Br$$

In the first application of inductive reasoning to the course of an organic reaction, Lucas assumed that the converse proposition held for the addition of hydrogen bromide to propylene.

$$CH_3{-}CH{=}CH_2 + HBr \rightarrow CH_3{-}CHBr{-}CH_3$$

The electron drifts were represented as shown below:

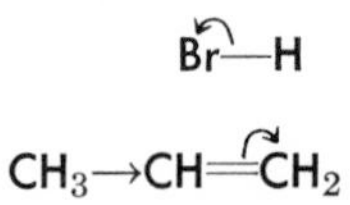

$$Br{-}H$$

$$CH_3{\rightarrow}CH{=}CH_2$$

Recently the concept of sigma-bond delocalization has also been applied to assumed explanations of this reaction:

$$\overset{\displaystyle H^+ \ \overset{\displaystyle Br^-}{} \ H^+}{H_2C=C-CH_2{}^-}$$

The two alternatives are nearly impossible to disentangle experimentally. It has also been proposed that the delocalization or resonance argument may be better presented by assuming that one intermediate is stabilized preferentially over the one formed by the alternative pathway,

$$\overset{\displaystyle H^+ \quad\quad H^+}{H_2C-CH=CH_2} \ \leftrightarrow \ \overset{\displaystyle H^+ \quad\quad H^+}{H_2C=CH-CH_2}$$

occurs rather than

$$\overset{\displaystyle H^+}{CH_2=CH-CH_3}$$

which has no symmetrical resonating form.

It may be assumed that both resonance and inductive effects are at work in the case of vinyl bromide, bromoethylene, which adds as shown below:

$$Br-CH=CH_2 + HBr \rightarrow Br-CHBr-CH_2$$

The electron drifts would be represented as follows:

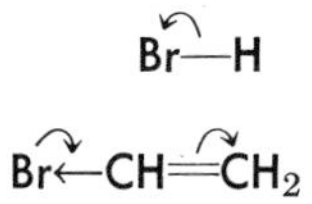

$$Br-H$$

$$Br\leftarrow CH=CH_2$$

The carboxyl group or the carboethoxy group could deactivate the beta carbon by resonance:

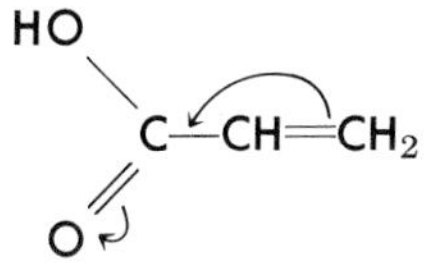

$$\overset{\displaystyle HO}{\underset{\displaystyle O}{\diagdown}} C-CH=CH_2$$

This would not greatly affect the electron availability at the alpha carbon. The effect on the alpha carbon should be largely inductive:

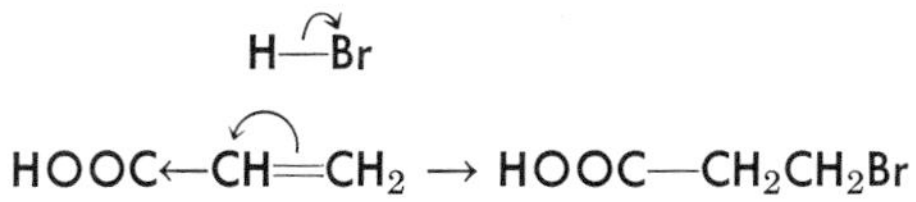

$$H-Br$$

$$HOOC\leftarrow CH=CH_2 \rightarrow HOOC-CH_2CH_2Br$$

The reader should recall that the Markovnikov rule (Section 11-4), which applies only to hydrocarbons, is that in the addition of HBr, the Br will go to a secondary carbon in preference to a primary. Since this is a special case of the application of electronic principles to the reaction of double bonds, it can be seen why the presence of highly polar groups with opposite electronic effects produces opposite results.

41–8   Inductive Effects: On Electrophilic Aromatic Substitution

As stated in the previous section, the principles used in the classification of directive influences on electrophilic addition to the double bond can also be applied to the classification of directive influences on electrophilic substitution in aromatic systems. First, let us consider the strongly electron-attracting substituents. Both the trimethylammonium group and the trifluoromethyl group are strongly deactivating, indicating that the withdrawal of electrons slows the reaction, as would be expected for an electrophilic attack. Following the schemes for electron drift given for the corresponding derivatives of ethylene, we should expect the patterns of electron drift to be as follows:

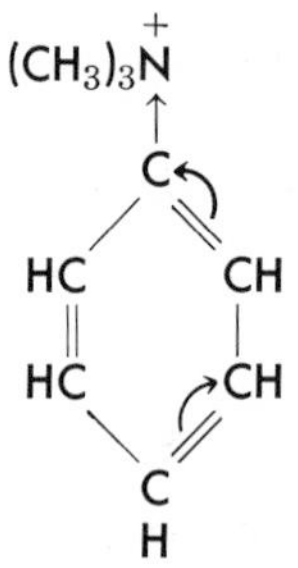

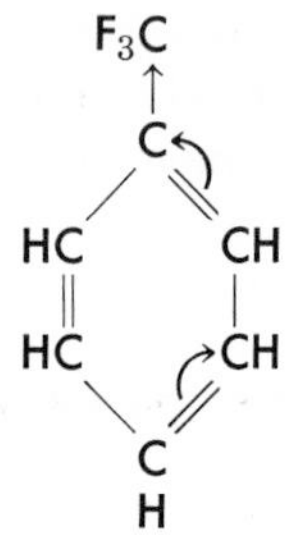

According to these patterns, we should expect the *para* (and the *ortho*) positions to be more strongly deactivated than the *meta* positions. However, since the inductive effect will cause a general electron drift in the molecule toward the electron-attracting group, we should also expect the *meta* position to be deactivated.

In fact, we find that in both cases the *ortho* and *para* positions are more strongly deactivated than the *meta*, leaving both substances predominantly *meta* directing. The first investigations of both compounds indicated that no *ortho* or *para* substitution took place. Recent work with improved analytical methods has shown, however, that 11% *para* substitution takes place in the phenyltrimethylammonium ion. It is to be presumed that a reinvestigation of the trifluoromethyl compound will produce a similar revision. Qualitatively, however, the results to be expected from the action of the inductive mechanism are borne out by the findings in either case.

41–9   Nitration of Toluene

For toluene, we should expect a similar effect in the opposite direction if the inductive mechanism were at work. That is, since the methyl group is electron releasing, we should expect all positions on the ring to be activated, and we should also expect greater activation at the *ortho* and *para* positions. This is in line with the experimental observations. The results of competitive reactions between benzene and toluene permit assignments of activities to the three positions on toluene relative to the activity of each position on the benzene ring which is taken as unity. These are:

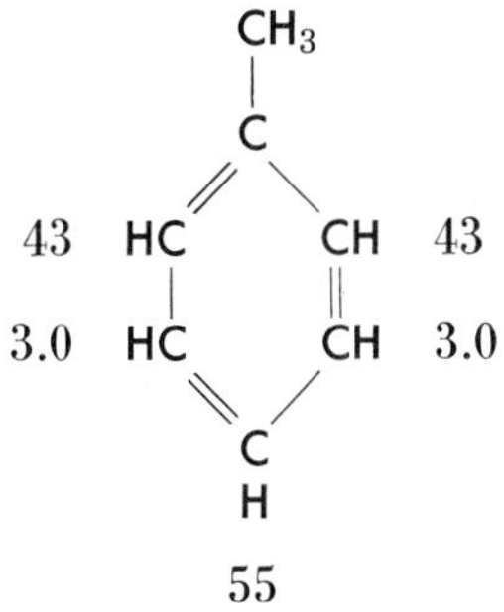

$$
\begin{array}{ccc}
 & \mathrm{CH_3} & \\
 & | & \\
 & \mathrm{C} & \\
43 \quad \mathrm{HC} & & \mathrm{CH} \quad 43 \\
3.0 \quad \mathrm{HC} & & \mathrm{CH} \quad 3.0 \\
 & \mathrm{C} & \\
 & \mathrm{H} & \\
 & 55 &
\end{array}
$$

It seems probable that the inductive mechanism is at work in the *meta* positions. Whether the inductive mechanism or sigma-bond delocalization is responsible for the activation of the *ortho* and *para* positions is not clear, however, since both would act in the same direction.

41–10   Nitration of Ethyl Benzoate

The nitration of ethyl benzoate leads to the following reactivities, compared with benzene as unity:

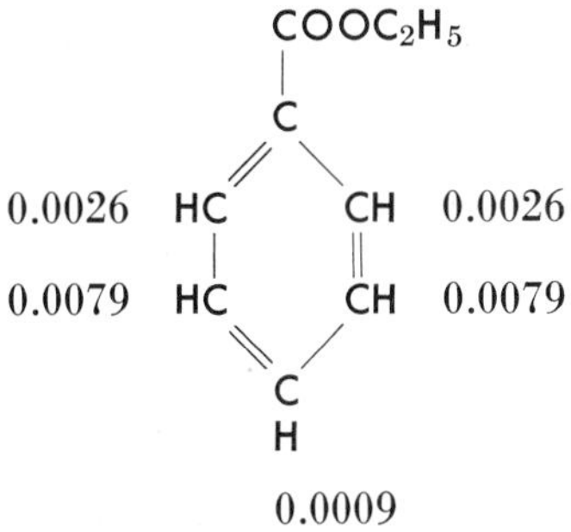

$$
\begin{array}{ccc}
 & \mathrm{COOC_2H_5} & \\
 & | & \\
 & \mathrm{C} & \\
0.0026 \quad \mathrm{HC} & & \mathrm{CH} \quad 0.0026 \\
0.0079 \quad \mathrm{HC} & & \mathrm{CH} \quad 0.0079 \\
 & \mathrm{C} & \\
 & \mathrm{H} & \\
 & 0.0009 &
\end{array}
$$

Again we see the pattern to be expected for a general inductive withdrawal of electrons with preferential withdrawal from the *ortho* and *para* positions.

41–11   Nitration of Chlorobenzene and Bromobenzene

The most interesting cases are those of the halogens, chlorine and bromine. In these cases, inductive and resonance mechanisms work in opposite directions so the outcome is not predictable. The experimental results are as shown on p. 546. The results below are interpreted, after the fact, as being due to inductive withdrawal of electrons from all three positions and resonance release of electrons to the *ortho* and *para* positions. Since the resonance effect would not release electrons to the *meta* position, this explanation seems reasonable.

41–12 Nitration of Phenyltrimethylphosphonium Ion

The substitution of phosphorus for nitrogen in the quaternary compound produces an anomalous result. The overall reactivity of the phenyltrimethylphosphonium ion is 4.8 times as great as that of the phenyltrimethylammonium ion. This should indicate greater inductive electron release and, consequently, more *para* substitution. Instead, it is observed that only 3% *para* is formed with the phosphorus compound, whereas 11% is formed with the nitrogen compound. This suggests that there is another mechanism for the withdrawal of electrons from the ring in addition to the inductive mechanism and that this additional mechanism works preferentially on the *para* position. It is known that the valence of nitrogen is limited to four, but that under some conditions, pentavalent compounds of phosphorus can be formed. An example is PCl_5, which, it will be recalled, has a structure compatible with the assumption that all bonds are equivalent. If we assume that a resonance effect can exist in which the phosphorus becomes pentavalent and draws electrons from the ring, we have an explanation for the effect observed in the nitration reaction. It is interesting that the anomalous order is reversed in the benzyl compounds, $C_6H_5CH_2N^+(CH_3)_3$ giving less *para* and more *meta* than $C_6H_5CH_2P^+(CH_3)_3$. Since the interposition of the methylene group would destroy the resonance effect, this result is in accord with our expectations.

41–13 Conclusion Concerning Aromatic Nitration

The results cited above concerning directive influences are selected from a large number of experiments which have been carried out in the field. They are representative, although results which differ in detail can be found when the experiments are performed under different conditions of solvent, temperature, or other critical variables. It may be concluded that a reasonably comprehensive correlation between electronic effects and the course of electrophilic aromatic substitutions has been worked out.

PROBLEMS

41-1 (a) Write a structure for toluene which demonstrates the electron drift by induction.

(b) Write a structure for toluene which illustrates resonance forms involving hyperconjugation.

(c) Do the same for chlorobenzene and for ethyl benzoate. In these cases, of course, we do not invoke hyperconjugation.

(d) Can you explain the relative rates of nitration of these compounds using this information?

(e) Demonstrate that the —$\overset{+}{P}$(CH$_3$)$_3$ substituent withdraws electrons by both inductive and resonance effects.

41-2 In Section 41-7, we saw that several lines of reasoning could be used to explain different orientations of HBr to substituted olefins. Consider the argument based on the stabilities of the competing carbonium ion intermediates.

(a) On this basis, how would HBr add to vinyl bromide? How would it add to acrylic acid?

(b) If the inductive effect and the resonance effects are in opposition, which effect is more important in determining the course of a reaction? Note that this may be answered no matter which approach we use to explain the hydrobromination of vinyl bromide. The rule is, in general, valid, although later we shall be able to define its limit of validity more accurately.

41-3 Which will brominate faster, the 2- or the 3-position of 1-naphthol?

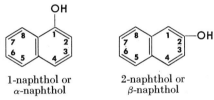

1-naphthol or
α-naphthol

2-naphthol or
β-naphthol

41-4 Which will brominate faster, the 1- or the 4-position in 2-naphthol?

41-5 Do you think it is safe to state which will be the most rapid reaction of those listed in Problems 41-3 and 41-4?

41-6 What product or products would you expect in predominant yield from the mononitration of the following compounds?

(a) *m*-xylene (b) *p*-methoxyphenylacetic acid (c) *p*-nitroanisole

(d) *m*-nitroanisole (e) biphenyl, (f) *p*-methylbiphenyl

41-7 Suppose that you wanted to make *p,p'*-dinitrobenzophenone from diphenylmethane. What sequence of steps would you employ? What sequence would you avoid?

41-8 Aniline supplies electrons by resonance to the *o*- and *p*-positions. But when aniline is nitrated with the usual nitrating mixture, the product contains almost half *m*-nitroaniline, and the reaction is relatively slow. Explain this. (What is the usual nitrating mixture? What would it do to amines?)

Do nucleophilic substitutions in the aromatic series proceed by the same mechanism as in the aliphatic series, or is a different mechanism operative? How can the reactions of aromatic type heterocyclic compounds be correlated with those of the substituted benzenes, both with respect to electrophilic substitution and with respect to nucleophilic substitution?

42

NUCLEOPHILIC AROMATIC SUBSTITUTION; SUBSTITUTION IN HETEROCYCLES

42-1 Nucleophilic Aromatic Substitution

In the presence of suitable activating groups, nucleophilic substitutions may occur in the aromatic series. Superficially, these resemble the nucleophilic aliphatic substitutions studied earlier. An example would be the replacement of chlorine as a substituent by ethoxide, hydroxide, or even iodide:

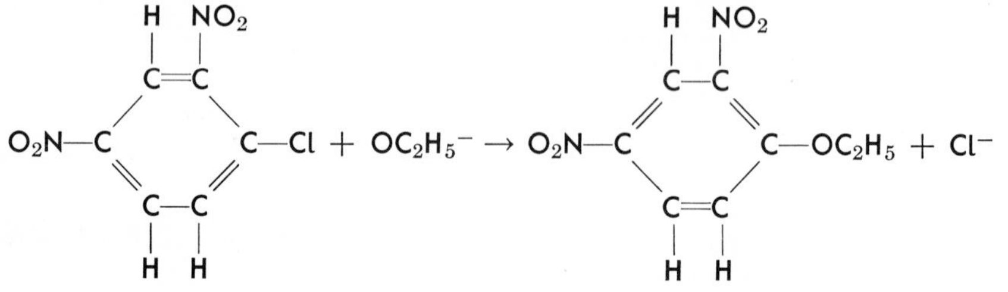

The use of dinitrofluorobenzene in the labeling of aliphatic amino acids is an example of this type of reaction.

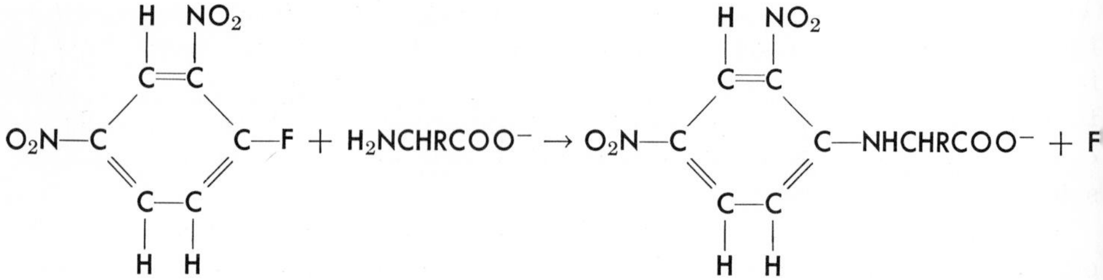

42–2 Kinetics of the Reaction

A kinetic study was made on the replacement of chloride by ethoxide in 2,4-dinitrochlorobenzene by Lulofs in 1901. He found that the reaction is second order. Other more recent investigators have confirmed this reaction order with a variety of such substitution reactions. The nucleophilic power of the attacking reagents follows the same order as that for nucleophilic aliphatic substitution. Hence the reaction may be classed as an S_N2 reaction. The mechanism of attack must necessarily be different from the attack on the aliphatic, however, since a backside attack would require the entering group to start from within the benzene ring, a stereochemical impossibility.

42–3 Intermediates in the Reaction

The mechanistic course of the reaction of nucleophilic aromatic substitutions is susceptible to direct investigation in a number of cases because the reaction intermediates are capable of isolation. An example is the replacement of the methoxy group by the ethoxy group in trinitroanisole; the intermediate was isolated by Meisenheimer.

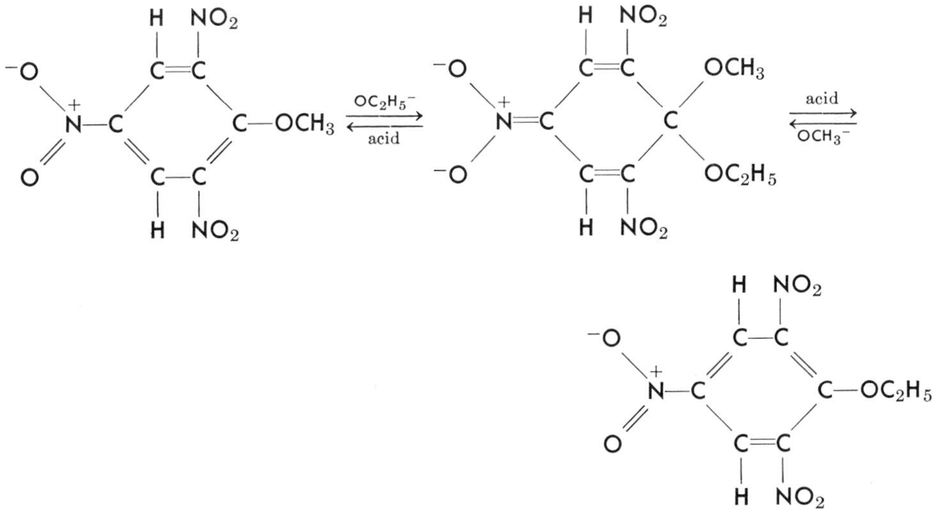

The ionic intermediate is obviously a resonating structure and its nature makes the role of the nitro group in the activation clear; its ability to form a salt derived from the pseudo-acid form stabilizes the negative charge on the intermediate and thus facilitates the reaction in much the same way as the stabilization of a positive charge on a similar intermediate is assumed to facilitate electrophilic aromatic substitution.

The negatively charged intermediate in nucleophilic aromatic substitution has one carbon with four groups attached at the center of substitution. For this reason, this carbon should have a relatively close approach to tetrahedral geometry. To form such a tetrahedral carbon, then, the approach of the entering group must be from above the plane of the benzene ring, and its entrance must drive the group being replaced downward from the ring. The general electron-deficiency which provides a driving force for the reaction must be in the pi cloud above and below the ring, which would be held more closely to the ring than normally by the electron-attracting effects of the nitro groups. The essence of the reaction, then, would be the donation of electrons by the nucleophile to the pi cloud above the ring, as sketched in Fig. 42–1.

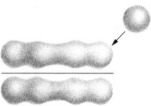

FIGURE 42–1

Even without the activating influence of the nitro group, nucleophilic substitution can be forced by high temperatures in benzene derivatives. This is the basis for the commercial process for the manufacture of phenol from chlorobenzene, a reaction which is run at a temperature of about 320°C. In this case, the reaction intermediate might involve delocalization of the negative charge to the *ortho* and *para* positions of the benzene ring.

Recently, experimental evidence has been accumulating that forcing conditions, such as high temperatures or extremely strong bases like the NH_2^- ion at lower temperatures, are capable of bringing an alternative mechanism into play. In this mechanism, an elimination reaction precedes further reaction. This elimination results in the formation of a highly reactive species called benzyne:

Benzyne

This intermediate is so unstable that it is incapable of existence for periods longer than a few microseconds. In the case of the formation of phenol, it would react immediately with the water present in the reaction mixture:

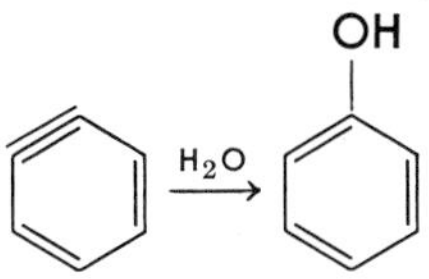

The presence of such an intermediate is made plausible by experiments performed with isotopic tracers and with ordinary labeling substituents. Thus the reaction of *p*-chlorotoluene leads to a mixture of *meta* and *para* cresols:

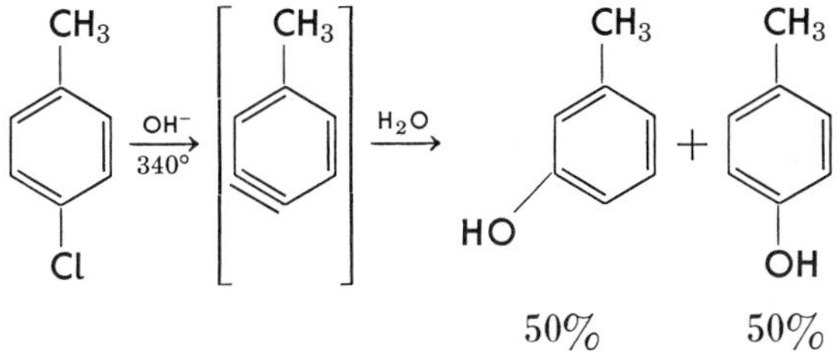

42–4   Heterocyclic Substitution Reactions

Among the heterocyclic compounds with aromatic characteristics, some characteristically give electrophilic substitutions, others nucleophilic substitutions. The general reaction type as well as the predominant directive influence can usually be correlated by means of the examination of the relative stabilities of the intermediates, as we have seen for the substitution of phenol and of dinitrochlorobenzene.

42–5   Substitution in the Pyrrole Ring

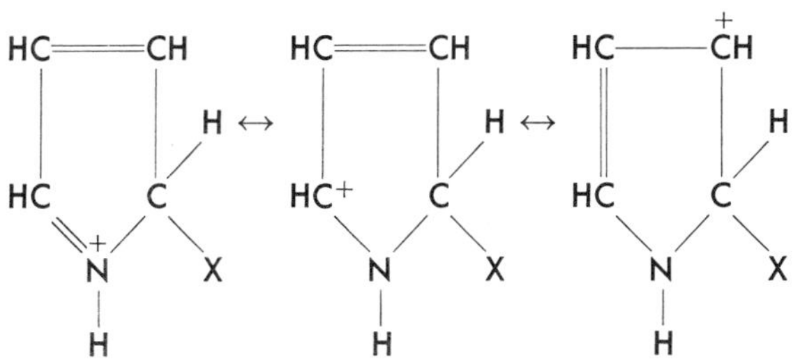

The first heterocycle that we shall consider is pyrrole. In this ring, we should expect deactivation of all positions by the inductive effect of the nitrogen atom. However, the ability of the nitrogen to assume a positive charge and to donate its electrons to any position of the ring would act to facilitate substitution. Thus the reaction intermediates could be formulated as follows: for alpha,

and for beta,

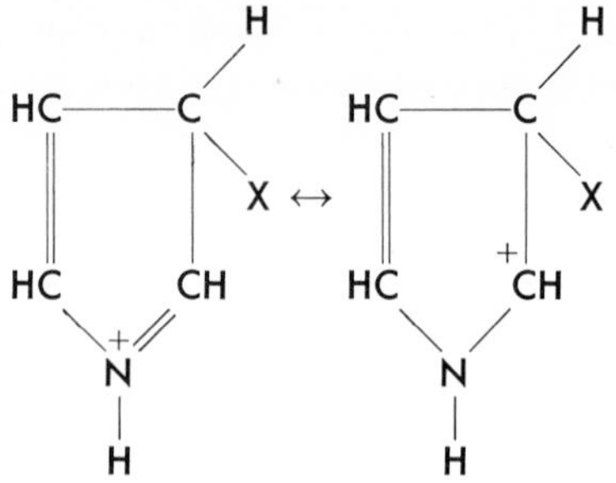

Substitution at either the alpha or the beta position permits the stabilization of the positive charge on nitrogen, all atoms having octets. Thus the reaction should be of the general order of ease of the substitution of phenol. It will be seen, in addition, that there is a possibility that the charge is on ring carbons, forming atoms with only a sextet of electrons. These would be less stable than the forms with octets and, for this reason, would not contribute so much to the stabilization of the reaction intermediates. For alpha substitution, however, the greater degree of delocalization possible should give an appreciably more stable intermediate than for the beta. For this reason, the theory would be consistent with the observation of greater ease of substitution at the alpha position than at the beta. Experiment shows this to be true. Actual kinetic measurements on the iodination reaction of highly substituted pyrroles show the alpha position to be approximately 25 times as reactive as the beta.

42–6   Intermediates in Pyrrole Substitution

Further investigation led to substantiation of the concept of the type of reaction intermediate sketched for this and other aromatic substitution reactions. Fu was able to isolate the bases corresponding to these intermediates by the use of hypochlorous, hypobromous, and hypoiodous acids on the following substituted pyrroles:

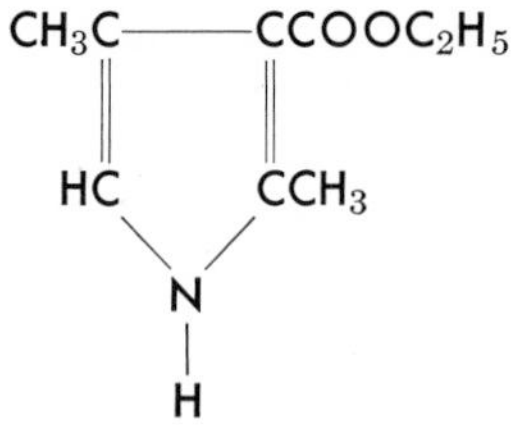

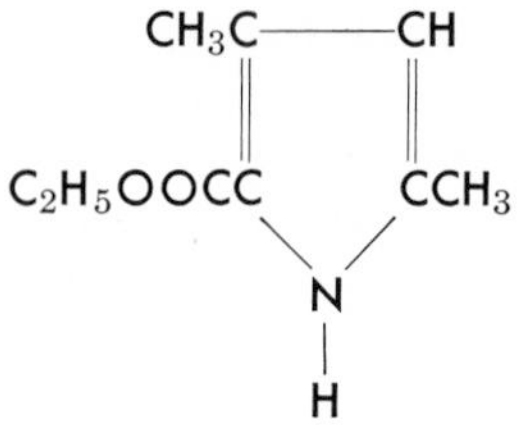

A base typical of this series is

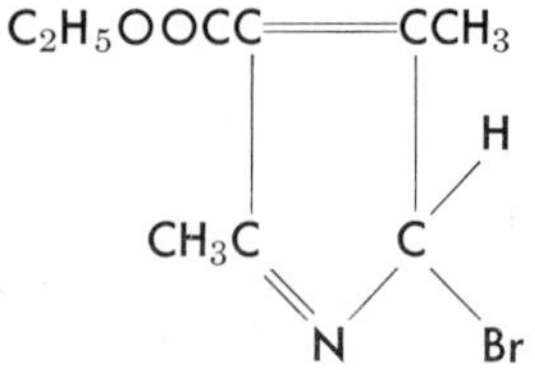

Treatment of this base with hydrogen bromide would be expected to regenerate the halogenation reaction intermediate and to permit the bromopyrrole to be formed by loss of a proton:

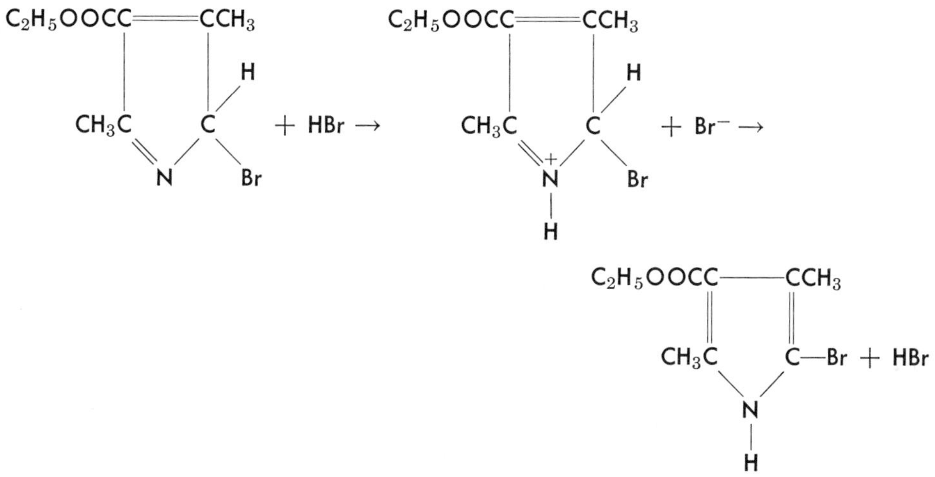

Thus the acid acts catalytically to convert the intermediate into the bromopyrrole. The isolation of the reaction intermediate relies on the exclusion of acid, using hypobromous acid as the halogenating agent:

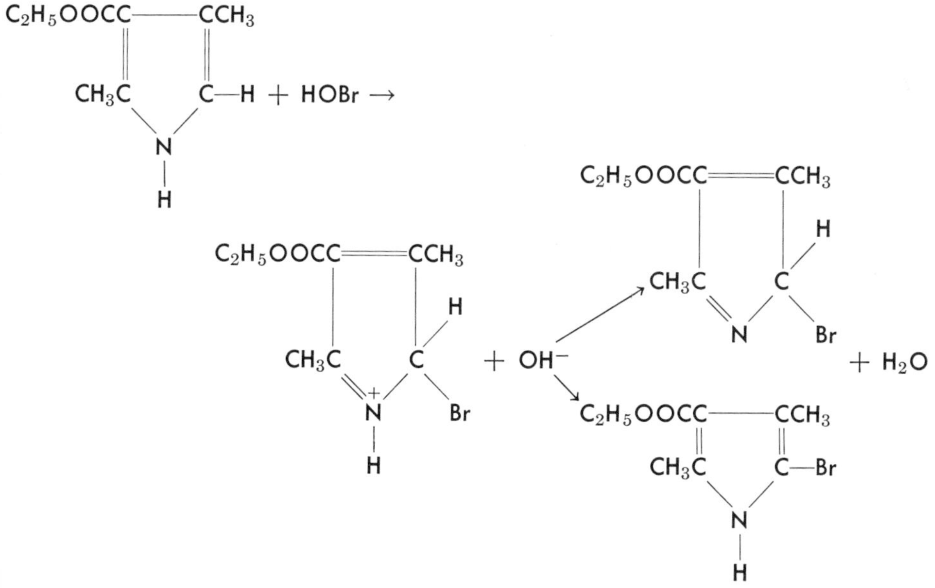

The desired product is formed in approximately 50% yield and can be separated by fractional crystallization. Its isolation and catalytic destruction by HBr provide excellent support for the reaction scheme for halogenation presented.

While we ordinarily associate basic properties with nitrogen, pyrrole as a base is of approximately the strength of acetamide as a base.   Deuterium-exchange experiments lead to the concept that even this basicity is not a result of the nitrogen atom, but is due to protonation in the α-position, the salt being of a structure similar to those formulated for the reaction intermediates in electrophilic attack:

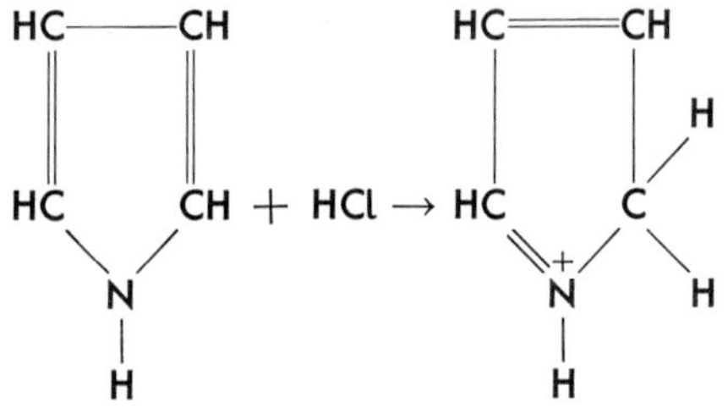

$$
\begin{array}{ccc}
\text{HC}\!-\!\!-\!\!\text{CH} & & \text{HC}\!=\!\!=\!\!\text{CH} \\
\| \qquad \| & & | \qquad\quad | \qquad \text{H} \\
\text{HC} \qquad \text{CH} + \text{HCl} \rightarrow \text{HC} \qquad \text{C} \\
\diagdown \;\; \diagup & & \diagdown\!\!\!\overset{+}{=}\!\!\!\diagup \quad\; \diagdown \\
\text{N} & & \text{N} \qquad \text{H} \\
| & & | \\
\text{H} & & \text{H}
\end{array}
$$

   Treatment of pyrrole with more concentrated acid results in the formation of a reddish resinous mass.

42–7   Substitution in the Pyridine System

Geometrical considerations prevent the formation of a tetravalent, positively charged nitrogen in the pyridine ring.   Such an atom would require a bond angle approaching 180°, which could not be accommodated within the compass of a ring as small as the pyridine ring:

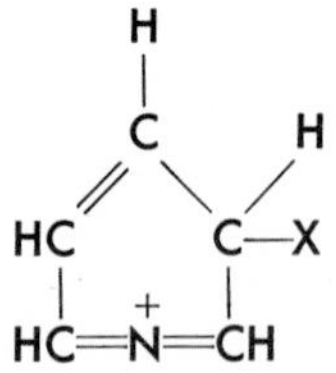

$$
\begin{array}{c}
\text{H} \\
| \\
\text{C} \qquad \text{H} \\
\diagup\!\!\| \qquad \diagup \\
\text{HC} \qquad \text{C}\!-\!\text{X} \\
| \quad\; \overset{+}{\;} \quad | \\
\text{HC}\!=\!\text{N}\!=\!\text{CH}
\end{array}
$$

Electrophilic substitution at the γ-position would require the formation of a positively charged nitrogen with only six electrons:

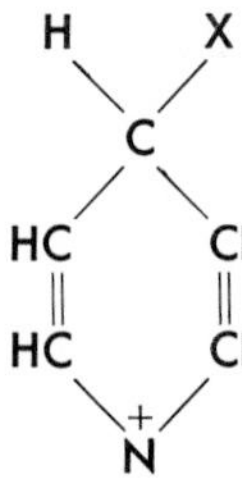

$$
\begin{array}{c}
\text{H} \qquad \text{X} \\
\diagdown \quad \diagup \\
\text{C} \\
\diagup \qquad \diagdown \\
\text{HC} \qquad\quad \text{CH} \\
\| \qquad\qquad \| \\
\text{HC} \qquad\quad \text{CH} \\
\diagdown \quad \overset{+}{} \quad \diagup \\
\text{N}
\end{array}
$$

Because of the electron-attracting property of nitrogen with respect to carbon, the removal of an electron pair from nitrogen would cost more energy than the removal of an electron pair from carbon.   For this reason, we should expect electrophilic substitution to occur even less readily with pyridine than with benzene. This is in line with the experimental observations.

Nucleophilic substitution on the pyridine ring, however, can take place with the accommodation of an electron pair on nitrogen and the preservation of all octets:

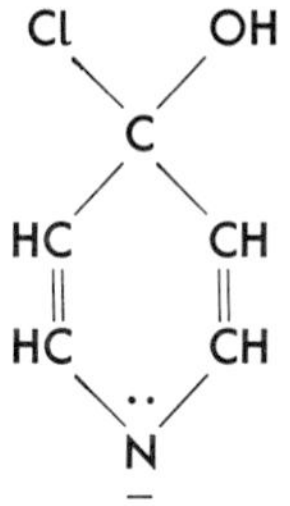

It is observed that this is a characteristic reaction of the pyridine ring. The nitrogen in the ring serves the same general purpose in substitution as do the oxygens attached to a nitro group in nitrobenzene. The relative ease of the two reactions can also be correlated. Thus the acids

$$CH_4 < NH_3 < H_2O < HF$$

are arranged in order of increasing acidity and their conjugate bases

$$CH_3^- > NH_2^- > OH^- > F^-$$

are arranged in the order of their diminishing basicity. This is another way of stating that the reaction

$$NH_2^- + H_2O \rightarrow NH_3 + OH^-$$

proceeds spontaneously (and violently) to the right. Thus the negative charge is more stable on the oxygen than on the nitrogen. Accordingly, we should expect the intermediate in the substitution of p-nitrochlorobenzene to be more stable than that in the substitution of γ-chloropyridine. This would imply that the nitro group would serve as a stronger activator for nucleophilic substitution than the ring nitrogen of pyridine. This reasoning is in accord with the experimental observation that the "hydrolysis" of nitrochlorobenzene proceeds more readily than that of γ-chloropyridine.

42–8   Substitution in the Pyrimidine Ring

The presence of a second ring nitrogen, in the pyrimidine ring, should reinforce the influence of the first nitrogen, so that the attack of hydroxide ion on chloropyrimidines should take place even more readily. We have already seen (Chapter 26) that this reaction is of preparative value in the pyrimidine series and that many of the characteristic transformations in the pyrimidine series take place by the nucleophilic-substitution mechanism. These reactions are intermediate in ease between those of the nitrochlorobenzenes and those of the dinitrochlorobenzenes.

42–9 Furane Substitution

The oxygen analog of pyrrole is furane.

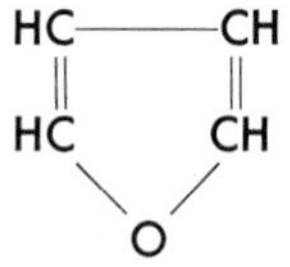

$$\begin{array}{ccc} HC & \!\!\!\!\text{------}\!\!\!\! & CH \\ \| & & \| \\ HC & & CH \\ & \searrow \quad \swarrow & \\ & O & \end{array}$$

The chemistry of furane is somewhat similar to that of pyrrole, being characterized by ready electrophilic substitution. We can rationalize the order of ease of substitution in this case by reference to the reaction:

$$H_3O^+ + NH_3 \rightleftarrows H_2O + NH_4^+$$

The fact that this reaction lies far to the right indicates that a positive charge on nitrogen is more stable than one on oxygen. We should expect the reaction intermediate for pyrrole to be more stabilized than that for furane, with the result that pyrrole should undergo more rapid electrophilic substitution. This is in accord with the experimental facts. Furane undergoes substitution reactions substantially faster than benzene but slower than pyrrole. As in the case of pyrrole, substitution takes place more rapidly at the α-position than at the β-position. This can be rationalized in the same manner as for pyrrole.

42–10 Thiophene Substitution

The sulfur analog of pyrrole and furane is thiophene. The story of the discovery of thiophene is interesting. In 1879, von Baeyer found that a blue color developed on mixing benzene with isatin and concentrated sulfuric acid.

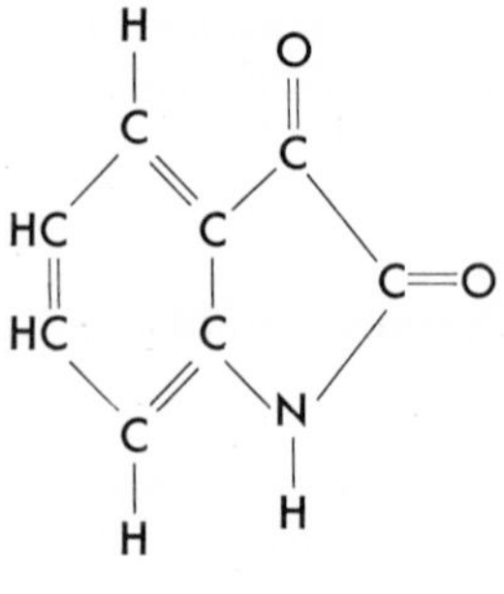

Isatin

This reaction was called the indophenin reaction. Three years later Victor Meyer attempted to present the Baeyer test as a lecture demonstration before a class. In spite of the fact that the experiment had worked for him many times before, this time it failed. Meyer immediately announced to the class that they had witnessed an observation of importance, and he then set about learning the cause for its failure. He found that the sample of benzene he was using for this particular experiment had been prepared by the decarboxylation of benzoic acid, whereas ordinarily benzene is prepared by distillation from coal tar. He verified that the source of the benzene was critical and immediately suspected that the benzene from coal tar contained an impurity responsible for the Baeyer test. Soon he was able to isolate the impurity, thiophene, and he followed this by an exhaustive study of the reactions of thiophene derivatives. The isatin test is an attack by an electrophilic reagent which takes place more readily with thiophene than with benzene. A laboratory method for the separation of the substances relies on the fact that the electrophilic mercuration of thiophene takes place much more readily than that of benzene, resulting in the separation of a mercurial derivative of thiophene:

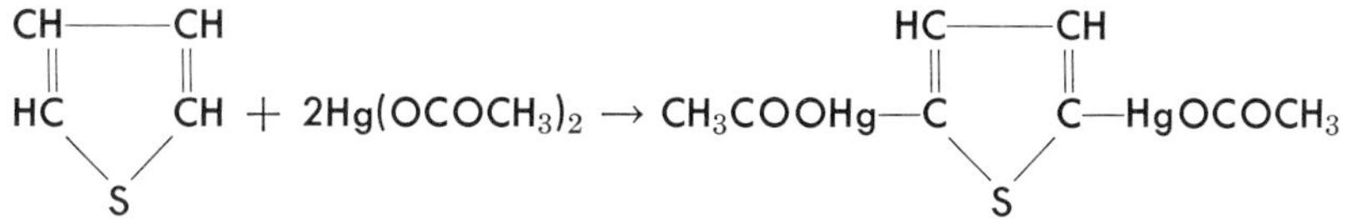

$$
\underset{\underset{S}{\diagdown\diagup}}{\overset{\text{CH}\text{---}\text{CH}}{\underset{\text{HC}\quad\quad\text{CH}}{\|\quad\quad\|}}} + 2\text{Hg(OCOCH}_3)_2 \rightarrow \underset{\underset{S}{\diagdown\diagup}}{\overset{\text{HC}\text{---}\text{CH}}{\underset{\text{CH}_3\text{COOHg}\text{---}\text{C}\quad\quad\text{C}\text{---}\text{HgOCOCH}_3}{\|\quad\quad\|}}}
$$

Mercurations of this sort with mercuric acetate proceed readily with phenols but not with the benzenoid hydrocarbons. It is estimated that thiophene is approximately 1000 times as reactive to electrophilic reagents as benzene.

The reactivity of thiophene, while greater than that of benzene, is less than that of phenol. The reactivity of furane is roughly comparable to that of phenol. The reactivity of pyrrole is still greater, being comparable to that of resorcinol, *m*-dihydroxybenzene. We may rationalize the difference in reactivity between furane and thiophene by pursuing further the analogy with the series of protonated derivatives. Hydrogen sulfide is a stronger acid and weaker base than is water. This is another way of saying that sulfur has less affinity for a positive charge than does oxygen. As a result, the resonance stabilization of the intermediate compound in thiophene substitution should be less than that in furane substitution and the substitution should proceed less readily. This is in accord with the experimental observations cited above. Both furane and thiophene resemble pyrrole in their reaction to strong acids, and resinous masses result.

42–11   Substitution in the Imidazole Ring; Imidazole

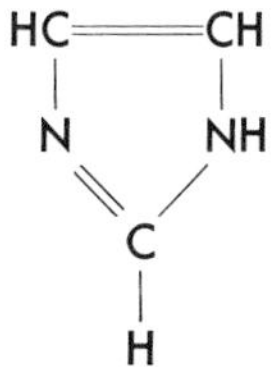

We have already referred to the chemistry of imidazole (Chapter 26) in connection with the structures of nucleic acids. The substance, shown at the right, has one pyrrolic nitrogen and one nitrogen resembling that in pyridine.

$$
\underset{\underset{\text{H}}{|}}{\underset{\text{C}}{\underset{\diagdown\diagup}{\underset{\text{N}\quad\quad\text{NH}}{|\quad\quad\quad|}}}}\overset{\text{HC}\text{===}\text{CH}}{}
$$

The nitrogen of pyrrole is characterized by very weak acidity, the N—H bond being comparable in acidity to that of diphenylamine, $(C_6H_5)_2NH$. Because of resonance stabilization of the anion, the acidic properties of imidazole are much more pronounced than those of pyrrole:

$$\begin{array}{ccc} HC{=\!=\!=}CH & & HC{=\!=\!=}CH \\ | \quad\quad | & & | \quad\quad | \\ N \quad\quad N^- & \leftrightarrow & {}^-N \quad\quad N \\ \diagdown \;\; \diagup & & \diagup \;\; \diagdown \\ C & & C \\ | & & | \\ H & & H \end{array}$$

Both pyrrole and imidazole are sufficiently reactive to undergo iodination readily. The iodination of imidazole is catalyzed by the presence of base, indicating that the species reacting is the anion. In this case, the reaction intermediate would be a neutral molecule:

$$\begin{array}{ccccccc} HC{=\!=\!=}CH & & HC{-\!-\!-}CH & & HC{=\!=\!=}CH & & HC{=\!=\!=}CH \\ | \quad\quad | & & || \quad\quad || & & | \quad\quad | & & | \quad\quad | \\ N \quad\quad N^- + I_2 \rightarrow & N \quad\quad N & \xrightarrow{OH^-} & N \quad\quad N^- & \xrightarrow{H_2O} & N \quad\quad NH + OH^- \\ \diagdown \;\; \diagup & & \diagdown \;\; \diagup & & \diagdown \;\; \diagup & & \diagdown \;\; \diagup \\ C & & C & & C & & C \\ | & & \diagup \;\; \diagdown & & | & & | \\ H & & H \quad I & & I & & I \end{array}$$

The directive influence is strongly in favor of the 2-position, as written. It is not clear why this should be true, nor has the mechanism of the reaction been studied in detail.

One of the most characteristic reactions of the imidazole ring is that of oxidative desulfuration. An example is the apparent reduction of 2-thiolimidazole by ferric chloride in acid or by a trace of bromine in aqueous acid. The reaction has been shown to involve preliminary oxidation of the sulfur followed by electrophilic attack by a proton:

$$\begin{array}{ccccccc} HC{=\!=\!=}CH & & HC{=\!=\!=}CH & & HC{-\!-\!-}CH & & HC{=\!=\!=}CH \\ | \quad\quad | & & | \quad\quad | & & || \quad\quad || & & | \quad\quad | \\ N \quad\quad NH & \xrightarrow{oxidation} & N \quad\quad NH & \xrightarrow{H^+} & N \quad\quad NH & \xrightarrow{H_2O} & N \quad\quad NH + H_2SO_2 + H^+ \\ \diagdown \;\; \diagup & & \diagdown \;\; \diagup & & \diagdown \;\; \diagup{}^+ & & \diagdown \;\; \diagup \\ C & & C & & C & & C \\ | & & | & & \diagup \;\; \diagdown & & | \\ SH & & SOH & & H \quad SOH & & H \end{array}$$

This reaction is of great value in imidazole chemistry and in purine chemistry where the sulfhydryl group serves as a removable protective group.

PROBLEMS

42-1 What direction of approach to the benzene nucleus would you expect the nitronium ion to take in the nitration of benzene if there is an intermediate pi complex between NO_2^+ and benzene? What direction if the substituted carbon becomes tetrahedral without an intermediate stage? How would the energy profiles of these possibilities differ?

42-2 Consider the general reaction, $HB \rightleftarrows H^+ + B^-$.

(a) Which proton will be lost most easily in α-picoline, one of the ring protons or one of those in the methyl group? Explain your answer in terms of resonance possibilities in the anion produced; there are also geometrical factors you should consider here.

(b) Which would you expect to incorporate deuterium more rapidly in $NaOD/D_2O$, α-picoline or β-picoline? β-picoline or γ-picoline?

42-3 Which position would you expect to be brominated most readily in indole? Remember that eight-electron forms are much more stable than six-electron forms.

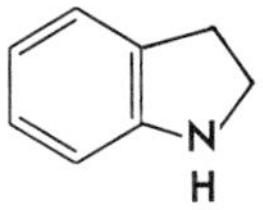

Indole

42-4 Show how the following choices may be resolved by drawing resonance forms for the reaction intermediates. Some of the answers will also be based on arguments involving inductive effects.

(a) Which would undergo replacement of Cl by OH more readily, 2-chloropyrimidine or 2-chloroimidazole?

(b) What product would you expect if one Cl group were replaced in 2,8-dichloropurine?

(c) Would the 8-Cl group in 8-chloropurine be more or less reactive than that in 2-chloroimidazole?

(d) Which would undergo oxidative desulfurization more readily, 2-thiopyrimidine or 2-thioimidazole?

(e) Which thiol group would be removed more readily in 2,8-dithiopurine?

(f) Would the remaining thiol group be more or less easily removed than that of 2-thiopyrimidine?

42-5 In the following reaction, which mechanism would better correlate the experimental facts, that of a benzyne intermediate or that of the type of intermediate isolated by Meisenheimer in nucleophilic substitution of aromatic nitro compounds?

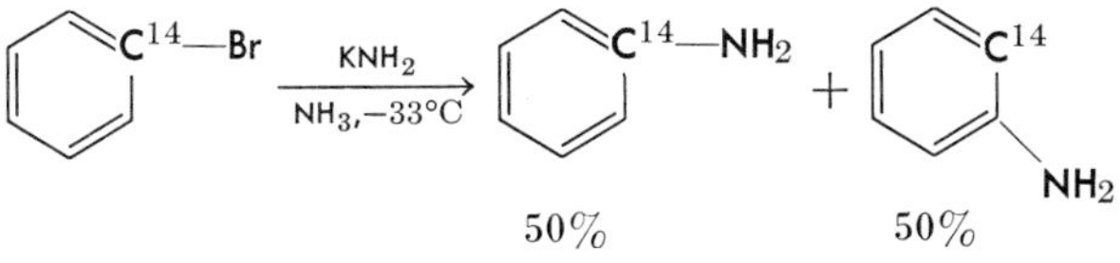

What is the mechanism of the process of diazotization? What is the mechanism of the diazo-coupling reaction? How can changes in coupling rates with structure be rationalized on the basis of the mechanism? What are the mechanisms of the preparative reactions by which the diazonium group is replaced by other groups on the benzene ring?

43

DIAZONIUM COMPOUNDS AND THEIR REACTIONS

43–1 Diazotization

Probably the most useful of the aromatic compounds from the point of view of preparation are the aromatic amines. In addition to having direct applications, these materials may be transformed into many other types of compounds because of the versatility of the aromatic diazonium compounds. Diazonium compounds are prepared by the treatment of aromatic amines with nitrous acid at ice temperatures. Many of them are unstable at room temperature, hence the precaution of preparing and using them in the cold.

The diazotization of aniline may be represented by the following equation:

$$C_6H_5NH_2 + HNO_2 + H^+ \rightarrow C_6H_5\overset{+}{N}{\equiv}N + 2H_2O$$

If the reaction is performed in hydrochloric acid solution, the product would be benzene diazonium chloride.

43–2 Kinetics of the Reaction

The mechanism of the formation of diazonium compounds has been studied under a variety of conditions. The rate has been shown by Taylor to be proportional to the concentration of the free amine and to the square of the concentration of the nitrous acid:

$$\text{Rate} = k(\text{amine})\,(HNO_2)^2$$

This rate expression is consistent with more than one mechanism. To narrow the field, the same manipulation was performed in this case as the one which proved successful in elucidating the nature of the reagent in aromatic nitration; that is, the reactivity of the amine was increased up to the point at which it was used so fast that the rate of formation of the nitrosating agent became critical in the control of the overall rate. This was accomplished by reducing the acidities of the solutions employed in such a way as to greatly increase the proportion of the free amine available for the reaction. Under these conditions the rate law was found to be:

$$\text{Rate} = k'(\text{HNO}_2)^2$$

This rate law is consistent with the assumption that the active nitrosating agent in dilute aqueous media is N_2O_3. The preparative chemist is aware that the solutions in which diazotizations are performed frequently exhibit the blue color of N_2O_3, making this assumption attractive. Studies in the presence of halide ions have shown that NOCl and NOBr may also be active nitrosating agents under these conditions. Indeed, it is occasionally advantageous to use preformed NOCl or NOBr as nitrosating agents when aqueous media are undesirable. In the presence of strong acids and with less water present, it can be shown that the NO^+ ion can be the nitrosating agent. The means employed to demonstrate this resemble those used in the demonstration of the presence of NO_2^+ in the nitration reaction, although the proofs of the presence of NO^+ are not so comprehensive as those of NO_2^+. Under still other conditions, N_2O_4, the mixed anhydride of nitric and nitrous acids, may be employed as a nitrosating agent. Thus the chemist has a wide choice of reagents to fit the conditions most appropriate for his reactions.

43–3 Mechanism of Diazotization

Assuming diazotization under ordinary dilute aqueous conditions, the mechanism of the formation of the diazonium compound would be:

$$C_6H_5-NH_2 + O=N-O-N=O \rightarrow C_6H_5-\overset{H}{\underset{H}{\overset{+|}{N}}}-N=O + NO_2^-$$

$$C_6H_5-\overset{H}{\underset{H}{\overset{+|}{N}}}-N=O \rightarrow C_6H_5-\overset{+}{N}\equiv N + H_2O$$

It is obvious that the last equation represents more than one step. In cases of this sort, it seems most reasonable to assume a series of bimolecular collisions, to avoid the less probable event of a higher-order collision. In collisions involving solvent molecules, higher orders may be postulated because of the very high concentration of the solvent. Otherwise, such collisions are very rare. Experimental methods for establishing the sequence of the rearrangement of protons and OH groups by a series of bimolecular exchanges are in an unsatisfactory state. Since definite means for deciding between possible paths are lacking, the usual method is to postulate a reasonable path through which the desired transformations could be secured. In the present instance, a possible sequence for the individual steps involved might be:

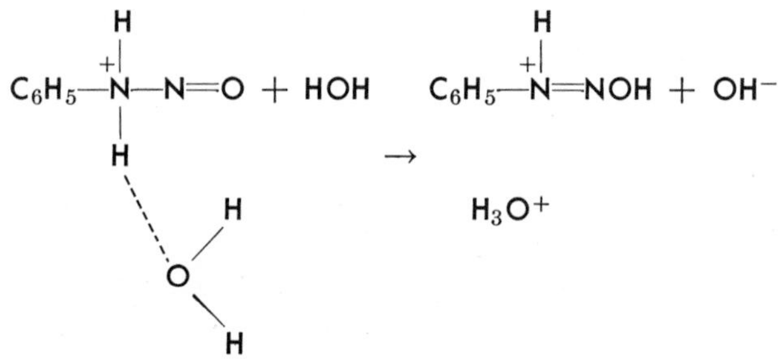

$$
\overset{\overset{\displaystyle H}{|}}{C_6H_5\text{—}\overset{+}{N}\text{—N}=O} + HOH \quad\quad C_6H_5\text{—}\overset{\overset{\displaystyle H}{|}}{\overset{+}{N}}=NOH + OH^-
$$

$$
C_6H_5\text{—}\overset{\overset{\displaystyle H}{|}}{\overset{+}{N}}=NOH + H_2O \rightarrow C_6H_5\text{—N}=NOH + H_3O^+ \rightarrow C_6H_5\text{—}\overset{+}{N}\equiv N + 2H_2O
$$

Compounds of the type $C_6H_5\text{—N}=NOH$ can be obtained in the form of their alkali metal salts by treatment of diazonium chlorides with alkali or by the reaction of nitrosobenzene with alkaline hydroxylamine:

$$
C_6H_5\text{—N}=O + H_2NOH + OH^- \rightarrow C_6H_5\text{—N}=N\text{—O}^- + 2H_2O
$$

As might be expected, they exist in two stereoisomeric forms. The reader should write structural formulas for these two forms.

43–4   The Coupling Reaction

One of the most important commercial applications of the aromatic amines is for the preparation of azo dyes. These substances are formed by the coupling of aromatic diazonium compounds with aromatic amines or phenols. An example is butter yellow:

$$
C_6H_5\text{—}\overset{+}{N}\equiv N \leftrightarrow C_6H_5\text{—N}=N^+ + C_6H_5N(CH_3)_2 \rightarrow C_6H_5\text{—N}=N\text{—}C_6H_4\text{—N}(CH_3)_2 (p)
$$

Butter yellow

Butter yellow is so named because it was once employed as a yellow dye for the artificial coloring of butter. Its use was banned in the United States many decades ago when it was discovered that it produced skin irritation in some persons who worked with it. Because of its cheapness, however, its use continued in the Orient until it was discovered that continued ingestion produces cancer of the liver. The material is now employed in research laboratories for the study of the mechanism of carcinogenesis.

43–5   Kinetics of Coupling with Phenol

The study of the mechanism of the coupling of diazonium compounds was initiated by Conant and Peterson in 1930. They found that the rate of coupling is second order. Studies of the dependence of the rate of pH lead to the conclusion that it may be formulated as follows:

$$\text{Rate} = k(\text{ArN}_2{}^+)(\text{Ar}'\text{O}^-)$$

that is, the rate of coupling is proportional to the product of the concentration of the diazonium ion and that of the phenolate ion. Early investigators had frequently assumed that the active agent in coupling was the diazohydroxide, Ar—N$=$NOH. Examination of Conant and Peterson's results show that they can also be formulated:

$$\text{Rate} = k(\text{ArN}_2\text{OH})(\text{Ar}'\text{OH})$$

that is, that the rate is proportional to the product of the concentration of the diazohydroxide and the free phenol. Hence these experiments alone are not sufficient to distinguish between the two possibilities. A distinction can be achieved by a simple qualitative experiment, however. It is observed that benzenediazonium chloride couples readily with phenol but not with anisole:

$$\text{C}_6\text{H}_5\overset{+}{—\text{N}}{\equiv}\text{N} + \text{C}_6\text{H}_5\text{OH} \rightarrow \text{C}_6\text{H}_5—\text{N}{=}\text{N}—\text{C}_6\text{H}_4—\text{OH}$$

$$\text{C}_6\text{H}_5\overset{+}{—\text{N}}{\equiv}\text{N} + \text{C}_6\text{H}_5\text{OCH}_3 \rightarrow \text{no reaction}$$

Since anisole is incapable of forming an anion in aqueous solutions, it may be assumed logically that the formation of the anion is prerequisite to coupling and, consequently, that the diazonium cation is the active attacking agent in coupling. Thus this reaction becomes an example of electrophilic substitution with the designation S_E2.

43–6   Kinetics of Coupling with Anilines

The conclusion that coupling is a reaction of the diazonium cation was confirmed by the studies of Wistar and Bartlett on coupling with aromatic amines. These were found to obey the rate law:

$$\text{Rate} = k(\text{ArN}_2{}^+)(\text{Ar}'\text{NR}_2)$$

For the reaction with phenols, making the solution more alkaline results in the diminution of the amount of the diazonium cation accompanied by a corresponding increase in the amount of the phenolate anion, with the result that decisive changes in rate are not obtained. For the coupling with amines, however, very little more amine will be formed in alkaline solutions, but diazonium ion will be destroyed with the formation of the diazotate. The experiment shows that the process of making the solution alkaline is accompanied by a decrease in the rate of the coupling with the amine, thus showing that the destruction of the diazonium ion is critical in determining the course of the reaction.

43–7   The Effects of Substituents on Coupling

Since the diazonium cation is an electrophilic reagent, it follows that the degree of its electron-attracting power should be capable of alteration by the use of substituents, that is, electron-attracting substituents should increase its attacking power and electron-donating substituents should diminish it. Hammett has recalculated the results of Conant and Peterson and has shown that the following rates hold to within 25% for the coupling of *para*-substituted phenyldiazonium ions with five different phenols:

—NO$_2$	—SO$_3^-$	—Br	—H	—CH$_3$	—OCH$_3$
1300	13	13	(1)	0.4	0.1

If we recall that the *para*-methoxy group is electron-donating due to its resonance effect, we see that the substituents are in the expected order. We have had no previous basis for comparing the sulfonate anion with bromine as a substituent, but it would be expected that both would be electron attracting.

43–8   Qualitative Experiments on the Mechanism of Coupling

Fifty years ago, the studies of Kurt Meyer yielded information which could have been interpreted in the same way as the more modern experiments, if organic chemists of the time had been inclined to draw mechanistic conclusions from experimental data. Meyer's experiments constituted a fitting operation between diazonium ions with increasing electron-attracting powers and aromatic nucleophiles with diminishing nucleophilic power. For example, we have seen that benzenediazonium chloride will not couple with anisole. Meyer found, however, that the extra activation achieved by the use of phloroglucinol trimethyl ether was sufficient to permit coupling to take place:

$$C_6H_5\overset{+}{N}_2 + HC \underset{\displaystyle CH_3O\ \ H}{\overset{\displaystyle CH_3O\ \ H}{\bigcirc}} C-OCH_3 \rightarrow C_6H_5-N=N-C_6H_2(OCH_3)_3$$

If the degree of activation was decreased by the subtraction of one methoxy group, then coupling would not take place unless a more powerful coupling agent was used:

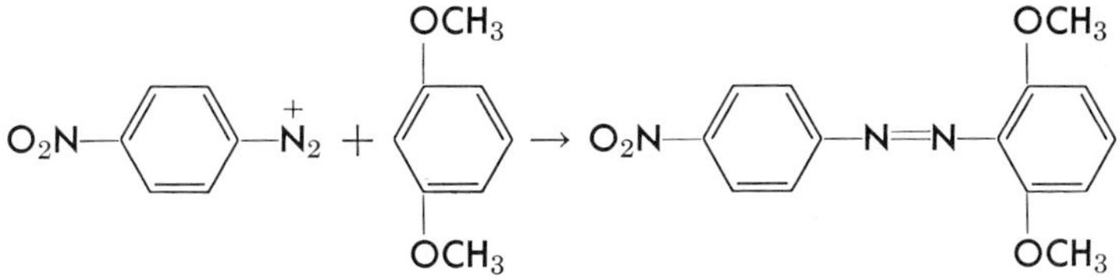

Similarly, the pairs:

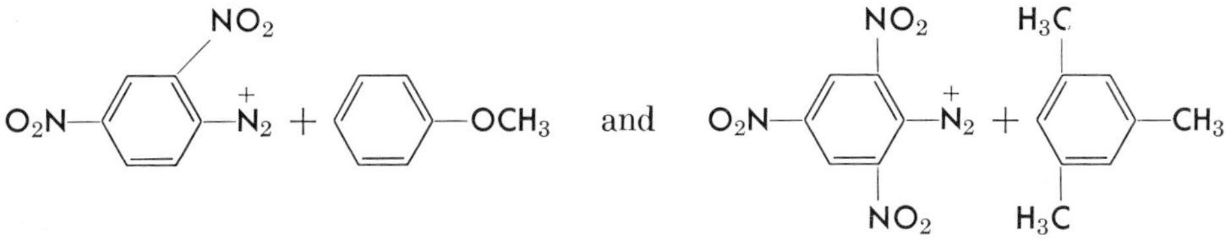

fit for the purposes of coupling. These qualitative experiments provide excellent substantiation for the mechanistic hypothesis advanced and provide the preparative chemist with a guide to the practical use of substituents in the management of projected syntheses.

43–9   Substituent Effects and Hammett Plots

In our discussion of acidities, we saw that Hammett plots could be prepared for variously substituted aromatic acids. Since acids are electrophilic reagents and have positive slopes (rho values) in the Hammett plots, we should expect the plots of the rates of coupling with substituted electrophilic diazonium salts to have positive rho values. Such plots have been prepared by Nachlas, Goldstein, Rosenblatt, Kirsch, and Seligman for a limited number of couplings with phenols, and found to have the expected positive rho values. In the case of coupling with amines, however, the positive slope of the curves is interrupted by a change in mechanism, the rate becoming independent of the nature of the diazonium salt when sufficiently powerful couplers are used. This phenomenon has not yet been adequately investigated for an explanation to be offered.

Substitution on the nucleophilic reagent in a coupling reaction should also produce a Hammett plot, this time with a negative rho value. The same investigators found this relationship to hold. From these results, we may conclude that the diazonium salt acts as the electrophile and the amine or phenol as the nucleophile in the coupling reaction. As in the case of nitration, the reaction intermediate may be formulated as shown on the right.

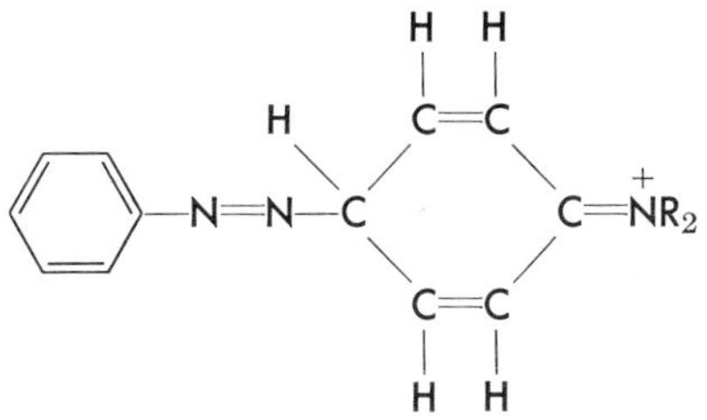

43-10   Uncatalyzed Decomposition of Diazonium Ions

One of the reasons for the versatility of the diazonium salts is the ease with which the diazonium group may be displaced by other groups, permitting wide latitude in synthetic reactions. Thus water converts a diazonium compound to a phenol, an alcohol to a phenol ether, halide ions to the phenyl halides, reducing agents to the hydrocarbon, and a variety of other substituting agents to their respective products. The mechanism of the reaction has been studied and found to be first order in the diazonium compound and independent of the concentration of the substituting reagent. The reaction is therefore classified as an aromatic S_N1 reaction. From this information, it was logical to assume that the rate-determining step is the decomposition of the diazonium ion according to the equation:

$$C_6H_5\overset{+}{-}N\equiv N \rightarrow C_6H_5{}^+ + N_2$$

According to this hypothesis, electron-releasing groups should favor the ionization reaction, since the nitrogen leaves with its electron pair. The kinetic effects of numerous substituents have been investigated and found to be characteristic. Groups which release electrons by a resonance effect, however, do not speed the reaction, since the net effect of their electron release is to form a double bond to the leaving nitrogen, thus strengthening its attachment:

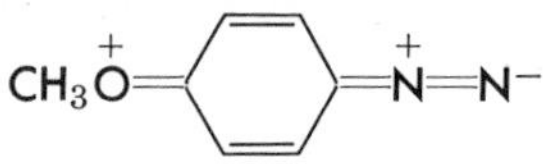

Thus the rate of decomposition of benzenediazonium chloride is approximately 6700 times that of the p-methoxy compound. The data calculated by Ingold from the results obtained by Crossley, Kienle, and Benbrook are as shown in Table 43-1.

43-11   Analysis of Substituent Effects on the Decomposition of Diazonium Ions

Certain regularities are immediately apparent. The four substituents listed below hydrogen in Table 43-1 are all electron attracting and each one slows the reaction in each position, as would be expected from the hypothesis. The four substituents above hydrogen would be expected to be electron releasing, but in the *para* position, each of them slows the reaction. For —OH, —OCH$_3$, and —C$_6$H$_5$, this effect can easily be ascribed to the existence of resonance to strengthen the C—N bond. In the case of methyl, the inductive effect would predict a speeding of the reaction, while electron release by sigma-bond delocalization or "hyperconjugation" would slow the release. Thus in this case, the evidence seems to favor the sigma-bond delocalization mechanism of electron release.

The contrasting effects of the phenyl and methyl groups in the *ortho* positions with the same groups in the *para* positions are rationalized by ascribing them to

Table 43–1

RATE OF DECOMPOSITION, $10^7 k$, sec^{-1}

Substituents	ortho	meta	para
—OH	6.8	9100	0.93
—OCH$_3$	—	3400	0.11
—C$_6$H$_5$	1100	1700	37
—CH$_3$	3700	3400	91
—H	740	740	740
—COOH	140	410	91
—SO$_3^-$	91	150	42
—Cl	0.14	31	1.4
—NO$_2$	0.37	0.69	3.1

the fact that the space-occupying properties of the *ortho* groups help to force the nitrogen out of the molecule. Closer inspection will reveal, however, that this explanation is not entirely adequate since the phenyl group, being larger, would be expected to exert a greater steric effect than the methyl group, whereas the opposite effect is observed. In spite of this, it seems reasonable to ascribe some of the increased effect to steric causes.

In the *meta* position, the four groups which can be electron releasing all exert their maximum effects. It may seem strange that electron release by a resonance mechanism should be thought of as originating from the *meta* position. The diagram would be represented as follows:

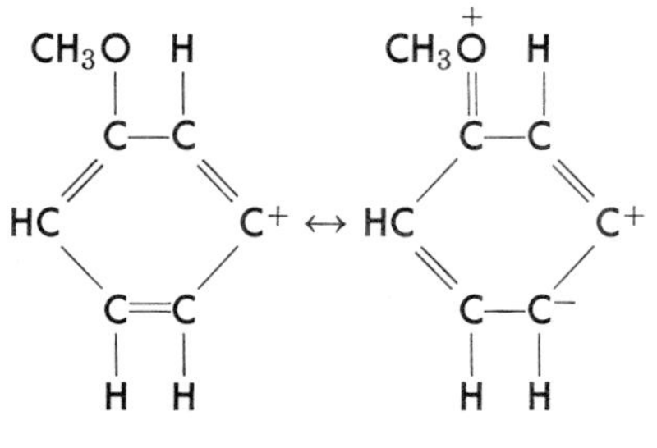

Several comments are in order. In the first place, the phenyl cation is not a resonating species; that is, delocalization of the positive charge will not take place readily through the pi-bond system. To verify this, the reader should try to move the positive charge from the hydrogen-deficient carbon. He will find that he produces either a carbon atom with only two bonds or one between two double bonds, both highly unlikely structures. The basic reason for this difficulty lies in the geometry of the system. It will also be easy to verify that in all the cases we have studied up to now, resonance interaction between substituents and the pi cloud of the benzene ring involves either unshared pairs of electrons or pi electrons in the substituents. Sigma bonds of substituents are not involved. The direction of sigma-bond orbitals is perpendicular to the benzene ring pi cloud, making overlap with it difficult. For the phenyl positive ion, the vacant orbital is a sigma orbital, at right angles to the pi cloud and therefore not readily available for overlap. Electrons originating in the unshared pair of the oxygen, on the other hand, can be delocalized into the pi-bond system, with contributions taking place in each of the positions *ortho* to the positively charged carbon. This positive charge will attract these electrons, as we have seen with positive charges originating in other pi-bond systems. Overall, this would be expected to cause a stabilization of the positive charge over an alternative system in which such electron donation was not possible. In essence, this is the reasoning used to rationalize the behavior of the electron-donating groups in the *meta* positions.

In summary, all the effects of the groups below hydrogen in Table 43–1 are easily coordinated by the hypothesis advanced concerning the S_N1 mechanism of the reaction. The case is not so clear for the groups above hydrogen in the table, and special explanations of their effects are required. While these explanations may be justified, they cannot be thought of as providing strong support for the theory, while at the same time they provide no evidence against it.

43–12   The Sandmeyer Reaction

Sandmeyer (Victor Meyer's assistant in the famous indophenin lecture demonstration mischance that led to the discovery of thiophene) discovered that still another group of reactions could be brought about on diazonium compounds by the use of catalysts. The catalysts employed were cuprous salts of the anions to be introduced. Thus cuprous chloride facilitates the introduction of chlorine, cuprous bromide the introduction of bromine, and cuprous cyanide the introduction of the cyano group. Experimental evidence indicates that this reaction proceeds by still another mechanism, involving free radicals. One piece of evidence in favor of the radical mechanism is the fact that the Sandmeyer reaction can be used to initiate the polymerization of acrylonitrile, $CH_2{=}CHCN$, a reaction known to be initiated by the presence of radicals. The reaction with cuprous chloride has been studied and found to be first order in diazonium ion and in the cuprous chloride complex, $CuCl_2^-$. The cuprous chloride is not consumed during the reaction. A formulation for the mechanism which accounts for the experimental observations is:

$$C_6H_5{-}\overset{+}{N}{\equiv}N + Cl{-}Cu{-}Cl^- \xrightarrow{\text{slow}} C_6H_5\cdot + Cl{-}Cu{-}Cl + N_2 \xrightarrow{\text{fast}} C_6H_5{-}Cl + CuCl$$

Either by the S_N1 mechanism or by the radical mechanism, replacements of the diazonium group by nitro, sulfhydryl, arsono, halomercuri, or aryl groups may be effected. Detailed mechanisms have not been worked out in each case but preparative methods are available for all these replacements.

PROBLEMS

43-1   Reactions of diazonium ions are of great synthetic value. A number of the following reactions have been mentioned in the text.

$$ArN_2^+ \xrightarrow{\;H_2O\;} ArOH$$

$$ArN_2^+ \xrightarrow{\;CH_3OH\;} ArOCH_3$$

$$ArN_2^+ \xrightarrow{\;CuX_2^-\;} ArX^*$$

$$ArN_2^+ \xrightarrow{\;HAsO_3^=\;} ArAsO_3H_2$$

$$ArN_2^+ \xrightarrow{\;HgCl_2\;} ArHgCl$$

$$ArN_2^+ \xrightarrow[\;CH_2=CHCOOC_2H_5\dagger\;]{\;CuCl_2\;} ArCH_2CHClCOOC_2H_5$$

$$ArN_2^+ \xrightarrow{\;Cu,OH^-,C_6H_6\;} Ar\!-\!C_6H_5$$

$$ArN_2^+ \xrightarrow{\;H_3PO_2\;} ArH$$

$$ArN_2^+ \xrightarrow[\;or\ H_2SO_3\;]{\;Zn,\ CH_3COOH\;} ArNHNH_2$$

How could you convert:

   (a) 3-nitro-4-chlorobenzenesulfonic acid into 4-chlorobenzenesulfonic acid?

   (b) *o*-chloronitrobenzene into *o*-chlorobenzoic acid?

43-2   Starting from benzene, show how you would prepare

   (a) *p*-bromobiphenyl and (b) *m*-chloroanisole.

43-3   The ionization constants of several substituted benzoic acids have been measured with the following results:

Substituent	K
H	6.4×10^{-5}
p-Br	10.7×10^{-5}
p-OCH$_3$	3.4×10^{-5}
p-CH$_3$	4.2×10^{-5}
p-NO$_2$	37×10^{-5}

Using this information, determine whether the data given in this chapter for the relative rates of coupling of benzenediazonium ions with phenols ought to be interpretable by a Hammett plot. If the data are good enough, decide on a value of ρ for the general reaction and interpret it.

---

* X is usually Cl, Br, CN.

† Other activated olefins may be used, as in the Michael reaction.

How do investigations of rearrangement reactions differ from those of reactions involving no structural change? What new concepts must be introduced into the mechanistic picture to include molecular rearrangements? What mechanistic tools have been applied to the study of the diazoamino rearrangement and the sulfamic acid rearrangement?

44

AROMATIC REARRANGEMENTS I

44-1 The Problem Posed by Molecular Rearrangements

In the study of the structures of organic chemicals, the reliability of a given reaction in a structural determination was always hedged by the restriction, "barring molecular rearrangements." In the great majority of reactions, it can be established that no rearrangement has taken place. The cases in which rearrangements do appear, however, have been cataloged and, with an increase in our knowledge of the mechanisms of organic reactions, it is possible to recognize in advance the reaction conditions most likely to lead to rearrangements. In some cases the problem posed by an unexpected reaction outcome has been turned to advantage in synthesis by using the reaction as a means for obtaining products which would have been unavailable without the special synthetic route afforded by the molecular rearrangement.

44-2 The Diazoamino Rearrangement

We have seen that the coupling of benzenediazonium chloride with dimethylaniline produces an azo dye, butter yellow. If the coupling is performed on aniline instead of dimethylaniline, a different result may be obtained under certain conditions. It was found by Peter Griess and C. A. Martius in 1866 that the product of coupling of aniline under neutral or alkaline conditions is not the expected azo dye, but is an isomer which can be rearranged under acid conditions to yield the azo dye. Because of its structural implications, the rearrangement interested Kekulé, who contributed studies in the field.

The reaction of benzenediazonium chloride with aniline produces a coupling product which has lost the basicity of the aniline amino group. It is therefore logical to formulate the coupling as having taken place on the amino group of the aniline:

$$C_6H_5 - \overset{+}{N} \equiv N + H_2N - C_6H_5 \rightarrow C_6H_5 - N = N - NH - C_6H_5 + H^+$$

The product is logically named diazoaminobenzene. Treatment with alcoholic acid or, better, with a mixture of aniline and aniline hydrochloride yields the azo dye which was expected from the coupling reaction:

$$C_6H_5 - N = N - NH - C_6H_5 \overset{H^+}{\longrightarrow} C_6H_5 - N = N - C_6H_4 - NH_2$$

This product is the amino derivative of azobenzene, $C_6H_5 - N = N - C_6H_5$, and is consequently called aminoazobenzene. The compound has regained the basic properties of an aromatic amine and the structural assignment follows from this.

44–3   Evidence for the Intermolecular Mechanism

The first question that must be answered concerning the mechanism of a molecular rearrangement is whether it is the result of a collision between two or more molecules with a resultant exchange of partners, that is, it is *inter*molecular, or whether it takes place entirely within the rearranging molecule itself, that is, it is *intra*molecular. Approximately twenty years after the discovery of the diazoamino rearrangement, the question was settled in this case by Nietzski who demonstrated an intermolecular transfer of the diazo group. This was accomplished by "tagging" the molecule with methyl groups.

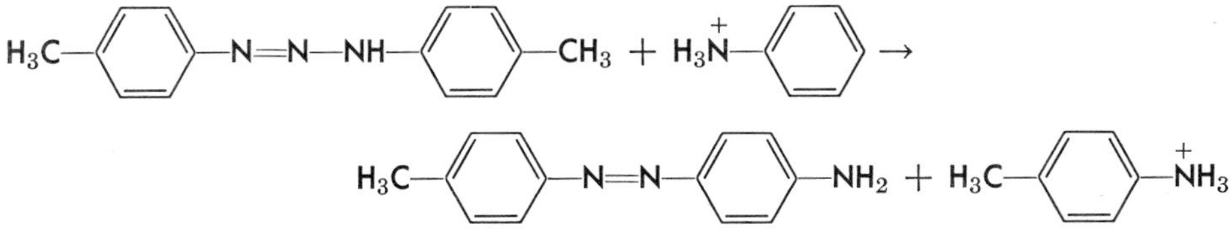

A parallel reaction was also performed with *ortho*-toluidine.

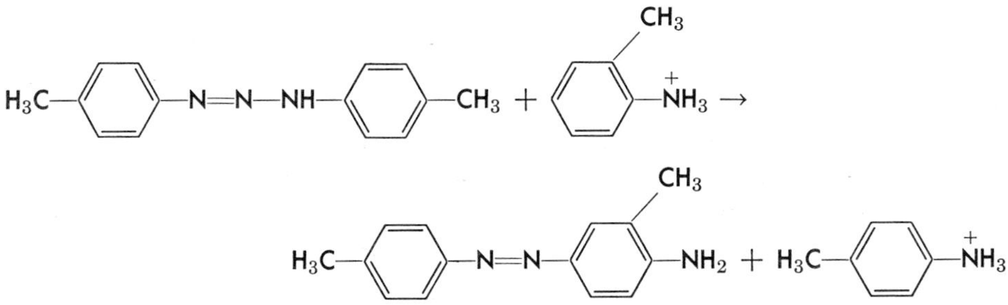

It was next shown that the molecule accepting the diazo group could be a phenol.

$$C_6H_5\text{---}N\text{==}N\text{---}NH\text{---}C_6H_5 + C_6H_5OH \xrightarrow{H^+} C_6H_5\text{---}N\text{==}N\text{---}C_6H_4\text{---}OH + C_6H_5\text{---}\overset{+}{N}H_3$$

Since this is the product obtained when benzenediazonium chloride and phenol are coupled under ordinary conditions, it was natural to assume that the rearrangement reaction of diazoaminobenzene in acid involved as its first step the acid cleavage of the diazoamino compound back to the diazonium ion and then the recoupling of this to give the aminoazo compound.

$$C_6H_5\text{---}N\text{==}N\text{---}NH\text{---}C_6H_5 + H^+ \rightarrow C_6H_5\text{---}\overset{+}{N}\text{≡≡}N + H_2N\text{---}C_6H_5 \rightarrow$$

$$C_6H_5\text{---}N\text{==}N\text{---}C_6H_4\text{---}NH_2 + H^+$$

This interpretation of the reaction was advanced by Friswell and Green in 1885.

44-4 The Goldschmidt Mechanism and Its Refinement

In the period between 1890 and 1900, Goldschmidt and his collaborators studied the kinetics of the diazoamino rearrangement and, in a pioneering mechanistic study, advanced what was essentially the modern mechanism for the reaction. Using aniline as the solvent for the reaction, these investigators found that the reaction is first order in the diazoamino compound. With strong acids, the reaction also approximates first order with respect to the acid concentration. This means that the rate-determining step involves both the diazoamino compound and the acid. These investigators also showed that the preparative trick of using aniline instead of an inert solvent exerts a strong "catalytic" effect on the reaction, presumably because the aniline is also a participant in the rate-determining portion of the reaction. For these reasons, they proposed that the rate-determining step was one which involved all three species, aniline, diazoamino compound, and acid. They thus formulated the reaction as a nucleophilic displacement of aniline by aniline:

$$H_2N\text{---}C_6H_5 + \underset{\underset{N\text{---}C_6H_5}{\|}}{N\text{---}\overset{+}{N}H_2\text{---}C_6H_5} \rightarrow H_2N\text{---}C_6H_4\text{---}\underset{\underset{N\text{---}C_6H_5}{\|}}{N} + H_2N\text{---}C_6H_5 + H^+$$

A further finding of these studies was that in the presence of weak acids, the reaction approaches second order in acid concentration. It is argued from this fact that under these conditions, one molecule of the acid functions as a proton donor, while the other functions to form its conjugate base, which acts to remove a proton from the reaction intermediate. We have seen that in other cases of aromatic substitution, the removal of the proton from the intermediate takes place rapidly after the rate-determining step. If the interpretation advanced for the dependence of the diazoamino reaction on acid concentration is correct, this reaction would be an exception to the rule concerning aromatic substitution. In this case, the reaction mechanism would be formulated as:

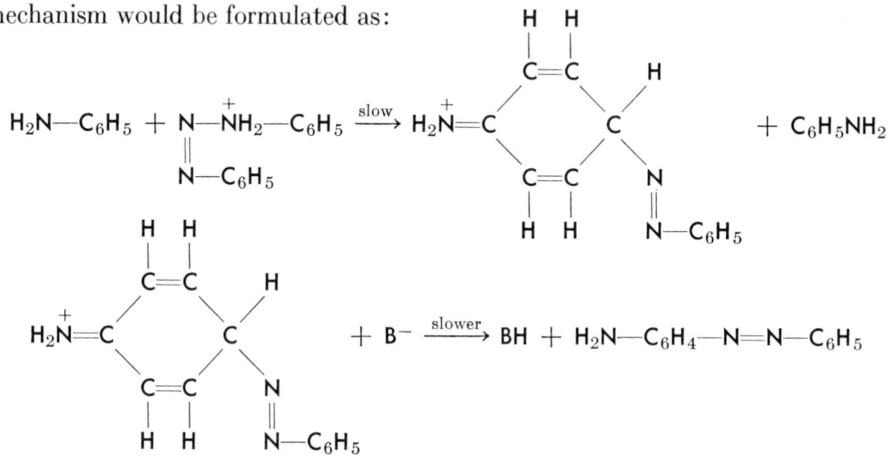

$$H_2N-C_6H_5 + \overset{+}{N}-\underset{\underset{N-C_6H_5}{\|}}{NH_2}-C_6H_5 \xrightarrow{slow} [\text{structure}] + C_6H_5NH_2$$

$$[\text{structure}] + B^- \xrightarrow{slower} BH + H_2N-C_6H_4-N=N-C_6H_5$$

The reader should formulate a critical experiment which would establish or disprove this hypothesis.

44–5   The Chloramine Rearrangement

In 1886 it was discovered that N-chloroacetanilide could be rearranged in aqueous hydrochloric acid to give a mixture of o- and p-chloroacetanilides:

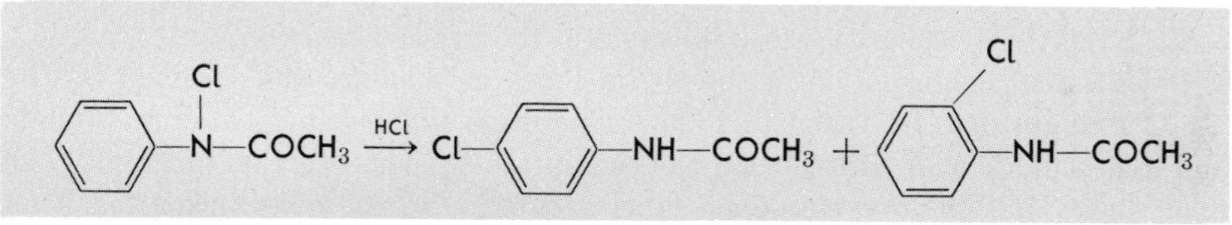

It was assumed, without experimental evidence, that this rearrangement involved intramolecular migration of the halogen.

44–6   Evidence for the Intermolecular Mechanism

In 1909, Orton and Jones undertook an experimental investigation of the chloramine rearrangement and came to the conclusion that the reaction is an intermolecular reaction, involving the liberation of chlorine through the action of the hydrochloric acid and subsequent chlorination of the acetanilide thus liberated by the free chlorine.

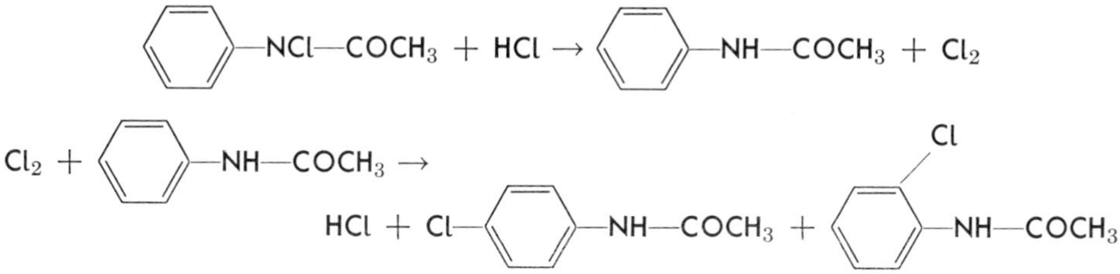

The evidence on which Orton and Jones based their hypothesis was that aspiration of air through the reacting mixture removed chlorine gas from the reaction and permitted the isolation of acetanilide from the mixture. Then, by making ring chlorination more difficult through the use of N-chloro-2,4-dichloroacetanilide, transfer of chlorine from the initial N-chloro compound to another more reactive aromatic nucleus could be achieved.

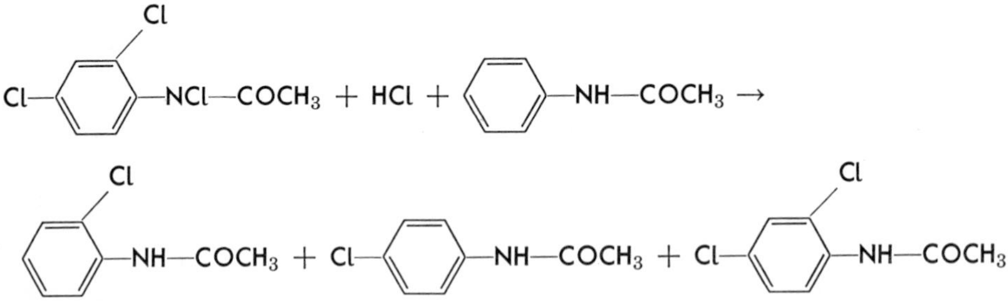

As in the transfer of the diazo group of the preceding rearrangement, this chlorine transfer demonstrates that the rearrangement is not intramolecular. It was found that the proportions of the *ortho* and *para* isomers formed in the transfer reaction was the same as in the rearrangement reaction. This permitted a very subtle test, since the proportion of the isomers formed is dependent on the nature of the solvent, more of the *para* isomer being formed in glacial acetic acid than in aqueous acetic acid. Even this peculiarity was duplicated in the transfer reaction.

Independent confirmation of the Orton-Jones mechanism was obtained by the use of radioisotopes by Olson in 1936. They used unlabeled N-chloroacetanilide and hydrochloric acid with labeled chlorine in the aqueous reaction medium. The final ring-bound chlorine contained labeled chlorine to the extent expected if all the chlorine of the starting material had been pooled with the labeled chlorine of the reaction medium.

44–7   Kinetics of the Rearrangement

It is known that ClBr is a brominating agent and ClI is an iodinating agent. The reader should be able to rationalize these observations. If N-chloroacetanilide is treated with HBr instead of HCl, a mixture of *ortho* and *para* bromoacetanilides results. If the N-chloro compound is treated with HI, a mixture of *ortho* and *para* iodoacetanilides results.

Kinetic studies on the bromination reaction with HBr showed that the rate is proportional to the concentration of the chloroamide, the hydrogen ion, and the bromide ion. Accordingly, the mechanism would be formulated:

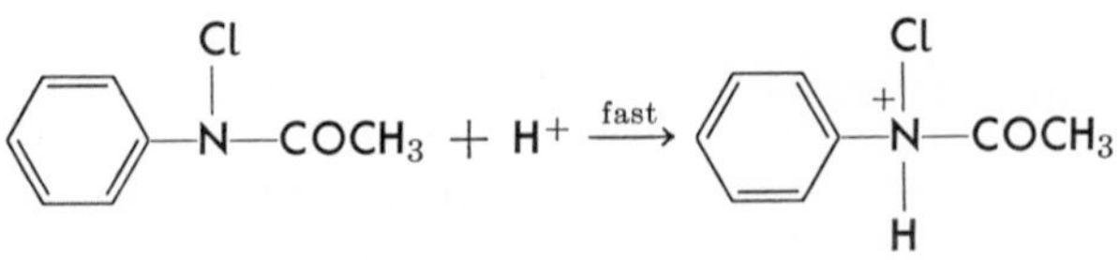

The mechanism for the reaction with bromide ion is:

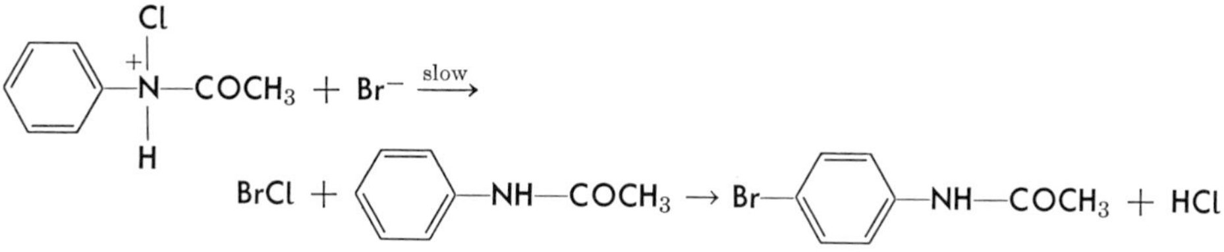

Thus the intermolecular mechanism proposed by Orton seems well established, the experimental evidence being of several types. In spite of this evidence, Orton himself stated that the existence of an alternative intramolecular mechanism under some conditions could not be excluded, even though evidence in favor of this had not been discovered.

44-8 The Sulfamic Acid Rearrangement

The direct sulfonation of aniline is an electrophilic substitution performed with sulfuric acid containing excess sulfur trioxide (oleum) and, as might be expected, the product obtained is predominantly the *meta* sulfonic acid, metanilic acid.

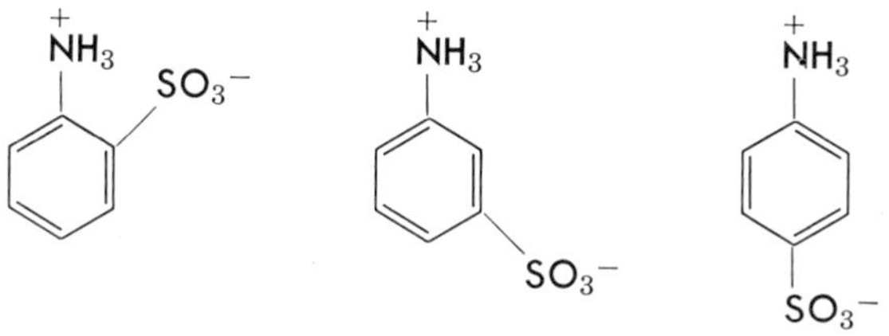

Orthanilic acid   Metanilic acid   Sulfanilic acid

This result occurs because the predominant species in strong sulfuric acid medium is the anilinium ion. When sulfanilic acid is desired, the method used for its preparation is the "baking process" in which dry anilinium acid sulfate is heated to 230°C. Alternatively, the acid sulfate may be heated to 180°C in concentrated sulfuric acid as the solvent. Sulfonation is a reversible process. By heating a sulfonic acid with aqueous sulfuric acid to a sufficiently high temperature, the parent aromatic compound may be regenerated:

$$C_6H_6 + H_2SO_4 \xrightarrow{80°} C_6H_5SO_3H + H_2O$$

$$C_6H_5SO_3H + H_2O \xrightarrow[150°]{H_2SO_4} C_6H_6 + H_2SO_4$$

We may safely assume, then, that during the baking process the less stable isomers of sulfanilic acid are brought into equilibrium with the more stable so that the final product of the reaction is the equilibrium mixture. Small amounts of orthanilic and metanilic acids are formed but the main product is sulfanilic acid.

44-9   The Bamberger Mechanism

In 1897 Bamberger proposed that sulfanilic acid is formed during the baking process by the following sequence of reactions:

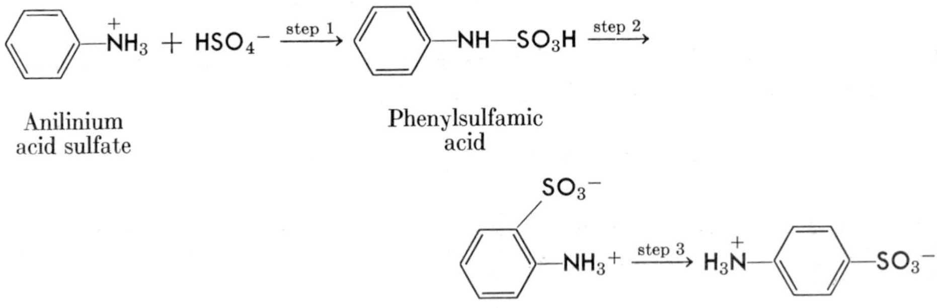

$$\text{Anilinium acid sulfate} \quad -\overset{+}{N}H_3 \; + \; HSO_4^- \xrightarrow{\text{step 1}} \quad -NH-SO_3H \xrightarrow{\text{step 2}}$$

Anilinium
acid sulfate

Phenylsulfamic
acid

$$\overset{SO_3^-}{\underset{}{}} \quad -NH_3^+ \xrightarrow{\text{step 3}} H_3\overset{+}{N}- \quad -SO_3^-$$

Orthanilic acid   Sulfanilic acid

Bamberger claimed to demonstrate steps 2 and 3 of the proposed sequence experimentally. On treatment of phenylhydroxylamine with sulfur dioxide, phenylsulfamic acid is formed:

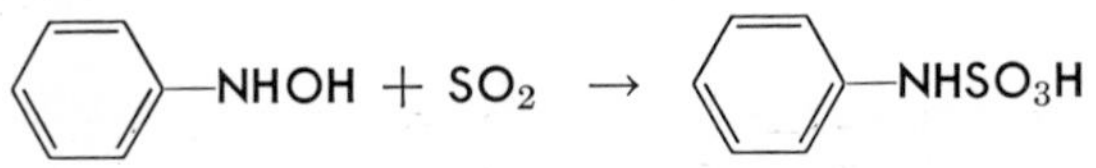

$$-NHOH + SO_2 \; \rightarrow \; -NHSO_3H$$

Phenylhydroxylamine   Phenylsulfamic acid

Bamberger stated that an acetic acid solution of phenylsulfamic acid at 16 to 17°C was converted to orthanilic acid by the addition of a trace of sulfuric acid as a catalyst. This demonstrated the validity of reaction 2, according to his reasoning. He then found that orthanilic acid could be heated to 180°C in sulfuric acid, conditions sometimes used for the formation of sulfanilic acid, and converted to sulfanilic acid. This demonstrated the validity of reaction 3. The only flaw in the reasoning as presented appeared to be that neither Bamberger nor any of his successors has been able to demonstrate reaction 1. Phenylsulfamic acid is so unstable to acids at low temperatures that it is doubtful that it would be capable of isolation from anilinium acid sulfate, even if it were formed.

44-10   Modern Evidence Concerning the Reaction Mechanism

Bamberger's results were accepted for over fifty years without specific verification, and theories attempting to explain the rearrangement of phenylsulfamic acid to orthanilic acid have appeared in the literature. Recently, however, Illuminati, working in the laboratories of Hughes and Ingold, has found that phenylsulfamic acid does not rearrange to orthanilic acid. Instead, both are formed simultaneously from phenylhydroxylamine and sulfur dioxide. Once it is completely purified, phenylsulfamic acid in acetic acid will dissociate under the catalytic influence of acids into sulfuric acid and aniline, but it will not rearrange to orthanilic acid. It is now assumed that the first material formed by the addition of sulfur dioxide to phenylhydroxylamine is a sulfitoamine:

$$C_6H_5NHOH + SO_2 \rightarrow C_6H_5NHOSO_2H$$

Hughes then assumed that this sulfitoamine can undergo a proton shift to yield an intermediate salt capable of forming orthanilic acid:

$$C_6H_5NH\text{---}OSO_2H \rightarrow C_6H_5\overset{+}{N}H_2\text{---}OSO_2{}^-$$

By a simple rearrangement of electrons and bonds, this internal salt can be transformed into the reaction intermediate for the formation of orthanilic acid:

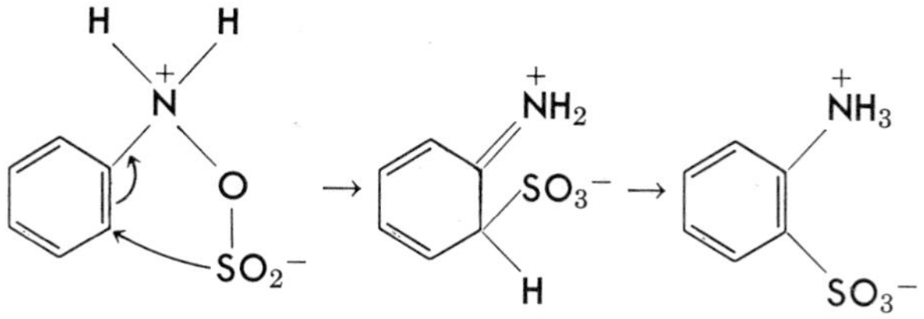

It may also be assumed that the sulfitoamine is an intermediate in the formation of phenylsulfamic acid, or alternatively, that this results from direct attack of the sulfur on the hydroxylamine nitrogen by a molecule of sulfur dioxide:

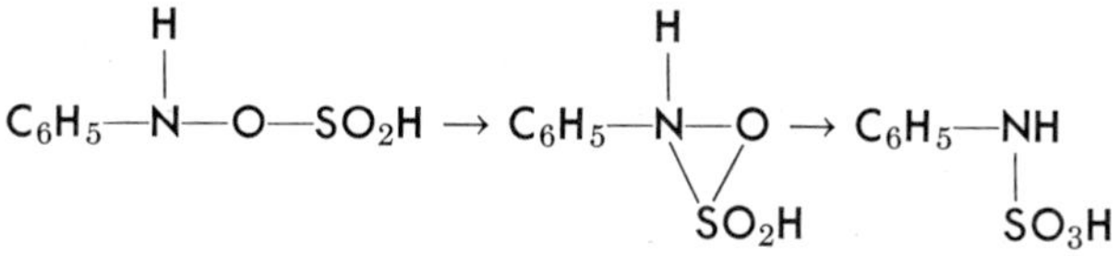

All these steps, including the assumed mechanism for the formation of orthanilic acid, are speculative, since the sulfitoamine has not been prepared.

Illuminati found that heating phenylsulfamic acid in dioxane at 100°C produces about 22% rearrangement to sulfanilic acid but that even under these rearranging conditions no orthanilic acid is formed. Dissociation of phenylsulfamic acid into aniline and sulfuric acid will not account for this rearrangement, since under these conditions of solvent and temperature, no sulfanilic acid is formed from aniline and sulfuric acid. A model of phenylsulfamic acid shows that while the spatial positions of the atoms are quite favorable for the reaction at the *ortho* position, which does not occur, they are not at all favorable for the reaction which does occur at the *para* position. It is possible that the dioxane plays a part in this reaction.

The study of the sulfamic acid rearrangement provides an interesting case history in the regression of our knowledge in the field. Whereas fifty years ago it appeared that chemists were in possession of a reasonable hypothesis for the formation of the aniline sulfonic acids, we must now confess that we know less than we thought we knew earlier. It still seems logical to assume that the formation of sulfanilic acid from orthanilic acid is caused by dissociation and resulfonation, but an unequivocal demonstration of this is still to come. The mechanism for the formation of sulfanilic acid from phenylsulfamic acid is still open, and the mechanism for the formation of orthanilic acid from phenylhydroxylamine and sulfur dioxide requires further investigation.

44-11 The Nature of the Aniline Sulfonic Acids

We should note that all three aminobenzenesulfonic acids are properly written as dipolar ions, as was orthanilic acid in the last formula. In the case of glycine we saw that acetic acid reacts with ammonia to form ammonium acetate. We therefore concluded that a substituted acetic acid, glycine, would react with a substituted ammonia, also glycine, to form a salt and for benzenesulfonic acid and aniline, the acid is so strong that salt formation takes place readily. Consequently, we should expect the substituted benzenesulfonic acid, sulfanilic acid, to react with substituted aniline, also sulfanilic acid, to form an internal salt. The melting point of aniline is low, $-6°C$, and that of benzenesulfonic acid is not high, 50 to 51°C, but the melting point of sulfanilic acid is so high, 288°C, that decomposition takes place at the melting point. This is one indication of salt formation. The same proposition is not true for the aminobenzoic acids, however. Aniline is a relatively weak base, weaker than ammonia by a factor of approximately 10^5, and as a result, the carboxyl group of benzoic acid is not sufficiently strong to convert aniline to its salt. It is for similar reasons that aminobenzoic acid is covalent in character. The melting point of *para*-aminobenzoic acid is 187°C, while that of benzoic acid is 122°C.

PROBLEMS

44-1 Phenylhydroxylamine undergoes a rearrangement in dilute sulfuric acid. The products, after neutralization, are a mixture of *o*- and *p*-aminophenol.

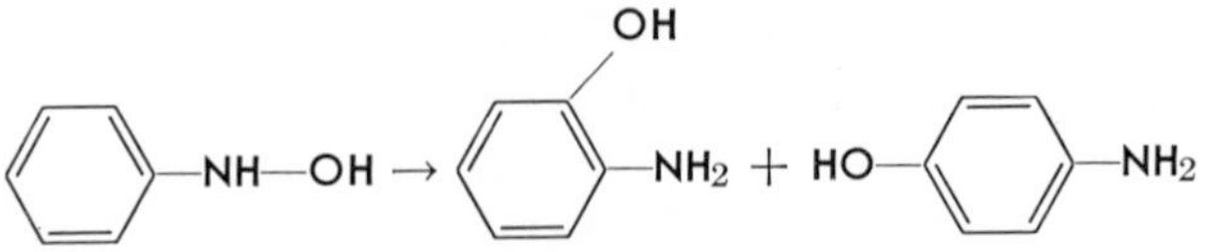

When the reaction is carried out in methanol or ethanol, methyl and ethyl ethers of *p*-aminophenol are produced in place of *p*-aminophenol.

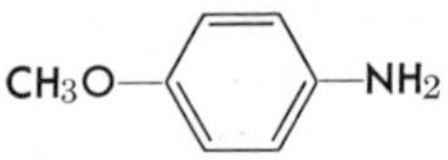

p-anisidine 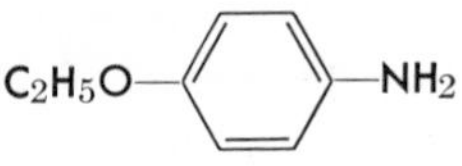   *p*-phenetidine

In the presence of chloride ion, chlorinated products are obtained.

(a) By analogy, what would the chlorinated products be?

(b) Does this reaction involve electrophilic or nucleophilic substitution? That is, do the various products suggest that attack on the ring is by electron-poor or electron-rich atoms (or ions)?

The dependence on the concentration of acid is unusual. In dilute acid the rate is proportional to the acid concentration, but as the concentration increases, the dependence on acid ceases. This has been interpreted as showing that the reaction involves the conjugate acid of phenylhydroxylamine.

(c) On which atom would you expect the additional proton to add? Remember that the electron pair of the nitrogen atom is delocalized by resonance with the ring.

When the reaction is carried out using p-tolylhydroxylamine, quinone-type products may be isolated.

(d) Noting the structure of this intermediate, and noting that the proper structure for the conjugate acid of phenylhydroxylamine provides a good leaving group and a remaining aromatic residue which is deficient in electrons, suggest a mode of cleavage of the N—O bond.

We have not determined whether entry of the new substituent is simultaneous with the departure of the leaving group. It has been noted, however, that when the compound is rearranged in the presence of chloride ion, the concentration of chloride ion does not enter into the rate expression.

(e) What does this suggest about the time order of the two steps in this case?

(f) Generalizing from these data, write a complete mechanism for the rearrangement of phenylhydroxylamine taking all the above information into account.

(g) What results would you expect if the reaction were studied in H_2O^{18}?

44-2 When aromatic esters are treated with aluminum chloride at moderately elevated temperatures, a rearrangement takes place to give a mixture of o- and p-hydroxyketones, after hydrolysis.

This reaction is called the Fries rearrangement.

The following information should suggest a mechanism for this reaction, though no mechanism is adequately defined by it. First, recall that aluminum chloride is a Lewis acid; mixtures of dimethyl ether and aluminum halide in nitrobenzene are conductors of current. This suggests that an ionic reaction has occurred, and the formation of a covalent bond between oxygen and aluminum at least formally produces a molecule which would be expected to have a large dipole moment:

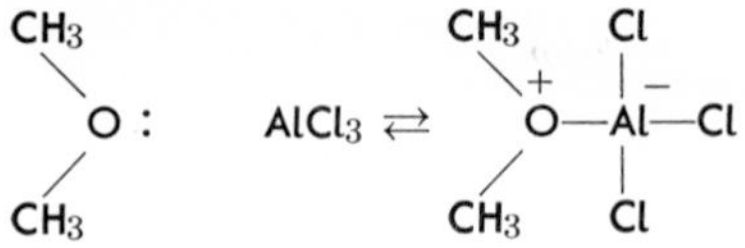

$$
\begin{array}{ccc}
CH_3 & & CH_3 \quad Cl \\
\backslash & & \overset{+}{\backslash} \quad | \quad \overset{-}{} \\
O: \quad AlCl_3 \rightleftarrows & & O-Al-Cl \\
/ & & / \quad | \\
CH_3 & & CH_3 \quad Cl
\end{array}
$$

(a) With which electronegative atoms in phenyl acetate might $AlCl_3$ coordinate?

The complex with $AlCl_3$ may undergo heterolysis to give a carbonium ion and an anion:

$$A\!-\!B \rightarrow A\!-\!\overset{+}{B}\!-\!\overset{-}{AlCl_3} \rightleftarrows A^+ + BAlCl_3^-$$

(b) The infrared spectrum of acetyl chloride has a carbonyl absorption at 5.53 microns. When a 1:1 complex of acetyl chloride and aluminum chloride is examined, this band has disappeared and a new one at 5.06 microns is present. What kind of structure does this suggest for the complex? By analogy, what kind of structure could be intermediate in the Fries reaction?

(c) The reaction does not proceed if there is a nitro, acyl, or carboxyl substituent in the aromatic ring. In other words, electron-withdrawing groups slow the reaction to an extreme degree. On this basis alone, is the attacking group which gives the rearrangement products an electrophile or a nucleophile?

(d) Would either of the ions suggested in part (b) be a suitable attacking group? That is, does either have the proper charge and the proper structure?

(e) On the basis of this reasoning by analogy, suggest a reasonable mechanism for the Fries rearrangement.

(f) A very high percentage of the *ortho* product is found, relative to *para*. Can you guess why this is so?

When the reaction is carried out on a mixture of esters, scrambling is found in the products:

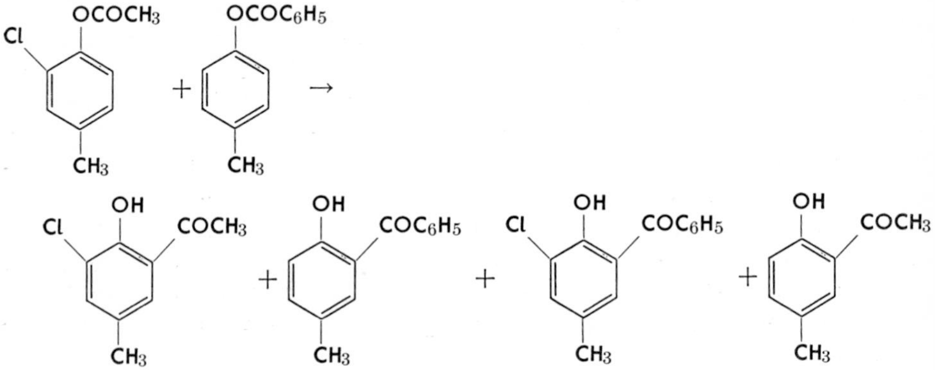

(g) Is the reaction intermolecular or intramolecular? Does this affect your answer to part (e)?

Often we postulate "reasonable" mechanisms based on analogy to known facts. These do not have the force of more carefully determined experiments, of course, but are useful guides for further study. You might find it of interest to devise experiments to substantiate your proposed mechanism. Some supporting evidence for the existence of this type of carbonium ion is given in Chapter 49.

*How is hydrazobenzene formed,
along with other products, by the reduction of benzene?
What is the mechanism of the benzidine rearrangement?*

45

AROMATIC REARRANGEMENTS
II: THE BENZEDINE REARRANGEMENT

45–1 Background

In the preceding chapter we examined a few of the many rearrangements which take place in aromatic systems. We shall continue our discussion of aromatic rearrangements by selecting for more detailed analysis a rearrangement which proceeds by an entirely different type of mechanism, the benzidine rearrangement. This is important because it is used industrially as a preparative method to produce tons of commercial intermediates and because it has probably been more carefully studied than any other aromatic rearrangement. It is characteristic of well-conducted research that as it answers the simpler questions first set as objectives, it opens new vistas of more and more detailed and complex studies. The studies on the benzidine rearrangement are no exception to this rule. The fact that some of the first obvious questions have been settled has led investigators to dig ever deeper with the result that there are now probably more unsettled questions in this field than there appeared to be twenty years ago. Thus it is a continuing object of careful study.

45–2 The Reduction of Nitrobenzene; Hydrazobenzene

The starting material for the benzidine rearrangement is hydrazobenzene. This is obtained by the reduction of nitrobenzene under controlled conditions. Before going deeper into the benzidine rearrangement, we shall digress for a moment to study briefly the reduction of nitrobenzene.

45–3 Formation of Phenylhydroxylamine

When it is conducted in acidic media with sufficiently strong reducing agents, the reduction of nitrobenzene proceeds all the way to aniline:

$$C_6H_5NO_2 \xrightarrow{\text{Sn or Fe, HCl}} C_6H_5NH_2$$

Early in the industrial study of this reaction, it was learned that reductions with other reagents under other sets of conditions gave other products. The complexities of the reduction of nitrobenzene were elucidated by Fritz Haber, using the technique of electrolytic reduction at controlled potentials (Fig. 45–1). Haber showed that the first expected product of the reduction, nitrosobenzene, is more rapidly reduced than nitrobenzene at the potentials required for the reduction of nitrobenzene. To reduce nitrosobenzene requires a smaller negative potential than that required to reduce nitrobenzene. In either case, if the potentials used are not high enough to carry the reduction to aniline, the product that can be isolated is phenylhydroxylamine:

$$C_6H_5NO_2 \xrightarrow{-0.78\ V} \searrow$$
$$C_6H_5NHOH \xrightarrow{CrO_3} C_6H_5NO$$
$$C_6H_5NO \xrightarrow{-0.49\ V} \nearrow$$

Nitrosobenzene   Phenyl-hydroxylamine

Nitrosobenzene can be obtained for study by the oxidation of phenylhydroxylamine with dichromate. We may rationalize the relative difficulty of reducing nitrobenzene and the ease of reducing nitrosobenzene by pointing out that in nitrobenzene the nitro group is stabilized by resonance which is lacking in the case of nitrosobenzene. The reader should verify this statement by drawing the resonating structures of nitrobenzene and of nitrosobenzene. The use of chemical reagents of relatively low potential (zinc and ammonium chloride, for example) produces phenylhydroxylamine from nitrobenzene.

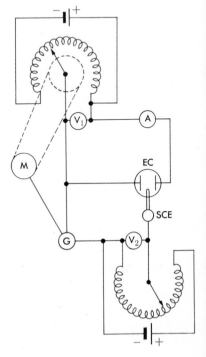

FIG. 45–1. Essentials of an apparatus for electrolytic reductions at controlled potentials; EC, electrolytic cell; SCE, standard calomel electrode; V_2, voltmeter on measuring circuit; G, galvanometer; M, controlling motor; V_1, voltmeter on power circuit; A, ammeter. Haber's apparatus was manually controlled. By using a controlling galvanometer and reversing motor, Lingane made the system automatic.

45–4   Nitrosobenzene as an Intermediate

Haber verified the intermediate formation of nitrosobenzene in an alcoholic-alkaline medium by trapping the material chemically. The trapping procedure was to allow the nitrosobenzene to react with hydroxylamine to form a diazotate which then coupled with α-naphthol:

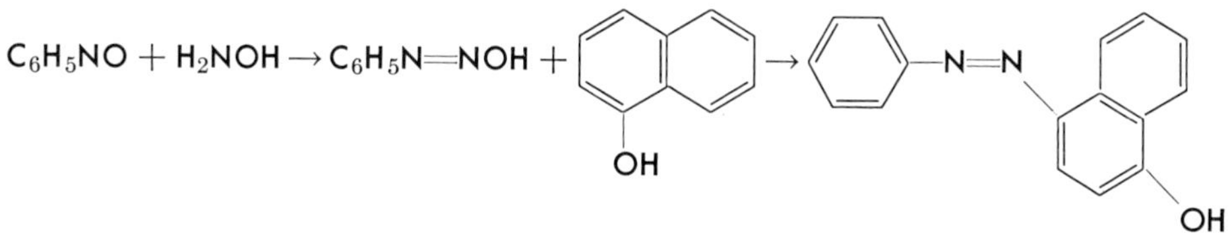

$$C_6H_5NO + H_2NOH \rightarrow C_6H_5N{=}NOH + \text{(α-naphthol)} \rightarrow \text{(azo dye)}$$

At a potential of -0.98 V in the presence of hydroxylamine and α-naphthol, the azo dye was formed during the reduction of nitrobenzene, thus establishing that nitrosobenzene was, in fact, an intermediate. A similar process was carried out in acidic solution except that α-naphthylamine was substituted for the α-naphthol. Again an azo dye was formed. The reader should write the formula for the dye formed and explain why Haber chose α-naphthol for the alkaline reduction trapping experiment and α-naphthylamine for the acidic trapping.

In spite of the fact that nitrosobenzene is more readily reduced than nitrobenzene, it may be prepared by the electrolytic reduction of nitrobenzene in a stirred cell with a nickel cathode for the reduction plus a lead anode. The lead anode is first oxidized to lead dioxide which then serves to oxidize the phenylhydroxylamine back to nitrosobenzene as it is formed.

45–5   Formation of Azoxybenzene

When phenylhydroxylamine and nitrosobenzene are allowed to interact, the product of the reaction is azoxybenzene:

$$C_6H_5{-}NHOH + C_6H_5{-}NO \rightarrow C_6H_5{-}\overset{\overset{\textstyle -O}{+|}}{N}{=}N{-}C_6H_5 + H_2O$$

Azoxybenzene

This reaction is analogous to the condensation of nitrosobenzene with hydroxylamine. For purposes of preparation, the reaction is best carried out in an alkaline medium. In this case, nitrobenzene is more readily reduced than azoxybenzene so that by limiting the potential, it is possible to prepare a good yield of azoxybenzene. Chemically the same result may be achieved by carrying on the reduction with sodium arsenite in sodium methoxide solution. In both cases, some nitrosobenzene is reduced to phenylhydroxylamine and this then condenses with new nitrosobenzene as it is formed.

45-6   Formation of Azobenzene

Phenylhydroxylamine is capable of condensing with itself to form azobenzene:

$$2C_6H_5\text{—NHOH} \rightarrow C_6H_5\text{—N}=\text{N—}C_6H_5 + 2H_2O$$
Azobenzene

By performing the reduction under slightly more drastic reducing conditions, all the nitrosobenzene is reduced to phenylhydroxylamine as the reaction proceeds, and its self-condensation yields azobenzene. Chemically, azobenzene may be prepared by the reduction of azoxybenzene by heating it with iron.

45-7   Formation of Hydrazobenzene

If the negative potential is raised still further to produce a more drastic reduction, the product formed will be hydrazobenzene:

$$C_6H_5\text{—N}=\text{N—}C_6H_5 \rightarrow C_6H_5\text{—NH—NH—}C_6H_5$$

When carrying out this reaction directly, it is necessary to perform the reduction in two stages. The nitrobenzene is first reduced to azobenzene; the reducing potential is then increased to carry the reduction to hydrazobenzene. Chemically, this reduction is performed by the use of metallic zinc and alkali. Hydrazobenzene may be reoxidized to azobenzene by the use of sodium hypobromite, and azobenzene may be oxidized to azoxybenzene by the use of hydrogen peroxide.

Drastic reduction of azoxybenzene, azobenzene, or hydrazobenzene will cleave the N—N bond with the formation of aniline. Thus careful control of the reaction conditions under which the reduction of nitrobenzene is carried out will permit the isolation of any one of a variety of products.

45-8   The Benzidine Rearrangement

In 1863, Hofmann discovered that the treatment of hydrazobenzene with acids yields benzidine:

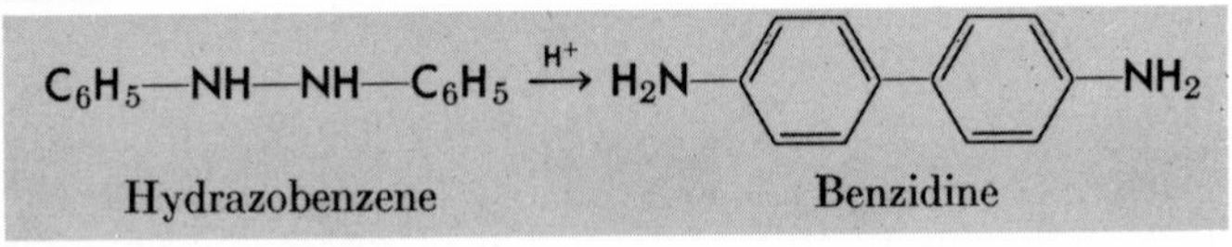

The compound had been prepared earlier by the nitration and reduction of biphenyl, thus establishing its constitution as diaminobiphenyl. Fifteen years after Hofmann's discovery, the field was complicated by more careful studies performed by Schmidt and Schultz. Schultz had just succeeded in establishing the positions of the amino groups on the biphenyl system. In examing the reaction products of the benzidine rearrangement, however, it was found that an isomer of benzidine was produced as a minor product. Structural investigations showed that this was an *ortho-para* derivative which was named diphenyline. Hence the course of the benzidine rearrangement had to be rewritten:

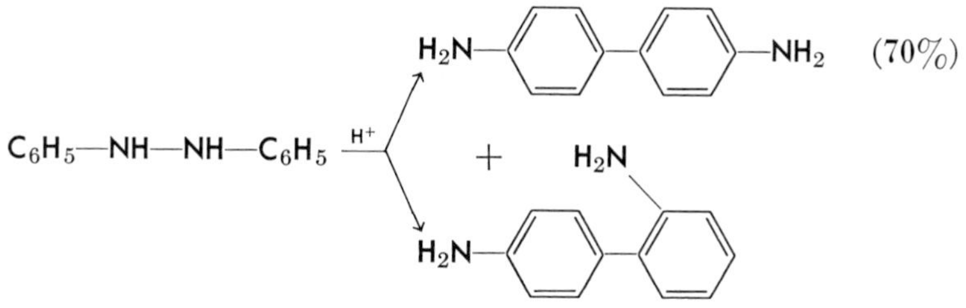

Diphenyline

45–9 Semidines and *Ortho*-Benzidines

In 1892 a thirty-year study of the benzidine rearrangement was begun by Jacobson. During this time many more complications were unearthed. For example, it was discovered that blocking one of the *para* positions of the benzene ring with an amino group gave a different type of reaction product, a so-called "*para*-semidine":

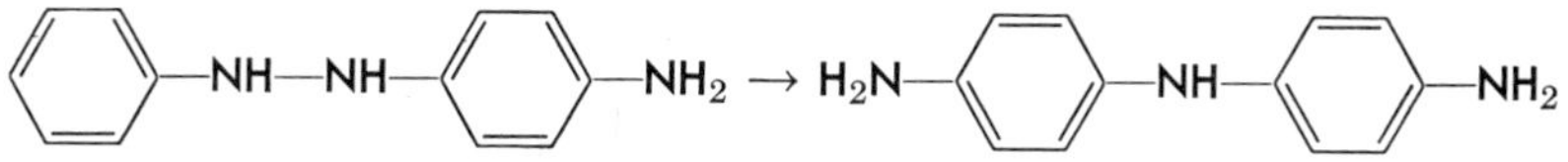

On the other hand, blocking the *para* position with a methyl or methoxy group produced an "*ortho*-semidine":

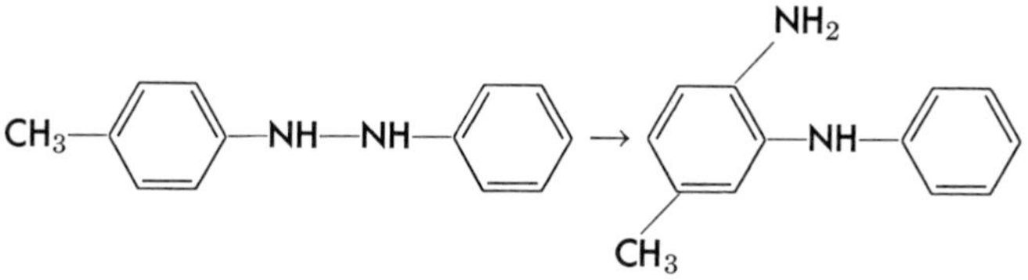

Finally, the rearrangement of 2,2'-hydrazonaphthalene yields an "*ortho*-benzidine" as might be expected:

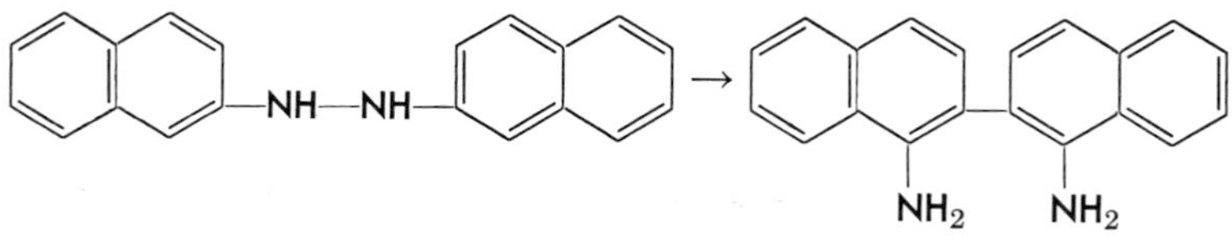

When carboxyl or sulfonic acid groups are present in the *para* positions, the rearrangement is not blocked, but the benzidine that forms has expelled the *para* groups. Various other substituents give mixtures of the products enumerated. The mechanistic problem is to construct a theory or a set of theories capable of correlating all the data unearthed by Jacobson.

45-10 Examination of a Free-Radical Mechanism for the Benzidine Rearrangement

In 1900, Gomberg announced the discovery of the triphenylmethyl radical,

$$(C_6H_5)_3C—C(C_6H_5)_3 \rightleftarrows 2(C_6H_5)_3C \cdot$$

As a result, the formulation of radical intermediates in reactions of various sorts became popular. In 1903 Tichwinsky proposed that the first step in the benzidine rearrangement should be regarded as the formation of two radicals by cleavage of the NH—NH bond in the center of the molecule. The radicals could then re-attach themselves at any point necessary to give the observed products. Some years later, Wieland succeeded in preparing radicals of the sort that would be formed by the dissociation of an N—N bond. Wieland's radicals were diphenyl-nitrogen radicals:

$$(C_6H_5)_2N—N(C_6H_5)_2 \rightleftarrows 2(C_6H_5)_2N \cdot$$

He showed that these radicals had no tendency to recombine in the *para* positions to give benzidine-type products.

Jacobson made an even more fundamental attack on the radical hypothesis for the benzidine rearrangement. He did this by studying the rearrangement of unsymmetrical hydrazobenzenes. If we represent such a starting material by the symbol AB, it is clear that dissociation into radicals would form both symmetrical and unsymmetrical reaction products:

$$A—B \rightarrow A \cdot + B \cdot \rightarrow \begin{matrix} A'B' \\ A'A' \\ B'B' \end{matrix}$$

Although it could be demonstrated that products of the expected sort were capable of separation, Jacobson was never able to find any evidence for the formation of such symmetrical rearrangement products. From this he concluded that the rearrangement not only involved no dissociation into radicals but that it involved no dissociation into free particles of any other type and was thus to be regarded as a true intramolecular reaction.

45-11 The Hypothesis of Ionic Particles

The possibility of dissociation into particles, either radicals or ions, is critical, so it has been investigated by modern techniques. One of the most sensitive methods for detecting the presence of an impurity in a mixture is through radiochemical labeling. This technique was applied to the benzidine rearrangement by Wheland and Schwartz. These investigators rearranged 2-methyl-2'-ethoxyhydrazobenzene with the methyl group labeled with radio carbon. If dissociation of any sort were to take place, this reaction would yield some *o*-tolidine:

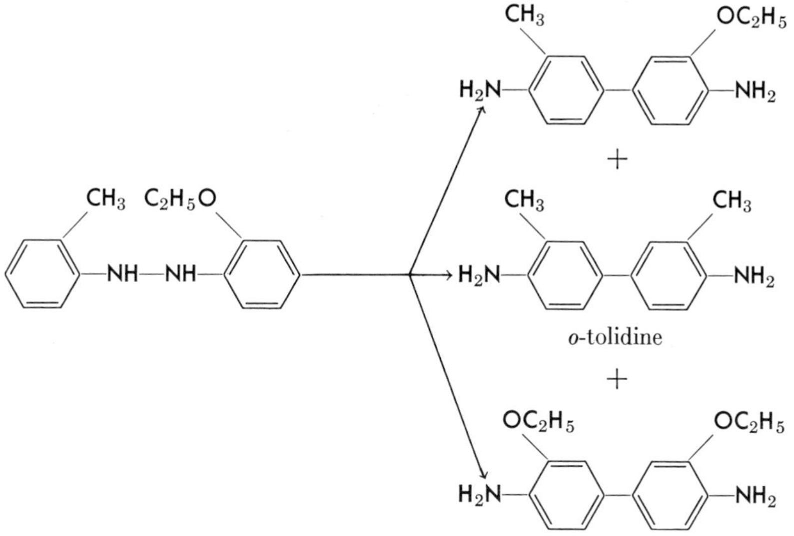

After completing the rearrangement, radiochemically inert *o*-tolidine was added to the mixture. The *ortho*-tolidine was then recovered from the reaction mixture. If any labeled *o*-tolidine was formed in the reaction, labeled carbon would be found in this product. None was found. Radiochemical labeling is a very sensitive test for the formation of even a fraction of a percent of a product which would be difficult to detect by any other method. Its absence in the recovered *o*-tolidine establishes conclusively that none is formed.

While the argument advanced on the basis of the foregoing experiments appears conclusive at first, there is one flaw in the reasoning. It may be argued that the nature of the substituents used in the unsymmetrical hydrazobenzenes will permit ionic dissociation to proceed all in one direction, producing a "lock and key" which, although dissociated, would only recombine in one manner. A theory for the benzidine rearrangement which would lead to this interpretation was advanced by Stieglitz in 1903. Essentially, the theory is as follows:

$$C_6H_5—NH—NH—C_6H_5 + H^+ \rightarrow$$

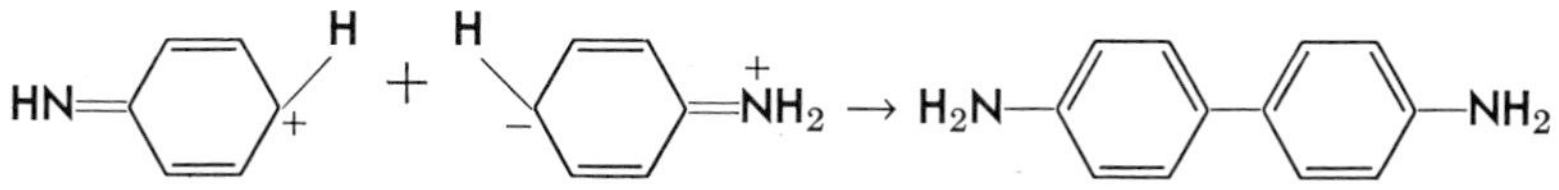

If tagging groups of sufficiently different polarities are attached to the two rings, it could be argued that the positive charge would always go to the more nucleophilic ring and the electron pair to the more electrophilic ring. Thus dissociation could take place, but only one product would be formed.

Ingold and Kidd designed an experiment to test this hypothesis. They started with an equimolar mixture of 2,2'-dimethoxy- and 2,2'-diethoxy-hydrazobenzenes. Thus the directive influences of the two groups were as nearly alike as possible, and each molecule would form one particle of the "lock" type and one of the "key" type. If such particles were to form, then cross reaction would be expected.

The mixture of alkoxy-hydrazobenzenes was rearranged and the product examined by means of the freezing-point diagram. This established that only two components were present in the product mixture and thus ruled out any cross-reaction.

From the failure of the various attempts to establish the possibility of radical or ionic particles as intermediates in the benzidine rearrangement, it may be concluded that the reaction is an intramolecular rearrangement.

45–12   Kinetics of the Benzidine Rearrangement

In recent years, kinetic studies have been made on the benzidine rearrangement. These have shown that the rate of the reaction is proportional to the concentration of hydrazobenzene and to the square of the hydrogen ion concentration. From this it is concluded that the transition state requires the attack of two protons on one molecule of hydrazobenzene. The ratio of benzidine to diphenyline has been investigated as a function of acid concentration and has been found to be independent of changes in acidity. From this it is concluded that both reactions are governed by the same kinetic equation.

45–13   The Nature of the Intermediate in the Benzidine Rearrangement

If we examine the resonance forms of hydrazobenzene, certain geometrical relationships emerge. One of these forms may be written:

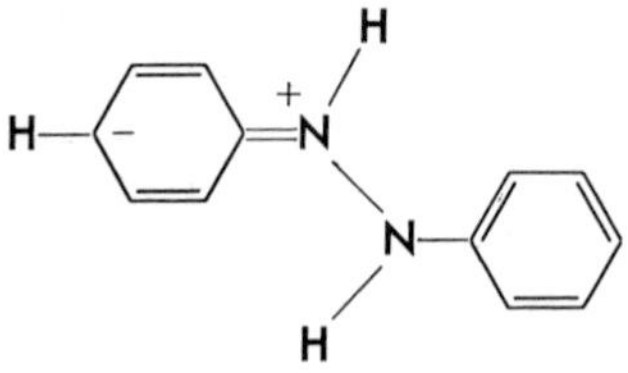

The requirement of an angle approaching 120° at the nitrogen represented with a double bond will impose the further requirement that the hydrogen and the nitrogen attached to it will be in the same plane with it. Another resonance form may be written:

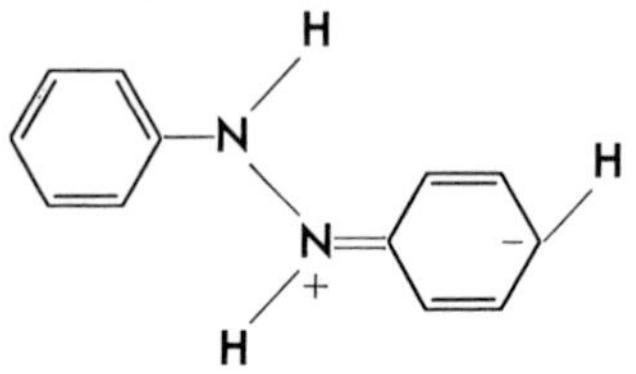

The same conditions must be met for this doubly bonded nitrogen as for the other. The consequence of resonance interaction between the nitrogens and the ring, then, would be that the rings, the attached nitrogens, and the attached hydrogens would all be in a single plane. This would effectively prevent approach of the *para* positions of the rings to each other.

The addition of a single proton to one nitrogen on the molecule would not be sufficient to destroy the geometrical relationships pictured above. The addition of two protons, however, would destroy the resonance interaction on both rings and would allow the N—N bond to rotate freely. The result of this would be that the possibility of reaction in the *para* positions would now be present.

One effect of the conversion of the two nitrogens to strong electron-attracting groups by protonation would be a shrinkage in the thickness of the pi clouds above and below the benzene rings. This would be a further factor tending to favor reaction between the rings. Both the formation of tetrahedral nitrogens and the shrinkage of the pi clouds would permit the formation of a structure that may be sketched as shown in Fig. 45–2.

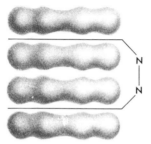

FIGURE 45–2

A rocking motion toward the *para* positions by high-energy collisions would stretch the N—N bond and make one benzene ring approach the other at an angle suitable for interaction between the pi clouds to be set up with resultant bond formation. The transition state would be one with a forming bond at the *para* position and a breaking bond at the N—N position. This can be represented conventionally as:

$$\overset{+}{H_2N} \cdots \overset{+}{NH_2}$$

The flow of electrons at the time of reaction may be represented as:

$$\overset{+}{H_2N} - \overset{+}{NH_2}$$

45-14 The Mechanistic Problem in the Semidine Rearrangement

An examination of the models of the diprotonated species of hydrazobenzene will show that very little stretching is required to bring the rings into positions suitable for the formation of diphenyline or of *ortho*-benzidine. Hence the theory is easily extended to fit these two cases. The situation with respect to the formation of semidines is quite different, however, and may contain the key to the further elucidation of the mechanism of the reaction. The precise course of the semidine rearrangement has not been investigated in as much detail as the benzidine rearrangement. To form a semidine from a reaction intermediate of the type pictured for the benzidine rearrangement, it would be necessary to imagine the two benzene rings "skating" on each other with a twisting motion to permit one ring to turn around with respect to the other. Whether or not further research will justify such a picture or will require that an entirely different approach be made to the semidine rearrangement remains to be determined.

PROBLEMS

45-1 It might be argued that the two charged aromatic rings would tend to repel each other in the benzidine rearrangement, rather than attract each other. How would you answer this objection?

45-2 The *p,p'*-dideuterio compound, I, reacts at essentially the same rate as unlabeled hydrazobenzene.

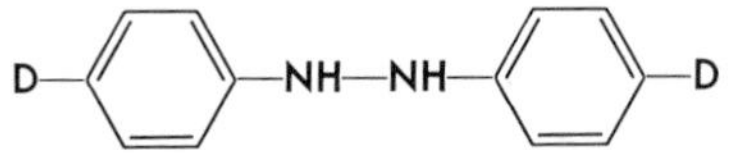

I

(a) What does this similarity of reaction rates suggest about the rate-determining step of the reaction?

(b) What possibilities still remain for the rate-determining step in the benzidine rearrangement?

45-3 Suggest a mechanism to explain the rearrangement

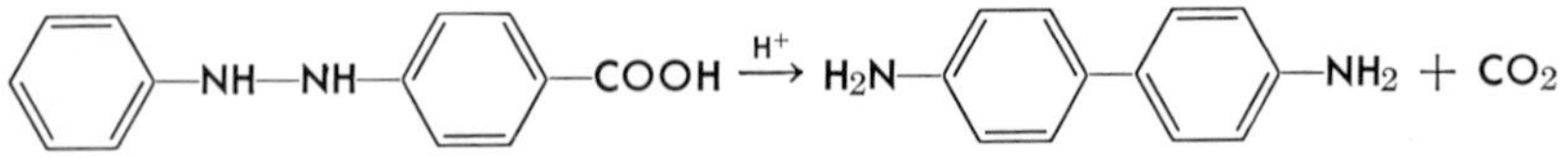

45-4 Would you expect electron-withdrawing substituents to accelerate or slow the reaction in Problem 45–2? State the experimental results that you would expect on the basis of each mechanism proposed in Problem 45–2.

45-5 Write mechanisms for the semidine rearrangement and the diphenyline rearrangement.

45–6 How would you prepare some of the unsymmetrical hydrazobenzenes used in these studies, for example:

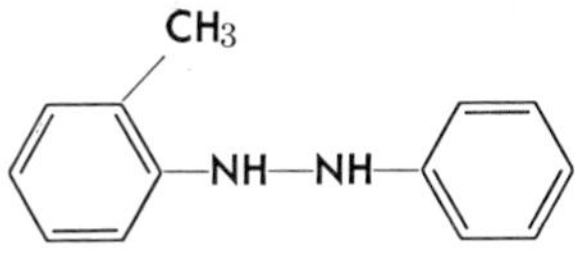

and

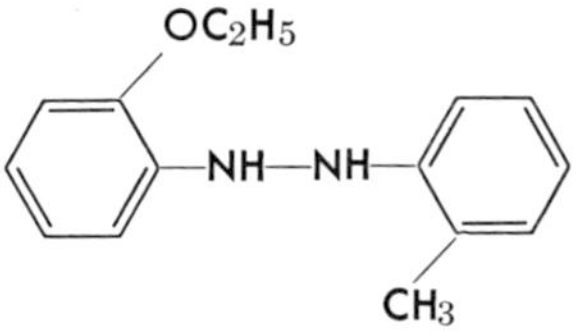

45–7 What do you expect would happen to compound II in a moderately acid solution?

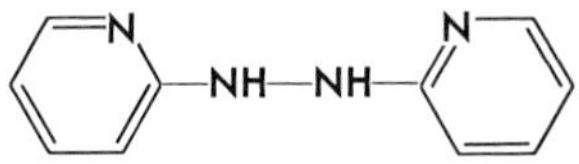

II

The basicity constants for pyridine and aniline are 1.7×10^{-9} and 3.8×10^{-10}, respectively. These molecules are so dissimilar that a rationalization of the order of basicities would be tenuous. However, you can use these constants as a base for your argument.

Part 5

SOME MECHANISMS APPLYING TO BOTH ALIPHATIC AND AROMATIC SYSTEMS

Some general processes, like reduction and oxidation, are as important in the aliphatic series as in the aromatic. Stereochemical effects and radical mechanisms, involving homolytic bond cleavages, also occur in both series. Part 5 is devoted to a consideration of processes important in both fields of chemistry.

Four processes are ordinarily used to accomplish reductions:
catalytic hydrogenation, electrolytic reduction, reduction by dissolving
metals, and reduction by electron exchange in solution.
What can be learned about the mechanisms of these processes?

46

MECHANISMS OF REDUCTION

46–1 Introduction

In the preceding chapter we saw how the alteration of conditions for the reduction of nitrobenzene could lead to the control of the reaction for selection among numerous possible products of the reaction. We may now examine reduction mechanisms in somewhat greater detail to learn what other possibilities for control may exist.

The majority of reductions performed by organic chemists are done with the aid of metals dissolving in acids or alkalis. The major portion of the remainder are catalytic hydrogenations performed on metallic surfaces. An increasing proportion of the rest is accomplished by electrolytic means at metallic cathodes. Because of the prominent part played by metals in reduction processes, a brief summary of the knowledge about the structures of metals is basic to an understanding of reductions.

46–2 The Structures of Metals

X-ray studies have established the fact that the atoms in metals are frequently arranged in the positions expected for close-packed spheres, or nearly so. The problem of the closest packing of spheres can be solved by acquiring a sufficiently large supply of marbles and studying their arrangements within a confining rack. Apparently, this simple exercise was first investigated systematically about eighty years ago by Barlow who came to the conclusion that, if spheres all with the same radius are used, two possible ways of arranging them would exist, one with cubic

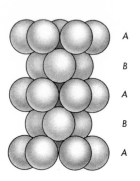

A
B
A
B
A

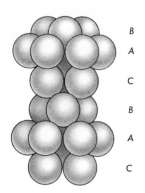

B
A
C
B
A
C

FIGURE 46–1   FIGURE 46–2

symmetry, the other with hexagonal symmetry. The differences between the two methods of arranging the spheres can be visualized by imagining the process of building the lattice a layer at a time. The first layer can be closest packed in only one way, A. This is the arrangement with each sphere in contact with six others. The second layer can be placed on the first in only one way, B. In this way each sphere is again in contact with six others in the same layer and with three in the layer below. The third closest-packed layer can, however, be placed in either of two positions. In the first, A, each sphere in the third layer is directly above one in the first layer. This gives hexagonal closest packing, Fig. 46–1. In the second arrangement, C, each sphere in the third layer is above a hole in the first layer. This gives cubic closest packing, Fig. 46–2. More than half the metals crystallize either in hexagonal closest-packing or in cubic closest-packing lattices or in both. Fifteen metals crystallize in body-centered cubes, a still different arrangement. In body-centered cubic lattices, each atom has eight nearest neighbors and six more near neighbors; in a closest-packed lattice there are twelve nearest neighbors.

A study of the bond distances in metals shows that they are usually somewhat longer than would be expected for covalent single bonds and much shorter than would be expected for nonbonded atoms. It is reasoned that the equilibrium positions assumed are the result of resonance extending in all directions between single-bonded structures with alternate bond positions. According to this concept, metals represent structures with three-dimensional resonance stabilization and with consequent freedom of the bonding electrons to move in any direction throughout the lattice. This is held to account for the electrical conductivity of metals.

46–3 Semiconductors

Because of the nature of carbon, nitrogen, and oxygen bonds, it does not seem possible to invent a purely organic structure with a true three-dimensional resonance. An approach to it may be made through pi complexes, however. These are believed to be formed through the interactions of the pi clouds of aromatic systems. For example the pi cloud of nitrobenzene is represented as polarized toward electron deficiency by the electron-attracting power of the nitro group and that of aniline toward electron excess by the electron-releasing property of the amino group. Admixture of nitrobenzene and aniline produces an orange color due to the formation of a weak complex, now called a pi complex. If such complexes are made up of molecules with somewhat greater areas, the intereactions become more pronounced. An example would be quinhydrone. The first step in building the quinhydrone lattice may be considered as the formation of a complex made up of equal numbers of quinone and hydroquinone molecules:

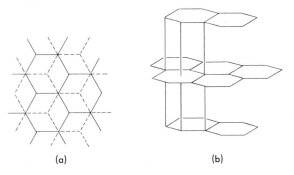

Many chains of this sort then form a high-molecular weight complex, which appears black in the solid state and deep orange in solution. This is represented as being held together by interaction between the chains. These interactions are between the pi clouds of one chain and those of an adjoining chain, forming multiple pi complex interactions. Similarly, large planar dye molecules such as the porphyrins interact between the planes, as shown by x-ray diagrams. As thicker and thicker layers of these are built up, the electrical properties of the crystals change and the materials become semiconducting. These organic semiconductors differ from metals in that they have much lower conductivities and lower positive temperature coefficients of conductivity, but their electrons have greater freedom of motion than ordinary organic substances. This is ascribed to the possibility of electrons passing from one pi cloud to the next to give a limited amount of three-dimensional mobility to the electrons. The ideal semiconductor is graphite (Fig. 46–3), which is composed of planes of hexagonal "benzene" rings fused to form a large aromatic compound with the layers of these rings interacting as described above for pi complexes. Substances such as these constitute the nearest approach among organic chemicals to the metallic structure.

(a)   (b)

FIG. 46–3. Graphite structure: (a) top view, (b) side view.

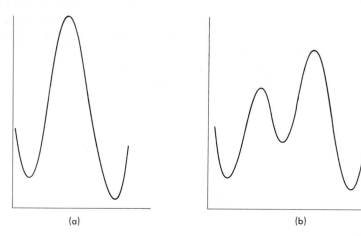

FIG. 46–4.   Energy diagrams showing lowering of activation energy through catalysis. (a) Uncatalyzed reaction; (b) catalyzed reaction.

46–4   Catalytic Hydrogenation

The heat evolved when ethylene is hydrogenated is approximately 33 kcal/mole. This means that the reaction tends strongly toward hydrogenation. In spite of this, a mixture of ethylene and hydrogen shows no tendency to react in the absence of a catalyst. Cobalt, iron, nickel, platinum, and palladium will serve as catalysts for the hydrogenation reaction. It can be shown that all these metals are capable of promoting the exchange between hydrogen and deuterium. In a mass spectrometer the three species H_2, HD, and D_2 can be distinguished. After passing a mixture of H_2 and D_2 over a catalytically active metal, HD is found to have formed on contact with the metal. This means that among other attributes, the metal has the power to break H—H and D—D bonds and combine the fragments to form H—D bonds. We thus arrive at a picture of a single-step process, addition of hydrogen to ethylene, being broken into more than one step, one of which is the initial cleavage of the hydrogen molecule into fragments by the metal surface. This fragmentation alters the reaction mechanism and may increase the rate by more than one means. In many cases that have been investigated, the height of the energy barrier has been found to be lowered in the catalyzed process as compared to the uncatalyzed process. The effect is shown in Fig. 46–4. It is also possible to increase the rate through an increase in the proportion of fruitful collisions due, presumably, to more favorable orientation at the catalyst surface. This effect will be recognized by a favorable change in the entropy of activation. This is calculated from the temperature-independent portion of the reaction rate constant.

46–5   Reactions Between Metals and Hydrogen

Palladium differs from most of the other catalytically active metals in the nature of its reaction with hydrogen. The fragments formed from hydrogen in palladium have freedom to move throughout the entire body of the metal. Thus a palladium plug sealed into a vacuum chamber can be heated in a hydrogen atmosphere, and it will be found that hydrogen diffuses into the chamber. For other catalytically active metals, the freedom of the hydrogen to roam the metal is apparently confined to the surface of the metal. Hydrogen introduced at one point on the surface of a metal can be withdrawn from another point on the surface. This has led some chemists to refer to hydrogen absorbed on a catalytically active metal as a "two-dimensional gas." We may imagine the hydrogen atoms as marbles of different radii interposed among the "holes" of the crystal surface of the metal with some bonding to each of the neighboring metallic atoms on the surface. Freedom to move on collision could be postulated as involving a rolling motion over a "valley" between two metal atoms into the next hole, a process that would leave the "bonding" to two of the neighbors intact. A hydrogen atom so held on the surface of a metal is not properly regarded as "atomic" hydrogen, nor is it to be regarded as a metal hydride of the type Me—H with a single covalent bond to a single metal atom. Rather, its bonding type more closely resembles the bonding of the metal atoms themselves. The ability of hydrogen to assume a type of bonding similar to true "metallic" bonding is illustrated by the ease with which hydrogen enters into the palladium lattice, passes through it, and emerges on the other side. In this property it resembles some of the alloys, which can be shown to permit the slow migration of metals right through their structures, a process requiring years, whereas only seconds are required for the passage of hydrogen. In spite of the time differential, the two processes may be thought of as similar.

Studies on the action of hydrogen on a nickel surface made by Germer by electron diffraction show that the introduction of hydrogen to the nickel surface causes a fundamental rearrangement of the positions of the nickel atoms. Thus the hydrogen may be regarded as forming a surface-layer "alloy" with the nickel, resembling to a limited degree the three-dimensional alloy formed with palladium. On the other hand, no such rearrangement appears to take place with platinum. Infrared studies on the platinum-hydrogen surface indicate the presence of essentially covalent Pt—H bonds, resembling the bonds of platinum to other coordinating species. It is obvious from these studies that a single theory of the mechanism of hydrogen interaction with metals is not adequate to explain all cases.

46–6 Stereospecificity

The hydrogenation of double bonds over a nickel catalyst has been found to be stereospecific. As an example, we may cite the hydrogenation of dimethylmaleic acid and that of dimethylfumaric acid:

This means that both hydrogen atoms which ultimately combine with the two carbons undergoing reaction must approach from the same side of the molecule. It does not mean that both must approach simultaneously. It is possible to interpret the stereochemical result in the sense that one hydrogen attacks one carbon and later the second hydrogen attacks the second carbon. The stereochemistry only requires that once the first hydrogen has attacked, no inversion can take place at the second atom. This result can be rationalized by assuming that the cleavage of the pi bond of the ethylenic linkage takes place on the surface of the metal with one carbon going to each of two adjacent "holes" on the surface. Neighboring "holes" would be occupied by hydrogens which could roll over the valleys one at a time to detach the carbons by successive reactions. The mechanism is presented schematically in Fig. 46–5.

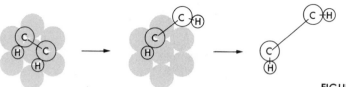

FIGURE 46–5

Studies currently being made using the electron microscope reveal the actual spacings between atoms on the various facets of metal crystals; correlations are being obtained between the amount of a metal surface having facets favorable to positioning the bonds of the material being acted on and the degree of catalytic activity.

46–7 Metal-Oxide Catalysts

It should be noted that not all catalytic hydrogenations are performed with metallic catalysts. In particular, organic chemists have found nickel and copper chromites, $NiCr_2O_4$ and $CuCr_2O_4$, to be highly useful in the hydrogenation of polar molecules such as esters and amides. It is reasoned that this activity is due to the alternating polarities of the atoms at the surfaces of the chromite catalysts which permit attachment of molecules with polar bonds, like the carbonyl bonds of the esters and amides.

46–8 Electrolytic Reductions

It is surprising that, although dissolving metals form the major reducing media used by organic chemists, not nearly so much study has been devoted to them as to electrolytic reductions, which are much less frequently used. The explanation probably lies in the fact that the factors governing electrolytic reductions can be much more carefully regulated and measured and have, especially in recent times, appealed to physical chemists as subjects for precise studies. On the other hand, it is gratifying that much of the material obtained from a study of electrolytic reductions can be applied to reductions with dissolving metals to elucidate the mechanisms of their actions.

When an electric current is passed through an aqueous solution of an acid, hydrogen is discharged at the cathode and oxygen at the anode at a potential of 1.2 V, provided that smooth platinum electrodes are employed. If lead is substituted for platinum at the cathode, a substantially higher potential will be required to bring about gas evolution. The difference in potential is called the *overpotential* or *overvoltage* at the lead electrode. Overpotentials of some metals in normal sulfuric acid are given in Table 46–1.

Table 46–1

OVERPOTENTIALS OF SELECTED
METALS, VOLTS

Cadmium	0.48
Tin	0.53
Lead	0.64
Zinc	0.70
Mercury	0.78

Experimentation has shown that most electrolytic reductions take place in the overpotential region. By using a metal with limited overpotential, it is possible to limit the power of the reduction so that intermediate reduction products can be obtained. The same result can also be accomplished by the use of a high overpotential electrode but with limited potential applied to the system. This is the method used by Haber in his studies on the reduction of nitrobenzene.

46–9   The Electrical Double Layer and Overpotential

Physical chemical explorations in the vicinity of operating electrodes have shown the existence of an "electrical double layer," a region that behaves in many respects like a condenser. When a potential is applied to a cathode, the first process to occur is a charging process, like the charging of a condenser, which continues until the electrical double layer has been completed. Eyring has formulated this process as follows:

$$M \left\{ + H_2O \rightarrow \bar{M} \left\{ \begin{array}{l} -H \\ -OH \end{array} \right. \rightarrow M \left\{ \begin{array}{l} -H \\ -OH^- \end{array} \right. \right.$$

In this diagram, $M\{$ represents the metal surface, and the negative charge indicates that the cathode serves as a source of electrons. The charging reaction is represented by the transfer of the electron to the OH, forming an adsorbed hydroxyl ion. This will attract H_3O^+ from the solution and thus form the double layer. By examining the results in the literature on the measurement of overpotentials in a variety of solvents, Eyring also concluded that in aqueous solutions only the water and its associated fragments could be involved in the process of building an overpotential, once the double layer had been completed. This process was represented as follows:

$$S\left\{ \begin{matrix} H \\ | \\ O \\ \diagdown \\ H \end{matrix} \quad + \quad \begin{matrix} H \\ | \\ \overline{O}- \\ | \\ H- \end{matrix} \right\} M \rightarrow S\left\{ \begin{matrix} H \\ | \\ \underset{-}{O} \end{matrix} \quad H \quad \underset{+}{\overset{H}{\overset{|}{O}-}} \quad \begin{matrix} \\ H- \end{matrix} \right\} \overline{M} \rightarrow S\left\{ \begin{matrix} H \\ | \\ \underset{-}{O} \end{matrix} \quad + \quad \begin{matrix} H_2O \\ \\ H- \end{matrix} \right\} M$$

| Initial state | Activated state | Final state |

In this representation, $S\{$ represents the solvent phase. In the initial state, collision between the bound H- and HO-fragments on the metal surface could produce water. In the final state, HO-fragments have been removed, leaving only H-fragments on the metal surface. When these fragments leave with their electron pairs, obtained from the cathode, they are equivalent to hydride ions, which can produce reductions. At sufficiently high potentials, their concentration will be great enough to cause a high probability of collisions with each other, thus forming hydrogen gas, while leaving the excess electrons on the electrode.

The electrolytic reduction of benzophenone, for example could then be represented as follows:

$$(C_6H_5)_2C{=}O + H{-}\bigg\} M \rightarrow (C_6H_5)_2\overset{\overset{H}{|}}{C}{-}O^- + \bigg\} M^+$$

The temporary electron deficiency caused at the metal surface by the departure of the hydrogen with its electron pair will be instantaneously corrected by an electron supplied by the current source, and the negative charge of the benzhydrylate ion will be neutralized by the solvent:

$$(C_6H_5)_2\overset{\overset{H}{|}}{C}{-}O^- + H_2O \rightarrow (C_6H_5)_2\overset{\overset{H}{|}}{C}{-}OH + OH^-$$

46–10   The Hydride Ion Mechanism

In many cases, it is sufficient to assume that the cathode, with its overpotential, is simply acting as a donor of H^- in reductions. Parallel to this assumption is Ingold's assumption from other evidence that the rate-determining reaction in reductions with dissolving metals is also the step of addition of H^-. Thus the reduction of acetone could be formulated:

$$CH_3\overset{\overset{O}{\|}}{C}{-}CH_3 + H^- \rightarrow CH_3{-}\underset{\underset{H}{|}}{\overset{\overset{O^-}{|}}{C}}{-}CH_3 \xrightarrow{H_2O} CH_3{-}\underset{\underset{H}{|}}{\overset{\overset{OH}{|}}{C}}{-}CH_3 + OH^-$$

We shall review some of this evidence presently.

46–11   Catalytic Hydrogenation at an Electrode

In some instances it is not sufficient to assume that electrolytic reductions or reductions with dissolving metals are simply the result of the donation of H^-. Two examples are immediately apparent from the literature. The first is the case in which the cathode is a catalytically active metal, such as platinum covered with platinum black, and a catalytic hydrogenation is performed with it. Compounds of low polarity such as olefins, are frequently difficult to reduce electrolytically, but sometimes they may be hydrogenated electrolytically, even without overpotential, if the metal is catalytically active.

46–12   Bimolecular Reductions

The second example of an obvious departure from the reduction result expected on the basis of the donation of H^- is the pinacol reduction. When acetone is reduced with dissolving metals, either of two products may be obtained. For the production of isopropyl alcohol, the best reducing agent appears to be aluminum amalgam containing a little zinc as an impurity. Most reagents give a mixture of isopropyl alcohol and pinacol. Magnesium containing magnesium iodide gives an excellent yield of pinacol. The reactions are:

Pinacol

The process by which pinacol is formed is frequently called a *bimolecular reduction* and occurs among many types of compounds. Examination will show that simple addition of a hydride ion could not produce pinacol. The process requires only a single electron per molecule of acetone instead of two electrons per molecule, as in the case of the formation of isopropyl alcohol.

It is of interest that the reducing agents which form pinacols in the best yields are those with the highest positions in the electromotive series of the elements. Thus sodium and magnesium are both extremely powerful reducing agents and both give good yields of pinacol. A parallel observation is made in electrolytic reductions. A special study has been made of pinacol reductions of substituted acetophenones by Allen. Contrary to some predictions, it was found that the two-electron reduction to the alcohol takes place at lower overpotentials, while the one-electron reduction to the pinacol takes place only at quite high overpotentials. The fact that two molecules must condense to form the pinacol makes it highly probable that the reaction takes place on the surface of the electrode. The situation may be rationalized by assuming that the great increase in cathode polarity induced by the high overpotential is sufficient to bring about a *chemisorption* reaction at the surface of the electrode, that is, an adsorption with the formation of a chemical bond. Two chemisorbed acetone molecules may then collide and leave with a single electron each in the form of the doubly charged pinacol anion. This would react with the solvent to form pinacol. In the diagram we shall represent a metal atom at the electrode with its electron as $\cdot \}$ M and a negatively charged electrode as $:\}$ M.

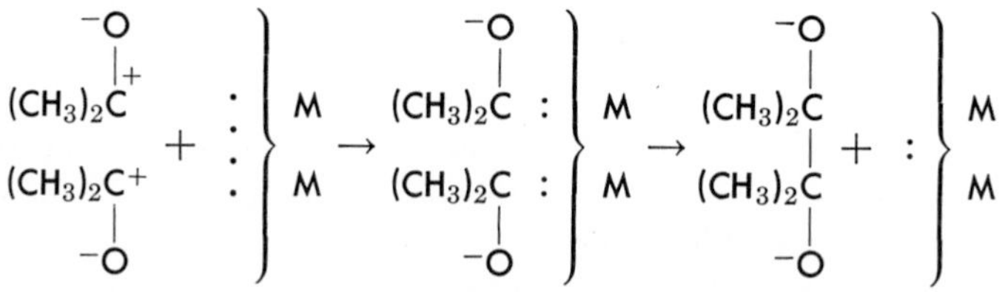

$$
\begin{array}{c}
^-\text{O} \\
|_+ \\
(CH_3)_2C \\
+ \\
(CH_3)_2C^+ \\
| \\
^-\text{O}
\end{array}
\left.\begin{array}{c} \\ \\ \\ \\ \\ \end{array}\right\}
\begin{array}{cc} \cdot & : \\ \cdot & : \end{array}
\begin{array}{c} M \\ M \end{array}
\rightarrow
\begin{array}{c}
^-\text{O} \\
| \\
(CH_3)_2C \quad : \\
(CH_3)_2C \quad : \\
| \\
^-\text{O}
\end{array}
\left.\begin{array}{c} \\ \\ \\ \\ \\ \end{array}\right\}
\begin{array}{c} M \\ M \end{array}
\rightarrow
\begin{array}{c}
^-\text{O} \\
| \\
(CH_3)_2C \\
| + \\
(CH_3)_2C \\
| \\
^-\text{O}
\end{array}
\begin{array}{c} : \end{array}
\left.\begin{array}{c} \\ \\ \\ \\ \\ \end{array}\right\}
\begin{array}{c} M \\ M \end{array}
$$

In this and some other reactions, the evidence favors the hypothesis that actual interaction with the electrode takes place. Interaction with the electrode can hardly be doubted in the reduction of acetone at a lead electrode. When care is taken to exclude air, one product of the reaction is tetraisopropyl lead, $[(CH_3)_2CH]_4Pb$.

46–13 Substituent Effects

The theory that electrolytic reductions of the ordinary type in aqueous media can be represented as additions of H^- is supported by the recent work of Manzhelei who charted the potentials at which a series of substituted nitrobenzenes were reduced in acidic media. According to this theory, electron-withdrawing groups should facilitate attack by H^- and vice versa. Experimentally, it was found that Cl, CHO, NH_2, (NH_3^+) and NO_2 all facilitate reduction, as would be predicted, and CH_3 retards it. In basic media the NH_2 group also retards reduction.

46–14 Reductions by Dissolving Metals

In 1929, Burton and Ingold presented a theory of reduction accomplished by dissolving metals which was essentially the same as that presented above for electrolytic reductions. They assumed that in most such reductions the reaction could be represented as the addition of H^- and that the polar effects which would control this would outweigh considerations based on the stability of the substances formed. This would be an example of *kinetic* control as opposed to *thermodynamic* control of the outcome of a reaction. They based their theory on a number of observations which had been made over the years with respect to the course of reductions.

Among the earliest systematic investigations of the outcome of reduction reactions were those of Baeyer in 1889 on the reduction of terephthalic acid with sodium amalgam. In this reaction the product isolated is demonstrably unstable with respect to two of its isomers which can be produced from it by treatment with alkali:

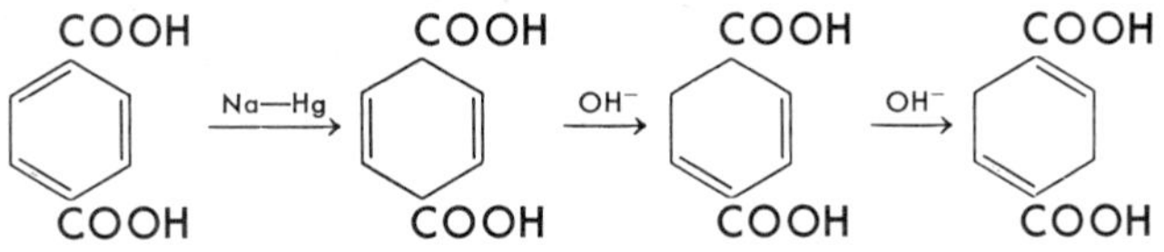

The 1,4-addition product formed initially has presumably added H^- at the most highly polar carbons next to the carboxyl groups. The positions of greatest stability, however, are those in which the double bonds in the ring are in conjugation with the carbonyl of the carboxyl group. Hence, on treatment with alkali, stepwise rearrangement can be brought about to the isomer in which both ring double bonds are in conjugation with the carboxyl groups.

Exactly similar results are obtained in straight-chain compounds:

$$HOOC—CH{=}CH—CH{=}CH—COOH \xrightarrow{Na—Hg}$$

$$HOOC—CH_2—CH{=}CH—CH_2—COOH \xrightarrow{OH^-} HOOC—CH{=}CH—CH_2—CH_2—COOH$$

$$C_6H_5—CH{=}CH—CH{=}CH—COOH \xrightarrow{Na—Hg}$$

$$C_6H_5—CH_2—CH{=}CH—CH_2—COOH \xrightarrow{OH^-} C_6H_5—CH_2—CH_2—CH{=}CH—COOH$$

These and similar instances of directive influences by polar groups make the H^- addition theory of reduction attractive. It should be remembered, however, that pinacol reductions are also performed with metals so that the same arguments which apply to the participation of the metal in electrolytic reductions to pinacols also apply to metallic reductions to pinacols. In addition, it seems highly probable that the considerations which relate to the selectivity of electrodes with respect to overpotentials and the control of reductions by control of potential are applicable to dissolving metals. The organic chemist's selection of these metals to perform specific tasks is probably based in part on the maximum potential which can be developed at a given metal surface and the maximum overpotential which can be developed at that surface. These considerations have not yet been adequately investigated.

46–15   Reduction by Electron Exchange

The organic chemist sometimes uses ionic reducing agents for his reactions. In these cases, the outcome of the reaction may be governed by the relative possibilities of one-electron steps and two-electron steps. The situation can be illustrated most clearly by an example from inorganic chemistry.

The reduction of ceric ion is a one-electron process:

$$Ce^{+4} + e \rightleftarrows Ce^{+3}$$

The reduction of thallic ion is a two-electron process:

$$Tl^{+3} + 2e \rightleftarrows Tl^{+1}$$

In spite of the fact that ceric ion is quite a powerful oxidizing agent and thallous ion is a powerful reducing agent, only a slow reaction takes place on mixing:

$$2Ce^{+4} + Tl^{+1} \rightarrow \text{Slow reaction}$$

This outcome is explained by the fact that the Tl^{+2} ion is a high-energy material difficult to form under ordinary temperatures, and cerium lacks a valence state which would permit a two-electron change. It has also been shown that the incidence of termolecular collisons is too small to account for the observed rate in the absence of a catalyst.

Manganese can exist in three oxidation states, +2, +3, and +4. If a small amount of a manganese salt is added to the mixture of ceric and thallous ions the reaction proceeds readily. The explanation advanced is summarized in the following equations:

$$Ce^{+4} + Mn^{+2} \rightleftarrows Ce^{+3} + Mn^{+3}$$
$$Ce^{+4} + Mn^{+3} \rightleftarrows Ce^{+3} + Mn^{+4}$$
$$Mn^{+4} + Tl^{+1} \rightarrow Mn^{+2} + Tl^{+3}$$

This principle probably accounts for the use of iron, manganese, and other additives in securing successful reductions both by the ionic mechanisms and by electrolytic and metallic reducing agents. In the latter case, however, care must be taken with the addition of impurities since these sometimes contaminate the reducing surfaces in such a manner as to reduce the available overpotentials and thus weaken the reducing power of the reagent.

PROBLEMS

46–1   The addition of one mole of sodium to one mole of benzophenone in a nonhydroxylic solvent produces a blue solution of sodium benzophenone ketyl. Magnetic-susceptibility studies indicated that this material is a free radical in equilibrium with its dimer.

(a) What dimer would you expect to be formed under these conditions? Remember that it would be a disodium salt.

(b) Write the equilibrium between the monomer and the dimer. Note that the monomer is a radical ion. Which atom bears the negative charge? Why is the radical stabilized?

You should note that resonance forms for radicals are counted by a slightly different process than for ions. In ions we write different forms distinguished by two-electron shifts.

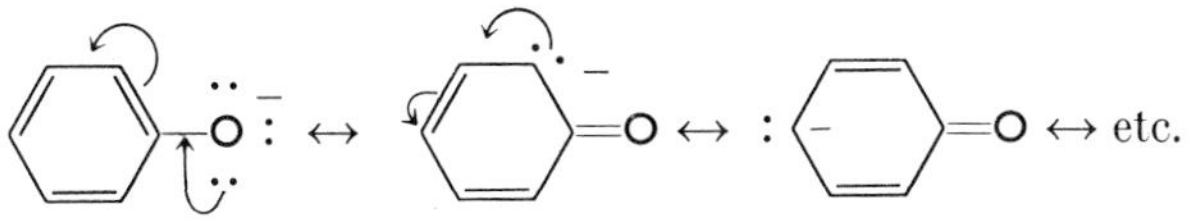

For radicals it is necessary to count forms by pairs of one-electron shifts:

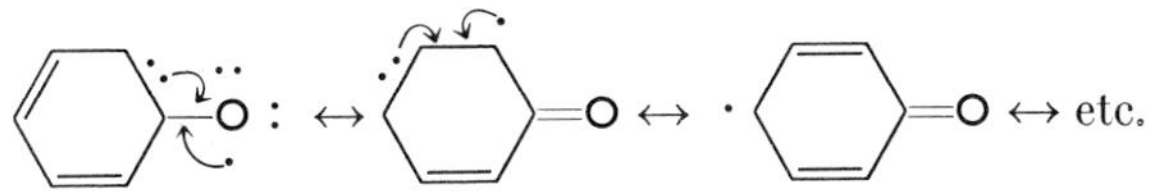

This method also incorporates a rationale for the effectiveness of electron-donating vs. electron-withdrawing substituents in stabilizing radicals.

(c) What then is more important in stabilizing a radical, withdrawal of charge, donation of charge, or the number of atoms over which the free electron may be spread?

(d) On the basis of resonance effects, where would the relative monomer-dimer equilibria lie in ketyls formed from the following ketones?

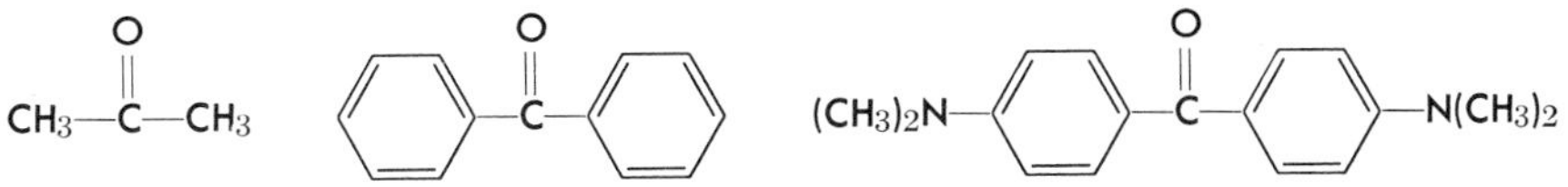

Michler's ketone

46-2 Would you expect the catalytic hydrogenation of butyne-2 by one mole of H_2 to yield *cis*- or *trans*-butene-2?

46-3 Write mechanisms to rationalize the following reductions. Discuss the role of the metals:

(a)

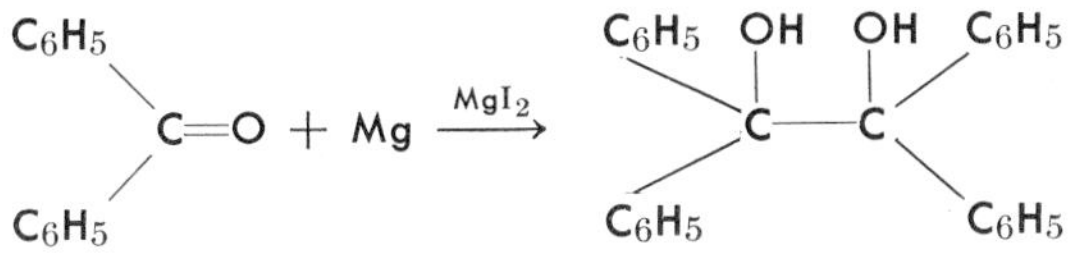

(After workup)

(b)

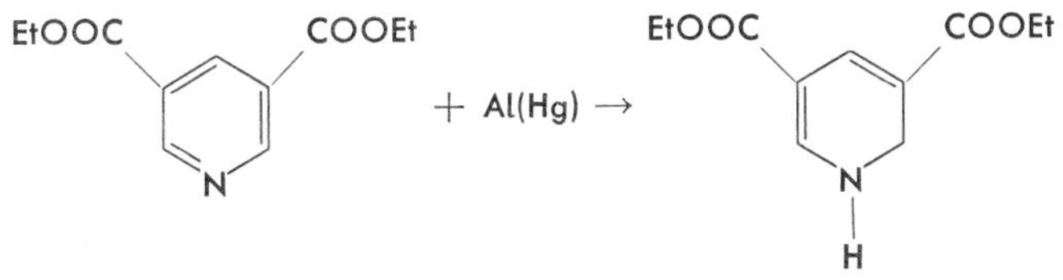

Is there possibility of kinetic control here? If so, draw a plausible first product of the reduction and include it in your reaction.

46-4 Acetophenone may be reduced by the Clemmensen method (Problem 12–4) to ethylbenzene. Under these conditions the corresponding alcohol (phenylmethylcarbinol) is not affected. Strong acid and a low concentration of the ketone are essential to obtain a good yield of the hydrocarbon. These are the main facts known. The requirement for a useful mechanism is that no step in it violate a known experimental fact.

(a) Make a list of data which must be included.

(b) Note those intermediates which must be excluded, for example, ions which might be formed from the carbinol.

(c) Write a mechanism accounting for the known facts. More than one might be possible, of course, with so little data on which to work.

46–5 The metal in the Clemmensen reduction must be amalgamated to effect reaction. This process also accelerates pinacol-type reductions. Suggest reasons for this observation.

*What experimental methods were used to establish the mechanisms
of the action of oxidizing agents in their attack on organic compounds?
What agents other than metallic oxides may be used in organic oxidations?*

47

MECHANISMS OF OXIDATION

47–1 Background

In Book 1, many examples were given of the use of oxidizing agents in the investigation of the structures of organic compounds. In spite of the fact that some of these reactions have been used since the beginning of organic chemistry, it is only within the last decade or so that a sound knowledge of the mechanisms involved has been obtained. Many reagents will attack one group of organic compounds by one mechanism and another group by another, so that it is possible to study mechanisms of oxidation from the point of view of the organic grouping being attacked, as well as from the point of view of the reagent performing the reaction. In our study, we shall classify reactions according to the reagents used for the oxidations.

47–2 Chromic Acid and Isopropanol

The oxidation of isopropanol to acetone by means of chromic acid has been studied carefully by Westheimer and his associates. An alternative approach has also been presented by Roček. Earlier measurements by organic chemists had established the nature of the equilibria between various species of Cr^{+6} present at different acidities. Thus studies on the rate of the oxidation reaction as a function of acidity served to identify the species primarily responsible for the oxidation. Under conditions in which the concentration of the neutral chromate ion, $CrO_4^=$, is high, the oxidation is slow. This eliminates this species from consideration as the oxidizing agent. At high concentrations of CrO_3, neutral chromate reacts to form $Cr_2O_7^=$. Under these conditions as well, oxidation is slow. Thus the dichromate ion is not the oxidizing agent. However, by proper adjustment of concentrations and acidities, the dichromate ion will react with water to form the acid chromate ion:

$$Cr_2O_7^= + H_2O \rightleftarrows 2HCrO_4^-$$

The acid chromate ion was found, by this study of concentrations and acidities, to be an effective oxidizing agent.

Curiously, the use of acetic acid as a solvent increases the oxidizing power of the chromate. Because of solubilities, the most favorable concentration is at 86.5% acetic acid. In this solution, the oxidation proceeds 2500 times as fast as in water. It is assumed that this may be due to the formation of the acetyl-chromate ion:

$$CH_3COOH + HCrO_4^- \rightleftarrows CH_3\overset{\overset{\textstyle O}{\|}}{C}OCrO_3^- + H_2O$$

In the course of the kinetic studies used to establish the nature of the chromium-containing species responsible for the oxidation, the reaction order was also established. It was shown that the reaction is proportional to the first power of the concentration of the acid chromate ion and also to that of the isopropanol. These facts must be taken into account in the formulation of the final mechanistic equation.

The next step was to examine other factors which might influence the rate of the reaction. It will be recalled (Chapter 40) that C—D bonds break less rapidly than C—H bonds. By isotopic substitution it is thus possible to learn whether or not the breaking of a C—H bond participates in the rate-determining step. Accordingly, 2-deuterio-isopropanol was prepared, and its rate of oxidation was studied. It was found that this substance oxidizes only one-sixth as fast as isopropanol itself:

$$(CH_3)_2\, CHOH \rightarrow (CH_3)_2C{=}O, \quad k = 1$$
$$(CH_3)_2\, CDOH \rightarrow (CH_3)_2C{=}O, \quad k = \tfrac{1}{6}$$

The interpretation is that the secondary hydrogen is removed in the rate-determining step. Thus a base must participate in this step.

Additionally, it is found that the reaction rate is proportional to the square of the hydrogen ion concentration. All of these factors may be combined by the rate expression:

$$\text{Rate} = k(\text{Alcohol})\,(HCrO_4^-)(H^+)^2(\text{Base})$$

47–3   Intermediate-Ester Hypothesis

To accommodate all these species in the collisions occurring up to and including the rate-determining step without assuming simultaneous collisions by a large number of species, which is highly improbable statistically, it is normal to assume that combination takes place between the species two at a time, thus building up a complex containing a number of species by a series of bimolecular collisions. A logical choice for an intermediate which could accommodate so many species would be the chromate ester of isopropanol:

$$(CH_3)_2CHO—CrO_2—OH$$

47-4 Verification of the Presence of a Chromium Ester

An attempt was made to isolate a chromium ester by extraction with benzene. Instead of the monoester, however, a diester was obtained by this procedure. The ester was so unstable that it was incapable of isolation in the pure state. However, its dilute solutions in benzene were sufficiently stable for chemical studies that could be completed within approximately half an hour. By these means it was shown that the ester is a neutral substance, incapable of being extracted from the benzene by bicarbonate. Its absorption spectrum agrees with that of the equivalent amount of chromate ion. It can be shown to have two equivalents of alcohol to one of chromium. Finally, treatment with a weak base, pyridine, is sufficient to destroy it immediately with the formation of acetone. Thus the properties of the diester with respect to its reaction with a base are identical with those postulated for the hypothetical reaction intermediate, the monoester. Since the monoester must be an intermediate in the formation of the diester, the case for the inclusion of the monoester in the reaction scheme seems complete.

47-5 Rate Dependence of the Reaction

To account for the dependence of the rate on the isopropanol concentration and the acid chromate concentration, the first reaction could be written:

$$(CH_3)_2CHOH + HCrO_4^- \rightleftarrows (CH_3)_2CHO—CrO_2—O^- + H_2O$$

To account for the participation of two hydrogen ions, the next two steps could be written:

$$(CH_3)_2CHO—CrO_2—O^- + H_3O^+ \rightleftarrows (CH_3)_2CHO—CrO_2—OH + H_2O$$
$$(CH_3)_2CHO—CrO_2—OH + H_3O^+ \rightleftarrows (CH_3)_2CHO—CrO_2—OH_2^+ + H_2O$$

The sequence of the three steps might be altered. However, the presence of a positive charge on the final product of the reaction series makes it particularly sensitive to attack by base. If the attack were to take place at the positive center, the only result would be reversion to the compound existing previously. This is the reaction shown by the reverse arrow in the last equation above. Attack on the hydrogen attached to the secondary carbon, on the other hand, would produce an essentially irreversible reaction:

$$
\begin{array}{cc}
H_2O{:}\,H & H_3O^+ \\
\quad\mid & \\
(CH_3)_2C—O—CrO_2—OH_2^+ & \rightarrow (CH_3)_2C{=}O + H_2CrO_3
\end{array}
$$

47–6 Oxidation States of the Chromium

The oxidation state of the chromium obtained from this sequence is $+4$. However, the overall stoichiometric reaction for the oxidation is:

$$3CH_3CHOHCH_3 + 2HCrO_4^- + 8H^+ \rightarrow 3CH_3COCH_3 + 2Cr^{+3} + 8H_2O$$

To convert the chromium from the tetravalent state to the trivalent by means of a series of bimolecular collisions, a scheme such as the following has been suggested:

$$2Cr^{+4} \rightarrow Cr^{+5} + Cr^{+3}$$
$$Cr^{+4} + Cr^{+5} \rightarrow Cr^{+6} + Cr^{+3}$$

Adding these equations we obtain the overall result:

$$3Cr^{+4} \rightarrow Cr^{+6} + 2Cr^{+3}$$

Evidence for the existence of all these intermediate oxidation states of chromium has been obtained by studies of the inorganic chemistry of chromium.

47–7 Mildly Basic Oxidation with Chromic Anhydride

Emphasizing the importance of the discovery that the rate-controlling step of the reaction is performed by a base, is the discovery that secondary alcohols which are too insoluble to be oxidized under the usual reaction conditions may be dissolved in pyridine and treated with anhydrous CrO_3 to effect their oxidation. The reagent is sometimes referred to as "Sarett's reagent." It is prepared by dissolving CrO_3 slowly in cold pyridine. Reversing the order of the addition usually results in a fire. The reagent is especially valuable because of its selectivity. It will oxidize secondary alcohols to ketones while leaving double bonds and thioethers untouched.

47–8 Chromic Acid and Tertiary Alcohols

As we have seen (Section 12–5) it is possible to oxidize tertiary alcohols with chromic acid-sulfuric acid mixtures. Kinetic studies on these oxidations have shown that their velocity is independent of the concentration of chromic acid. The rate-determining step in these reactions is the dehydration of the alcohol to the olefin:

$$(CH_3)_3COH \xrightarrow{H^+} (CH_3)_2C{=}CH_2 + H_2O$$

The remainder of the reaction is then the cleavage of the carbon-carbon double bond by the oxidizing agent, a reaction whose mechanism we shall study in the next section.

47–9   Chromic Acid and Olefins

Under comparable conditions, the oxidation of an olefin by chromic acid is slower than that of a primary or secondary alcohol. As a consequence, glycols which may be formed as intermediates cannot be isolated. This makes the investigation of the course of the oxidation more difficult than for the alcohols, and less definitive detail is available on the course of the reaction. Studies of the equilibria involved have led to the formulation of the active oxidizing agents as the species $HCrO_3^+$. This is a highly electrophilic reagent which can attack the π-electrons of the double bond. An example is the oxidation of tetramethylethylene.

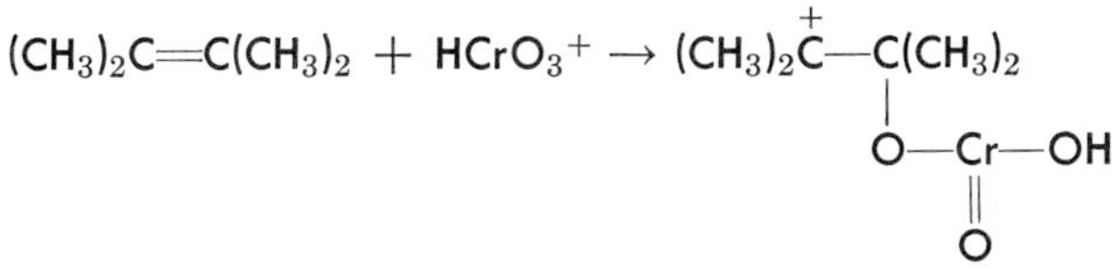

$$(CH_3)_2C{=}C(CH_3)_2 + HCrO_3^+ \rightarrow (CH_3)_2\overset{+}{C}{-}C(CH_3)_2$$
$$\underset{\underset{O}{\overset{\|}{|}}}{O{-}Cr{-}OH}$$

Under nonhydrolytic conditions, it is possible to isolate an epoxide from the reaction. This could be formed by the cleavage of the $O{-}Cr$ bond:

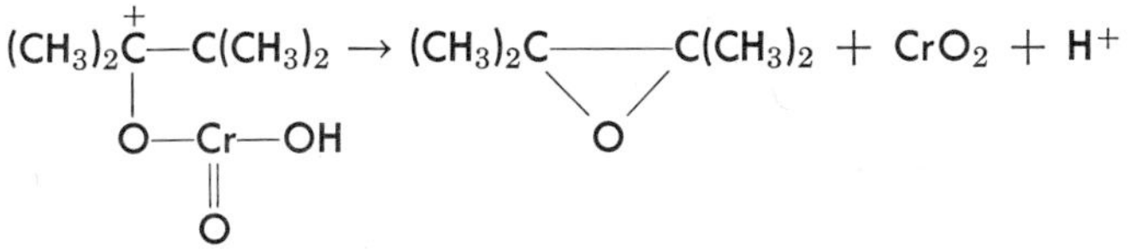

$$(CH_3)_2\overset{+}{C}{-}C(CH_3)_2 \rightarrow (CH_3)_2C{-\!-\!-}C(CH_3)_2 + CrO_2 + H^+$$

Under hydrolyzing conditions, on the other hand, either the epoxide or its assumed precursor would be expected to react with water to give a glycol:

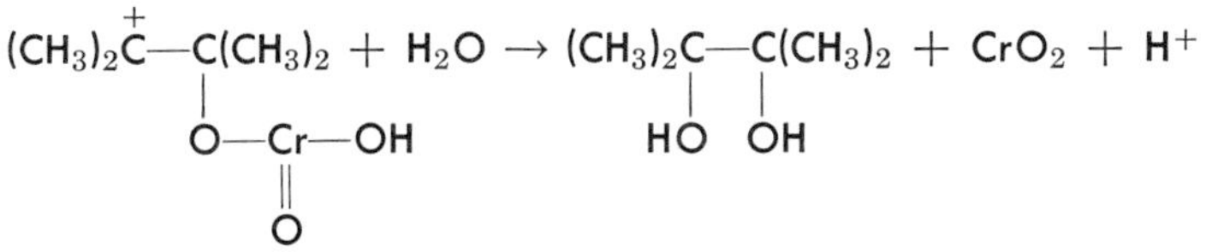

$$(CH_3)_2\overset{+}{C}{-}C(CH_3)_2 + H_2O \rightarrow (CH_3)_2C{-}C(CH_3)_2 + CrO_2 + H^+$$
$$O{-}Cr{-}OH \qquad\qquad HO \quad OH$$

The glycol thus formed, pinacol, readily oxidizes to acetone under the conditions of the reaction and has not been isolated as an intermediate.

47–10   Chromic Acid and Glycols

While still other byproducts have been isolated from the reaction mixture, the key reaction from the point of view of double-bond cleavage is the formation of acetone from the hypothetical intermediate, pinacol. The oxidation of pinacol to acetone has been studied directly. Pinacol is a ditertiary alcohol but it is readily oxidized under conditions of low acidity such that tertiary butanol, for example, remains completely unattacked. Evidently the proximity of two alcoholic groups favors the reaction.

47-11 The Cyclic-Ester Hypothesis

A reasonable hypothesis would be that, in the case of the 1,2-diols, a cyclic ester with chromium is capable of formation. Roček and Westheimer tested this hypothesis by studying the relative rates of oxidation of a pair of *cis* and *trans* isomers whose conformations were locked by being held in a cyclopentane ring:

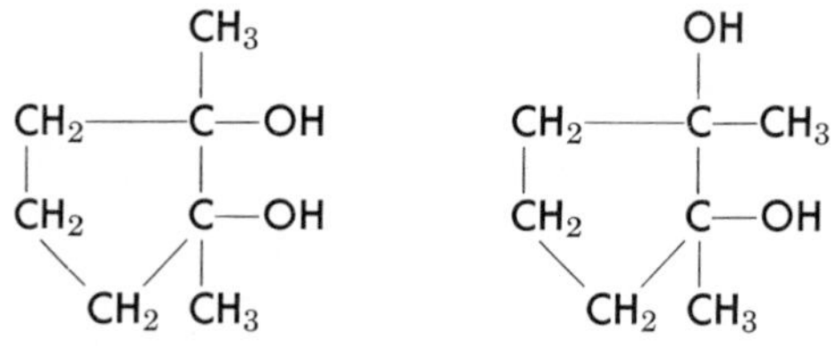

$$k = 1700 \qquad\qquad k = 1$$

The *cis* isomer oxidizes 1700 times as fast as the *trans* isomer, thus verifying the prediction based on the cyclic-ester concept. This isomer also reacts 47 times as fast as does pinacol, indicating that the flexibility of the pinacol molecule makes cyclic-ester formation somewhat slower than in the case of the sterically favored compound. At the same time, however, pinacol reacts 36 times as fast as the *trans* compound, whose conformation is sterically unfavorable to cyclic-ester formation. Thus it is reasonable to formulate the bond cleavage in the sterically favored glycol as follows:

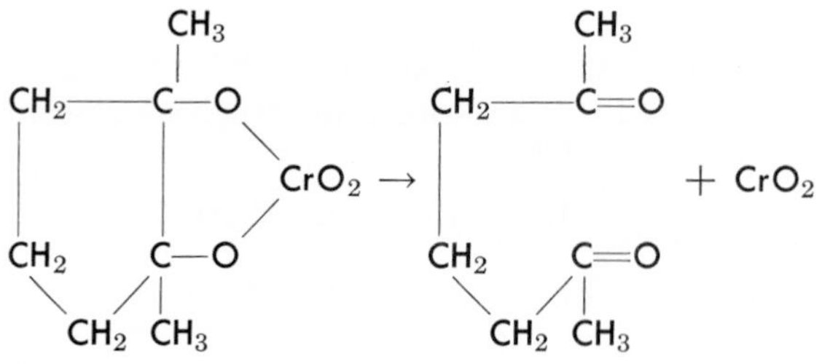

47-12 The Pinacol-Pinacolone Rearrangement

Under acidic conditions, pinacol is known to rearrange to form pinacolone and it has been found possible to isolate pinacolone from the reaction products of the chromic acid oxidation of tetramethylethylene. Independent study of the pinacol-pinacolone rearrangement has made the presence of a carbonium ion intermediate in the reaction highly probable:

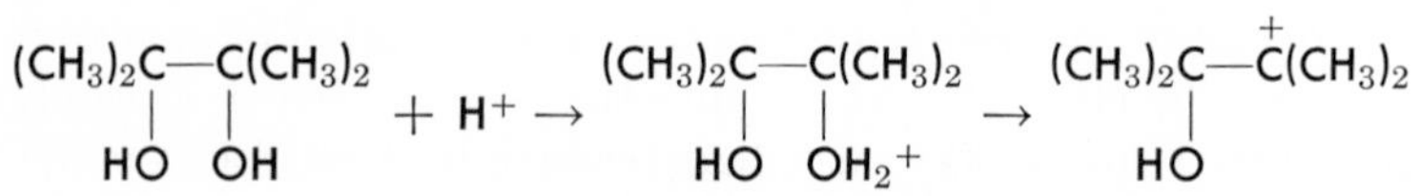

This ion then is assumed to undergo rearrangement by migration of a methyl group with its bonding electron pair:

$$\underset{\substack{H_3C \quad OH \\}}{\overset{\substack{CH_3 \qquad CH_3 \\}}{C\text{—}C}} \xrightarrow{\ \ } \underset{\substack{HO^+ \qquad CH_3 \\}}{\overset{\substack{CH_3 \quad CH_3 \\}}{C\text{=}C}} \rightarrow CH_3\text{—}\underset{\substack{O \\}}{\overset{\substack{CH_3 \\}}{C}}\text{—}\underset{\substack{CH_3 \\}}{\overset{\substack{\\}}{C}}\text{—}CH_3 + H^+$$

Pinacolone

Thus the isolation of pinacolone is taken as confirmatory evidence for the presence of a carbonium ion, although this could well be the carbonium ion with chromium attached, since this would also be capable of giving the same rearrangement. It also serves to establish the presence of pinacol as an intermediate in the reaction, thus confirming the mechanism advanced for the oxidation.

47–13   Oxidation with Permanganate

Another reagent which was found useful in structural studies is acidic permanganate. The mechanism of its action on benzaldehyde has been studied by Wiberg and Stewart. They found that the rate is proportional to the hydrogen ion concentration and to that of the benzaldehyde, as well as to the concentration of the permanganate ion. This observation makes the occurrence a series of two-body collisions before the rate-determining step a probability. It was also observed that C_6H_5CDO oxidizes at one-seventh of the rate of C_6H_5CHO. This indicates that the cleavage of the CH bond takes place in the rate-determining step. Finally, it was observed that permanganate labeled with ^{18}O leaves the labeled oxygen on the benzoic acid formed from the reaction, indicating bond formation between the permanganate ion and the benzaldehyde during the course of the reaction. All these observations can be rationalized by the assumption of the formation of a permanganate ester with protonated benzaldehyde:

$$C_6H_5CH\text{=}O + H^+ \rightleftarrows C_6H_5\overset{+}{C}HOH + {}^*OMnO_3^- \rightleftarrows C_6H_5\text{—}\underset{\substack{*O\text{—}MnO_3 \\}}{\overset{\substack{OH \\ |}}{\underset{|}{C}}}\text{—}H \xrightarrow{\text{slow}}$$

$$C_6H_5\text{—}\underset{\substack{*O \\}}{\overset{\substack{OH \\ |}}{C}} + H^+ \qquad MnO_3^-$$

This mechanism would also lead to the deduction that electron-withdrawing groups on the phenyl ring would make protonation more difficult and thus diminish the concentration of the protonated intermediate, slowing the reaction. This deduction has been verified experimentally. For example, each of the three nitrobenzaldehydes oxidizes less rapidly than benzaldehyde.

47-14 Periodic Acid; the Cyclic Ester

In the oxidation of sugars, it was found that periodic acid is a useful and selective reagent. The mechanism of its reaction was studied by Bunton and his co-workers, who found that periodic acid reacts with 1,2-glycols to form cyclic esters sufficiently stable to be detected spectroscopically. These decompose slowly to form the observed reaction products. In their papers, no specific formulation is adopted for periodic acid. However, we shall adopt the formula on the right. In this formula we shall assume octahedral coordination of the oxygens on the iodine. The rate of the reaction is proportional to the concentration of the singly charged species, represented as $H_4IO_6^-$. The reaction is formulated as:

$$\begin{array}{ccc}
\begin{array}{c} CH_2\text{—}OH \\ | \\ CH_2\text{—}OH \end{array}
& + H_4IO_6^- \rightleftarrows &
\begin{array}{c} CH_2\text{—}O \quad OH \quad O^- \\ \diagdown \quad | \diagup \\ I^+ \\ \diagup \quad | \diagdown \\ CH_2\text{—}O \quad OH \quad O^- \end{array}
& + 2H_2O
\end{array}$$

$$\begin{array}{ccc}
\begin{array}{c} CH_2\text{—}O \quad OH \quad O^- \\ \diagdown \quad | \diagup \\ I^+ \\ \diagup \quad | \diagdown \\ CH_2\text{—}O \quad OH \quad O^- \end{array}
& \rightarrow &
\begin{array}{c} CH_2\text{=}O \\ \\ CH_2\text{=}O \end{array}
& + IO_3^- + H_2O
\end{array}$$

Ability to make direct observations on the cyclic periodate esters permits a more complete analysis of the factors governing the rate of the overall reaction than is possible in most cases. Thus it is possible to measure the positions of the equilibria of the reactions of ester formation, showing the order of stability of the esters. The following stability series was observed by this method:

$$\begin{array}{c} CH_2\text{——}CH_2 \\ | \qquad | \\ O \qquad O \\ \diagdown \; \overset{+}{} \diagup \\ HO\text{—}I\text{—}OH \\ \diagup \quad \diagdown \\ {}^-O \qquad O^- \end{array}
>
\begin{array}{c} CH_3CH\text{——}CH_2 \\ | \qquad | \\ O \qquad O \\ \diagdown \; \overset{+}{} \diagup \\ HO\text{—}I\text{—}OH \\ \diagup \quad \diagdown \\ {}^-O \quad \cdot \quad O^- \end{array}
>
\begin{array}{c} CH_3 \\ | \\ CH_3C\text{——}CH_2 \\ | \qquad | \\ O \qquad O \\ \diagdown \; \overset{+}{} \diagup \\ HO\text{—}I\text{—}OH \\ \diagup \quad \diagdown \\ {}^-O \qquad O^- \end{array}
>$$

$$>
\begin{array}{c} CH_3CH\text{——}HCCH_3 \\ | \qquad | \\ O \qquad O \\ \diagdown \; \overset{+}{} \diagup \\ HO\text{—}I\text{—}OH \\ \diagup \quad \diagdown \\ {}^-O \qquad O^- \end{array}
>
\begin{array}{c} H \qquad CH_3 \\ | \qquad | \\ CH_3C\text{——}CH \\ | \qquad | \\ O \qquad O \\ \diagdown \; \overset{+}{} \diagup \\ HO\text{—}I\text{—}OH \\ \diagup \quad \diagdown \\ {}^-O \qquad O^- \end{array}
>
\begin{array}{c} CH_3 \qquad H \\ | \qquad | \\ CH_3C\text{——}CCH_3 \\ | \qquad | \\ O \qquad O \\ \diagdown \; \overset{+}{} \diagup \\ HO\text{—}I\text{—}OH \\ \diagup \quad \diagdown \\ {}^-O \qquad O^- \end{array}$$

In most five-membered ring systems, it has been observed that increasing alkyl substitution increases ring stability. This is due to the fact that the alkyl groups are larger than hydrogens and that the exterior angles on a pentagon tend to be larger than the normal $109\frac{1}{2}°$ tetrahedral angle. Thus alkyl groups help to fill the external "void" created by the internal bond strain. Additionally, periodic acid is an electrophilic reagent whose affinity for the glycol oxygens should be increased by electron-donating groups. Some other factor must be at work in this series to reverse these two tendencies toward greater stability with increasing methyl substitution.

47–15   Steric Explanation of the Stability Series

Bunton and his collaborators ascribe the inverted stability order to a steric effect but do not support this hypothesis with specific models. They do show, however, that the rate-determining step in the formation of the cyclic ester is the formation of the intermediate monoester:

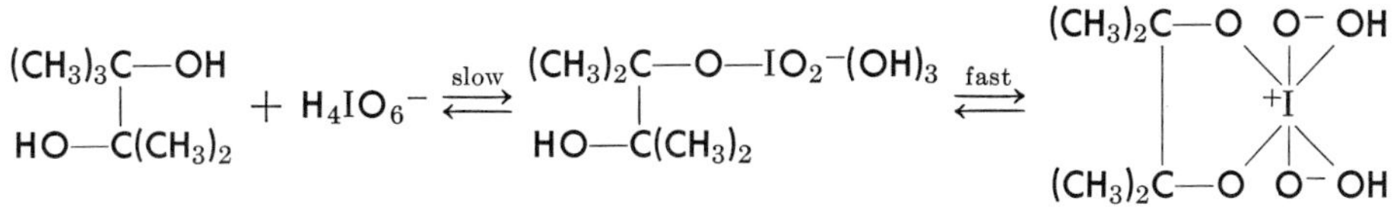

$$(CH_3)_3C-OH$$
$$|$$
$$HO-C(CH_3)_2$$ $$+ H_4IO_6{}^-$$ $$\xrightarrow{\text{slow}}$$ $$(CH_3)_2C-O-IO_2{}^-(OH)_3$$
$$|$$
$$HO-C(CH_3)_2$$ $$\xrightarrow{\text{fast}}$$

$$(CH_3)_2C-O \quad O^-\,OH$$
$$| \qquad \qquad \diagdown \diagup$$
$$\qquad \qquad \qquad {}^+I$$
$$| \qquad \qquad \diagup \diagdown$$
$$(CH_3)_2C-O \quad O^-\,OH$$

The relative rates of these reactions can be deduced from the fact that the concentration of the cyclic ester can easily be determined spectroscopically, while the concentration of the monoester is so low that it cannot be detected. It is therefore converted to the more stable cyclic diester essentially as fast as it is formed.

Using the formulation given for the cyclic diester and setting the six groups around iodine at octahedral angles, a model shows that there is no steric overlap between the hydroxyl groups on the iodine and the hydrogens on the carbon of ethylene glycol (Fig. 47–1a). As methyl groups are added, however, steric interference appears between the hydrogens on the methyl groups and the oxygens on the iodine as shown in Fig. 47–1(b). This is appreciably greater on the optically active butanediols than on the *meso* form and is greater when two methyl groups are present on one carbon than when they are distributed between them. Thus the

(a)   (b)   FIGURE 47–1

steric hypothesis is a reasonable one. According to this hypothesis, steric interferences would increase the rates of the back reaction in the ester formation as
methyl groups are added and thus would diminish the stabilities of the more highly
substituted esters, as observed.

47–16 Steric Explanation of the Rate Series

The same steric influence which controls the stabilities of the cyclic esters with
respect to their reversion to the monoesters also controls their stabilities with
respect to their irreversible decomposition reactions. These reactions are the rate-
determining steps in the oxidations. In these oxidations it is observed that the
more highly substituted diols oxidize faster than the less highly substituted ones.
Thus a steric explanation of both the ester stability and the oxidation rate series
is reasonable. In the irreversible reaction the steric crowding would tend to promote
fragmentation of the ring:

$$(CH_3)_2C-O\diagdown OH \diagup O^- \qquad (CH_3)_2C=O$$
$$I^+ \qquad \longrightarrow \qquad + IO_3^- + H_2O$$
$$(CH_3)_2C-O \quad OH \quad O^- \qquad (CH_3)_2C=O$$

The outcome in the case of the *cis*- and *trans*-cyclohexane-1,2-diols is also consistent with the cyclic-ester hypothesis. Because the *trans* diol is di-equatorial,
ring formation should be favored in this case over that of the *cis* diol, which is
axial-equatorial. This deduction is verified by the spectroscopic observation of the
relative ring stabilities. On the other hand, the oxidation of the *cis* diol takes place
more rapidly than that of the *trans* diol. Since the irreversible ring cleavage is the
rate-determining step in the oxidation, this observation is in line with expectations.

47–17 Lead Tetraacetate

Still another oxidizing agent for 1,2-diols which has enjoyed wide popularity with
organic chemists is lead tetraacetate. Criegee and his collaborators introduced
this reagent. They formulate the reaction mechanism as follows:

$$(CH_3)_2C-OH$$
$$\qquad\qquad + Pb(O-COCH_3)_4 \xrightarrow{\text{slow}}$$
$$(CH_3)_2C-OH$$

$$(CH_3)_2C-OPb(O-COCH_3)_3$$
$$\qquad\qquad\qquad\qquad + HO-COCH_3$$
$$(CH_3)_2C-OH$$

$$(CH_3)_2C-O-Pb(O-COCH_3)_3$$
$$\qquad\qquad\qquad \rightleftarrows$$
$$(CH_3)_2C-OH$$

$$(CH_3)_2C-O\diagdown \qquad O-COCH_3$$
$$Pb \qquad \xrightarrow{\text{fast}}$$
$$(CH_3)_2C-O \diagup \qquad O-COCH_3$$

$$(CH_3)_2C=O$$
$$\qquad\qquad + Pb(O-COCH_3)_2$$
$$(CH_3)_2C=O$$

In this case monoesters of the type of the first intermediate have been isolated, but the cyclic esters have not been. On the other hand, it has been found that *cis* glycols of both five-membered and six-membered *alicyclic* rings, that is, ring compounds of the aliphatic series, oxidize much faster than the isomeric *trans* glycols. Since this is consistent with the hypothesis of cyclic-ester formation, it is taken as indirect verification of the hypothesis in this case.

47–18 Catalytic Oxidations

As for hydrogenations, catalytic oxidations have been performed, usually with platinum or palladium catalysts. However, these reactions are very much more difficult to control than are the hydrogenations, particularly when it is necessary to conduct them under pressure. A history of explosions accompanying such attempts has usually discouraged investigators from intensive study of this field. On the other hand, catalytic oxidations are frequently performed with air bubbling through a solution at atmospheric pressure. In these cases, a transition metal soap is frequently employed as the catalyst. Oxidations by atmospheric oxygen usually involve radical chain mechanisms and will be discussed briefly in Chapter 50. In addition, oxidizing agents containing metallic elements can oxidize organic compounds by pathways that involve one-electron changes, which initiate radical reactions.

47–19 Electrolytic Oxidations

Electrolytic oxidations have also been performed on occasion by organic chemists. These have not been studied nearly as carefully as electrolytic reductions. It has been argued that electrolytic oxidations are strictly comparable to oxidations with hydrogen peroxide, but cases are known which do not fit this category. In particular, it is possible to perform anodic halogenations when an organic material is dissolved in strong hydrochloric or hydrobromic acid. The field for exploration of these oxidation reactions at controlled potentials is only beginning to be exploited and holds promise for future research.

PROBLEMS

47–1 Not all oxidations with lead tetraacetate involve cyclic mechanisms. A useful application of this reagent is the preparation of certain kinds of aldehydes from the corresponding alcohols.

Write a reasonable mechanism for this transformation, assuming that lead diacetate, the expected inorganic product, is formed.

47-2   The *t*-butyl group, because of its bulk, maintains an equatorial position when it is attached to a cyclohexane ring. Thus the four *t*-butylcyclohexanols illustrated below have the indicated conformations.

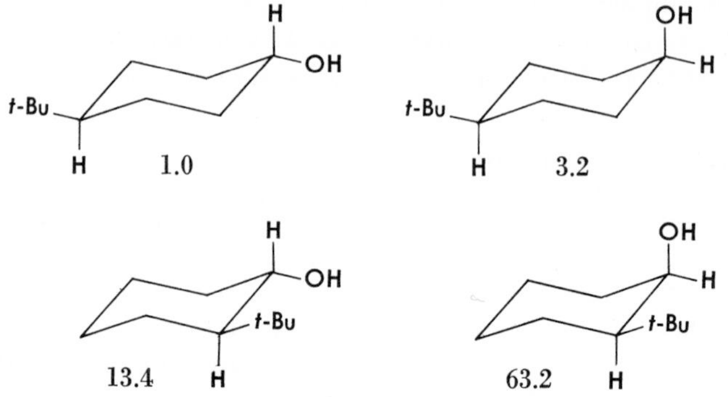

The number below each figure indicates the relative rate of its oxidation to the corresponding ketone with chromate. What rationale can you use to explain this observation?

47-3   (a) When H_5IO_6 containing O^{18} is used to oxidize pinacol, there is no appreciable O^{18} found in the acetone. Show how this distinguishes between two mechanisms for the formation of the cyclic periodate ester, one in which periodate acts as an electrophile and another in which it acts as nucleophile.

(b)   Periodate is also known to oxidize 1,2-diketones to two moles of carboxylic acid:

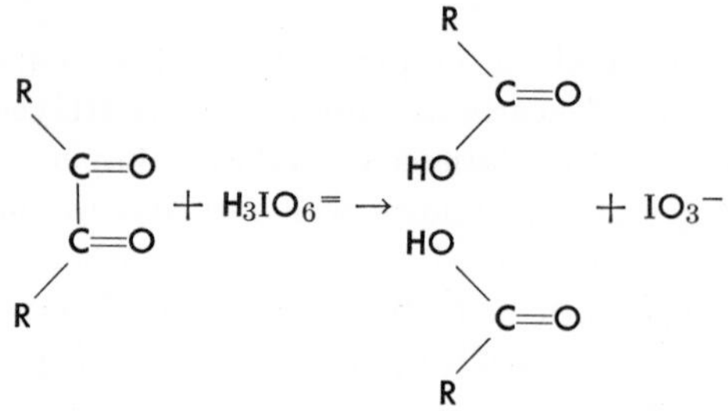

Diacetyl, $CH_3COCOCH_3$, was equilibrated with H_2O^{18} in the presence of base.

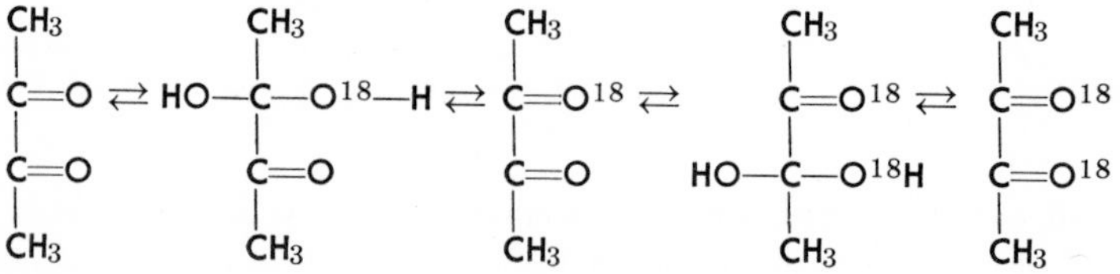

The isotopically labeled diacetyl was then treated with unlabeled $H_3IO_6^=$ in the same solution. Under these conditions it was determined experimentally that $H_3IO_6^=$ exchanges oxygen considerably more slowly than does diacetyl, and that part of the diacetyl is hydrated. To examine alternative mechanistic possibilities, suppose that the periodate acted as an electrophile. What percentage of the original O^{18} would you expect to find in the product, acetic acid? Demonstrate your answer with a postulated mechanism.

(c) Suppose alternatively that the periodate acted as a nucleophile in the reaction. What percentage of the original O^{18} would be found in the acetic acid?

(d) Suppose that the periodate acted once as a nucleophile and once as an electrophile in the two steps required to form the cyclic ester. What then would be the percentage of O^{18} in the acetic acid?

(e) The experimental result of such a determination was the incorporation of a percentage of O^{18} between 50% and 75%. Show that recognition of the *slow* exchange of $H_3IO_6^=$ with the H_2O^{18} indicates that periodate is a nucleophile in this case.

47–4 Several synthetically important oxidations and reductions involve the transfer of hydrogen with a pair of electrons. For example, the following reaction may be considered as the formal transfer of a hydride ion:

$$\begin{array}{c}
\underset{\substack{R \\ |}}{R}\!\!\diagdown\!\!\overset{O^-}{\underset{|}{C}}\!\!\diagup \quad + \quad O\!\!=\!\!C\overset{R'}{\diagdown_{R'}} \quad \rightleftarrows \quad \overset{R}{\underset{R}{\diagup}}C\!\!=\!\!O \quad + \quad \overset{O^-}{\underset{|}{C}}\overset{R'}{\diagdown_{R'}}
\end{array}$$

(a) When optically active 2-methylbutanol-1 in equilibrium with a small amount of its sodium salt is heated, no reaction occurs. Addition of a small amount of benzophenone, however, causes the alcohol to lose its optical activity rapidly. Account for this on the basis of the illustration above, recalling that hydrogens next to carbonyl groups are somewhat acidic (Chapter 38).

(b) Depending on the purpose of the experiment, a reaction of the type illustrated may be considered either an oxidation of the molecule on the left or a reduction of the one on the right. Thus aluminum isopropoxide is used to reduce a ketone to the corresponding alcohol in the Meerwein-Pondorff-Verley reduction. Alternatively, the aluminum salt of an alcohol may be oxidized by an excess of acetone to give a ketone in the Oppenauer oxidation. The alcohol salt is usually formed by equilibration of the alcohol with aluminum *tert*-butoxide. Write out the sequence of steps involved in the Oppenauer oxidation of benzhydrol, $(C_6H_5)_2CHOH$, to benzophenone, and explain the driving force for each step of the reaction. Show how 2-cyclohexenone might be converted to 2-cyclohexenol with aluminum isopropoxide.

(c) Is there a reason for the choice of aluminum as the metal ion in this reaction? (See Problem 44–2.) Show that coordination of the reacting species could lead to an especially favorable six-membered transition state.

(d) How might you prepare 1-deuterio-2-cyclohexenol, using this reaction?

(e) Show how the Oppenauer oxidation would be particularly useful in the oxidation of easily rearranged enols such as cholesterol. What product should be obtained without migration of the double bond? Why do reaction conditions prohibit the use of permanganate and dichromate?

How can a steric effect on the rate of a reaction
be distinguished from an electronic effect?
Are the details of esterification and ester hydrolysis consistent
with explanations for hindrance based on steric grounds?

48

STERIC HINDRANCE; THE MECHANISMS OF ESTERIFICATION AND ESTER HYDROLYSIS

48–1   Development of the Concept of Steric Hindrance

In the preceding chapters we have reviewed the evidence that there are at least two types of electronic effects which are important in the systemization of reaction mechanisms. One of these is the inductive effect, the other the resonance effect. At times both of these operate in one direction with respect to the speeding or slowing of a reaction, while in other situations they may act in opposition. The concept of steric hindrance was originally introduced to explain reaction velocities which could not be explained on the basis of electronic effects. Early opponents of the concept argued that it was merely a "wastebasket" into which otherwise inexplicable effects were swept. It seems clear from an examination of the development of the concept, however, that this criticism is not well grounded, even though it is probable that some early proponents of steric explanations for reactions were overenthusiastic in their advocacy.

The idea of steric hindrance was first clearly stated by Victor Meyer in 1894. Before that time there had been much study devoted to the *"ortho* effect," that is, the anomalous low reactivity frequently observed in *ortho*-substituted benzene compounds. One of the careful investigators in this field was Fittig at Tubingen. It is interesting to note that Remsen studied with Fittig on the *ortho* effect and that many of Remsen's students contributed careful measurements of reaction velocities in these reactions before the turn of the century. At that time chemists were still groping their way toward mechanistic explanations for chemical reactivities, but the investigations leading to sound explanations were being accumulated by studies such as those of Fittig, Remsen, and their students.

48–2   Effects Due to Electronegativity

In his efforts to systematize organic reactions, Victor Meyer referred to electronegativity. He had in mind at that time the idea that we now have when we speak of the inductive effect. The idea of the resonance effect had not been clearly formulated then but the germs of it were present. In 1885 Laar spoke of the interchange between chemical formulas taking place with the speed of light. He called this change "tautomerism," a word which we now reserve for a different meaning. In spite of this, the concept has persisted and it is customary in England to refer to the resonance effect as the "tautomeric" or "mesomeric" effect. Laar did not give his concept the extra twist which has been applied in modern thought, that is, that such changes taking place with the speed of light stabilize the compounds under study. Hence the "electrochemical" thinking of the times was limited to the concepts of the inductive effect being exerted by "electronegative" and "electropositive" groups. Meyer realized that these two opposite types of "electrical" effects affected chemical reactivities in opposite ways. He recognized that in benzene substitution, the methyl group belonged to one class, the nitro group to the other.

48–3   Effects Not Due to Electronegativity

Meyer found that benzoic acids with substituents in each of the *ortho* positions to the carboxyl are extraordinarily resistant to esterification by the usual methods. He made several dozen such compounds in an attempt to find a compound where this rule was not obeyed. He drew attention to the fact that the groups which accomplished this effect belonged both to the strongly "electronegative" groups, such as nitro, chloro, bromo, and carboxyl, and to the "electropositive" groups, such as methyl and hydroxyl. He also noted that the three least effective groups in accomplishing this hindrance were the smallest, fluoro, methyl, and hydroxyl. He reasoned, on this basis, that the hindrance was due to the "space-occupying" properties of the groups, not to their electronegativity.

Meyer next used a reagent of opposite type to the acid catalyst employed in esterifications. This was the nucleophilic hydroxide ion, used for ester hydrolysis. Meyer had shown previously that the esters could be prepared by reacting silver salts with alkyl iodides, even when steric hindrance prevented their preparation by acid esterification. The esters made available by this process were shown also to be subject to steric hindrance in hydrolysis. Thus neither the charge on the reagent nor the electronegativity or electropositivity of the substituent group affected the outcome of the reaction, only its size. Meyer also showed that steric hindrance did not affect the esterification of substituted phenylacetic acids, although it did affect the esterification of benzoic acids. See the structures shown at the right.

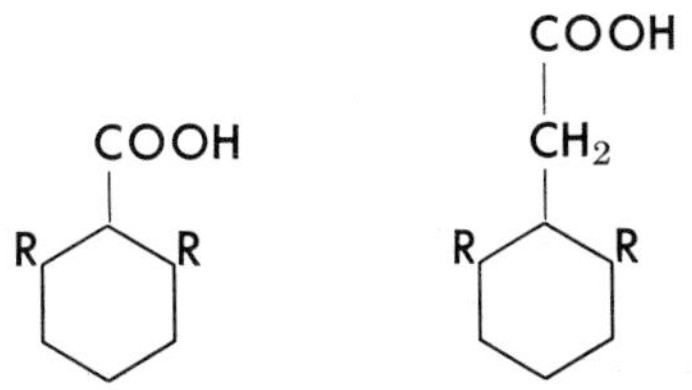

Hindered   Not hindered

48–4 Objections to the Concept of Steric Hindrance

As we have seen, Meyer argued that it should be possible to observe different degrees of steric hindrance and that the degree of hindrance produced would be proportional to the bulk of the group. Unfortunately, however, Meyer's only measure for the space-occupying power was mass. He pointed out that the effects produced by the halogens increased with the atomic weight of the halogen. His opponents retorted however, that the effects of groups did not accurately follow the sequence of their masses and, consequently, that Meyer's argument based on space-occupying properties was not tenable. It was essentially because of these quantitative discrepancies that Meyer's arguments went without general acceptance for a number of decades.

48–5 The Existence of a Solution to the Problem

In this case, as in a number of others that we have examined previously, the clue to the correct answer to Meyer's dilemma had already been published when Meyer did his work. As we saw in Section 8–6, van der Waals put forth his equation of state in 1879. This equation permits the modern student of chemistry to calculate the volumes occupied from molecules and from these it is possible to deduce atomic interference radii. By themselves, they would not have produced results of high precision, but reliance on them alone would have been sufficient to solve the problem of the space-occupying effects of groups with enough precision for Meyer's purposes. The fundamental difficulty of the time lay in a barrier to communication rather than in one of measurement.

While means of communication between various disciplines have greatly improved since Meyer's time, the modern investigator is still faced with this problem. Indeed, in some ways it has intensified, since the mass of material has increased to such proportions that its digestion by any single investigator is a difficult task. The modern investigator must be especially alert that ideas originating in unexpected places have an opportunity for a hearing.

As we have recounted in the study of the design of models, knowledge of interatomic distances was beginning to accumulate some thirty years after Meyer's hypothesis was advanced. Models made of spheres on the basis of interatomic distances still failed to account adequately for effects which many organic chemists regarded as steric, however. Finally, it was realized that interference radii larger than the interatomic distances had to be incorporated into the design of the models. Many such models use radii smaller than the van der Waals radii, however, since use of full van der Waals radii with models of impenetrable wood or plastic makes it difficult to build models of some molecules. We must conclude that really satisfactory models for the purpose of the organic chemist have not yet been devised. In spite of this, however, it is possible to picture steric effects with modern models much more satisfactorily than was possible in Meyer's day. Using our models, the hypothesis of steric hindrance acquires much greater credibility than it had earlier. As we refine our knowledge, however, we always find new difficulties. In this case, difficulties occur because of the limitations of our knowledge of the angle from which an approaching group must attack to bring about the reaction.

48-6 Mechanism of Esterification

To understand the reason for the steric effects of groups on esterification in the *ortho* positions, it is necessary to know the facts concerning the mechanism of this reaction. The equilibrium between ester and acid can be displaced in either direction by control of the amounts of reagents used. This demonstrates that acid-catalyzed hydrolysis of an ester and acid-catalyzed esterification of an acid are the reverse of each other. If water is withdrawn in the presence of excess alcohol, esterification will proceed. For a water-immiscible alcohol such as *n*-butanol, this may be accomplished by azeotropic distillation. If water is added, hydrolysis will occur.

48-7 Which Bond Cleaves?

In hydrolysis, the first question to be answered concerns the position of bond cleavage. The cleavage might take place either between the alkyl group and the oxygen or between the acyl group and the oxygen:

$$
\underset{\displaystyle \overset{\displaystyle O}{\|}}{C_6H_5C}-O \cdot \frac{}{}\cdot CH_3 \quad \text{or} \quad \underset{\displaystyle \overset{\displaystyle O}{\|}}{C_6H_5C}\cdot \frac{}{}\cdot O-CH_3
$$

Structural changes can be made which will permit either possibility to develop. It has been established, however, that the ordinary reaction takes place between the acyl group and the oxygen. This was shown in three ways. The first method was to show that the ester of an optically active alcohol whose center of asymmetry lay at the bond with the oxygen did not lose asymmetry on hydrolysis. This reaction was first carried out on the ester of malic acid with acetic acid by Holmberg in 1912:

$$
\underset{\displaystyle \overset{\displaystyle O}{\|}}{CH_3C}-O-\underset{\displaystyle \underset{\displaystyle COOH}{\underset{\displaystyle |}{CH_2}}}{\overset{\displaystyle \overset{\displaystyle COOH}{\overset{\displaystyle |}{}}}{CH^*}} \;\rightarrow\; \underset{\displaystyle \overset{\displaystyle O}{\|}}{CH_3C}-OH \;+\; HO-\underset{\displaystyle \underset{\displaystyle COOH}{\underset{\displaystyle |}{CH_2}}}{\overset{\displaystyle \overset{\displaystyle COOH}{\overset{\displaystyle |}{}}}{CH^*}}
$$

After the hydrolysis had been completed, it was found that the malic acid had retained its optical activity. It was reasoned that cleavage between the optically active carbon and the oxygen would have caused inversion or racemization, hence that the cleavage did not take place at that point.

    The second method used involved the preparation of an ester whose carbonium ion would be a resonating hybrid that would give two identifiable products if formed. This method was applied by Ingold and Ingold:

$$
\underset{\displaystyle \overset{\displaystyle O}{\|}}{CH_3C}-O-\underset{\displaystyle \overset{\displaystyle CH_3}{\overset{\displaystyle |}{}}}{CH}-CH{=}CH_2 \;\rightarrow\; \underset{\displaystyle \overset{\displaystyle O}{\|}}{CH_3C}-OH \;+\; HO-\underset{\displaystyle \overset{\displaystyle CH_3}{\overset{\displaystyle |}{}}}{CH}-CH{=}CH_2
$$

The alternative course of the reaction would be:

$$CH_3\overset{\displaystyle O}{\overset{\|}{C}}-O-CH_2-CH{=}CHCH_3 \rightarrow CH_3\overset{\displaystyle O}{\overset{\|}{C}}-OH + HO-CH_2-CH{=}CHCH_3$$

The hybrid that would be formed if cleavage took place at the alkyl-oxygen link would be:

$$CH_3\overset{+}{C}H-CH{=}CH_2 \leftrightarrow CH_3CH{=}CH-\overset{+}{C}H_2$$

Had this been formed, one or the other of the two esters would have given a rearranged alcohol or both would have given the same mixture of the two. When the experiment was performed, however, each isomer was obtained pure, showing that the carbonium ion was not formed as an intermediate.

A recent method for the examination of the esterification-hydrolysis equilibrium involves the use of labeling with O^{18}. This has the advantage that it can be performed on any ester and no special structure is required for the operation of the method. The reaction was applied to ethyl, isopropyl, and *tert*-butyl benzoates. The method was to use water enriched with H_2O^{18} for the hydrolysis. If cleavage were to take place between the alkyl group and the oxygen, alcohol would be recovered containing O^{18}. When the reaction was performed it was found that all of the O^{18} that had entered into the products was in the carboxyl group:

$$C_6H_5\overset{\displaystyle O}{\overset{\|}{C}}-O-C_2H_5 + H_2O^* \rightarrow C_6H_5\overset{\displaystyle O}{\overset{\|}{C}}-\overset{*}{O}-H + C_2H_5OH$$

This establishes that the bond cleaved is between the acyl group and the oxygen.

48-8   Kinetics of Esterification

The kinetic order of the reaction between ethanol and acetic acid, as well as that of other esterifications, was established by Goldschmidt in 1895. He found the rate proportional to the concentration of H^+ and CH_3COOH. In the hydrolytic reaction, Friedmann and Elmore found in 1941 that the rate of hydrolysis of methyl acetate in acetone is proportional to the water concentration. This implies that the esterification reaction taking place in the opposite direction would be found to have a rate proportional to the alcohol concentration. Hence the transition state would be one that involved all three species: for esterification, the acid, the alcohol, and the solvated proton, and for hydrolysis, the ester, the water, and the solvated proton. At least two formulations are consistent with these observations. The first is the formation of an intermediate addition compound (I) involving all species by the reaction shown on the next page.

In the second possible mechanism, it may be assumed that the replacement of water by ethanol or of ethanol by water is a nucleophilic-substitution reaction and that no stable compound such as (I) is formed:

Mechanism I

$$C_2H_5OH_2^+ + C_6H_5\overset{\overset{O}{\|}}{C}{-}OH \underset{fast}{\overset{slow}{\rightleftharpoons}} C_2H_5OH + C_6H_5\overset{\overset{O}{\|}}{C}{-}\overset{+}{O}H_2 \underset{fast}{\overset{slow}{\rightleftharpoons}}$$

$$\underset{\underset{C_2H_5}{|}}{\overset{\overset{H}{\diagdown}}{\underset{+}{O}}}{-}\underset{\underset{C_6H_5}{|}}{\overset{\overset{O^-}{|}}{C}}{-}\overset{+}{O}H_2 \underset{fast}{\overset{slow}{\rightleftharpoons}} \underset{\underset{C_2H_5}{|}}{\overset{\overset{H}{\diagdown}}{\underset{+}{O}}}{-}\underset{\underset{C_6H_5}{|}}{\overset{\overset{O}{\|}}{C}} + H_2O \underset{fast}{\overset{slow}{\rightleftharpoons}} C_2H_5O{-}\underset{\underset{C_6H_5}{|}}{\overset{\overset{O}{\|}}{C}} + H_3O^+$$

I

Mechanism II

$$C_2H_5OH + \underset{\underset{C_6H_5}{|}}{\overset{\overset{O}{\|}}{C}}{-}\overset{+}{O}H_2 \rightarrow \left[C_2H_5O \cdots \underset{\underset{C_6H_5}{|}}{\overset{\overset{O}{\|}}{C}} \cdots \overset{\overset{H}{|}}{O}H_2 \right]^+ \rightarrow C_2H_5{-}\overset{\overset{H}{|}}{\underset{+}{O}}{-}\underset{\underset{C_6H_5}{|}}{\overset{\overset{O}{\|}}{C}} + OH_2$$

II

48–9   Position of the Energy Barrier

Formula (II) represents a transition state at the top of an energy barrier, while formula (I) represents a metastable compound at the bottom of an intermediate energy trough. Bender has been able to demonstrate by means of experiments with labeled oxygen that the actual reaction is described by mechanism (I) rather than (II). He accomplished this by allowing an ester-hydrolysis reaction to proceed only part of the way to completion and then showing that labeled oxygen from the solvent phase had been incorporated into the residual ester. This reaction sequence may be represented as follows:

$$H_2\overset{*}{O} + \underset{\underset{C_6H_5}{|}}{\overset{\overset{O}{\|}}{C}}{-}\overset{\overset{H}{\overset{|}{}}}{\underset{+}{O}}{-}C_2H_5 \rightleftharpoons H_2\underset{*}{O}{-}\underset{\underset{C_6H_5}{|}}{\overset{\overset{O^-}{|}}{C}}{-}\overset{\overset{H}{\overset{|}{}}}{\underset{+}{O}}{-}C_2H_5$$

III

$$C_6H_5\overset{*}{C}\overset{+}{O_2}H_2 + C_2H_5OH$$

$$H_2O + \overset{*}{O}{=}\underset{\underset{C_6H_5}{|}}{C}{-}\overset{\overset{H}{\overset{|}{}}}{\underset{+}{O}}C_2H_5 \rightleftharpoons {}^-O{-}\underset{\underset{C_6H_5}{|}}{\overset{}{C}}{-}\overset{\overset{H_2O^+}{}\overset{H}{}}{\underset{*}{O}}{-}C_2H_5$$

IV

The species (III) must persist long enough for a proton exchange to take place so that it may be converted into species (IV) to accomplish the exchange of labeled

oxygen into the ester without hydrolysis. From that it is apparent that the intermediate species is more stable than the transition state (II) and that a molecule
with a finite survival time must represent the intermediate. While (III) is not the
only possible formulation for such an intermediate species, it is one which accounts
for all the known facts with economy. All the alternatives which have been proposed
have the feature in common with (III) that they are tetrahedral and have three
oxygens on the carboxyl carbon. They differ in their distribution of protons.

48–10 Alkaline Hydrolysis of Esters

In the alkaline hydrolysis of esters, experiments similar to those performed in acid
established that the reaction is second order and that the cleavage which occurs is
an acyl-oxygen fission, not an alkyl-oxygen fission. Again the question arises as to
the nature of the intermediate, that is, whether there is a single transition state or
an intermediate unstable molecule. Labeling experiments establish that in this case
again, the metastable molecule is the intermediate. The reader should write equations for the labeling experiments with heavy oxygen that would establish this
point. From these experiments, the intermediate in the hydrolysis of ethyl benzoate
is identified as:

$$C_6H_5-\overset{\overset{\displaystyle O^-}{|}}{\underset{\underset{\displaystyle OH}{|}}{C}}-OC_2H_5$$

At one critical point, however, the reactions in acid and alkali differ. In the case
of alkaline hydrolysis, the carboxylic acid formed from the intermediate reacts
with the excess alkali present. This removes it from the reaction and effectively
prevents reversal of the reaction.

$$C_6H_5-\overset{\overset{\displaystyle O^-}{|}}{\underset{\underset{\displaystyle OH}{|}}{C}}-OC_2H_5 \rightleftarrows C_6H_5-\overset{\overset{\displaystyle O}{||}}{C}-OH + {}^-OC_2H_5 \rightarrow C_2H_5OH + C_6H_5-\overset{\overset{\displaystyle O}{||}}{C}-O^-$$

For this reason, alkali-catalyzed esterification does not occur.

48–11 The Cause of Steric Hindrance

It is evident that there are substantial reasons for formulating the change which
takes place on esterification or hydrolysis of benzoates and other carboxylic acid
derivatives as involving the formation of a tetrahedral
carbon from a trigonal carbon. A model of either
benzoic acid or ethyl benzoate will show that the
carboxyl group can assume the planar position which
permits resonance interaction with the benzene ring.

On the other hand, 2,6-dinitrobenzoic acid and its esters suffer extensive steric interaction between the carbonyl oxygens and the oxygens of the nitro groups.

Even though all the bonds involved are 120°, the models show that the fact that the two nonbonded oxygens, one from the nitro and one from the carbonyl groups, are not truncated for bonding but have full interference radii makes them overlap to a considerable extent. This interference can only be relieved if the nitro group and the carboxyl group each move a little out of the plane of the benzene ring, the bonds of each group deing bent a little and stretched a little to allow a number of small accommodations take place. Moving far out of the plane would reduce stability by interrupting resonance interaction.

Replacing the trigonal carbonyl group by a tetrahedral carbon, as would be necessary to form the reaction intermediate in either esterification or hydrolysis, will increase the crowding materially. Part of the accommodation of the carbonyl group can be removed by increasing the angle above 120°. When the normal angle has been reduced to approximately 109°, this source of relief is much less effective. The models show that at all possible conformations, the intermediate compound is tightly locked by the adjacent nitro groups, indicating even greater steric stress on the reaction intermediate than on the starting material. Thus the formation of the reaction intermediate necessary for esterification or hydrolysis leads to a substantial increase in steric stress, increasing the amount of energy necessary to form the intermediate and thus raising the height of the energy barrier to the reaction. This is held to account for the steric effects of groups in the *ortho* positions of the benzene ring.

48–12 Model Research

An important contribution to the understanding of reaction mechanisms can often be secured through the use of good models. It is unfortunate that no all-purpose models are available for study. In spite of this, the chemist frequently knows what kind of a steric effect he should look for in a given situation, and he can then choose models which are designed to permit the visualization of this particular effect.

In the case of the "*ortho* effect," it cannot be assumed without verification that all reactions in *ortho* positions are subject to steric influences. In each case, it is advisable to construct a model to see whether or not there is interference to the approach of an entering group or to the stability of a reaction intermediate in a given reaction sequence. Thus by using models it is possible to secure a verification of the possibility of the existence of a steric effect in a given reaction.

PROBLEMS

48–1   One of Remsen's students, Reid, in his doctoral dissertation examined the rates of hydrolysis of substituted benzamides. The work was published in 1899 and 1900 and is another example of very precise determinations gathered years before their chemical significance was fully realized.

Second-order rate constants for HCl-catalyzed
hydrolysis of substituted benzamides

$$C_6H_5CONH_2 = 217 \times 10^{-4}$$

p-Cl	208×10^{-4}	o-Cl	33.3×10^{-4}
p-NO$_2$	245×10^{-4}	o-NO$_2$	5.6×10^{-4}
p-CH$_3$	183×10^{-4}	o-CH$_3$	22.7×10^{-4}
p-Br	204×10^{-4}	o-Br	17.7×10^{-4}
p-OCH$_3$	131×10^{-4}	o-OCH$_3$	121×10^{-4}
p-I	164×10^{-4}	o-I	11.0×10^{-4}

(a) Is the reaction very susceptible to electronic effects? To answer this, examine the effects of *para* substituents. Is the value of ρ very large?

(b) In addition to inductive and resonance effects, there are large steric effects of the *ortho* groups. Suppose that we wished to estimate the importance of steric interaction for these groups. We might begin by assuming that the inductive and resonance effects of an *ortho* substituent are fairly similar to those of the same group in the *para* position. Is this assumption justified? Draw structures to demonstrate your point.

(c) Does the relative susceptibility of the reaction to electronic effects make this assumption any safer in this particular case?

(d) We now might write:

$$k_{ortho \text{ (electronic)}} = k_{para}$$

There is now a steric factor which decreases the rates of hydrolysis of the *ortho*-substituted products:

$$k_{ortho} = k_{ortho \text{ (steric)}} \times k_{ortho \text{ (electronic)}}$$

Determine the steric factors for each substituent. How do these values compare with the space-filling properties for models based on the van der Waals radii?

(e) Does the steric factor for the nitro group indicate whether the nitro group is nearly parallel with the ring or twisted out of the plane by a large angle? Compare this figure with the others to justify your answer.

48–2   The ester interchange reaction is used to convert one ester into another ester in the presence of acid:

$$RCOOCH_3 + C_2H_5OH + H^+ = RCOOC_2H_5 + CH_3OH + H^+$$

(a) Write a mechanism for this reaction, noting the apparent similarities between this reaction and acidic hydrolysis.

(b) Define the conditions under which it would be experimentally feasible.

(c) The above reaction shows exchange of the alcohol portion of the ester. Is it possible to exchange the acid portion for a different acid? Try to write a mechanism for this reaction.

48–3 The basic hydrolysis of alkyl toluenesulfonates is known to be an S_N-type reaction (see Section 36-9).

(a) Write a mechanism for the hydrolysis of ethyl toluenesulfonate.

(b) The hydrolysis of phenyl toluenesulfonate, however, in 60% aqueous dioxane in the presence of H_2O^{18} yields phenol with no incorporation of excess O^{18}. Show that this information demonstrates a different mechanism for the hydrolysis of phenyl toluenesulfonate.

$$
\begin{array}{ccc}
 & O & \\
 & \diagup\;\diagdown & \\
CH_2 & & CH_2 \\
| & & | \\
CH_2 & & CH_2 \\
 & \diagdown\;\diagup & \\
 & O &
\end{array}
$$

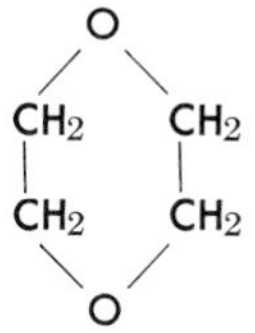

Dioxane

(c) Why would nucleophilic substitution be unlikely in this case? What structural feature was found to be required for nucleophilic aromatic substitution?

48–4 The hydrolysis of optically active 2-octyl nitrite in 91% aqueous dioxane in the presence of acid leads to complete retention of configuration in the alcohol product.

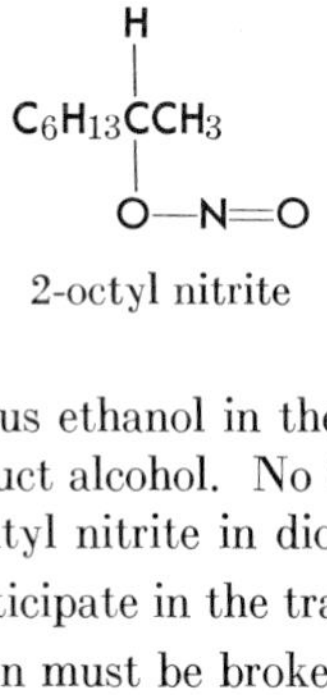

$$
\begin{array}{cc}
\quad H & \quad H \\
\quad | & \quad | \\
C_6H_{13}CCH_3 & C_6H_{13}CCH_3 \\
\quad | & \quad | \\
O\!-\!N\!\!=\!\!O & ONO_2 \\
\text{2-octyl nitrite} & \text{2-octyl nitrate}
\end{array}
$$

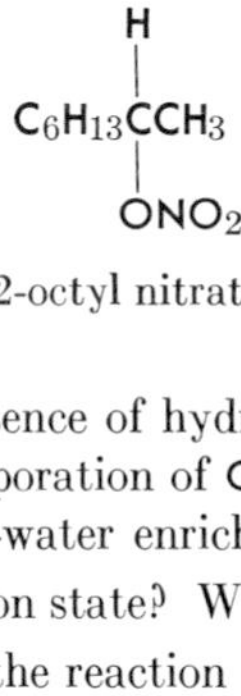

Hydrolysis in 91% aqueous ethanol in the presence of hydroxide also leads to retention of configuration in the product alcohol. No incorporation of O^{18} was observed in the acid-catalyzed hydrolysis of t-butyl nitrite in dioxane-water enriched with H_2O^{18}.

(a) Does the dioxane participate in the transition state? What is its role in the reaction?

(b) Which bond to oxygen must be broken in the reaction in acid? In base?

(c) Write mechanisms for the acid- and base-catalyzed hydrolysis of alkyl nitrites consistent with this information. It may not be possible to write a *uniquely* determined mechanism in either case. You need only give one proposal which is consistent with the facts.

These hydrolysis mechanisms involve critical tetrahedral intermediates. Arriving at them involves a number of proton transfers, and the formation of C—O bonds. Recall that H^+ and H_2O are the species available in acid, and OH^- and H_2O, in base. The sequence of steps may look almost arbitrary when you eventually find a way to account for the intermediate. You should therefore try to justify the likelihood of each step in your sequence—for example, be sure that you attach protons to basic centers, and that water or hydroxide performs nucleophilic attacks.

(d) After you have worked out a reasonable series of steps, note the similarities and differences between these reactions and the acidic and basic hydrolysis of esters.

48–5 The hydrolysis of 2-octyl nitrate, on the other hand, under neutral conditions (78% aqueous acetone in the presence of $CaCO_3$) gives alcohol with 15% retention and 85% inversion of configuration. In the presence of base (OH^-) in 64% aqueous dioxane, the product has 71% retention and 29% inversion.

(a) Which bonds are broken in these reactions?

(b) The percent inversion might also be expressed as a fraction of racemization. The neutral hydrolysis might thus be 30% racemization and 70% inversion. How would the basic hydrolysis be stated in these terms?

(c) Part of the reaction proceeds through the usual ester hydrolysis mechanism and part through nucleophilic substitution. What part of the mechanism is affected by the reinterpretation of part (b)?

(d) Write mechanisms for these hydrolyses as you did for Problem 48–3. Where the experimental facts do not resolve mechanistic ambiguities, more than one mechanistic interpretation, must be considered, as in part (c).

(e) How might you resolve the ambiguity experimentally? Would O^{18} studies be useful?

(f) Formulate a reason for the difference in product stereochemistry between nitrites and nitrates. On the basis of your distinction, what would you propose for the basic hydrolysis of alkyl sulfates? Alkyl hypochlorites?

Can steric effects accelerate a reaction instead of decelerating it?
What evidence has been gathered to establish the validity
of the hypothesis of steric damping of resonance?

49

STERIC FACILITATION;
DAMPING OF RESONANCE

49–1 Behavior of Oxygen Bases in Sulfuric Acid

In studying the ionization of nitric acid in sulfuric acid, we saw how Hammett and his students perfected the techniques of working with sulfuric acid as a cryscopic solvent. Their major objective at that time was to examine the behavior of carboxylic acids and other oxygen-containing substances for the weakly basic properties which they should exhibit, due to their unpaired electrons. They found, for example, that benzoic acid dissolved in 100% sulfuric acid has a van't Hoff i-value of 1.76 to 2.07, indicating that two particles are formed in solution. This indicates that benzoic acid is protonated under these conditions, the other species formed being the bisulfate ion. It is possible to write two formulas for the protonated benzoic acid:

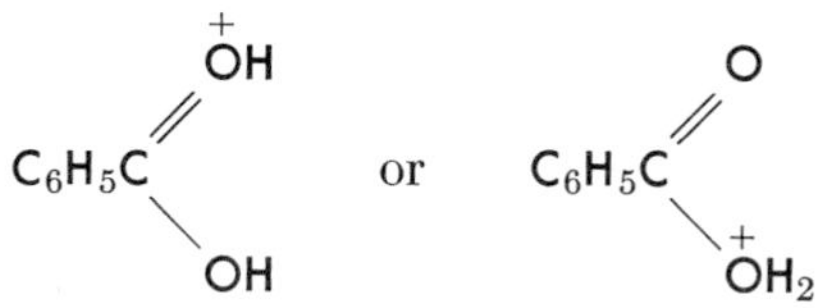

The first of these formulations represents a resonance hybrid, and it would be stabilized by delocalization. It is thus probably the major species in the solution. The second formula, on the other hand, takes cognizance of the fact that alcohols are stronger bases than carbonyl compounds, just as amines are also stronger bases than imines. It is probable that this form is present to a limited extent. However,

633

since only the second form leads to the further reactions presented below, we shall use it to represent the cation. The equation for the reaction in sulfuric acid can then be written:

$$C_6H_5COOH + H_2SO_4 \rightleftarrows C_6H_5C\begin{matrix} O \\ \diagup \\ \diagdown \\ O^+H_2 \end{matrix} + HSO_4{}^-$$

Treffers and Hammett examined a number of methyl-substituted benzoic acids and found the *i*-values listed in Table 49-1.

Table 49-1.   IONIZATION OF
BENZOIC ACIDS IN SULFURIC ACID

Benzoic acid	*i*
2-methyl	1.95 to 2.02
2,4,5-trimethyl	2.00 to 2.20
2,4-dimethyl	1.98

49-2   Abnormal Ionization of Certain Acids in Sulfuric Acid

Two substituted benzoic acids, on the other hand, gave results which were substantially different. These results are listed in Table 49-2.

Table 49-2.   IONIZATION OF
BENZOIC ACIDS IN SULFURIC ACID

Benzoic acid	*i*
2,6-dimethyl	2.87 to 3.53
2,4,6-trimethyl	3.25 to 3.98

For 2,4,6-trimethylbenzoic acid, ionization to four particles is essentially complete. Hammett formulated this reaction as follows:

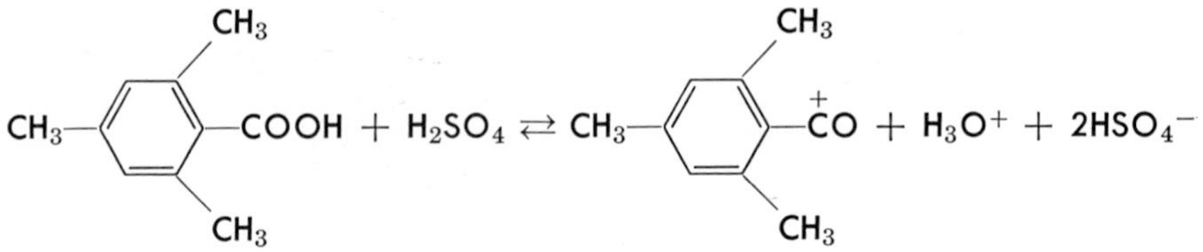

$$CH_3\text{—}\underset{CH_3}{\overset{CH_3}{\bigcirc}}\text{—COOH} + H_2SO_4 \rightleftarrows CH_3\text{—}\underset{CH_3}{\overset{CH_3}{\bigcirc}}\text{—}\overset{+}{C}O + H_3O^+ + 2HSO_4{}^-$$

49-3   Mechanism of Acyl Ion Formation

For 2,6-dimethylbenzoic acid, the reaction is incomplete. This suggests that a portion of the solute is present in the form of the cation similar to that formed with benzoic acid, while the remainder has proceeded to the formation of the acyl cation. This, in turn, suggests that the process of acyl ion formation is a two-step process:

$$(CH_3)_2C_6H_3COOH + H_2SO_4 \rightleftharpoons (CH_3)_2C_6H_3C\overset{O}{\underset{\overset{+}{O}H_2}{\diagdown}} + HSO_4^-$$

$$(CH_3)_2C_6H_3C\overset{O}{\underset{\overset{+}{O}H_2}{\diagdown}} + H_2SO_4 \rightarrow (CH_3)_2C_6H_3\overset{+}{C}{=}O + H_3O^+ + HSO_4^-$$

In the second step of this process, a water molecule leaves with its electron pair. This reaction strongly resembles the ionization of tertiary butyl chloride. In consequence, one would expect it to be affected by the same types of electronic factors that affect the formation of alkyl cations: electron-releasing groups should favor the reaction and electron-attracting groups should diminish the extent of the reaction. This explanation has been used to account for the fact that 2,6-dimethylbenzoic acid forms an acyl ion to a lesser extent than does 2,4,6-trimethylbenzoic acid. We may reason that the methyl group in the 4-position favors the reaction by its electron-releasing properties.

49–4   Steric Effect in Acyl Ion Formation

The contrast between 2,4,5-trimethylbenzoic acid and 2,6-dimethylbenzoic acid must be laid to other grounds, however. As we saw in the preceding chapter, 2,6-dimethylbenzoic acid is subject to steric effects: the methyl groups overlap the oxygens of the carboxyl group in such a manner as to require accommodation by bond bending, bond stretching, and turning from the preferred position of co-planarity. A sketch and a model showing the degree of overlap is given in Fig. 49–1.

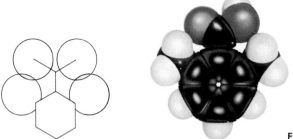

FIGURE 49–1

Formation of the acyl ion eliminates one of the space-occupying oxygens; the remaining oxygen is attached through a C—C—O bond with an angle of 180°. This forms a molecule with interferences as illustrated in Fig. 49–2.

Thus it may be concluded that the reaction of acyl ion formation is favored by a steric effect which helps to expel the water molecule as well as by an electronic

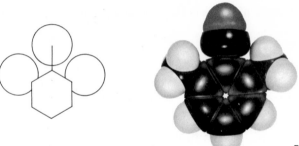

FIGURE 49–2

effect that helps to donate electrons to the leaving oxygen atom in the water molecule.

Treffers and Hammett have strengthened this argument by demonstrating that the addition of electron-attracting groups diminishes the extent of the acyl ionization. For example, 2,4,6-trimethyl-3,5-dibromobenzoic acid has an i-value of 1.87 to 2.63, indicating a distinct diminution in the extent of the acyl ionization.

49–5   Preparative Application of Acyl Ions

Newman has demonstrated that the reaction of acyl ion formation can be put to preparative use. When benzoic acid is dissolved in 100% sulfuric acid and the solution is then poured into cold methanol, unchanged benzoic acid is recovered, showing that the benzoic cation does not esterify under these conditions. When, on the other hand, 2,4,6-trimethylbenzoic acid is dissolved in 100% sulfuric acid and the solution poured into cold methanol, a high yield of the methyl ester of 2,4,6-trimethylbenzoic acid is obtained. This constitutes by far the most convenient method for the preparation of this highly hindered ester. The reaction is formulated:

$$(CH_3)_3C_6H_2CO^+ + 2CH_3OH \rightarrow (CH_3)_3C_6H_2COOCH_3 + CH_3\overset{+}{O}H_2$$

The interpretation of the cryoscopic results as the result of acyl ionization is further confirmed by Newman's observation that the methyl ester of 2,4,6-trimethylbenzoic acid gives an i-value of 5 in sulfuric acid. This is interpreted by the equation:

$$(CH_3)_3C_6H_2COOCH_3 + 3H_2SO_4 \rightarrow (CH_3)_3C_6H_2CO^+ + H_3O^+ + CH_3HSO_4 + 2HSO_4^-$$

Pouring this solution into ice water forms 2,4,6-trimethylbenzoic acid, whereas methyl benzoate, under the same conditions, can be recovered unchanged.

49–6   Effect of Substituents on the Alcohol Group

The electronic effect of substituents on the reaction of acyl ionization can be carried over to the alcohol side of the ester. On the carboxyl side, an electron-*releasing* substituent should facilitate the reaction. On the alcohol side, an electron-

attracting substituent should facilitate the reaction, since it would increase the attraction of the leaving oxygen for its electrons. This hypothesis was tested by Kuhn and Corwin. The results of the measurements are given in Table 49–3. The benzoyl ion formed in these reactions is not a stable entity, as shown by the fact that pouring the mixture into cold methanol does not produce esterification. Hence it must be assumed that the benzoyl ion reacts with bisulfate ion to produce benzoyl acid sulfate:

$$C_6H_5CO^+ + HSO_4^- \rightarrow C_6H_5COOSO_3H$$

This reaction reduces the number of particles by one and means that for esters with uncharged alcohols, i should have a maximum value of 4, while with the charged ester of the last line of Table 49–3, i should have a maximum value of 5, because of the extra bisulfate ion formed in this case. The results show that electron-attracting substituents in the beta position of the ethyl group on the alcohol increase the degree of acyl ionization in benzoic esters, the greatest effect being observed when a full positive charge is introduced by protonation of the beta oxygen of the ester group by the sulfuric acid. In this manner, it is possible to secure acyl ionization of benzoic acid itself by purely electronic effects without the necessity for steric facilitation.

Table 49–3

Ester	i
$C_6H_5COOC_2H_5$	1.86 to 2.05
$C_6H_5COOCH_2CH_2Cl$	2.21 to 2.24
$C_6H_5COOCH_2CCl_3$	2.74 to 2.87
$C_6H_5COOCH_2CH_2\overset{+}{O}\!\!\overset{H}{\diagup}\underset{C_2H_5}{\diagdown}$	4.27 to 4.47

Table 49–4

Ester	i
$CH_3COOC_2H_5$	1.91 to 1.94
$CH_3COOCH_2CH_2Cl$	2.98 to 3.05
$CH_3COOCH_2CCl_3$	3.50 to 3.53
$CH_3COOCH_2CH_2\overset{+}{O}\!\!\overset{H}{\diagup}\underset{C_2H_5}{\diagdown}$	5.25 to 5.45

49–7   Transient Formation of Acetyl Ions

These observations were then extended to secure acyl ionization of acetates, as shown in Table 49–4. The results of the experiments summarized in Table 49–4 indicate that the acetyl ion is somewhat easier to form than the benzoyl ion and may be slightly more stable.

49–8   Remote Steric Hindrance

The results obtained with anisic acid, $p\text{-}CH_3OC_6H_4COOH$, were unexpected. In spite of the fact that there is no *ortho* substituent, anisic acid in sulfuric acid gives an i-value of 3.38, indicating extensive acyl ion formation. Pouring the solution into cold methanol gives approximately 15% of the methyl ester, indicating that some of the anisoyl ion remains in the solution. Thus the strongly electron-releasing property of the methoxyl group is sufficient to permit the departure of the water molecule from anisic acid with formation of some anisoyl ion. In contrast, Treffers and Hammett found that 3,4,5-trimethoxybenzoic acid has a normal *i*-value of 2.02. Thus the presence of two methoxy groups in the *ortho* positions to that in the 4-position inhibits the formation of the more highly substituted anisoyl ion. For the methoxy group in the 4-position to exert its electron-releasing effect, it would have to be capable of assuming coplanarity with the benzene ring. In the case of the 3,4,5-trimethoxy compound, the two groups in the *ortho* positions to the 4-methoxyl are large enough to interfere sterically, thus preventing the 4-methoxyl from being coplanar with the ring. The relative positions of the groups are shown in Fig. 49–3. The effect of this steric action is to produce hindrance at a reaction site remote from the point at which the steric effect is observed. For this reason, the effect has been called *remote steric hindrance*. This effect was produced by steric damping of resonance.

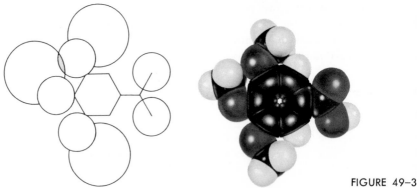

FIGURE 49–3

49–9   Summary of Effects Influencing Acyl Ion Formation

We may summarize by saying that through favorable combinations of steric and electronic effects it is possible to demonstrate the existence of acyl ions and that their existence can be utilized preparatively. The electronic effects are those that would be expected to favor cleavage of a C—O bond, with electron-releasing groups on the C side and electron-attracting groups on the O side favoring the reaction.

49–10   Steric Damping of Resonance

Spitzer and Wheland performed a group of parallel reactions on nitro- and cyano-substituted benzenes. In these, the nitro group, as we have seen, would be subject to steric effects while the cyano group, because of the 180° bond angle, would not be expected to be susceptible. The reactions which were performed were conden-sations with piperidine, using an activated derivative of bromobenzene to undergo nucleophilic substitution:

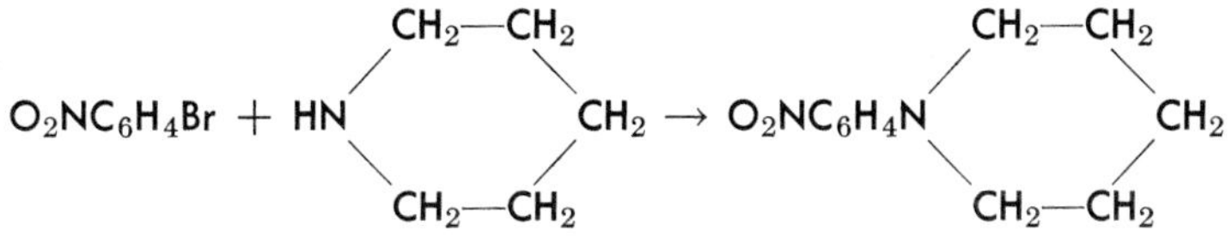

$$O_2NC_6H_4Br + HN\begin{matrix} CH_2-CH_2 \\ \diagup \qquad \diagdown \\ \qquad\qquad CH_2 \\ \diagdown \qquad \diagup \\ CH_2-CH_2 \end{matrix} \rightarrow O_2NC_6H_4N\begin{matrix} CH_2-CH_2 \\ \diagup \qquad \diagdown \\ \qquad\qquad CH_2 \\ \diagdown \qquad \diagup \\ CH_2-CH_2 \end{matrix}$$

In each case the velocity constant of the reaction was measured. Compounds used and their rate constants for the condensation with piperidine are given in Table 49–5.

Table 49–5

RELATIVE RATE CONSTANTS FOR CONDENSATION WITH PIPERIDINE

Nitro	Rate constant	Cyano	Rate constant	Approximate ratio NO_2/CN
(1) O_2N—⬡—Br	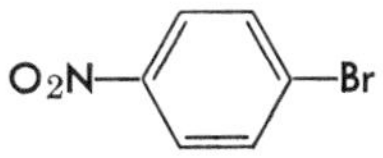 92 to 100	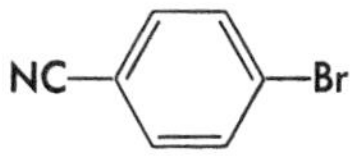 NC—⬡—Br	16 to 17	5.7
(2) O_2N—⬡—Br (2,6-di-CH₃)	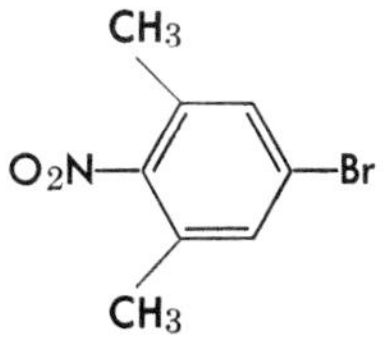 2.5 to 3.1	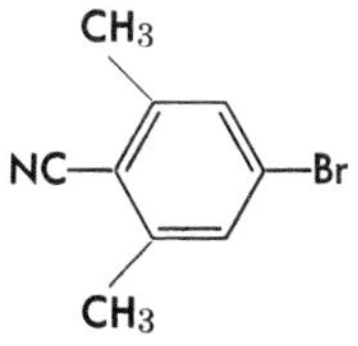 NC—⬡—Br (2,6-di-CH₃)	4.5 to 5.3	0.55
(3) O_2N—⬡—Br (3,5-di-CH₃)	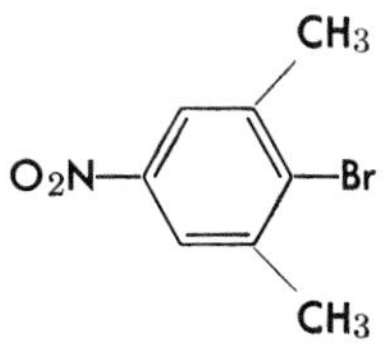 0.43 to 0.81	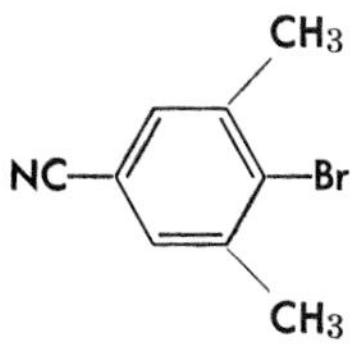 NC—⬡—Br (3,5-di-CH₃)	0.16	2.7 to 5
(4) ⬡—Br (ortho NO₂)	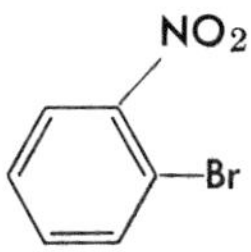 1700 to 1730	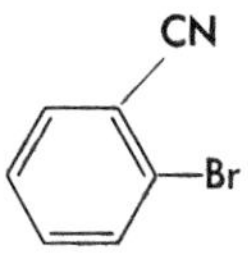 ⬡—Br (ortho CN)	17 to 18	100
(5) ⬡—Br (CH₃, NO₂, CH₃)	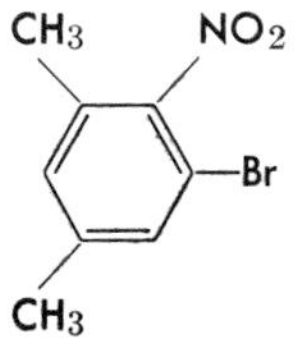 16	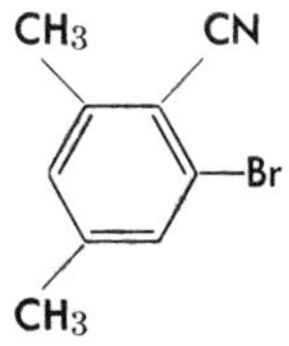 ⬡—Br (CH₃, CN, CH₃)	5.7 to 5.9	2.8

The reactions of line (1) show the nitro-substituted compound to be over five times as reactive as the cyano compound. Substitution of methyl groups in the *ortho* positions to the groups (line 2) reduces the reactivity of the nitro compound to just over half that of the cyano compound. Thus the effect of the methyl groups was much greater on the nitro compound than on the cyano compound. It is argued that the effect of the nitro group in nucleophilic aromatic substitution is due to its ability to withdraw electrons from the reaction site, making attack by the nucleophile take place more readily. This electron withdrawal will depend on the ability of the nitro group to assume a position coplanar to the benzene ring. A substitution of methyl groups in the *ortho* positions to the nitro group interferes with coplanarity and, by this steric damping of resonance, a marked inhibition of the reaction velocity is brought about. This is still another case of remote steric hindrance.

For the piperidine ring to attack the benzene carbon holding the bromine atom, the benzene carbon must be converted from a trigonal shape to a tetrahedral shape. As we have seen in the preceding chapter, this can introduce hindrance if the positions of the groups are right. The case here differs from the case of the esterification of benzoic acids in that the tetrahedral atom formed is in the benzene ring instead of immediately adjacent to it. Examination of a model will show that in this case the hindrance is not nearly so great as in the case of the benzoic acids but that some hindrance is present. The intermediate from the reaction of line (3) is shown below:

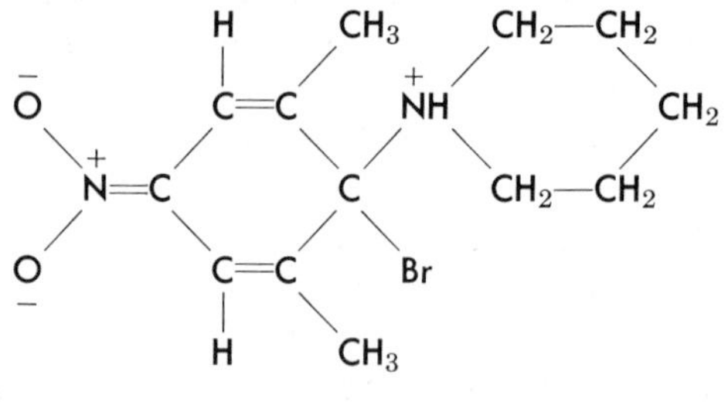

$$
\overset{-}{O}\diagdown\underset{\overset{+}{N}=C}{}\diagup\overset{\overset{\displaystyle H}{\,\mid\,}}{C}=\overset{\overset{\displaystyle CH_3}{\diagup}}{C}\diagdown\ \overset{\overset{+}{NH}}{}\diagup\overset{CH_2-CH_2}{}\diagdown CH_2 \cdots
$$

The carbon next to the nitrogen of the piperidine ring might be expected to interfere with the hydrogens of the methyl group. If coplanarity were required, the interference would be large. With some freedom to rotate on the part of the piperidine group, a major portion of the interference can be eluded but some will remain. Thus the reactivity of the nitro compound is reduced in approximately the same degree as that of the cyano compound by the combined steric and electronic effects of the methyl groups.

In line (4), the nitro compound is approximately 100 times as reactive as the cyano compound. Interference with its coplanarity, in line (5), reduces the factor in favor of the nitro compound to approximately 3, again demonstrating the greater inhibiting effect of the damping of resonance on the nitro group.

These reactions are interpreted as buttressing the argument that coplanarity is an essential prerequisite to strong resonance interaction of a group with a benzene ring and that interference with coplanarity diminishes the resonance effect.

49–11   Steric Damping in Ester Hydrolysis; Remote Steric Facilitation

A similar group of observations was made by Westheimer and Metcalf on the effect of steric damping on the reaction velocities of the alkaline hydrolysis of substituted ethyl benzoates. In each case, the logarithm of the reaction velocity was compared to that of the compound with hydrogen as a substituent as a standard. The results of their experiments are shown in Table 49–6. The last column gives the direct ratio of velocities.

Table 49–6

Substituent (para)	log (k/k_H) Ethyl benzoates	log (k/k_H) Ethyl 3,5-dimethyl benzoates	Difference, (log H,H) — (log R,R)	Ratio
H	0.00	0.00		
NO$_2$	2.02	1.60	0.42	2.6
NH$_2$	−1.63	−1.29	0.34	2.2
N(CH$_3$)$_2$	−1.53	−0.26	1.27	18.6

In this case, the nitro group speeds up the alkaline hydrolysis of the unsubstituted ethyl benzoate by a factor of over 2.6 times the amount of the effect which it exerts on the dimethyl-substituted ester. This is reflected in a difference of 0.42 units in the logarithm. Similarly, the amino group slows down the attack on the unsubstituted ethyl benzoate by a factor of 2.2 greater than for the dimethyl-substituted compound. These two comparisons permit the estimation of the magnitude of the differences to be expected between the two sets of compounds. If everything remained the same, the dimethylamino compounds would also be expected to be slowed down in the same degree as the amino compounds. Instead, however, we find that the difference in amount for the unsubstituted compound as compared with the substituted compound is 1.27 logarithmic units, that is, a factor of approximately 18.6. Thus the dimethylamino group is much more effective in slowing down the reaction in the unsubstituted ethyl benzoate than in the dimethyl-substituted compound. In the latter compound, the methyl groups are in a position to exert maximum interference with the coplanarity of the dimethylamino group:

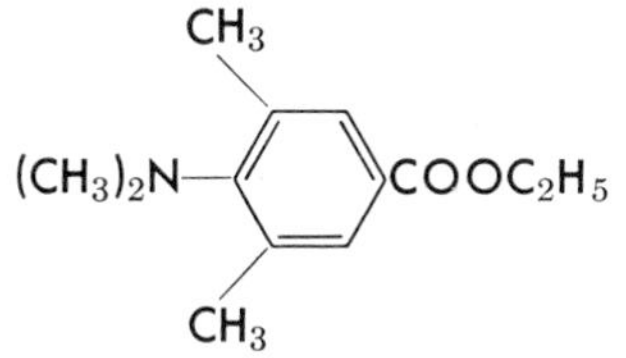

It is argued that by their steric effect, the two methyl groups prevent the dimethylamino group from assuming a coplanar position. But for the group to exert maximum electron-releasing effect, it would have to be coplanar. Hence it is argued that the effect of the methyl groups is a steric damping of resonance. Since this effect accomplishes a speeding up of the reaction, compared with the velocity of the unsubstituted compound, this case may be called an example of "remote steric facilitation" of a reaction. Thus, by their effects on the damping of resonance, groups may exert a remote effect of facilitation, when the group interfered with is an inhibiting group, or of hindrance, when the group interfered with is a facilitating group.

PROBLEMS

49–1 We saw earlier that acid chlorides form esters on treatment with alcohols. This is usually a fairly slow reaction. The hydrolysis of 2,4,6-trimethylbenzoyl chloride, however, is "immeasurably fast" under conditions where the rates of alcoholysis of other aromatic acid chlorides can be studied. Explain this fact.

49–2 The study of carbonium ions of the type RCO^+, sometimes called the oxocarbonium or acylonium ions, has been carried to the point where stable crystalline salts of these ions have been isolated and characterized. Such information lends support to mechanisms where they are postulated (see Problem 44–2). A further example of reactions of this sort is the acylation of aromatic compounds.

$$CH_3COCl + C_6H_6 \xrightarrow{AlCl_3} CH_3COC_6H_5 + HCl$$

(a) Suggest a mechanism for this reaction. The rate of this reaction has been found to be proportional to the product of the concentrations of the halide, the catalyst, and the aromatic compound.

(b) Would you expect a plot of logarithms of rates of reaction vs. sigma values of various RC_6H_5 with benzoyl chloride to have a positive or negative ρ?

(c) This reaction is also known for alkyl halides instead of acyl halides. Ethylbenzene may be prepared either from ethyl chloride, benzene, and aluminum chloride, or from ethylene, benzene, and sulfuric acid. What intermediate is the same in both of these reactions?

(d) Benzene dissolves in strong H_2SO_4. If D_2SO_4 is used, replacement of H by D is observed. Write a mechanism to account for this.

(e)

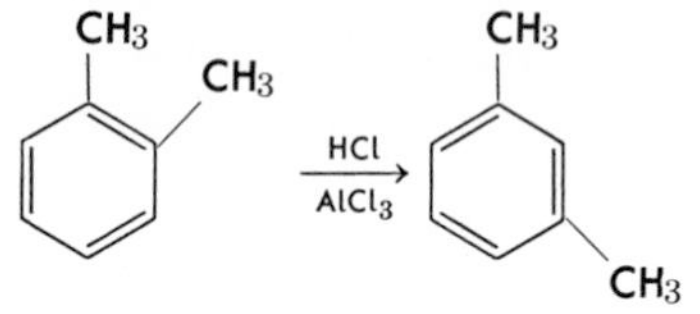

Keeping your answer to (d) in mind, write a plausible mechanism for the rearrangement.

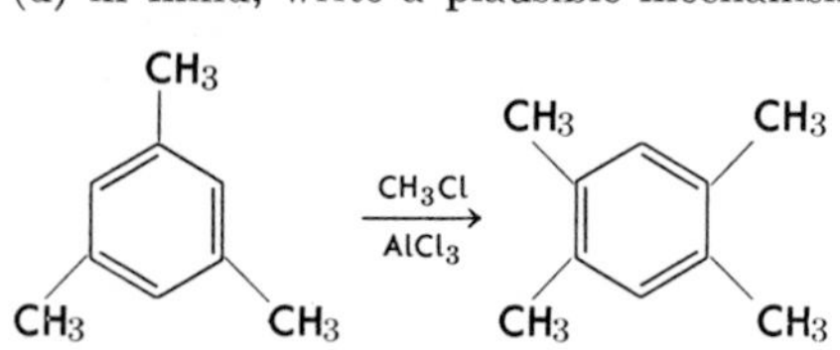

Mesitylene   Durene

Give a mechanism for the above reaction.
Why do you think that durene is formed in preference to the other tetramethylbenzenes?

49-3 The following reaction is observed.

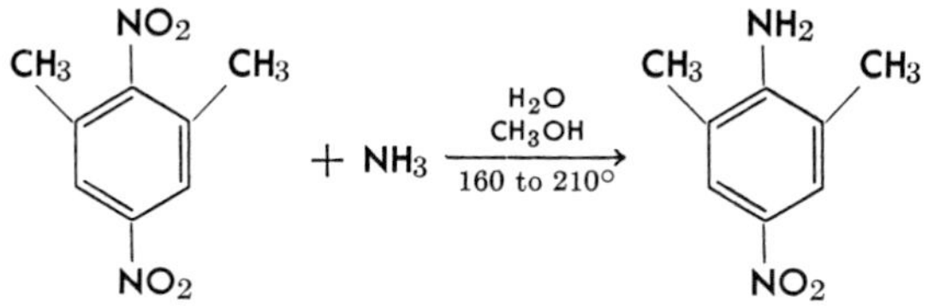

(a) What would the intermediate in this reaction be?

(b) Would the electronic effects of the methyl groups favor this reaction?

(c) Would they favor reaction with the 4-nitro group?

(d) With due regard to your answers to (b) and (c), how would you explain the formation of the product observed?

Do modern experimental techniques furnish a basis for verification
of the hypothesis that free-radical reaction intermediates exist?
What types of reaction mechanisms are best explained on the
assumption of the existence of free radicals? What techniques can distinguish
radical mechanisms from ionic or polar mechanisms?

50

RADICAL MECHANISMS

50–1 Background

In the first half of the nineteenth century, organic chemists thought that their analytical evidence provided them with grounds for formulating many of their compounds as radicals. It was not until Cannizzaro pointed out the importance of molecular-weight determinations that they realized that the substances they had regarded as radicals were molecules of double the assigned molecular weight. As a result of this discovery, radicals were in disrepute for the next forty years. At the turn of the century, however, Gomberg provided unequivocal evidence for the existence of the triphenylmethyl radical as a stable entity. This was prepared by a Wurtz reaction:

$$2(C_6H_5)_3CCl + 2Na \rightarrow 2NaCl + (C_6H_5)_3C-C(C_6H_5)_3 \rightleftarrows 2(C_6H_5)_3C \cdot$$

The radical was identified by its orange color (hexaphenylethane should be colorless), by the abnormal freezing-point depression which it gave to cryoscopic solvents in molecular-weight determinations, and by its extreme reactivity with atmospheric oxygen:

$$2(C_6H_5)_3C \cdot + O_2 \rightarrow (C_6H_5)_3C-O-O-C(C_6H_5)_3$$

For the next dozen years, organic chemists occupied themselves with studies on other radicals more or less resembling the triphenylmethyl radical. An event which took place in 1912 was passed over for nearly twenty years before its significance to organic chemistry was appreciated. This was the preparation of atomic hydrogen by Langmuir. Langmuir found that by heating hydrogen to approximately 2500°C it would dissociate into atoms:

$$H_2 \underset{\longleftarrow}{\overset{2500°}{\longrightarrow}} 2H \cdot$$

In 1924 R. W. Wood of the physics department at The Johns Hopkins University found a more convenient method for the preparation of atomic hydrogen. Wood's method consisted of drawing hydrogen through an electrical discharge tube. It was found that uncombined atoms could be detected at distances as great as 100 cm from the discharge. This discovery provided a convenient method for the preparation of atomic hydrogen for chemical studies, and Smallwood and Urey undertook physical and chemical studies on its properties.

50-2 Properties of Atomic Hydrogen

It was expected that atomic hydrogen would be a powerful reducing agent. Experimentation, however, showed that this concept was erroneous. Instead, atomic hydrogen proved to be a powerful chain initiator, causing many polymerization reactions. As an example the reaction of atomic hydrogen with ethylene, studied by Taylor, may be cited:

$$H \cdot \; + \; CH_2{=}CH_2 \rightarrow CH_3{-}CH_2 \cdot \; + \; CH_2{=}CH_2 \rightarrow CH_3CH_2C_2H_4 \cdot \; + \; C_2H_4 \rightarrow$$

$$CH_3CH_2(C_2H_4)_2 \cdot \; + \; \cdots$$

In the presence of an excess of ethylene, the polymerization process continues until two radicals collide to terminate it. It is thus possible to build oils and waxy materials. It is true that the resulting hydrocarbon is reduced from the original ethylene, but it has only added two hydrogens per chain rather than two hydrogens per ethylene, as in catalytic hydrogenations. It is for this reason that older theories of reductions based on mechanisms involving atomic hydrogen had to be discarded when the actual reactions of atomic hydrogen were investigated.

50-3 The Paneth Experiment

Perfection of techniques for working with atomic hydrogen laid the groundwork for the next step of interest to organic chemists, the Paneth experiment. In 1929, Paneth and Hofeditz studied the thermal decomposition of tetramethyl lead. They introduced the material into an evacuated tube, heated it to red heat, and found that it produced a lead mirror. Interest immediately centered on the nature of the organic products from this reaction. To investigate these, the experimenters repeated the first experiment under slightly altered conditions. A previously deposited mirror was placed downstream from the decomposition zone, while a second mirror was being deposited. It was found that the organic products from the upstream decomposition were capable of removing the downstream mirror. The apparatus used for the experiment is sketched in Fig. 50-1.

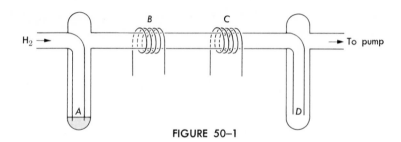

FIGURE 50–1

In the Paneth experiment, pure hydrogen at 1- to 2-mm pressure is used for a carrier. The first trap has tetramethyl lead at A. The temperature of this trap is regulated to produce any desired vapor pressure of the $Pb(CH_3)_4$. Furnace C is then heated to a temperature greater than 600°C and the issuing products are examined for undecomposed $Pb(CH_3)_4$ by catching them in the second trap at D. When temperatures in excess of 600° are used, it is found that the organometallic compound is completely decomposed. At the same time, a lead mirror is deposited at C. For the second part of the experiment, the portion of the tube at C is allowed to cool and that at B is heated to a temperature greater than 600°. A new lead mirror is now formed at B. Simultaneously, the mirror at C disappears. The equation for the reaction at B may be written:

$$Pb(CH_3)_4 \xrightarrow{600°} Pb + 4X \tag{1}$$

It was argued by some that the material removing the mirror at C might be some form of "hot molecule," perhaps a hot hydrogen molecule. This possibility was investigated by an examination of the products trapped in D. It was found that unlike the first portion of the experiment, when the mirror at C had been formed and no $Pb(CH_3)_4$ was to be found at D, the second portion of the experiment, with mirror removal at C, produced $Pb(CH_3)_4$. Hence we may write the equation for the reaction occurring at C as:

$$4X + Pb \rightarrow Pb(CH_3)_4 \tag{2}$$

It follows that the only logical solution to the problem of the identity of X in Eqs. (1) and (2) is that $X = CH_3\cdot$; this argument was buttressed by a similar experiment using zinc mirrors. Zinc forms no volatile hydride and, for this reason, could not be removed by hydrogen alone. Zinc-mirror removal by the fragments from the decomposition of either $Pb(CH_3)_4$ or $Zn(CH_3)_2$ is accompanied by the formation of $Zn(CH_3)_2$.

Paneth's announcement of the production of methyl radicals was greeted with polite skepticism, a reaction which heightened when investigators in a number of other laboratories were unable to duplicate his work. Paneth's reply was to invite anyone interested to come to his laboratories and learn the new technique. It was then discovered that the reason for many failures to reproduce the experiment was the lack of sufficiently "aseptic" precautions in the prosecution of the experiment.

In particular, small traces of oxygen are sufficient to coat the metallic mirrors with oxide and render them unreactive to radicals. It is an illuminating commentary on the care with which Paneth worked that he was able to succeed in this difficult experiment without any directions to guide him. One is tempted to inquire what the course of this branch of science might have been if someone with less careful technique had set up the experiment, experienced a failure, and announced that the concept was invalid. That such a possibility existed was proved by the fact that even with directions, some investigators were unable to secure the results which the experiment was capable of producing. This experience should serve as a warning to future investigators who are inclined to abandon promising lines of research after their first experimental rebuffs.

50–4 Reactions of Aliphatic Radicals

One chemist who was very much interested in Paneth's work and who took advantage of the invitation to visit the laboratory was F. O. Rice. Rice then proceeded to organize and prosecute a vigorous campaign of investigation of the thermal decomposition of organic compounds. We shall summarize briefly below the results of this work and of that of other laboratories in the field.

As might be expected, it was found that the main reaction of methyl radicals not exposed to a metallic mirror is that of recombination:

$$2CH_3 \cdot \; \rightarrow \; CH_3CH_3$$

Ethyl radicals formed at 500°C in sufficient concentration to undergo many collisions with each other give recombination to butane, but they also give other reactions:

$$100 \; C_2H_5 \cdot \; \rightarrow \; 28.6 \; C_4H_{10} + 14.9 \; C_2H_6 + 28.3 \; C_2H_4 + 12.0 \; H_2$$

This analysis of the reaction products establishes that one reaction of the ethyl radical at 500°C is decomposition:

$$C_2H_5 \cdot \; \rightarrow \; C_2H_4 + H \cdot$$

This decomposition at elevated temperatures contrasts with the relative stability of radicals at ordinary reaction temperatures which permits them to survive long enough to undergo polymerization reactions, as we have seen for the polymerization of ethylene. It is also evident that the atomic hydrogen formed by this process is capable of abstracting another hydrogen atom from an ethyl radical to give gaseous hydrogen:

$$H \cdot + C_2H_5 \cdot \; \rightarrow \; H_2 + C_2H_4$$

Thus one of the reactions of a radical, in this case atomic hydrogen, with a hydrocarbon radical (and also with a hydrocarbon) is the abstraction of an atom of hydrogen. The ethane formed in the reaction must come from disproportionation. Formulation will show that this is exactly the same reaction of hydrogen abstraction:

$$C_2H_5 \cdot \; + \; H—C_2H_4 \cdot \; \rightarrow \; C_2H_5—H \; + \; C_2H_4$$

50-5 The Thermal Decomposition of Hydrocarbons

After he had studied the general reactions of aliphatic radicals, Rice was in a position to examine the thermal decomposition of aliphatic hydrocarbons under controlled reaction conditions. He chose a temperature of 600°C for most of his studies and arranged the flow of the hydrocarbon through the cracking tube such that only a very small percentage of the material would be decomposed. This permitted him to study the primary reactions of the decomposition process. Any radicals formed could collide only with hydrocarbons, under these conditions, thus preventing the recombination reaction from occurring. It was found that radicals larger than the ethyl radical underwent even more extensive decomposition than the ethyl radical. It was also found that the rate of abstraction of hydrogens from different types of carbon atom were different in the ratio primary:secondary:tertiary = 1:2:10. Rice formulated a relatively simple scheme for the prediction of the outcome of the decomposition of aliphatic hydrocarbons, based on his analytical observations. Some years later, Rice and Kossiakoff made revisions in this scheme to permit greater quantitative precision to be obtained. The more precise scheme is more complicated, however, and since the simpler scheme illustrates the method, can be remembered easily, and permits reasonably good predictions of the outcome of these complicated reactions, we shall confine our attention to it.

The first step in the decomposition of an aliphatic hydrocarbon was found to be the formation of radicals. These were identified by analysis of the products of mirror removal. In the next step, the radical abstracts a hydrogen from one of the carbons of the hydrocarbon under study, forming a new radical. This is a chain-initiating step. The new radical will then react or decompose in its characteristic manner, with the formation of still another radical. This is the chain-propagating step. Under the conditions used, it was found that the chain length is approximately 100. This means that the chain-propagating step is repeated about 100 times before the chain is terminated due to collision of two radicals or to a wall reaction. Thus there are four steps in the decomposition reaction: (1) radical formation, (2) chain initiation, (3) chain propagation, (4) chain termination. We shall illustrate these processes by using the thermal decomposition of propane as an example.

50-6 Thermal Decomposition of Propane

When propane is heated to 600°C, radical formation takes place by cleavage of the weakest bond, the C—C bond:

$$CH_3—CH_2—CH_3 \; \rightarrow \; CH_3 \cdot \; + \; \cdot CH_2—CH_3$$

These can be identified by performing the decomposition in the presence of a lead mirror in which case tetraalkyl leads are formed. The methyl and ethyl radicals so formed react with the excess of propane in which they are carried to abstract hydrogen:

$$CH_3 \cdot \; + \; CH_3{-}CH_2{-}CH_3 \rightarrow CH_4 \; + \; \cdot CH_2{-}CH_2{-}CH_3$$

$$C_2H_5 \cdot \; + \; CH_3{-}CH_2{-}CH_3 \rightarrow C_2H_6 \; + \; \cdot CH_2{-}CH_2{-}CH_3$$

This hydrogen-abstraction reaction serves to initiate the chain. However, in the chain-propagation reaction two different hydrogen abstractions are possible:

$$R \cdot \; + \; CH_3{-}CH_2{-}CH_3 \rightarrow RH \; + \; \cdot CH_2{-}CH_2{-}CH_3 \tag{1}$$

$$R \cdot \; + \; CH_3{-}CH_2{-}CH_3 \rightarrow RH \; + \; CH_3{-}\overset{\cdot}{C}H{-}CH_3 \tag{2}$$

Because there are six primary hydrogens and only two secondary, we might expect these reactions to occur in the proportions of 6:2. As stated above, however, it was found that secondary hydrogens are abstracted approximately twice as readily as primary. This gives a weighting factor which corrects the ratio from the expected value of 6:2 to the weighted value of 6:4. Hence we may write two chain-propagation reactions in the following proportions:

$$6R \cdot \; + \; 6CH_3{-}CH_2{-}CH_3 \rightarrow 6RH \; + \; 6 \cdot CH_2{-}CH_2{-}CH_3 \tag{1}$$

and

$$4R \cdot \; + \; 4CH_3{-}CH_2{-}CH_3 \rightarrow 4RH \; + \; 4CH_3{-}\overset{\cdot}{C}H{-}CH_3 \tag{2}$$

The characteristic reaction of the *n*-propyl radical will be decomposition at the weakest bond, a C—C bond. One of these would give a methylene radical and an ethyl radical:

$$\cdot CH_2{-}CH_2{-}CH_3 \rightarrow \; \cdot CH_2 \cdot \; + \; \cdot CH_2{-}CH_3$$

The methylene radical is a higher-energy form than the monovalent radicals, so this reaction would require a considerable increase in energy. On the other hand, decomposition at the other bond would yield another radical and a stable olefin:

$$\cdot CH_2{-}CH_2{-}CH_3 \rightarrow CH_2{=}CH_2 \; + \; CH_3 \cdot$$

This reaction, because of the formation of ethylene, would be exothermic instead of endothermic. Hence, this is the decomposition to be expected. This means that one of the chain-propagating radicals will be the methyl radical.

The characteristic reaction of the *i*-propyl radical cannot be cleavage at either carbon, since either would yield the same divalent radical:

$$CH_3{-}\overset{\cdot}{C}H{-}CH_3 \rightarrow CH_3{-}\overset{\cdot}{C}H \cdot \; + \; \cdot CH_3$$

For this reason, the next stronger bond will have to break in this radical, that is, a CH bond. This gives the reaction:

$$CH_3—\overset{\displaystyle .}{C}H—CH_3 \rightarrow H\cdot + CH_2{=}CH—CH_3$$

Therefore the second chain-propagating radical will be the hydrogen atom.

We may now complete the formulation of the chain-propagating step, with the components properly weighted:

$$6\cdot CH_2—CH_2—CH_3 \rightarrow 6CH_2{=}CH_2 + 6CH_3\cdot \qquad RH = CH_4$$

$$4CH_3—\overset{\displaystyle .}{C}H—CH_3 \rightarrow 4CH_2{=}CH—CH_3 + 4H\cdot \qquad RH = H_2$$

From this analysis, we may write the prediction for the outcome of the reaction as follows:

$$10C_3H_8 \rightarrow 6CH_2{=}CH_2 + 6CH_4 + 4CH_2{=}CH—CH_3 + 4H_2$$

Thus 10 volumes of propane originally taken will expand to 20 volumes and the analysis should be $\frac{6}{20}$ ethylene, $\frac{6}{20}$ methane, $\frac{4}{20}$ propylene, and $\frac{4}{20}$ hydrogen. A few percent, 1% or 2%, of methane and ethane should also be formed from the primary-radical decomposition, but this will be far outweighed by the fact that this takes place once while the chain itself has many links.

The outcome of the experiment is shown below.

	H_2	CH_4	C_2H_4	C_2H_6	C_3H_6
Predicted	20	30	30	0	20
Found	23	26	22	2	25

As stated, the revised scheme will give a still closer approach to the observed value. However, since most mechanistic theories do not even attempt to predict yields, this simple scheme for predicting yields from a thermal decomposition is quite adequate as a quick "rule-of-thumb."

50–7   Decompositions of Methane, Ethane, and Ethylene

Among the most unexpected results obtained in this work were those on the thermal decomposition of methane, ethane, and ethylene. Let us consider ethane first. Experiment shows that the chain-initiating step is the formation of methyl radicals, as might be expected. These then abstract hydrogens and the ethyl radicals so formed decompose:

$$CH_3\cdot + CH_3—CH_3 \rightarrow CH_4 + \cdot CH_2—CH_3 \rightarrow H\cdot + C_2H_4$$

The chain-propagating radical is the $H\cdot$ atom, RH is H_2, and the products of the decomposition are hydrogen and ethylene. To the organic chemist accustomed to thinking of ethylene as more reactive and "unstable" than ethane, it requires a readjustment of the frame of reference to regard ethylene as more stable than ethane. With respect to thermal stability, this is certainly so, however. Ethane decomposes at 600°C whereas ethylene is stable to approximately 800°C.

Methane requires a temperature of approximately 750°C to bring about its decomposition. This demonstrates the greater stability of the CH bond than of the $C-C$ bond. The primary products of the decomposition of methane would be methyl radicals and hydrogen. Collision of either with more methane could result in the formation only of more methyl radicals. Ultimately, two of these must collide, giving ethane. This would then be decomposed by the methyl radicals present to give ethylene and hydrogen. Hence the final products of the decomposition of methane are hydrogen and ethylene:

$$2CH_4 \rightarrow C_2H_4 + H_2$$

At temperatures above 800°C, the decomposition of ethylene can be accomplished with the formation of hydrogen and acetylene. The reader should be able to write the mechanism for the reaction. Again, the stability of acetylene requires a readjustment of the organic chemist's thinking. Acetylene can be formed by passing hydrogen through a carbon arc at 4000°C and is thus the most stable of the hydrocarbons to thermal effects.

50–8   Other Thermal Decompositions

The thermal decomposition of many substances other than hydrocarbons has been studied systematically. One of the decompositions which is used commercially is that of acetone to give ketene. The mechanism has been shown to be as follows:

$$CH_3COCH_3 \rightarrow CH_3\cdot + \cdot COCH_3 \rightarrow CO + \cdot CH_3$$
$$CH_3\cdot + CH_3COCH_3 \rightarrow CH_4 + \cdot CH_2COCH_3$$
$$\cdot CH_2COCH_3 \rightarrow CH_3\cdot + CH_2{=}CO$$
$$\text{Ketene}$$

Again we see an instance of the instability of radicals at elevated temperatures. The acetyl radical decomposes at 600°C, whereas it could persist long enough to undergo a number of collisions at room temperature.

Ketene is a very reactive substance and can be used for a variety of acetylations:

$$CH_2{=}CO + H_2O \rightarrow CH_3COOH$$
$$CH_2{=}CO + CH_3OH \rightarrow CH_3COOCH_3$$
$$CH_2{=}CO + CH_3COOH \rightarrow (CH_3CO)_2O$$

$$CH_2{=}CO + CH_2{=}CO \rightarrow \begin{array}{c} CH_2{=}C{-}O \\ | \quad\quad | \\ CH_2{-}C{=}O \end{array} + CH_3OH \rightarrow CH_3COCH_2COOCH_3$$

Ketene dimer

50–9   Stable Radicals; Autoxidations

We have seen that electrons tend to distribute between orbitals according to Hund's rule before they pair. The result is a large number of substances with unpaired electrons which may be regarded as stable radicals. The characteristic physical property of unpaired electrons is their ability to be attracted to a magnet. The magnetic properties of iron, nickel, and some other metals are due to this structural feature.

More surprising, however, is the existence of a number of stable free radicals of low molecular weight. Of these NO and NO_2 can be formulated in no other manner, since the molecules have an odd number of electrons. The most surprising case, however, is that of oxygen. Ordinary gaseous oxygen does not obey the usual octet rule and has two unpaired electrons. Thus its formula is

$$\cdot \ddot{O} : \ddot{O} \cdot$$

As a result, it is able to initiate many reactions which proceed by radical-chain mechanisms. These are ordinarily called *autoxidations*. An example is the air oxidation of benzaldehyde. This reaction is catalyzed by ferric ions. Thus the brown bottles frequently used for the storage of chemicals actually promote the destruction of benzaldehyde. A mechanism which is in agreement with all the known facts is:

$$C_6H_5CHO + Fe^{+3} \rightarrow C_6H_5\overset{\bullet}{C}{=}O + Fe^{++} + H^+$$

$$C_6H_5\overset{\bullet}{C}O + O_2 \rightarrow C_6H_5\overset{O}{\overset{\|}{C}}{-}O{-}O\cdot$$

$$C_6H_5\overset{O}{\overset{\|}{C}}{-}O{-}O\cdot + C_6H_5CHO \rightarrow C_6H_5\overset{O}{\overset{\|}{C}}{-}O{-}O{-}H + C_6H_5\overset{\bullet}{C}O$$

Here we see the contrast in radical stability due to the lowering of the temperature from the conditions of thermal-decomposition reactions. The benzoyl radical in this room-temperature reaction is sufficiently stable to carry the radical chain effectively. The perbenzoic acid formed in this reaction will decompose in time to give benzoic acid and hydrogen peroxide.

50–10   The Addition of HBr to Propylene

Pure propylene, when treated with HBr, adds according to Markovnikov's rule:

$$CH_3CH{=}CH_2 + HBr \rightarrow CH_3CHBrCH_3$$

In studying the reaction, however, the results from different laboratories were so conflicting that Kharasch undertook a reinvestigation of the reaction. He discovered that the results obtained depended on the purity of the sample of propylene used. Samples which had stood in the air were found to have acquired peroxides which altered the course of the reaction. By the addition of peroxide, he found that another, faster reaction could be made to supersede the normal addition:

$$CH_3CH=CH_2 + HBr \xrightarrow{\text{peroxide}} CH_3CH_2CH_2Br$$

This is thus an "anti-Markovnikov" addition. The peroxide-catalyzed reaction was found to involve a radical chain:

$$RO-OH \rightarrow RO\cdot + \cdot OH$$
$$RO\cdot + HBr \rightarrow ROH + Br\cdot$$
$$Br\cdot + CH_3CH=CH_2 \rightarrow CH_3\overset{\cdot}{C}HCH_2Br$$
$$CH_3\overset{\cdot}{C}HCH_2Br + HBr \rightarrow CH_3CH_2CH_2Br + Br\cdot$$

The bond in HCl is too strong to be broken by peroxides, hence the reaction does not work in this case. In the case of HI, the reagent reduces the peroxides and thus prevents the initiation of the chain. For this reason, the reaction only succeeds for additions of HBr.

50–11 Homolytic and Heterolytic Mechanisms

The foregoing reactions are only examples of the many homolytic reactions that occur. In general, these reactions are chain reactions. They can frequently be identified by their ability to start other chains, such as polymerization chains. Chains can also be identified by the fact that as a rule, their kinetics are complicated and do not follow integral orders. In spite of the great mass of homolytic reactions known, however, their number is dwarfed by the number of heterolytic reactions which occur. Consequently, it is advisable to place the major emphasis in reaction mechanisms on the heterolytic reactions, as has been done in this presentation.

PROBLEMS

50–1 Give qualitative rationalizations of the following observations:

(a) Both the *para*-methoxy and the *para*-nitro substituents in analogs of hexaphenylethane increase the dissociation of triarylmethyl radicals.

(b) Hexamethylethane, which does not dissociate into free radicals, has an abnormally long C—C bond length between the central carbons.

(c) Hexa(*o*-tolyl)ethane (I) has a dissociation equilibrium constant more than 1000 times larger than that of hexa(*p*-tolyl)ethane (II) in benzene at 25°C.

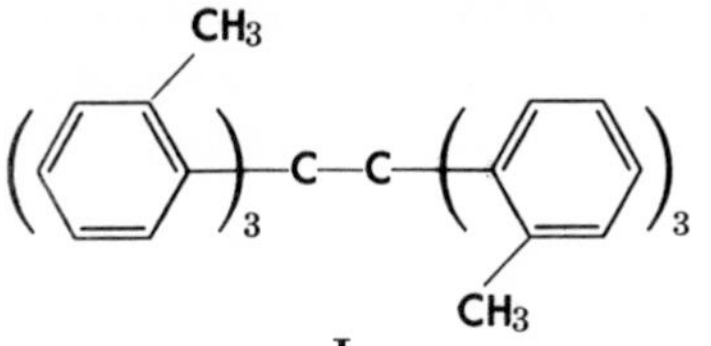

I 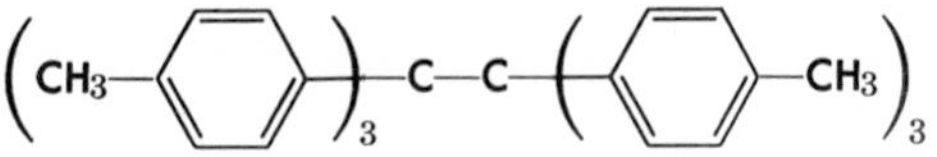   II

(d) The rates of removal of a hydrogen atom from a primary, a secondary, and a tertiary carbon are in the ratio 1:2:10.

50–2   Give the products and approximate yields expected for the decomposition of neopentane and isobutane at 600°C.

50–3   What products would you expect from the thermal decomposition of acetaldehyde? The relative rate of the process

$$R\cdot \; + \; RCH \rightarrow RH + R\dot{C}{=}O$$
$$\qquad\;\; \underset{O}{\|}$$

is much greater than any competing abstraction of hydrogen.

Part 6

FURTHER APPLICATIONS
OF SPECTROSCOPY

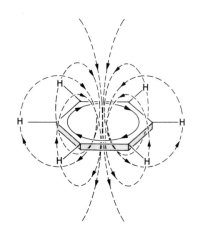

In earlier chapters we hinted at the utility of infrared and x-ray spectroscopy and mass spectrometry to organic chemists in structural studies and in relating chemical reactivity to structure. Other spectroscopic correlations have also been used frequently. For example, visible and ultraviolet spectroscopy are widely used in qualitative studies and in quantitative measurements. Colored substances are chosen for the visualization, for qualitative purposes, of the presence or absence of reactive materials in both chemical and physiological fields. In the latter field, they are invaluable in the localization of chemically different substances and of reactive sites. In quantitative studies, the determination of color intensity forms one of the favorite general methods for quantitative analysis in areas as diverse as organic, inorganic, physical, and biological studies. Finally, the advent of convenient and precise measurements of the interaction of nuclear spins with magnetic fields provides yet another method for the resolution of structural problems.

The chemist who wishes to take the fullest advantage of the wealth of spectroscopic material available for the study of diverse mechanisms, both chemical and biochemical, will need to understand the rudiments of the theory of energy absorption, together with some practical applications.

What is color? Which entities within a molecule are responsible for the absorption of light? What happens to these entities when light is absorbed? What are the general relationships between the absorption of light and chemical structure?

51

THEORY OF ELECTRONIC ABSORPTION SPECTRA

51-1 The Importance of Color Theory

Through the study of the spectra of the elements, physicists have been able to achieve a quantitative understanding of the energy relationships that are fundamentally responsible for chemical bonding. Our theories of the number, arrangements, and interrelationships between atomic orbitals have been based on spectroscopic measurements. In examining the details of chemical bonding, chemists have attempted to adapt and expand the theories of atomic orbitals to permit their application to the problems concerned with the nature of bonds, their relative strengths, and their interrelationships. Thus the study of molecular spectra provides the chemist with the materials for the quantitative examination of bond energies and other bond characteristics based on an approach quite different from the study of chemical reactivity. For this reason, information derived from this source which supports theories based on chemical reactivity helps to substantiate these theories, while information which diverges may well point the way toward new chemical approaches.

51-2 The Basis of Modern Color Theory

Quantum-mechanical approaches to the problem of light absorption have been based on the valence-bond theory and on the molecular-orbital theory. As we have seen, the valence-bond theory has many applications in chemical work which make it convenient for the organic chemist to use. For some other applications, the molecular-orbital theory is more convenient. In the case of color theory, the molecular-orbital theory has the advantage that it is patterned on the atomic-orbital theory and is thus able to use materials from the physical study of spectra by casting them into similar patterns. It is for this reason that the molecular-orbital theory has been found to be the more convenient in the correlation of structure with light absorption. Accordingly, we shall approach the problems of color from this point of view.

51–3   What is Color?

White light is a mixture of all the wavelengths of light that are visible to the human eye. A filter that is capable of removing all the wavelengths except yellow would obviously create the physiological impression of yellow light. A pigment on a cloth or piece of paper that removed all the wavelengths except yellow would reflect only the yellow light and would thus appear yellow. On the other hand, this is not the only mechanism by which the impression of yellowness can be created. If a pigment removes only the violet portion of the white light, the resulting impression to the eye is that of the complementary color, namely, yellow. Most dyes and pigments create the impression of color by this process, that is, they have a wavelength of maximum absorption in the visible, and by removing light of this wavelength, the eye perceives the complementary color. Hence the problem of color theory is to correlate the positions and intensities of light absorptions by different compounds with their structures.

51–4   Witt's Chromophore Theory

In 1876 Witt propounded his *chromophore* theory of color. In modern terms, this would be regarded as a descriptive correlation between color and structure, not as a mechanistic approach. Since the descriptive terms employed by Witt remain in current use, however, the reader should become familiar with them. Witt stated that two types of group are ordinarily present in colored compounds. The fundamental color-bearing group he called a *chromophore*. He thought of the $N{=}N$, $C{=}O$, and NO_2 groups as chromophores. Later a number of other chromophores were added, of which the most important was the quinoid grouping:

Quinone   A quinoid or quinonoid grouping

Groups such as the phenolic hydroxyl and the amino or dimethylamino groups, Witt called *auxochromes*, that is, groups which increase color. In modern usage, the combination of a chromophore with an auxochrome is more likely to be regarded as a new chromophore, rather than simply as a combination. Finally, Witt spoke of two types of color shift caused by the introduction of substituents, a *bathochromic* shift, that is, a deepening of shade caused by a shift in absorption to longer wavelengths, and a *hypsochromic* shift, that is, a lightening of shade caused by an absorption shift to shorter wavelengths.

We now recognize that the "unsaturation" that Witt and his contemporaries regarded as essential to color is a phenomenon associated with the pi electrons. The first question that must be asked, then, is whether or not color can be associated with other types of electrons.

51–5　Energy Absorption by Sigma Electrons

If we move far enough into the ultraviolet, thereby increasing the energy of the light, we shall ultimately find a wavelength whose absorption by hydrogen causes one of the binding electrons to dissociate from the molecule with the formation of the species H_2^+. Thus this absorption is connected with a sigma electron of the hydrogen molecule. As this wavelength is approached, definite absorption bands appear in the spectrum whose spacing gets progressively closer until the bands are finally so close together that they are incapable of resolution. This is the wavelength at which ionization takes place. This region is in the portion of the spectrum where absorption by oxygen and nitrogen takes place, so that spectrometers for its study have to be operated in a vacuum. It is thus called the *vacuum ultraviolet*. The vacuum ultraviolet extends below 175 mμ. The region between 185 and 175 mμ can be reached in an atmosphere of nitrogen but not in oxygen.

Examination of methane shows a similar absorption region for it in the vacuum ultraviolet. This can also be shown to be due to the imparting of enough energy to a sigma electron to cause ionization. The C—C single bond absorbs at longer wavelengths. None of these absorptions can be said to cause color, in the physiological sense, since they take place in the vacuum ultraviolet, and the lower limit of perception by the eye is about 400 mμ. (See Fig. 51–1.)

Since the absorptions due to sigma electrons which occur in the regions of longest wavelength do not cause dissociation of the molecules, it must be possible to promote sigma electrons, through the absorption of electromagnetic energy, into higher energy states without disruption of bonding. The excited states formed by this energy absorption do not lend themselves readily to formulation by the usual bonding notations used by the organic chemist. Reference to Chapter 31 will show some of the higher energy levels which must be considered for the representation of the excited states. A compromise may be reached by formulating a $\sigma \rightarrow \sigma^*$ transition as follows:

$$H \updownarrow H \xrightarrow{h\nu} H \downarrow \uparrow H$$

This notation is intended to show that the electrons originally paired in the ground state remain paired even though one of them has moved to a higher energy level.

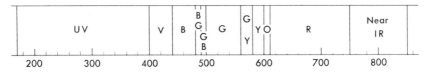

FIGURE 51–1

51–6   Energy Absorption by Pi Electrons

Ethylene has absorption bands in the C—H and C—C regions of the vacuum ultraviolet where methane and ethane absorb. In addition, however, it has bands at longer wavelengths. The longest wavelength at which a strong absorption occurs is at 203 mμ. Because this represents substantially less energy than is present in the vacuum ultraviolet, the absorption must be due to electrons less firmly held than the sigma electrons. Accordingly, it is logical to ascribe this absorption to the pi electrons. In conjugated systems of increasing length, the absorption bands appear at still longer wavelengths, that is, at still lower energies.

The absorption of electromagnetic energy by ethylene may be represented as follows:

$$\text{H}_2\text{C} \; \updownarrow \; \updownarrow \; \text{CH}_2 \xrightarrow{h\nu} \text{H}_2\text{C} \; \updownarrow \; \downarrow\uparrow \; \text{CH}_2$$

51–7   The Energies of Hydrogen Emissions

It will be recalled that light results when an electron which has been previously excited to a higher level undergoes a transition to a lower energy level. The early spectroscopic investigators found that the energies associated with these emissions fell into series which obeyed simple numerical relations. The Lyman series of the hydrogen spectrum is made up of transitions from energy levels 2, 3, 4, 5, etc., down to the energy level 1. Calculation of the energies of the various levels shows that they may be represented by the series

$$E_1 = C(1/1^2), \qquad E_2 = C(1/2^2), \qquad E_3 = C(1/3^2), \qquad E_n = C(1/n^2).$$

The constant, C, is related to more fundamental physical constants by the equation

$$C = -\frac{2\pi^2 m e^4}{h^2},$$

where m is the mass of the electron, e is its charge, and h is Planck's constant.

In the transition from a higher energy level to a lower level, the energy emitted will be the difference between the two levels: $(E_1 - E_2), (E_1 - E_3), \ldots$ The relationship between energy and the frequency of the emitted light is given by the equation

$$E = h\nu,$$

where h is Planck's constant and ν is the frequency. Energy is given in ergs. Hence we may write for the energies involved in the Lyman series:

$$E_1 - E_2 = h\nu_1 = C(1 - \tfrac{1}{4}), \qquad E_1 - E_3 = h\nu_2 = C(1 - \tfrac{1}{9}) \ldots$$

The figures derived from these simple relationships are in excellent agreement with the experimental observations.

51-8   Energies of Pi Electron Absorption

Since the process of energy absorption is the reverse of that of emission, it is reasoned that the absorptions of pi electrons may be cast into a model resembling that of the hydrogen atom. It is obvious from this statement that the relative precisions of the two calculations will be of a different order, since the complexity of the molecule is much greater than that of the atom, and many more forces are at work in the molecule. For this reason, it is also obvious that while the pattern may be useful, fitting and modifying will be essential to secure a workable result.

51-9   Absorption by Ethylene

Let us consider ethylene first. There will be two pi electrons, and in the ground state both will be in a single orbital. The lowest energy absorption band will involve the transition of one of these electrons to the lowest unoccupied orbital. We may diagram this as illustrated in Fig. 51–2. The problem is to find the energy required for the transition.

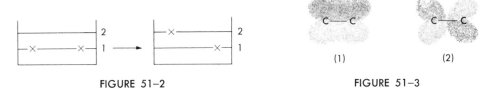

FIGURE 51–2   FIGURE 51–3

Following the convention used in organic spectroscopy, energies are calculated in wave numbers, that is, reciprocal centimeters, rather than in ergs. In this case, the formula for the energy of an electron in the nth state is given, to a first approximation, by the formula

$$E_n = B(n^2/L^2),$$

where n is the number of the orbital, L is the length of the orbital and B is a constant equal to $h/8mc$, where c is the velocity of light, h is Planck's constant, and m is the mass of the electron. For the transition indicated, the values would be:

$$E_1 = B/L^2, \qquad E_2 = 4B/L^2, \qquad E_2 - E_1 = 3B/L^2.$$

A study of the symmetries of the orbitals of ethylene, which can be conducted by means of the study of polarization phenomena, leads to the conclusion that the lowest vacant orbital, represented by the level 2 in Fig. 51–2, has a node in the center. The general shapes of the first two orbitals of ethylene are shown in Fig. 51–3.

A formula for the energy of a spectroscopic transition such as that given above can only be tested for the general order of magnitude of its fit in a single case, because of the possibility of adjusting L. To give the formula a better test, it was applied to the polyenes.

51–10   Absorption by Butadiene

The ground state of butadiene has four π-electrons occupying the two lowest-lying orbitals. The diagram is given in Fig. 51–4. Again the transition is from the highest occupied level to the lowest unoccupied level, giving the longest wavelength transition. In this case L would be 3(C—C).

$$CH_2\!=\!CH\!-\!CH\!=\!CH_2$$

$$C\!-\!C \quad C\!-\!C \quad C\!-\!C$$

Because of the zig-zag shape of the molecule, the actual distance would be somewhat less than that indicated. The shapes assigned to the four lowest-lying orbitals of butadiene are shown in Fig. 51–5.

Comparing the wavelengths calculated for butadiene and higher polyenes with those actually observed, we find that the simple formula given was not close enough to the observed values to be considered satisfactory. Accordingly, modifications were made.

It will be recalled that the first unoccupied orbital of H_2^+, as well as that of the hydrogen molecule itself, is an *antibonding* orbital. Promotion of an electron into such an orbital in a polyene weakens the bond between the carbons with the result that the dimensions of the excited state are larger than those of the ground state. Accordingly, the first modification made in an effort to fit the formula to the observations was to use a different and larger value of L for the first excited state than for the ground state. This alteration resulted in an improvement of the fit between the formula and the observed values.

The simple diagrams of Figs. 51–2 and 51–4 assume that the "potential wells" holding the electrons in ethylene and butadiene are rectangular boxes. In fact, however, they are electrical force fields of much greater complexity in shape than rectangular boxes. One shape assumed for the force fields holding the electrons in butadiene is given by the dashed line in Fig. 51–6. Calculations based on a shape as irregular as that indicated by the dashed line are complex and tedious to make. Accordingly, a compromise was arrived at by assuming a sine-curve potential well whose values would approximate the average of the more complex curve. This well is shown in Fig. 51–6. This further modification of the shape of the box permitted a still closer approximation to the spectroscopic values observed.

The process given in outline in the preceding argument will suffice to illustrate the general approach to the solution of a quantum-mechanical problem as complex as that of the spectra of large molecules. Rigorous solutions are out of the question because of the computational difficulties involved. The nature of the models which are successful in giving reasonably good fits to the data are useful, however, in giving a closer approximation to the nature of the ground states and the electronically excited states in molecules. This information is frequently of such a nature that the quantitative findings may be translated into qualitative differences of value to the organic chemist.

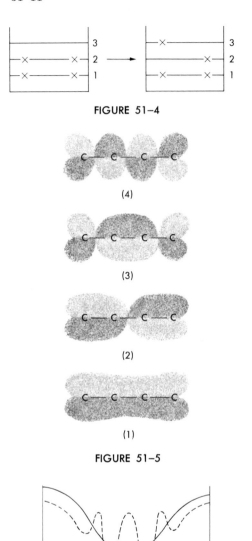

FIGURE 51–4

FIGURE 51–5

FIGURE 51–6

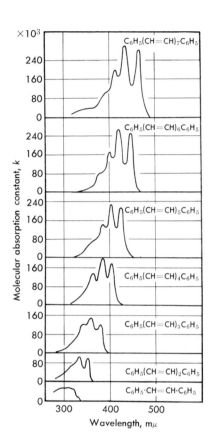

FIG. 51–7. Absorption spectra of diphenylpolyenes in benzene. [Reproduced by permission from A. E. Gillam and E. S. Stern, *An Introduction to Electronic Absorption Spectroscopy in Organic Chemistry*, London: Edward Arnold (Publishers) Ltd., 1958.]

51–11 Spectra of Polyenes

Figure 51–7 shows the absorption spectra of a series of diphenylpolyenes, C_6H_5—$(CH{=}CH)_n$—C_6H_5. Two features of these spectra are apparent from the figure. The first is that the wavelength of the first absorption band moves closer and closer to the visible as the number of carbons in the conjugated system increases. The second is that the intensity of the absorption also increases as the wavelength increases.

With respect to the positions of the absorption maxima, the formula for calculating the absorptions of the polyenes correlates with the finding that the positions of the maxima should move to lower energies as the number of carbons in the conjugated chain increases. Using the rough approximation that each double bond in the conjugation lengthens the chain by one C—C unit, which we shall designate as d, the lowest energy absorption of ethylene would be $3B/d^2$. That of butadiene would be $(9 - 4) = 5B/(3d)^2$ or $\frac{5}{9}B/d^2$. Hexatriene would be $(16 - 9) = 7B/(5d)^2$ or $\frac{7}{25}B/d^2$. Thus as the series lengthens, the fraction of B/d^2 diminishes, and the energy of the transition diminishes. This is the relationship illustrated by Fig. 51–7.

51–12 The Intensity of Absorption

The intensity of an electronic absorption is measured by the area under the absorption curve at a given transition. We may assume that the light used to irradiate the sample is kept constant from sample to sample. Then a lower absorption intensity would correspond to a smaller fraction of the photons impinging on the molecule being absorbed. With most organic substances, only a very tiny fraction of the photons colliding with a molecule is absorbed. The major portion of the collisions is rejected by the molecule and brings about no transition. Thus the area under the curve is said to measure the *transition probability*, that is, the probability that a collision between a photon of the right wavelength for absorption and a molecule will produce a transition in the molecule to an excited state.

The formula for calculating the transition probability in a polyene system resembles that used to calculate the energy of transition but is somewhat more complex. It is also inverted in its effect from that for energies, since the transitions between higher levels which have the lower energies have the higher transition probabilities.

PROBLEMS

51–1 Arrange the following molecules in order of increasing energy of the first electronic transition and then in order of decreasing transition probability.

Benzene 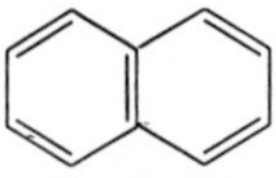   Naphthalene 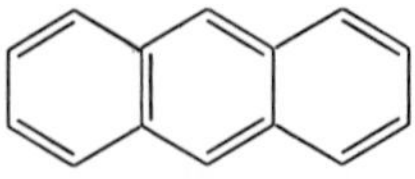   Anthracene 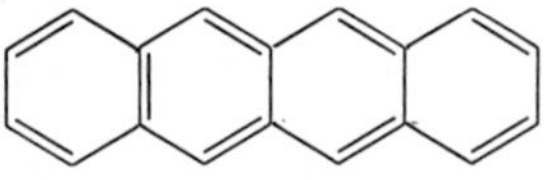   Naphthacene

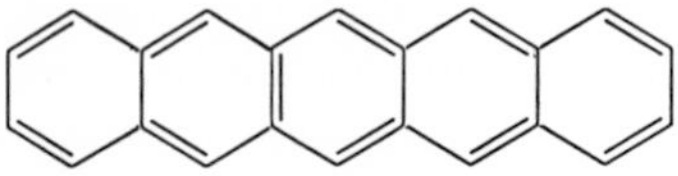

Pentacene 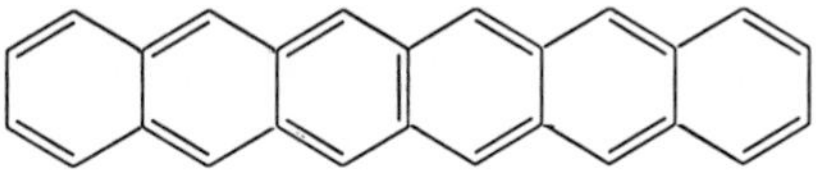   Hexacene

51-2   The first absorption maximum for hexacene occurs at 686 mμ, and that for hexaphene occurs at 459.5 mμ. Rationalize this fact.

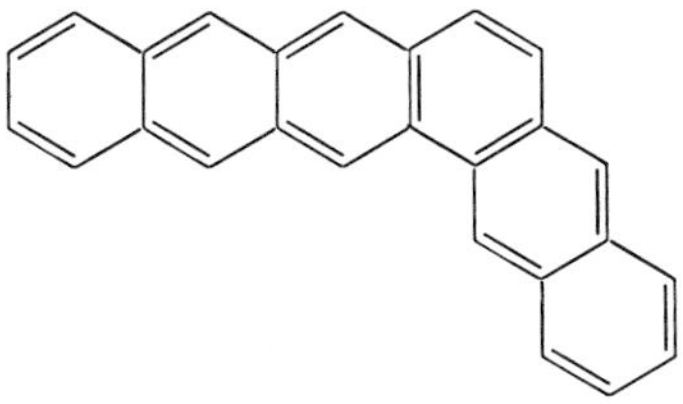

Hexaphene

51-3   Rationalize the following: *trans*-stilbene (diphenylethylene) has maximum absorption at 295.5 mμ, but *cis*-stilbene absorbs maximally at 280 mμ; in addition, the transition probability for the latter compound is much less. The absorption of 2,4,6-trimethyl-*trans*-stilbene is similar to that of *cis*-stilbene rather than that of *trans*-stilbene.

51-4   Anthracene and 1,1-diphenylethylene in ethanol or hexane solutions have dissimilar ultraviolet spectra. Is this to be expected? In concentrated sulfuric acid, their spectra are very similar. What does this imply about the position of protonation in these molecules? Draw structures for the protonated forms consistent with the observation.

How can the theory of molecular orbitals be applied to rationalize the observed facts concerning light absorption in organic molecules? What effects do molecular vibrations and rotations have on visible and ultraviolet spectra? How is it possible to perform calculations on the excited states of molecules which permit estimation of their bond lengths and angles?

52

TYPES OF ABSORPTION AND EMISSION SPECTRA

52–1 The Orbitals of Benzene

The six pi electrons of benzene are assigned to three orbitals. The lowest-lying of these encompass the whole molecule and may be represented by enclosing the whole area of the ring within one shaded area, as in Fig. 52–1. This orbital has a node in the plane of the benzene ring but otherwise occupies the whole force field of the six-carbon system. The next higher energy levels are represented by different electron distributions but have identical energies. Their nodes are shown in Fig. 52–2. The relationship between the diagrams of Figs. 52–1 and 52–2 may be compared to the vibration of a string in which the lowest-lying energy level corresponds to the vibration of the whole string, the fundamental tone, while the next higher energy level corresponds to the vibration with a node at the center, the first overtone. In the ground state of the molecule, each of these orbitals is assigned two electrons.

The first two unoccupied orbitals of the benzene molecule are assigned the orbitals sketched in Fig. 52–3. These also have identical energies. The highest energy orbital is represented by Fig. 52–4. Energetically, we may represent the levels by the diagram of Fig. 52–5.

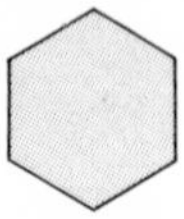

FIGURE 52–1   FIGURE 52–2 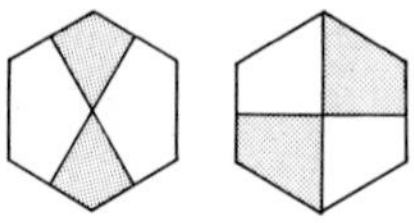   FIGURE 52–3 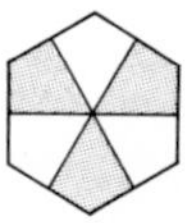   FIGURE 52–4

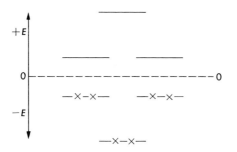

FIGURE 52–5

52–2 Transitions of Benzene

Inspection will show that the orbitals of benzene differ in their symmetries. As a consequence, transition of an electron from a state with one symmetry to one with a different symmetry would require the action of a light "vector" with a special asymmetry of its own, that is, the light would have to be polarized at a definite angle to accomplish the transition. Certain symmetry changes cannot be accomplished in a single step. These are said to be "forbidden." The transition from the highest occupied to the lowest unoccupied orbital of benzene is a forbidden transition.

52–3 Forbidden Transitions

In spite of the fact that some transitions are formally forbidden, it is frequently found that they occur. That they can occur is due to the fact that symmetry changes can be brought about in two steps. The first step is a change caused by a collision of the molecule which brings it into a vibrationally or rotationally excited state with a different symmetry from the ground state. This vibrationally or rotationally excited state may then have a symmetry such that a transition to the electronically excited state becomes possible. Of course, there will never be as many of these particular vibrationally excited molecules present as there will be molecules in the ground state or in some other unsuitable vibrationally excited states. As a consequence, absorption by molecules at "forbidden" frequencies by this mechanism is always much more limited in extent than absorptions at "allowed" frequencies.

Another mechanism which sometimes permits a forbidden transition between two electronic levels is due to the difference in geometry between these levels. We have already seen that as a rule, the excited state of a molecule is larger than the ground state. Since an electronic transition takes place in such a short time that essentially no movement of atomic centers is possible in this time interval, the

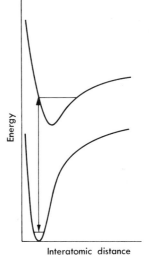

Interatomic distance

FIGURE 52–6

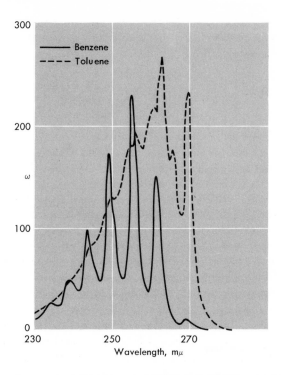

FIG. 52–7. Absorption spectra of benzene and toluene, dissolved in cyclohexane. [Adapted by permission from A. E. Gillam and E. S. Stern, *An Introduction to Electronic Absorption Spectroscopy in Organic Chemistry*, London: Edward Arnold (Publishers) Ltd., 1958.]

dimensions of the excited state which is actually reached must be the same as those of the ground state and thus smaller than the equilibrium dimensions of the excited state. But such a size represents a compressed condition of the excited state, obtained only during a vibration. It therefore belongs to a vibrationally excited species of the electronically excited state. This vibrationally excited species will usually have a different symmetry from the lowest energy level of the electronically excited state and may represent an allowed transition. These relationships are known as the Franck-Condon principle and are illustrated in Fig. 52–6.

One of the important effects of the introduction of substituents on molecules containing pi-bond systems is to alter the vibrational modes of the molecules. Thus while the electronic effect of a substituent may be important in the determination of color changes produced by it, the electronic effect may be entirely outweighed by the change in vibrational modes which produces a change in the steps necessary to permit an otherwise forbidden transition. An example of such an effect is contained in the change from benzene to toluene. Figure 52–7 shows the spectra of these two substances, dissolved in cyclohexane. It will be seen that in most cases, the positions of the absorption maxima are not shifted much on going from benzene to toluene. In spite of this, the relative intensities of the bands are appreciably altered. If these bands were in the visible, the effect would be to produce a sensible difference in shade, due mainly to differences in the transition probabilities of the various bands.

52–4 n-π^* Transitions

The absorption spectra of the polyenes and of benzene result from transitions of pi electrons from their normal orbitals to higher-energy orbitals of the pi system. These are therefore designated as π-π^* transitions. In molecules with unshared pairs, still a different type of transition is possible. This would be a transition of an electron from the unshared pair in the ground state to a pi orbital in the excited state. Such a transition is called an n-π^* transition. The letter n signifies that the ground-state electron is nonbonded, that is, it is not part of a bond but one of an unshared pair. Most unshared pairs are somewhat basic in nature and in a molecule with such electrons it is sometimes easy to identify an n-π^* transition. Protonation will bind the unshared pair, and if it does not produce a complete change in the chromophore, such protonation will at least make the transition of the electron from the unshared pair much more difficult, that is, it will move it a very substantial amount toward shorter wavelengths. Indeed, complete protonation is not necessary in most cases. Simple solution in a hydroxylic solvent such as methanol is frequently sufficient to cause a measurable shift toward shorter wavelengths due to hydrogen bonding. Thus it is sometimes possible to test for the type of transition by a controlled change in solvent.

52–5 n-σ^* Transitions

In addition to the σ-σ^* transitions of the type found in the hydrogen molecule, we may also have n-σ^* transitions. An example is the absorption responsible for the purple color of iodine vapor.

52–6   Broadening of Bands

We have already seen that the superimposition of vibrational modes on electronic absorptions can alter the spectra of organic molecules. In particular, vibrational excitation and rotational excitation can lift a molecule to a slightly higher state than the ground state, and in the electronically excited state, vibrational and rotational excitations can also be superimposed. The result is that in organic molecules, electronic transitions are seldom sharp, but instead are broadened. This result may be represented by the diagram in Fig. 52–8. By starting at one of the several levels of the ground state which are rotationally or vibrationally excited above the lowest level, an electronic transition would require less energy to reach the first electronically excited level. By starting at the lowest level of the ground state and moving to one of the vibrationally excited levels of the first electronically excited state,

FIGURE 52–8

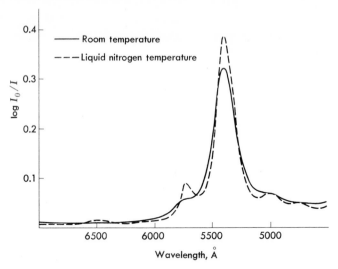

FIG. 52–9.   Sharpening of the absorption band on cooling.   [From G. D. Dorough and K. T. Shen, *J. Am. Chem. Soc.* **72**, 3940 (1950).]

more energy would be required than in the former case. Thus the "center of gravity" of the electronic system can be displaced on both the high- and the low-energy sides, causing a widening of the band.

In practice, it is observed that cooling organic materials to liquid air temperatures usually accomplishes a marked sharpening of the absorption band, due to freezing out of the rotations and some of the vibrations. This change is accomplished without an appreciable alteration of the area under the absorption curve, that is, without altering the transition probability. The effect is sketched in Fig. 52–9. This sharpening due to cooling is sometimes useful in the analysis of spectra.

52–7   Spectroscopic Examination of the Excited State

The most powerful tool for the analysis of the vibrational and rotational spectra of excited states lies in their examination in the gaseous state. In the gaseous state, absorption spectra reveal much greater detail in "fine structure" than in the liquid state. The result is that measurements with greater precision and greater possibilities for refined interpretation can be obtained for molecules which are stable enough to be examined at leisure in the gaseous state. Since the fine structure revealed in the gaseous state is due to rotational and vibrational modes superimposed on the electronic absorption, their presence permits an examination of the vibrational and rotational spectra of the molecule. In the ground state, vibrational spectra can be examined in the infrared, and rotational spectra in the long-wavelength infrared and microwave regions. With the excited state, however, no such examination can be made because of the extremely short survival time of the species. It is possible to examine these spectra, nevertheless, by the analysis of the fine structure of the gaseous absorption spectrum. In this way, information about

Table 52–1

Bond	Ground state	Excited state	
Length			
C=O	1.22 Å	1.32 Å	(C—O single bond 1.42 Å)
C—H	1.09	1.09	
Angle			
H—C—H	120°	122°	
Out of plane	0°	20°	(Single bond about 50° out of plane)

vibrational modes, bond stretching and bending frequencies, and bond lengths and angles of an excited state can be obtained from a careful examination of the gaseous absorption spectrum.

52–8   The Spectrum of Formaldehyde

The spectrum of formaldehyde has been examined by all the techniques noted above, recent work having been performed by Robinson and DiGiorgio. Using the methods indicated, it was established that the longest wavelength transition of formaldehyde, at 353 mμ, is an n-π^* transition. The measurement of the bond lengths and bond angles of the excited state are given in Table 52–1.

It is reasoned that the promotion of an unshared electron to an antibonding pi orbital weakens the C=O bond with a resulting increase in bond length. This bond is still a double bond, however, and hence has a bond length less than that of a C—O single bond. Excitation produces no effect on the C—H bond. It does destroy the symmetry of the carbonyl group, with the result that the oxygen bends 20° out of the H—C—H plane.

It is worthy of particular note that the electron which has been promoted from the nonbonded state to an excited pi orbital still has its spin state unchanged. It is thus still paired with its ground-state partner.

52–9   Organic Dyes

Crystal violet may be chosen as a typical organic dye. The formula is shown at the right. The unshared pairs of the nitrogen atoms enter into the pi-electron system of the molecule in the resonance hybrid. The result is a semantic difficulty in the designation of these electrons as pi electrons or n-electrons. Protonation bleaches the color from deep blue-violet to yellow. It can be argued that this is caused by binding of the n-electrons or by altering the pi electrons of the chromophoric system. Examina-

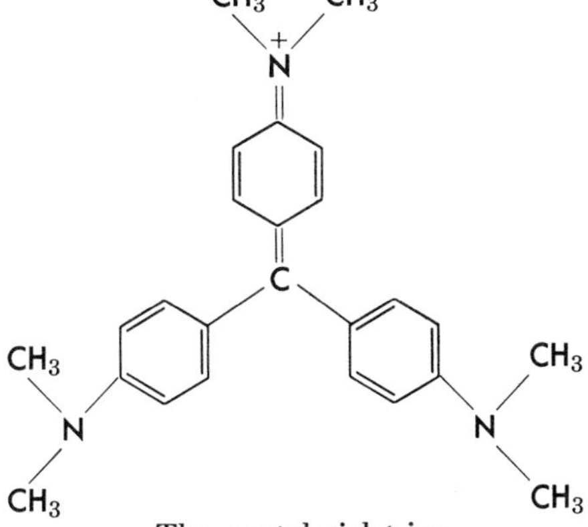

The crystal violet ion

tion of the details of the spectrum shows, however, that in spite of the deep color which the dye possesses, the transition which causes the absorption is a forbidden transition. The same turns out to be true for many of the useful and apparently intensely colored substances with which the dye chemist deals.

52–10   Fluorescence

Energy absorbed in an electronic transition is quickly lost by the excited state. Many organic substances lose energy mainly by thermal degradation, that is, by collisions which impart part or all of the energy to surrounding molecules. In some cases, on the other hand, it may be lost by light emission. In most cases the light emitted by such a process appears as fluorescence.

In recent years, the perfection of high-speed electronic instruments has made it possible to measure the survival time of an excited state which emits light. Essentially, the method is to put a pulse of light energy into a colored substance and then find out how long the resultant decay curve persists. The fluorescent excited states of organic substances are found to have survival times ranging from as short as 10^{-8} sec to about 10^{-5} to 10^{-4} sec. These short survival times are only possible because no externally aided process is required to permit the electron to radiate its energy and resume its ground state. Partly on this basis, fluorescent emissions are assigned transitions which require no change in spin state of the electrons. Since they resemble the type of emission which produces single lines in atomic spectra, these emissions are referred to as singlet-singlet transitions. In singlet-singlet transitions in either direction, no change in spin state occurs and the electrons remain paired throughout the absorption-emission cycle.

52–11   Phosphorescence

Under certain experimental conditions, such as low temperatures or solution in a glass, organic dyes may emit light of a different type from that found in fluorescence. Characteristically, such light has a different wavelength from the fluorescent emission and persists longer, in some cases up to several seconds. The characteristics of the fluorescence and phosphorescence of fluorescein dissolved in boric acid glass are shown in Fig. 52–10. The solution is obtained by melting boric acid with fluorescein and then allowing the melt to solidify.

Fluorescein (salt form)

The fluorescent emission is represented by the line α, the phosphorescence by the line β in Fig. 52–10. Because of its longer life, the excited state leading to phosphorescence can be irradiated before it decays and its absorption spectrum determined. Such a transition is represented by the line γ in Fig. 52–10.

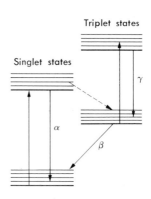

FIGURE 52–10

Phosphorescent emissions arise from states which have been characterized by spectroscopists as triplet states. Magnetic measurements have been made on such states and it has been shown that they are paramagnetic; that is, they have unpaired electrons. The presence of the unpaired electrons accounts for their relatively long survival times, since the process of changing the spin state of an electron requires collision or acquisition of energy by some other process which requires waiting time for its consummation. The emission represented by the line β would be a triplet-singlet transition and that represented by the line γ would be a triplet-triplet transition.

The measurement of fluorescence and phosphorescence have both become feasible for the organic chemist in recent years due to the perfection of instruments for the purpose. By the insertion of a polarizer and an analyzer, it is possible to find the relationship between the angle of polarization of the exciting light beam and that of the light emitted by the organic substance, and from this information, to calculate the differences in symmetry between excited states and the ground state.

52–12 Chemiluminescence

Very occasionally light is emitted from a chemical reaction. Such emitted light has been found, in cases studied so far, to be associated with one of the species present in the reaction mixture; some molecule emits light in falling from an excited to a ground state. The energy for formation of this excited state is chemical, rather than electronic, so that instead of absorbing light from an irradiating source, the molecule is formed in an excited state by virtue of absorption of energy from some exothermic process. One example which is fairly well understood is the reaction of luminol with oxygen and base:

The emitted light in this case corresponds to the fluorescence of the aminophthalate ion. It was concluded that the reaction of oxygen with the dianion eventually produces the product aminophthalate in an excited singlet state.

PROBLEMS

52–1 Sketch what the pi-electron cloud distribution of benzene must approximate, using the discussion of the symmetry diagrams given in the chapter. (For example, the lowest orbital resembles Fig. 31–19.)

52–2 Would you expect the fluorescence spectrum and the phosphorescence spectrum of a given compound to be identical? If not, which would appear at generally longer wavelengths?

52–3 The usual effect of cooling a sample is to sharpen its ultraviolet spectrum, as we have seen. Suppose that you had an anomalous sample, in which cooling the solution to −196°C (liquid nitrogen) produced a shift of 15 mμ in the spectrum.

(a) Would you expect two species related by an ionization (e.g., triphenylcarbinol and triphenylcarbonium ion) to have the same spectrum?

(b) Would you expect two tautomers to have the same spectrum?

(c) Why might effects of this sort explain the wavelength shift in the case in point?

52–4 (a) Which would have the longer wavelength absorption, triphenylcarbinol or triphenylcarbonium ion?

(b) Suppose a dimethylamino group, $(CH_3)_2N$—, were substituted in the *para* position of each phenyl ring in the triphenylcarbonium ion. Would you expect a shift to longer or shorter wavelengths?

52–5 Pyridine absorbs at 252 mμ in ethanol solution; in concentrated sulfuric acid it absorbs at 252.5 mμ, essentially the same position. What type of transition must be taking place in this absorption?

52–6 Glyoxal appears yellow to the eye; its absorption maximum is 267.5 mμ.

(a) This maximum is well into the ultraviolet and there are no absorption maxima closer to the visible. Why should it appear yellow?

1,3-Butadiene has a maximum at 217 mμ.

(b) Draw the molecular orbitals for glyoxal and butadiene and show what transitions can be expected to correspond to these absorptions. Explain the large difference in energy between the two absorptions.

52–7 Benzophenone and acetophenone in alcohol solution undergo a type of one-electron transfer reduction to the corresponding pinacols under the influence of light. 1-Naphthaldehyde (I) and 2-acetonaphthone (II) on the other hand, do not.

This reduction is believed to proceed through a triplet state intermediate and the lowest-lying triplet state for benzophenone and acetophenone occurs at about the same place as that for acetone and other alkyl ketones.

(a) This implies that the transition of all these species is connected with the carbonyl group. What type of transition might this be?

(b) Solvent studies indicate a shift to shorter wavelengths with hydroxylic solvents, as opposed to hydrocarbons:

Solvent	Absorption of acetone
Hexane	279 mμ
Ethanol	272 mμ
Water	264.5 mμ

What does this imply about the electron promoted?

(c) The transition in the naphthalene compounds, on the other hand, takes place at longer wavelengths than these earlier ones, and the solvent dependence does not follow the pattern suggested by the other ketones. This implies a different type of promotion. What might that be?

(d) Why would this type be more favored in the naphthalene system?

(e) Why does this type of promotion cut off the photochemical pinacol formation?

*What physical process occurs
in nuclear magnetic resonance?
How can this process be used as an experimental
tool in organic chemistry?*

53

NUCLEAR MAGNETIC RESONANCE

53-1 Background

In the preceding chapter we saw that vibrational and rotational interactions modify the energies of electronic absorptions. Because of this fact, it is possible to use electronic spectra to determine vibrational and rotational characteristics of species like excited states which are not available for direct study. This is done through spectroscopic analysis of the fine structure of the spectra of materials in the gaseous state.

Careful study of the electronic spectra of substances at high spectral resolution showed that in addition to the fine structure resulting from vibrational and rotational modes, still smaller perturbations were visible under some conditions. These were called the *hyperfine* structure. In 1924 Pauli suggested that the hyperfine structure of spectral lines might be ascribed to the action of fields caused by nuclear magnetic dipoles on the electrons undergoing transition. This concept was soon confirmed and it became possible by a detailed study of the hyperfine structures of the individual elements to determine the magnitudes of the nuclear magnetic moments of the elements. This method is indirect and time-consuming, however, and is therefore not applicable to routine study of molecular spectra.

In 1933 Stern and Estermann made a direct magnetic determination of the magnetic moment of the proton. This started a series of magnetic measurements which, with improved electronic instrumentation, has made available one of the most powerful tools which we possess for the investigation of organic chemical structures and electronic force fields. Modern instrumentation has developed along lines initiated by Bloch and Purcell, who were awarded the Nobel Prize in Physics in 1952 for their discoveries.

53-2   Nuclear Magnetic Moments

We saw in Chapter 48 that the spin of an electron creates a magnetic field which is ultimately responsible for paramagnetism. In exactly the same manner, proton spin produces a magnetic field in the opposite direction to that produced by the spin of an electron. Thus a spinning nucleus may be treated as a tiny bar magnet whose axis is the same as the axis of spin. The magnetic moment due to the spin of an elementary particle is inversely proportional to its mass. Since the proton is of the order of 1000 times as heavy as the electron, its magnetic field would be expected to be no greater than 0.001 times that due to an electron. However, proton magnetic susceptibilities turn out to be proportional to the square of the magnetic moment, cutting the susceptibilities to the order of 10^{-6} times those due to electrons. It is obvious, then, that highly refined measurements are necessary to permit their direct observation.

The unexpected observation with respect to nuclear magnetic moments was that the spin of a neutron generates a magnetic field, just as the spin of an electron or a proton does. This result has been explained by assuming that the neutron is dissociated for a fraction of the time into a proton and a negative meson. The moment of the meson is larger than that of the proton and of opposite sign. Thus the spin of the neutron can give rise to an overall magnetic moment. The magnetic moment of a neutron is not accessible to direct measurement but can be inferred

Table 53-1

Element	A	P	N	Class*	I	Q
Neutron	1	0	1		$\frac{1}{2}$	
Proton	1	1	0		$\frac{1}{2}$	
H	2	1	1	c	1	+
H	3	1	2	a	$\frac{1}{2}$	
He	3	2	1	b	$\frac{1}{2}$	
He	4	2	2	d	0	
Li	6	3	3	c	1	+
Li	7	3	4	a	$\frac{3}{2}$	−
Be	9	4	5	b	$\frac{3}{2}$	+
B	10	5	5	c	3	+
B	11	5	6	a	$\frac{3}{2}$	+
C	12	6	6	d	0	
C	13	6	7	b	$\frac{1}{2}$	
C	14	6	8	d	0	
N	14	7	7	c	1	+
N	15	7	8	a	$\frac{1}{2}$	
O	16	8	8	d	0	
O	17	8	9	b	$\frac{5}{2}$	−
O	18	8	10	d	0	
F	19	9	10	a	$\frac{1}{2}$	

*All isotopes in Class d have zero magnetic moment.

from the moments of the various atomic isotopes. Just as the electron is assigned a spin quantum number of $\frac{1}{2}$, so the proton and neutron each have a spin quantum number of $\frac{1}{2}$, that is, the moment will be $\frac{1}{2}$ the constant $h/2\pi$, where h is Planck's constant. Nuclear spins sometimes pair, as electronic spins do, and sometimes remain parallel, causing addition of their moments. The rules that govern pairing or nonpairing are not simple, like Hund's rule for electrons. They are related to the number of protons and the number of neutrons in the isotope. The distributions of protons and neutrons in isotopes fall into four classes. If we designate the number of protons by P and the number of neutrons as N, the four classes are: (a) P odd, N even; (b) P even, N odd; (c) P odd, N odd; (d) P even, N even. Table 53–1 gives the values of A, the atomic mass, P, N, the class, and I, the nuclear spin quantum number of a series of isotopes of interest to the organic chemist. In addition, the table gives the sign of Q, the quadrupole moment, when one exists. The quadrupole moment will be explained later.

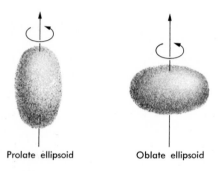

Prolate ellipsoid   Oblate ellipsoid   FIGURE 53–1

53–3   Nuclear Quadrupole Moments

Nuclei with spin quantum numbers of $\frac{1}{2}$ behave as though they were spherical spinning nuclei. Such nuclei are said to have a quadrupole moment of 0. Nuclei with spin quantum numbers greater than $\frac{1}{2}$ behave as though they were spinning ellipsoids. Such nuclei react to an electrical charge differently depending on the direction of approach and are said to have a *quadrupole moment*. If the ellipsoid is elongated (prolate) like an egg, the quadrupole moment, Q, is positive. If the ellipsoid is flattened (oblate), the quadrupole moment is negative. (See Fig. 53–1.)

53–4   The Nuclear-Magnetic-Resonance Spectrometer

An nmr-spectrometer consists of four essential parts: (1) a radiofrequency oscillator, usually of fixed frequency; (2) a radiofrequency receiver; (3) a powerful electromagnet which produces a homogeneous field; (4) a sweep generator capable of varying the magnetic field over a small range. Figure 53–2 shows a schematic diagram of an nmr-spectrometer.

The sample, S, is placed between the poles of the electromagnet which has coils so arranged that the sweep generator, SG, can vary the magnetic field. The field

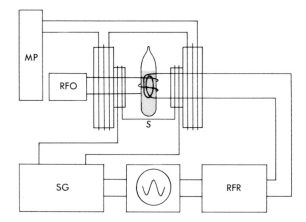

FIGURE 53-2

is on the x-axis. The sample is also in the field of a coil connected to a radio-frequency oscillator, RFO. To achieve precision, the oscillator is usually set to a predetermined constant frequency. Its field is set on the y-axis at right angles to the magnetic field. Still another coil is set on the z-axis at right angles in space to both the magnetic field and the oscillator coil. This third coil is connected to a radiofrequency receiver, RFR, which monitors the output from the sample. When a sample of material with a suitable nuclear spin is in the sample chamber exposed to the constant radiofrequency oscillations, absorption of RF-energy will take place at certain magnetic field strengths. If another spectrometer with a different oscillator frequency is used on the same sample, a different value of the magnetic field will give energy absorption for the same system. Thus the position of energy absorption is a function of both the oscillator frequency and the field strength of the magnet. When energy absorption occurs, a signal is observed on the RFR-detector system.

53-5   The Origin of nmr-spectra

In an assemblage of atoms with nuclear spin quantum number $\frac{1}{2}$ and in the absence of a magnetic field, there will be no bias toward either of the two possible values of the quantum number $+\frac{1}{2}$ or $-\frac{1}{2}$. In the presence of a magnetic field, however, a bias will exist toward the value of $+\frac{1}{2}$ in which the nuclei are aligned in the direction of the field. Opposing this is thermal agitation which tends to destroy the bias created by the magnetic field. The RF-generator produces a rotating magnetic field, which can interact with the field of the nuclei at the exact field-frequency relationship at which it is in tune with them. This causes them to flip from the stable configuration to the unstable with absorption of energy. The process has certain features reminiscent of the excitation of molecular vibrations by infrared energy. The spin-excited state produces a field perpendicular to its original direction. Since this is the direction in which the receiver is oriented, a signal is produced in the receiver by these excited nuclei.

53–6 The Chemical Shift

Changing the chemical environment of atoms causes a concomitant change in their magnetic environment. The result is that even with the same nucleus, such as a hydrogen nucleus, changes in the neighbors cause changes in the magnetic field required to bring a fixed-frequency oscillator into resonance. Two variables are of interest to the chemist. The first is the field at which resonance occurs; the second, the area under the curve at a given frequency. A typical resonance spectrum at low resolution is that for ethanol, shown in Fig. 53–3.

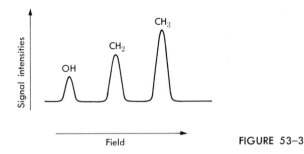

FIGURE 53–3

In this spectrum, the differing field strengths at which resonance occurs correspond to different chemical environments. The effect is called the *chemical shift*. The differing areas under the curves are proportional to the number of nuclei causing the signals. Thus it is possible to tell that there is one proton causing the first signal, two causing the second, and three causing the third and that the molecule in question has six protons. Absolute calibration of the number of protons can only be attained by the use of an internal standard of reference added to the solution being tested.

53–7 Shielding

The chemical shift is caused primarily by interactions of nuclear magnetic fields with electronic magnetic fields. In a powerful magnetic field such as that maintained in an nmr-spectrometer, electron clouds respond by setting up a small induced magnetic field in opposition to the external field. This induced field shields the nuclei so that a higher external field than would be necessary for a bare proton must be placed on them to cause the resonance absorption to take place. This is called the *shielding effect*. It obviously varies with changes in the electronic clouds in the neighborhood of the protons under investigation. In addition, *deshielding effects* of smaller magnitude may occur due to electronic interactions. These may be important in determining the relative positions of resonance frequencies of different protons.

A typical example of shielding occurs in the interactions of the ring electrons with the protons attached to the benzene ring, as shown in Fig. 53–4. When the magnetic field, H_0, is applied in the direction shown, a ring current will be present in the benzene ring, due to the motion of the aromatic pi electrons. This current will be in the direction indicated by the arrows on the ring enclosed in the hexagon. This ring current will generate an opposing magnetic field, indicated by the dashed lines. This field is sufficiently large to envelop the hydrogens on the benzene ring, thus shielding their protons partially from the action of the applied field. The shielding effect falls off with distance but is still measurable at the distance of one methylene group from the ring. Thus the magnetic fields surrounding a benzene ring may be used for exploring atoms attached in the vicinity of the ring. This possibility has resulted in valuable stereochemical applications of nmr-spectroscopy.

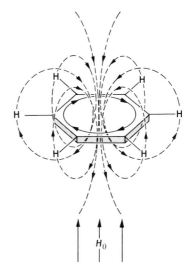

FIG. 53–4. Shielding of protons on the benzene ring.

53–8   Nuclear-Magnetic-Resonance Units

Chemical shifts have been reported in several different ways. The commonest way is in τ-units with τ defined by the equation

$$\tau = 10 - \frac{(\nu - \nu_r)}{\text{Oscillator frequency}} \times 10^6 \text{ cps,}$$

where ν_r is the frequency of the reference standard, usually tetramethyl silane $(CH_3)_4Si$. Some τ-values are given in Table 53–2.

Table 53–2

	τ
SO_3H	-1.0 to -1.3
$-COOH$	-0.2 to -1.3
$-CHO$	0 to $+0.3$
ArH	$+2.8$
CH (tertiary)	$+7.0$ to $+7.2$
$C_6H_5-CH_3$	$+7.7$ to $+7.8$
$R-NH_2$	$+7.2$ to $+7.3$
CH_3-C	$+8.8$ to $+9.1$
$(CH_3)_4Si$	10

Chemical shifts are sometimes altered by changes in concentration. This is especially true when hydrogen bonding or other association effects are important. In such cases, a good practice is to determine the shift at several different concentrations and then to plot the values against concentration with extrapolation to infinite dilution. Such a process carried out for ethanol causes the OH resonance frequency to change from a position on the left of the CH$_2$ peak to one on the right of the CH$_3$ peak, showing the strong effect of hydrogen bonding.

53-9 Chemical Shifts and Hammett's Constants

Table 53-2 suggests a relationship between the electronegativity of the group to which the proton is attached and the chemical shift. While such relationships are not always reliable, due to deshielding effects, a number of plots of chemical shifts on one axis against Hammett sigma values on the other show linear relationhips approximately as reliable as those of the original correlations of sigma values with reactivity. This suggests an independent method for investigating electro-negativities.

53-10 Spin-Spin Coupling

When the nmr-spectrum of ethanol is observed under higher resolution than that which gave the spectrum shown in Fig. 53-3, it is found that resolution of the methylene and methyl bands into fine structure occurs. The spectrum of these two bands at higher resolution is shown in Fig. 53-5.

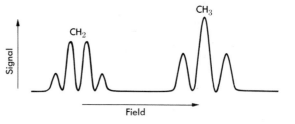

FIGURE 53-5

Investigation of this effect has shown that it is due to coupling of the spins of adjacent nuclei, an effect which can take place when the bond angle and distance relationships are suitable. The four bands of the methylene group result from a coupling interaction with the methyl group, and the three bands of the methyl group result from interaction with the methylene group.

Let us consider the resolution of the methyl group into three components under the influence of the methylene group. The methylene group, which will produce a coupling effect on the methyl group, has four possible orientations of the spins of the two nuclei. These are represented in Fig. 53-6.

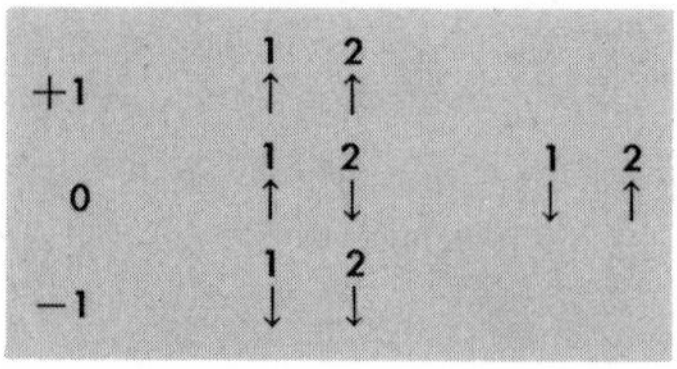

FIGURE 53-6

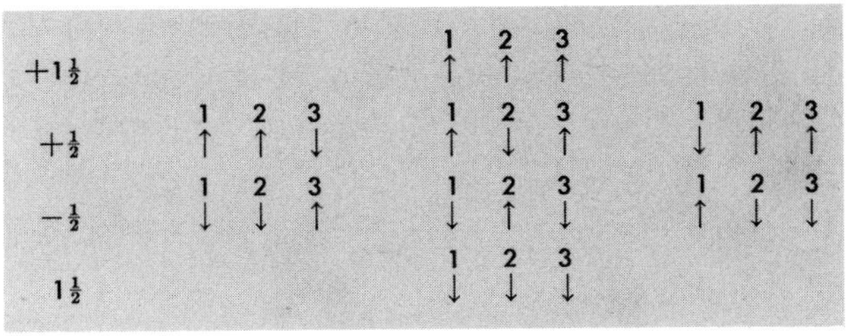

FIGURE 53-7

The interaction of the orientation with a moment of $+1$ will cause the protons of the methyl group to respond with resonance slightly sooner than with an unaffected proton. There will be no interaction with the two orientations which have zero moment, thus giving resonance at the unaffected value. Finally, interaction with the orientation with -1 moment will cause resonance slightly later in the sweep than for the unaffected value. Hence there will be three distinct peaks. The intensities of these peaks may be calculated on statistical grounds. One-quarter of the molecules will be in the $+1$ orientation, one-half in the zero orientation and one-quarter in the -1 orientation. Therefore the relative intensities of the three peaks will be $1:2:1$.

The interactions of the methyl group on the methylene can be calculated in similar manner. The possible orientations of the three nuclear spins of the three methyl protons are shown in Fig. 53-7. The reader should be able to carry the reasoning through and rationalize the number and intensities of the fine-structure bands of the methylene group in Fig. 53-7.

53-11   Kinetic Applications of nmr

One important application of the nmr-technique is to determine the survival time of species in which rapid transfer of protons is taking place. For example, hydroxyl groups in different alcohols are constantly exchanging protons. If the rate is slow compared with the resonance excitation time of the nmr-determination, then the spectrum will be that of the two different species. If the rate is fast with respect to the excitation time, then each hydroxyl will have had a number of protons connected with it during the excitation. The result will be that the instrument will see the average between the two rather than either one singly.

The classical example of such an exchange was the determination of water in water-acetic acid mixtures by Gutowsky. The spectrum of pure acetic acid is shown in Fig. 53-8, and the spectrum of water is given in Fig. 53-9. The spectrum of a $1:1$ mixture of acetic acid and water is given in Fig. 53-10.

Figure 53-10 shows an **OH** frequency which is an average between those of water and acetic acid. By standardizing with known mixtures of the two, a calibration curve may be prepared and used for the analysis of mixtures. The experiment was performed with an instrument with a resonance frequency of 40 megacycles/sec. Since this frequency showed averaging instead of separation of the

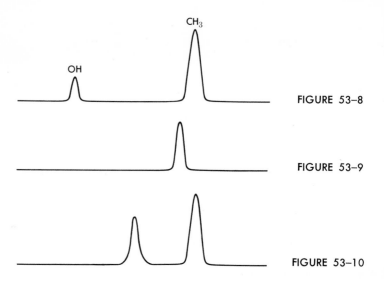

FIGURE 53–8

FIGURE 53–9

FIGURE 53–10

two chemical shifts, the survival time of the proton on the oxygens must have been less than 7×10^{-4} sec. This is calculated by observing the separation between the peaks in cycles per second, and then taking its reciprocal.

Examination of ethanol-water mixtures at room temperatures shows separate peaks. Heating causes the two peaks to disappear and an average peak to form. This shows that the survival time is of the order of 7×10^{-4} sec. Even at room temperature, addition of water in excess of about 20% causes a decrease in the amount of the separate signals that can be found until finally only the average is observed. This shows that the addition of water to the mixture speeds the proton exchange.

53–12   Structural Determinations

By far the most frequent use of nmr in organic chemistry is in the determination of structures of unknown organic substances and the confirmation of structural conclusions drawn by other methods. An investigator in a certain field will gradually build up a reference library of nmr-spectra of substances in the field with known structures. This will catalog the extent of the chemical shifts to be expected in the different situations which occur. When a new compound is prepared, an nmr-spectrum will frequently reveal critical structural information which can be correlated with the information obtained from the catalog. Use of spin-spin coupling will frequently reveal the environment of the protons giving splitting of bands into fine structures, and integration of the areas under the curves permits accounting for all the protons in the compound. The sum of this information may sometimes make a structural determination possible based on nmr-spectra alone. While such a single-method determination should not be accepted as conclusive, it can be arrived at without destruction of sample. Infrared determinations can also be made for confirmatory evidence without destruction of sample. Mass spectra can also be determined with the destruction of only minor amounts of sample. This leaves the main body of the sample intact for any confirmatory chemical evidence that needs to be gathered. Many difficult structural determinations are now performed with remarkable speed by these methods.

PROBLEMS

53–1 Nuclear-magnetic-resonance spectra are as useful a tool in structural determination as infrared spectroscopy or ultraviolet spectroscopy. The utility of each lies in the fact that infrared spectroscopy points up the presence of functional groups, ultraviolet spectroscopy allows comparison of carbon-skeletal conjugated systems, and nuclear magnetic resonance demonstrates the electronic surrounding of each proton in the molecule. The different resonances may be summed to give a total, and the fractional areas found at each chemical shift may be compared to determine the protons per molecule responsible for the absorption.

In addition to the ratios of the integrated areas, the other important factors to consider in assigning absorptions in high-resolution nmr-spectra are the chemical shift and the spin-spin splitting. Briefly, depletion of electrons usually causes a shift toward lower τ. A simple rule to remember for spin-spin splitting is that n equivalent protons on adjacent carbons will split a resonance into $n + 1$ peaks.

The spectra in Figs. 53–11, 53–12, and 53–13 were recorded on a 60-megacycle nuclear-magnetic-resonance spectrometer. The units at the bottom are δ-units, related to τ-units by the formula $\delta = 10 - \tau$. Since most technical journals express an editorial preference for reporting data in τ-units, the accompanying material uses them. The peak at $\tau = 10$ is the resonance of tetramethylsilane, the reference peak in the spectrum.

The data summarized below are from the spectra of C_3H_8O (compound 1) and $C_3H_7NO_2$ (compound 2). (See Fig. 53–11.)

	Compound 1			Compound 2	
τ	Multiplet	Relative area	τ	Multiplet	Relative area
6.00	Septet	1	5.33	Septet	1
8.40	Singlet	1	8.45	Doublet	6
8.80	Doublet	6			

(a) How many protons are responsible for the area under the 6.00 peak in spectrum 1? Under the 8.40 peak? Under the 8.80 peak?

(b) How many protons of equivalent character (i.e., identical electronic environment) cause the splitting of the peak at 6.00? At 8.40? At 8.80?

(c) Draw a structure for compound 1 which accounts for all these facts. Show that other possibilities may be discounted. One proton would be expected to exchange rapidly and not be influenced by the others.

(d) Do the same for compound 2. Show by simple inspection that the compounds are related.

(e) Why in both cases is the doublet more shielded than the septet?

(f) Explain the great deshielding of the septet in compound 2 relative to compound 1 (by 0.67 τ-units).

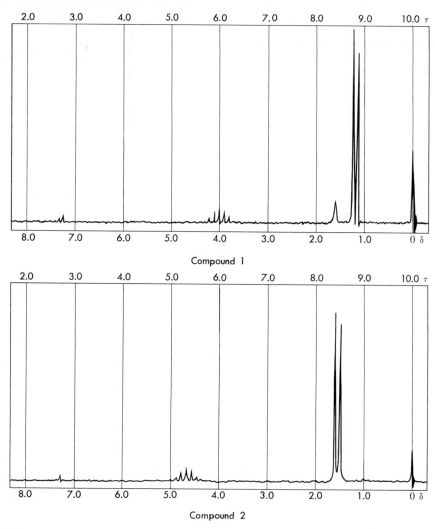

FIG. 53–11. Nuclear-magnetic-resonance spectra. (Reproduced by permission from N. S. Bhacca, L. F. Johnson, and J. N. Shoolery, *NMR Spectra Catalog*, Varian Associates, Palo Alto, California.)

(g) Why is the shift of the doublet from 1 to 2 less (0.35 τ-units)?

53–2   Compound 3 is C_2H_4O, and compound 4 is C_3H_6O. (See Fig. 53–12.) One peak in the spectrum of compound 3 ran off the paper, and was recorded at an arbitrary place. The value below is correct.

Compound 3			Compound 4		
τ	Multiplet	Relative area	τ	Multiplet	Relative area
0.20	Quartet	1	5.27	Triplet	4
7.80	Doublet	3	7.28	Quintet	2

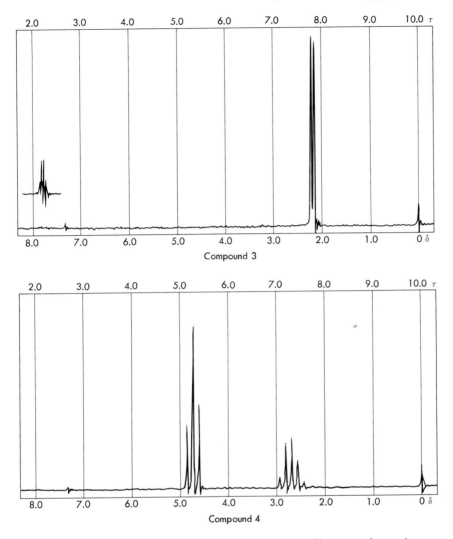

FIG. 53–12. Nuclear-magnetic-resonance spectra from Bhacca *et al., op. cit.*

(a) What kind of proton is so greatly deshielded in spectrum 3?
(b) Which of these compounds would have ultraviolet absorption at the longer wavelength?

53–3 Identify compounds 5 and 6 in Fig. 53–13.

Compound 5 = $C_3H_6Cl_2$		Compound 6 = C_8H_{12}	
τ	Relative area	τ	Relative area
6.30	2	4.42	1
7.80	1	7.62	2

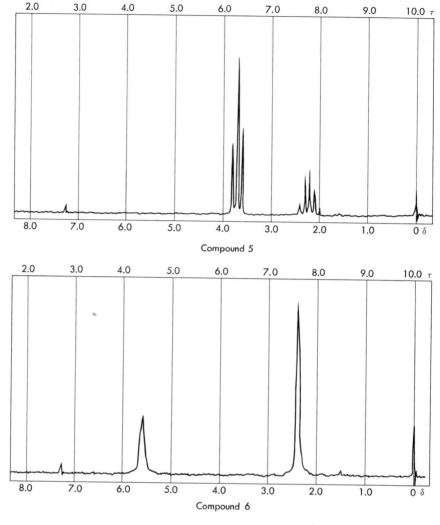

FIG. 53–13. Nuclear-magnetic-resonance spectra from Bhacca *et al., op. cit.*

These are remarkable spectra for the uninitiated. In compound 5, is there experimentally any interaction with the spin on the Cl atoms? The orientation of Cl nuclei is apparently changing so rapidly that interaction disappears. Compound 6 is obviously highly symmetrical, since there are only two resonances. The fact that there is only faintly discernible spin-spin splitting would not be expected on the basis of our discussions so far, but the weakness of apparent interaction may be related to rapid ring flipping.

Part 7

EPILOGUE

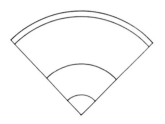

We have devoted much effort to the study of the elements of organic chemistry. We started with a bird's eye view of the field and proceeded to an examination of the methods used by chemists to determine the structures of organic materials. This determination involves the use of many chemical reactions. The factors governing the general course of these reactions were then examined in their turn. It now remains to attempt to view the general position of organic materials within the scheme of things. Although this particular bird's eye view will be brief, it should suggest to the alert reader many types of interesting and humanly significant applications of the knowledge which he has gained from this study. This is the goal of Part 7.

How did organic matter originate on the earth? Is it possible to perform in modern laboratories experiments which simulate the primitive conditions on the earth and from these experiments to produce organic chemicals? Can we understand the chemistry of the origin of life? What current trends pose problems which the chemist will be able to study? What chemical problems may arise in the future which may be critical to the continuance of life?

54

ORGANIC CHEMISTRY: PAST, PRESENT, AND FUTURE

54–1 The Problem of Origins

Scientific attempts to probe the origins of the earth or of life processes frequently come into opposition to certain religious beliefs. Examination will show, however, that scientific methods are still powerless to cope with the problem of *true origins*. The origin of matter is a phrase that can be repeated glibly, but philosophers who have studied the problem have conceded that the phrase has no real meaning to the human mind. This is because the human mind is as yet incapable of grasping the concept of nothingness. We can conceive of the removal of any given object, but true nothingness requires that there be no objects to remove. The concept of ultimate creation would require that the human mind first firmly grasp the concept of nothingness and then conceive a process by which nothing can become something. No approach to this conceptualization has yet been possible. Religious doctrine sidesteps the question of nothingness by conceiving the eternal existence of a deity. Until philosophers and scientists can conceive of nothingness and its transformation into matter, science will be in no essential conflict with religious beliefs. The problems that scientists can consider are those of the transformation of the physical forms of matter, once the matter is assumed to exist for purposes of transformation. The concept of the "origin of the earth," then, is a concept embodying the rearrangement of matter. The concept of the "origin of life" is also one of the rearrangement of matter. Neither of these concepts involves a true material creation. A deity capable of creating matter would also be able to transform nonliving matter into living matter. This would be a

691

secondary miracle, not the primary miracle of creation. Once the admission is made of the possibility of a primary miracle, then the possibility of secondary miracles also must be taken into account. Such events, however, conflict with the doctrine of the immutability of natural laws, a doctrine which has proved highly useful in the pursuit of scientific studies. Again, it is not possible to prove, *a priori*, that the doctrine of immutability of natural laws is true. It is, however, the basic assumption of modern science and it is by the pursuit of this doctrine that the vast storehouse of scientific knowledge now available has been built. For this reason, the scientist, while not denying the possibility of a primary miracle in the creation of matter, will wish to examine the alternatives to secondary material miracles with respect to the transformations giving rise to the earth and to life on the earth.

54–2 Early Development of the Earth

Modern research in geology has led to a great increase in understanding of the processes leading to the formation of the earth. Much of this information has come from the study of the parent-daughter element relationships in radioactive disintegrations. Thus U^{238}, which occurs in granites to the extent of approximately four parts per million, disintegrates into Pb^{206}. Since Pb^{204} does not change with time, the ratio of Pb^{204}/Pb^{206} can be used to calculate the amount of Pb^{206} formed from uranium, and the U^{238}/Pb^{206} ratio can be used to calculate the length of time that a given sample of rock has been subject to radioactive disintegration. Similar calculations can be performed on other pairs, for example the Rb^{87}/Sr^{87} ratio. It can be demonstrated by studies of heat loss that the major portion of the radioactivity of the earth is in the earth's crust and the upper reaches of the mantle immediately beneath the crust. From the information on radioactive decay, it is possible to extrapolate back in time to the point at which the temperature must have been great enough for the crust to have been molten. These calculations lead to the conclusion that the separation of the core and the mantle of the earth (Fig. 54–1) must have taken place approximately 4.5 billion years ago.

Various hypotheses, most of them based on the study of meteorites, have been advanced to extend the story back in time before the geologic record began. One geologic hypothesis placed the age of the earth and the planets as about 5 billion years. In this time scale, the age of the sun would be approximately 6 billion years and that of the galaxy about 6.5 to 7 billion years. Figures such as these are subject to revision as new evidence comes in.

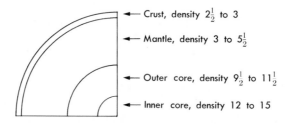

FIG. 54–1. General structure of the earth.

54-3   The Inorganic Phase

After the separation of the core from the mantle of the earth, a period of external cooling is assumed to have taken place from a temperature of approximately 2200°C, the melting point of the earth's crustal rocks. During this time, precrustal rocks formed. At this time, radioactivity was approximately 15 times as great as it is at present. The process of cooling could not progress rapidly until some of the heat from radioactive disintegration had exhausted itself. After the passage of approximately 1.7 billion years, it is calculated that cooling had progressed far enough to permit a lasting crust to develop on the earth. This was a necessary precondition to the beginning of life.

54-4   Thermostable Organic Materials

In the period of the formation of precrustal rocks, many changes could have taken place preparatory to the beginning of life. Temperatures somewhat below 2200°C are not too high for the existence of primitive forms of organic matter. The most stable "organic" species known is the $CN\cdot$ radical. The reaction

$$NC\!-\!CN \rightleftarrows 2CN\cdot$$

takes place at about 1500°C, and the $CN\cdot$ radical formed by this process is stable to temperatures of at least 10,000°C. It is formed on the interaction of numerous forms of carbon and nitrogen, so there is no reason to suppose that it was not relatively abundant in early atmospheres. It is a highly reactive species and is capable of entering into a variety of reactions that might be of synthetic importance.

The next most thermostable species is acetylene. As stated earlier, acetylene can be generated by the action of a carbon arc in an atmosphere of hydrogen at 4000°C. Again, there is no reason to suppose that acetylene would not have been present in early atmospheres. Its presence in the upper reaches of the atmosphere in modern times has been demonstrated. Acetylene is a highly reactive substance, also capable of entering into numerous reactions to form more complicated organic molecules.

A third primitive species capable of existence at high temperatures is CO. The reaction

$$2CO_2 \rightleftarrows 2CO + O_2$$

is in equilibrium at a temperature of 2000°C. During the process of cooling, CO would have been available. It is also a reactive species, capable of undergoing numerous reactions; however, most reactions require the presence of suitable catalysts.

The foregoing statements illustrate the method that the chemist is forced to adopt in considering the possibilities of the origin of organic matter. It is impossible to retrace our steps to the times examined in this phase of research. Instead, we must create conditions in the laboratory resembling as closely as possible those under which the transformations of interest occurred, and then examine the various possibilities experimentally. This technique is being applied in a number of laboratories in an attempt to learn how living matter might have evolved.

54–5   The Primitive Atmosphere

Spectroscopic examination of the atmospheres of other planets in the solar system reveals the presence of methane and ammonia. Recent evidence obtained by The Johns Hopkins Laboratory of Astrophysics shows that water vapor is present in the atmosphere of Venus. Because of these findings, it is reasonable to speculate that the atmosphere of the earth once contained these substances as well. To organisms now living, the most important constituent of the atmosphere is oxygen. There are reasons for believing that oxygen was not present in the primitive atmosphere of the earth. Oxygen is now formed by the process of photosynthesis. The stoichiometry of the photosynthetic reaction, although not its actual course, may be represented by the equation:

$$CO_2 + H_2O \rightarrow CH_2O + O_2$$

Thus for each atom of carbon present in a living organism or in a fossil fuel, there should be one molecule of oxygen formed. Rough calculations show that there is approximate equivalence between the total amount of oxygen in the atmosphere and the amount of "fixed carbon" present in living and fossil materials. Since the latter figure is not known with precision, such calculations can only be rough at present. The approximate equivalence suggests, however, that all the oxygen of the atmosphere was formed by photosynthesis.

54–6   "Anaerobic" Organic Synthesis

If the primitive atmosphere contained no free oxygen, the environment would have been much more favorable to the production of organic chemicals than the present oxygenated atmosphere. Consequently, modern experimentation has proceeedd on the assumption that this was the case. It has been shown that the simple carbon compounds referred to above can form more complex carbon compounds under conditions of irradiation with high-energy radiation. The usual type of experiment is to use water, carbon dioxide, methane, hydrogen, and ammonia and treat the mixture either with the high-energy beams of a cyclotron or with short-wave ultraviolet light. When only carbon dioxide and water are used, formic acid, acetic acid, and succinic acid have been obtained. When ammonia is added to the gas mixture, it is possible to isolate amino acids such as glycine, alanine, β-alanine, and others.

Because of the absence of the shielding effect of oxygen and, more particularly, of ozone in the primitive atmosphere, it is assumed that high-energy ultraviolet rays were able to penetrate the atmosphere. Thus the environment was favorable to the synthesis of many simple organic molecules, among these, the building blocks of proteins. Further experimentation has shown that if some process existed to permit points of concentration of these amino acids, melting them together in glutamic acid as a solvent results in the formation of peptide chains of considerable length. Thus substances can be formed in the laboratory, which may be considered protein precursors, under the inorganic conditions of a primitive reducing atmosphere in the presence of either ionizing radiation or of ultraviolet light.

54–7 First Steps Toward Reproduction

One of the products of irradiation in the presence of methane and ammonia is ammonium cyanide. By heating ammonium cyanide to a temperature just below 100°C it is possible to produce a black polymer from which a number of recognizable compounds can be extracted. One of these is adenine. The formation of adenine in this manner suggests a mechanism by which bases necessary for the formation of nucleic acids can be generated.

The first step toward reproduction would be the development of an autocatalytic process. While an autocatalytic process with survival value sufficient to give its product a competitive advantage over products not possessing this attribute would require a fair degree of organization, autocatalytic processes occur among simple molecules. Thus the formation of acetic acid from ethyl acetate is autocatalytic:

$$CH_3COOC_2H_5 + H_2O \underset{}{\overset{CH_3COOH}{\rightleftarrows}} CH_3COOH + C_2H_5OH$$

This system will continue to generate acetic acid as long as the "food," ethyl acetate and water, is fed in and the "waste," ethanol, is removed.

When polyphosphate is added to a mixture of amino acids, the temperature at which the formation of proteinoid material begins is markedly reduced from that required in the absence of the polyphosphate. Thus this slightly more complex mixture will use up a supply of amino acids faster than the less complex mixture which lacks the polyphosphate. It may thus be said to have "survival value" with respect to the uncatalyzed mixture in competition.

54–8 The Gap Between Organic Chemicals and Anaerobic Organisms

Numerous tentative steps along the road to a simple living system have been taken in the laboratory. Even so, a large gap still remains in our knowledge. This is one of the fascinating fields of current experimentation by organic chemists with biochemical inclinations. If we assume that in the 1.7 billion years when the earth's crust was forming, the formation of organic molecules of ever-increasing complexity was going on, then the conditions were ripening for the organization of simple organisms. The oldest fossil remains that have been found are estimated to be approximately 1.6 billion years old. This leaves a gap of approximately 1.2 billion years during which the earth had a crust and conditions were present which would permit the formation and first steps in the evolution of organisms. This was a period in which removal of organic matter by combustion did not occur and ultraviolet radiation was at a high level of intensity. In addition, irradiation due to radioactive decay occurred at a rate at least five times as great as it is at present. All these factors combined to permit a high rate of "biological experimentation" so that favorable combinations could be formed and finally gain ascendency.

54–9 The Advent of Chlorophyll and Photosynthesis

The earliest known fossil remains are those of microscopic algae which resemble present-day organisms that have the power of photosynthesis. We may conclude that it is probable that the process of photosynthesis began approximately 1.6 billion years ago, when an organism capable of performing it was formed. To carry on photosynthesis, it was necessary for the organism to possess chlorophyll, a structure that we may regard as relatively complex. In fact, iron-porphyrin catalysts occur among organisms more primitive than those which have the power of photosynthesis, and the biogenesis of chlorophyll has been shown by Granick to proceed through protoporphyrin, the heme pigment. Because of the peculiar arrangement of the groups in protoporphyrin, it has frequently been assumed that its synthesis must involve the action of a forming template which would necessarily be more complex than the molecule itself. Recent work has shown that this assumption is not necessary, however.

54–10 Postulated Mechanism for the Formation of Natural Porphyrins

Let us abbreviate the formula for the precursor of protoporphyrin as:

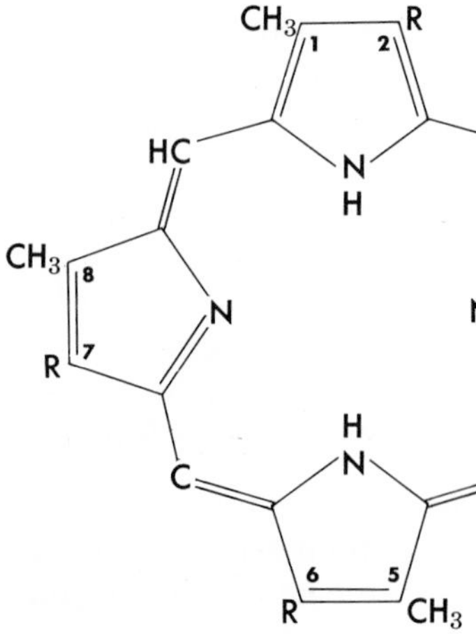

The methyl groups are formed from the decarboxylation of acetic acid groups, $RCH_2COOH \rightarrow RCH_3$. The simple pyrrole which is the precursor of the heme pigments is porphobilinogen.

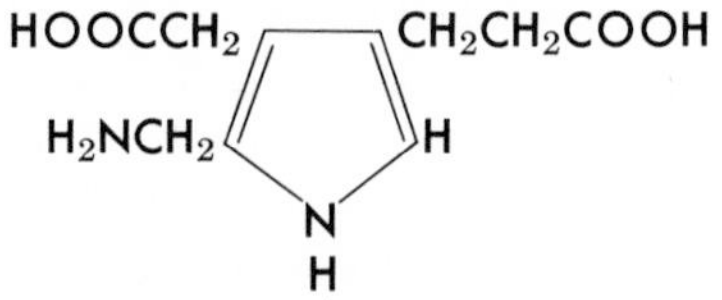

Porphobilinogen

One would expect a linear condensation of porphobilinogen to yield a substance with acetic acid groups in the 1-, 3-, 5-, and 7-positions.

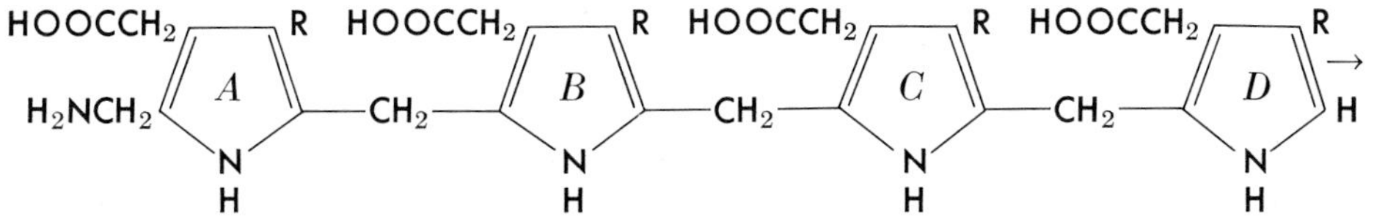

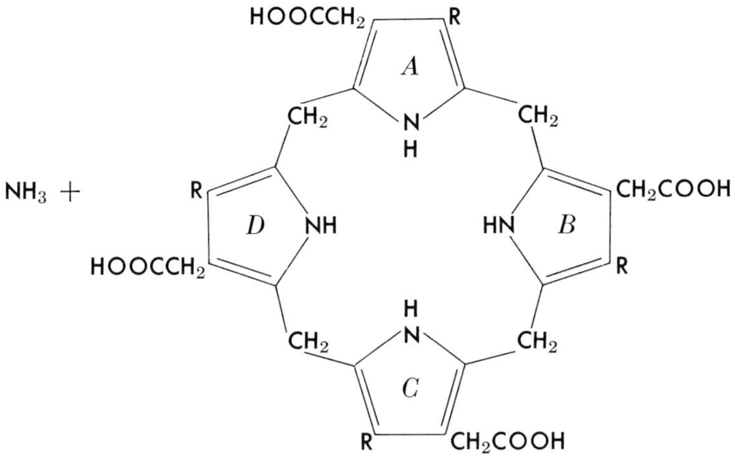

The structural peculiarity of the system is the "inversion" of the order of the groups in positions 7 and 8. Instead of the expected sequence of 1, 3, 5, 7, the sequence appearing is 1, 3, 5, 8.

Work with models shows that the stereochemistry of the system is such that the most readily available position for condensation is not the terminal pyrrole hydrogen of the linear tetrapyrryl compound but a position opposite to this.

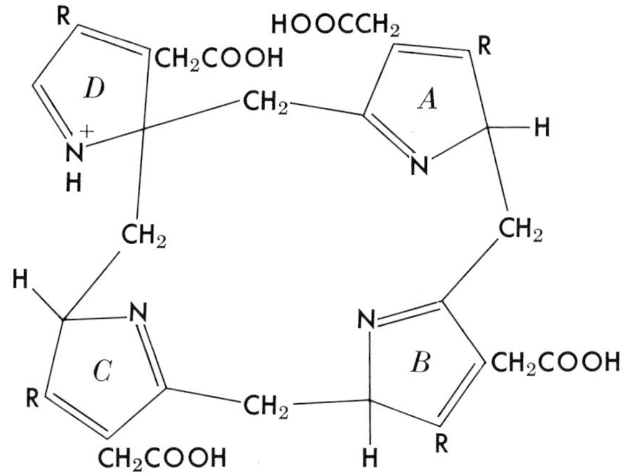

Subsequent breaking of the bond between rings C and D and reforming under R in ring D permits the process to proceed with "inversion" of the sequence of substituents. Such an inversion has actually been observed in acid-catalyzed test-tube reactions taking place spontaneously and not under enzymatic influence. Thus a template for the determination of the sequence of substituents in chlorophyll and the heme pigments is not necessary. This greatly simplifies the conceptual scheme necessary for the formation of photosynthetically active organisms.

54–11   The Discontinuity Created by the Start of Photosynthesis

Once the process of photosynthesis started, the organisms possessing this power had two survival advantages over the organisms which preceded them on the earth. The first was that they were able to manufacture their own food. The second was that by emitting oxygen into the atmosphere, they "poisoned" the anaerobes which had preceded them, in all but especially protected locations. The initiation of processes of combustion produced a far-reaching and irreversible process on the face of the earth. The primitive conditions under which life could form were destroyed and all future life had to depend on the unbroken continuation of the threads then in existence.

54–12   Some Current Problems

During the course of this text we have seen many of the strictly professional types of study which engage organic chemists. We have also seen some of the derived problems which the peculiar properties of organic substances make technologically and socially valuable. Our brief study of the current work on the origins of organic chemicals indicates a continuation of the studies on living processes which the organic chemist is peculiarly adapted to perform. These are studies on the processes which permit normal physiological chemical reactions to proceed. Among the most fascinating of these are the reactions which take place in the brain and which are ultimately responsible for the present, let us hope not temporary, dominance of man in the biological hierarchy. The unique power of abstract reasoning which is one of the distinguishing characteristics of mankind deserves careful and extended study, since it is this power which is primarily responsible for man's position. Chemists have made an excellent start toward classifying the physiological processes responsible for individuality and for the power of individual thought that is our greatest asset. These studies are more complex than the materials presented in this course and would form a natural succeeding step for interested students.

54–13   Problems of the Immediate Future

Experiments on skin grafting and organ transplantation establish the fact that with the exception of identical twins, every individual is distinct in his chemical makeup. Attempts to classify living organisms according to biological classifications are valuable for study purposes, but in the final analysis, the basic fact of biology is chemical individuality. Research in the past decades has resulted in finer and finer classifications of humans according to blood groups. The means now exist for achieving absolute chemical differentiation between individuals by the study of the amino acid sequences of their body proteins. It is predictable that such identifications will be achieved in the relatively near future. This will lay the groundwork for the understanding of one of the most prized of human possessions, individuality.

With the first protein synthesis, that of insulin, the way has been opened to a second attack on the problem of individuality, the production of artificial proteins with altered amino acid sequences. Thus the solution to the protein portion of the problem of immunological specificity can be foreseen with confidence. Our tools for the study of immunologically active polysaccharides still lag behind those for the study of proteins.

During the past few years, the first chemotherapeutic agents for the counter-action of virus diseases have been synthesized. Because of the close similarity between the essential structures of virus "molecules" and genes, this promises first steps toward the control of genetic processes. As the thalidomide tragedy so amply demonstrated, chemicals now exist which are capable of altering genetic charac-teristics. Experimentation upon these "mutagens" has been in progress for years and more precise control over the results are predictable, even though the time schedule for such control is not. The ultimate political consequences of a successful program in this field are frightening to contemplate in states in which the propensity toward regulation of the individual by the central government is dominant.

Biochemical studies such as the foregoing spread exciting vistas of useful ac-complishments in the promotion of human welfare before the student of organic chemistry. While they represent some of the more spectacular achievements that are now foreseeable, applications of the methods of the organic chemist to large numbers of other fields of human endeavor promise results that will be of the greatest importance to commerce and society.

54–14   Future Problems

While the solution to problems of individual survival through the control of disease can now be confidently contemplated, the development of modern civiliza-tion is presenting us with an increasing threat to the survival of the race, in ad-dition to the much-publicized nuclear threat. Our civilization has brought with it an increase in population density and a closeness of human interaction that is unprecedented in the life of the race. Extension of the lines of thought presented earlier in this chapter leads us logically to the consideration of problems arising from population density that will become more serious as time progresses and present trends continue. One of these is the threat posed by possible depletion of the food supply, another the problem created by the disposal of steadily increasing amounts of waste.

The problem of food supply arises because in all times, including the present, the growth of population outstrips the food supply. With modern communication, this situation is becoming less and less tolerable and the condition in which the large majority of the people of the earth is born to starvation is one which will not be tolerated indefinitely. Two courses of action are open. One is to limit the population, the other is to increase the food supply. In either of these endeavors, the organic chemist can play a key role. Continued study will undoubtedly uncover safer and more effective chemical means for the controlled limitation of population. With respect to the food supply, improved fertilizers and crop- and pest-control measures are constantly increasing the potential output of our farms. We must exercise care to see that these chemical measures never cause damage which outweighs their benefits. This is also a problem for chemical research.

The problem of waste disposal is also an ever-recurring one. One of the great advances of the twentieth century has been the large-scale introduction of sewage-disposal facilities for the human population. However, a much more subtle problem remains, that of increasing air pollution. As our knowledge of the nature of the pollutants increases, we find that some of them can be lethal. The lethal ones are mainly organic chemicals whose control and destruction lies in the hands of chemists. However, one of the most insidious of the air pollutants may turn out to be one that is regarded as innocuous, that is, carbon dioxide. As our consumption of fossil fuels for industrial and automotive power increases, a larger amount of carbon dioxide moves into the air. Physical studies have indicated that this increases the absorption coefficient of the atmosphere for heat, creating a "greenhouse" effect which may be responsible for the large-scale changes in the weather that we are now witnessing. Thus in the long run, control over major changes in weather patterns may depend on our learning how to control the emission of carbon dioxide into the atmosphere. The amount of carbon dioxide formed by combustion would be greatly reduced if sources of energy other than fossil fuels were exploited on a large scale. An additional hazard of the long-continued use of fossil fuels would arise when their exhaustion point approached. If, by some magic of prospecting, we were able to find the last bit of coal, petroleum, and peat in the earth and consume it for power, then its combustion into carbon dioxide would consume perilously close to the last trace of oxygen in the atmosphere.

Long before we have exhausted our fossil fuel, we shall be utilizing new sources of energy. It lies within the power of the chemist to invent means by which the fixation of energy by photosynthetic or parallel means may be accelerated, postponing the exhaustion of fossil fuels. It is even more probable that within the relatively near future, the process of nuclear fusion will afford us with large sources of energy not dependent on fossil fuels. It is predictable that in the transformation of these power sources into packages small enough to be utilized by the ultimate consumer, the organic chemist will play a decisive role. In general, the function of the organic chemist is to bring about the transformation of matter into forms that can serve the needs of mankind and, in this endeavor, his powers and capabilities are now rapidly increasing.

We may conclude our introduction to the study of organic chemistry with the thought that the more advanced practice in this field holds challenges to the student ranging from minor and immediate to major and long range. The field is so broad and its practice so versatile that there is ample opportunity in it for all who feel its fascination.

INDEX OF SYNTHETIC METHODS

REACTION INDEX

INDEX OF SYNTHETIC METHODS

$$RCHO \xrightarrow[(Br_2, H_2O)]{HOBr} RCOOH \qquad\qquad 309, 330$$

$$C_6H_5R \xrightarrow[\text{or } KMnO_4, OH^-]{CrO_3, H^+} C_6H_5COOH \qquad\qquad 77$$

$$RMgX + CO_2 \rightarrow RCOOH \qquad\qquad 170$$

$$RCOCH_3 + NaOX \rightarrow RCOOH + CHX_3 \qquad\qquad 204, 213$$

$$CH_2{=}C{=}O + H_2O \rightarrow CH_3COOH \qquad\qquad 651$$

Alcohols

$$RCOOR' + H_2O \xrightarrow[OH^-]{H^+ \text{ or}} R'OH \qquad\qquad 43, 476, 625$$

$$RI + NaOH \rightarrow ROH \qquad\qquad 43, 51, 469$$

$$R_2C\overset{O}{\overset{\triangle}{\underline{\qquad}}}CR_2 + H_2O \xrightarrow[OH^-]{H^+ \text{ or}} R_2COH{-}CR_2OH \qquad\qquad 346$$

$$RCOOH + LiAlH_4 \rightarrow RCH_2OH \qquad\qquad 67$$

$$RCOOR' + Na + EtOH \rightarrow RCH_2OH + R'OH \qquad\qquad 67$$

$$R_2C{=}O + LiAlH_4 \rightarrow R_2CHOH \qquad\qquad 178$$

$$R_2C{=}CHR + H_2O \xrightarrow{H^+} R_2COHCH_2R \qquad\qquad 154$$

$$R_2C{=}O + Al(O{-}i\text{-}Pr)_3 \rightarrow R_2CHOH \qquad\qquad 621$$

$$R_2C{=}O + 2H^+ + 2e \rightarrow R_2CHOH \qquad\qquad 602$$

$$R_2C{=}O + H_2 \xrightarrow{Pt \text{ or } Pd} R_2CHOH \qquad\qquad 178$$

$$R'MgX + R_2CO \rightarrow R'CR_2OH \qquad\qquad 170$$

$$R'MgX + RCOOEt \rightarrow R'_2CROH \qquad\qquad 170$$

Aldehydes

$$RCHOH{-}CHOHR + HIO_4 \rightarrow RCHO + RCHO \qquad\qquad 321$$

$$RCH{=}CHR + O_3 \rightarrow \text{ozonide} \xrightarrow[Pt]{H_2} RCHO + RCHO \qquad\qquad 158$$

$$CHCl_3 + C_6H_5OH + OH^- \rightarrow HOC_6H_4CHO \qquad\qquad 319$$

(In favorable cases, aldehydes are formed by the partial oxidation of alcohols.)

Alkanes

$$RCH{=}CHR + H_2 \xrightarrow{Pt, Pd, \text{ or } Ni} RCH_2CH_2R \qquad\qquad 120$$

$$RMgX + HOH, \text{ etc.} \rightarrow RH \qquad\qquad 171$$

$$R_2CO + Zn(Hg) \rightarrow R_2CH_2 \qquad\qquad 178$$

$$R_2CO + NH_2NH_2 + OEt^- \rightarrow R_2CH_2 \qquad\qquad 178$$

$$RCOONa + \text{soda lime} \xrightarrow{400°} RH \qquad\qquad 63$$

$$RI + Na + H \text{ source} \rightarrow RH \qquad\qquad 310$$

$$2RI + Na \rightarrow R{-}R \qquad\qquad 51, 113$$

Alkenes

$$RCH_2CH_2OH \xrightarrow{Al_2O_3,\ 450°} RCH{=}CH_2 \qquad\qquad 120$$

$$RCH_2CH_2OH \xrightarrow{H_2SO_4} RCH{=}CH_2 \qquad\qquad 154,\ 155$$

$$RCH_2CH_2OH \xrightarrow{P_2O_5} RCH{=}CH_2 \qquad\qquad 240$$

$$RCH_2CH_2Br + KOH \xrightarrow{alcohol} RCH{=}CH_2 \qquad\qquad 162,\ 516$$

$$RCH_2CH_2\overset{+}{N}R_3OH^- \xrightarrow{heat} RCH{=}CH_2 \qquad\qquad 222$$

$$RCOOCH_2CH_2R' \xrightarrow{600°} RCOOH + H_2C{=}CHR \qquad\qquad 237$$

$$RCHO + OH^- + H_2CA_2\ (A\ activating) \rightarrow RCH{=}CA_2 \qquad\qquad 241$$

$$RCHBrCHBrR + Zn \rightarrow RCH{=}CHR \qquad\qquad 513$$

Alkynes

$$CaC_2 + H_2O \rightarrow HC{\equiv}CH \qquad\qquad 162$$

$$RI + NaC{\equiv}CH \rightarrow RC{\equiv}CH \qquad\qquad 163$$

$$RCH_2CHCl_2 + KOH \xrightarrow{alcohol} RC{\equiv}CH \qquad\qquad 162$$

Amides

$$RCOOR' + NH_3\ (NH_2CH_3) \rightarrow RCONH_2\ (RCONHCH_3) \qquad\qquad 266,\ 273$$

$$RCOCl + NH_3 \rightarrow RCONH_2 \qquad\qquad 224$$

$$RCOO^-\,NH_4{}^+ \xrightarrow{heat} RCONH_2 \qquad\qquad 182$$

$$RCON_3 + H_2NR \rightarrow RCONHR + HN_3 \qquad\qquad 280$$

Amines

$$RX + NH_3 \rightarrow RNH_2 + R_2NH + R_3N \qquad\qquad 219,\ 220$$

(Phthalimide synthesis, 267)

$$RCN + H_2 \xrightarrow{Ni} RCH_2NH_2 \qquad\qquad 182$$

$$RNO_2 \xrightarrow[\text{Sn or Fe}]{HCl} RNH_2 \qquad\qquad 77$$

$$RCONH_2 \xrightarrow[H_2O]{HOBr} RNH_2 \qquad\qquad 276$$

$$R_2C{=}NOH \xrightarrow[Pt]{H_2} R_2CHNH_2 \qquad\qquad 265$$

Epoxides

$$CH_2{=}CH_2 + O_2 + Ag \rightarrow CH_2\overset{\displaystyle O}{\underset{}{\diagup\diagdown}}CH_2 \qquad\qquad 254$$

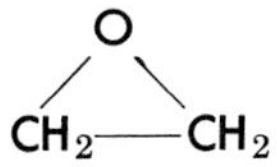

$$ClCH_2CH_2OH + NH_3 \rightarrow CH_2\overset{\displaystyle O}{\underset{}{\diagup\diagdown}}CH_2 \qquad\qquad 342$$

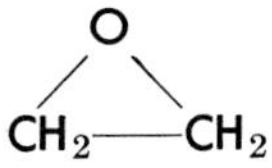

Esters

$$RCOOH + R'OH \xrightarrow{H^+} RCOOR' \qquad\qquad 52$$

$(RCO)_2O$ or $RCOCl + R'OH \rightarrow RCOOR'$ ... 52

$RCOOH + NaOH + (CH_3)_2SO_4 \rightarrow RCOOCH_3$ ... 324

$ROH + CH_2{=}C{=}O \rightarrow CH_3COOR$ ... 651

Ethers

$RI + NaOR' \rightarrow ROR'$ ... 51, 476

$ROH + OH^- + (CH_3)_2SO_4 \rightarrow ROCH_3$ ... 324

$C_6H_5N_2^+ + ROH \rightarrow C_6H_5OR$ ... 566, 569

See also epoxides.

Glycols

$R_2C{=}CR_2 + KMnO_4 + H_2O \xrightarrow{\text{neutral}} R_2COHCR_2OH$ ... 138

$R_2C{=}CR_2 + OsO_4 + H_2O_2 \rightarrow R_2COHCR_2OH$ ... 139

$R_2C{=}O \xrightarrow[H^+]{1e \text{ or } h\nu} R_2COHCR_2OH$ ... 603, 674

See also alcohols.

Halogen compounds

$ROH + HI \rightarrow RI$ ... 61

$ROR + HI \rightarrow 2RI$ ... 61

$RCH{=}CH_2 + HX \rightarrow RCHXCH_3$ ... 541

$RCH{=}CH_2 + HX + H_2O_2 \rightarrow RCHCH_2X$ ... 653

$RH + X_2 + \text{light} \rightarrow RX$ ... 206

$RCH{=}CHR + X \rightarrow RCHXCHXR$ ... 120, 137, 207, 494

$RCOCH_3 + NaOX \rightarrow RCOOH + CHX_3$ ... 204, 213

H_2CA_2 (A activating) $+ X_2 \rightarrow A_2CHX$ or A_2CX_2 ... 191, 211, 273, 503

$ROSO_2R' + NaI \rightarrow RI + NaOSO_2R'$ ... 310

$R_2CO + PCl_5 \rightarrow R_2CCl_2$ ... 162

$HC{\equiv}CH + 2HBr \rightarrow CH_3CHBr_2$ ... 163

$C_6H_6 + X_2 + FeX_3 \rightarrow C_6H_5X$ ... 77, 208, 534

$C_6H_5N_2^+ + CuX + HX \rightarrow C_6H_5X$ ... 568, 569

Hemiacetals

$R_2CO + ROH \underset{\text{H}^+ \text{ or OH}^-}{\rightleftharpoons} R_2C\begin{smallmatrix}OH\\\\OR\end{smallmatrix}$ ... 312

Hydrazides

$RCOOR' + NH_2NH_2 \rightarrow RCONHNH_2$ ... 273

Ketones

$R_2C{=}CR_2 \xrightarrow[\text{KMnO}_4, \text{ OH}^-]{\text{CrO}_3, \text{ H}^+ \text{ or}} R_2CO + R_2CO$ ... 151, 613

$R_2C{=}CR_2 \xrightarrow{O_3}$ ozonide $\xrightarrow{H_2}{Pt}$ $R_2CO + R_2CO$ 158

$RC{\equiv}CH + H_2O \xrightarrow[H_2SO_4]{HgSO_4} RCOCH_3$ 163

$RMgX + RCOOEt \xrightarrow{-80°} RCOR$ 170

$R_2CHOH \xrightarrow[KMnO_4,\ OH^-]{CrO_3,\ H^+\ or} RCOR$ 240, 609

$HOCR_2CR_2OH \xrightarrow{H^+} RCOCR_3$ 615

$HOCR_2CR_2OH \xrightarrow[or\ H_5IO_6]{Pb(OAc)_4} 2R_2CO$ 618

$R_2CHOH \xrightarrow[CH_3COCH_3]{Al(OR)_3} R_2CO$ 621

$RCOX + C_6H_6 \xrightarrow{AlCl_3} RCOC_6H_5$ 642

Mercaptans

$RI + NaSH \rightarrow RSH$ 51

Nitriles

$RI + CN^- \rightarrow RCN$ 65

$R_2CO + HCN \rightarrow R_2C\genfrac{}{}{0pt}{}{\diagup OH}{\diagdown CN}$ 249, 642

$RCONH_2 + P_2O_5 \rightarrow RCN$ 327

$C_6H_5N_2^+ + CuCN + HCN \rightarrow C_6H_5CN$ 568, 569

Nitrobenzenes

$C_6H_6 + HNO_3 \xrightarrow{H_2SO_4} C_6H_5NO_2$ 71, 77, 560

Sulfoxides

$R_2S + H_2O_2 \rightarrow R_2S^+{-}O^-$ 106

Thioesters

$RCOOH + R'SH \xrightarrow{H^+} RCOSR'$ 52

See also esters.

Thioethers

$RI + NaSR' \rightarrow RSR'$ 51

REACTION INDEX

Acid anhydrides and chlorides

$RCOCl + RCOONa \rightarrow (RCO)_2O$	44, 52
$RCOCl$ or $(RCO)_2O + H_2O \rightarrow RCOOH$	52
$RCOCl$ or $(RCO)_2O + ROH \rightarrow RCOOH$	52
$RCOCl$ or $(RCO)_2O + NH_3 \rightarrow RCONH_2$	224
$RCOCl$ or $(RCO)_2O + C_6H_6 \xrightarrow{AlCl_3} RCOC_6H_5$	642

Acids, carboxylic

$RCOOH + ROH \xrightarrow{H^+} RCOOR$	44, 52
$RCOOH + PCl_5 \rightarrow RCOCl$	44, 52
$RCOOH + LiAlH_4 \rightarrow RCH_2OH$	67
$RCOOH + CH_2{=}C{=}O \rightarrow RCOOCOCH_3$	651
$RCOONa + \text{soda lime} \xrightarrow{400°} RH$	63
$RCOO^-NH_4^+ + \xrightarrow{heat} RCONH_2$	182
$RCOCR_2COOH \xrightarrow{heat} RCOCHR_2$	190, 201

Active hydrogen compounds

$A_2CH_2 + \text{base} \rightarrow A_2CH^-Na^+$	189
$RX + A_2CH^- \rightarrow A_2CHR$	190, 476
$A_2CH_2 + X_2 \rightarrow A_2CHX$	191, 211, 273
$RCOOEt + A_2CH^- \rightarrow RCOCHA_2$	196, 200
$A_2CH^- + RCHO \rightarrow A_2C{=}CHR$	241

Alcohols

$$ROH + R'COOH \xrightarrow{H^+} R'COOR \qquad\qquad 44, 52$$

$$ROH + (R'CO)_2O \text{ or } R'COCl \to R'COOR \qquad\qquad 52$$

$$ROH + CH_2{=}C{=}O \to CH_3COOR \qquad\qquad 651$$

$$R_2CHOH \xrightarrow[\text{KMnO}_4,\ \text{OH}^-]{\text{CrO}_3,\ \text{H}^+ \text{ or}} R_2CO \qquad\qquad 240, 610$$

$$RCH_2OH \xrightarrow[\text{KMnO}_4,\ \text{OH}^-]{\text{CrO}_3,\ \text{H}^+ \text{ or}} RCOOH \qquad\qquad 65, 610$$

$$RCH_2CH_2OH \xrightarrow{\text{Al}_2\text{O}_3,\ 450^\circ} RCH{=}CH_2 \qquad\qquad 120$$

$$RCH_2CH_2OH \xrightarrow{\text{H}_2\text{SO}_4} RCH{=}CH_2 \qquad\qquad 154$$

$$RCH_2CH_2OH \xrightarrow{\text{P}_2\text{O}_5} RCH{=}CH_2 \qquad\qquad 240$$

$$ROH + HI \to RI \qquad\qquad 61$$

$$ROH + HNCO \to ROCONH_2 \qquad\qquad 261$$

$$R_2CHOH \xrightarrow[\text{CH}_3\text{COCH}_3]{\text{Al(OR)}_3} R_2CO \qquad\qquad 621$$

Aldehydes and Ketones

$$R_2CO + LiAlH_4 \to R_2CHOH \qquad\qquad 178$$

$$R_2CO + H_2 \xrightarrow{\text{Pt or Pd}} R_2CHOH \qquad\qquad 178$$

$$R_2CO \xrightarrow{\text{Al(O}-i\text{-Pr)}_3} R_2CHOH \qquad\qquad 621$$

$$R_2CO + Zn(Hg) \to R_2CH_2 \qquad\qquad 178$$

$$R_2CO + NH_2NH_2 + OEt^- \to R_2CH_2 \qquad\qquad 178$$

$$R_2CO + CHA_2^- \to R_2C{=}CA_2 \qquad\qquad 241$$

$$R_2CO + H_2NOH \to R_2C{=}NOH \qquad\qquad 152$$

$$R_2CO + H_2NNHR \to R_2C{=}NNHR \qquad\qquad 153$$

(Osazones, 303)

$$R_2CO + CH_3OH \xrightleftharpoons{\text{H}^+ \text{ or OH}^-} R_2C{\overset{OH}{\underset{OCH_3}{<}}} \qquad\qquad 312$$

$$R_2CO + CH_3OH \xrightleftharpoons{\text{H}^+} R_2C(OCH_3)_2 \qquad\qquad 312$$

$$R_2CO + HCN \to R_2C{\overset{OH}{\underset{CN}{<}}} \qquad\qquad 249, 642$$

$$R_2CO + HSO_3^- \to R_2C{\overset{OH}{\underset{SO_3^-}{<}}} \qquad\qquad 312, 322$$

$RCOCH_2R + X_2 \rightarrow RCOCHXR$ 503

$R_2CO + PCl_5 \rightarrow R_2CCl_2$ 162

$R_2CO + 2e + 2H^+ \rightarrow R_2CHOH$ 602

$R_2CO + 1e + H^+ \rightarrow R_2COH-CR_2OH$ 603

$CH_3COCH_3 \xrightarrow{600°} CH_4 + CH_2{=}C{=}O$ 651

$(C_6H_5)_2CO \xrightarrow{Na} (C_6H_5)_2\dot{C}O^- Na^+$ 606

$R_2CO \xrightarrow{h\nu} R_2COH-CR_2OH$ 674

Special reactions of aldehydes

$RCHO \xrightarrow[KMnO_4, OH^-]{CrO_3, H^+ \text{ or}} RCOOH$ 152, 160

$RCHO \xrightarrow[(Br_2, H_2O)]{HOBr} RCOOH$ 309, 330

$C_6H_5CHO + Cl_2 \rightarrow C_6H_5COCl$ 53

Special reaction of methyl ketones

$RCOCH_3 + NaOX \rightarrow RCOOH + HCX_3$ 204, 213

Alkanes

$RH + X_2 + \text{light} \rightarrow RX$ 206

$RH \xrightarrow{600°} \text{pyrolysis products}$ 648

Alkenes

$RCH{=}CHR + H_2 \xrightarrow{Pt, Pd, \text{ or } Ni} RCH_2CH_2R$ 120

$RCH{=}CHR + X_2 \rightarrow RCHClCHClR$ 120, 137

$RCH{=}CHR \xrightarrow[OsO_4, H_2O_2]{\text{neutral } KMnO_4 \text{ or}} RCHOH-CHROH$ 139

$RCH{=}CR_2 \xrightarrow[KMnO_4, OH^-]{CrO_3, H^+ \text{ or}} RCOOH + R_2CO$ 141, 151

$RCH{=}CR_2 + H_2O \xrightarrow{H^+} RCHOHCHR_2$ 154

$RCH{=}CR_2 + HX \rightarrow RCH_2CR_2X$ 541

$RCH{=}CR_2 + HX + H_2O_2 \rightarrow RCHXCHR_2$ 653

$RCH{=}CR_2 \xrightarrow{O_3} \text{ozonide} \xrightarrow{Pt}_{H_2} RCHO + R_2CO$ 158

$R_2C{=}CR_2 \text{ (activated)} \xrightarrow[ROH]{Na} R_2CHCHR_2$ 605

Alkynes

$RC{\equiv}CH + Na \rightarrow RC{\equiv}C^- Na^+$ 163

$RC{\equiv}CH + Cu^+ \text{ or } Ag^+ \rightarrow \text{acetylides}$ 163

$RC{\equiv}CH + H_2O \xrightarrow[H_2SO_4]{HgSO_4} RCOCH_3$ 163

$HC{\equiv}CH + 2HBr \rightarrow H_3CCHBr_2$ 163

See also alkenes.

Amides

$RCONHR + H_2O \xrightarrow{H^+ \text{ or } OH^-} RCOOH + RNH_2$	278, 284
$RCONH_2 + HOBr \xrightarrow{H_2O} RNH_2$	276
$RCONH_2 + P_2O_5 \rightarrow RCN$	327

Amines

$RNH_2 + RX \rightarrow R_2\overset{+}{N}H_2X^-$, etc.	219, 220, 476
$HO^-\ R_3\overset{+}{N}CH_2CH_2CH_3 \xrightarrow{heat} R_3N + CH_2{=}CHCH_3$	222
$R_2NH + RCOCl \rightarrow RCONR_2$	224
$R_2NH + RCOOEt \rightarrow RCONR_2$	266, 273
$RNH_2 + C_6H_5NCS \rightarrow$ A substituted thiourea	226
$RNH_2 + HNO_2 \rightarrow CH_3OH + N_2$	352
$C_6H_5NH_2 + HNO_2 + HCl \rightarrow C_6H_5N_2{}^+ Cl^-$	352, 560

Aromatic nucleus

$C_6H_6 + HNO_3 \xrightarrow{H_2SO_4} C_6H_5NO_2$	71, 77, 525
$C_6H_6 + X_2 \xrightarrow{FeX_3} C_6H_5X$	77, 208, 534
$C_6H_6 + H_2SO_4 \rightarrow C_6H_5SO_3H$	575
(Position of substitution, 77, 537)	
$C_6H_5CH_3 \xrightarrow[\text{KMnO}_4,\ OH^-]{CrO_3,\ H^+ \text{ or}} C_6H_5COOH$	77
$C_6H_6 + H_2 \xrightarrow{Ni} C_6H_{12}$	74, 148
$C_6H_6 + RX \xrightarrow{AlCl_3} RC_6H_5$	642

Diazonium ions

$C_6H_5N_2{}^+ + C_6H_5R$ (R donating) $\rightarrow C_6H_5N{=}NC_6H_4R$	562
$C_6H_5N_2{}^+ + H_2O \rightarrow C_6H_5OH$	566, 569
$C_6H_5N_2{}^+ + ROH \rightarrow C_6H_5OR$	566, 569
$C_6H_5N_2{}^+ + X^- \rightarrow C_6H_5X$	566
$C_6H_5N_2{}^+ + H_3PO_2 \rightarrow C_6H_6$	566, 569
$C_6H_5N_2{}^+ + CuCN + HCN \rightarrow C_6H_5CN$	568, 569
$C_6H_5N_2{}^+ + CuX + HX \rightarrow C_6H_5X$	568, 569
$C_6H_5N_2{}^+ + H_2NC_6H_5 \rightarrow C_6H_5N{=}NNHC_6H_5$	571
$C_6H_5N_2{}^+ + Cu + H_2O + OH^- + C_6H_6 \rightarrow C_6H_5{-}C_6H_5$	569
$C_6H_5N_2{}^+ + HAsO_3 \rightarrow C_6H_5AsO_3H_2$	568, 569
$C_6H_5N_2{}^+ + HgCl_2 \rightarrow C_6H_5HgCl_2$	568, 569
$C_6H_5N_2{}^+ + Zn, HOAc \rightarrow C_6H_5NHNH_2$	569
$C_6H_5N_2{}^+ + H_2SO_3 \rightarrow C_6H_5NHNH_2$	569
$C_6H_5N_2{}^+ + CuCl + CH_2{=}CH_2R \rightarrow C_6H_5CH_2CH_2R$	569

Epoxides

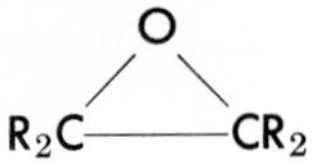

$$R_2C\overset{O}{\overbrace{}}CR_2 + H_2O \xrightarrow{H^+ \text{ or } OH^-} R_2COH\text{—}COHR_2 \qquad 346$$

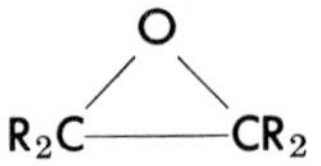

$$R_2C\overset{O}{\overbrace{}}CR_2 + NH_3 \rightarrow HOCR_2CR_2NH_2 \qquad 254$$

See also ethers.

Esters

$RCOOR' + H_2O \xrightarrow{H^+ \text{ or } OH^-} RCOOH + R'OH$	52, 476, 625
$RCOOR' + Na + EtOH \rightarrow RCH_2OH + R'OH$	67
$RCH_2COOR' + X_2 \xrightarrow{P} RCHXCOOR$	211
$RCOOR' + NH_3 \rightarrow RCONH_2$	224, 273
$RCOOR' + NH_2NH_2 \rightarrow RCONHNH_2$	273, 280
$RCOOCH_2CH_2R \xrightarrow{600°} RCOOH + CH_2{=}CHR$	237
$RSO_2OR' + NaI \rightarrow RSO_3Na + R'I$	310
$C_6H_5OCOR \xrightarrow{AlCl_3} RCOC_6H_4OH$	579
$ROXO_n \xrightarrow[\text{or } OH^-]{H_2O,\ H^+} ROH + HOXO_n$	631

Ethers

$ROR' + HI \rightarrow RI + R'I$	61
(R aromatic, products = $ROH + R'I$, 272).	

Glycols

$RCHOHCHOHR \xrightarrow[KMnO_4,\ OH^-]{CrO_3,\ H^+ \text{ or}} RCOOH + RCOOH$	138, 241
$RCHOHCHOHR + HIO_4 \rightarrow RCHO + RCHO + HIO_3$	321, 616
$RCHOHCHOHR + R_2CO \xrightarrow{H^+} \text{cyclic acetal}$	310

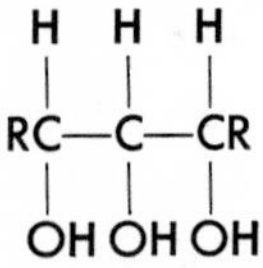

$$\underset{\underset{OH\ OH\ OH}{|\ \ \ |\ \ \ |}}{\overset{\overset{H\ \ H\ \ H}{|\ \ \ |\ \ \ |}}{RC\text{—}C\text{—}CR}} + 2HIO_4 \rightarrow RCHO + HCOOH + RCHO + 2HIO_3 \qquad 321$$

$HOCR_2CR_2OH \xrightarrow{H^+} RCOCR_3$	615

See also alcohols.

Grignard reagents

$R'MgX + R_2CO \rightarrow R'CR_2OH$	170
$R'MgX + RCOOR'' \xrightarrow{-80°C} R'COR$	170
$R'MgX + RCOOR'' \xrightarrow{20°C} R'_2CROH$	170

$RMgX + CO_2 \rightarrow RCOOH$ 170

$RMgX + H_2O$, etc. $\rightarrow RH$ 171

Halogen compounds

  $RI + NaOH \rightarrow ROH$ 44, 51, 469

  $RI + NaSH \rightarrow RSH$ 44, 51

  $RI + NaOR \rightarrow ROR$ 44, 51

  $RI + NaSR \rightarrow RSR$ 44, 51

  $RI + NaCN \rightarrow RCN$ 65

  $RX + Mg \rightarrow RMgX$ 169

  $RCH_2CH_2X + KOH \xrightarrow{\text{alcohol}} RCH{=}CH_2$ 162

  $RCHBrCHBrR + Zn \rightarrow RCH{=}CHR$ 513

  $RX + NH_3 \rightarrow RNH_2 + R_2NH + R_3N + R_4N^+X^-$ 219, 220

  $RCH_2CHCl_2 + KOH \xrightarrow{\text{alcohol}} RC{\equiv}CH$ 162

  $RI + NaC{\equiv}CH \rightarrow RC{\equiv}CH$ 163

  $CHCl_3 + C_6H_5OH + NaOH \rightarrow HOC_6H_4CHO$ 319

  $RX + C_6H_6 \xrightarrow{\text{AlCl}_3} RC_6H_5$ 642

  $RI + Na + H$ source $\rightarrow RH$ 310

  $2RI + Na \rightarrow R{-}R$ 51

  $RI + CHA_2^- \rightarrow RCHA_2$ 190, 476

Hydrazides

  $RCONHNH_2 + HNO_2 \rightarrow RCON_3$ 280

Ketene

  $CH_2{=}C{=}O \xrightarrow{H_2O} CH_3COOH$ 651

  $CH_2{=}C{=}O \xrightarrow{ROH} CH_3COOR$ 651

  $CH_2{=}C{=}O \xrightarrow{CH_3COOH} (CH_3CO)_2O$ 651

  $2CH_2{=}C{=}O \rightarrow$ dimer   651

Nitriles

  $RCN + H_2O \xrightarrow{H^+ \text{ or } OH^-} RCONH_2 \rightarrow RCOOH$ 65, 327

  $RCN + H_2 \xrightarrow{Ni} RCH_2NH_2$ 182

Nitro compounds

  $RNO_2 \xrightarrow[\text{Fe or Sn}]{HCl} RNH_2$ 77

Thioethers

  $R_2S + H_2O_2 \rightarrow R_2S^+{-}O^-$ 106

Reactions of reduction products of nitrobenzene

(1)

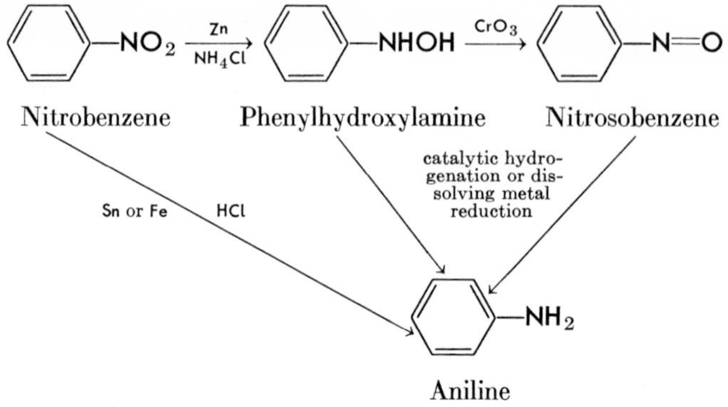
NO2
Zn
NH4Cl
NHOH
CrO3
N=O
Nitrobenzene
Phenylhydroxylamine
Nitrosobenzene
Sn or Fe
HCl
catalytic hydrogenation or dissolving metal reduction
NH2
Aniline

See page 582.

---

(2)

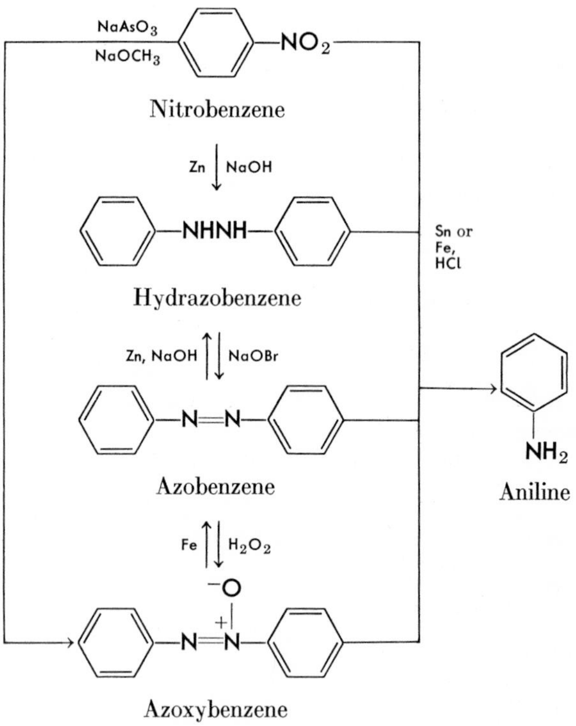
NaAsO3
NaOCH3
NO2
Nitrobenzene
Zn
NaOH
NHNH
Hydrazobenzene
Sn or
Fe,
HCl
Zn, NaOH
NaOBr
N=N
Azobenzene
NH2
Aniline
Fe
H2O2
O
N=N
Azoxybenzene

See pages 583, 584.

Reactions of reduction products of nitrobenzene (continued)

(3)

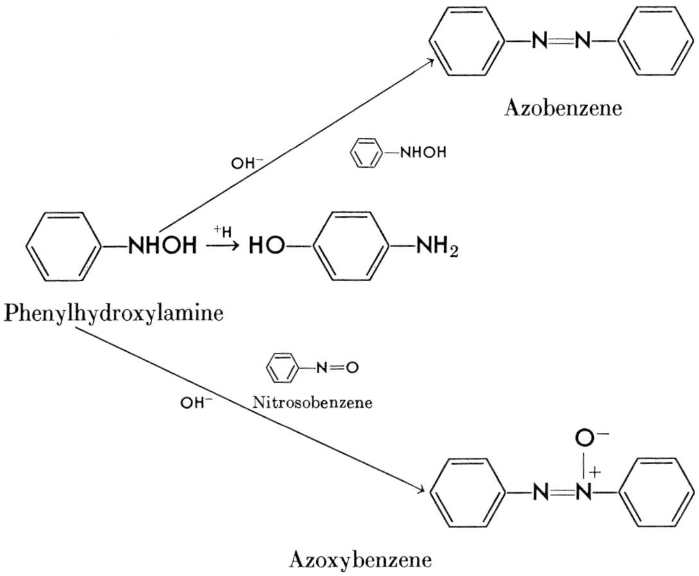

Azobenzene

Phenylhydroxylamine

Nitrosobenzene

Azoxybenzene

See pages 578, 583, 584.

---

(4)

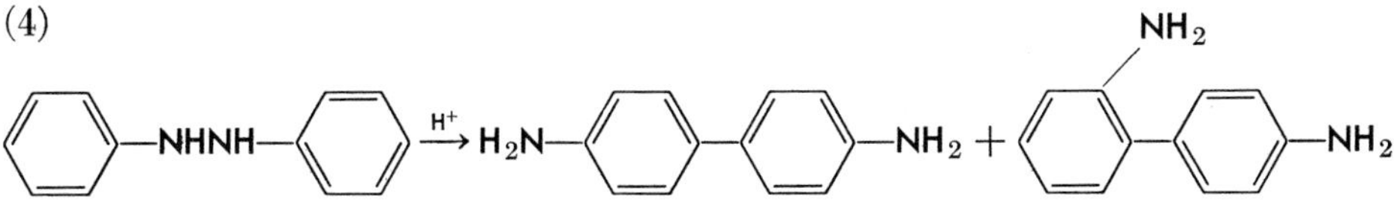

Hydrazobenzene   Benzidine   Diphenyline

and with appropriately substituted compounds

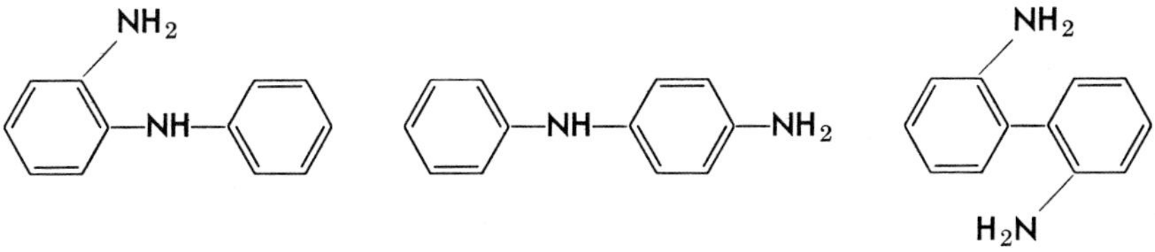

ortho-semidine   para-semidine   ortho-benzidine

See pages 584, 585.

GENERAL INDEX

GENERAL INDEX

A

Abderhalden, 283
absolute configuration, 103, 104
absolute zero, 127
absorption, intensity, 664
abstraction by radicals, 647–650
acetaldehyde, 159
   preparation, 163
   thermal decomposition, 654
acetals, 310, 312, 313
acetamide, 182, 417
acetate, as nucleophile, 489
acetates, ionization, 637
acetazide, 280
acethydrazide, 280
acetic acid, 44, 62, 63, 64, 65, 66, 94, 143,
      152, 185, 694
   dielectric constant, 439
acetic acid dimer, 289
acetic anhydride, 44
   dielectric constant, 439
acetoacetic acid, 200
acetoacetic ester, 196–201, 348
   synthesis, 200–202
acetobromogentiobiose, 327
acetobromoglucose, 319, 328, 339
2-acetonaphthone, 674

acetone, 151, 152, 156, 197, 201
   basicity of, 504–505
   bromination, 503–506
   dielectric constant, 439
   reduction, 602–604
   thermal decomposition, 651
acetonedicarboxylic acid, 247, 259
acetonylacetone, 196, 202
acetophenone, 157, 674
   dielectric constant, 439
   infrared spectrum, 418, 457
   pK, 509
acetophenones, substituted, reduction, 603
acetylacetone, 156, 510
   enol content, 506
acetylation, 85
acetyl chloride, 44
acetylene, 49, 111
   bond angle, 398
   orbitals, 428–429
   reaction with heavy metals, 162
   stability at high temperature, 651
   synthesis, 162
   thermal stability, 693
acetylenedicarboxylic acid, 111
acetyl ion, 637
acetylides, 163
acetylserine, 373

M